MW00634926

FOSSILS OF OHIO

STATE OF OHIO
George V. Voinovich, Governor

DEPARTMENT OF NATURAL RESOURCES
Donald C. Anderson, Director

DIVISION OF GEOLOGICAL SURVEY
Thomas M. Berg, Chief

BULLETIN 70

FOSSILS OF OHIO

Rodney M. Feldmann, Editor-in-Chief
Department of Geology
Kent State University

Merrianne Hackathorn, Managing Editor
Division of Geological Survey
Ohio Department of Natural Resources

Contributors:

Robert L. Anstey
Department of Geological Sciences
Michigan State University

William I. Ausich
Department of Geological Sciences
The Ohio State University

Loren E. Babcock
Department of Geological Sciences
The Ohio State University

Stig M. Bergström
Department of Geological Sciences
The Ohio State University

Alan H. Coogan
Department of Geology
Kent State University

Aureal T. Cross
Department of Geological Sciences
Michigan State University

Richard Arnold Davis
Department of Chemistry & Physical Sciences
College of Mount St. Joseph, Cincinnati

William H. Gillespie
Department of Geology & Geography
West Virginia University

Joseph T. Hannibal
The Cleveland Museum of Natural History

Michael C. Hansen
Division of Geological Survey
Ohio Department of Natural Resources

Richard D. Hoare
Department of Geology
Bowling Green State University

F. D. Holland, Jr.
Department of Geology & Geological Engineering
University of North Dakota

Royal H. Mapes
Department of Geological Sciences
Ohio University

Barry B. Miller
Department of Geology
Kent State University

J. Keith Rigby
Department of Geology
Brigham Young University

Michael R. Sandy
Department of Geology
University of Dayton

Barbara A. Schwimmer
The Cleveland Museum of Natural History

Alison J. Smith
Department of Geology
Kent State University

Walter C. Sweet
Department of Geological Sciences
The Ohio State University

Ralph E. Taggart
Department of Geological Sciences
Michigan State University

John R. Tillman
Department of Geology & Geography
Ohio Wesleyan University

Mark A. Wilson
Department of Geology
College of Wooster

Columbus
1996

Scanning, creation of some illustrations, composition, and layout by Lisa Van Doren

ISBN 0-931079-05-5

Frontispiece: *Isotelus maximus*, the official Invertebrate Fossil of Ohio.

Cover illustration: restored skull and thoracic shield of *Dunkleosteus terrelli*. This ferocious arthrodire fish was a predator in the Devonian seas of Ohio. This specimen, which is nearly 1.4 meters long, is from the Cleveland Shale Member of the Ohio Shale (Upper Devonian) in Cuyahoga County, Ohio. Photo courtesy of the Cleveland Museum of Natural History.

Dedication

John Strong Newberry

TO JOHN STRONG NEWBERRY

It is appropriate that the manuscripts for this volume were being compiled in 1992, the 100th anniversary of the death of Dr. John Strong Newberry, who, more than any other individual, brought attention to the remarkable paleontological riches of Ohio. Through his determination and scientific genius, Newberry alerted the world to the diversity of Ohio's Paleozoic fossils.

Newberry was born in Windsor, Connecticut, in 1822 but moved to Ohio with his family soon after his birth. His father founded the community of Cuyahoga Falls and, in 1828, established coal mines near Tallmadge, Summit County (Stevenson, 1893). As a young boy, Newberry became fascinated by the fossil plants preserved as carbonized impressions in the roof shales of his father's coal mines. At the age of 19, Newberry guided James Hall, the famous New York geologist and paleontologist, on a trip through northeastern Ohio. This encounter sparked Newberry's lifelong pursuit of geology and paleontology and a friendship with Hall that would last throughout their lives.

John Strong Newberry's long, productive, and diverse career has been chronicled by Kemp (1893), Stevenson (1893), and Waller (1943). He rose to national and international fame as a geologist and paleontologist and spent most of his career at the Columbia School of Mines (now Columbia University) in New York City. However, he maintained his Ohio ties and served as the second State Geologist of Ohio (1869-1882). He is buried in Lake View Cemetery in Cleveland (Hannibal and Schmidt, 1988).

Newberry's tenure as State Geologist was the greatest episode in Ohio paleontology. His plan was to describe all of the state's fossils in three volumes, each illustrated by numerous engraved plates of specimens. Newberry undertook the description of fishes and plants, his specialties, and employed prominent paleontologists to describe the remaining groups. The first volume (Ohio Geological Survey, Volume 1, Part 2, Paleontology), was issued in 1873 and included descriptions of Lower Paleozoic invertebrates by F. B. Meek and fossil fishes and fossil plants by Newberry. The second volume (Volume 2, Part 2, Paleontology), issued in 1875, included descriptions of fossil fishes by Newberry, Silurian invertebrates by James Hall and R. P. Whitfield, Silurian and Devonian corals by H. A. Nicholson, Carboniferous invertebrates by F. B. Meek, Pennsylvanian tetrapods by E. D. Cope, and Mississippian plants by E. B. Andrews. Most of the Pennsylvanian tetrapod specimens described by Cope had been collected by Newberry from the famous Linton locality in Jefferson County. These two volumes totaled 834 pages plus 107 full-page plates of the described fossils.

These monumental works served as the foundation of Ohio paleontology. They were instrumental in establishing correlations of Ohio rocks and fundamental in the understanding of the history of Paleozoic life. From the beginning of the Second Geological Survey, Newberry had to defend his decision to investigate and describe the state's fossils. He wrote, in the Ohio Geological Survey Report of Progress for 1870, "There are, however, yet some intelligent men, even editors and members of legislature, who cherish the notion that there is nothing which has any value in this world but that thing which has a dollar in it, and that so plainly visible as to be seen by them. Such men, to quote the language of one of them, 'don't care a row of pins for your clams and salamanders, but want something practical.' "

Newberry recommended printing only 5,000 copies of the paleontology volumes, but the legislature demanded that 20,000 copies be printed and distributed free of charge to their constituents. By 1874, appropriations for the Survey were discontinued and Newberry's plan for a third volume on paleontology was abandoned, even though manuscripts and plates had been prepared by several paleontologists. Through the efforts of Edward Orton, Newberry's assistant, who succeeded him as State Geologist, the reports by R. P. Whitfield on Paleozoic invertebrates and by E. O. Ulrich on Ordovician pelecypods were published in Volume 7 (1893). Orton added chapters by C. L. Herrick on Mississippian invertebrates, A. F. Foerste on Silurian invertebrates, and E. W. Claypole and A. A. Wright on Devonian fishes. Thus, Newberry's plan was completed.

John Strong Newberry published 37 papers and reports on Ohio fossils, beginning in 1853. Twenty-two reports were on fossil fishes, 13 on fossil plants, and two on fossil mammals. His greatest contributions to paleontology were his descriptions of Devonian fishes, particularly the remarkable arthrodires from the Ohio Shale, and the unique accumulation of nonmarine vertebrates in Pennsylvanian rocks at Linton, Ohio. This lifelong endeavor of Newberry culminated in 1889 with publication of his U.S. Geological Survey monograph, *Paleozoic fishes of North America*, which described and figured many Ohio specimens.

This brief outline includes but a fraction of the contributions of Dr. Newberry. He was a man of both vision and accomplishment. His original scientific contributions to paleontology and geology, in Ohio and on a national scale, form the foundation of our science. His organizational abilities and leadership as State Geologist of Ohio resulted in perhaps the most productive era in Ohio geology. Today's citizens of Ohio still benefit greatly from his contributions.

Thomas M. Berg
State Geologist and Chief

CONTENTS

FIGURES

TABLES

Preface

Fossils are fascinating for people of all ages and backgrounds. The most popular book in the history of the Division of Geological Survey has been Bulletin 54, *Ohio Fossils*, published in 1955 and reprinted 13 times. This book, Bulletin 70, *Fossils of Ohio*, is the long-awaited successor to that book.

Whether fossils are collected as a record of the biological history of the Earth or as curios and objects of aesthetic appeal, there is always a desire to learn more about them and to seek an identification. "What is it?" is perhaps the most frequently heard question about fossils. Other questions include "How old is it?" "Where did it come from?" "Are they hard to find?" It is these questions, and more, that *Fossils of Ohio* attempts to address.

Ohio has a remarkable fossil record. Rocks of Ordovician through Permian age are exposed along hillslopes and stream valleys and in manmade excavations along highways and in quarries across the state. Nearly all of these rocks are fossiliferous, and, thus, an excellent record of fossil vertebrate and invertebrate animals as well as plants (particularly in the Pennsylvanian Period) is available for collection. Some Ohio localities are, in fact, internationally known. Fossils of Late Ordovician age from Cincinnati, fossils of Middle Devonian age from the vicinity of Toledo, and plants from the coal-bearing rocks of Pennsylvanian age in eastern Ohio are found in paleontology collections throughout the world. These and other fossils in Ohio commonly are abundant, beautifully preserved, and relatively accessible for collection and study.

Accessibility to collecting localities is, however, becoming more difficult. Throughout this book, localities for fossil collecting are listed; some are accessible to the public, but most are on private land and never available for collecting without permission. The listing of a locality in this book does not constitute permission to enter the property or to collect fossils; landowner permission is always required. If no reference is made to collecting sites, this is not an error of omission. Typically, some collecting sites for each of the groups of fossils treated will be mentioned; however, if the fossils are particularly rare or the probability of damaging fossils by collecting them is extremely high, collecting localities are simply not stated.

Because of the widespread and abundant fossil record in Ohio, it is not surprising that a relatively large number of professional paleontologists and geologists were initially stimulated by fossil-collecting experiences in Ohio. It is also not coincidental that Ohio has a large number of outstanding paleontologists devoted to teaching paleontology and conducting research on the fossil record. Paleontology is taught at most colleges and universities throughout the state, and excellent degree programs emphasizing paleontology are available at several of these universities and colleges. Thus, when the decision was made to have experts in each of the groups of fossils serve as authors of chapters dealing with the details of their specialty group, it became immediately apparent that I could find eminently qualified experts in nearly all of the fossil groups working in Ohio. Using these specialists as authors guaranteed high quality and modern interpretation of the organisms. The authors of each of the chapters are well-known, highly respected authorities in paleontology and they bring to this work the unique blend of expertise, years of experience, and enthusiasm. In finalizing this book, the Managing Editor and I tried to maintain a consistent style and approach, but the number of authors, as well as the diversity of the fossils, required some variation in presentation.

The number of species of organisms preserved in the fossil record is seemingly endless, and no one can become expert in all groups. However, it is possible to learn to recognize major groups to which fossils belong and to make an approximate identification. In some cases these identifications will be quite accurate because there are very few organisms with which your fossils may be confused. On the other hand, some groups of animals are extraordinarily difficult to study and only an approximation of the identification can be made. Furthermore, many fossils are microscopic in size. Their study requires specialized techniques and, generally, specialized equipment, including a microscope. The intent of this volume is to deal with fossils that may be collected at the surface in Ohio and that may be recognized, studied, and appreciated by novices as well as professional paleontologists. Thus, the general emphasis is on megafossils—those that are large enough to be seen and studied with the unaided eye—although some groups of microfossils that have an excellent fossil record in Ohio also are discussed.

Because the number of fossil types is vast, it is impossible to treat all of the species that have been collected and identified in Ohio. Rather, the most commonly encountered fossils, and those that are representative of most major groups having a fossil record, are emphasized throughout the book. It should also be noted that these fossils are not uniformly abundant. Some of the animals and plants that are discussed are extremely common at some localities and others may be quite rare. Identification may be quite easy or extremely difficult. There is also the possibility of finding a fossil that has never been described before. Specimens may require little or no preparation in order to examine them, or it may require extensive work to extract them from the rocks. To be properly identified, some fossils may need to be cleaned, or to be cut for examination of internal parts. The range of possibilities and techniques for attacking these problems are thoroughly discussed.

Because most scientific investigations use the metric system for measurements, this book uses the International System (SI) metric units. Where road distances are given, the kilometer value is followed by the mile equivalent in parentheses. A table for conversion to English (inch-pound) units is provided below.

Multiply SI units	by	to obtain inch-pound units
micrometer (micron) (μm or μ)	0.00003937	inch
millimeter (mm)	0.03937	inch
centimeter (cm)	0.3937	inch
meter	3.281	foot
kilometer (km)	0.6214	mile
gram (g)	0.03527	ounce (avoirdupois)
kilogram (kg)	2.205	pound (avoirdupois)

Several individuals, other than those listed as authors of chapters, have contributed an enormous amount of effort in the preparation of this volume. Where appropriate, individuals are acknowledged in the various chapters. In order to assure accuracy, scientific credibility, and to improve uniformity of presentation, nearly all the chapters were subjected to an external review by F. D. Holland, Jr., emeritus professor at the Department of Geology and Geological Engineering, University of North Dakota, and Ellis L. Yochelson, U.S. Geological Survey (retired). These individuals were selected as reviewers because both of them have vast experience in the fossil groups known from Ohio. Their careful reviews of the chapters dealing with invertebrate fossils and trace fossils, as well as the introductory chapters, have significantly improved the quality of the work. Their efforts are greatly appreciated and gratefully acknowledged.

Many of the specimens that were used in the course of preparing these chapters were generously made available for study by curators of paleontology collections in university and museum collections throughout Ohio and adjoining states. I acknowledge the efforts of the curators of those collections for making the material available. Similarly, the line drawings in this book were prepared by a number of artists too numerous to acknowledge individually. The majority of the drawings were rendered by students employed by the Department of Geology at Kent State University.

Specific thanks are due to Karen Smith, Department of Geology, Kent State University, for her enormous help throughout the project in reading and criticizing parts of the text, formatting, translating word-processing programs, and generally helping with the sometimes difficult mechanical processes of preparing manuscripts for final editing at the Ohio Division of Geological Survey. This work could not have been done without her. Finally, I extend special thanks to Merrianne Hackathorn, Editor at the Ohio Division of Geological Survey and Managing Editor of this book. Her expertise in technical editing and keen attention to detail is sincerely appreciated.

The ultimate goal of the work is to enjoy and to learn more from the fossil record so that novices and professionals alike can gain a greater appreciation for the vast array of creatures that have inhabited the Earth through geologic time. So, enjoy *Fossils of Ohio*, use it, and savor the most fascinating subject in the world.

Rodney M. Feldmann
Editor-in-Chief

Scenes of Paleozoic and Pleistocene life

The reconstructions of past environments on the following pages provide a glimpse of what life may have been like during the various time periods in Ohio's geologic history. The photographs of the Paleozoic dioramas are courtesy of the Carnegie Museum of Natural History, Pittsburgh; the representation of the Pleistocene is from Folger (1992) and is reproduced with permission of Discover Magazine.

ORDOVICIAN

Orthoconic cephalopods dominate this scene; several trilobites are in the lower right. Also shown are corals, crinoids, brachiopods, pelecypods, macrophytic algae, and jellyfish.

SILURIAN

Eurypterid arthropods are the predominant creatures. Also shown are gastropods, crustaceans, macrophytic algae, and jellyfish.

DEVONIAN

Corals, bryozoans, orthoconic cephalopods, trilobites, and crinoids typical of Middle Devonian time are shown.

MISSISSIPPIAN

Stalked echinoderms (crinoids and blastoids) predominate. Also shown are asteroid echinoderms (starfish), horn corals, and macrophytic algae.

PENNSYLVANIAN—MARINE

Brachiopods, coiled cephalopods, corals, sponges, echinoderms, fish, and macrophytic algae are shown.

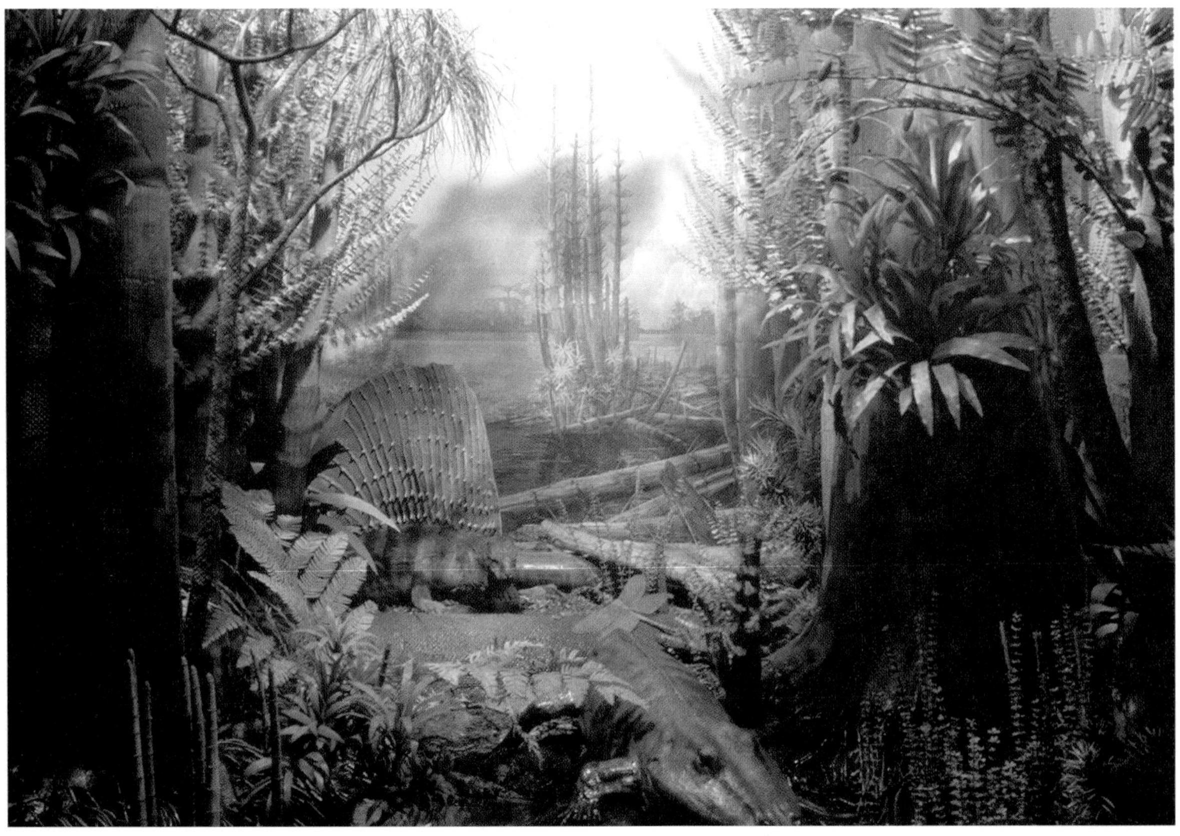

PENNSYLVANIAN—TERRESTRIAL

A fin-backed reptile, an amphibian, and a large dragonfly are shown amidst a flora of sphenopsids, lycopods, and ferns.

PERMIAN

Two fin-backed reptiles and an amphibian are surrounded by sphenopsids and ferns.

PLEISTOCENE

A depiction of the Burning Tree mastodon site in Licking County. The mastodon stands in a plant-filled bog; a conifer forest is in the background. Artist: Steven Kirk, ©1992, The Walt Disney Co.

Abstract

Ohio has a rich record of fossil plants and animals preserved in rocks spanning the Ordovician through the Permian Periods of the Paleozoic Era and the Pleistocene Epoch of the Cenozoic Era. The fossils are relatively abundant in many of the gently dipping rock units of Paleozoic age, which are overlain in all but the southeastern third of Ohio by Pleistocene-age sediments. Generally speaking, the oldest Paleozoic rocks exposed at the surface, which are of Ordovician age, are present in southwestern Ohio, and the youngest Paleozoic rocks, of Permian age, are exposed along the southeastern margin of the state. Most of the rock sequence and the enclosed fossils were deposited in marine environments; however, in the Pennsylvanian Period, a remarkable, diverse terrestrial plant and vertebrate assemblage is present. Plants do occur throughout the rock record in the state but generally are less conspicuous than the animals. The Pleistocene fossil record is contained in sediments associated with the glaciations that covered Ohio during the Pleistocene Epoch. A wide array of plants and vertebrate and invertebrate animals are known from terrestrial and freshwater habitats.

For those unfamiliar with paleontology, Chapter 1 discusses the preservation of fossils, describes and illustrates the major groups of organisms commonly preserved as fossils, and provides a key to assist in determining the major group to which a fossil belongs. Chapter 2 describes common collecting and preparation techniques that facilitate development of a correctly identified collection. Chapter 3 is an overview of the geology of Ohio. Chapters 4 through 25 each describe in detail a group of organisms preserved as fossils. Keys are again provided to more precisely identify fossils. Most fossils discussed also are illustrated by photographs. Accessible fossil-collecting localities are listed. Extensive references permit more detailed research into the fossils of Ohio. A glossary of terms is included, and names of genera and species are indexed.

Chapter I

INTRODUCTION

by Rodney M. Feldmann

THE NATURE OF FOSSILS

A fossil is defined as any direct evidence of ancient life. The fossil may be in the form of something as subtle as a sinuous trail, now preserved on a rock surface, originally made by an organism that has long since died and decayed. It may be something as spectacular as a nearly complete skeleton of a fish that lived several hundred million years ago. Whatever the fossil remains might be, they are the primary physical evidence of the history of life on our planet. They serve as the clues used by paleontologists to unravel this history. Fossils are of interest not only to paleontologists and other geologists, they are also of considerable interest to anyone who has a curiosity about the natural world. At one time or another, almost everyone has picked up a piece of rock containing objects resembling seashells and recognized that they were holding an amazing artifact of past life. It is virtually impossible not to have wondered how the seashell came to be entombed within the rock and to have recognized that if the history of that little animal could be unraveled, a fascinating story would result.

Many aspects of the history of animals and plants preserved in the fossil record can be deciphered. It is the purpose of this book to introduce the reader to the study of paleontology by describing the fossils that are common in the state of Ohio. As an aid to readers, terms that may be unfamiliar are shown in **boldface** at their first occurrence in a chapter and are defined in the glossary at the end of this book.

The fossil record in Ohio is rich and varied. In Ohio, stratified rocks containing fossils span an interval of time in Earth history from about 500 million years to about 245 million years ago, an interval of geologic time referred to as the Paleozoic. Chapter 3 discusses in more detail geologic time and the time terms that are used in studying paleontology.

In addition to these ancient Paleozoic rocks, many parts of Ohio are blanketed by a thin veneer of much younger sediments accumulated within the past 2 million years during the Pleistocene Epoch, a time when glacial ice covered much of the state. Associated with the deposits from these glaciers are sediments that accumulated in lakes, streams, and upland regions populated by a host of plants and animals, some of which are preserved as fossils. Thus, Ohio offers the opportunity to collect and study some ancient fossil organisms that have long since become extinct and to study some of the youngest of fossils accumulated during and after the ice ages.

MODES OF PRESERVATION OF FOSSILS

Any direct evidence, however meager or obscure, of ancient life may be considered a fossil. A wide variety of preservational types may be observed in the fossil record (fig. 1-1). When plants and animals die, decomposition of the soft tissue occurs almost immediately. As this process of decomposition continues, progressively more information about the nature of the organism is lost. At one end of this range, animals that lived in areas of glaciation during the Pleistocene are known to have died by falling into ice crevasses and being frozen almost immediately. Along with bones and teeth, these animals have soft tissues, hair, and skin preserved in almost the same condition as when the animal was alive. Unfortunately, none of these soft-tissue remains is known from Ohio. At the other end of the range

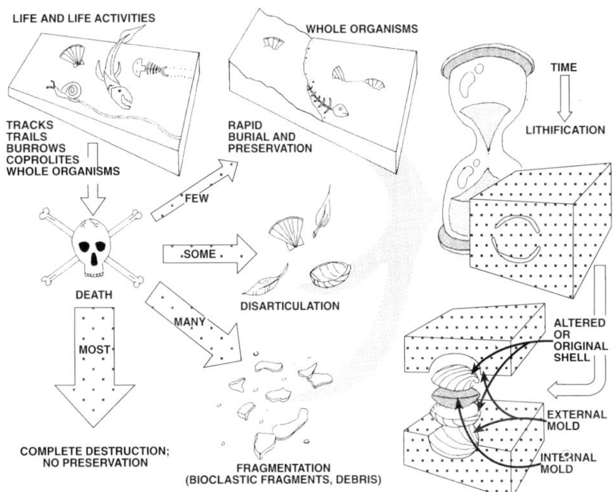

FIGURE 1-1.—Schematic illustration of several of the possible methods by which living material can be preserved in the fossil record.

of preservation, many kinds of fossils are mere traces on rock surfaces, providing evidence of the activity of an animal that has long since disappeared and that is not preserved for examination. Understanding the kind of fossil preservation, therefore, helps us, not only when we try to identify fossils, but also when we try to interpret their significance. Fossils in which physical remains of the organism are preserved are referred to as **body fossils**, whereas the records of activity in which the physical remains of the organism are not preserved are called trace fossils, or **ichnofossils**.

When coal or petroleum is referred to as a fossil fuel, use of the term "fossil" has great significance. These energy resources are, in fact, the highly altered remains of plants and animals that populated the Earth many millions of years ago. Their remains have been so significantly altered that it is generally impossible to identify the specific nature of the organisms involved. Although there may be excellent fossils associated with coal deposits or rocks containing petroleum, coal and petroleum are not commonly the subject of paleontological investigations.

Most fossils consist of the hard parts of animals or plants. Fossils may be large enough to see with the naked eye (**macrofossils**) or they may be microscopic (**microfossils**). As indicated above, decomposition quickly destroys soft tissue; the skeletal remains, or hard parts, decompose and are lost at a very much slower rate. When one walks along a seashore and examines the seashells that have been washed up on the shore by wave activity, it is rare to find bits of soft tissue attached to the shells. Commonly this material has decayed or been eaten by scavengers so that the only thing that remains is the shell material. Such hard parts are the raw materials for the fossil record.

Upon death and decomposition of the soft tissue, there are many pathways that the hard parts may follow on their way to becoming fossils. All involve burial within sediments—sand, silt, or mud. Burial has the effect of enclosing and protecting the remains. The sediments and the enclosed remains may subsequently be altered by processes of **diagenesis**, which result in the formation of sedimentary rocks. Exposure of these remains at some later date might lead to the discovery and study of the specimens. If the remains have been buried and preserved in such a way that skeletal material has been unchanged chemically, the fossils are considered unaltered. This type of preservation is rare except in the relatively recent Pleistocene deposits. Most fossils have been enclosed within rock for many millions of years, and it is nearly impossible to visualize settings in which they would have been totally unaffected by water or heat or pressure over that interval of time. Customarily, therefore, fossil remains have been altered to some degree. Thus, it is very likely that the chemical composition of the fossil is very different from the original composition of the skeletal material produced by the organism. Alteration of the original material can take several forms, but they can be summarized by considering just a few possibilities. The skeletal material of plants and animals is invariably porous, that is, tiny spaces exist within the structure. If water containing dissolved minerals permeates this porous material, minerals can crystallize in the open spaces. This process, referred to as **infiltration**, has the effect of filling up the available pore spaces. It is also possible that some or all of the skeletal material may be dissolved by the water and replaced by inorganic mineral material; this style of preservation is referred to as **replacement**. Infiltration and replacement have both been called **permineralization** because they involve the deposition of additional minerals from percolating ground water. Although the minerals calcite ($CaCO_3$) and quartz (SiO_2) are probably the most common, replacement minerals in Ohio fossils include pyrite (FeS_2), marcasite (also FeS_2), and sphalerite (ZnS), among others. The process of replacement may produce superb fossils with delicate detail in many cases, but the fine structure of the original material is typically lost.

Another form of alteration, which is more common in plant fossils than in animal fossils, is **carbonization**. Plant material, rich in the element carbon, may be subjected to enough heat and pressure, simply as a result of burial, to drive off the less stable compounds and squeeze the remainder. The result is a thin film of carbon material, a **compression**, which can preserve the structure of the plant remains in great detail.

Another consequence of the action of water on organic material is that the original skeletal material may be dissolved and lost entirely. In that event, it is still possible that fossils may result as impressions, or **molds**, which are the negative forms of the fossil in rock material. For example, if one were to visualize the burial of a clam in mud and the subsequent careful removal of the clam shells when the mud has hardened (see fig. 1-1), the process would produce two quite different kinds of impressions of the clam shells. The outer surface of the clam shell would leave a concave depression preserving the details of the shell exterior, forming a fossil termed an **external mold**. The interior of the clam, that is, the material between the two shells, would leave a nut-shaped, convex impression exhibiting details of the shell interior, forming a fossil termed an **internal mold**. Another term for an internal mold is **steinkern** ("stone kernel"). This kind of fossil preservation is extremely common in some rock units in Ohio, notably the Silurian rocks of western Ohio. Internal molds of the clam *Megalomoidea* have been found that exceed 20 cm in length. If the actual cavity originally occupied by the shell of the clam were to be filled by mineral material, the result would be a replica of the original shell, a **cast**. Natural casts are not common.

Internal and external molds of organisms represent one kind of fossil preservation in which the original skeletal remains have been totally lost. In these cases, however, the form of the skeleton is still very much in evidence. In other instances, organisms may leave some trace in the rock that clearly demonstrates activity of an organism. These trace fossils record activity of an animal rather than the actual shape of the organism making the trace. Perhaps the most spectacular trace fossils are the footprints of vertebrate animals that were made as an animal walked across a soft or muddy landscape. Although footprints of land animals are exceedingly rare, traces made by the activity of invertebrate animals (those without backbones) are found in many rock units in Ohio. These traces resulted from the feeding, resting, moving, and burrowing activity of organisms. Trace fossils may take many different forms, some of which are illustrated in Chapter 25.

Invariably, fossils provide us with some evidence of ancient life. This evidence is clear and unequivocal when we look at a fossilized tree trunk or a preserved snail shell, but the interpretation becomes more difficult when one examines trace fossils. When a specimen is collected that is suspected to be a fossil, it is necessary to ask whether or not there is some kind of process, other than organic activity, which might have produced this structure. Recognition of fossils may be tricky because there are inorganic processes which produce structures that can be confused with fossils. Typically, there is a kind of symmetry or design in animal and plant forms that is difficult to reproduce by inorganic processes. On the other hand, there are inorganic structures, such as ripple marks, made by water washing across sediments, that have distinct patterns but that can be interpreted in terms of common, well-known processes occurring today at many places on the surface of the Earth. These structures, referred to as **pseudofossils**, may have a wide variety of form; however, invariably, careful study of a pseudofossil will lead to a correct interpretation. The most common pseudofossils are produced by the precipitation of minerals from water. Beautiful, well-formed crystals are easily recognized for what they are. However, some minerals may not form well-shaped crystals but may form very delicate leaflike structures on the surfaces of rocks. These structures, called dendrites, are extremely thin mineral encrustations which, upon careful examination, do not reveal any organic structures such as **venation** or precise definition of leaf margins. Growth of minerals by inorganic processes also can occur in cracks within rocks. The cracks form by drying of sediment, which shrinks and cracks into multi-sided, angular units. The cracks, when filled in by calcite or some other mineral, produce a veined, solid mass. These septaria may superficially resemble turtle shells or some other kind of animal remains. Careful examination of septarian structures will reveal that the patterns are superficially symmetrical but irregular. Carlson (1991) discusses dendrites and septaria in his bulletin on *Minerals of Ohio*.

Understanding the process of fossil preservation is important because it provides valuable information regarding both the identity and the interpretation of the fossils. Furthermore, a thorough understanding of fossil preservation permits us to recognize many kinds of structures as having been formed by organic processes and, thus, to be fossils.

THE OCCURRENCE OF FOSSILS

Fossils occur in most kinds of sedimentary rocks, that is, rocks that accumulated in layers at or near the surface of the Earth. (Sedimentary rocks are discussed in Chapter 3.) However, the accumulation of fossils is not uniform throughout these rocks. It is possible to increase one's chances of locating and collecting fossils by considering a few of the conditions under which fossils accumulate. Fossilization occurs unevenly. The probability of any plant or animal being preserved for millions of years is exceedingly remote. To increase the chances of finding fossils, therefore, it is necessary to look at rocks that were formed in a setting in which large numbers of animals lived originally and were preserved. As a general rule, shallow, sunlit sea floors in warm-water regions of the world have the largest concentration of animals. These sites are also typically locations where rapid accumulation of sediments enhances the chances of burial of organic remains and traces. So, deposits of warm, shallow seas are the most likely ones in which to find fossils. Some terrestrial regions also have a very large concentration of animals and plants. However, land areas are commonly characterized by processes of erosion rather than deposition of sediments. For that reason, former land areas are less likely places to find large numbers of individuals preserved.

As will be described in detail in Chapter 3, many of the rocks exposed at the surface in Ohio were deposited as sediments in warm, shallow seas during the Paleozoic Era. Animal and, to a lesser extent, plant life was abundant in these marine settings. Because sediments accumulated rapidly enough to bury remains of these organisms, the fossil record of marine rocks tends to be good. However, just as animals and plants are not uniformly distributed around the surface of the Earth today, it is important to recall that there is little reason to expect that all rock units would have the same kinds of fossils or the same concentration of fossils. Continued examination of rocks in Ohio has revealed that there are certain localities at which fossils are exceedingly abundant and other localities, perhaps even in the same rock units, where fossils are relatively uncommon. Collecting sites in Ohio are detailed in subsequent chapters. Ohioans are fortunate that the sedimentary rock record in Ohio tends to be richly fossiliferous.

Fossil collecting is generally confined to areas where rocks are exposed at the surface. About two-thirds of Ohio is covered with glacial deposits that are tens to hundreds of meters thick. In all of Ohio, soil—the accumulation of deeply weathered rock and organic material—and vegetation blanket most of the ground surface and obscure the fossiliferous rock. Rock is exposed in areas where the soil and/or the glacial deposits have been stripped away to reveal the fresh rock beneath. Common types of exposures are road cuts and ditches along highways and stream valleys where river erosion has cut into hillsides. Quarrying and strip mining also remove the soil and weathered upper layers of rock and expose the fresh rock beneath. Weathered blocks around quarries and spoil piles from mines may yield fossils to the collector more readily than fresh, unweathered rock. Although these exposures are the most likely places to collect fossils, extreme care must be taken and permission must be obtained from the property owner.

COLLECTING FOSSILS

Relatively little equipment is necessary to develop a collection of fossils. A hammer and perhaps some chisels, material for wrapping the fossils, a sack or some other container to transport the fossils, and a pencil and notebook are all that are essential. More advanced techniques for collection, preservation, and preparation of fossils are numerous and many require specialized equipment. Chapter 2 briefly discusses some of these techniques. Details of these procedures have been described by Feldmann, Chapman, and Hannibal (1989).

Please remember that all of Ohio is the property of someone, and it is necessary to obtain the landowner's permission to collect fossils. Although exposures along highways and along navigable streams may be part of the public domain, there are limitations to collecting even in these areas. It is illegal to stop and collect from exposures along interstate highways. Access to exposures along streams generally crosses private property and requires permission from the landowner. Permission is always necessary when collecting on private property. Permission is particularly important in areas of active strip mining and quarrying operations. Laws governing the safe maintenance of open-pit mining require that the operators control access to these very dangerous areas. Many quarries are now off limits for collecting. If permission from the owner or operator is granted to collect in a quarry or a strip mine, you should determine what areas are available for collecting.

Collecting without explicit permission is prohibited in metropolitan, county, state, and federal parks, with very few exceptions. As exceptions, collecting is allowed in Lodi City Park (Medina County) and at Caesar Creek State Park (Warren County) and Hueston Woods State Park (Preble County), although at Caesar Creek a permit must be obtained at the park Visitor Center. Severe financial penalties can be imposed for violating restrictions on collecting. Although there are laws against trespassing and collecting on state or federal land, there are no Ohio laws governing collection (with permission) on private land or ownership of fossil remains. The State of Ohio cannot stop or delay excavations on private land or confiscate fossils, a common misconception, particularly in regard to large Pleistocene mammals (see Chapter 21). Safe, careful, and respectful adherence to these simple rules of access will make collecting an enjoyable experience for you and for future generations.

CLASSIFICATION OF ORGANISMS

Animals and plants, whether they are fossil or living organisms, are classified in a hierarchy according to the degree of relationship that they show with other organisms. A formal system of classification, called **taxonomy**, was developed in the 1700's by Linnaeus (hence the term Linnean classification) and has been in use for over 200 years to express the degree of morphological similarity between organisms and inferred biological relationships. In that sense, the system could be thought of as an elaborate family tree.

The largest category in this hierarchy is the kingdom. Modern biologists recognize five kingdoms of organisms: Plantae, Animalia, Protista, Fungi, and Monera ("blue-green algae" and bacteria). We will deal with the first three of these in our treatment of the fossils of Ohio. The common green plants belong to the kingdom Plantae, whereas the kingdom Animalia comprises the "animals" of the world, including clams, snails, lobsters, fish, and people. The kingdom Protista includes organisms that have a single-celled or acellular construction and whose characteristics do not permit placement in either the animal or the plant kingdom. Typically protists are relatively small (most are microscopic), but nonetheless they can provide valuable information for interpreting Earth history.

Animals and protists are further subdivided into phyla (singular = phylum), and plants are subdivided into divisions. Phyla and divisions represent the major groupings of organisms. Thus, when we speak of the Arthropoda or the Mollusca or the Chordata, we are speaking of a group of organisms that share some characteristics that unite the organisms at the phylum level. Phyla and divisions, in turn, are subdivided into progressively smaller and smaller categories, referred to as classes, orders, families, genera (plural of genus), and species (both singular and plural). To illustrate this hierarchy, the nomenclature of a common Ohio trilobite is given below.

Kingdom	Animalia
Phylum	Arthropoda
Class	Trilobita
Order	Asaphida
Family	Asaphidae
Genus	*Isotelus*
Species	*Isotelus maximus*

Each of these subdivisions is a group of organisms whose members show progressively greater morphologic similarity and, presumably, biological relationship. The smallest of the subgroups with which we will deal, the species, encompasses a group of organisms that are so closely related that they are capable of reproducing with other members of their species to produce fertile offspring. One species is reproductively isolated from other species.

The formal system of naming organisms is called **nomenclature**. A named group of organisms is referred to as a **taxon**. Genus and species names, by biological convention, are *italicized* when written. The species name always includes the genus name, although the genus name may be abbreviated, for example, *I. maximus*. Another biological convention is to include the name(s) of the person(s) who originally named the species, for example, *Isotelus maximus* Locke. If a genus or species name has been redefined by a later worker the name of the original author is placed in parentheses, as in *Flexicalymene meeki* (Foerste).

In some cases, a scientist may formally indicate uncertainty in the identification of an organism through the use of open nomenclature (Bengtson, 1988). The authors of the chapters in this book have indicated uncertain identification in a number of ways:

- **aff.** (abbreviation for Latin term "affinis") relates a new (undescribed) taxon to a named taxon. Example: *Cystiphylloides* aff. *C. americanum*.

- **cf.** (abbreviation for Latin term "confer") means that the new taxon resembles a named taxon, but the identification is provisional. Example: *Pleurodictyum* cf. *P. problematicum*.

- a question mark (?) means that the identity is uncertain. Examples: *Acidapsis brevispinosa*? (species name is in question); *Odaria*? *eurypetala* (genus name is in question but species name is not).

- sp., or ichnosp. in the case of a trace fossil, means that the genus has been identified but the species has not. Examples: *Isotelus* sp., *Cruziana* ichnosp.

- quotation marks (". . .") indicate that a former taxonomic assignment is now obsolete. Example: "*Flexicalymene*" *celebra*.

From the hierarchy of classification given above, it should be clear that each subdivision contains one or more categories beneath it, so that there must be more genera than families and more families than orders. It has been estimated by a variety of methods that there are several million species of organisms living in the world today. If we extend this estimate back into geologic time, it is likely that several tens or even hundreds of millions of species have lived on Earth through geologic time. Nearly all of those species, however, are now extinct. Learning to identify more than a tiny fraction of these organisms is difficult, and no one can identify them all! For this reason, biologists and paleontologists rely heavily upon identification keys, texts and references, and photographic illustrations to summarize points of identification. It is our aim that this book will aid you in the identification of major groups of fossil organisms and provide you with adequate information on the identity of the common genera of animals and plants preserved as fossils in the rocks of Ohio. The major groups that are the subjects of the various chapters in this book are generally of the phylum or class level. Within each chapter, the common genera of that group are discussed and illustrated. (For most groups the orders and families are not discussed for sake of brevity.)

In most of the ensuing chapters, the description of illustrated fossils includes the location, or **repository**, of the specimen, identified by an abbreviation and a number. The abbreviations for the various repositories are listed in table 1-1. Many of the descriptions refer to **type specimens**, the specific fossil designated to represent the characteristics of the species. This system is carried further by designating a **type species** for each genus.

TABLE 1-1.—LIST OF ABBREVIATIONS FOR MUSEUMS AND OTHER REPOSITORIES

Abbreviation	Location
AMNH	American Museum of Natural History
BGSU	Bowling Green State University Department of Geology
BMNH	British Museum, Natural History
CiMNH	The Cincinnati Museum of Natural History
ClMNH	The Cleveland Museum of Natural History
CM	Carnegie Museum, Pittsburgh
CMUMP	Central Michigan University Museum of Paleontology
CW	The College of Wooster
FMNH	Field Museum of Natural History
IUPC	Indiana University Paleontological Collection
KSU	Kent State University Department of Geology
MCGM	Marietta College Geology Museum
MCZ	Museum of Comparative Zoology, Harvard University
MS	M. R. Sandy Collection, Department of Geology, University of Dayton
MSU	Michigan State University Department of Geological Sciences
MUGM	Miami University Geology Museum
NYSM	New York State Museum
OHS	Ohio Historical Society
OSU	The Ohio State University Orton Geological Museum
OU	Ohio University Department of Geological Sciences
SUI	University of Iowa Department of Geology
UCGM	University of Cincinnati Geology Museum
UI	University of Illinois Department of Geology
UM	University of Missouri
UMMP	University of Michigan Museum of Paleontology
UMMZ	University of Michigan Museum of Zoology
USNM	U.S. National Museum of Natural History

IDENTIFICATION OF FOSSILS

Fossils are identified by examining the shape and structure, or morphology, of the preserved remains. In this regard, there is very little difference between the identification of fossils and the identification of other objects in nature, such as birds, butterflies, or trees. Certain characteristics of the morphology of these organisms are typical of a species and are used to identify that species. Thus, the shape of leaves, the nature of the seeds and flowers, and the characteristics of bark are all properties that are used to identify species of trees. The size and location of the tree are not particularly important characteristics because any given species of tree may grow in a variety of localities and, of course, the size increases as the tree gets older. When undertaking the identification of any kind of object, including fossils, it is important to know the characteristics of the morphology that are crucial for identification. The characteristics that are important for identification of the common Ohio fossils are listed in the following chapters. The identification of fossils can be more difficult than identifying living species of organisms because not all the parts necessary for identification may be preserved. It is possible that some specimens which you collect will not be identifiable because of inadequate or incomplete preservation. It is recommended that as you begin learning to identify fossils you confine your initial efforts to working with well-preserved, relatively complete specimens. In that way, you will become familiar with the major groups of animals preserved as fossils. With experience, you will discover that it is possible to identify progressively less complete material.

To aid in the identification process, a series of keys based upon important characters of morphology have been constructed. A key to the various groups of Ohio fossils begins in this chapter on page 6. Keys to fossils within a particular group are provided in the appropriate chapters.

Keys are used to identify and classify fossils. The keys in this book provide a series of alternatives, each of which limits the number of organisms to which the fossil may be related. Start the identification process at the beginning of the key and carefully read each of the alternatives (1A and 1B) to decide which of the alternatives is more probable or more nearly correct. Having made that decision, proceed to the next part of the key indicated by the number. If you have successfully worked through the key to a group of organisms, for example, Gastropoda, you will have successfully identified the fossil to group. More detailed identification of that particular fossil is made by proceeding to the keys in the chapter in the text dealing with gastropods. This technique gives you a relatively rapid and efficient way to identify an unknown fossil by observing its morphology.

Not all fossils can be keyed out, for several reasons. One reason is that the group of animals that you are attempting to key may not be included in the key. Only those groups that are commonly preserved as fossils in Ohio are included. Graptolites and tentaculitoids are not included in the key, although they are described in chapters in this book. Alternatively, the preservation of your fossil material may not be adequate to make certain determinations in the key. If that is so, the probability of properly identifying the fossils is reduced. Finally, it is possible that because the morphology of animal and plant groups is so variable, some types of fossils may not possess the morphology described in the key. In the event that the alternatives presented to you appear to be equally possible, follow both pathways and see which yields the best results. Remember that the key is only an aid to the identification of organisms and that the key characters do not include all of the points of definition of any of the groups, so that in some cases you will not arrive at a unique solution. Nonetheless, for every step that you make in the key, you eliminate large groups of organisms from consideration. Each process of elimination means you are closer to the proper identification for your fossil material.

The chapters that form the bulk of this book describe the groups of organisms commonly preserved as fossils in Ohio and have aids to identify the most common fossils within each group. It is likely that, as you continue collecting, you will encounter specimens that are not identifiable using the information in this book. That is understandable when one considers that, of the thousands of species of fossils that have been described from Ohio, only a few hundred are described herein. Continued collecting results in the discovery of progressively rarer species, requiring more sophisticated identification aids. In fact, if you collect actively, it is probable that you will collect species that have not been named and are unknown to scientists. Rare species commonly can be identified by resorting to the use of additional reference books, some of which are noted in individual chapters and listed in the references at the end of this book. If no identification is possible, having consulted these references, it is worthwhile to show the specimen to a specialist. Paleontologists affiliated with natural history museums, with the state geological survey, and with geology departments in universities and colleges in Ohio typically are eager to see unusual fossil material and will make every attempt to provide an identification for you. Consultation with professional paleontologists contributes in a very real way to adding information regarding the geologic history of our state.

KEY TO THE IDENTIFICATION OF MAJOR GROUPS OF ORGANISMS PRESERVED AS FOSSILS IN OHIO

(accompanying drawings are not to scale)

1A. Fossil large enough to examine with the naked eye 2

1B. Fossil very tiny, barely visible to naked eye or microscopic, typically less than 1 mm in greatest dimension 19

2A. Fossil appears to be track, trail, burrow, or footprint with no indication of the remains of the organism .... trace fossil (ichnofossil, Chapter 25)

2B. Fossil represents some of the physical remains of the organism or an impression of those remains 3

3A. Fossil remains are twigs, leaves, or wood, commonly black or dark brown .... plant (Chapters 22-24)

3B. Fossil remains are seashells, bones, or teeth; typically light colored, but may be blue gray to black 4

4A. Fossil remains are pieces of bone, teeth, or scales; commonly white, bluish gray, or yellowish brown, may be black .... Chordata (vertebrates, Chapter 21)

4B. Fossil remains are seashells or skeletal remains of various shapes; may be composed of one or many parts 5

5A. Fossil has weakly developed skeletal structure, tiny hairlike or needlelike pieces, or numerous layers 6

5B. Fossil generally has well-developed hard parts 7

6A. Fossil flat or domelike, layered structure in cross section and irregularly sculpted on surface .... stromatoporoids (Chapter 5)

6B. Fossil of variable shape; may have tiny needlelike, starlike, or hairlike elements .... Porifera (Chapter 4)

7A. Fossil is, or appears to have been, constructed of two shells of equal or unequal shape and size 8

7B. Fossil not composed of two shells; is tubular, conical, or composed of many elements 11

8A. Two shells of fossil not similar in shape or size; one shell typically larger than the other .... Brachiopoda (Chapter 16)

8B. Two shells of fossil similar in size and shape 9

9A. Fossil shell very thin, amber to black, leathery, mostly smooth .... Brachiopoda (Chapter 16)

9B. Fossil shell relatively thick, typically light colored 10

10A. Two shells of fossil tightly closed, having a long, straight junction on one side, open at one or both ends .... Rostroconchia (Chapter 11)

10B. Either one or both fossil shells preserved, typically not open at the ends if joined .... Pelecypoda (Chapter 12)

11A. Fossil appears to be regular or irregular cone or pyramid, may be straight to tightly coiled 12

11B. Fossil does not have general form of a cone 16

12A. Fossil a four-sided pyramid having ribbed structure, commonly bluish gray or black .... Conulariida (Chapter 6)

12B. Fossil a cone more or less circular in cross section 13

13A. Cone straight or slightly curved, circular to ovoid in cross section 14

13B. Cone tightly coiled, generally not circular in cross section 15

14A. Interior of cone filled with transverse and longitudinal structures .... Cnidaria (Chapter 7)

14B. Interior of cone has widely spaced transverse partitions (may appear only as lines on outside) .... Cephalopoda (Chapter 14)

15A. Interior of cone has widely spaced transverse partitions, typically coiled in one plane .... Cephalopoda (Chapter 14)

15B. Interior of cone without partitions, typically coiled out of one plane, like a corkscrew .... Gastropoda (Chapter 13)

16A. Fossil appears to be constructed of numerous, similar units in a group (**colony**) 17

16B. Fossil consists of one or many parts, but does not resemble numerous, similar, individual living spaces 18

17A. Individual units of fossil tiny, less than 1/2 mm in diameter; colony may be twig or branch shaped, dome-like, or a thin encrusting sheet .... Bryozoa (Chapter 15)

17B. Individual units of fossil generally larger than 1 mm in diameter, interior of units typically, but not always, partitioned by transverse and/or longitudinal structures .... Cnidaria (Chapter 7)

18A. Fossil appears to be flower or bud shaped, constructed of washer-shaped or many-sided plates, commonly light colored .... Echinodermata (Chapter 17)

18B. Fossil appears to be "bug"-shaped, segmented individual with head and tail sections, typically dark amber to black .... Trilobita (Chapter 8) (see also Other Arthropoda, Chapter 10)

19A. Fossil consists of microscopic toothlike structures, amber colored .... Conodonta (Chapter 18)

19B. Fossil not toothlike 20

20A. Fossil disk shaped, amber to black .... plant **spore**, *Tasmanites* (Chapter 22)

20B. Fossil not disk shaped, typically light colored to earthy 21

21A. Fossil consists of two very tiny shells resembling clams .... Ostracoda (Chapter 9)

21B. Fossil consists of many chambers; coiled or spindle shaped; spindle-shaped forms as much as 10 mm long .... Foraminiferida (see Protista below)

OVERVIEW OF THE MAJOR GROUPS OF FOSSIL ORGANISMS

PROTISTA

The kingdom Protista includes a wide variety of organisms, each of which is composed of a single cell or lacks well-defined cellular structures. These organisms are almost always microscopic, and the vast majority of them lack hard skeletal remains. Therefore, they are rare in the fossil record. Some protists, however, are capable of secreting hard skeletons composed of either opaline silica (SiO_2) or calcite ($CaCO_3$). In Ohio, the only protists that have a significant fossil record are in the order Foraminiferida, which is related to the modern, soft-bodied *Amoeba*. The Foraminiferida are marine organisms that range in age from the Cambrian to the Recent (see Chapter 3 for an explanation of geologic time units). Most foraminiferans secrete a skeleton composed of calcite. Some types bind sand grains together into a skeleton, and a few have organic **tests**.

The skeleton of all foraminiferans, or forams, is essentially one or more tiny chambers, the shape and arrangement of which is unique to each species within the group (fig. 1-2). In forms with a relatively simple morphology, the organism begins growth in a single chamber, the **proloculus**, and grows by increasing the size or length of this chamber or by addition of more chambers. Much of the protoplasm of the organism is enclosed within the skeleton. However, tubular or lobose extensions of protoplasm extend out an opening, called the **aperture**, in the last chamber or through pores in the chamber walls. These extensions of protoplasm are used for mobility and for food gathering. Foraminiferans occur in the modern ocean in staggering numbers and provide one of the basic food resources for all other life in the sea.

The diversity of foraminiferans has increased through geologic time. In Ohio, relatively few fossil foraminiferans are of significance, and, because of their small size, it is unlikely that many will be encountered in normal collecting. However, one group, the Fusulinina, occurs in large numbers in Upper Paleozoic, especially Pennsylvanian, rocks of eastern Ohio. Fusulinids tend to be giant foraminiferans; they may attain lengths of 2 cm or more, although most are less than 0.5 cm long. Their skeletons are composed of tiny hairlike crystals of calcium carbonate, which give the skeleton a dull, commonly brown or earthy, appearance. As with the other members of the Foraminiferida, fusulinids grew by addition of chambers about an initial proloculus. The chambers are arranged in a coiled fashion and each of the chambers tends to be elongate, so that the overall form of fusulinids is that of a wheat grain or tiny football. Some fusulinids from Ohio attain maximum lengths in excess of 1 cm and, therefore, are readily visible with the naked eye. Unfortunately, identification of species of fusulinids can be made only by microscopically examining details of their internal structure, which can be very complex. Making these determinations requires specialized grinding and polishing equipment for preparation of **thin**

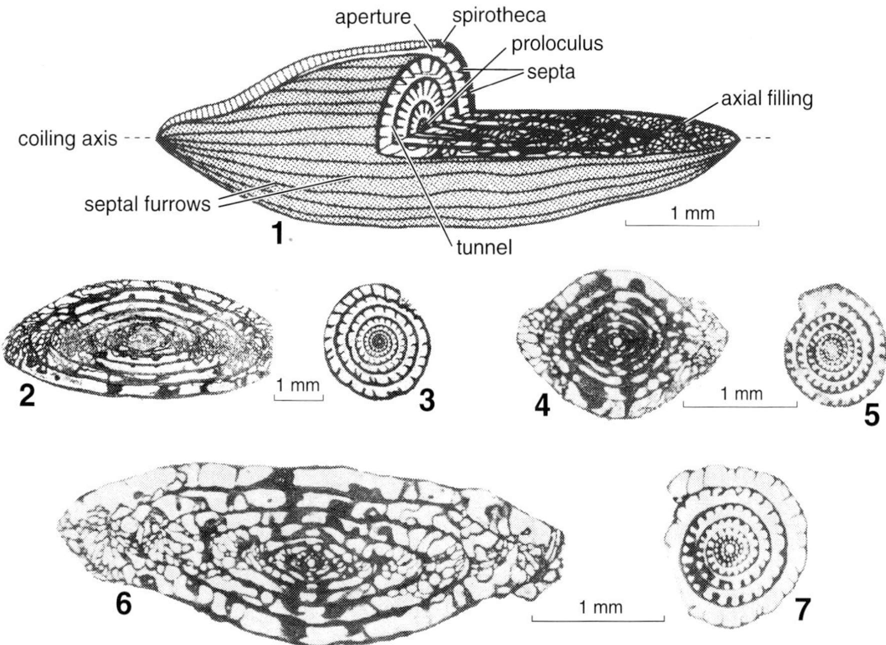

FIGURE 1-2.—Schematic diagram of a fusulinid foraminiferan and representative fusulinids from Ohio. **1**, schematic diagram illustrating the exterior and part of the interior, in cutaway view, of a typical fusulinid showing the arrangement of parts. **2**, **3**, longitudinal (USNM 368928) and cross-sectional (USNM 368929) views of *Triticites ricei* Douglass from the Ames limestone (Conemaugh Group, Pennsylvanian). **4**, **5**, longitudinal (USNM 368909) and cross-sectional (USNM 368915) views of *Fusulinella iowensis* Thompson from the Mercer limestone (Pottsville Group, Pennsylvanian). **6**, **7**, longitudinal (USNM 368897) and cross-sectional (USNM 368903) views of *Beedeina leei* (Skinner) from the Putnam Hill limestone (Allegheny Group, Pennsylvanian). Figures 2-7 from Douglass (1987, pls. 15, 16).

sections, slices of rocks or fossils that are thin enough to allow light to pass through so the specimen can be examined through a microscope. A discussion of the identification procedures of these organisms is beyond the scope of this work.

PHYLUM PORIFERA

The Porifera, or sponges, are organisms in which the body consists of a sacklike structure and the skeleton is constructed of needlelike units called **spicules** (figs. 1-3, 1-4). These skeletal elements may be composed of calcite ($CaCO_3$), opaline silica (SiO_2), or a complex organic material called spongin, the stuff of natural bath sponges. Sponge spicules are united to form the skeleton of sponges in a variety of ways, but they generally do not form a well-defined, rigid skeleton. As a result, when a sponge dies and the tissue decomposes, either the spicules tend to be scattered on the sea floor and lost or the sponge may collapse, preserving the arrangement of spicules, to some degree, but not preserving the shape of the living sponge. Their preservation makes the study of fossil sponges extremely difficult and has resulted in the recognition of relatively few species of fossil sponges, although they were probably much more diverse than the known fossil record would indicate.

The group is mainly marine and has a mainly marine geologic history. A few fossil sponges are known from freshwater habitats. Sponges are sedentary animals that typically are attached to some firm object on the sea floor. Food is extracted from water as the water flows through canal systems in the animal. Fossil sponges have been reported in rocks as old as the Precambrian, although they are more common in Cambrian and younger rocks. The group is still

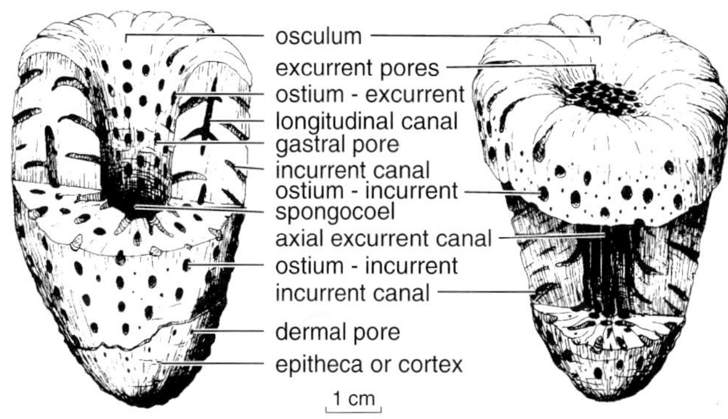

FIGURE 1-3.—Schematic diagrams showing the parts of a typical living sponge.

represented by a diverse array of genera and species in modern habitats.

One group of sponges, the stromatoporoids (fig. 1-5), differs from other sponges in secreting a calcareous skeleton of thin **laminae** separated by vertical **pillars**. Stromatoporoids are locally common in Ohio. Because they are substantially different in structure from other sponges, they are treated in a separate chapter (Chapter 5).

PHYLUM CONULARIIDA

The Conulariida is a relatively small phylum of extinct organisms whose geologic range extends from the Cambrian Period to the Triassic Period. Their fossil remains are known from marine rocks at numerous localities in Ohio, especially from Mississippian rocks. The **exoskeleton**, or **integu-**

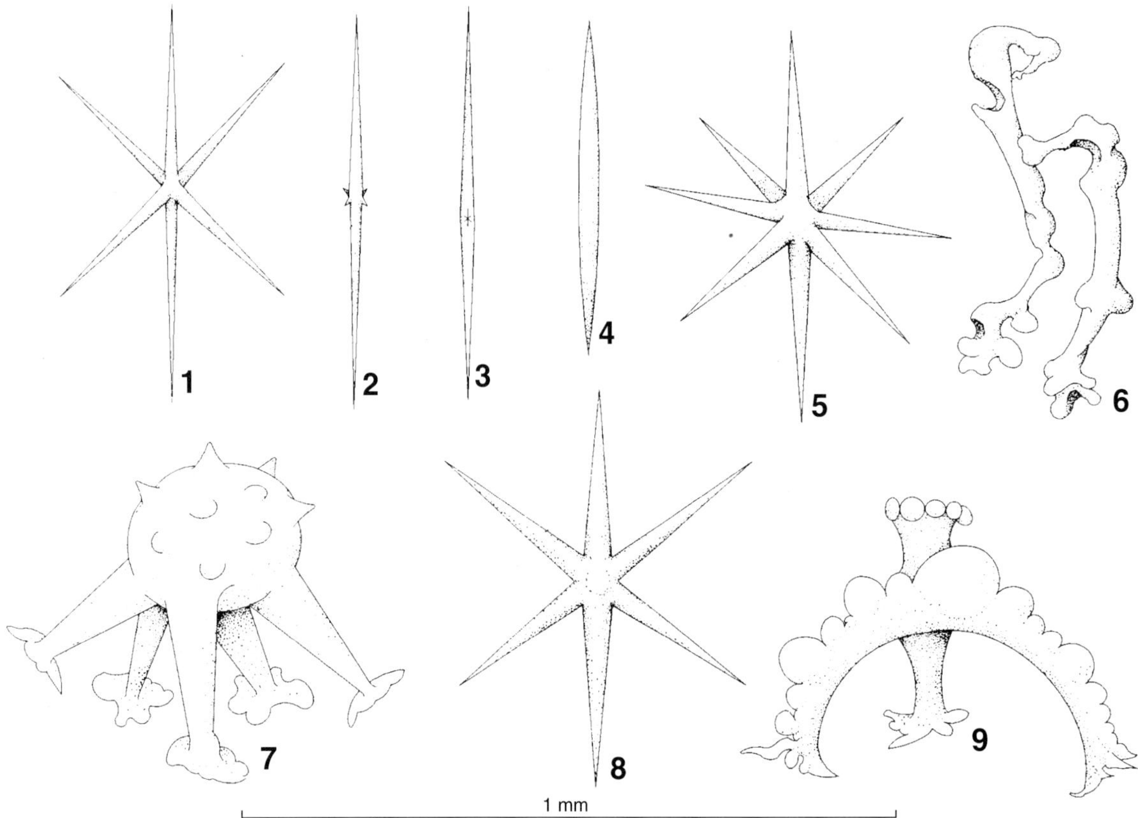

FIGURE 1-4.—Sketches of spicule types that occur in sponges of Ohio. **1**, normal hexactine; **2**, **3**, rhabdodiactines with short, lateral rays or an axial cross as ray remnants; **4**, oxea; **5**, octactine; **6**, two generalized heloclones; **7**, sphaeractine with swollen centrum and radiating rays; **8**, sexiradiate, a modified octactine that lacks vertical rays like ones shown in **5**; **9**, tricranoclone. Numerous other varieties of spicules are developed in other fossil sponges, but these illustrated forms are the common spicules in the sponges of Ohio.

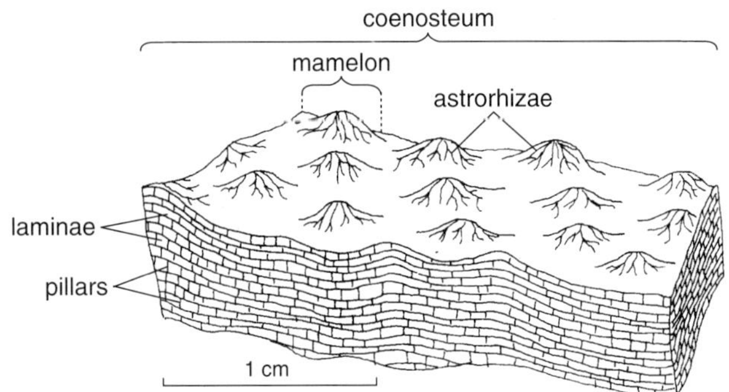

FIGURE 1-5.—Schematic diagram of part of a stromatoporoid showing morphology of the surface and a cross-sectional view.

ment, of a conulariid forms an elongate, four-sided pyramid that has a closed **apex** at the narrow end and an open aperture at the wide end (fig. 1-6). As preserved, the skeleton is composed of a phosphate-rich mineral, apatite. Each of the four sides, or **faces**, is crossed by pairs of narrow, curved **ridges** that meet at a **midline**. At each corner, a **corner groove** is present. Conulariids typically range in size from 1 cm to more than 30 cm in complete adult length. The conulariid skeleton was evidently somewhat flexible, and they are commonly preserved as flattened fossils. Rarely, specimens are found that show a narrow **stalk** extending from the apex. The stalk attached the animal to the sea

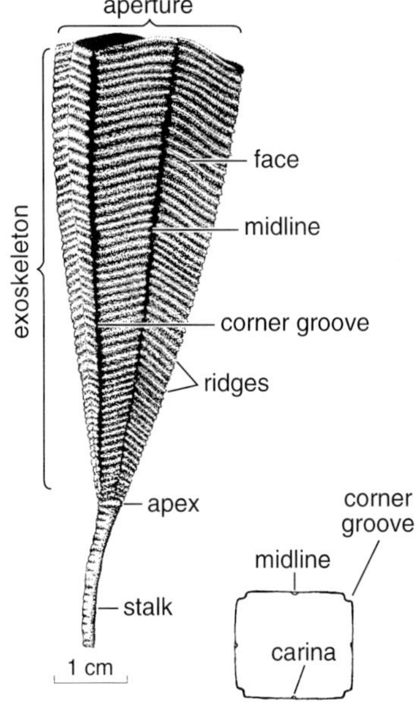

FIGURE 1-6.—Schematic diagram of a typical conulariid and cross-sectional view through the exoskeleton.

floor. The general architecture of the exoskeleton and the overall form make conulariids difficult to confuse with members of the other phyla of invertebrate animals.

PHYLUM CNIDARIA

The Cnidaria (formerly part of the phylum called Coelenterata) includes such marine animals as sea anemones, jellyfish, and corals. Because they are soft bodied, most types of cnidarians are rare in the fossil record. However, because corals have hard parts, they have had a long, and at times prolific, geologic record from the Late Precambrian to the Recent. Corals are common in some fossiliferous rocks in Ohio.

The outer skeleton, or **corallum**, of corals is composed of aragonite or calcite (both $CaCO_3$) and may consist of a single individual or many individuals living in a **colony**. The exoskeleton of an individual coral is generally conical, although it may be irregularly curved and twisted (fig. 1-7). The conical form of the skeleton may not be immediately obvious in colonial corals, in which many individual skeletons, called **corallites**, are fused together to form a larger unit (fig. 1-8). Whether a coral lives as a solitary individual or in a colony, three types of partitions are variously developed in the interior of the skeleton. The most common partitions are **septa**, which are longitudinal and extend from the beginning point of growth, the apex, to the open end of thc conc. Other partitions, called **tabulae**, cut across the cone as a series of platelike structures or shelves. Some corals have bubble-shaped partitions called **dissepiments**. The shape, arrangement, number, and relative strength of development of septa, tabulae, and dissepiments are significant characters in the identification of corals. Another feature that may be observed in some coral skeletons is the **columella**, a thickened structure that defines the axis of the coral skeleton. The exterior of the skeleton may exhibit **growth lines** representing progressive stages in the growth of the organism. Coral colonies exhibit a variety of growth forms. Some are branching, bushlike colonies that have trumpet-shaped corallites. Others are **encrusting** and superficially look like encrusting bryozoans. Most corals attached to the sea floor or some other hard surface during some part of their life cycle.

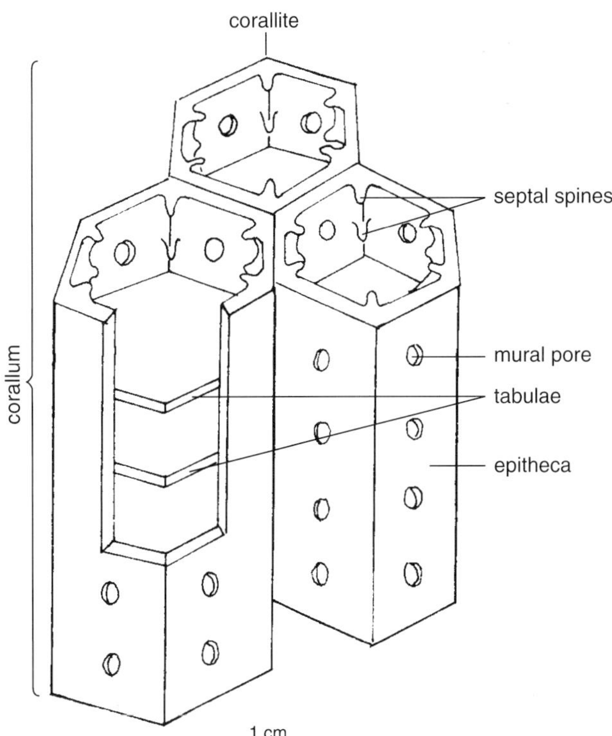

FIGURE 1-8.—Schematic diagram of a typical colonial tabulate coral.

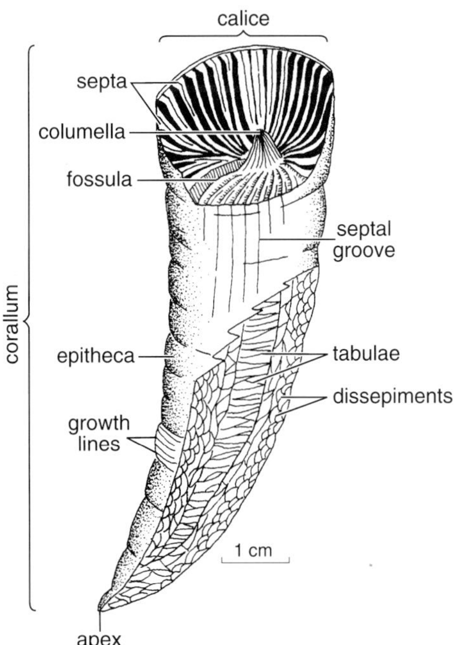

FIGURE 1-7.—Schematic diagram of a typical solitary rugose coral skeleton with a cutaway view showing internal morphology.

PHYLUM ARTHROPODA

The Arthropoda is the largest and the most diverse phylum of invertebrate animals. The Arthropoda includes insects (fig. 1-9), spiders, centipedes, millipedes, pill bugs, trilobites (fig. 1-10), crabs, lobsters, barnacles, ostracodes (fig. 1-13), and many other groups. Arthropods have a complex exoskeleton that is composed primarily of **chitin**, a complex celluloselike organic material that covers the outer surface of the animal. The chitinous exoskeleton may be either relatively thin and flexible or partly **calcified** and hardened into the more rigid skeleton typical of crabs and lobsters. Because all arthropods have bodies composed of many segments, that segmentation is generally reflected in the skeletons of the animals. Thus, arthropod fossils commonly can be recognized because they show some kind of jointing or articulation that allowed major parts of the body and the appendages, or legs, to be moved and flexed.

Arthropods have a long geologic record extending from the Cambrian to the Recent. Some possible arthropods of Precambrian age also have been described. Arthropods thrive in nearly all habitats—marine, freshwater, brackish water, and terrestrial. Arthropods are everywhere! Most fossil arthropods are known from marine rocks. Terrestrial arthropods are limited to rather unusual preservational settings. In Ohio, fossil insects, arachnids, and millipedes have been identified from rocks associated with coal depos-

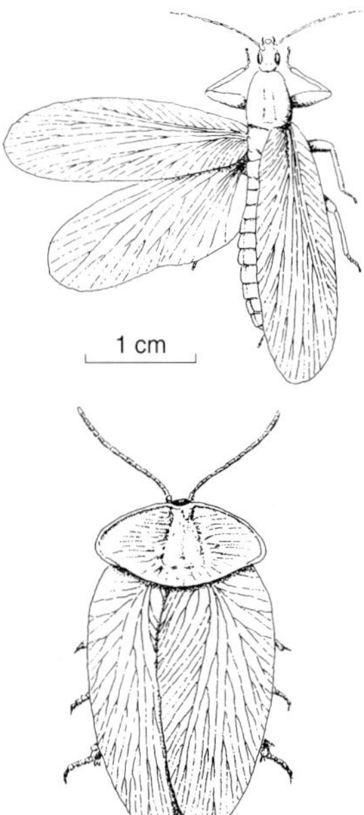

FIGURE 1-9.—Schematic diagrams of a fossil dragonfly (top) and a fossil cockroach (bottom), which are representative of fossil insects that have been collected in Ohio.

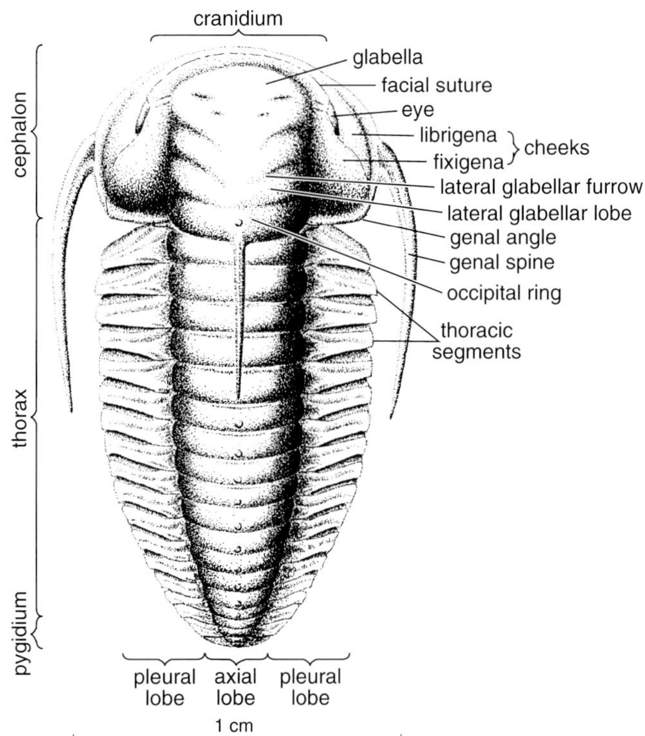

FIGURE 1-10.—Schematic diagram of the dorsal surface of a trilobite, *Triarthrus spinosus* Billings.

its of Pennsylvanian age, but they are exceedingly rare.

Certainly the most prominent larger arthropods in the Paleozoic Era were the trilobites (fig. 1-10). The class Trilobita is an extinct group of marine arthropods characterized by a chitinous exoskeleton covering a head shield, or **cephalon**; a flexible, multisegmented midsection, or **thorax**; and a tail shield, the **pygidium**. The exoskeleton is calcified in most species. The name trilobite comes from the fact that there is also a three-part (tri-lobed) longitudinal subdivision of the skeleton. A central **axial lobe** is flanked by two lateral **pleural lobes**. The head in most species possesses compound **eyes**. **Facial sutures**, which separate the fixed **cheeks** (**fixigenae**) from the free cheeks (**librigenae**) of the cephalon, are present in most species (fig. 1-11). These facial sutures were zones of weakness on the trilobite exoskeleton that could rupture during the **molting** process, permitting the animal to escape the old exoskeleton and grow. The thorax consists of articulated segments that permitted the animal to flex or curl. Many trilobites are found tightly enrolled. The pygidium of a trilobite may be small to large, and with or without distinct segmentation. The appendages of trilobites were situated underneath the animal and are almost never preserved. The only parts of the underside of trilobites that are commonly preserved are the bottom margin of the cephalon, the **doublure**, and a plate situated in front of the mouth region, the **labrum** (fig. 1-12).

Recognition of trilobites when collecting fossils is generally not difficult. Commonly they are dark amber colored or black. Most other fossils, with the notable exception of inarticulate brachiopods, tend to be lighter colored because the skeletons of the other common invertebrate animals are composed of calcium carbonate. However, identification of genera of trilobites may be difficult. Because the skeleton is flexible and because trilobites molt, the skeletal remains of trilobites are commonly broken into smaller parts and the entire animal is not collected; for example, only the head or the tail region of the animal may be collected. Less commonly, isolated segments of the thorax may be the only fossils found.

Also notable in the fossil record of arthropods in Ohio are representatives of the class Crustacea. The most common crustaceans are the Ostracoda, a subclass of tiny organisms that has a geologic record spanning the Cambrian to the Recent. Although they are related to crabs and lobsters, ostracodes have a very different kind of skeleton—it consists of two calcareous **valves** that are joined along one edge by a **hinge** to form a **carapace** (fig. 1-13). Ostracodes are typically identified on the basis of the shape and **ornamentation** of the exterior of the valves as well as on the shape and arrangement of hinge parts and **muscle scars** on the interior of the valves. The shape of the carapace may range from a simple bean-shaped, smooth form to a quadrate, highly ornamented form. The carapace may be ornamented with **spines**, ridges, or cross-hatched patterns. Ostracodes live in a wide variety of aquatic habitats from marine to freshwater. Living forms are found in virtually every body of water in Ohio. Chapter 9 tells how to collect some living ostracodes. Fossil forms are present in many ancient strata in Ohio. Ostracodes occur in enormous numbers in some rocks, but their small size tends to make them an inconspicuous element of fossil assemblages. Because of their size, they must be studied using a hands lens or a microscope.

Another subclass of crustaceans, the Phyllocarida, may be found in moderate numbers in some Devonian rocks of northern Ohio. Phyllocarids are known from marine settings in modern habitats but have never had a particularly good fossil record. Most of them are small, and the chitinous exoskeleton tends to be weakly calcified. Upon death of these animals, the exoskeletons tend to be broken, scavenged, or decomposed. One notable exception is *Echinocaris*,

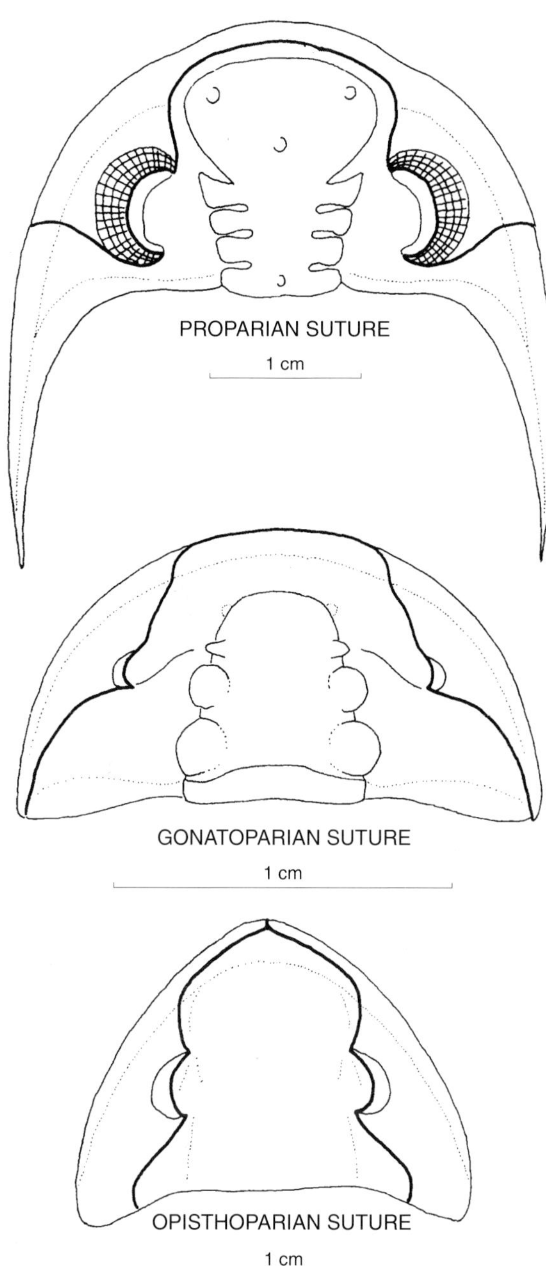

FIGURE 1-11.—Diagrams depicting the most common types of facial sutures (heavier lines) visible on the cephala of trilobites.

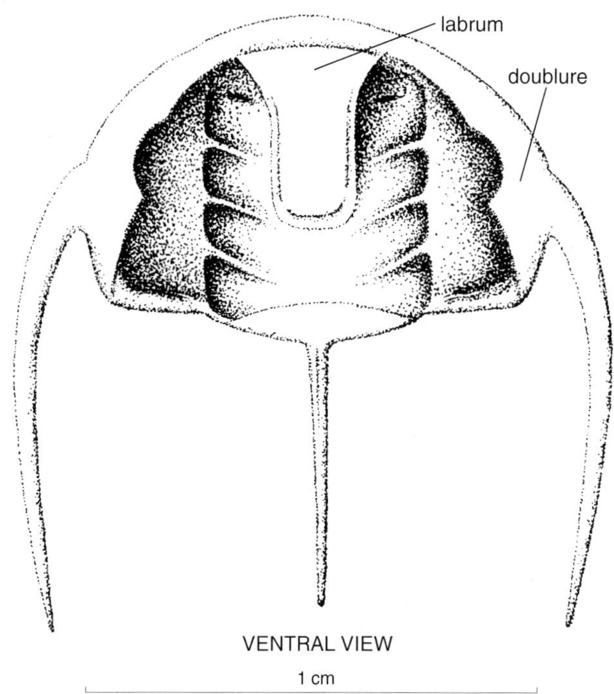

FIGURE 1-12.—Schematic drawing of the underside of the cephalon of a trilobite.

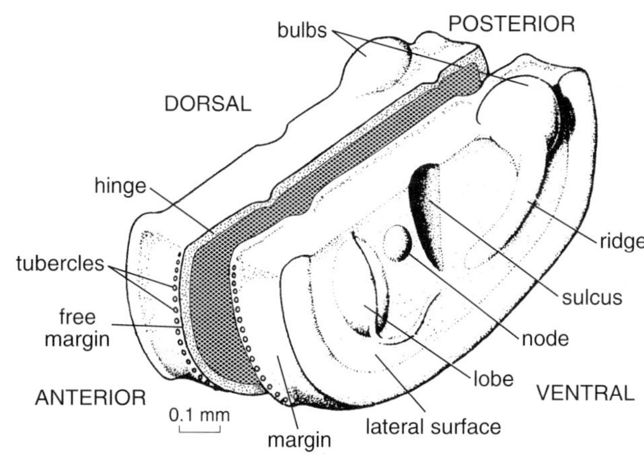

FIGURE 1-13.—Schematic drawing of the bivalved carapace of an ostracode. Modified from Benson and others (1961, fig. 16).

a phyllocarid genus that attains a length of several centimeters (fig. 1-14). *Echinocaris* is known from Middle and Upper Devonian rocks in the Toledo and Cleveland areas. The skeleton, or carapace, of *Echinocaris* consists of two valves that are joined along a relatively inflexible hinge. The valves are ornamented by a series of ridges, grooves, and nodes. The tail portion of *Echinocaris* is a jointed extension of the **abdomen**, which extends from the posterior part of the bivalved carapace and terminates in a three-spined **telson**. As with other arthropods, the skeleton tends to break up upon molting or death so that the most common fossils of *Echinocaris* are the carapaces. Entire animals, including tail sections, are extremely rare.

PHYLUM MOLLUSCA

The Mollusca is an extremely diverse phylum of organisms that has a geologic history spanning the Cambrian to the Recent. In modern marine environments, the mollusks include clams, oysters, snails, squids, octopuses, and the pearly nautilus. Clams and snails also live in freshwater environments. Snails are unique among the mollusks in inhabiting terrestrial environments. Within each major class of mollusks, the majority of species are characterized by having a rigid outer skeleton composed of calcium carbonate. Because the shells of representatives of each of the classes are so distinctive, it is not particularly useful to de-

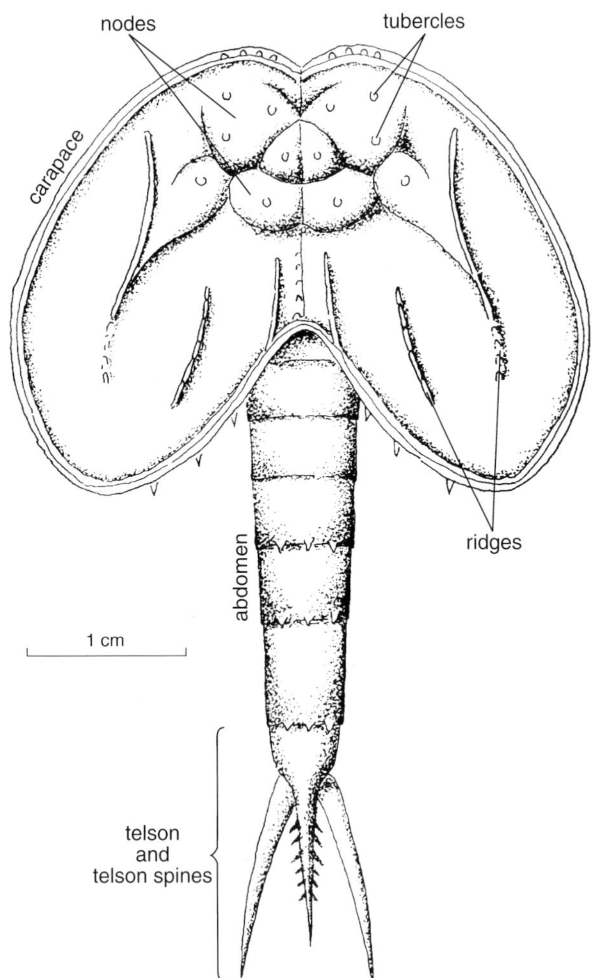

FIGURE 1-14.—Schematic diagram of the phyllocarid crustacean *Echinocaris* Whitfield.

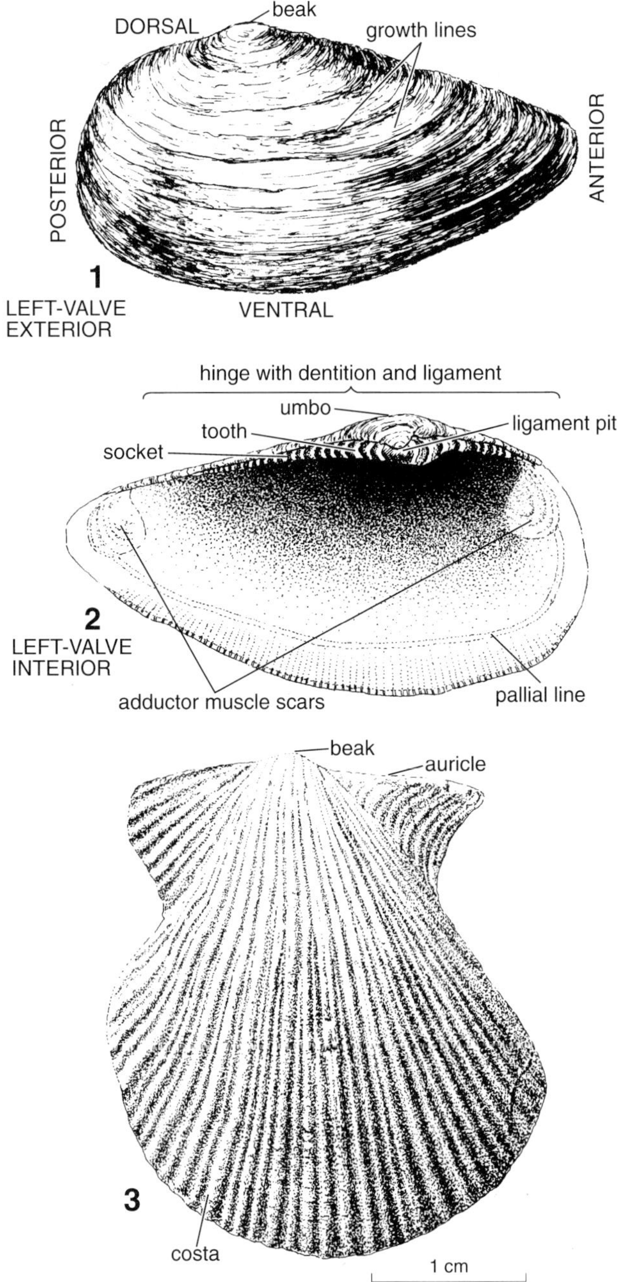

FIGURE 1-15.—Schematic diagrams of representative Paleozoic pelecypods illustrating some of the morphological terms used in the text. **1**, **2**, exterior and interior views of a bivalve like *Palaeoneilo* Hall. **3**, exterior view of a pectiniform pelecypod like *Aviculopecten* M'Coy.

scribe the morphology of the mollusk shell here. Instead, each class of mollusk is best described separately.

Seven classes of mollusks have a substantial fossil record; three of these—the Pelecypoda (clams), the Gastropoda (snails), and the Cephalopoda (cephalopods)—occur widely throughout the rocks of Ohio. Representatives of the other classes—the Monoplacophora, the Rostroconchia, the Polyplacophora (chitons), and the Scaphopoda (tusk shells)—are rare.

The Pelecypoda (also called Bivalvia or Lamellibranchiata) is a class of bivalved organisms (fig. 1-15) whose geologic record spans nearly all of the Paleozoic to the Recent. Modern pelecypods may be found in both marine and freshwater habitats. Lakes, rivers, and streams in Ohio are populated with a wide variety of pelecypods today. In the fossil record in Ohio, pelecypods are moderately common constituents of marine rocks of Paleozoic age and of freshwater deposits associated with the Pleistocene glaciation.

The shell of a pelecypod or clam consists of two valves that are joined at a hinge. The shell opens and closes about the hinge, which is generally constructed of a series of **teeth** and **sockets** in each of the valves. A flexible, organic ligament along the hinge or in a centrally located pit serves as a spring to open the two valves when the animal relaxes the **adductor muscles**. The ligament typically is not preserved. The shells are closed by one or two adductor muscles, which leave impressions, or muscle scars, on the interior of the clam shells. Muscle scars are as important in the identification of the genera of clams as is the general shape, size, and outline of the shell. In general, the two valves of the clam shell tend to be mirror images of one another, that is, a plane passing through the hinge line and between the valves divides the animal into symmetrical halves. The valves to the right and left of this plane tend to be similar in shape and proportion. This pattern of symmetry aids in distinguishing clam shells (plane of symmetry passes along the hinge line and between the valves) from the superficially similar, but unrelated, brachiopods (plane of symmetry passes through the valves at right angles to the hinge line; see fig. 1-26). The outline of clam shells ranges from the irregular form of oysters to very rounded forms with straight hinges, such as the pectens (scallops; see fig. 1-15.3), to nearly spherical forms. The range in size of clams is very great, but most of those known from rocks in Ohio range from about 1 cm to about 10 cm in length. The exterior of the shells typically exhibits growth lines marking successive stages in the growth of the animal. In many genera, these growth lines are crossed by more prominent ribs (**costae**), ridges, or grooves which further ornament the shell.

As with living representatives of this class, fossil pelecypods are known from marine and freshwater deposits. Most clams are able to move about by using a fleshy foot that can be extended along and beyond the margin of the valves opposite the hinge line. Pelecypods circulate water through the shell interior, where oxygen and waste gases are exchanged by gills and food is captured by soft structures surrounding the mouth.

The class Rostroconchia (fig. 1-16) is a group of mollusks that, until recently, had been considered to be pelecypods. However, although their shell appears to consist of a pair of generally symmetrical valves, the rostroconchs differ from pelecypods in several essential ways. Rostroconchs lack a functional hinge, and what appears to be two valves is thought to be a single valve that has been folded over. The initial, larval shell of rostroconchs is a single cap-shaped valve. If the interior of the valve is examined, muscle scars and other structures of attachment of the soft tissue to the shell interior are recognizably different from comparable structures in the pelecypods. The soft-bodied portion of rostroconchs communicated with the shell exterior by means of openings in the shell at either end of the valve. Food and oxygenated water could be drawn into and expelled out of the shell by means of these openings. Little is known about the biology of rostroconchs, however, because they are extinct. Their geologic record extends through the Paleozoic. Representatives of this class have been found in Ordovician, Devonian, Mississippian, and Pennsylvanian rocks in Ohio.

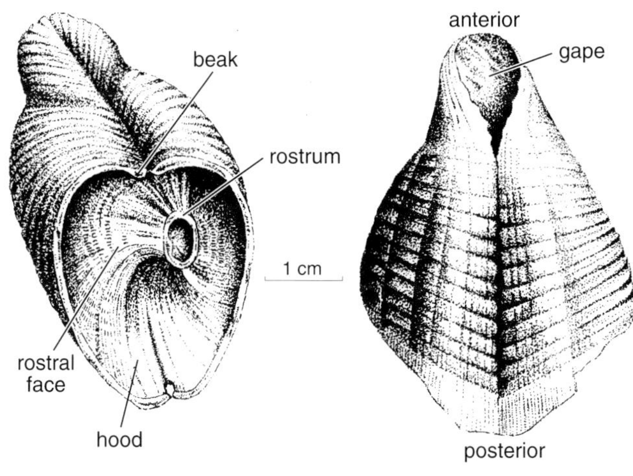

FIGURE 1-16.—Schematic diagrams of a rostroconch.

The class Gastropoda, which includes the modern-day snails and slugs, has a geologic history spanning most of the Paleozoic to the Recent. Modern gastropods are known to live not only in marine and freshwater habitats but also on land. Thus, they are ecologically the most diverse class of mollusks. The skeleton of gastropods consists of a hollow, conical tube which is generally coiled into some form of spiral, similar to a corkscrew (fig. 1-17). The apex, or point of origin of growth of the conical skeleton, is readily distinguishable and the shell can be seen to spiral away and downward from that apex toward the open end, the aperture. The angle of coiling may differ markedly, producing a shell with a very high **spire** (fig. 1-17.1) or one in which the apex is elevated only slightly above the plane of coiling. In some forms the shell is coiled in a single plane (**planispiral**; fig.1-17.2). Thus, variations in the mode of coiling largely determine the general appearance of gastropod shells. The aperture may vary in cross-sectional shape. The surface of the shell may be variously ornamented by growth lines, ribs, grooves, cross-hatched patterns, or spines. These variations in coiling, aperture, and ornamentation are the features typically used to distinguish one genus of gastropod from another.

The class Cephalopoda includes the modern-day squids and octopuses as well as a shelled form, the pearly nautilus (fig. 1-18). Although most modern cephalopods lack an external skeleton, the fossil record from the Cambrian to the Recent includes a vast array of cephalopods which did se-

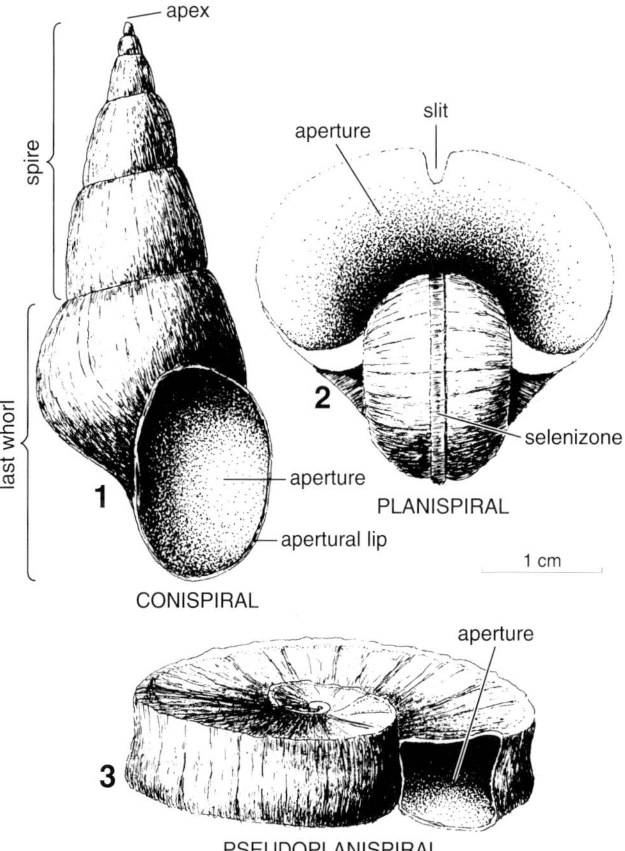

FIGURE 1-17.—Schematic diagrams of three gastropods illustrating variation in manner of coiling of the shell and some morphological terms.

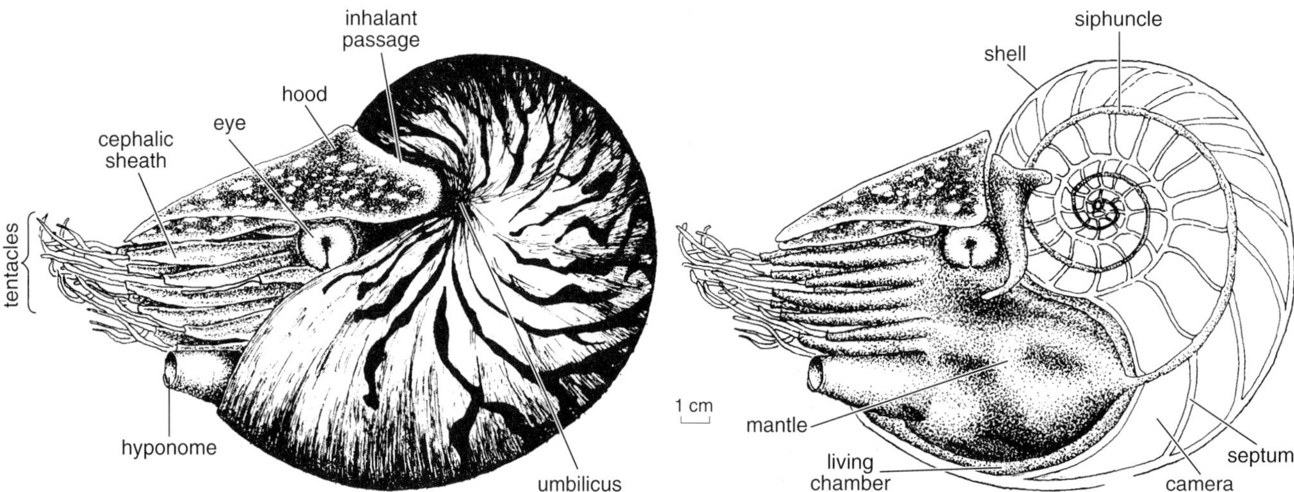

FIGURE 1-18.—Schematic views of the exterior (left) and interior (right) of the living shelled cephalopod, *Nautilus*.

crete, as does the pearly nautilus, a calcium carbonate skeleton, or **conch**. Therefore, cephalopods are important elements in the fossil record.

The shell of a cephalopod may be a coiled, conical tube, similar to that of a gastropod, or it may be straight or slightly curved (fig. 1-19); however, unlike most gastropods, the shell of a cephalopod tends to be partitioned internally by a series of transverse septa (fig. 1-20). These septa close off the initial and successive portions of the cephalopod shell so that the main body of the animal resides only in the actively growing, widest part of the cone. The animal has a thin fleshy stalk, the **siphuncular cord**, that extends through an opening in each of the septa to the tip of the shell in a more or less mineralized tube or sheath called the **siphuncle** (fig. 1-21). Cephalopods are exclusively marine organisms. The siphuncular cord permits gas and fluid exchange into the chambers in the older portion of the shell to adjust buoyancy so that the animal is able to float or swim at various levels in the ocean. The gas and fluid exchange through the siphuncular cord also allowed some of the early cephalopods to deposit complex mineral structures along the siphuncle and in the chambers (see fig. 1-20). Although these structures are important in exact identification of straight cephalopods, they can rarely be seen without sectioning the conch. The septa that divide the interior of cephalopod shells may be nearly flat, slightly concave, or intensely folded and corrugated. The septa are not visible from the shell exterior, but the pattern made by the junction, or **suture**, of the septa with the walls of the cone is important in the identification of genera of cephalopods (fig. 1-22). The suture pattern can be observed only in broken conchs or in internal molds.

Also important in cephalopod identification are the overall shape, size, and manner of coiling of the cephalopod shell. The form of cephalopod shells ranges from straight or nearly straight (**orthoconic**), to slightly arcuate (**cyrtoconic**), to very tightly coiled; in very tightly coiled forms only the last coil is visible from the exterior. Most coiled cephalopods tend to be coiled in a single plane so that a cut through the center of the aperture and down the midline of coiling produces symmetrical right and left sides. Most of the cephalopods known from the fossil record in Ohio tend to be of moderate to small size; the smallest may be about 1 cm in diameter,

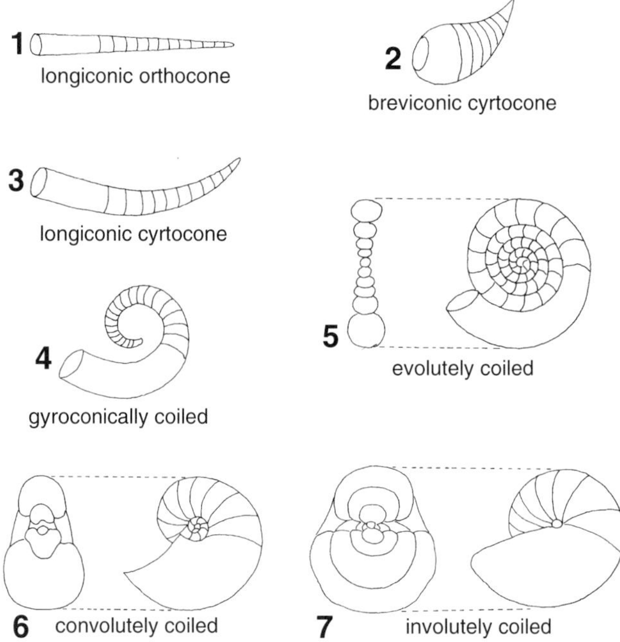

FIGURE 1-19.—Manner of coiling and cross-sectional shape (left-hand diagrams in **5**, **6**, **7**) of whorls of representative cephalopods. Modified from Sturgeon and others (in press).

and the largest about 10 cm in diameter. As preserved in the Paleozoic rocks of Ohio, straight forms rarely exceed 40 cm in length, although whole individuals may have been much longer.

The other classes of mollusks known from Ohio must be considered exceedingly rare and, therefore, it is unlikely that they would be encountered in collecting. The class Polyplacophora includes the modern-day chiton, which has a skeleton composed of eight separate plates which cover much of the upper surface of a flattened, sluglike body. When these animals are preserved in the fossil record, the plates tend to become separated from one another; the breakup of the plates, coupled with their relatively small size (commonly less than a centimeter across), makes polyplacophorans relatively difficult to recognize. Members of the class Scaphopoda, or tusk shells, have a conical, slightly arcuate shell that is open at both ends. Although scaphopods are known to range from Ordovician to Recent, they have never been a large or diverse group and have only rarely been collected from rocks in Ohio. The class Monoplacophora includes cap-shaped mollusks that have multiple, paired muscle scars in the shell. Although they are known from Paleozoic rocks, fossils of this group are not known so far from Ohio.

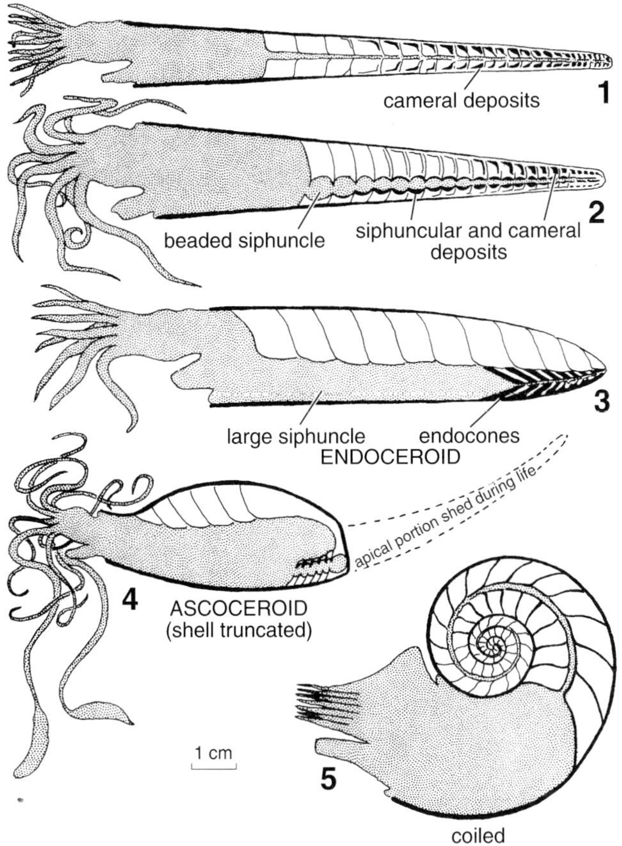

FIGURE 1-20.—Outline drawings of several forms of cephalopods showing straight or slightly curved septa; the regions occupied by soft tissue (stippled pattern), including the head region with tentacles, the body, and the siphuncular cord; and types of deposits (cameral and siphuncular deposits, endocones) that helped keep the living animal in a more-or-less horizontal position. After Moore, Lalicker, and Fischer, (1952).

PHYLUM BRYOZOA

Members of the phylum Bryozoa are exclusively colonial organisms (fig. 1-23). Although modern bryozoans are known from both freshwater and marine settings, only the marine forms have hard skeletons composed of calcite. Thus, marine bryozoans are the only forms that have a substantial fossil record. Individual bryozoans, called **zooids**, within a colony are extremely tiny. Each zooid secretes an individual external skeleton, called a **zooecium** (plural = zooecia). Zooecia never attain diameters greater than 1 mm. However, when joined together into a colony, or **zoarium** (plural = zoaria), bryozoans may form encrusting mats or

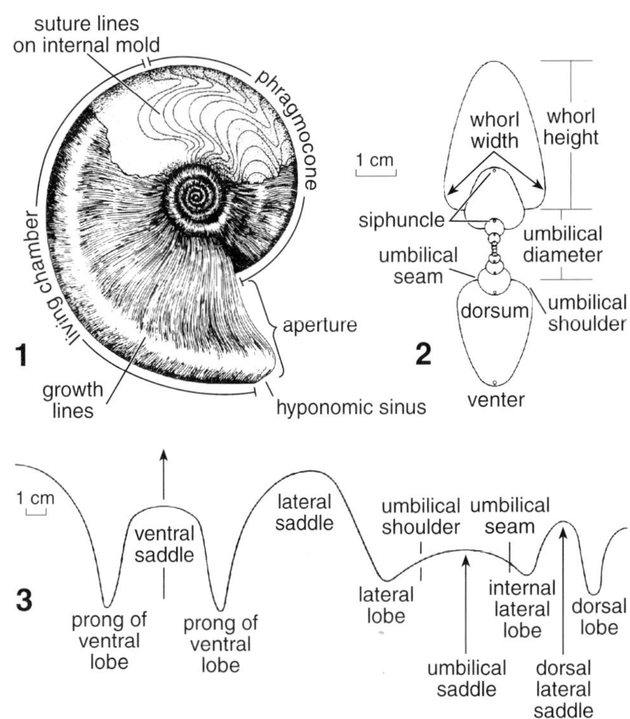

FIGURE 1-22.—Schematic diagrams of a coiled ammonoid cephalopod with complexly folded septa. **1**, shell exterior and suture pattern exposed on a portion of the specimen on which the shell exterior has been removed. **2**, transverse cross section showing outline of whorls and position of the siphuncle. **3**, diagrammatic representation of a suture pattern, constructed by projecting the curved suture line onto a flat surface. The arrow points toward the aperture and marks the middle of the venter. Modified from Mapes and others (in press).

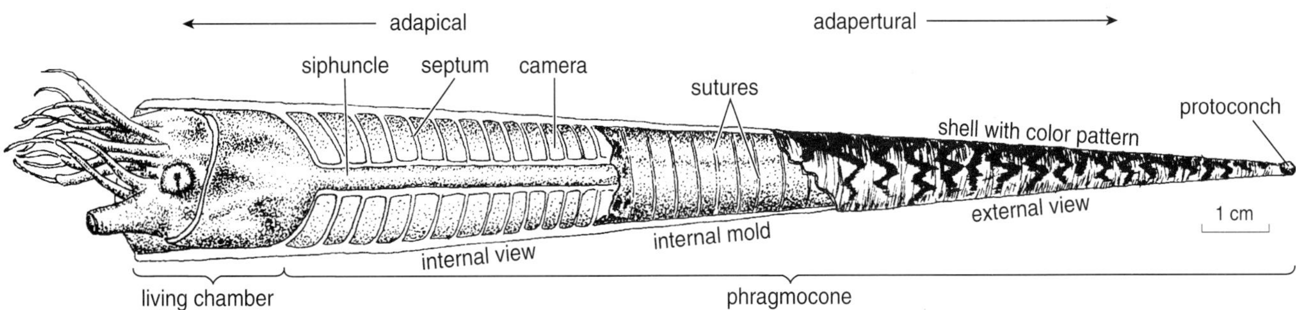

FIGURE 1-21.—Schematic diagram of a straight (nautiloid) cephalopod showing the shell exterior with preserved color pattern and, in cutaway view, the weakly concave septa, the siphuncle, and the form of the sutures on an internal mold.

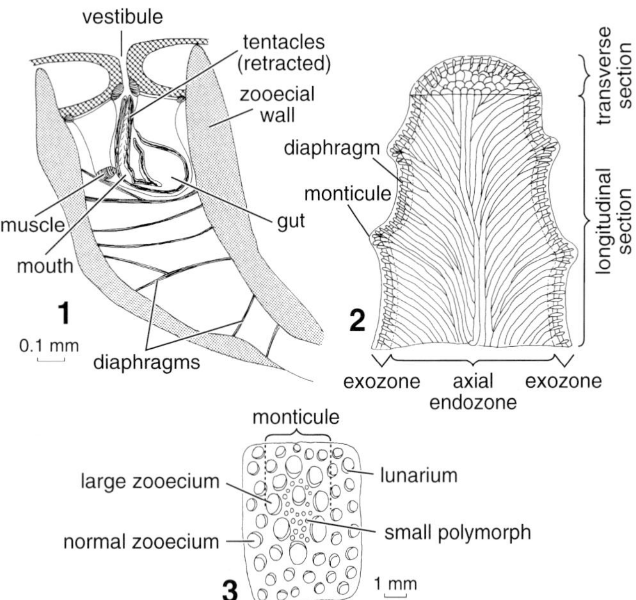

FIGURE 1-23.—Schematic views of bryozoans. **1**, cross section of a zooecium showing the position occupied by an individual zooid retracted into the zooecium. **2**, longitudinal and transverse (top of diagram) sections through a zoarium showing the pattern of growth of a colony, which is a useful character in identification. **3**, tangential section through the exozone of a zoarium showing the variation in the form of zooecia.

dome-shaped or fan-shaped colonies consisting of several hundred individuals and attaining dimensions of a meter or more. Individual zooecia have various shapes, ranging from boxlike structures to elongate vase-shaped skeletons to extremely elongate, cylindrical forms which are typically partitioned by transverse platforms termed diaphragms. Precise identification of bryozoans involves examination of internal structures in thin sections under a microscope. Identification of some of the common bryozoan genera of Ohio, however, can be made by determining the growth habit of the colony and the shape and arrangement of individuals within the colony.

PHYLUM BRACHIOPODA

The Brachiopoda (figs. 1-24, 1-25) is a phylum of exclusively solitary, marine organisms that has an extensive record from the Cambrian Period to the present. In the Paleozoic marine rocks of Ohio, brachiopods are among the most common fossils. The phylum is subdivided into two classes, the Inarticulata and the Articulata, which can readily be distinguished on the basis of several key features of morphology.

The shell of inarticulate brachiopods consists of two valves, a **pedicle valve** and a **brachial valve**, held together by muscles. The valves are composed typically of a leathery, commonly amber to black, organic material impregnated with calcium phosphate; shells of a few species of inarticulate brachiopods are composed of calcite. The valves may not have much ornamentation, although the outer surface typically exhibits growth lines. The growth lines are concentric about the **beak**, the initial point of origin of the valve. The outline of the shells may be circular to elongate or spade shaped. In some species the valves are similarly shaped, whereas in other species one valve is cemented to a hard

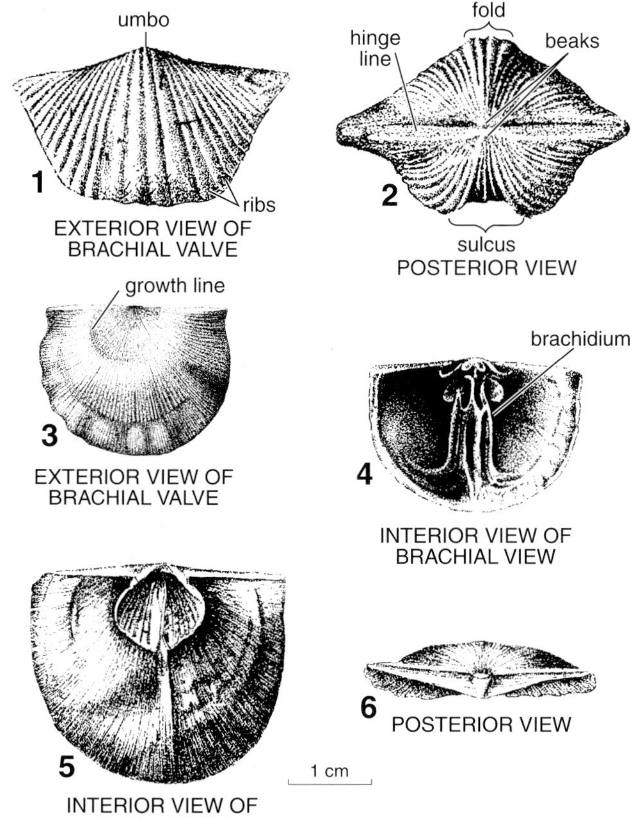

FIGURE 1-24.—Schematic diagrams of representative Paleozoic articulate brachiopods. **1**, **2**, *Platystrophia*. **3-6**, *Strophomena*.

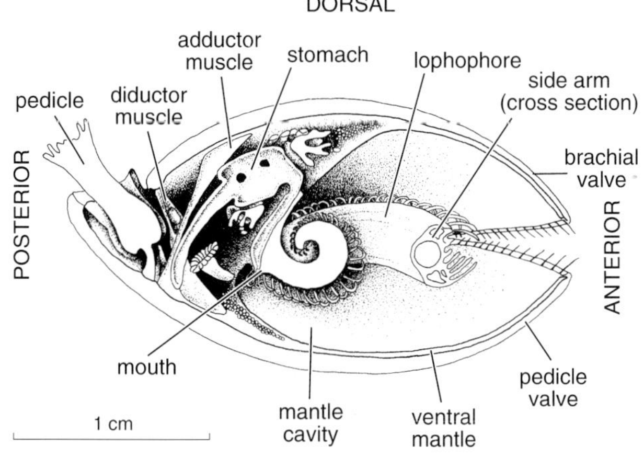

FIGURE 1-25.—Cross-sectional view of a typical living articulate brachiopod, *Terebratulina*, illustrating the morphology of soft tissues and orientation. Modified from Williams and others (1965, p. H6).

surface, such as another brachiopod shell, and the upper valve is a cap-shaped cover. Individual inarticulate brachiopods typically range in length from less than 1 cm to 2 or 3 cm.

Articulate brachiopods have pedicle and brachial valves composed of calcite. Unlike the inarticulates, articulate brachiopods have a hinge along one side of the paired valves.

The **hinge line** may be extremely short or it may be the widest part of the shell. In either case, however, the hinging mechanism includes postlike teeth on the pedicle valve which fit securely into pits, or sockets, on the brachial valve. This tooth-and-socket arrangement permits the valves to be opened around the hinge but prevents the two valves from becoming misaligned. At the center of the hinge, the **pedicle opening** allows a fleshy stalk, the **pedicle**, to extend out from the shell interior. The animal attaches to the sea floor and may rotate by means of this pedicle. In some species, the pedicle opening is partially or entirely closed by accessory plates.

The shape of brachiopod shells is variable; the outline ranges from nearly circular to extremely wide with a drawn-out hinge to shield-shaped, flattened forms. In side view (**profile**), brachiopods range from **biconvex** (both valves convex), to **plano-convex** or **convexi-plane** (one valve flat), to **concavo-convex** or **convexi-concave** (one valve curved toward the other) (fig. 1-26). An ornament of heavy ribs or fine ridges radiating from the beak is common. Some forms have spines over the surface of the shell or along the hinge. Although it is difficult to generalize about the shape of the brachiopod skeleton, most forms are symmetrical. If a plane were passed through the two valves from the beaks to the opposite edges of the valves, the right and left halves would be mirror images of one another (fig. 1-26.1). The two valves, however, are not mirror images of one another; one valve is normally longer or larger than the other.

The interior of the brachiopod shell exhibits a wide variety of features which are important for the identification of the animals. Notable are the adductor and **diductor muscle** scars, pits for attachment of the adductor and diductor muscles used for closing and opening the shell, respectively. A complex set of structures, collectively referred to as the **brachidium**, is extremely important in the classification of articulate brachiopods. The brachidium supports the **lophophore**, a fleshy organ bearing many short tentacles. The lophophore is responsible for circulating food and oxygenated water to the animal inside the shell.

PHYLUM ECHINODERMATA

The Echinodermata (figs. 1-27 to 1-32) is a very large phylum of exclusively marine organisms whose record extends from the Precambrian to the Recent. In modern seas the echinoderms are represented by starfishes, brittle stars, sea urchins, sand dollars, sea cucumbers, and crinoids ("sea lilies"). Modern echinoderms are so diverse, in fact, that they are grouped into five separate classes. The diversity of echinoderms was even greater in the Paleozoic—more than 20 classes of echinoderms have been defined. However, all but five had become extinct by the close of the Paleozoic. These organisms occur in truly staggering numbers in modern as well as ancient marine habitats.

The skeleton of all echinoderms consists of a series of plates of calcium carbonate, each of which is a single crystal of calcite. The plates are enclosed within a leathery covering, or integument. Depending upon the degree to which the individual plates are fused to one another and the degree to which the plates are bound by connective tissue, the individual types of echinoderms may by extremely flexible or very rigid. When an echinoderm dies, the connective tissue decomposes and the individual plates of the skeleton may be separated from one another and scattered about the sea floor. As a result, most groups of echinoderms have a relatively sparse fossil record, at least in terms of complete or nearly complete specimens. On the other hand, some Paleozoic limestones, including some in Ohio, consist almost entirely of the disarticulated, or broken, fragments of echinoderms.

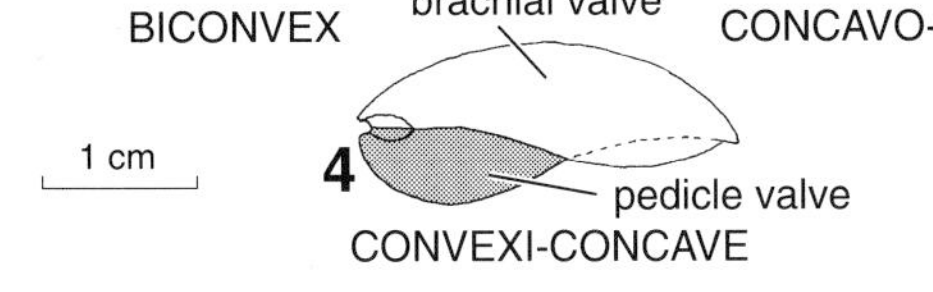

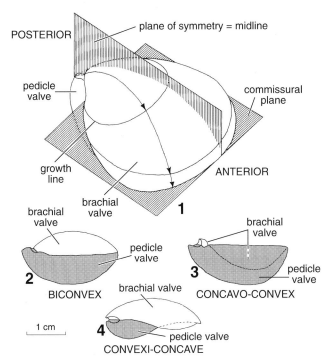

FIGURE 1-26.—Schematic diagrams of brachiopods illustrating terms describing orientation, symmetry, and convexity. Modified from Williams and others (1965, p. H62).

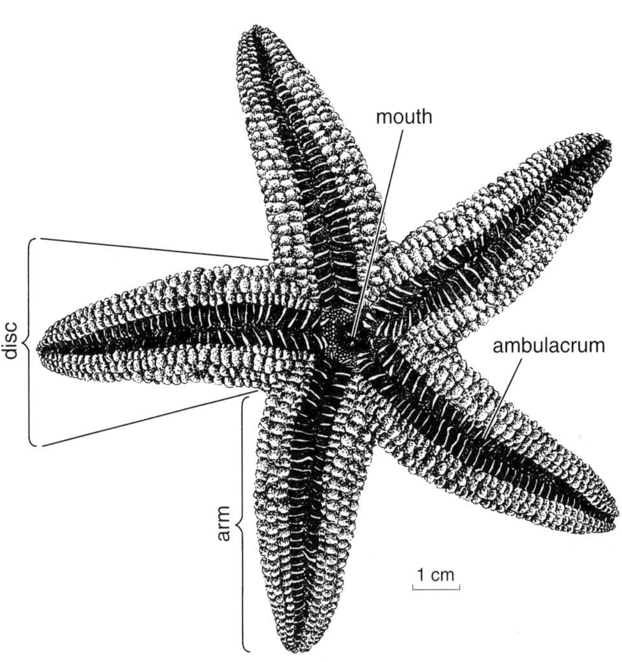

FIGURE 1-27.—Generalized schematic diagram of a starfish, an asteroid echinoderm, illustrating morphological terms used in the text.

Of the numerous classes of echinoderms known from the fossil record, only three, the Crinoidea, the Rhombifera, and the Edrioasteroidea, are common enough in the rocks of Ohio to be considered significant elements of the fossil fauna. The Crinoidea is certainly the most abundant. Other classes of echinoderms that are discussed briefly in Chapter 17 include the Asteroidea (starfishes) (fig. 1-27), the Ophiuroidea (brittle stars), the Echinoidea (sea urchins and sand dollars) (fig. 1-28), the Blastoidea (sea buds) (fig. 1-29), and the Diploporita (fig. 1-31.1).

The class Crinoidea (fig. 1-30) consists of organisms with a sacklike or spherical body, the **calyx**, which is generally elevated above the sea floor on a flexible stem or stalk, called the **column**. This column is composed of a series of washer-shaped plates, called **columnals**, stacked one upon another. The **holdfast** extends from the base of the column and attaches the animal to the sea floor or other hard surface. Crinoid columnals are among the most common fossils in the marine rocks of Ohio. The body of the crinoid is composed of a series of plates. A circle of five, or some multiple of five, **arms** extends above the body. These arms, which have additional branchlets, contain grooved regions, the **ambulacra**, that serve to collect food and transport it to the animal's mouth, which is situated on the upper surface of the body within the circle of arms. This ambulacral system and the **pentameral symmetry** (five-part) are the primary characters defining all of the Echinodermata. The identification of crinoids is based upon the presence or absence of a column; the shape and arrangement of plates on the body; and the shape, development, and arrangement of arms. In most occurrences, fossil crinoid remains are limited to isolated columnals and plates. Rarely, whole bodies without the arms and column are found. Crinoids are seldom preserved as entire specimens, although there are several places in Ohio where they do occur.

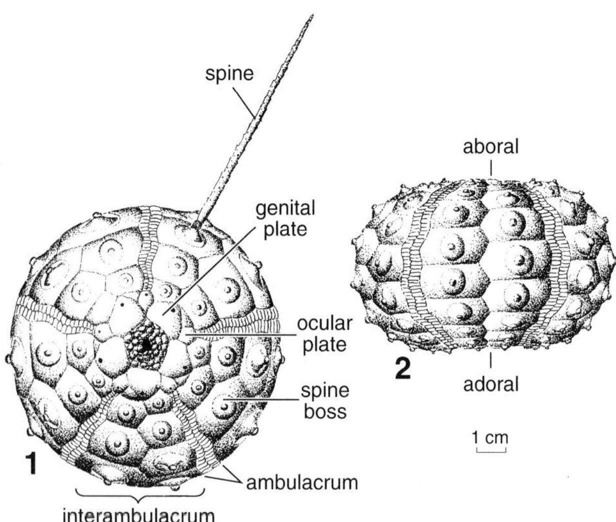

FIGURE 1-28.—Generalized top (**1**) and lateral (**2**) views of a sea urchin, an echinoid echinoderm, illustrating morphological terms used in the text.

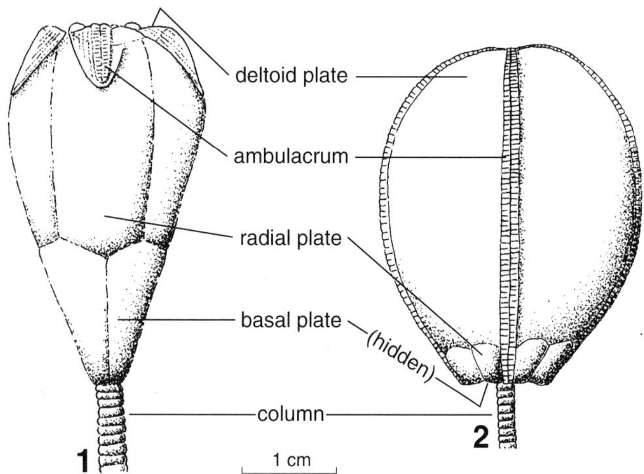

FIGURE 1-29.—Schematic diagrams of blastoid echinoderms illustrating morphological terms used in the text. **1**, *Heteroschisma*. **2**, *Eleacrinus*.

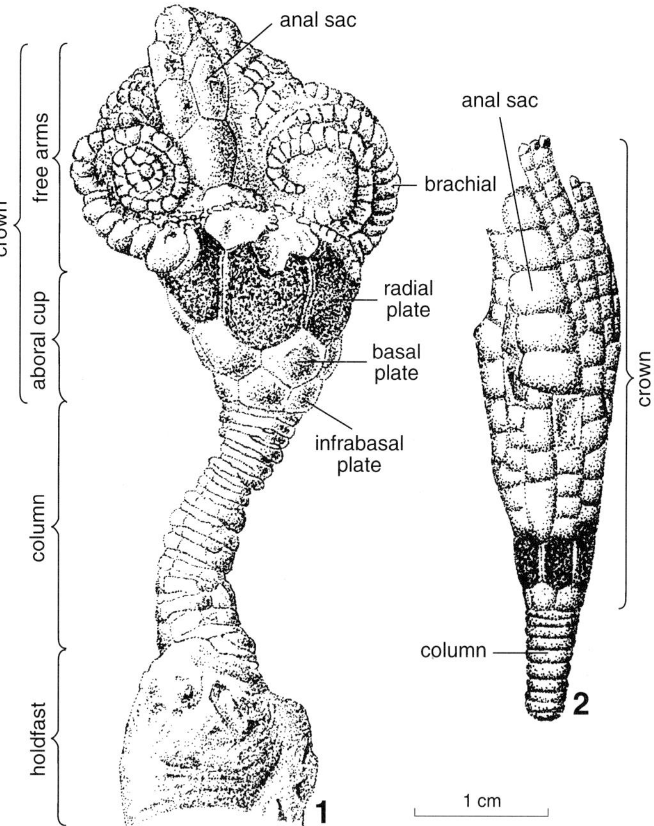

FIGURE 1-30.—Schematic diagrams of typical crinoid echinoderms illustrating morphological terms used in the text. **1**, *Euspirocrinus*. **2**, *Ohiocrinus*.

The class Rhombifera (fig. 1-31.2), previously part of the Cystoidea, consists of species that are superficially like the Crinoidea. Rhombiferans have a sacklike body, called a **theca**, that is elevated above the sea floor by a column. However, the body structure of rhombiferans is somewhat different from that of the crinoids. The basic body of the theca is composed of four plate circlets and pore systems, commonly in a rhombic (diamond-shaped) pattern crossing plate boundaries. Rhombiferans generally have five **brachioles** that extend as simple, unbranched appendages above the body. The ambulacral regions on these brachioles carry food particles to the mouth on the upper surface of the body. Fossil rhombiferans are known throughout much of the Paleozoic but are now extinct. The number of genera of rhombif-

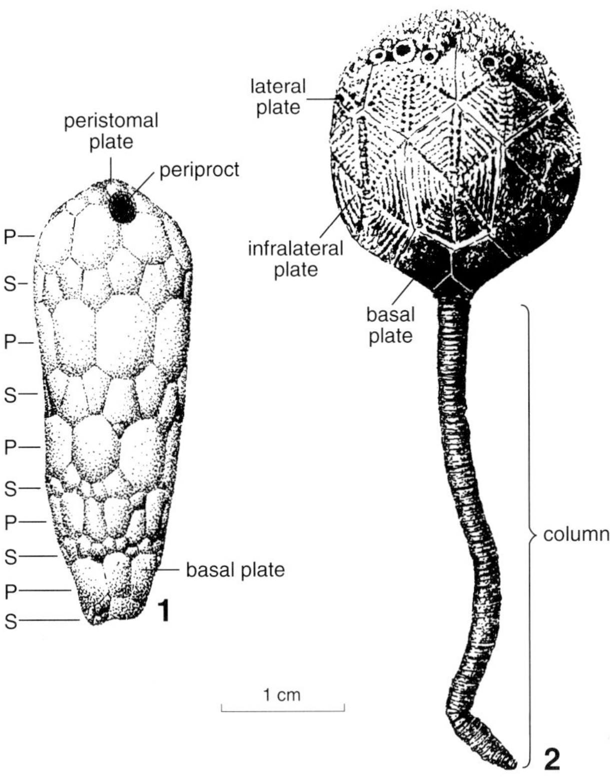

FIGURE 1-31.—Schematic diagrams of diploporan (**1**) and rhombiferan (**2**) echinoderms illustrating morphological terms used in the text. **1**, *Holocystites*. P = primary plate, S = secondary plate. **2**, *Caryocrinites*.

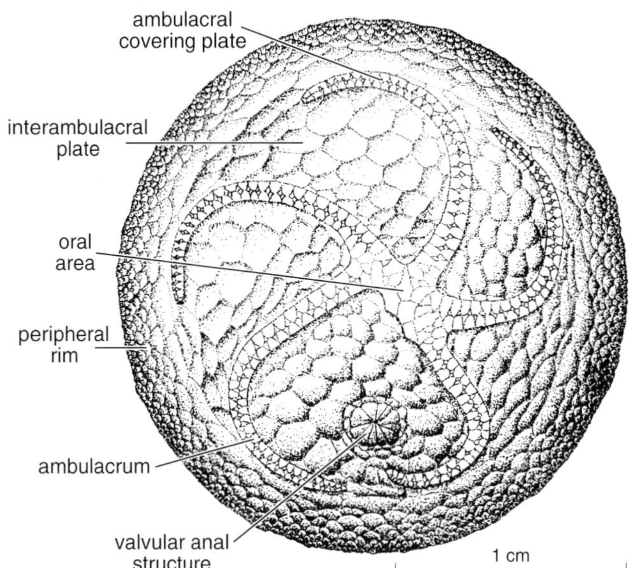

FIGURE 1-32.—Schematic diagram of the edrioasteroid echinoderm *Isorophus* illustrating morphological terms used in the text.

erans is not as great as that of the crinoids, and they are not common in the fossil record. Most fossil rhombiferans are incomplete, consisting only of the theca of the animal with the brachioles and column missing.

Members of the class Edrioasteroidea (fig. 1-32) are probably even rarer than rhombiferans. Edrioasteroids are generally small—less than 2 cm in diameter—and have a disk-shaped body that is attached to some firm surface, commonly the shell of a flat brachiopod. Fossil edrioasteroids in Ohio are known primarily from rocks of Ordovician age in the Cincinnati area. The architecture of edrioasteroids is markedly different from that of crinoids and rhombiferans. The outer margins of the body are defined by a series of small, imbricate plates defining the circular body. The main dome of the body is formed of somewhat larger plates, and the ambulacral region, formed of five sinuous arms reminiscent of the arms of a starfish, is incorporated into the upper surface of this dome. In life, the edrioasteroid was probably inflated into a bulbous form, but, upon death, the structure collapsed to form a nearly flat encrustation. Edrioasteroids are readily recognized on the basis of the sinuous five-rayed ambulacral regions.

OTHER FOSSIL INVERTEBRATE GROUPS

Several other invertebrate groups may be encountered as fossils in Ohio rocks. Some of them are either poorly known or their classification is not well understood. However, because they are common as fossils, it is important that they be mentioned. In general, these fossils are all small—the only feature they have in common.

The most important of these groups is the Conodonta. Conodont fossils consist of small, microscopic to barely visible, amber-colored, toothlike **elements** (fig. 1-33). The morphology of conodont elements is quite variable and ranges from simple tusk-shaped forms to comblike forms that have a serrated edge, to forms that have a broad platform with **denticles** of various shapes situated upon it. Conodonts have been identified in rocks ranging in age from Cambrian to Triassic and, in Ohio, might be anticipated in any of the marine rocks of Paleozoic age. Because conodonts are so variable and they changed very rapidly through time, conodonts are among the best age indicators of all fossils. However, because they are very small, the recognition and identification of conodont elements require extremely careful examination of rock surfaces or microscopic examination of the residue from rock that has been broken into small bits (disaggregated), washed, and sieved. This process is relatively tedious but can result in the collection of thousands of specimens of these interesting organisms. Procedures for making such collections are described in Chapter 2 as well as in Chapter 18. Most manuals dealing with paleontological preparations (see, for example, Feldmann, Chapman, and Hannibal, 1989) give additional, more detailed procedures.

The biological relationship of conodonts is not well understood because nothing quite like them lives today. It is known that a single animal may have possessed several different types of conodont elements, arranged in a predictable pattern, referred to as a conodont **apparatus** (fig. 1-34). Conodont apparatuses, in turn, have been found associated with elongate traceries of soft tissue, and these have led various authors to conclude that conodonts were (1) primitive chordates, distantly related to the vertebrates; (2) arrow worms, representatives of the modern phylum Chaetognatha; or (3) representatives of an extinct phylum, not directly related to any living today. Recent evidence tends to support the first view.

Another enigmatic group is the tentaculitoids (figs. 1-35, 1-36), including the styliolinids. These fossils are small, conical shells, mostly less than 1 cm in length, which are com-

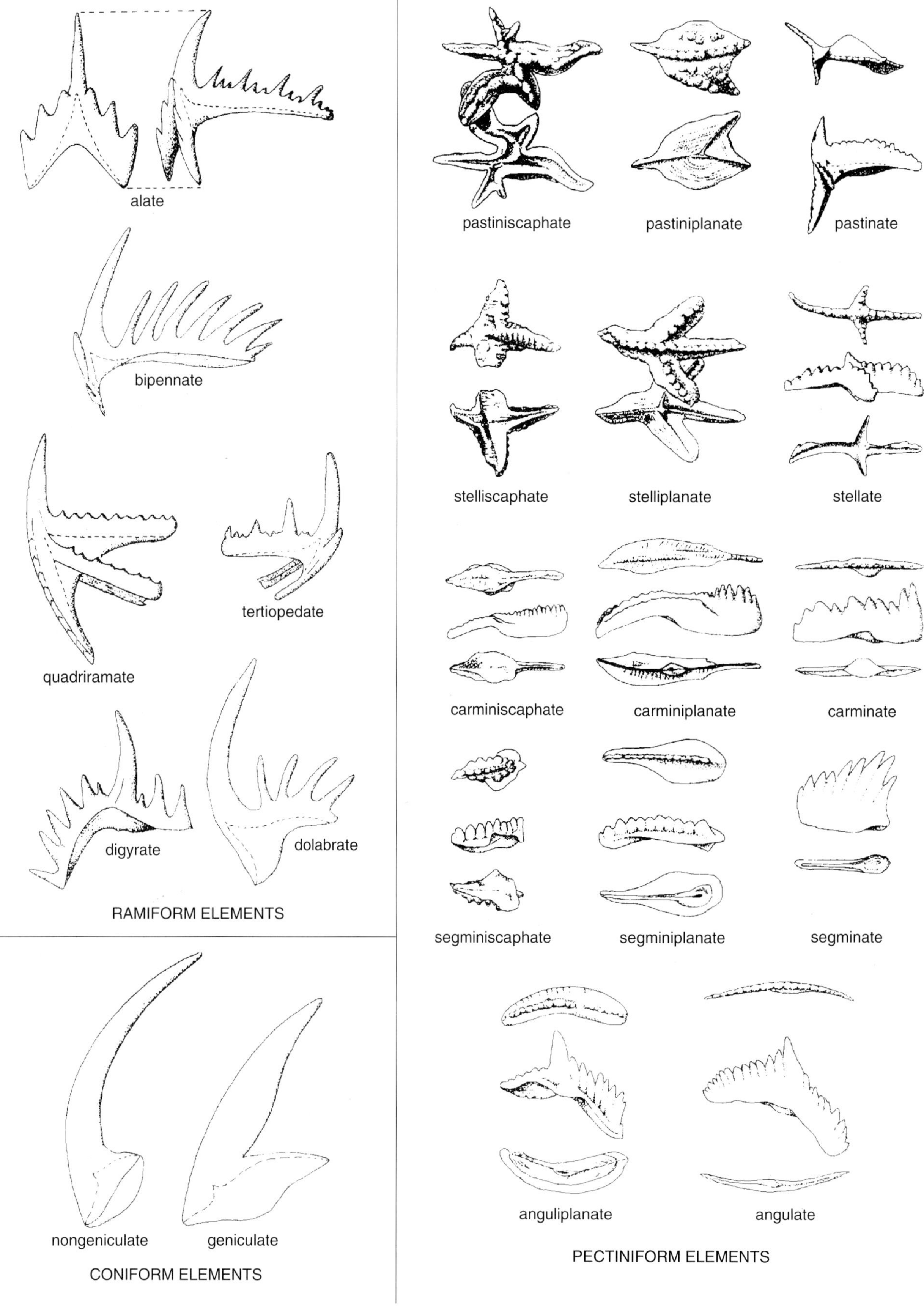

FIGURE 1-33.—Ramiform, coniform, and pectiniform shapes of conodont elements. All elements are less than 1 mm long.

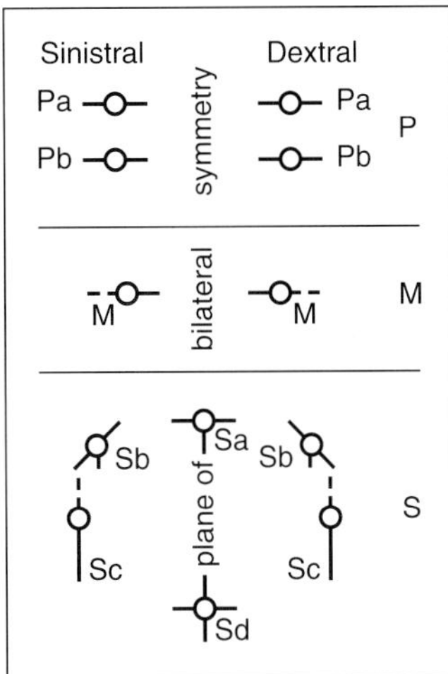

FIGURE 1-34.—Organization of the conodont apparatus. Most conodont apparatuses are composed of three types of elements in regions termed S, M, and P. S-region elements are mostly ramiform; M-region elements are ramiform or coniform; and P-region elements are pectiniform in most species. In many primitive conodonts, however, apparatuses were formed entirely of coniform elements, and in the vast majority of apparatuses both right-handed (dextral) and left-handed (sinistral) versions of the same types of elements occurred. Thus we infer that conodonts were bilaterally symmetrical.

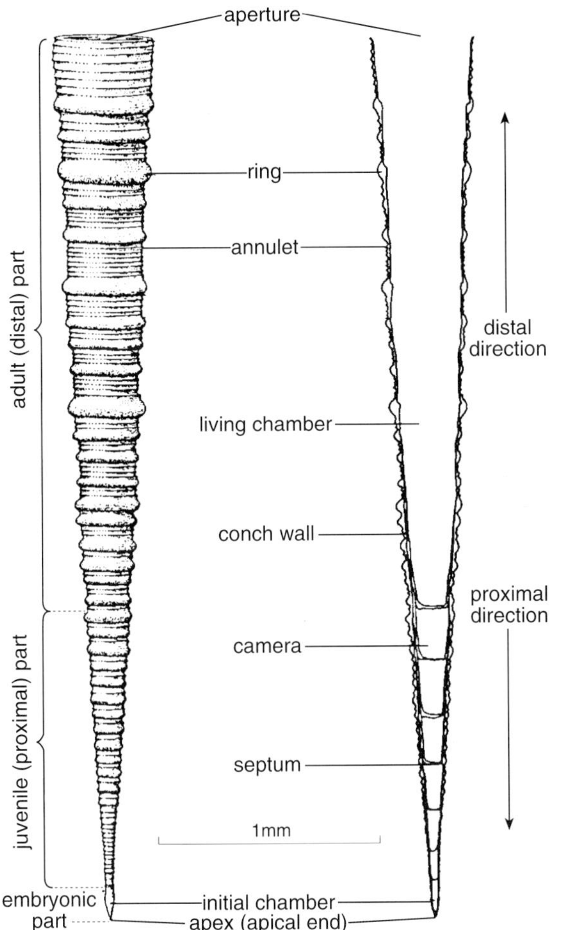

FIGURE 1-35.—Morphological terminology of tentaculitoids. Figure slightly modified from Larsson (1979).

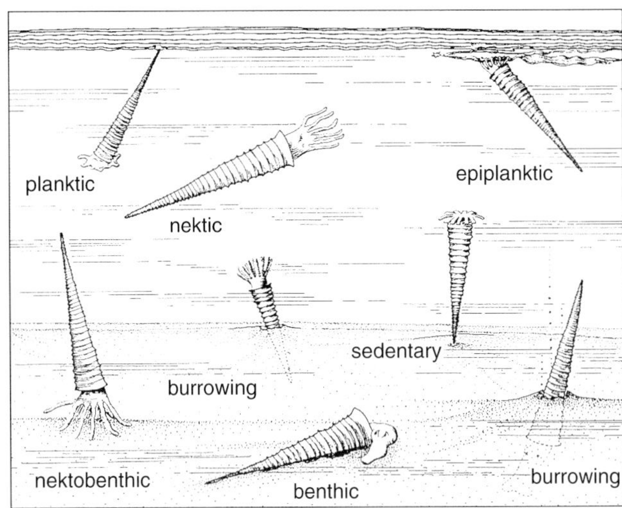

FIGURE 1-36.—Possible modes of life of tentaculitoids. Thick-shelled and relatively heavy forms are likely to have been benthic (bottom dwelling), whereas thin-walled and relatively light forms may have been planktic (floating) or nectic (swimming).

posed of calcium carbonate. Tentaculitoid shells have transverse rings ornamenting the outer surface of the hollow conical tube, whereas styliolinid shells are relatively smooth and either straight or slightly arcuate. Remains of both groups are relatively common in Middle Devonian rocks near Toledo and Columbus, and they may be encountered in Upper Ordovician to Devonian rocks of Ohio. These creatures have been assigned variously to the Mollusca, as the skeletons of tiny mollusks; to the Brachiopoda, as spines; or to other groups. Each of the suggested relationships is flawed and unclear. Tentaculitoids and styliolinids remain interesting fossils whose biological affinities are unknown.

The Graptolithina (fig. 1-37) is a group of invertebrate fossils that are relatively rare in Ohio rocks. Graptolites formed colonies that are either elongate and contain up to a few tens of individuals, or fan shaped and made up of several hundred individuals. The skeleton is composed of a thin organic material, which, upon preservation, tends to be compressed on the rock surface, carbonized, and preserved as a thin black film. Graptolite fossils tend to be small, ranging from about 1 to 3 cm in maximum dimension, but some colonies may reach 1 meter in size. Individuals within the colony are in most cases less than 1 mm across. Those colonies that are formed as single strips have the general appearance of a coping-saw blade. Identification of graptolites is based on the shape of the individuals within the colony as well as on the shape of the overall colony. Although graptolites are rare in Ohio rocks, they do occur in fair numbers in certain rocks of Ordovician age in the Cincinnati region.

VERTEBRATE FOSSILS

Vertebrate fossils consist of the preservable remains of fishes (including sharks), amphibians, reptiles, birds, and mammals. The geological record of vertebrates extends from the Cambrian to the Recent. A large number of species of vertebrates are known from marine, aquatic, terrestrial, and aerial habitats in the Recent; however, fossils of these animals are not particularly abundant in Ohio. In Devonian and Pennsylvanian rocks, a variety of bones and dermal (skin) plates of fish have been identified. The best known

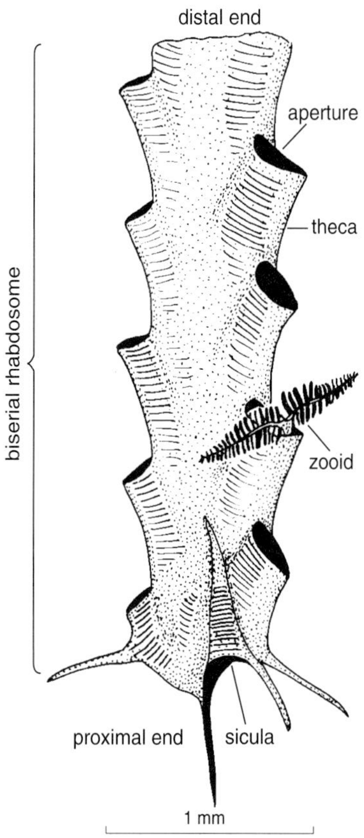

FIGURE 1-37.—Schematic diagram of a graptolite illustrating morphological terms used in the text.

deposits of fossil fishes of this age are in the vicinity of Cleveland, Ohio. Fossil remains of **tetrapods** and fishes of Pennsylvanian and Permian age have been found in Ohio and are abundant at a few localities. Although the entire gamut of vertebrate groups might be anticipated in sediments associated with Pleistocene glaciation, they are generally rare. The most common vertebrate remains from this epoch are large bones, teeth, and tusks of mammals, including mastodons, mammoths, and peccaries.

The identification of vertebrate remains, other than the recognition of them as vertebrate remains, can be relatively difficult. Entire fish fossils in which the outline of the fish is distinguishable can be identified with some ease. However, most vertebrate fossils consist of disassociated bones, teeth, etc. and are extremely difficult to interpret. Whenever fossil vertebrates are encountered, they should be brought to the attention of a specialist so that a determination can be made.

PLANT FOSSILS

Although plants have a fossil record from the Precambrian to the present and are known from marine, freshwater, and terrestrial settings throughout most of this history, the occurrence of plant fossils in any but terrestrial settings is uncommon. Most of Ohio's marine sedimentary rocks contain few plant remains. By far, the best and most likely places to find plant fossils are in the rocks associated with the coal beds of Pennsylvanian age. Here, plant fragments occur in huge quantities and many of them are well enough preserved that they can be identified.

Plant fossils generally can be subdivided into four types of remains: leaves, stems, fruits, and spores or pollen. Fossil leaves are identified on the basis of the overall shape of the leaf, the nature of the leaf margin, the pattern of venation, and the arrangement of leaves on stems. Fragments of plant stems and trunks may be identified on the basis of the pattern of stem branching, scars from leaf bases, and the pattern of bark or scales. The size, shape, and surface texture of fossilized fruits, which are not common, form the basis for their identification. Fossil spores and pollen are identifiable on the basis of their surface morphology, but must be examined under a microscope. Although fossil spores and pollen occur in huge numbers in some sedimentary rock sequences, they are typically extremely tiny and can be extracted from the rocks for study only with great effort. Thus, description and identification of these plant remains is not appropriate here. Only one fossil spore, *Tasmanites*, is large enough and common enough to be noteworthy. *Tasmanites* occurs as small amber or black disks, less than 0.5 mm in diameter, in rocks of Devonian and Mississippian age in northeastern Ohio. These disks are extremely resistant to weathering and, in many cases, have also been identified from lake and stream deposits of Pleistocene age. In these occurrences, the disks have weathered free from the underlying older rocks and have been redeposited with the Pleistocene sediments.

ICHNOFOSSILS

Ichnofossils, or trace fossils, are indirect evidence of the existence of the organisms that constructed them. They represent the activity of animals primarily, although casts of root systems and marks made on the sediments surface by plants wafted back and forth by water currents could also be classified as trace fossils. In all cases, the actual remains of the trace maker are not an integral part of the trace fossil.

Trace fossils may document various types of activity, including resting, feeding, walking, crawling, and burrowing. In addition, a burrow or other permanent living site, termed a domicile, and fossil dung or fecal remains, called coprolites, are considered to be trace fossils. In all cases, the morphology and the identity of the trace maker can only be inferred from the size, symmetry, shape, and details of morphology of the trace. In many cases, the trace maker is unknown; however, in some cases the trace is of such a distinctive form that the identity of the trace maker can be suggested with confidence. In very rare cases, the organism responsible for construction of the trace may be preserved along with the trace fossil so that positive identification is possible. The discovery of such an example should be brought to the attention of a paleontologist.

SUMMARY

Most of these fossil groups are discussed in more detail in subsequent chapters, which contain illustrations and keys to the identification of common genera. Because the chances of fossilization of any organism are relatively slight, all fossils provide important clues about the past if they are kept with data about their geologic and geographic occurrence. In the event that the fossils you collect cannot be related to groups that are described and illustrated in this book or in other common references, you might take them to a specialist for help in identification.

The number of species of fossil organisms is almost limitless, specimens can range in size from microscopic to gigantic, and the manner of preservation can greatly affect the appearance of the material. Thus, it is not possible to treat all the types of fossils that may be encountered in Ohio. Instead, the common fossils of Ohio and some examples of rarer organisms from Ohio are included herein. To pursue the study of paleontology further, it is necessary to consult texts and references with more specific treatment.

The literature on paleontology is vast! However, several modern textbooks and general reference works are available that cover the morphology, classification, and identification of fossils in more detail than is done in this book. A number of these general references are cited at the end of this volume, and the reader is encouraged to examine these works as the need arises. Most of these books are available in larger city libraries, college and university libraries, and in the reference collections of natural history museums.

Many species of fossil organisms remain to be recognized, identified, and described. The time and effort that you take to bring any unusual fossils to the attention of a paleontologist may substantially advance our understanding of the history of life.

Chapter 2

PREPARATION TECHNIQUES

by Rodney M. Feldmann, Alison J. Smith, and F. D. Holland, Jr.

INTRODUCTION

Collecting and identifying fossils does not require extensive or expensive equipment. However, fossils may require some special preparation. It may be necessary to remove rock material that obscures a part of the specimen, or special techniques may be necessary because the fossils are tiny. Fossils that you collect may be fragile, or broken, and repair is warranted. In some cases, which will be discussed in subsequent chapters, it may be desirable to examine internal structures. There are techniques for preparation and preservation of fossils that require little specialized equipment and these will be described below. Extremely sophisticated, and expensive, equipment is available to perform all of these tasks, and several books have been written on the subject of the preparation of fossils. Some of the currently available works, listed in the references at the end of this book, are Feldmann, Chapman, and Hannibal (1989), Rixon (1976), and Kummel and Raup (1965).

COLLECTING EQUIPMENT

Relatively little equipment is necessary to develop a collection of fossils. At many exposures, weathering loosens fossil material so that specimens can be picked up directly from the surface. If the fossils are not lying free on the surface but are enclosed in resistant rock, a hammer and chisels may be needed to extract them. Although a carpenter's hammer would probably suffice, most paleontologists use a mason's or brick-layer's hammer, which has a hammerhead on one end and a chisel edge on the other end. A pry bar is useful for separating rock slabs along bedding planes (surfaces that visibly separate layers of sedimentary rocks). The hammer, when used in combination with a variety of sizes of cold chisels, permits extraction of fossils from all but the most resistant rocks.

Some fossils in hard limestone may be removed by cracking the edges of slabs pried loose from the outcrop. A specimen on a weathered surface can be removed, in many cases, by carving a channel in the rock completely around the specimen. Use the hammer to repeatedly tap a 1/4" or 3/8" cold chisel in a circle around the specimen. Point the chisel away from the fossil at a 45° angle to the surface of the rock. Continue chipping until the channel is about half as deep as the fossil is wide. The intent is to get the channel as deep as the fossil extends into the rock. When the channel has been cut as deeply as appears necessary, place the edge of a slightly wider chisel, slanted toward the fossil, at the bottom of the channel. Strike the chisel a sharp blow while exerting downward pressure on the fossil with the heel of the hand holding the chisel. If you can perform this contortion, with great good fortune, the fossil and the rock immediately surrounding it will pop loose from the main block of rock. You should probably not attempt further removal of rock from such a specimen, for the fossil may have been weakened by the jarring.

Because working with hammers and chisels is potentially dangerous, be sure to work in an area and in a manner where you will cause no harm to yourself or to people around you. Never use a hammer as a chisel, that is, never strike one hammer with another hammer. It is also wise to wear a hard hat, safety glasses, and stout gloves when using hammers and chisels to avoid being cut by pieces of flying rock or small chips of steel which may break loose from the hammer or chisel.

In addition to equipment for extracting fossils, it is also necessary to have supplies for wrapping and transporting the fossils. Newspaper that can be torn into appropriate-sized pieces and small paper bags are generally quite sufficient; facial tissue or toilet paper is handy for wrapping delicate fossils. Also useful are a hand lens or pocket magnifier to examine fossils or rock surfaces in the field and a tote bag or day pack of some sort to carry the hammers, chisels, wrapping, and specimens.

RECORDING INFORMATION ABOUT FOSSILS

The value of a fossil is severely diminished if information regarding the rock unit and especially the site of the collection is not recorded. Therefore, collecting equipment must include a pencil (not ball-point or nonpermanent felt-tip pen, as such inks tend to smear or run), small notebook, and a permanent marker for recording pertinent data about the site. This information should include the date of the collection, the precise geographic location of the collection, the type of rock and name of the rock unit (if known) from which the fossils were collected, the name of the collector, and other information (such as associated fossils or distance above road, ditch, or stream level) that you think is pertinent. This information should be written with pencil in the notebook, and similar information should be recorded on a loose piece of paper that is wrapped with the fossil or is placed in the bag with the fossil. Many collectors carry masking or adhesive tape for labeling and wrapping large specimens or bedding-plane slabs. Most collectors develop a specimen or collection numbering system, using a separate number for each site or for each unit at each locality, so that the same number can be placed on the specimen, on the collecting bag, and in the notebook. In this way, critical information regarding your collection can be retained. If specimens from a distinct rock unit at a site are given the same number, one can later establish the associated fauna (or flora) for each fossil. This information aids in paleoecological reconstruction.

GLUES AND PRESERVATIVES

Some fossils, particularly those collected from fine-grained rocks such as siltstone and shale, may be extremely fragile when collected and become even more fragile as the rocks dry out. Therefore, it is very useful to have some kind of hardening material available to protect the fossils as they are extracted from the rock and dried. Although several commercial products are available for this purpose, an excellent hardener can be made by diluting hobbyists' cement (such as Duco Cement or similar products) with acetone to the thinness of water. Dilution of the cement in acetone produces a very thin fluid that can be painted onto the dry surface of the fossil and which will soak in deeply enough to cement the rock tightly and preserve the fossil material. Great care must be exercised in working with acetone because it is highly volatile. Be sure to use this technique only outdoors or in well-ventilated areas. Clear nail polish diluted with nail-polish remover (acetone) also will work.

It should be noted that the use of acetone-soluble glues either as a cementing agent or as a hardening material is highly desirable because the material can be readily removed by solution in acetone. Other kinds of adhesives and hardeners may be permanent or very difficult to remove so that the specimen may be permanently altered. Therefore, materials such as ordinary shellac, varnish, hide glue, and casein glue should be avoided. An important governing principle is to do no harm to the specimen. Never apply enough hardener so that it builds up to a shiny or glossy surface on the specimen.

REMOVAL OF ROCK MATERIAL FROM FOSSILS

When fossils are collected, there will almost invariably be some rock material that adheres to the surface of the specimen. Depending upon the rock type, the rock may be removed easily, or it may adhere to the fossil so securely that any attempt to clean the surface will result in damage to the specimen. As a general rule, attempt to use delicate techniques in the initial stages of preparation and proceed to more harsh techniques only as required. If a sufficient amount of the specimen is exposed to permit identification, it may not be necessary to prepare the specimen at all. Unnecessary preparation introduces the risk of damage.

The surface detail of most fossils can be enhanced by washing the specimen in soapy water. A toothbrush, or other soft brush, can be used to remove loosely adhering rock. Care must be taken to assure that brushing does not abrade the surface of the fossil. Washing is a useful technique in preparing almost any fossil for examination or display. However, great caution must be exercised when attempting to wash fossils preserved in shale. Although the shale may be readily removed by the process, the fossil may become extremely fragile so that the risk of breakage outweighs the possible advantage of cleaning.

If washing does not satisfactorily remove the rock material, somewhat more drastic measures may be necessary. Needles or pins, secured in a pin vise, or dental picks make excellent tools for carefully flaking rock material from the surface or around the edge of fossils. Sewing needles are sharp, strong, and inexpensive tools. Pin vises can be obtained from hobby stores; dental picks, perhaps with broken tips, generally can be obtained from a dentist or at flea markets. These devices can be sharpened when necessary on an ordinary whetstone. When using picks to clean fossils be certain to work carefully so the surface of the fossil is not scratched. Typically, it is advisable to work away from the fossil and to attempt to remove material by flaking the rock rather than by scraping the surface.

A small hammer and delicate chisel also can be used to chip away rock material. In many cases there is a surface of weakness between the rock and the fossil so that a blow of the hammer, with the chisel slanted downward toward the specimen, will dislodge it from the rock. Look for incipient fractures in the rock and orient the chisel in a way to take advantage of them.

Finally, concretions—solid, spheroidal to irregularly shaped masses of rock that commonly contain a fossil at the center (fig. 2-1)—in some cases can be opened by freezing and thawing. (See Carlson, 1991, for more information on concretions in Ohio.) Place the concretions in a coffee can or other container, add sufficient water to cover the concretions, and allow the specimens to soak in the water for several hours. Place the water-filled container in a food freezer. Be certain not to fill the container with so much water that the container will overflow as freezing takes place. When the water has frozen, remove the container and allow the ice to melt. Repeat the process several times. If the procedure is going to be successful, some of the concretions should break after two or three cycles of freezing and thawing. Some concretions can be split with a hammer. Hold the concretion on edge, between thumb and forefinger, and tap the edge with your hammer. Most concretions will split along a plane of weakness past a fossil inside; some might break across the fossil.

It is possible that none of these techniques will sufficiently clean the fossil. In that case, it will probably be necessary to refer to one of the reference works on the subject and to employ more sophisticated techniques and equipment. With practice, however, the simple techniques described above will probably suffice to prepare your fossils for further study.

PREPARATION OF ACETATE PEELS

Examination and identification of certain types of fossils, including corals, stromatoporoids, bryozoans, and some cephalopods, may require study of their internal structures. Such thorough study requires special preparation. Study of **thin sections**, slices of rocks or fossils cut thinly enough that light will pass through the section for microscopic examination, is one common means of studying internal structures. However, thin sections are difficult to prepare and require specialized equipment. A more rapid technique that yields excellent results for examining fossils is the preparation of a **polished section** or an **acetate peel** (fig. 2-2). An acetate peel is a replica of a polished and etched surface impressed in a thin sheet of transparent cellulose acetate, the material of which most ordinary plastic sheets and report covers is made. The materials and procedure for making a polished section and an acetate peel are listed below.

MATERIALS:

- a diamond saw, hack saw, or other device that will make a cut through the fossil; for fossils composed of calcite, an ordinary hack saw will suffice.

- carborundum paper or cloth (wet-dry paper or cloth typically used for sanding metal) or carborundum grit, at least as fine as 600 mesh (available in most rock shops).

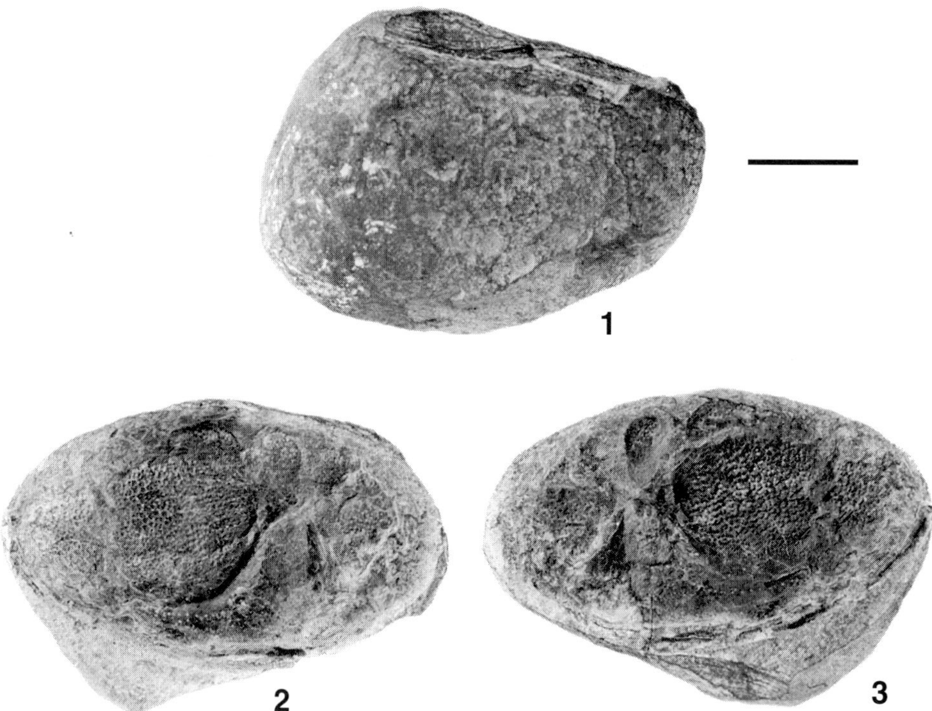

FIGURE 2-1.—A small nutlike concretion, similar to those found in many fine-grained sedimentary rocks throughout Ohio. Although the exterior of the concretion may appear to be nothing more than a pebble, many concretions contain fossils. **1**, exterior of the concretion. **2**, **3**, part and counterpart of a fossil arthropod, *Echinocaris* sp., exposed when the concretion was broken open by gently tapping around the margins. Scale bar equals 1 cm.

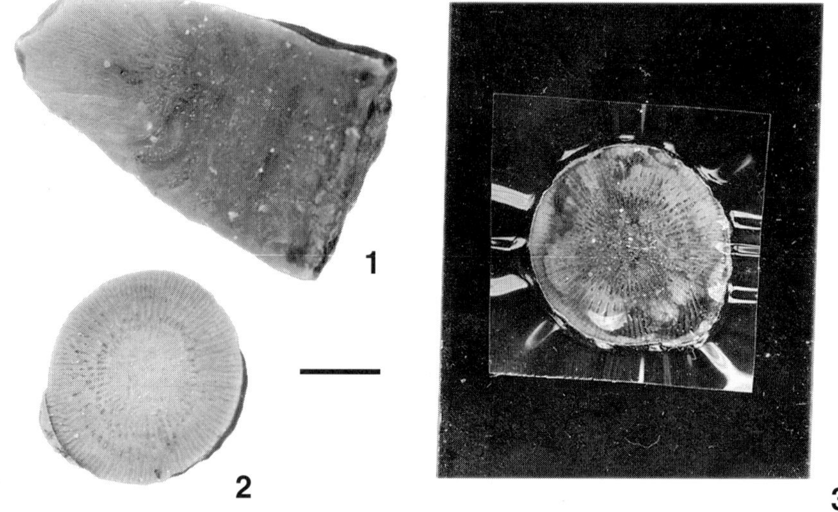

FIGURE 2-2.—Internal structures of many fossils can be examined readily by preparing polished sections and acetate peels. **1**, longitudinal polished section of an Ordovician coral, *Streptelasma* sp. **2**, transverse polished section of another specimen in the same genus. **3**, acetate peel of the specimen shown in **2**. The peel, a small piece of cellulose acetate on which the etched surface of the coral has been impressed by using acetone, is mounted between two glass microscope slides. Note that the detail of the internal features of the coral is more clearly seen on the peel than on the polished section. Scale bar equals 1 cm.

• glass dishes, shallow and flat-bottomed but large enough to encircle the specimen to be peeled.

• Dilute (10%) hydrochloric acid (HCl); muriatic acid used for cleaning concrete and brick will suffice. Be careful with acid—do not get it on skin, clothes, paint, or wood surfaces. If you spill any or get acid on your skin, immediately flush the surface with ample water.

• Acetone. Caution also must be exercised when using acetone. Work in an extremely well ventilated area, preferably in an area where a household fan can gently blow the vapors out an open window.

• Acetate sheets. Various thicknesses can be purchased in graphic supply and office supply stores as report covers or overhead projection transparencies. Sheets of 5 mils thickness are recommended.

• Glass slides (1" x 3", 2" x 2", or 2" x 3"), magic mending tape, pencil.

PROCEDURE:

1. Select the specimen from which the peel is to be made and determine the desired orientation of the surface to be peeled.

2. Using the saw, cut the fossil in the appropriate place. Take care to assure that the cut is properly oriented. In the event that only a small amount of rock must be removed, it may be possible to avoid cutting and simply grind the specimen using coarse carborundum paper. A grinding wheel does not produce satisfactory results ordinarily because the surface to be peeled must be absolutely planar.

3. Using carborundum paper or successively finer abrasive grits wetted and spread on a flat glass plate, grind the section until the surface is smooth and flat. Make certain that there are no scratches on the surface and that the surface is completely flat. The smoother the surface, the higher the polish, and the better the resulting peel. You now have a polished section (fig. 2-2.1, 2-2.2). Stop at this stage and examine the polished surface with a hand lens or a low-powered (10X or 15X) binocular microscope. Internal structure you wish to see may show up without further effort. The polished surface can be preserved from scratching by waxing or by coating with thinned, clear nail polish or Duco Cement thinned with acetone. If you want to photograph the structures, moisten them with water or glycerine.

4. To make an acetate peel (fig. 2-2.3), etch the polished surface by immersing the entire section in dilute HCl placed in a glass dish. The purpose of etching is to dissolve enough of the crystal boundaries so that each crystal will be well defined. Do not etch too deeply as this will result in a poor replica. An initial etching time of about 5-10 seconds may result in a proper etch of **calcareous** material. However, the amount of time needed to etch a given specimen will vary, depending on the composition, and requires some adjustment based on experience.

5. Immediately rinse the surface in gently flowing fresh water. Do not touch the etched surface! When the specimen is rinsed, allow it to air dry.

6. Cut a piece of acetate to a size greater than that of the surface to be peeled. Ideally, the acetate sheet should extend 4-5 cm beyond the margin of the specimen on all sides. Place the acetate on two or three sheets of paper towel that have been placed on a glass plate or other firm, flat surface.

7. Pour some acetone into a container that will be broad enough to permit the immersion of the entire specimen surface. Be extremely careful with the acetone and remember to work in a well-ventilated area. While it is still wetted with acetone, transfer the specimen directly onto the acetate sheet. Do not get acetone between the paper towel and the acetate. Press the specimen firmly, but carefully, on the acetate; do not press too hard, as you might rotate or displace the specimen. After a few seconds of applying steady pressure, the specimen with acetate sheet adhering to it can be turned over and the surface examined. If good contact was made, your peel will be firmly adherent to the surface and there will be no apparent bubbles. Cover the acetone and acid while preparing to make a peel of another specimen.

8. Allow the acetate to dry for at least several minutes or, ideally, overnight. Carefully peel back the acetate from the specimen. The peel should then be trimmed and mounted between two glass slides to keep the peel from crinkling or being scratched. Magic mending tape can be used to tape the slides together.

9. Label your slide; the tape also forms a writing surface on which the slide can be identified.

10. When properly prepared, acetate peels can be examined by holding them up to the light or by placing them under a microscope. The peel can also be used as a photographic negative in an enlarger and photographic prints prepared from it. The preparation of an acetate peel, once a smooth surface has been produced, requires just a few minutes, but the results are spectacular.

11. When you are through making peels, clean up your work area. Pour acid or acetone into the sink only while the water is running. Let the water run for several minutes to flush the acid completely through the drain.

SAMPLE PREPARATION FOR MICROFOSSILS

Preparation of **microfossil** samples basically consists of (1) disaggregating the sample, (2) removing fine sediment by decanting or by washing through sieves, (3) drying the washed residue, and (4) hand-picking microfossils under the microscope. These procedures are described in detail below. It is relatively easy to separate ostracodes or tiny gastropods from Pleistocene silt, mud, or clay; it is more difficult to free ostracodes, conodonts, or juvenile specimens of **macrofossils** from Paleozoic shale or consolidated mudstone or soft limestone. The more lithified the sample, the harsher the treatment. Most methods of freeing microfossils begin by soaking and washing the sample to soften and loosen the matrix surrounding the fossils. Phosphatic microfossils such as conodonts or fish teeth and scales can be extracted from limestone using dilute (10-15%) acetic acid. This procedure is described briefly in Chapter 18. The procedure for extracting pollen from peat is described in Chapter 24.

All washing and decantation should be done outside with a gentle stream from a garden hose in order to avoid putting a lot of mud down the sink drain. If you must use a sink, keep a good stream of water flowing from the faucet to flush fine sediment through the trap. Never wash sand, or anything coarser, down the drain.

PROCEDURE FOR PREPARING MICROFOSSIL SAMPLES:

1. DISAGGREGATION. Place ½ to 1 kg of sediment or broken chunks of shale in a small bucket or a metal saucepan. It may help disaggregation to dry the sample thoroughly before beginning. Fill your container about half full of water. Mix and swirl the sample about and stir the sediment with your hand, squeezing pieces of clay and breaking up any small chunks with your fingers. Soaking overnight may help. The sample should start to disaggregate and the water become very muddy. The fine suspended sediment can be removed either by repeated decantation (pouring off the liquid) or by washing the sample through sieves (Step 2 below).

If the sample does not readily break down, further dissaggregation may be necessary. Several relatively easy and safe processing techniques may be used to help recover microfossils from shale or soft limestone:

• *Heating*. Transfer your water and soaked sample to a metal saucepan; add 2 or 3 tablespoons of Calgon and let soak. Simmer the mixture for a few hours. Do not boil. Remove the fine suspended sediment by repeated decantation or wet-sieving (Step 2 below). If the chunks still do not disintegrate, add water and Calgon and simmer again; then slowly add 1 or 2 tablespoons of 3% hydrogen peroxide, available from most drugstores. Remove the pan from the heat, cool to room temperature, and decant or wet-sieve.

• *Freeze-thaw*. Repeated freeze-thaw is particularly effective on some shales. Place some of the smaller pieces of shale in a small plastic bucket (a 1-quart pail works well) and cover the pieces with a little water. Place the bucket in a freezer and let the water freeze solid. Thaw. As soon as it is thawed, slowly decant the water, and then add boiling water. Repeat if necessary, or go to the heating method described above.

• *Scrubbing*. Scrubbing is effective on beds of soft, fossiliferous limestones with thin, bedding-plane partings of shale. In a small dishpan or a bucket, scrub the bedding plane, under water, with a hard-bristled tooth brush, a nail brush, or other small, stiff brush. Save the material removed from the limestone by scrubbing and proceed to Step 2.

2. REMOVAL OF FINE SEDIMENT. Decantation or sieving may be used to remove fine sediment.

• *Decantation*. After slowly swirling the water and sample about in a pan of water, pause to let the mixture settle 5 to 10 seconds. Slowly decant (pour off) the muddy water. Watch the lip of the pan to see that no coarse grains go over the edge. Refill the pan with water, stir the sediment, pause, and repeat the slow decantation. Do this as many times as necessary to produce clear, unmuddy water. If the sediment is very clay rich, you may need to repeat the Step 1 procedure of gentle squeezing with your fingers. If the clay or shale chunks will not break up, try the techniques for further disaggregation described in Step 1.

• *Sieving*. Sieving separates the microfossils from the very fine sediment, once the original sample has been partly dissolved or suspended in the water. Instructions for obtaining or making sieves are given below. A stack of at least two sieves is used; a sieve with larger diameter openings (to catch larger fossils, rock fragments, and those sediment particles that have not disaggregated) is put on top of a sieve with smaller openings (to catch objects that are between 0.3 and 1 mm long—the microfossils). The entire sample can be placed onto the coarse sieve and slowly washed through the stack of sieves with running water. Continue washing until the water runs clear.

A sieve of large-diameter mesh can be made by tacking a 9" x 9" piece of window screen over an 8" x 8" frame made from 1" x 1" wooden strips. For the bottom sieve, stretch a nylon stocking over a second 8" x 8" frame. Alternatively, you might buy two sets of 8" embroidery hoops to use for your sieve frames. Stretch plastic screen from the hardware store across one set of hoops for the top sieve and a nylon stocking across the other set of hoops for the bottom sieve. If you are planning on doing a lot of microfossil collecting, you might want to invest in a market-grade, 100-mesh, 8"-diameter brass sieve, but these are expensive. Sets of 6"- or 7"-diameter plastic sieves are much more reasonable. Brass sieves are available through a number of biology and geology equipment-supply catalogs; satisfactory plastic sieves are available from several supply houses, especially ones that furnish equipment for junior high or high school life science or earth science labs.

• *Drying*. When the water runs clear from decanting or wet-sieving, gently remove the clean residue from the pan, or the fine sieve, with a small card onto a thickness or two of paper towel on a foil pie pan. Put a label (or your sample number) on the towel or on a piece of paper in the pan. Dry in the oven on very low heat or allow to air dry in a safe, draft-free place.

3. PICKING MICROFOSSILS. Examine the washed, dried residue, a little at a time, on a white card, under a low-powered (10X or 20X) binocular microscope illuminated with a bright light (small study lamp or high-intensity light). If you have used decantation instead of wet-sieving in Step 2 above, it will be helpful to pick out all the larger fragments by hand first, or pass the dry residue through a set of at least two sieves before examining under the microscope. If all the sand grains, fossil fragments, and microfossils appear dusty when magnified, repeat a gentle washing as in Step 2. Pick microfossils or juvenile specimens, one at a time, from the clean residue with a slightly moistened, 00 or 000 sable brush, obtainable from an art-supply store. Transfer the microfossils with the dampened brush to a small, labeled vial or a capsule.

In all steps of the preparation and study of microfossils, be very careful to keep all vessels, sieves, vials, slides, brushes, and work areas clean to avoid contamination of one sample with microfossils from another. It is important in all paleontological procedures to keep samples from different localities or geologic units labeled and separate, but special caution needs to be exerted with microfossils; they are so tiny they may be carried from one sample to another under your fingernails. Be neat and careful!

Chapter 3

OHIO'S SURFACE ROCKS AND SEDIMENTS

by Alan H. Coogan

INTRODUCTION

This chapter is an overview of the sedimentary rocks and glacial deposits of Ohio as a background for fossil collecting. Sedimentary rocks are rocks deposited in layers at or near the surface of the Earth. The main topics in this chapter are the geologic time scale, the geologic maps of Ohio, characteristics of sedimentary rocks, the geologic history of Ohio, and regional **stratigraphy** of Ohio. The section on sedimentary rocks includes information on identifying rocks and common stratigraphic concepts.

Because the fossil-bearing rocks represent only a portion of Ohio's total sedimentary deposits, fossils from only portions of the geologic time periods are found in the rocks that are at the surface. Fossils in subsurface rocks are known from rock cores and cuttings from wells drilled deep below the surface. Fossils also are found in relatively recent unconsolidated glacial, river, cave, and lake deposits.

GEOLOGIC TIME SCALE

The Earth is about 4.5 billion years old, and more than 99 percent of its history took place before any written or oral record could be made. Geologists have been studying the rock layers of the Earth for several hundred years and have devised a framework time scale that arranges the rock layers in units from oldest to youngest. Each rock unit is placed into its relative position compared to other units in the time scale. The unit may then be dated in terms of millions of years before present using radioactive isotopes. The results of two centuries of dating efforts are summarized in the geological time scale (fig. 3-1). There are four main divisions of the time scale. The Cenozoic Era extends from the present to about 66 million years ago and includes glacial and postglacial sediments. The Mesozoic Era extended from 66 to 245 million years ago and has no known representative rocks in Ohio. The Paleozoic Era extended from 245 to 570 million years ago and includes the surface rocks of Ohio. The Precambrian is an informal term for the all the time from 570 million years ago to the origin of the Earth. The eras are subdivided into periods, and the periods into epochs.

Ohio's surface rocks range in age from the Late Ordovician Period (about 455 million years ago) to the Early Permian Period (about 280 million years ago). Nearly all the significant fossil-collecting localities in Ohio are in these Paleozoic-Era rocks. For most of the past 245 million years, during the Mesozoic Era and the Tertiary Period of the Cenozoic Era, Ohio has been subjected to extensive uplift, erosion, and weathering. Within the past 2 million years, sediments of the Quaternary Period were deposited. The Quaternary Period consists of the Pleistocene Epoch, commonly referred to as the Ice Age, and the Holocene Epoch, also called the Recent.

Even the substantial thicknesses of Paleozoic rocks contain evidence of erosional events. Surfaces between the rock layers that indicate erosion or nondeposition are called unconformities. Unconformities result from uplift of the land surface or lowering of sea level. Major unconformities generally are related to collisions of continental plates and mountain building. In relation to present-day Ohio, such events took place mainly to the east. Unconformities and the movement of continental plates (plate tectonics) are described in more detail in later sections of this chapter.

THE GEOLOGIC MAPS OF OHIO

The map of the bedrock geology of Ohio (fig. 3-2) shows the distribution of Paleozoic rocks at or near the land surface, but beneath any Quaternary sediments. The glacial deposits map (fig. 3-3) of Ohio shows the extent and type of Pleistocene sediments.

Three main geologic structures (fig. 3-4) influence the outcrop pattern of the surface rocks in Ohio. A series of positive structural features, the Cincinnati Arch, the Findlay Arch, and the Indiana-Ohio Platform, extend from southwestern Ohio to Lake Erie. The axes of the arches plunge gently to the north-northeast. As a result, Ordovician rocks are at the surface in the vicinity of Cincinnati, but are in the subsurface farther north. Near Dayton, younger, Silurian rocks are at the surface, overlying Ordovician strata. North of Findlay and on the Bass Islands in Lake Erie, even younger Silurian rocks are at the surface. The Ordovician and Silurian rocks that are at the surface in southwestern Ohio are buried hundreds of feet in the subsurface to the north. Northwest of the Findlay Arch, bands of Devonian and Mississippian rocks curve across the northwestern corner of the state. These rocks dip northwestward toward a sedimentary-rock-filled depression called the Michigan Basin. East of the Findlay and Cincinnati Arches, a band of Devonian rocks can be traced from the Ohio River northward through the center of the state to Lake Erie and then eastward along the lake to Pennsylvania and beyond. This north-northeast trend outlines the western edge of the Appalachian Basin. Rocks east of the arches dip eastward (fig. 3-5) into the basin, so that progressively younger rocks are at the surface farther east and older ones are more deeply buried. Silurian rocks that are at the surface on the Findlay Arch are buried 1,200-1,500 meters below the surface near the Ohio-Pennsylvania line. The thickness of Paleozoic rocks ranges from about 760 meters in western Ohio to more than 4,000 meters in southeastern Ohio.

Ohio's geologic maps indicate where fossils of certain ages can be found. In the Cincinnati area are the very fossiliferous Upper Ordovician rocks. Farther north are the moderately fossiliferous Silurian rocks. In the hill country of east-

Years before present, in millions of years	Eras and duration in years	Periods and and duration in years	Area of outcrop in Ohio and principal rock types
	CENOZOIC 66+ million	QUATERNARY 1.5-2 million	northwestern 2/3 of Ohio—unconsolidated sand, gravel, clay
1.6		*TERTIARY 62.5 million*	*NOT PRESENT IN OHIO*
66.4	*MESOZOIC 179 million*	*CRETACEOUS 78 million*	
144		*JURASSIC 64 million*	
208		*TRIASSIC 37 million*	
245	PALEOZOIC 325 million	PERMIAN 41 million	southeastern Ohio—shale, sandstone, coal, clay, limestone
286		PENNSYLVANIAN 34 million	eastern Ohio—shale, sandstone, coal, clay, limestone
320		MISSISSIPPIAN 40 million	east-central, northeastern, and northwestern-most Ohio—shale, sandstone, limestone
360		DEVONIAN 48 million	central, northeastern, and northwestern Ohio—shale, limestone
408		SILURIAN 30 million	western Ohio—dolomite, limestone, shale
438		ORDOVICIAN 67 million	southwestern Ohio—shale, limestone
505		CAMBRIAN 65 million	NOT EXPOSED IN OHIO — Cambrian sandstones, shales, and carbonates and Precambrian sedimentary, igneous, and metamorphic rocks present in subsurface
570	PRECAMBRIAN 3,400 million		

FIGURE 3-1.—Chart showing divisions of geologic time and their representation in Ohio. Dates are from Palmer (1983). Wavy lines indicate a major unconformity (period of erosion or nondeposition) in Ohio.

ern Ohio are Pennsylvanian and Permian rocks, some of which are quite fossiliferous. In the areas between are sparsely to very fossiliferous Devonian and Mississippian rocks.

Geologic maps are important to our society as a whole and particularly to fossil collectors and paleontologists. Geologic maps show the location of fossil-bearing formations over large areas. If a fossil hunter is able to read a geologic map, he or she can identify new and perhaps remote fossil-collecting localities that others may never have visited. The Division of Geological Survey has numerous geologic maps available, including a series of regional geologic maps for the state (Schumacher, 1993; Larsen, 1994; Swinford and Slucher, 1995; others in preparation).

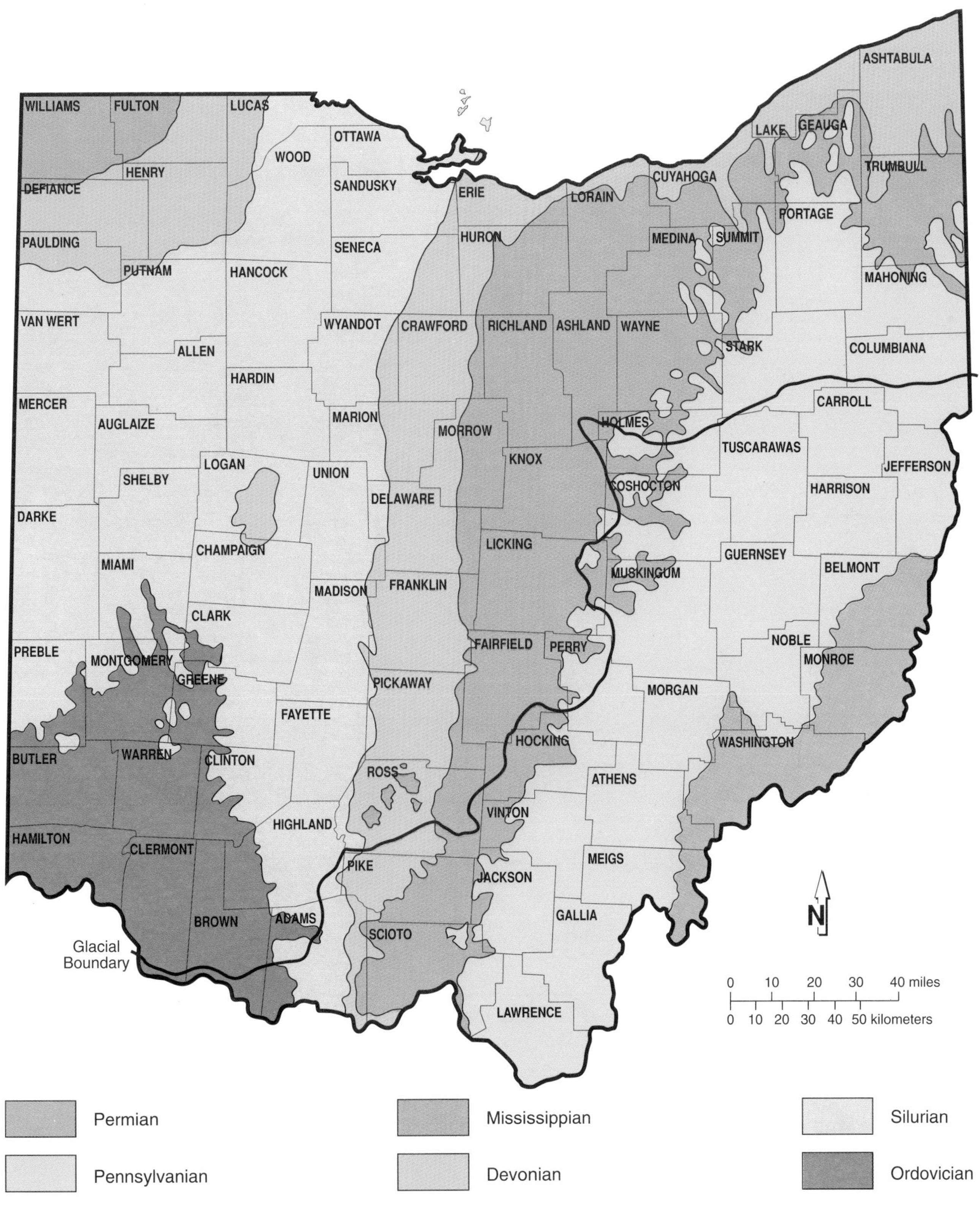

FIGURE 3-2.—Bedrock geology of Ohio, showing the pattern of surface rocks across the state.

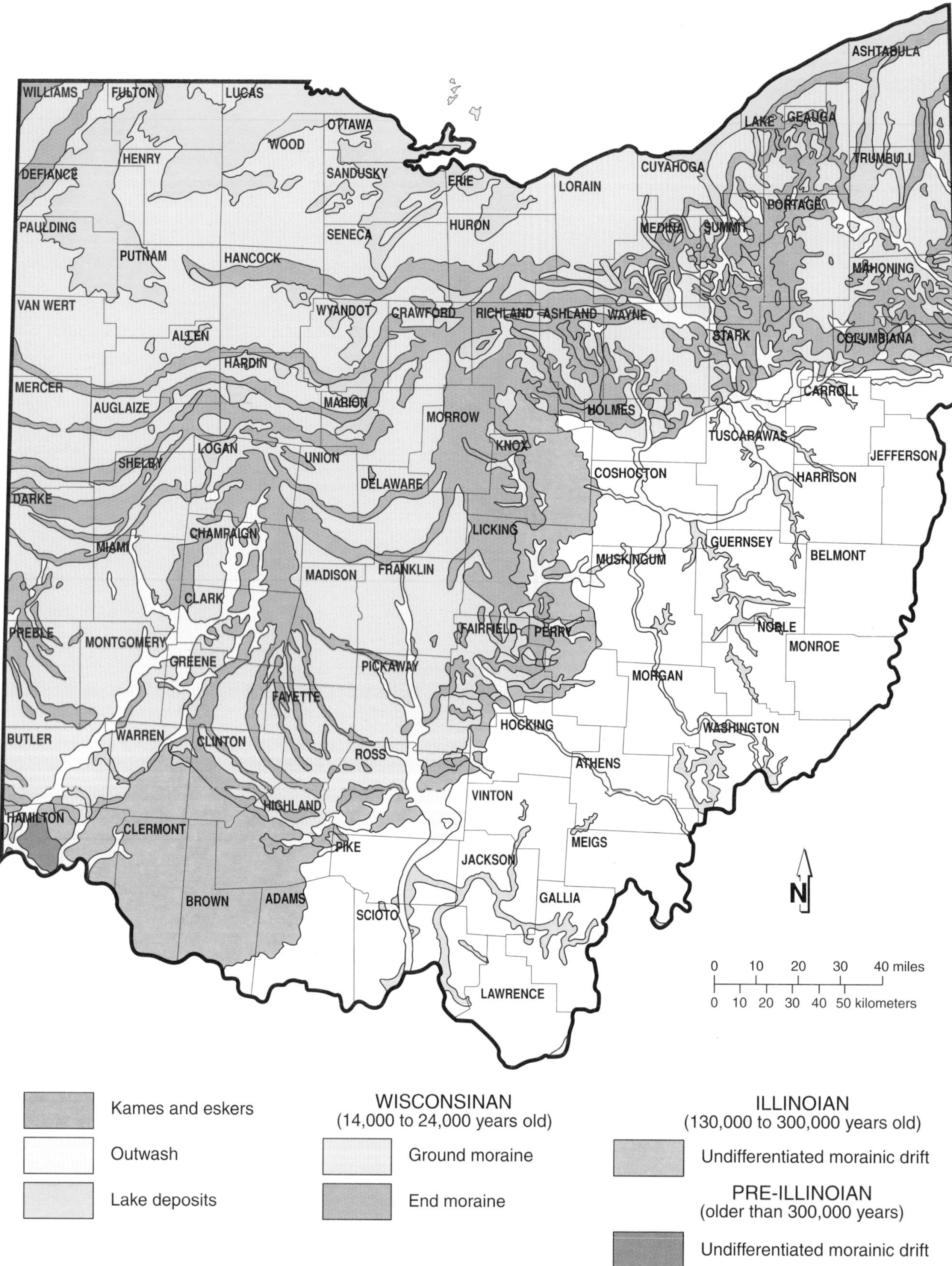

FIGURE 3-3.—Glacial deposits of Ohio. The terms Wisconsinan, Illinoian, and Kansan are subdivisions (ages) of the Pleistocene Epoch.

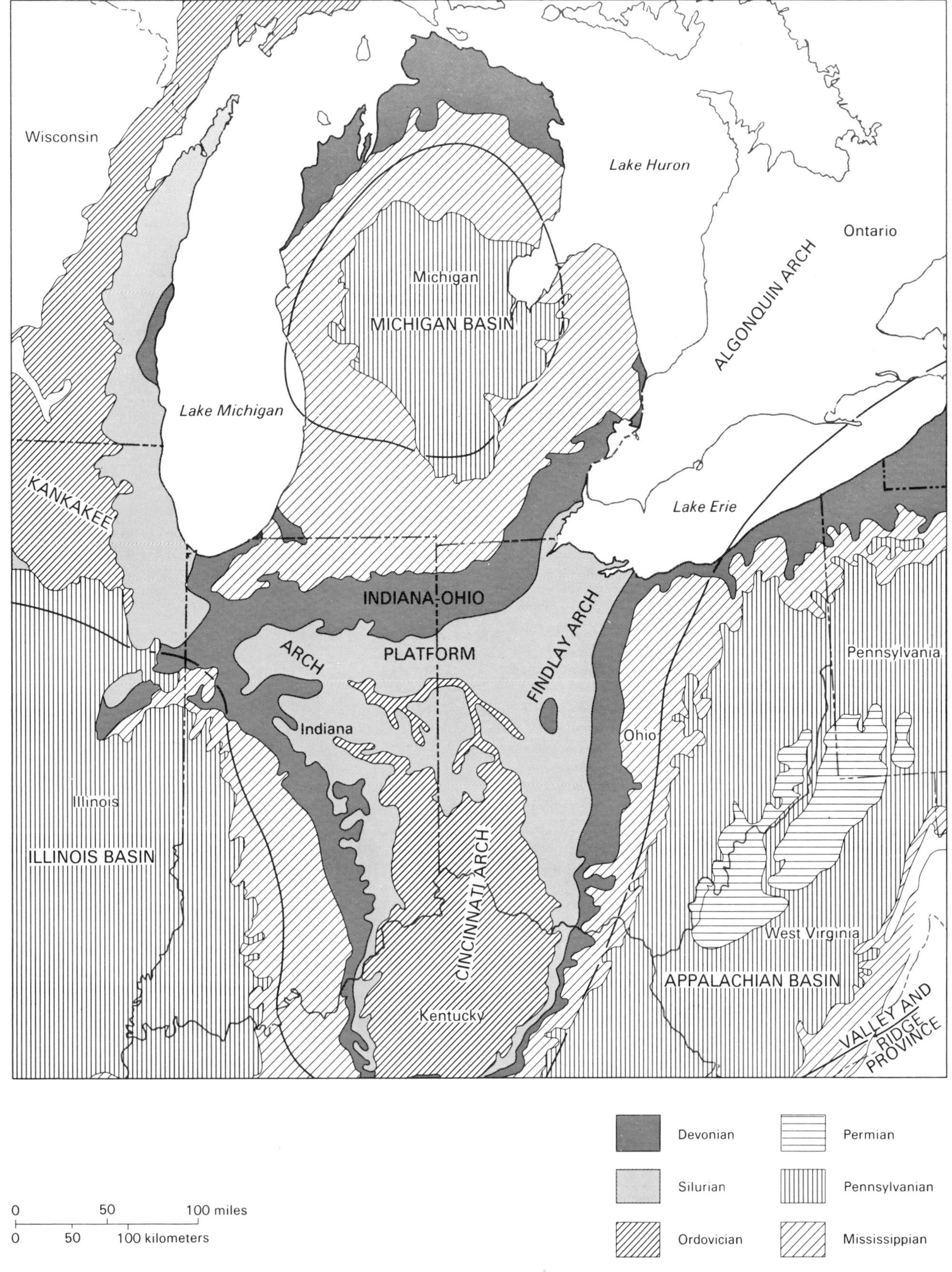

FIGURE 3-4.—Regional geologic structures of Ohio and adjacent states (from Carlson, 1991, fig. 4).

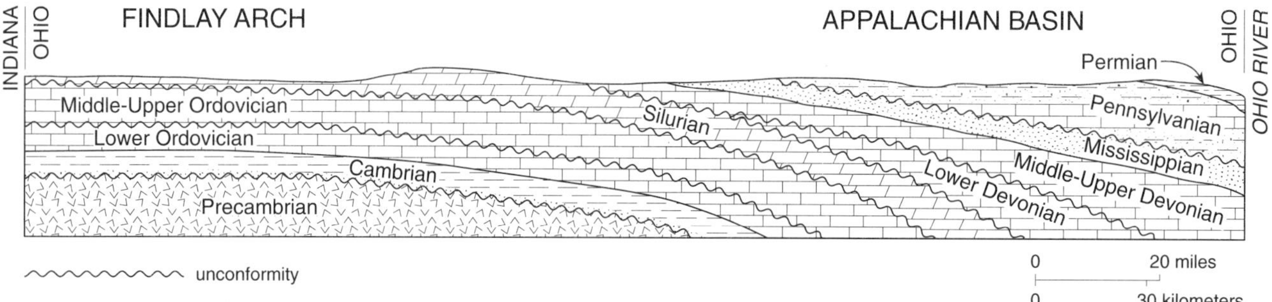

FIGURE 3-5.—Cross section through the rocks of central Ohio from the Indiana-Ohio border to the Ohio River.

CHARACTERISTICS OF SEDIMENTARY ROCKS

The primary characteristic of sedimentary rocks is that they are stratified, that is, deposited layer upon layer. A bed is a layer of rock, commonly less than 1/2 meter thick, that has a distinct surface, or bedding plane, that separates it from other beds above and below it. Thinner layers, commonly less than 1 cm thick, are called laminae. Beds record changes in sedimentary conditions at the time of deposition or changes due to subsequent burial of the bed by later sediments.

ROCK TYPES

There are two main types of sedimentary rocks: siliciclastic and chemical (tables 3-1 and 3-2). Siliciclastic rocks consist of weathered particles of pre-existing **siliceous** rocks that were eroded and transported by rivers and deposited in alluvial plains, deltas, and open seas as fragmental sediments (see fig. 3-8). Siliciclastic sediments are **lithified** (hardened into rock) by compaction and cementation by minerals precipitated from sea or ground water. Chemical rocks, as the term is used in this chapter, form by the precipitation of minerals from sea water or by the cementation of fragments of seashells. The precipitates are mainly calcite, silica, gypsum, anhydrite, and halite, or salt. The shells of many fossil organisms are made of calcite. Calcite may be replaced by the mineral dolomite or by silica. More information on the rocks and minerals of Ohio is provided in Carlson (1991).

TABLE 3.1.—NAMES FOR SILICICLASTIC SEDIMENTS AND ROCKS

Particle name	Particle size	Rock name
pebble or larger	>2 mm	conglomerate if fragments are rounded, breccia if fragments are angular
sand	1/16-2 mm	sandstone
silt	1/16-1/256 mm	siltstone (particles barely discernible; has gritty feel)
clay	<1/256 mm	shale or clay shale if laminated, claystone if massive (particles not discernible; has smooth feel)

For many types of sedimentary rocks, the names are formed by adding "-stone" to the sediment name, for example, sand/sandstone. Other rock names are mineralogic terms (such as dolomite) or century-old names (such as breccia, shale) used by builders, quarrymen, and stonemasons.

Rocks may have other distinctive characteristics that are used for identification. These characteristics may be added as modifiers to the basic rock name. For example, rock color can be important and may be part of the description, as in black shale. The kind of cement also can be added—for example, **calcareous** (calcite cement) shale, ferruginous (iron-rich cement) sandstone, or siliceous (silica cement) limestone. Other constituents, such as fossil richness (fossiliferous), and combinations of several characteristics may be included in rock descriptions. An example of a carefully described rock might be: fossiliferous, ferruginous, and calcareous red siltstone.

TABLE 3.2.—NAMES FOR CHEMICAL ROCKS

Mineral name	Chemical composition	Rock name
calcite or aragonite	calcium carbonate, $CaCO_3$	limestone[1]
dolomite	calcium-magnesium carbonate, $CaMg(CO_3)_2$	dolomite[1]
gypsum	hydrous calcium sulfate, $CaSO_4 \cdot 2H_2O$	gypsum[2]
anhydrite	anhydrous calcium sulfate, $CaSO_4$	anhydrite
halite	sodium chloride, NaCl	salt
silica (quartz)	silicon dioxide, SiO_2	chert, flint
various iron minerals		ironstone

[1]Limestones and dolomites commonly are referred to as carbonate rocks or carbonates. Most dolomites are the result of chemical alteration of limestones. Some geologists prefer to use the term "dolostone" for a rock composed of the mineral dolomite.

[2]Gypsum, anhydrite, and salt commonly are referred to as evaporite rocks or evaporites.

OTHER FEATURES OF SEDIMENTARY ROCKS

Some features of sedimentary rocks result from water-current flow, burrowing, and biologic growth. These features, called sedimentary structures, may resemble traces of biological activity. Trace features of biological origin are described and illustrated in the chapter on trace fossils (Chapter 25). Various sedimentary structures such as ripple marks or drag marks are indicative of sea-bottom or river-bed conditions and generally are observed on bedding planes.

Current-flow bedding is common in river, delta, shoreline beach and bar, and shallow sea deposits that were affected by wind, waves, or currents. Beds or laminae may be at an angle to the lower or upper bed surface. This angled bedding within a larger, more or less flat bed is called cross-bedding. Angles may be up to 35° from the horizontal and dip in the direction of the ancient flow. Cross-bedding is common in sand-size rocks such as sandstones and some carbonates. Mississippian-age sandstones and Devonian-age limestones contain many such cross-beds, which are easily observed on weathered surfaces. Ripple marks are the usual expression of small cross-laminations on the exposed surface of a bed.

Many rocks lack current cross-beds and appear homogeneous or massive throughout. Sandstones and siltstones may show churned and mixed grain sizes that are highlighted by a mottled color pattern. Churned bedding typically is the result of burrowing by animals (bioturbation), although there generally is no clear trace of fossils present. Churned bedding may also result from nonbiological deformation of soft, wet sediments in shallow lagoons or close to the seashore.

SEDIMENTARY-ROCK CONCEPTS

A few sedimentary-rock concepts and terms are helpful in understanding the occurrence of fossils. The topics discussed here are superposition and original horizontality, stratigraphic terminology, unconformities, sedimentary facies and environments, faunal succession, and plate tectonics.

Superposition and original horizontality

Centuries of observation of sedimentary processes show that sediments are deposited mainly one bed at a time, one on top of the other. Sediments deposited on gently sloping sea bottoms are the most likely to be preserved because they are less likely to be disturbed or eroded. Allowing for the small differences in slope of the sea floor and in the current flow that produces cross-bedding, sedimentary beds are so arranged that three conclusions can be drawn:

1. Older beds were deposited first and lie below younger beds, so that beds are successively younger upward.
2. Beds that tilt at high angles from the horizontal were moved by tectonic forces after the beds were lithified.
3. Beds that cut across, or cut out, other beds are younger than the beds they cut.

Stratigraphic terminology

Sedimentary rocks are categorized using different kinds of features, such as rock type, age, and fossil content. These categories are (1) rock-stratigraphic, or lithostratigraphic, units, (2) time-stratigraphic, or chronostratigraphic, units, (3) geologic-time units, and (4) biostratigraphic units.

A lithostratigraphic unit is based on rock type, or lithology, and is defined at a specific locality, called a type area. The fundamental lithostratigraphic unit is the formation. It is based on designated beds of rocks of a specific lithology (such as shale or sandstone) that are thick enough to be shown on a geologic map. Formations are named for a place (such as Columbus) and a rock type (such as limestone) to make the formal formation name: the Columbus Limestone. If the rock unit contains more than one rock type, the word "formation" is used with the place name, as, for example, the Dayton Formation, which is limestone and shale. Formations may be combined into larger units called groups (example: Detroit River Group) or subdivided into smaller units called members and beds (example: Cleveland Shale Member of the Ohio Shale). Descriptions of fossil-collecting localities generally refer to the group, formation, member, or bed that contains the fossils. These lithostratigraphic units are used in the following chapters to describe the occurrence of fossils.

A chronostratigraphic (time-stratigraphic) unit is a body of rock deposited during a defined unit of geologic time, such as a period. Chronostratigraphic units are closely related to geologic-time units. The primary chronostratigraphic unit is the system. The correspondence between chronostratigraphic and geologic-time units is shown below.

Geologic-time unit	Chronostratigraphic unit	Example
Era	Erathem	Paleozoic Era/Erathem
Period	System	Ordovician Period/System
Epoch	Series	Cincinnatian Series
Age	Stage	Edenian Stage
Chron	Zone	

For some units, the terms "upper" and "lower" or "late" and "early" are used. "Upper" and "lower" are used with lithostratigraphic terms (example: Upper Ordovician Waynesville Formation); "late" and "early" are used with time terms (example: Late Ordovician time). The term "middle" applies to both lithostratigraphic and time units.

A biostratigraphic unit is defined on the basis of its fossil content. The primary biostratigraphic unit is the zone or biozone, which encompasses a series of beds defined by the presence of a particular fossil or group of fossils. The boundaries of a biostratigraphic unit may or may not coincide with the boundary of a lithostratigraphic unit; there is no inherent relationship between them. An interval zone encompasses all rocks deposited and preserved during the time span of the existence of the particular genus or species on which it is based. An example of an interval zone is the *Foerstia* (*Protosalvinia*) Zone in the Devonian-age Ohio Shale; this zone is named for a fossil plant. An assemblage zone is a zone based on the unique and joint occurrence of three or more species or genera and is named for one of them. An example is the *Rhynchotrema* Assemblage Zone, an assemblage of bottom-dwelling marine organisms in Upper Ordovician strata that is named for a brachiopod.

Unconformities

Unconformity surfaces represent periods of erosion or nondeposition. They may be nearly smooth or have high relief, and they may be local or widespread. Unconformities commonly are represented by wavy lines on stratigraphic charts (fig. 3-1) and cross sections (fig. 3-5). There are three main types of unconformities: angular unconformity, disconformity, and paraconformity (fig. 3-6).

In an angular unconformity (fig. 3-6, top) the bedding planes between two groups of rocks are not parallel; generally, older (lower) rocks lie at an angle to the overlying (younger) rocks. The creation and preservation of an angular unconformity requires major deformation such as substantial uplift or mountain building, erosion of the deformed strata, resubmergence, and subsequent deposition. Angular unconformities in Ohio are generally very subtle (shallow angle) and can be recognized only by geologic mapping over large areas. The time required to form an angular unconformity is generally in excess of several million years.

A disconformity (fig. 3-6, middle) characterizes surfaces between parallel or nearly parallel beds in which the underlying beds have been eroded. A disconformity indicates a significant interruption in the sedimentary sequence. The disconformable rock surface is commonly visibly irregular or uneven.

A paraconformity (fig. 3-6, bottom) characterizes surfaces between parallel beds in which the surface generally is not discernible without careful study, especially of the faunal changes across the boundary. Paraconformities are common, even within formations.

Sedimentary facies and environments

All sediments are deposited in specific environments. Early Paleozoic environments were characterized by tropical and subtropical, shallow to moderately deep seas where mud banks, sand bars, and reefs abounded (fig. 3-7). Limestones and calcareous shales were the dominant deposits. A comparable modern-day environment is the Caribbean Sea. Later Paleozoic environments were characterized by streams, deltas, coal swamps, and nearshore seas (fig. 3-8). Sandstones, siltstones, and shales were the dominant deposits. A comparable modern-day environment is the Mississippi delta. The Paleozoic and Pleistocene reconstructions on pages xvi to xix provide a sense of what the environments may have looked like. These environments differed extremely from the environments of the Ice Age glaciers or even today's rivers and lakes in our temperate, continental environment. Overall, sedimentary environments vary with climatic change, which in turn reflects shifting continental plates and proximity to mountain building and erosion (see sections on plate tectonics and geologic history of Ohio).

Sedimentary environments may differ from place to place even at the same time. The deposits of different lithologies and sedimentary environments laid down at the same time in different places are different aspects—called facies—of the overall sedimentary unit (fig. 3-9). Lithofacies are based mainly on differences in rock type. Biofacies are based mainly on differences in fauna. Environmental or sedimentary facies are based on differences in depositional environments. Knowledge of facies and environments helps to understand how fossil organisms lived and died, as well as how the fossils are distributed in a rock unit.

Faunal succession

By collecting fossils from strata that were in known, regular, stratigraphic order, geologists more than a century and a half ago established conclusively that fossil faunas do not repeat themselves and do not occur out of order, unless the rocks containing them have been deformed and rearranged. However, a specific fauna may be missing from a certain series of beds because of lack of preservation, erosion of the beds, or for paleoecologic reasons. This principle of faunal succession explains why different fossils are found in different rock units. For example, a particular assemblage of species of brachiopods, bryozoans, corals, and clams is unique to a period of time and place because of the prior evolutionary history of the individual species, local environmental

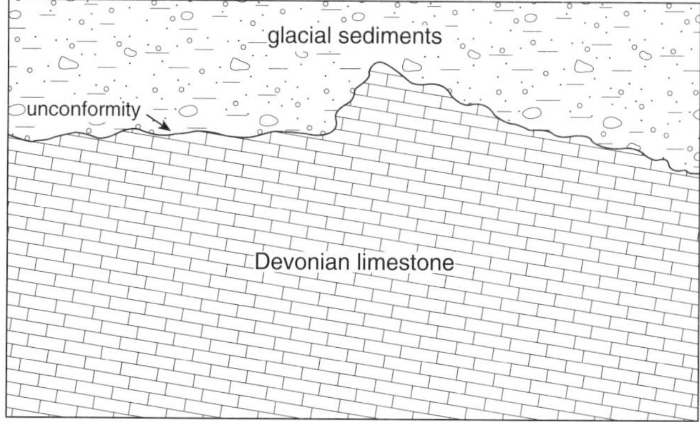

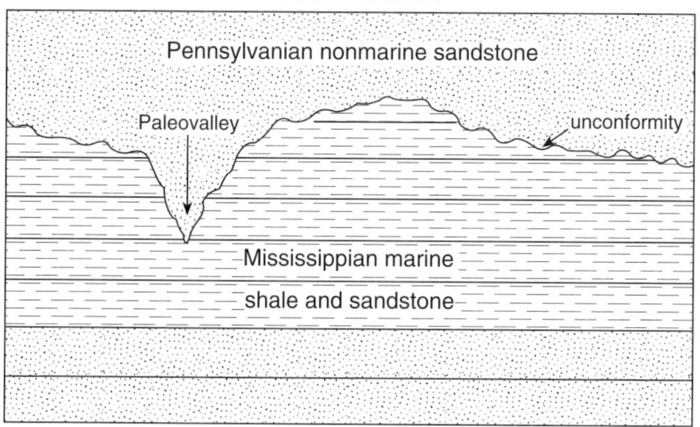

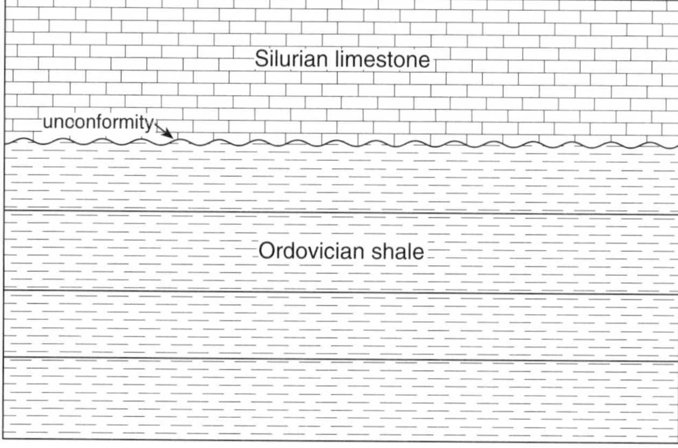

FIGURE 3-6.—Types of unconformities. In the illustration of an angular unconformity, flat-lying glacial sediments overlie dipping, eroded Devonian limestone. In the illustration of a disconformity, nearly flat-lying Pennsylvanian nonmarine sandstone overlies eroded hills and valleys of Mississippian marine shale and sandstone. In the illustration of a paraconformity, nearly flat-lying, shallow-water Silurian limestone overlies nearly flat-lying deeper water Ordovician marine shale; units are separated by an unconformable surface of nondeposition.

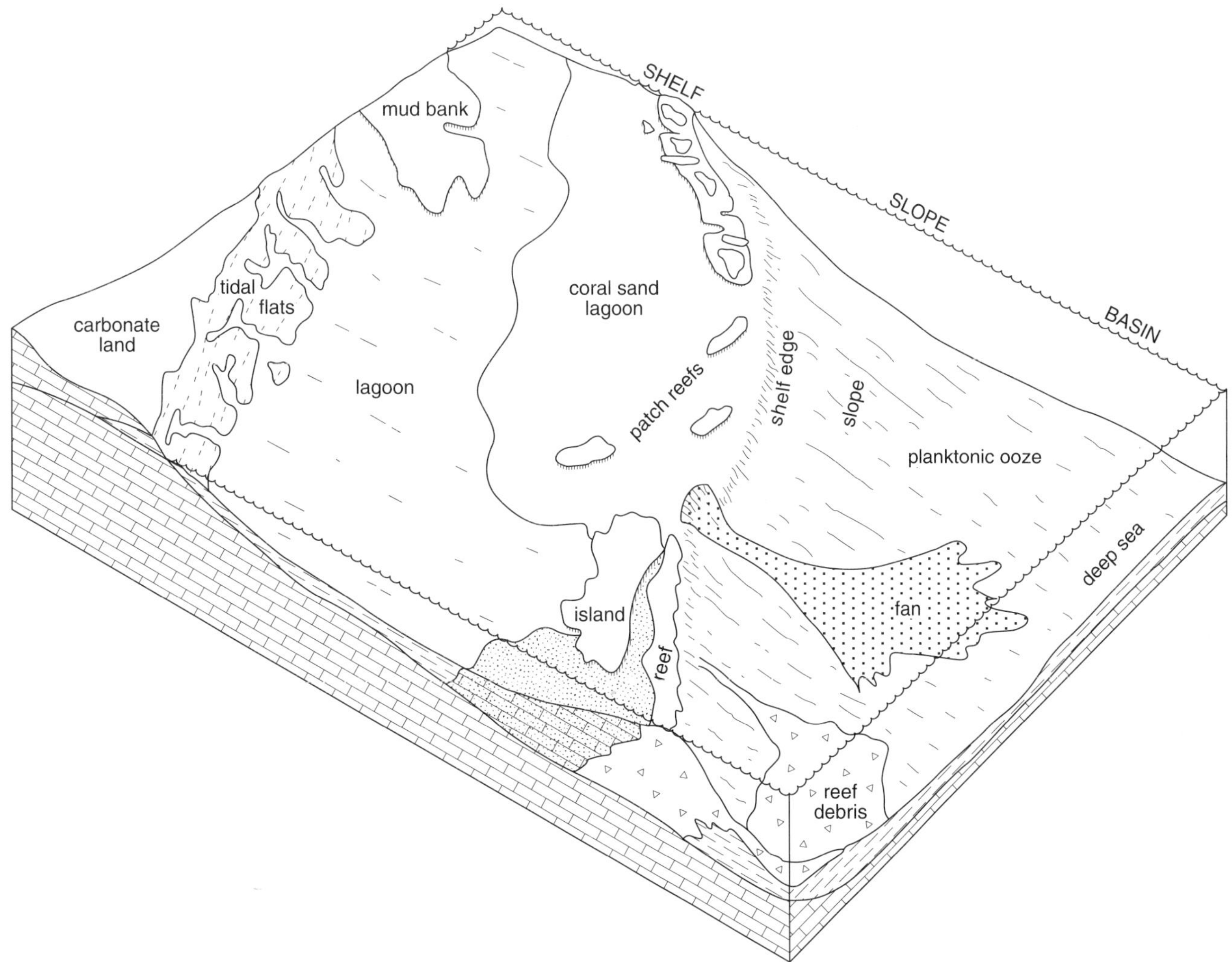

FIGURE 3-7.—Generalized block diagram showing typical carbonate sedimentary environments. These environments were common in earlier Paleozoic time (Ordovician, Silurian, and Devonian Periods).

conditions, and subsequent geologic events such as mass extinctions and changes in relative sea level. So, even though Ordovician, Silurian, and Devonian fossil assemblages may contain brachiopods, bryozoans, corals, and clams, the species and genera are distinctly different, making each assemblage unique from older and younger ones. The change in faunal assemblages over time is the result of extinction of species and organic evolution. The rate of evolutionary change in marine environments is sufficiently fast that new faunal assemblages are recognizable at intervals of about 5 to 20 million years. For some marine organisms, evolutionary rates are so fast that faunal changes can be measured in an interval of thousands of years or less.

A fossil genus (or rarely a species) that is relatively common, occurs over a large geographic area, and has a narrow stratigraphic range is called an **index** or **guide fossil**. The index fossil is a key to identifying the whole faunal assemblage and establishing its age.

Plate tectonics

The rock record in Ohio is the result of local geological and climatological conditions throughout geologic time, the changing geographic position of Ohio through time, and tectonic forces that result in folding, faulting, and vertical movement of the rocks and the surfaces upon which they were deposited. Tectonism is a general term for the movement or deformation of the rocks that form the crust of the Earth. Folding is the bending of rock layers due to stress. Faulting is the fracturing and displacement of rock layers due to stress.

The forces that have physically changed Ohio's geographic position as well as deformed its surface are closely related to the movement of pieces of the Earth's crust, a process called plate tectonics. Plate-tectonic activity is driven by the flow of plastic mantle material within the Earth. Although detailed treatment of plate tectonics is not possible here, it is useful to understand the basic process. Excellent, more detailed treatments of the subject can be found in many modern geology textbooks.

The outer portion of the Earth is called the lithosphere. It can be thought of as a thin, rigid skin floating on a very hot, plastic interior, called the asthenosphere (fig. 3-10). The asthenosphere is in constant motion, much as water moves as it is heated on a stove. As the asthenosphere slowly moves, the lithosphere is dragged along. In this process, large, rigid

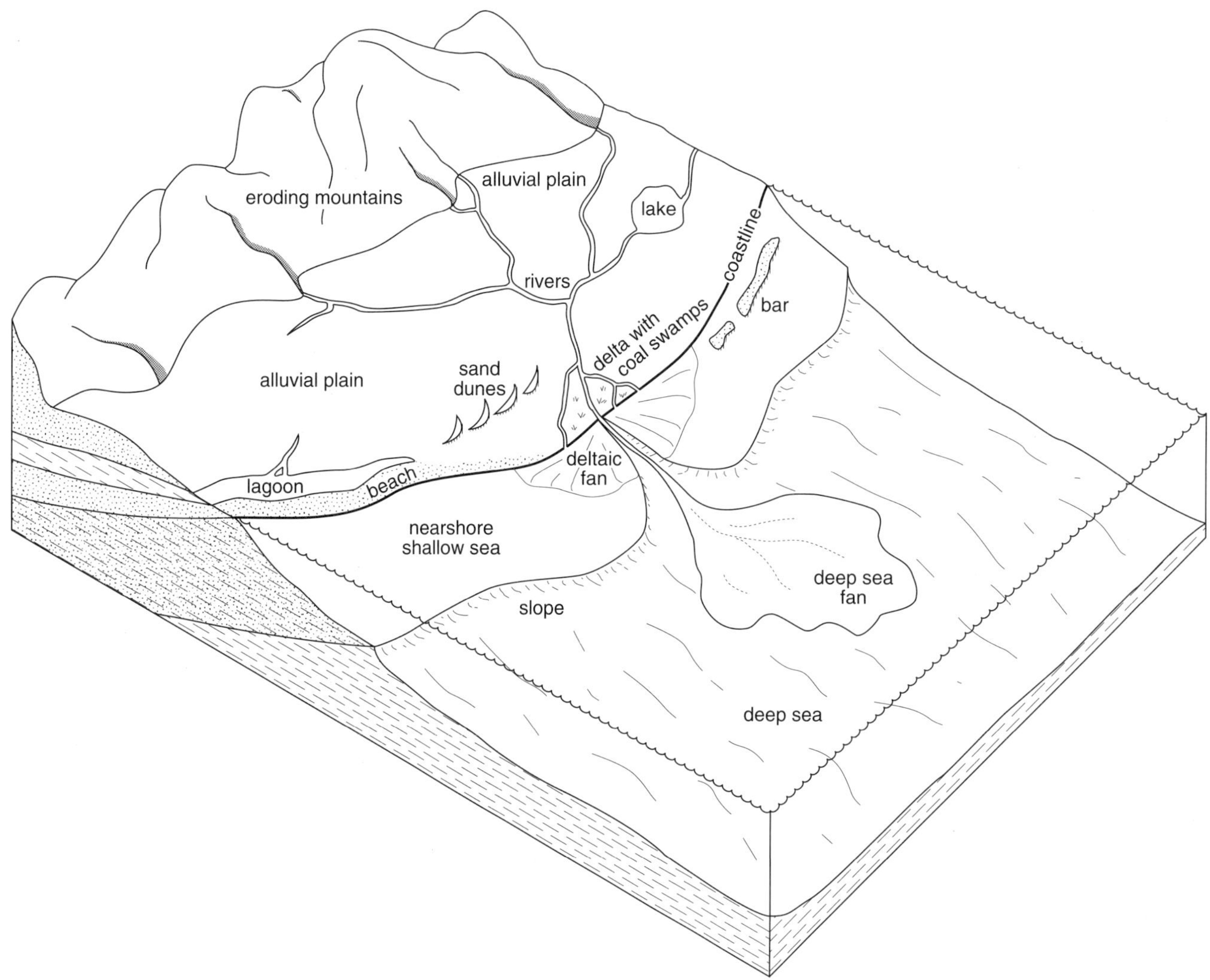

FIGURE 3-8.—Generalized block diagram showing typical siliciclastic sedimentary environments. Environments range from terrestrial alluvial plains to marginal-marine lagoons, to relatively deep, marine seas. These environments were common in later Paleozoic time (Mississippian, Pennsylvanian, and Permian Periods).

Lithofacies (W – E)	Formation and member names	
buff cross-bedded sandstone facies	Berea Sandstone	
red shale facies	"Red Bedford"	Bedford Shale
blue siltstone facies	Euclid Member	Bedford Shale
gray shale facies	"Gray Bedford"	Bedford Shale
black shale facies	Cleveland Member	Ohio Shale
gray shale facies	Chagrin Member	Ohio Shale
black shale facies	Huron Member	Ohio Shale

FIGURE 3-9.—Facies diagram showing relationship of Devonian-Mississippian rocks in northeastern Ohio.

sections of the lithosphere, called plates, move relative to one another. The modern Earth consists of six major plates and several smaller plates.

There are three types of plate movement. At convergent boundaries, plates collide to form major folded mountain chains and fault zones. The Appalachian Mountains are examples of the effects of plate collisions. At divergent or spreading boundaries, plates move away from one another. The great Mid-Atlantic ocean ridge system is a spreading center. At transform fault boundaries, plates slide past one another. The San Andreas fault in California is an example of a transform fault boundary. Much of the earthquake and volcanic activity on the Earth occurs at the margins of plates and can be attributed to plate-tectonic motion.

Within plate boundaries, where Ohio is located, folding and faulting tend to be less severe. In many areas, tectonism is confined to subtle warping and minor ruptures or fractures, called joints, in the rocks. Over long periods of geological time, flexing within plates may cause the plate surface to rise and fall. This motion, coupled with the rise and fall of sea level, due in part to changes in the amount of ice

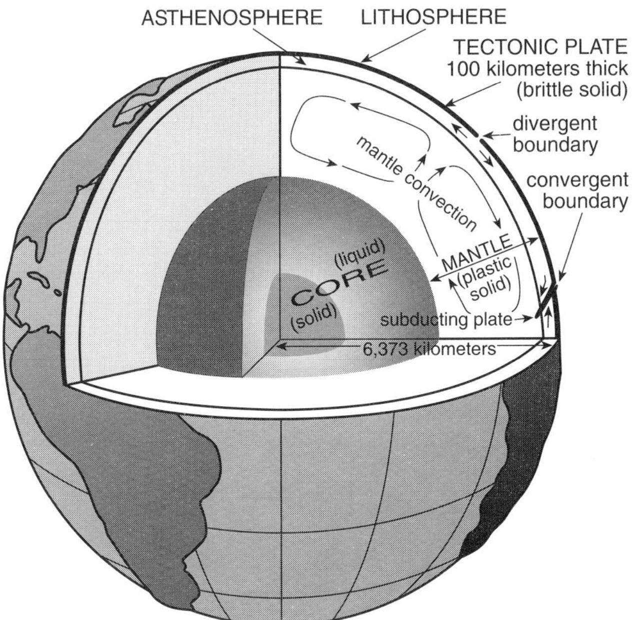

FIGURE 3-10.—Cross section of the Earth showing tectonic plates and convergent and divergent boundaries (modified from Washington Division of Geology and Earth Resources Information Circular 85, 1988).

stored on continents, helps explain the accumulation of sediments during part of geological history (when the surface is lower) and erosion of sediments at other times (when the surface is higher).

Ohio has been situated within the bounds of the North American Plate (see figs. 3-14, 3-15) from Precambrian time to the Recent. Thus, since the end of the Precambrian, there has been no major deformation of the area that is Ohio other than fracturing at the close of the Paleozoic Era. Nonetheless, global plate-tectonic motions have been responsible for movement of Ohio and the North American continent from a tropical location 15-20° south of the Equator during the Paleozoic to its present temperate location between 38° and 42° north of the Equator. Furthermore, the surface of this area was depressed during most of the Paleozoic to the extent that much of the time it was beneath the sea and fossiliferous sedimentary rocks formed. Since the Late Paleozoic, the region has been elevated, apparently above sea level, and the sedimentary rocks have largely been weathered and eroded. The historical sequence outlined below provides more detail about the changes that occurred in Ohio.

GEOLOGIC HISTORY OF OHIO

The earliest record of the geologic history of Ohio is preserved in the igneous and metamorphic Precambrian rocks of the deep subsurface. These rocks, which geologists commonly call the basement, are known only from deep well drilling and have been dated at more than 1 billion years old. Central and eastern Ohio are underlain by metamorphic rocks of the Grenville Province, the remains of a Precambrian plate that collided with the older portion of the North American continent, the Superior Province, 1 to 2 billion years ago to form the Grenville Mountains. The western edge of the Grenville Province is delineated by the Grenville Front, which is several tens of kilometers wide. The Grenville Front parallels and partly underlies the Cincinnati and Findlay Arches. West of this front, buried deep in the subsurface, is a rift or series of rifts in the basement, similar to the Red Sea rift of modern times. A rift is an area where a continental plate began to split apart. But, in the case of the western Ohio rifts, separation during the Precambrian was incomplete. The western Ohio rift, known as the East Continent Rift Zone, is quite deep and is filled with up to 6 km of undeformed sandstones and other siliciclastic rocks. West of the rift zone are older igneous and metamorphic rocks of the Superior Province. The ancient Grenville Mountains were eroded to an undulating plain bounded on the west by rift valleys (see fig. 3-11) by the time of onset of the early Paleozoic deposition in Ohio.

By Late Cambrian time, shallow seas covered Ohio and sediments were deposited and preserved, beginning a record of mainly marine and deltaic deposition, interrupted by periods of erosion (resulting in unconformities), which lasted until Early Permian time. Nonmarine deposition was intermittently common in the Pennsylvanian and Permian Periods. From what we can surmise from deposits and fossils found elsewhere, the area that is now Ohio has been an exposed continental area since the close of the Permian. In the Late Paleozoic, North America was part of a northern landmass called Laurasia, which collided with a southern landmass called Gondwana to form the supercontinent of Pangea (see fig. 3-15). Laurasia and Gondwana broke up in the Mesozoic, and the plates separated to create the Atlantic Ocean and the Gulf of Mexico. The area of Ohio remained high and dry, undergoing erosion for most of the past 245 million years of Earth history. The next substantial record is preserved as glacial deposits (see fig. 3-1).

PALEOZOIC HISTORY

Cambrian through Early Ordovician time

During the Cambrian Period, which began about 570 million years ago, Ohio was part of a broad coastal plain, comparable to the modern Gulf Coast of the U.S. In Middle to Late Cambrian time, the sea slowly spread across and eventually covered the area, onlapping the underlying, faulted Precambrian igneous and metamorphic rocks (figs. 3-11, 3-12A). Initially, sand and mud were deposited, then carbonate sediments accumulated. These sediments were lithified into sandstone, shale, limestone, and dolomite; these rocks (Mount Simon Sandstone, Eau Claire and Rome Formations, Knox Dolomite) are encountered only by drilling into the subsurface. Accumulation of several hundred meters of these rocks ended with withdrawal of the sea, followed by erosion (fig. 3-13) in Early Ordovician time, about 500 million years ago. The sea receded owing to uplift resulting from collision between the North American Plate and part of another plate to the east of Ohio. The related mountain-building event was the beginning of the Taconic Orogeny.

Middle Ordovician through Early Devonian time

In Middle Ordovician time, about 475 million years ago, the center of the North American continent lay astride the Equator, and Ohio lay south of the Equator (fig. 3-14). The sea again onlapped the continent, resubmerging the eroded land surface. Limestones were deposited widely as carbon-

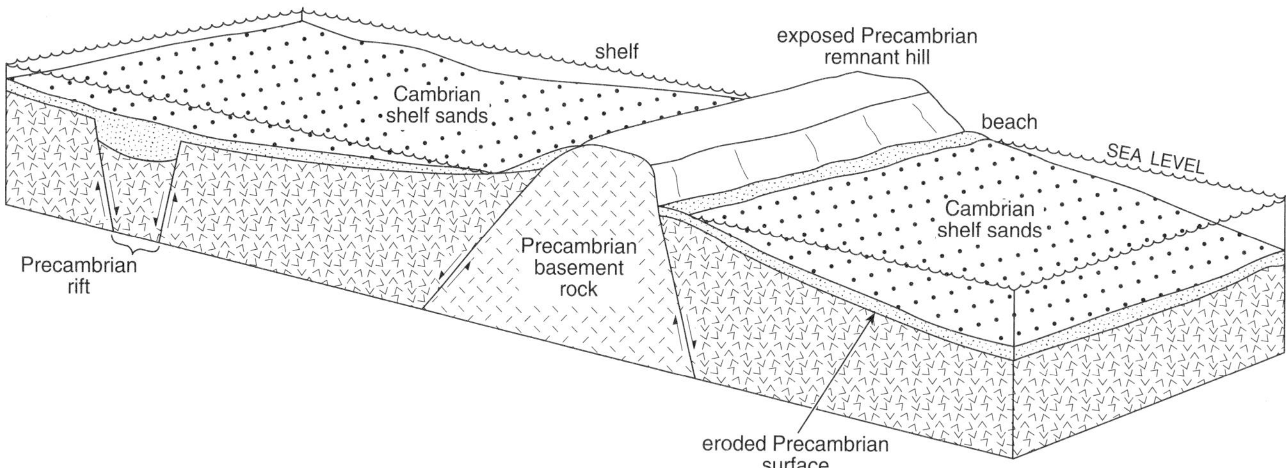

FIGURE 3-11.—Block diagram showing the onlap of the Precambrian basement rock by the Late Cambrian seas, deposition of basal Cambrian shelf sands over the faulted and eroded basement, and the Precambrian rift zone in western Ohio.

ate banks, reefs, and lagoonal and bar deposits (see fig. 3-7) during a time of only slight tectonic activity. These Middle Ordovician rocks in Ohio are known only from subsurface drilling.

The oldest exposed rock unit in Ohio, the Point Pleasant Formation of Middle to earliest Late Ordovician age, crops out along the Ohio River near Cincinnati. This rock unit represents the transition between shallow-water carbonate-bank limestones of the Middle Ordovician and the overlying, deeper water shales and limestones of the Late Ordovician (about 445 million years ago). These shales and limestones of the Late Ordovician Cincinnatian Series were deposited offshore (fig. 3-12B) in an epicontinental sea that was receiving sediment input from the mountains that formed in the early part of the Taconic Orogeny. The tropical environment and warm seas produced beds that are richly fossiliferous. These Upper Ordovician strata are exposed in numerous outcrops throughout a broad area in southwestern Ohio. Exposures on the hillsides and in stream and road cuts around Cincinnati are the best of Ohio's fossil-hunting areas. The State Invertebrate Fossil—the trilobite *Isotelus* (see frontispiece)—and many other well-preserved fossils can be found in the shales and limestones of the Cincinnatian Series (see Ordovician diorama on p. xvi and fig. 3-17). In latest Ordovician time, at the culmination of the Taconic Orogeny, the area that is Ohio was part of a rapidly subsiding (sinking) basin. The record of Ordovician deposition ends with a paraconformable break at the top of the Drakes Formation, toward the end of the Ordovician, about 438 million years ago. This break is widely attributed to a fall in sea level owing to glaciation in the Southern Hemisphere.

Silurian deposition began about 438 million years ago when sea level rose and flooded the exposed Ordovician surface. In their outcrop area on the east and west flanks of the Cincinnati Arch and on the crest of the Findlay Arch, the Silurian rocks consist of shallow-water, subtropical, carbonate-bank deposits (fig. 3-12C). Part of the bank had reefs, as in the Lower Silurian Lockport Dolomite. There are evaporite deposits (gypsum, anhydrite, and halite) between the reefs and overlying them. The Silurian carbonate rocks are moderately fossiliferous, but preservation is commonly poor.

The final stages of Silurian deposition reflect a subsiding but otherwise stable, shallow, marine environment that periodically experienced lowered sea level and evaporation of the sea water to form the thick salt beds of the Salina Group in eastern Ohio. These salt beds are mined more than 500 meters beneath Lake Erie at Cleveland (Cuyahoga County) and Fairport Harbor (Lake County).

In Early Devonian time, another plate collision along the northeastern margin of North America resulted in uplift and erosion. Deposition of sediments was essentially continuous in the Appalachian Basin in eastern Ohio. Lower Devonian rocks (Helderberg Limestone and Oriskany Sandstone, about 408 million years old) occur in the subsurface in eastern Ohio (Dow, 1962). A very limited deposit of Lower Devonian rocks (Holland Quarry Shale) was exposed in a quarry in Lucas County in northwestern Ohio, but this quarry has been long abandoned and is now reclaimed. Elsewhere, particularly along the present-day Devonian outcrop from southern Ohio to Lake Erie, a major unconformity separates Upper Silurian rocks from Middle Devonian dolomites and limestones. The uplift and related mountain-building activity that ended Middle Ordovician to Early Devonian deposition are referred to as the Acadian Orogeny.

Middle Devonian through Mississippian time

Middle Devonian sedimentation began in clear seas about 386 million years ago with deposition of the sediments that would become the richly fossiliferous Columbus Limestone east of the Findlay Arch and its approximate equivalents on the western side of the Findlay Arch, including the carbonates of the Detroit River Group (see fig. 3-19). These strata overlie the eroded Upper Silurian beds in a slight angular unconformity; the surface is characterized at some outcrops by phosphate-rich bone beds containing fish scales and teeth. The Columbus Limestone and the overlying Delaware Limestone crop out in a north-south band from south of Columbus (Franklin County) to Sandusky County and on Kelleys Island in Lake Erie. The best exposures of these fossiliferous units are in quarries along this belt. The quarries provide limestone for road construction, cement, and other building materials.

Toward the end of Middle Devonian time, carbonate deposition gave way to deposition of clay and organic matter that would become dark-brown to black marine shales (Olentangy

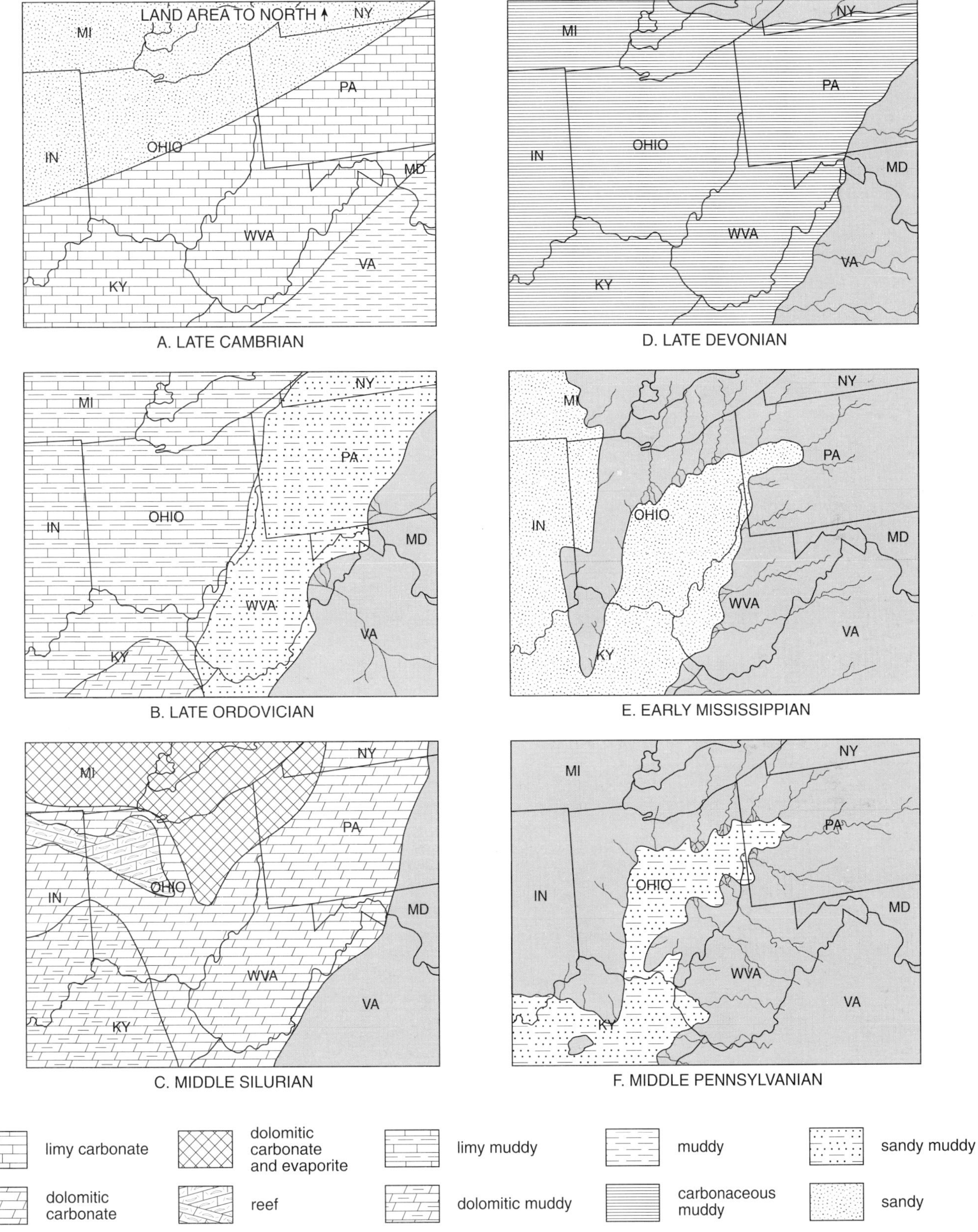

FIGURE 3-12.—Generalized paleogeographic maps of Ohio and surrounding areas during various Paleozoic periods. Land areas are shown by screen pattern. **A** modified by Ronald A. Riley from Dott and Batten (1976) and Palmer (1974). **B** modified by E. Mac Swinford from Weir and others (1984). **C** modified by by E. Mac Swinford from Dott and Batten (1976) and Droste and Shaver (1983). **D-F** modified from Hansen (no date).

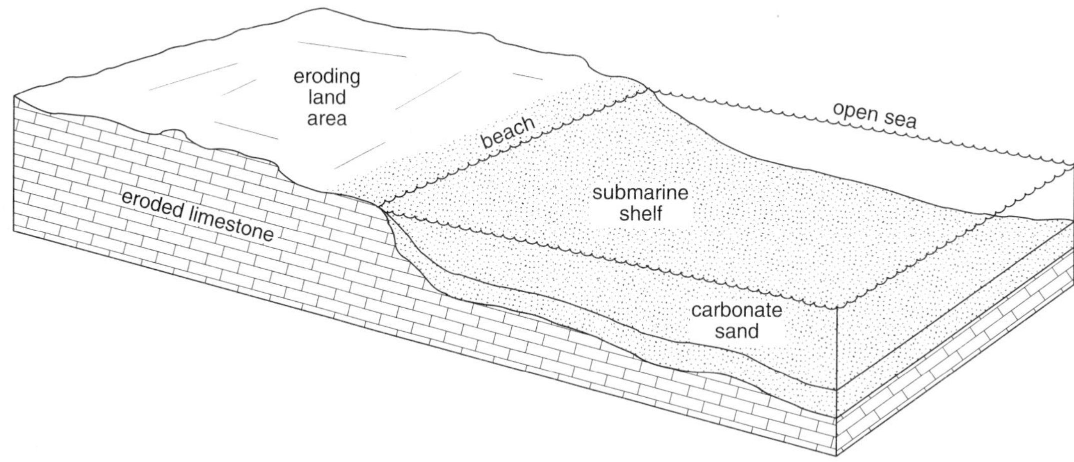

FIGURE 3-13.—Block diagram of erosion at low stand of sea level. As the sea recedes from left to right, the rocks are exposed and eroded.

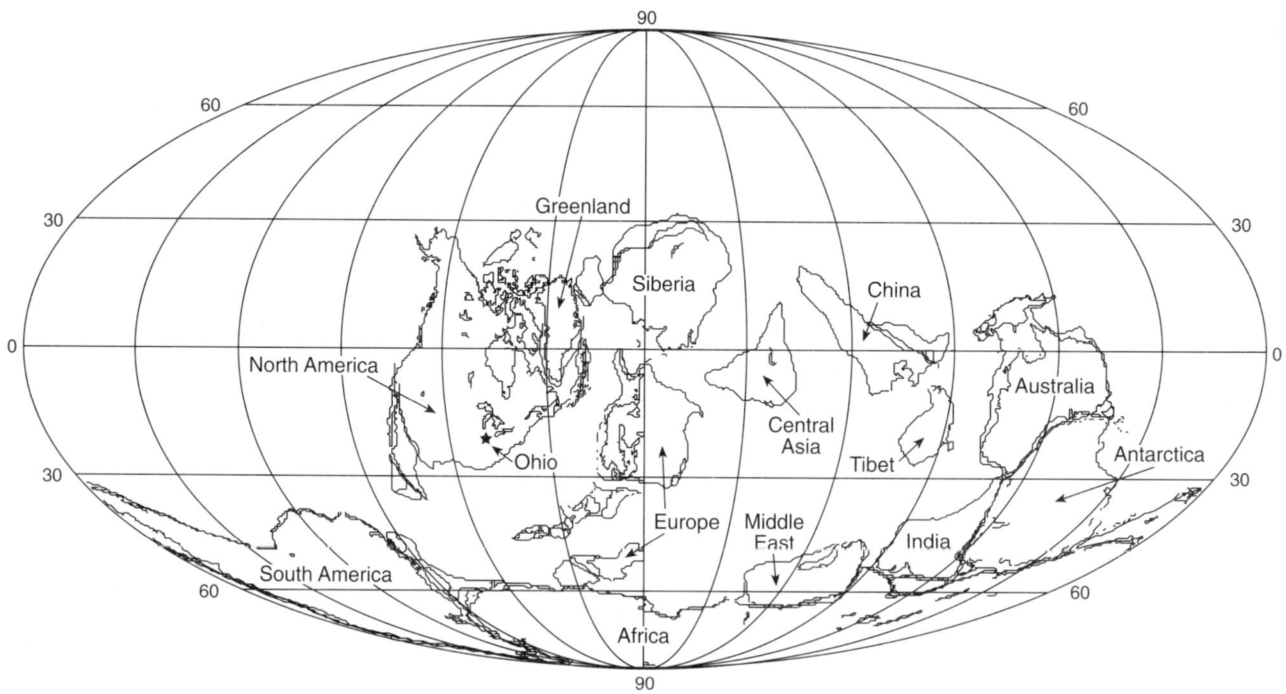

FIGURE 3-14.—Postulated position of the continents in the Early Paleozoic (Late Ordovician) (modified from Scotese and Denham, 1988).

Shale and Ohio Shale). These sediments began to fill a more rapidly subsiding, relatively stagnant offshore marine basin. The Olentangy Shale and the Ohio Shale (Huron, Chagrin, and Cleveland Shale Members) overall are poorly fossiliferous, but locally contain brachiopod and arthropod faunas and spectacular fish remains, especially shark and arthrodire fossils, such as the *Dunkleosteus* armor featured on the cover of this book. These shales crop out in a north-south band from Scioto County on the Ohio River through central Ohio to Erie County on the Lake Erie shore and then east to Pennsylvania and beyond to New York. The shoreline of this basin was in central Pennsylvania (fig. 3-12D).

By the end of the Devonian and beginning of the Mississippian, about 340 million years ago, the offshore marine basin was partly filled. The dark marine shales of the Late Devonian were covered by fluvial, deltaic and marginal-marine clastic sediments deposited in basin and shelf tectonic settings (fig. 3-12E) (see Pashin and Ettensohn, 1995). The Bedford Shale, the Berea Sandstone, the Cuyahoga Formation, and the Logan Formation (see fig. 3-20) were deposited in these environments. The black Sunbury Shale represents a brief return to stagnant basin conditions between the Berea Sandstone and the Cuyahoga Formation.

The western edge of the Mississippian outcrop belt parallels the north-south Devonian shale outcrop belt through central Ohio and then eastward parallel to the Lake Erie shore. Mississippian strata form a band of hills 5-10 km south of the present Lake Erie shoreline. The Mississippian rocks display various characteristics of deltaic and nearshore marine deposition (see fig. 3-8). The Cuyahoga and Logan Formations are moderately fossiliferous, containing brachiopod- and mollusk-rich faunas. Some excellent crinoid assemblages have been found in localized pockets in the Cuyahoga Formation.

Another major erosional event ended Mississippian deposition in Ohio and removed younger Mississippian strata, except for remnants of the Rushville and Maxville Formations in eastern Ohio. Valleys were carved by Mississippian and Early Pennsylvanian streams into the underlying Mississippian rocks. Pennsylvanian rocks were deposited on this irregular erosional surface.

Pennsylvanian and Permian time

The first record of renewed uplift to the east and/or subsidence (relative lowering of the Earth's surface) at the western edge of the Appalachian Basin is the sediments of the Early to Middle Pennsylvanian Sharon sandstone of the Pottsville Group (see fig. 3-21). Pennsylvanian and Permian rocks are primarily siliciclastic, consisting of nonmarine shales, sandstones, underclays, coals, ironstones, and limestones, as well as marine shales, limestones, ironstones, and flints. Moreover, unlike the deltas of earlier times, those of Pennsylvanian time were covered with lush vegetation. Although land plants were common in the Devonian and Mississippian, they did not overwhelm the landscape until the Pennsylvanian. Grand tree ferns, early conifers, reeds, and rushes grew in profusion in and around the swamps of the Pennsylvanian deltas. As the vegetation died, it accumulated in the water as peat, which was later compressed and heated deep underground to form Ohio's extensive coal deposits.

Rivers, lakes, deltas with peat (coal) swamps, open marine embayments, lagoons, beaches, and barrier bars characterized the final episodes of Paleozoic deposition in the Pennsylvanian and Early Permian. The four main subdivisions of the Pennsylvanian, the Pottsville, Allegheny, Conemaugh, and Monongahela Groups, as well as the Upper Pennsylvanian-Lower Permian Dunkard Group, display progressively more terrestrial environments of deposition consistent with the ongoing development of the supercontinent of Pangea (fig. 3-15).

Fossils in these upper Paleozoic strata are indicative of marginal-marine and terrestrial environments (fig. 3-12F). The climate was warm and tropical because the area that is now Ohio was near the Late Paleozoic Equator. Pennsylvanian strata are exposed in spectacular road cuts along Interstate Route 77 from Canton (Stark County) south to Marietta (Washington County) and along Interstate Route 70 from Cambridge (Guernsey County) to Bridgeport (Belmont County). There are equally impressive exposures of Pennsylvanian and Permian rocks in the cliffs along the Ohio River from Marietta north to East Liverpool (Jefferson County). The Pennsylvanian marine zones, mostly limestones and calcareous shales, generally are the most fossiliferous. Plant fossils are more common in freshwater shales. Permian (Dunkard Group) strata are present only in southeastern Ohio and are mainly continental fluvial-deltaic and lacustrine deposits which contain fossil vertebrates such as reptile and amphibian bones, fossil plants, and some fossil freshwater invertebrates.

MESOZOIC AND CENOZOIC HISTORY

During the Mesozoic Era and the Tertiary Period of the Cenozoic Era, an interval of about 245 million years, uplift, erosion, and weathering removed all traces of any deposits of these ages (if indeed there were any). Extensive systems of stream valleys dissected the entire surface of Ohio before the Pleistocene glaciations and may have removed several hundred meters of rock. The most recent chapter in Ohio's geologic history began about 2 million years ago when, in response to the cooling of the Earth's climate, continental glaciers moved south from Canada to cover about two-thirds of Ohio at their maximum extent (see fig. 3-3). Except for the continental deposits of the Pleistocene Ice Age and the sediments of the postglacial Recent, there is no observable record of Mesozoic and Cenozoic deposition in Ohio. Fossils in Pleistocene and Recent sediments consist of plant frag-

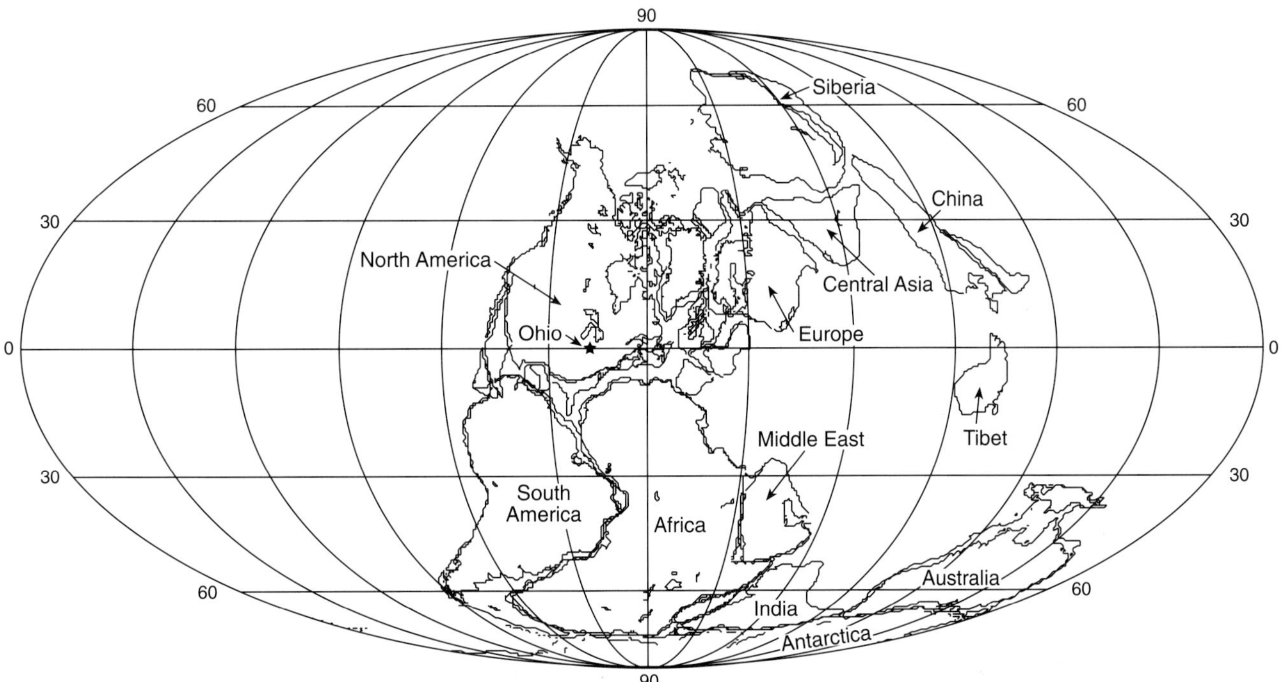

FIGURE 3-15.—Postulated position of the continents in the Late Paleozoic (Middle Pennsylvanian) (modified from Scotese and Denham, 1988).

ments, bones of land animals, and remains of lake and river dwellers such as clams, snails, and fish. Although they are comparatively rare, these fossils can be spectacular, as in the case of mastodon bones.

REGIONAL STRATIGRAPHY

The present pattern of rock outcrops (see fig. 3-2) is the result of the position of rock units in relation to geologic structures, the various erosional regimes, and the distribution of glacial deposits. On one hillside or in one stream or road cut, only a hundred meters or so of rock are typically exposed, that is, generally just one or two formations can be seen at one locality. A few kilometers away, another set of formations may be exposed. Unfortunately, not all the formations of Ohio can be described in this volume. The following paragraphs describe and illustrate composite sections of Paleozoic formations, many fossiliferous, for five general areas of Ohio shown in figure 3-16.

SOUTHWESTERN OHIO

This area is characterized by abundant outcrops of Upper Ordovician shales and limestones (fig. 3-17) in the hills of Cincinnati and surrounding areas. All of the units are highly fossiliferous. Fossil collecting is permitted at Caesar Creek State Park (see Shrake, 1992) in Warren County and Hueston Woods State Park (see Ohio Division of Parks and Recreation, no date) in Butler and Preble Counties.

CENTRAL OHIO

In eastern Adams, Highland, and Clinton Counties, relatively fossiliferous Silurian-age rocks of the Brassfield, Bisher, and Lilley Formations are exposed (fig. 3-18). Around Dayton (Montgomery County) and Springfield (Clark

FIGURE 3-16.—The five areas of Ohio that are discussed in the text and represented in the regional stratigraphic columns in figures 3-17 through 3-21. The boundaries of the geologic systems from figure 3-2 also are shown.

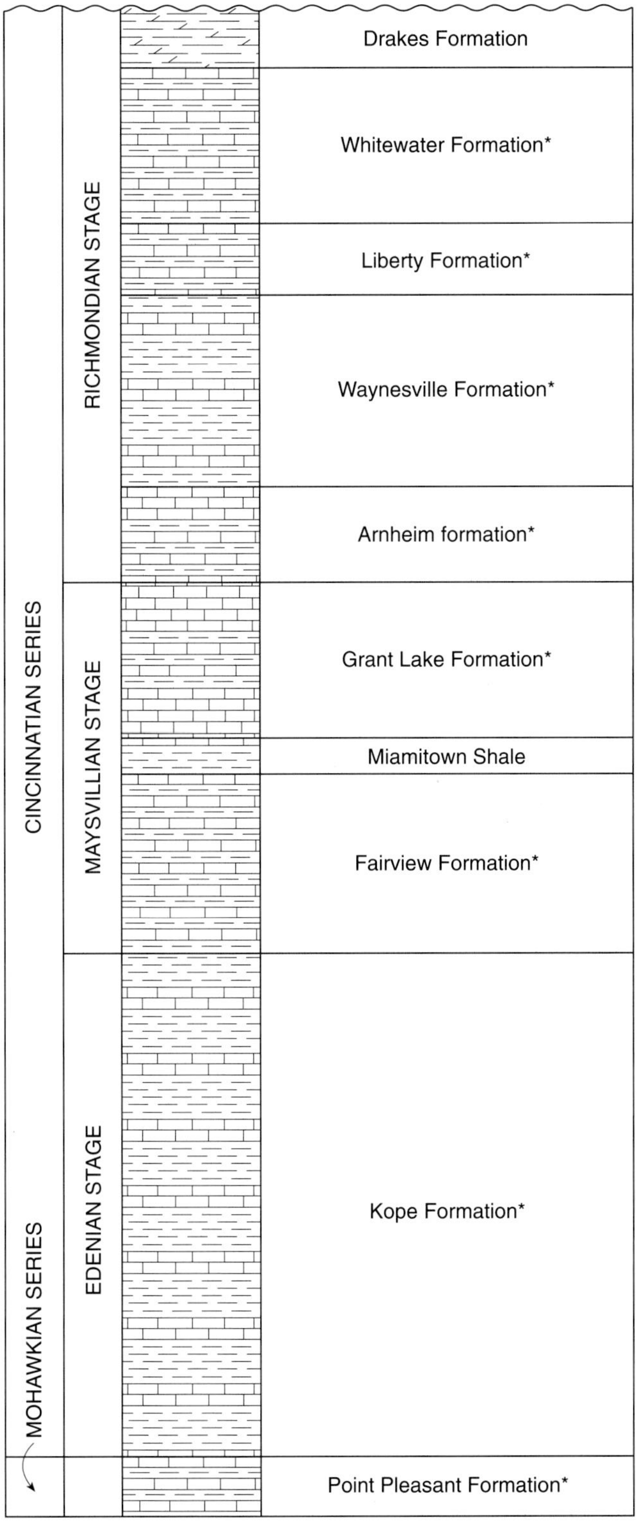

CINCINNATIAN SERIES
MOHAWKIAN SERIES
RICHMONDIAN STAGE
MAYSVILLIAN STAGE
EDENIAN STAGE
Drakes Formation
Whitewater Formation*
Liberty Formation*
Waynesville Formation*
Arnheim formation*
Grant Lake Formation*
Miamitown Shale
Fairview Formation*
Kope Formation*
Point Pleasant Formation*

FIGURE 3-17.—Generalized section of Middle and Upper Ordovician formations in southwestern Ohio. Asterisks indicate units that have fossils illustrated in Chapters 4 to 25. This composite section represents about 225 meters of rock exposed across the area. The section is not to scale, but the thicknesses indicated are proportional. The term Cincinnati Group is used in much of the geologic literature for southwestern Ohio for rocks of the Kope Formation through the Drakes Formation. Other nomenclature also has been used for these rocks. See figure 3-18 for explanation of rock types.

County), Silurian formations exposed in quarries and river valleys include the moderately fossiliferous Dayton Formation. The Silurian formations are not as fossiliferous as the Ordovician formations. Farther east, in south-central Ohio, Devonian and Mississippian shales and sandstones (Ohio, Bedford, and Sunbury Shales and Berea Sandstone) crop out. Plant and fish fossils are locally abundant in the Ohio Shale. In central Ohio, the Ohio and Olentangy Shales and the Columbus and Delaware Limestones crop out. The Columbus Limestone is very fossiliferous. The Ohio State House in Columbus is built of Columbus Limestone, and many fossils can be seen in the steps, pillars, and walls (see Melvin and McKenzie, 1992).

NORTHWESTERN OHIO

On the crest and flanks of the Findlay Arch, Lower and Upper Silurian and Middle and Upper Devonian formations are the surface rocks (fig. 3-19). Except for the island area of Lake Erie and some deeper river valleys, these rocks are exposed only in quarries. Some of these units are moderately fossiliferous and some are very fossiliferous, such as the world-famous Silica Formation at Sylvania (Lucas County) (see Stewart, 1927) and the Columbus Limestone at Marblehead (Ottawa County) and on Kelleys Island. Ancient reefs dominated by stromatoporoids, corals, and bryozoans are common in the Lockport Dolomite.

NORTHEASTERN OHIO

Siliciclastic rocks of Late Devonian through Early Pennsylvanian age crop out in the deeper valleys and in quarries and road cuts in northeastern Ohio. Exposures of Devonian and Mississippian rocks are common in the Cuyahoga Valley and along the Lake Erie shore from Erie County to the Pennsylvania line (fig. 3-20). Farther south, other Mississippian formations and Lower Pennsylvanian rocks are exposed. Spectacular fish remains have been found in the Cleveland Shale Member of the Ohio Shale in the Cleveland area. The Chagrin Shale Member has produced some excellent arthropod fossils. The Cuyahoga Formation also is fossiliferous in places and is particularly noted for its crinoid fossils.

EASTERN OHIO

The surface rocks in eastern Ohio are primarily of Pennsylvanian and Permian age; Mississippian rocks are present in the western part of this area. The area is largely unglaciated south and east of Canton (Stark County). Stream and road cuts expose Pennsylvanian-age interbedded sandstones, shales, coals, and thin limestones (fig. 3-21). The marine limestones and shales are moderately fossiliferous, especially the Lower Mercer, Putnam Hill, Vanport, Brush Creek, Cambridge, and Ames units. Plant fossils are abundant in the shales and sandstones. Permian rocks are limited to southeasternmost Ohio.

ACKNOWLEDGMENTS

Reviewers for this chapter included Thomas M. Berg, Merrianne Hackathorn, Michael C. Hansen, Dennis N. Hull, Gregory A. Schumacher, David A. Stith, and E. Mac Swinford (Ohio Division of Geological Survey) and Loren E. Babcock (The Ohio State University).

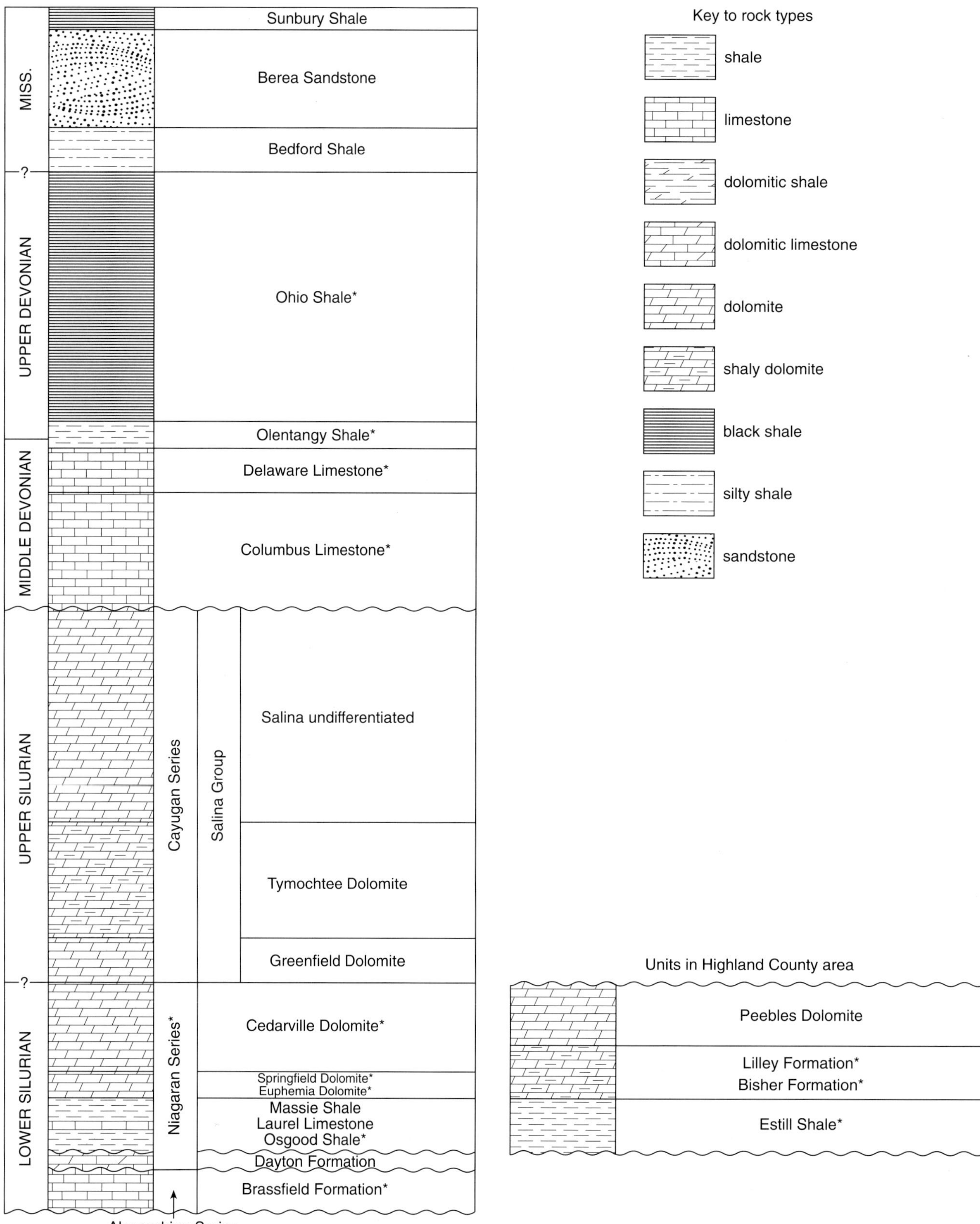

FIGURE 3-18.—Generalized section of Silurian, Devonian, and Mississippian formations in west-central and south-central Ohio. Asterisks indicate units that have fossils illustrated in Chapters 4 to 25. This composite section represents about 330 meters of rock exposed across the area. The section is not to scale, but the thicknesses indicated are proportional.

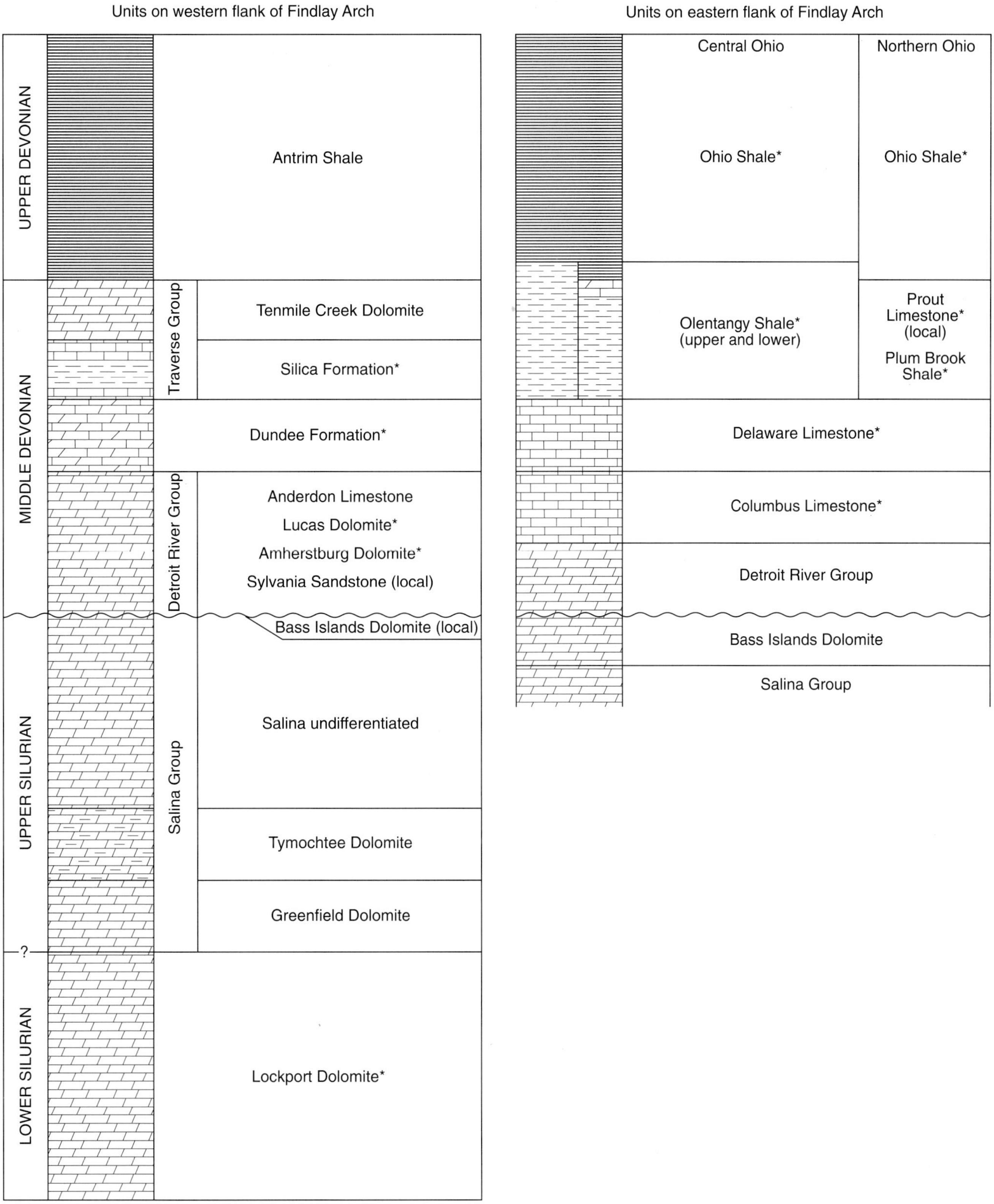

Units on western flank of Findlay Arch

Series	Group	Unit
UPPER DEVONIAN		Antrim Shale
MIDDLE DEVONIAN	Traverse Group	Tenmile Creek Dolomite
	Traverse Group	Silica Formation*
		Dundee Formation*
	Detroit River Group	Anderdon Limestone Lucas Dolomite* Amherstburg Dolomite* Sylvania Sandstone (local)
UPPER SILURIAN		Bass Islands Dolomite (local)
	Salina Group	Salina undifferentiated
	Salina Group	Tymochtee Dolomite
	Salina Group	Greenfield Dolomite
—?— LOWER SILURIAN		Lockport Dolomite*

Units on eastern flank of Findlay Arch

Central Ohio	Northern Ohio
Ohio Shale*	Ohio Shale*
Olentangy Shale* (upper and lower)	Prout Limestone* (local) Plum Brook Shale*
Delaware Limestone*	
Columbus Limestone*	
Detroit River Group	
Bass Islands Dolomite	
Salina Group	

FIGURE 3-19.—Generalized section of Silurian and Devonian formations in northwestern Ohio. Asterisks indicate units that have fossils illustrated in Chapters 4 to 25. This composite section represents more than 300 meters of rock exposed across the area. The section is not to scale, but the thicknesses indicated are proportional. See figure 3-18 for key to rock types.

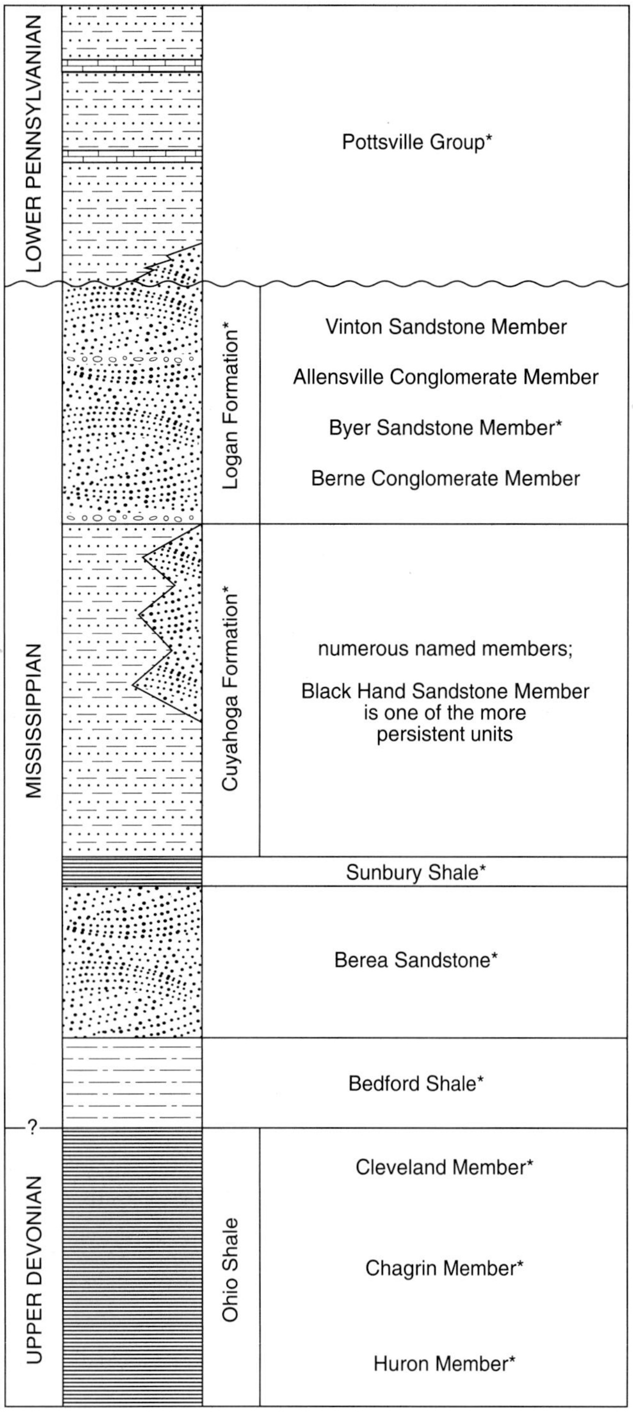

Period	Formation	Unit
LOWER PENNSYLVANIAN		Pottsville Group*
MISSISSIPPIAN	Logan Formation*	Vinton Sandstone Member
		Allensville Conglomerate Member
		Byer Sandstone Member*
		Berne Conglomerate Member
	Cuyahoga Formation*	numerous named members; Black Hand Sandstone Member is one of the more persistent units
		Sunbury Shale*
		Berea Sandstone*
		Bedford Shale*
?		
UPPER DEVONIAN	Ohio Shale	Cleveland Member*
		Chagrin Member*
		Huron Member*

FIGURE 3-20.—Generalized section of Upper Devonian, Misissippian, and Lower Pennsylvanian formations in northeastern Ohio. Asterisks indicate units that have fossils illustrated in Chapters 4 to 25. This composite section represents about 400 meters of rock exposed across the area. The section is not to scale, but the thicknesses indicated are proportional. The term "Waverly" is used in the older literature to refer to Mississippian rocks in Ohio. Some geologists use the European term "Carboniferous," which encompasses the Missisippian and Pennsylvanian Periods of the U.S. Many units have been named within the Cuyahoga Formation, but most units are local and cannot be traced over great distances. The Black Hand Member is a spectacular massive sandstone that is fairly widespread but discontinuous. See Hyde (1953), Hoover (1960), and Collins (1979) for more information on Mississippian rocks in Ohio. See figure 3-18 for explanation of rock types.

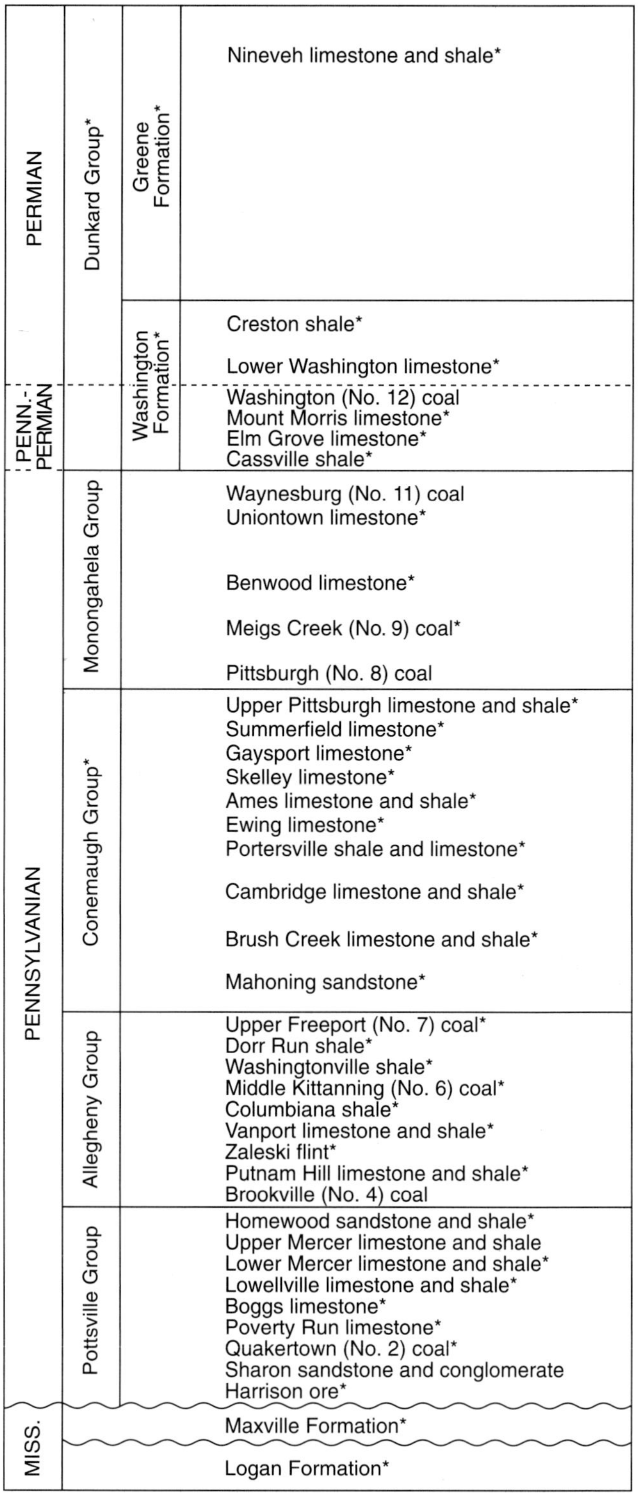

Period	Group	Formation	Units
PERMIAN	Dunkard Group*	Greene Formation*	Nineveh limestone and shale*
		Washington Formation*	Creston shale* Lower Washington limestone*
PENN.-PERMIAN			Washington (No. 12) coal Mount Morris limestone* Elm Grove limestone* Cassville shale*
PENNSYLVANIAN	Monongahela Group		Waynesburg (No. 11) coal Uniontown limestone* Benwood limestone* Meigs Creek (No. 9) coal* Pittsburgh (No. 8) coal
	Conemaugh Group*		Upper Pittsburgh limestone and shale* Summerfield limestone* Gaysport limestone* Skelley limestone* Ames limestone and shale* Ewing limestone* Portersville shale and limestone* Cambridge limestone and shale* Brush Creek limestone and shale* Mahoning sandstone*
	Allegheny Group		Upper Freeport (No. 7) coal* Dorr Run shale* Washingtonville shale* Middle Kittanning (No. 6) coal* Columbiana shale* Vanport limestone and shale* Zaleski flint* Putnam Hill limestone and shale* Brookville (No. 4) coal
	Pottsville Group		Homewood sandstone and shale* Upper Mercer limestone and shale Lower Mercer limestone and shale* Lowellville limestone and shale* Boggs limestone* Poverty Run limestone* Quakertown (No. 2) coal* Sharon sandstone and conglomerate Harrison ore*
MISS.			Maxville Formation*
			Logan Formation*

FIGURE 3-21.—Uppermost Mississippian, Pennsylvanian, and Permian units in eastern and southeastern Ohio. Asterisks indicate units that have fossils illustrated in Chapters 4 to 25. This composite section represents more than 500 meters of rock exposed across the area. The section is not to scale, but the thicknesses indicated are proportional. The only formally defined units in the Pennsylvanian of Ohio are the groups. There are more than 100 named beds, but many of them are local and cannot be traced over great distances. Only the bounding units of the groups and the fossiliferous units are shown. See Stout (1943) and Collins (1979) for more information on Pennsylvanian rocks in Ohio.

Chapter 4

PHYLUM PORIFERA, SPONGES

by J. Keith Rigby

INTRODUCTION

Only a relatively few fossil sponges have been described from Ohio, particularly when compared with the abundant and diverse brachiopods, bryozoans, and corals. Fossil sponges are known only locally, as for example in Lower Mississippian rocks of northeastern Ohio and in Upper Ordovician rocks of southwestern Ohio. Their apparent rarity may be an artifact of collection, for fossils sponges could easily be overlooked because they commonly appear nondescript and have obscure structure when compared with brachiopods, gastropods, or even bryozoans. Diverse sponge assemblages have been collected elsewhere, where paleontologists have hunted for them, from rocks similar to those exposed in Ohio.

Figures 1-3 and 1-4 in Chapter 1 show sponge morphology and **spicule** types. Expanded discussion of morphology and classification of fossil sponges and additional references are given in Broadhead (1983).

KEY TO SOME GENERA OF FOSSIL SPONGES FROM OHIO

1A. Sponge spherical or subspherical 2
1B. Sponge not spherical or subspherical 6

2A. Outer surface smooth, without **spongocoel** or deep surface grooves 3
2B. Outer surface with deep surface grooves 5

3A. Large interior canals straight and radiate from center 4
3B. Large interior canals subvertical and curved parallel to exterior and in radially arranged rows that open on summit .... *Astylospongia* (figs. 4-1.5, 4-1.9)

4A. Spicules are tricranoclones in prominent radial series .... *Hindia* (figs. 4-1.1 to 4-1.4)
4B. Spicules are sphaeroclones in less prominent series .... *Carpospongia* (fig. 4-1.11, 4-1.18 to 4-1.21)

5A. Sponge has deep grooves on sides and summit into which empty large radial canals in rows; lacks spongocoel; spicules are sphaeroclones .... *Caryospongia* (figs. 4-1.10, 4-1.12 to 4-1.14)
5B. Upper sides of sponge grooved; shallow spongocoel on summit; large vertical canals parallel to surface and open into spongocoel on top but not on sides; spicules are sphaeroclones .... *Astylospongia* (figs. 4-1.5, 4-1.9, 4-1.15 to 4-1.17)

6A. Walls thick 7
6B. Walls thin and have prominent rectangular structure 13

7A. Walls lack rectangular or **reticulate** structure 8
7B. Walls have regular three dimensionally reticulate bundles of spicules; skeleton is tubular cylindrical to branched, composed of oxeas .... *Heliospongia* (fig. 4-4.6)

8A. Sponge saucer or bowl shaped; skeleton of large irregularly oriented octactines .... *Astraeospongium* (fig. 4-2.1)
8B. Sponge not bowl shaped 9

9A. Sponge has appearance of hollow of hand, with fingerlike digitations; prominent spongocoel; skeleton of irregularly oriented hexactines .... *Brachiospongia* (fig. 4-2.2 to 4-2.4)
9B. Sponge cylindrical, twiglike, or massive 10

10A. Without spongocoel 11
10B. With spongocoel; walls have secondary gross overgrowths on polyactines and finer polyactines in a dermal layer .... *Regispongia* (fig. 4-4.1 to 4-4.5)

11A. Sponge small, twiglike; surface porous; skeleton upward divergent, fibrous; spicules are obscure heloclones .... *Heterospongia* (fig. 4-1.6, 4-1.7)
11B. Sponge massive or large sticklike 12

12A. Sponge massive, has coarse, thick **root-tuft** and multilobate surface without coarse pores; skeleton of irregular hexactines .... *Pattersonia* (figs. 4-2.5, 4-3.3)
12B. Sponge massive or irregularly lobate to sticklike or fingerlike; lacks root-tuft; surface crowded with coarse and fine pores; skeleton upward divergent, fibrous, of obscure heloclones .... *Dystactospongia* (fig. 4-1.8)

13A. Sponge vaselike and has ring of **nodes** in lower part above flattened base .... *Cleodictya* (figs. 4-3.5 to 4-3.7)
13B. Sponge conico-cylindrical or vaselike to goblet shaped without ring of nodes 14

14A. Sponge cylindrical, not upward flaring; skeleton uniformly quadrate 15
14B. Sponge goblet shaped or upward flared; lotus-blossom-like profile from flat base above stem or stalklike root-tuft; upper margin variously reflexed .... *Thamnodictya* (figs. 4-3.1, 4-3.2, 4-3.4)

15A. Body of sponge annulate .... *Ectenodictya* (= *Calathospongia*) (fig. 4-3.8)
15B. Sponge regularly conico-cylindrical, lacking annulations, may have cylindrical stem; skeleton gridlike, three dimensional .... *Clathrospongia* (fig. 4-2.6)

LOWER PALEOZOIC SPONGES

The genus *Pattersonia* Miller includes sponges that are massive, irregularly lobate structures (figs. 4-2.5, 4-3.3). They lack a spongocoel and have a prominent, thick root-tuft at the base. The tuft may be massive and very long and is composed of relatively smooth, long, hexactine-derived spicules. Individual lobes may be earlike and occur in more or less horizontal rows on the surface. Overall form is somewhat conical, flattened and deeply indented, longitudinally, on opposite sides. Solid lobes may be slightly pendent and tuberose (having an irregular, rootlike shape). The entire sponge may range up to 9 cm high and up to 11 cm in diameter across the maximum width, near the base. *Pattersonia aurita* (Beecher) (Beecher, 1889, p. 28) ranges up to 136 mm high and has a maximum diameter of about 138 mm. Earlike lobes point downward and are somewhat more regularly arranged in concentric rows than in *P. tuberosa* (Beecher) (fig. 4-3.3). The skeleton of *Pattersonia* consists of irregularly oriented hexactines and hexactine-derived spicules in an irregular felted mass, but includes some large hexactines that are oriented with some rays tangent to the outer surface. Some irregularly lobate specimens may be compound, consisting of individuals that have grown together. Canal systems include two sizes of openings; larger ones continue into the body and were perhaps excurrent, smaller intervening ones were perhaps incurrent.

Pattersonia difficilis Miller and *P. ulrichi* Rauff (fig. 4-2.5) are reported from the Upper Ordovician Corryville Shale Member of the McMillan Formation (= Grant Lake Formation of Ohio terminlogy) at Cincinnati. *Pattersonia aurita* is reported from the Middle Ordovician Bigby Limestone of Franklin County, Kentucky. *Pattersonia tuberosa* (fig. 4-3.3) is reported from the Upper Ordovician Bellevue Limestone Member of the McMillan Formation at Turners Station, Kentucky.

Sponges of the genus *Brachiospongia* Marsh have a handlike appearance, consisting of a central, somewhat tubular or cup-shaped spongocoel from which radiate 6-12 fingerlike projections from near the base (figs. 4-2.2, 4-2.4). These hollow projections curve outward and downward, somewhat like bent fingers that support the palm of the hand above a surface. They have walls of essentially the same thickness as the upper cuplike or subcylindrical part of the sponge and the upward-arched base. The exterior may be smooth, as in *Brachiospongia digitata* (Owen), or tuberose, as in *B. tuberculata* (James). The skeleton is apparently composed of irregularly oriented hexactines in a nonparallel arrangement of a felted mass, but with an "armor" of prominent larger hexactines or pentactines (fig. 4-2.3). The latter have four tangential rays subparallel to the surface and a prominent ray extending into the skeleton. These spicules are not arranged in regular fashion, but are irregularly oriented with respect to one another. Small pores are developed across the outer surface of the sponge, except on the base, and are seemingly related to canals. No root-tuft is evident. One species may have bifurcating or divided petal-like digitations rather than the subcylindrical fingerlike projections from the base. The general digitate handlike shape is diagnostic of this sponge. The genus is reported from the Middle to Upper Ordovician of Ohio, Kentucky, and Tennessee in the U.S. and Ontario and Manitoba in

Canada (see Rigby, 1970).

Representatives of the genus *Dystactospongia* Miller are massive to irregularly lobate or digitate sponges that lack a central spongocoel. They may be up to 10 cm long and wide, where massive, or somewhat smaller where tuberose or digitate. Their surfaces are marked by polygonal to circular pores of two sizes that are openings of canals which penetrate into the sponge (fig. 4-1.8). Larger canals may be approximately 2 mm in diameter and smaller ones less than 1 mm in diameter. Larger ones may be clustered into possible excurrent openings; the smaller ones occur in intervening spaces and apparently were incurrent openings. The latter tend to be more crowded and polygonal at the surface. Canals in the interior may be clustered in a vertical or steeply ascending axial zone, but spread out in an outer zone where canals are more nearly horizontal. The skeletal net consists of fibers of closely spaced heloclone spicules that may appear vermiform or like spaghetti that has been packed so closely that elements interfere and mutually accommodate by some change in shape. The net appears as a confused fibrous mass at first glance, but generally consists of upward and outward radiating tracts of heloclone spicules. Canal openings are less regular than in tabulate corals and considerably larger and more irregular than in bryozoans.

Dystactospongia occurs in the Middle to Upper Ordovician of Illinois, Ohio, and Indiana. *Dystactospongia madisonensis* Foerste was described by Rigby (1966) from Indiana, and apparently Foerste (1909c) recovered some material of the same species from Ohio. Ulrich (1889, p. 243) reported the occurrence of *D. minima* from the top of the "Trenton beds" near Hanover, Butler County, Ohio. It is indistinguishable from *D. minor* Ulrich & Everett (fig. 4-1.8) from Trentonian rocks near Dixon, Illinois. *Dystactospongia insolens* Miller was reported (S. A. Miller, 1882) as limited to "middle Trenton" beds.

The genus *Heterospongia* Ulrich includes branching, twiglike to lobate sponges (figs. 4-1.6, 4-1.7) without a central spongocoel. Their exteriors may be smooth or somewhat nodose and may have circular, polygonal or elongate skeletal pores of irregular size and distribution. Larger pores appear to be openings of excurrent canals and smaller ones of incurrent canals. The skeletal net generally consists of subvertical principal fibers along the axial region that curve upward and outward toward the outer surface. These fibers are connected in an irregular way by fibers essentially normal to the principal ones. Both types of fibers are composed of closely packed heloclonid monaxial spicules and perhaps other smooth monaxons, arranged basically parallel to the fiber surface, although the skeletal structure is not well defined.

Heterospongia appears similar to *Dystactospongia* Miller but differs in having a finer textured skeleton, a more twiglike growth form, and the possible possession of oxeas or styles (monaxons with one blunt end and one pointed end) in the skeleton. *Heterospongia* occurs in Upper Ordovician (Cincinnatian Series) rocks of Kentucky, Ohio, and Minnesota.

The genus *Hindia* Duncan includes distinctly spherical sponges that are 2 mm to 5 cm in diameter; most are approximately 1 or 2 cm in diameter (figs. 4-1.1, 4-1.4). Their exteriors are smooth and generally without surface grooves, and most specimens lack a spongocoel or even a shallow depression. The skeleton is made of radially oriented tricranoclones, which look like a three-legged chair with legs pointing toward the exterior (fig. 4-1.2). In general, spicule size increases radially. Ends of rays articulate with "shoulders" of adjacent spicules, somewhat like human hands on the shoulders and around the neck of a person. Canals are straight and radial and expand slightly toward the exterior (fig. 4-1.3), where generally three sizes of pores mark the surface. Larger ones were probably excurrent canals and intermediate and smaller canals were probably incurrent ones. Radiating straight oxeas may occur in canal openings or in other places throughout the skeleton.

Hindia gregaria (Miller & Dyer) occurs in Upper Ordovician rocks near Cincinnati and may appear as grapelike clusters of a few individuals. Other species such as *H. subrotunda* (James) may appear as somewhat ovoid or bowl shaped. *Hindia sphaeroidalis* Duncan is the most common species of the genus and occurs in rocks of the Edenian, Maysvillian, and Richmondian Stages of the Cincinnatian Series (Upper Ordovician) in the hills of Cincinnati (Ulrich, 1889, p. 245).

The genus *Astylospongia* Roemer includes subglobular to deep bowl-shaped sponges (figs. 4-1.5, 4-1.9, 4-1.15 to 4-1.17). They may have a prominent, simple spongocoel or shallow depression in the upper surface or may have a nearly smooth, slightly upward-arched, central upper surface. These sponges range in diameter from approximately 1 cm to approximately 5 cm and are perhaps somewhat less high. Canals are of two general sizes. The larger canals are in radially concentric, distinctly aligned rows and are arcuate parallel to the outer or dermal surface (fig. 4-1.9); they are the excurrent series. The smaller are cross-connecting, radial, relatively straight canals that appear to have their point of origin or convergence in the upper central part of the sponge; they are the incurrent series. The skeleton is composed of characteristic sphaeroclones that are essentially of one size and have a spherical centrum (middle part of spicule) and rays concentrated on one side, like stacked stools or chairs. These rays are fused to centra of adjacent spicules, somewhat like the arms and hands of several people being placed on the head (centrum) of another individual, and with that individual's arms and hands (rays), in turn, fused to the heads of adjacent or lower individuals.

Species of *Astylospongia* are common in Silurian formations to the south, west, and north of Ohio and should be expected in Ohio, although they have not yet been reported. *Caryospongia* and *Carpospongia* have similar distributions and also should be expected in Ohio. They are included here in part because of that expectation and in part for comparison to other spherical sponges such as *Hindia*.

The Silurian genus *Carpospongia* Rauff includes essentially spherical sponges that have a consistent radial skeleton and canal system (figs. 4-1.11, 4-1.18 to 4-1.21). Canals are of two general sizes, and both radiate from near the center of the sponge. They are not arranged in stacked series, but are distributed throughout the sponge body. Spicules are sphaeroclones and their size increases outward from the center. These sponges are widespread in Tennessee, Indiana, and southern Ontario.

Members of the genus *Caryospongia* Rauff are spherical to subglobular sponges that generally lack a prominent spongocoel (figs. 4-1.12 to 4-1.14). They have large canals that radiate as almost straight openings in the middle and lower parts of the sponge, but these canals curve outward and upward to become subvertical in the upper part of the sponge (fig. 4-1.10). These large canals occur in radial rows and generally emerge in grooves on the tops and sides of the sponges. A prominent series of smaller, straight canals radiate from near the center of the sponge and cross-connect the larger canals. Skeletons consist of sphaeroclones that are arranged in a distinctly regular radial pattern. Spicule size increases from the center toward the exterior.

The genus *Astraeospongium* Roemer includes generally saucer-shaped or low bowl-shaped to low conical sponges that have thick walls and lack canals. Their skeletons are composed of an irregularly felted but unfused mass of octactines that produce distinct starlike elements on the surface (fig. 4-2.1). Spicules are generally large and have straight rays, although some species may have some rays that are bent or irregular. Surface spicules may lack some rays and appear as sexiradiates. Spicules in the interior may be of three distinct sizes, all irregularly oriented and stacked. Individual sponges may range from bowl-shaped forms 2 or 3 cm in diameter to large platterlike forms up to 15 cm across.

Mostly only isolated spicules of the genus are recorded from Ohio. Isolated coarse octactine spicules may occur as fragments in Ordovician and Silurian rocks, in particular. *Astraeospongium ohioensis* Wells was described (Wells, 1943) from loose spicules recovered from the Middle Devonian Columbus Limestone in central and northern Ohio.

A spectacular isolated occurrence of the genus *Hydnoceras* Conrad was discovered in the 1970's in the Chagrin Shale Member of the Ohio Shale (Upper Devonian) along Euclid Creek in Cuyahoga County. The specimens are at the Cleveland Museum of Natural History, but have not been described or illustrated in the geological literature.

UPPER PALEOZOIC SPONGES

Sponges included in the genus *Ectenodictya* Hall (= *Calathospongia* Hall & Clarke) are generally cylindrical, but some may have minor annulations or contractions and expansions (fig. 4-3.8). Their exteriors are unusually smooth and unornamented, except for these irregularities. The skeleton is a distinctly quadrate mesh of relatively uniform texture, although horizontal bands are commonly slightly more prominent than vertical ones. The genus lacks nodes like those of *Cleodictya* (figs. 4-3.6, 4-3.7).

De Laubenfels (1955) included *Calathospongia* as a junior synonym of *Ectenodictya*, known from the Lower Mississippian of Pennsylvania. Several species of *Calathospongia* have been reported from Ohio. *Calathospongia carceralis* was reported from the Lower Mississippian "Waverly Group" at Richfield, Summit County (Hall and Clarke, 1898, p. 157); *C. redfieldi* (Hall) was originally described from a yellowish sandstone of the "Waverly Group" near Harrisville, Medina County, and in the Cuyahoga shale of the "Waverly Group" at Akron (Summit County) and at Richfield (Hall and Clarke, 1898, p. 156); *C. tiffanyi* Hall & Clarke was reported (Hall and Clarke, 1898, p. 160) as from only the "Waverly Group, Ohio."

Members of the genus *Clathrospongia* Hall & Clarke are vaselike (fig. 4-2.6) to regularly funnel-like sponges, perhaps with a pointed base, that lack the very rapid upward-flaring expansion of the flowerlike *Thamnodictya* (see fig. 4-3.1). Some species of *Clathrospongia* may be goblet shaped and have a subcylindrical stem. Both *Clathrospongia* and *Thamnodictya* have three-dimensional gridlike skeletons with boxlike openings of various ranks in the skeleton, in a structure that appears like tiny cardboard separation grids between bottles in a packing case. This three-dimensional structure is in contrast to skeletons of other similar or related sponges that generally have thin, rectangular, screenlike skeletons of straplike tracts or bundles of spicules. Rectangular primary openings in skeletons of *Clathrospongia* may be 4-6 mm across, and the boxlike or gridlike separating divisions may be up to 2 mm deep. The wall is subdivided into progressively smaller and smaller gridlike structures. These sponges may range up to 15 cm tall, although they are generally broken because of their delicate structure. Spicules are presumed to be hexactines, although they are not widely preserved in the generally **mold** impressions of the sponge.

Clathrospongia caprodonta Hall & Clarke was reported (Hall and Clarke, 1898, p. 154) from the Lower Mississippian "Waverly Group" at Portsmouth, Scioto County.

The genus *Cleodictya* Hall includes subcylindrical vaselike forms that expand upward from a moderately flattened base to a horizontal ring of low nodes or slight bulges at about one-third height (figs. 4-3.6, 4-3.7). Above this ring the sponge contracts and continues chimneylike to a smooth, cylindrical upper rim. The skeleton is made of smooth, straplike clusters of spicules that form a quadrate mesh. The base is probably flat. Specimens may range to approximately 20 cm tall and wide through the ring of lower nodes. These sponges also may flair slightly in the uppermost part, where complete, or may be straight and almost tubular. Spicules are hexactines and hexactine-derived forms (fig. 4-3.5), perhaps including long rhabdodiactines. The complex reticulate skeletal net includes a variety of small anchorlike and associated spicules.

Cleodictya occurs in Lower Mississippian rocks of Indiana and Ohio. *Cleodictya claypolei* Hall & Clarke was reported (Hall and Clarke, 1898, p. 163) from the Lower Mississippian "Waverly Group" at Akron.

Members of the genus *Thamnodictya* Hall are moderately large, gobletlike to lotus-blossom-like or thistle-tube- or funnel-shaped sponges that have a narrow stalk or stem (figs. 4-3.1, 4-3.2). The stem flares abruptly into a broad, vaselike main body that has an uppermost flared and reflexed margin. The flared, lotus-blossom-like side view is distinctive. The skeletal net consists of relatively coarse intersecting spicule tracts or bands in a rectangular skeletal structure (fig. 4-3.4) that is generally characteristic of this group of sponges. A dense central root-tuft may be present rather than a reticulated narrow stalk; these sponges also may have an upward folded or invaginated base. The skeletal wall is thin and may appear grooved if the sponge is flattened. Primary rectangular skeletal grids are three dimensional, as in *Clathrospongia*, and may be 3 or 4 mm wide and high and outlined by tracts up to 0.4 mm wide. Rectangular openings are subdivided into smaller orders by narrower tracts. The exterior is generally smooth or marked by weak ribs or grooves. *Thamnodictya newberryi* (Hall) is approximately 9 cm wide when flattened. This size is probably large for most species, although Hall and Clarke (1898) cited a nearly complete specimen 150 mm high.

Thamnodictya newberryi was reported by Hall and Clarke (1898, p. 162) as occurring in beds of the Lower Mississippian "Waverly Group" from Richfield and Cuyahoga Falls, Summit County. Hall and Clarke (1898, p. 162) reported *T. ortoni* from the Cuyahoga shale of the "Waverly Group" at Moot's Run, Licking County. Both species were named to honor State Geologists of Ohio—John Strong Newberry (see Dedication of this volume) and Edward Orton.

Members of the genus *Regispongia* Rigby are cylindrical to irregular conico-cylindrical sponges (figs. 4-4.4, 4-4.5).

They have a shallow to somewhat irregular axial spongocoel and thick walls composed of profusely rayed polyactines, which may be obscured by **calcareous** overgrowths (figs. 4-4.1 to 4-4.3). These overgrowths result in the main skeletal net being generally strongly fused. The skeleton is perforated by irregularly radial small canals. The thin outer dermal layer also is composed of polyactines, but they are distinctly smaller than those in the main skeleton. These sponges may look like irregularly ropy trace fossils or burrow fillings, but the small dermal spicules clearly define the sponge. *Regispongia* from Ohio localities may range up to 9 cm tall and to approximately 2 cm in diameter. Larger specimens are known elsewhere.

Rigby (1978) separated sponges originally described as *Wewokella* into the genera *Regispongia*, which has polyactine spicules, and *Wewokella*, which has a principal skeleton based on triactines. The dermal layer of *Regispongia* may include minor triactines and octactines, and the dermal layer of *Wewokella* may include minor octactines and polyactines, as well. *Regispongia* and *Wewokella* are both relatively common in sediments that accumulated in muddy environments. The **type species** of *Regispongia*, *R. contorta* (King), was described from Pennsylvanian rocks of Texas (King, 1943, p. 27-28). The type species of *Wewokella*, *W. solida*, was described by Girty (1915) from the Wewoka Formation of Oklahoma. *Regispongia* differs from *Wewokella* in basic skeletal makeup, although the two are similar in being grossly **calcified** and in general growth form. Like most early fossils described as *Wewokella* outside the type area, the wewokellid sponges from Ohio should be included in *Regispongia*.

Regispongia is reported (Hoare and Sturgeon, 1968) as relatively rare in the following Pennsylvanian units: Vanport shale (Allegheny Group) along Coal Run in Milton Township, Jackson County; Upper Mercer shale (Pottsville Group) in Wayne Township, Tuscarawas County; and Putnam Hill shale (Allegheny Group) in the Crow strip mine in Elk Township, Vinton County.

The genus *Heliospongia* Girty includes large cylindrical to conico-cylindrical, in some cases branching, sponges whose skeleton is a regular three-dimensionally reticulate net of fibers (fig. 4-4.6). The major cylindrical elements are pierced by a relatively narrow axial spongocoel (**S** in fig. 4-4.6). Moderately large circular canals interrupt the regular skeletal net as openings through the wall. Horizontal tracts flex downward sharply around the periphery and produce an upward bulging appearance to the skeleton as seen in cross section. On a microscopic scale, both the horizontal and ascending tracts are made of bundles of parallel, smooth oxeas. Horizontal tracts are spaced approximately 1 mm apart in a regular structure. Entire sponges may be more than 20 cm high. Branches of *Heliospongia ramosa* Girty described from Ohio average about 22 mm in diameter and are pierced by a 7-mm-wide central tubular spongocoel. Specimens of *H. ramosa* have been reported (Hoare, 1978) in Ohio from the Pennsylvanian Cambridge limestone (Conemaugh Group) near the junction of Ohio Routes 662 and 209 in Adams Township, Guernsey County.

FIGURE 4-1.—Ordovician and Silurian sponges. All figures are natural size (scale bar A equals 1 cm), except figures 4-1.2 and 4-1.3, which have adjacent scale bars. Figures 4-1.1, 4-1.3 to 4-1.5, and 4-1.12 to 4-1.21 are modified from Rauff (1894); figure 4-1.2 is modified from Rigby (1983); figures 4-1.6 and 4-1.7 are modified from Ulrich (1889); figure 4-1.8 is modified from Bassler (1932); figures 4-1.9 to 4-1.11 are modified from Rigby (1986).

1-4	*Hindia sphaeroidalis* Duncan. **Silicified** specimen. Ordovician, near St. Petersburg, Russia. **1**, broken surface through spherical sponge showing straight, radiating canals (dark areas) and skeletal structures (light areas). **2**, drawing of enlarged spicule showing nature of fusion of ray tips to the central capstanlike vertical ray; scale bar equals 0.5 mm. **3**, example of common preservation in silicified specimens in which the canals between the spicule rows have been filled with silica, and the spicules have been preserved as molds in the vertical, radial, linear series; enlarged, scale bar equals 2 mm. **4**, characteristic spheroidal specimen showing smooth outer surface marked only by regular pores.
5, 9	*Astylospongia verrucosa* Rauff. Silicified specimen. Silurian, Tennessee. **5**, outer view. **9**, vertical section showing, in black, the canals of radiating and concentric series.
6	*Heterospongia knotti* Ulrich. Arnheim Formation (Upper Ordovician), near Lebanon, Kentucky.
7	*Heterospongia subramosa* Ulrich, showing characteristic twiglike form and moderately open small canals. Arnheim Formation (Upper Ordovician), Lincoln County, Kentucky.
8	*Dystactospongia minor* Ulrich & Everett. Larger openings were apparently excurrent canals and smaller openings incurrent canals between the irregular skeletal tracts. Carters Limestone (Middle Ordovician), Tennessee.
10	*Caryospongia juglans* (Quenstedt). Vertical section showing characteristic arrangement of the small radiating incurrent canals and the coarser variously curved excurrent canals. Silurian, Altenburg, Germany.
11	*Carpospongia globosa* (Eichwald). Generalized vertical section showing characteristic radial patterns of both small incurrent and coarse excurrent canals. Based on Silurian specimen from near Ostrowitt, Germany.
12-14	*Caryospongia edita* (Klöden). Silicified, transported clast. Ordovician, collected on Island of Sylt, Germany. Side (**12**), top (**13**), and bottom (**14**) views showing characteristic coarse excurrent canals in vertical grooves of this pumpkinlike genus.
15-17	*Astylospongia praemorsa* (Goldfuss). Silicified specimens. Silurian, Neustadt, Germany. **15**, side view. **16**, top view showing shallow spongocoel into which the concentric series of excurrent canals empty. **17**, bottom view.
18-21	*Carpospongia stellatim-sulcatum* (Roemer). **18**, clast or transported silicified specimen. Ordovician, Gotland. **19-21**, spheroidal specimens showing characteristic grooved exteriors. Brownsport Formation (Silurian), Decatur County, Tennessee.

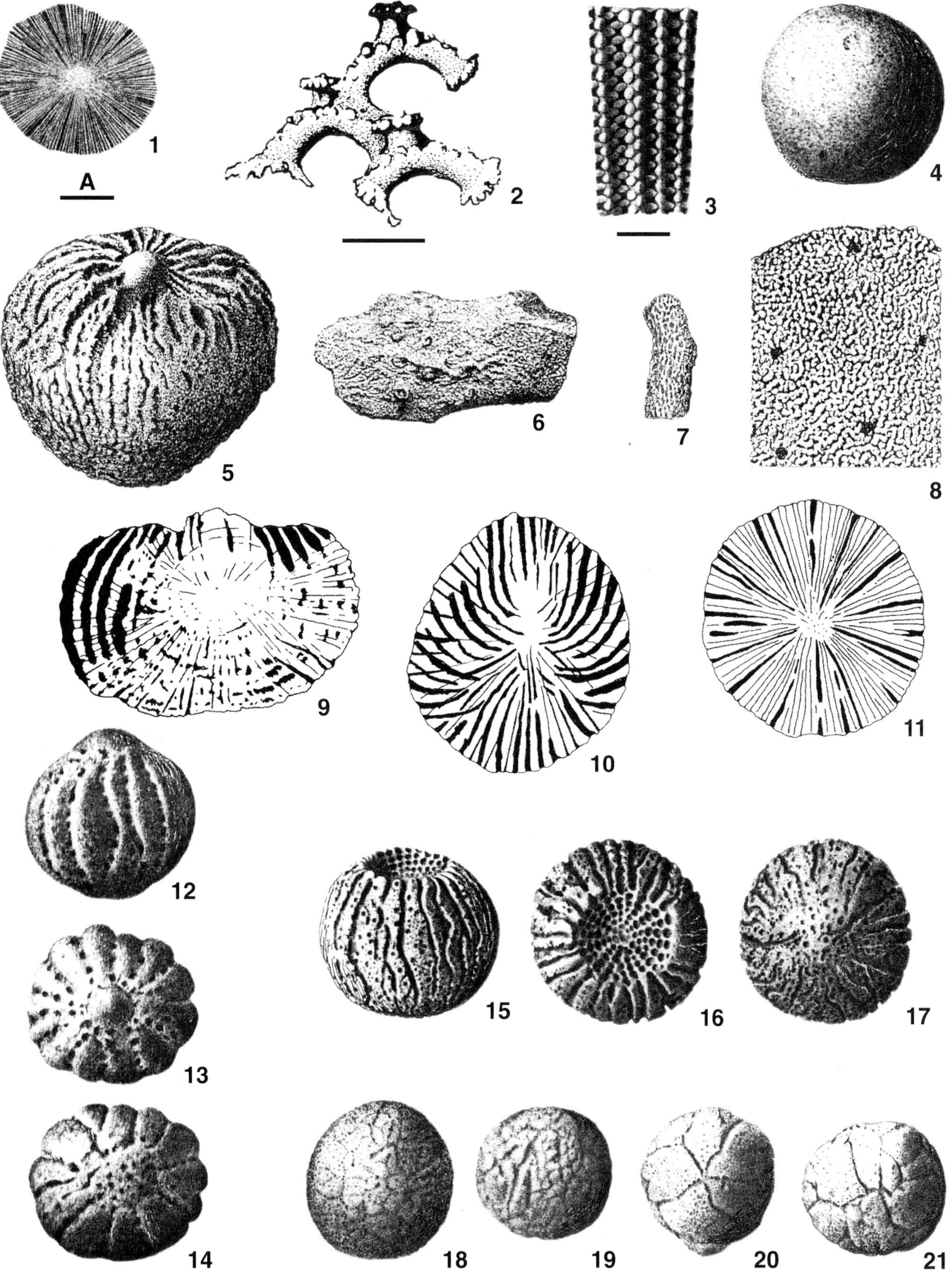
1
A
2
3
4
5
6
7
8
9
10
11
12
13
14
15
16
17
18
19
20
21

FIGURE 4-2.—Ordovician, Silurian, and Mississippian sponges. Figures 4-2.1, 4-2.5, and 4-2.6 are natural size (scale bar A equals 1 cm). Figures 4-2.2 to 4-2.4 have adjacent scale bars. Figure 4-2.1 is modified from Rigby (1987); figures 4-2.2 to 4-2.5 are modified from Rauff (1894); figure 4-2.6 is modified from Hall and Clarke (1898).

1 *Astraeospongium meniscus* (Roemer), showing the very coarse octactine spicules in the saucerlike specimen. Brownsport Formation (Silurian), Tennessee.

2-4 *Brachiospongia digitata* (Owen). Trenton Group (Middle Ordovician), Bridgeport, northern Kentucky. **2**, top view showing chimneylike central spongocoel and radiating, blunt digits of the hollow handlike specimen; scale bar equals 5 cm. **3**, drawing of an enlarged surface of *Brachiospongia* showing the coarse armoring pentactines with tangential rays reflexed into the finer skeleton of irregularly oriented smaller hexactines, all in a felted arrangement; scale bar equals 1 mm. **4**, side view cut away to show more or less complete fingerlike digits and the hollow chimneylike upper part of the sponge; scale bar equals 5 cm.

5 *Pattersonia ulrichi* Rauff, showing irregular lobate nature of the massive skeleton, which is composed of irregularly oriented small hexactines. McMillan Formation (= Grant Lake Formation) (Upper Ordovician), hills at Cincinnati, Ohio.

6 *Clathrospongia caprodonta* Hall & Clarke, showing the characteristic quadrately arranged straps of the skeleton in the steeply conico-cylindrical species. "Waverly Group" (Lower Mississippian), Portsmouth, Ohio.

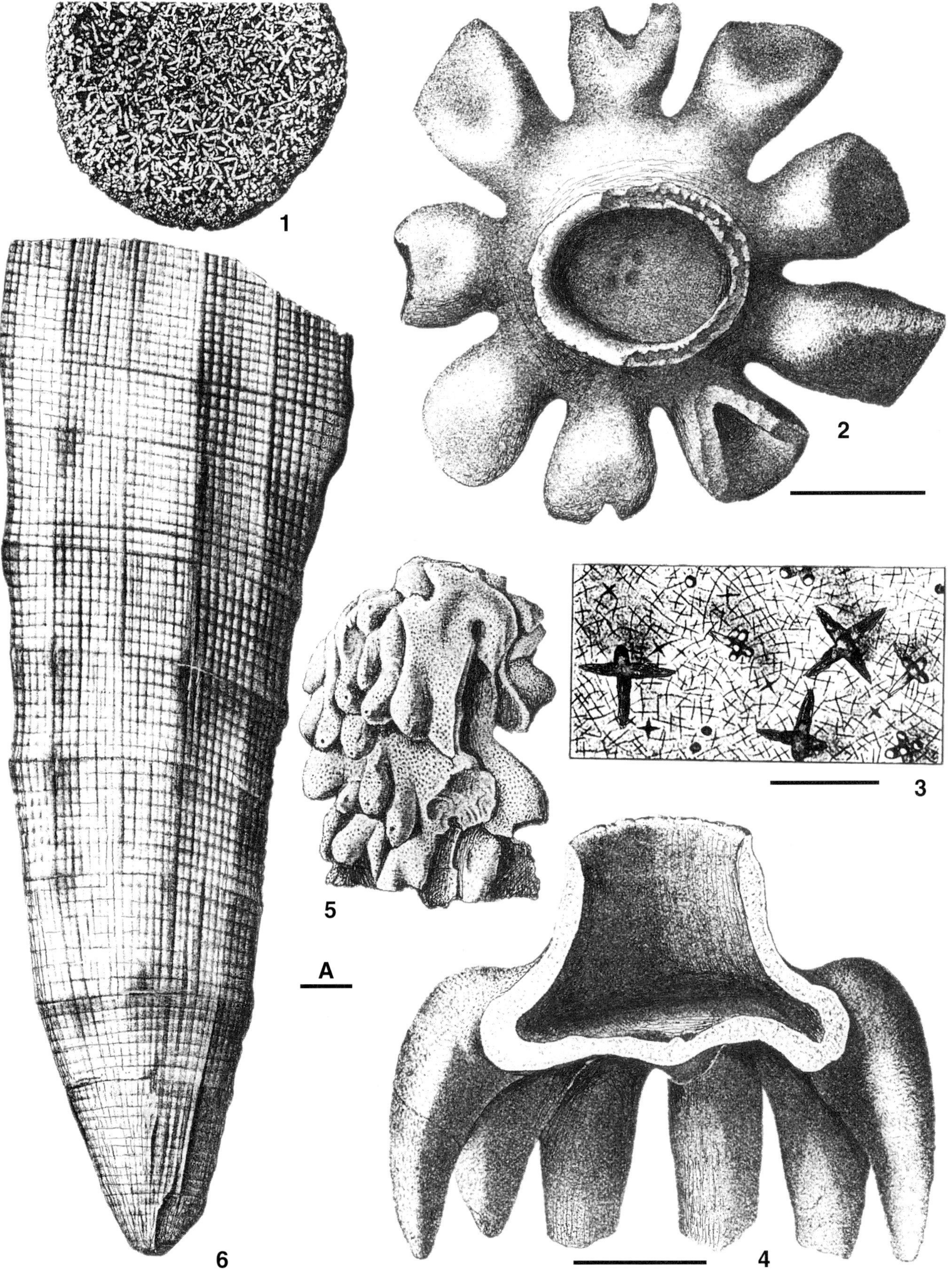
1
2
3
4
5
A
6

FIGURE 4-3.—Ordovician and Mississippian sponges. Figures 4-3.1, 4-3.3, 4-3.6, and 4-3.8 are natural size (scale bar A equals 1 cm). Scales of others are shown by adjacent scale bars. Figures 4-3.2, 4-3.5, and 4-3.7 are modified from de Laubenfels (1955); figures 4-3.1, 4-3.4, 4-3.6, and 4-3.8 are modified from Hall and Clarke (1898); figure 4-3.3 is modified from Rauff (1894).

1, 2, 4 — *Thamnodictya newberryi* (Hall). "Waverly Group" (Lower Mississippian), Cuyahoga Falls, Ohio. **1**, side view showing flaired shape and rectangular skeletal grid. **2**, growth form of the species; scale bar equals 2 cm. **4**, enlargement of **cast** showing the gridlike nature of the skeleton; scale bar equals 5 mm.

3 — *Pattersonia tuberosa* (Beecher), showing the massive, irregular lobate or earlike external sculpture and prominent root-tuft of parallel hairlike spicules at the base. upper Trenton sandstones (Middle Ordovician), Turners Station, northern Kentucky.

5 — *Cleodictya mohri* Hall, showing spicules common in this sponge but rarely preserved in the sandstone molds in which most of these fossils are preserved in Ohio; scale bar equals 0.5 mm. Osage Group (Lower Mississippian), Crawfordsville, Indiana.

6, 7 — *Cleodictya claypolei* Hall & Clarke. **6**, side view showing the characteristic vaselike growth form with nodes in the lower part below the chimney, which is shown restored in **7**; scale bar for **7** equals 2 cm. "Waverly Group" (Lower Mississippian), Akron, Ohio.

8 — *Ectenodictya* (= *Calathospongia*) *carceralis* Hall & Clarke, showing the characteristic narrowed, subcylindrical growth form of the species, which has a moderately prismatic exterior and a pronounced reticulate skeletal net made of tracts or "ropes" of spicules of various ranks. "Waverly Group" (Lower Mississippian), Richfield, Ohio.

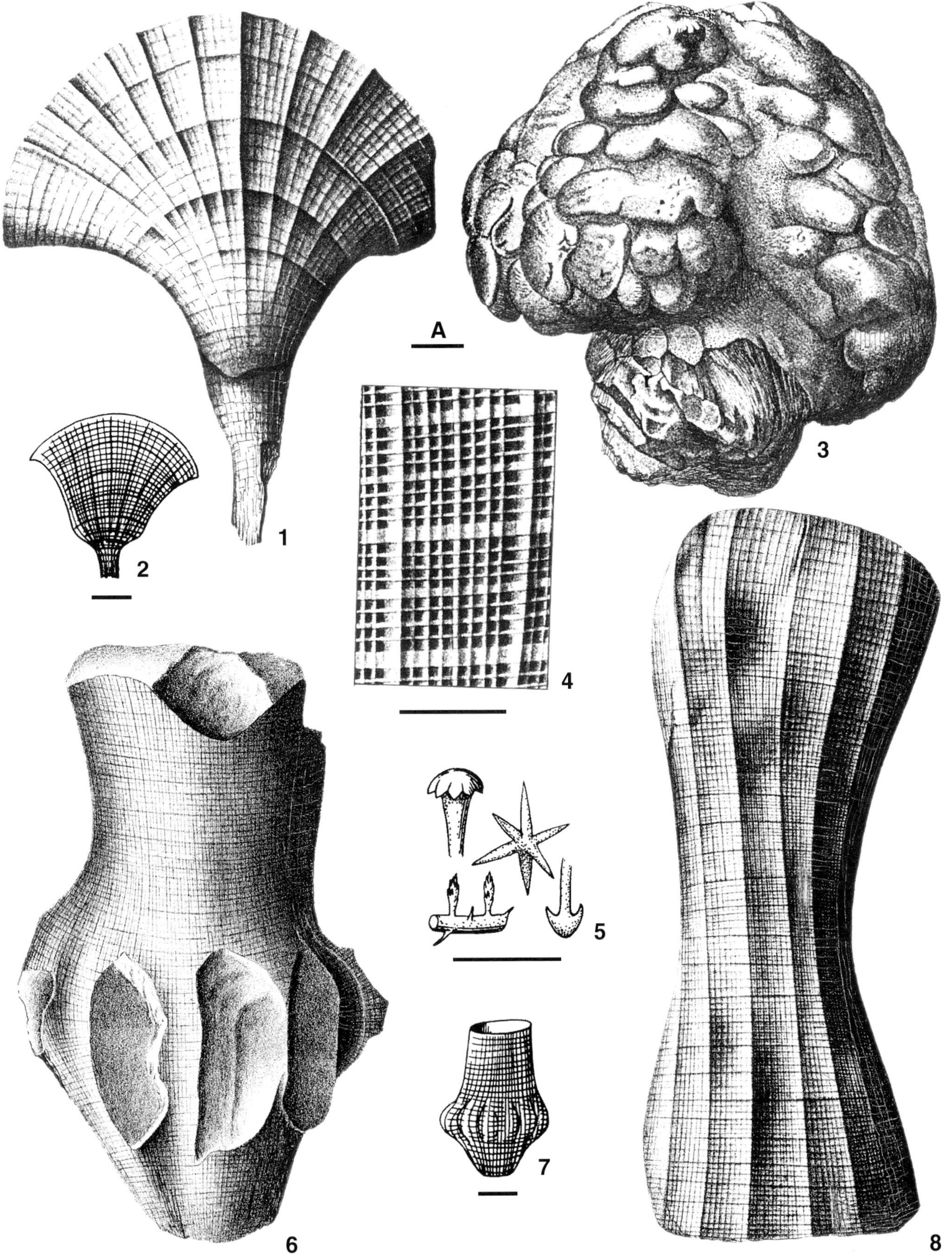
A
1
2
3
4
5
6
7
8

FIGURE 4-4.—Pennsylvanian sponges. Figures are natural size (scale bar A equals 1 cm) except spicules in figures 4-4.1 to 4-4.3, which have an adjacent scale bar (= 1 mm). Figures 4-4.1 to 4-4.3 are from Rigby (1978); figures 4-4.4 and 4-4.5 are modified from Hoare and Sturgeon (1968); figure 4-4.6 is modified from Girty (1908).

1-5 *Regispongia contorta* (King). **1**, **2**, small polyactine dermal spicules showing the beginning of secondary calcification. Chainman Shale (Mississippian-Pennsylvanian), western Millard County, Utah. **3**, partially calcified and obscured large body spicules; rounded openings are part of the radiating canals; secondary carbonate has obscured the original polyactine form of the basic skeleton. Chainman Shale (Mississippian-Pennsylvanian), western Millard County, Utah. **4**, nearly complete specimen, originally identified as *Wewokella solida* Girty, from the Putnam Hill shale (Allegheny Group), Elk Township, Vinton County, Ohio. **5**, smaller specimen with moderately preserved coarse skeletal fibers, originally identified as *Wewokella solida* Girty, from the Vanport shale (Allegheny Group), Milton Township, Jackson County, Ohio.

6 *Heliospongia ramosa* Girty, showing the characteristic growth form of the genus and species and a prominent spongocoel (**S**) in the natural section through the specimen in the lower center. The distinctive skeletal structure and canals in upward arcuate rows are visible in the several specimens. Allen Member of the Plattsburg Limestone, Chanute, Kansas.

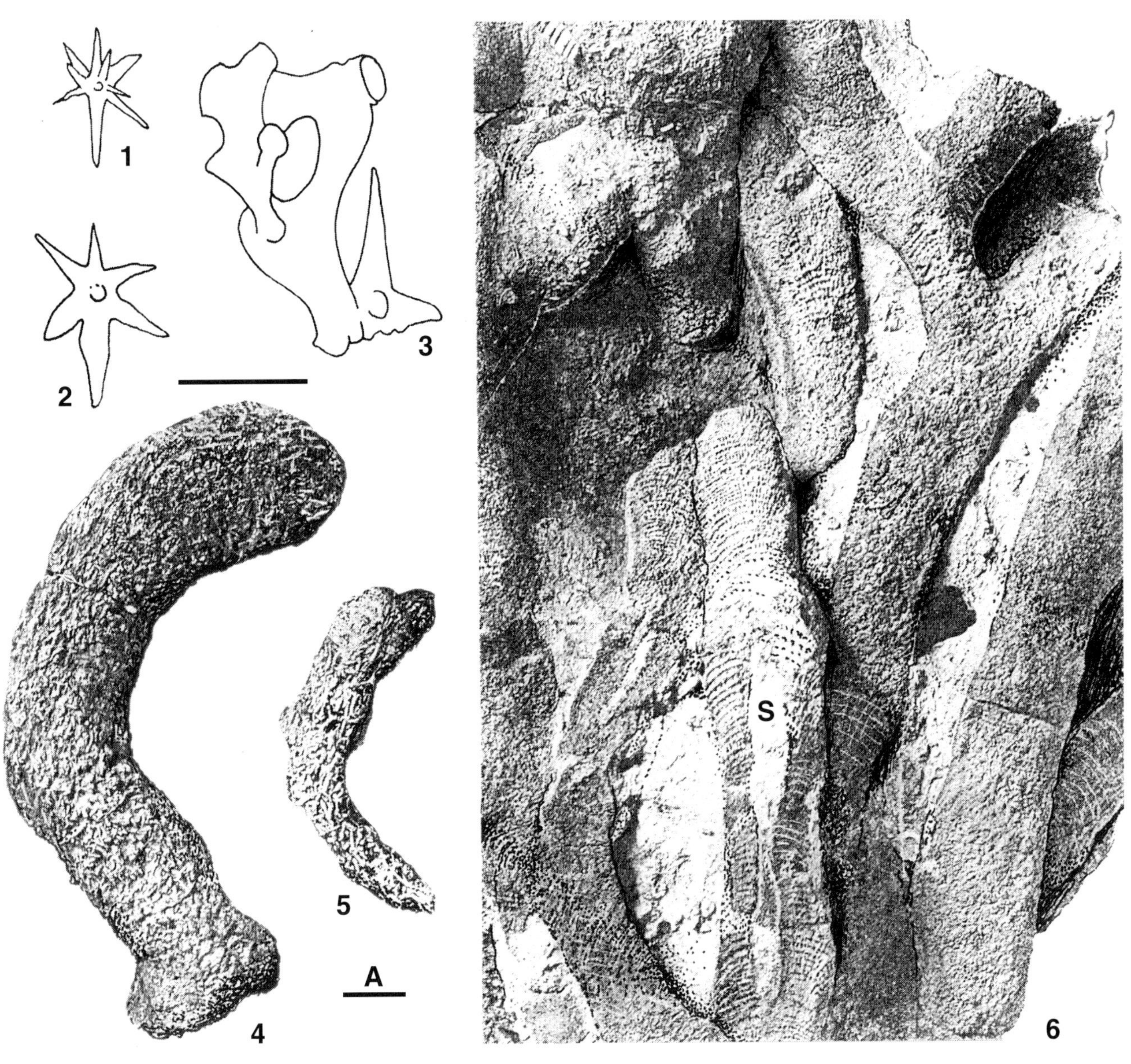
1
2
3
4
5
A
6
S

Chapter 5

PHYLUM PORIFERA, STROMATOPOROIDS

by Loren E. Babcock

INTRODUCTION

Stromatoporoids are an informal group of coralline marine sponges that construct domal, **encrusting**, or branching **calcareous** skeletal structures. The stratigraphic range of stromatoporoid-type sponges extends from the Ordovician to the present. Living stromatoporoids, which include some "sclerosponges" (Stearn, 1972, 1975), are known from the Caribbean Sea, the Mediterranean Sea, and the Pacific Ocean (Wood, 1990).

The skeletal structure of a stromatoporoid is referred to as a **coenosteum** (see fig. 1-5). It is formed of a series of **laminae**, or thin, broad layers that spread across (or nearly across) the coenosteum (figs. 5-1.1, 5-1.2), and **latilaminae**, or thick, broad layers (figs. 5-1.1, 5-1.2); the laminae and latilaminae are connected by small vertical **pillars** (fig. 5-1.2). Spaces between laminae are called **galleries** (fig. 5-1.2). The surface of each lamina characteristically shows numerous starlike canal systems called **astrorhizae** (fig. 5-1.3). The astrorhizae are evidently traces of an excurrent-water canal system. In some forms, the astrorhizae are centered on low bumps, called **mamelons** (fig. 5-1.3). Although fossil stromatoporoids commonly are composed of calcite ($CaCO_3$) or dolomite ($CaMgCO_3$), most stromatoporoid-type coenostea probably were secreted as aragonite (also $CaCO_3$, but different crystal structure). Living stromatoporoids contain small calcareous **spicules**, which are a defining characteristic of sponges. The spicules remain free within the soft tissue rather than being incorporated in the calcareous skeleton. Such spicules are rarely recognized in fossil sponges of stromatoporoid grade because of rapid dissolution and dispersal following death of the animal.

A coenosteum can take many shapes, and growth form is apparently related to environmental conditions. Commonly, stromatoporoids are domal or flattened in overall shape, but branching, twiglike forms also are known. Stromatoporoids were important components of shallow-marine reef communities, particularly during intervals of the middle Paleozoic and middle Mesozoic. Some coenostea reached massive proportions, likely weighing 1,000 kg or more and exceeding 1 meter in thickness.

In Ohio, stromatoporoids are present in rocks of Ordovician, Silurian, and Devonian age (Nicholson, 1875; Parks, 1936; Galloway, 1957; Galloway and St. Jean, 1957; Stearn, 1980; Fagerstrom, 1982; Bjerstedt and Feldmann, 1985). In Upper Ordovician rocks of southwestern Ohio, stromatoporoids typically are scattered in limestone, whereas in Silurian and Devonian rocks they are common in the limestone or dolostone of reef lithofacies. Among the most spectacular stromatoporoid buildups are ones in the Devonian-age Lucas Dolomite exposed on the north shore of Kelleys Island, just north of Glacial Grooves State Memorial (Bjerstedt and Feldmann, 1985).

For many years, the stromatoporoids have been difficult to classify at both high and low **taxonomic** levels. Until the recent recognition that they are related to living coralline sponges or "sclerosponges" (Stearn, 1972, 1975; Wood, 1990), they were commonly considered to belong to the phylum Cnidaria, which includes corals, anemones, jellyfishes, and hydrozoans. Stromatoporoids are currently regarded as a grade, or level of evolutionary organization, within the phylum Porifera (sponges).

Ancient stromatoporoid genera and species are identifiable only from **polished sections** or **thin sections** that exhibit details of the internal microstructure (Galloway, 1957; Galloway and St. Jean, 1957; Stearn, 1980). Identification can be hindered by variability in internal structure and growth form. **Diagenetic** changes, which occur after death and final burial, can destroy microscopic features that are critical for identification. For these reasons, individual genera are not treated in this chapter. The interested collector should consult either the published references cited at the back of this book or a specialist.

ACKNOWLEDGMENTS

Dale M. Gnidovec (Orton Geological Museum of The Ohio State University) loaned specimens for illustration from the collections under his care. Margaret T. Wilson (Columbus, Ohio) read an early version of the manuscript. Beth A. Daye (The Ohio State University) printed the photographs.

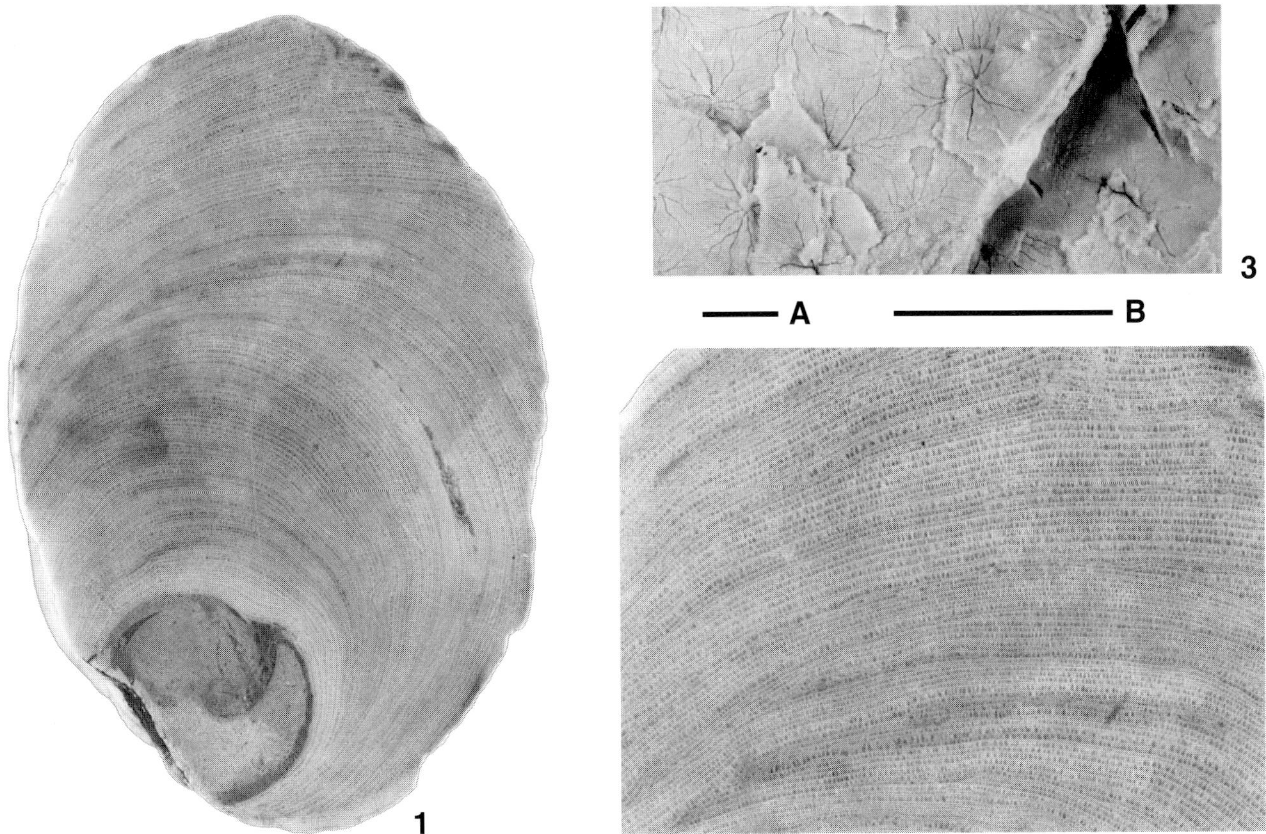

FIGURE 5-1.—Stromatoporoids. Scale bars equal 1 cm. Scale bar A applies to figures 5-1.1 and 5-1.3; B applies to figure 5-1.2. Specimens photographed without a whitening agent.

1, 2 *Anostylostroma substriatella* (Nicholson). Upper part of Lucas Dolomite (Devonian), Kelleys Island, Erie County, Ohio; OSU 21376. **1**, vertically oriented polished section of coenosteum that has broad, curved laminae and latilaminae and has grown over a large gastropod shell (lower left of specimen). **2**, enlargement of part of the same specimen showing broadly curved laminae and latilaminae, vertical pillars, and galleries.

3 *Stromatopora larocquei* Galloway & St. Jean. Surface view of **holotype** coenosteum showing astrorhizae and large, low mamelons. Upper part of Columbus Limestone (Devonian), Marblecliff, Franklin County, Ohio; OSU 21380 (part of same specimen = IUPC 5404).

Chapter 6

PHYLUM CONULARIIDA

by Loren E. Babcock

INTRODUCTION

Conulariids are extinct marine organisms characterized by an elongate, four-sided, pyramidal **exoskeleton** of phosphatic composition. Their unique exoskeleton, which is commonly whitish, black, blue, or multicolored because of its phosphatic nature, makes them among the most distinctive and interesting of Ohio's fossils.

The exoskeleton (see fig. 1-6) has an **aperture** (opening) at the widest end, and tapers to a closed, slightly rounded **apex**. The apex is rarely preserved. As viewed externally, each of the four sides, or **faces**, is crossed by numerous pairs of transverse, curved, narrow **ridges** that meet at a distinct longitudinal **midline**. On the inside of the exoskeleton along the midline of some species, a distinct longitudinal thickening, called a **carina**, is present. Ridges seemingly are formed by local thickenings in the layers of the exoskeleton. These thickenings, which have been called **rods**, probably provided some support to an otherwise thin, and rather flexible, exoskeleton or **integument**. In some species, the rods are ornamented with **nodes** or **spines**. If spines are present, small **crests** between and at right angles to the ridges may be evident externally. Adjacent faces meet at a longitudinal groove called a **corner groove**.

The placement of conulariids in the Linnaean classification system has been a troublesome issue for more than 200 years. Because of their skeletal shape or composition, they have been, at various times, classified as mollusks, worms, cnidarians (especially jellyfishes), protochordates, or chordates. Most of the reasons used to support these interpretations have been demonstrated to be erroneous (Babcock, 1991). As currently understood, conulariids do not seem to be closely related to any living group of organisms. On the best available evidence, they seem to be so unlike any other known group as to warrant their classification in a separate, extinct phylum of animals (Babcock and Feldmann, 1986a).

Much of the critical evidence for placing conulariids in a separate phylum came from specimens preserved in Mississippian rocks of Ohio (Babcock and Feldmann, 1986a, 1986b). Specimens are locally abundant at some localities in the Sunbury Shale and the Cuyahoga and Logan Formations. Some well-preserved, three-dimensional specimens from the Cuyahoga and Logan Formations showed that, although the exoskeleton has four faces, it actually has a subtle **bilateral symmetry**. The bilateral symmetry is evident in the fact that opposite sides are of the same width, whereas adjacent sides are of slightly different widths. The wider faces are called **major faces**, and the narrower faces are called **minor faces** (fig. 6-1.1). Another indication of bilateral symmetry is that pairs of ridges on opposite faces articulate, or meet, in the same way at the midline, whereas on adjacent faces they commonly articulate in a slightly different way. Specimens collected from the Sunbury Shale (Feldmann and Babcock, 1986) showed that after death the phosphatic exoskeleton could disarticulate into tiny pieces, including rods (fig. 6-1.6). Conulariids evidently became disarticulated quickly after death if not covered by sediment. The presence of rods inside a phosphatic exoskeleton is apparently unique in the animal kingdom. Since the time that conulariid rods were first discovered in Cuyahoga County, they have been found in a variety of other localities in North America, South America, and Europe. Preliminary work suggests that they will provide a better indication of the original geographic and stratigraphic distributions of these animals.

Other specimens from Ohio helped paleontologists to develop remarkable new insight into the paleobiology of conulariids (Babcock and Feldmann, 1986a, 1986b). One specimen from the Chagrin Shale Member of the Ohio Shale (Devonian) in Cuyahoga County was preserved with a **stalk** attached at the apical end (fig. 6-1.5). The stalk was a flexible structure that permitted the animal to attach to a shell or other object on the sea floor. Previously, it was widely thought that conulariids either floated in the water column similar to jellyfishes or attached to such floating organisms as seaweed. At various localities, conulariids were found in small clusters, typically of two (fig. 6-1.5) to four specimens. This suggested a gregarious lifestyle and the capability for sexual reproduction. Some specimens showed infoldings of the faces near the aperture (fig. 6-1.7). In the past, these infoldings were thought to have been flaps, or lappets, that closed off the aperture when the living animal was retracted inside the exoskeleton. Specimens from Ohio and elsewhere, however, showed that the exoskeleton was naturally somewhat flexible. Furthermore, the apertural flaps or lappets are due simply to bending or crushing of the thin and somewhat flexible exoskeleton after the death of the animal.

Most large conulariid specimens are broken in the apical region (the small end of the exoskeleton). Commonly such specimens reveal a smooth, rounded structure called an **apical wall**, which was an internal, transverse partition.

REPRESENTATIVE CONULARIID GENERA FROM OHIO

The exoskeleton of *Conularia* Sowerby can be up to 30 cm in length. Ridges are closely spaced and commonly look as though they continue across the midline of each face rather than being significantly offset. Crests are present between the ridges. *Conularia* is present in the Cincinnatian Series (Upper Ordovician) of southwestern Ohio (fig. 6-1.1). Rare specimens are known from Silurian and Devonian rocks. The genus is common at some localities in the Meadville and Wooster Members of the Cuyahoga Formation (Mississippian) in northeastern Ohio and in the Byer Sandstone Member of the Logan Formation (Mississippian) in southern Ohio (fig. 6-1.4). Some specimens from the Cuyahoga Formation reach 30 cm in length and are among the largest conulariids known from anywhere in the world.

The exoskeleton of *Paraconularia* Sinclair can be up to 20 cm in length; it is generally rather narrow. Ridges are generally widely spaced and distinctly offset at the midline. Crests may be present between the ridges. *Paraconularia* is locally common in Mississippian rocks of Ohio, especially in the Sunbury Shale (fig. 6-1.6) , the Cuyahoga Formation (fig. 6-1.7), and the Logan Formation (figs. 6-1.2, 6-1.3). It is present, but typically uncommon, in marine units of Late Devonian (fig. 6-1.5) and Pennsylvanian age.

ACKNOWLEDGMENTS

Frederick J. Collier (formerly of U.S. National Museum of Natural History), Dale M. Gnidovec (Orton Geological Museum of The Ohio State University), Joseph T. Hannibal (The Cleveland Museum of Natural History), and Joe H. Marak (Miami University) arranged loans of specimens from collections in their charge. Margaret T. Wilson (Columbus, Ohio) read an early version of the manuscript. Beth A. Daye (The Ohio State University) printed the photographs.

FIGURE 6-1.—Conulariids. Scale bars equal 1 cm. Scale bar A applies to figure 6-1.7; B applies to figures 6-1.2 to 6-1.4; C applies to figure 6-1.1; D applies to figures 6-1.5, 6-1.6.

1	*Conularia formosa* Miller & Dyer. Crushed exoskeleton showing subtle difference in width between major face (left) and adjacent minor face (right). Whitewater Formation (Ordovician); Cowan Lake, Vernon Township, Clinton County, Ohio; OSU 37310.
2, 3	*Paraconularia missouriensis* (Swallow). Corner view (**2**) and view of major face (**3**) of three-dimensional specimen preserved in siderite. Byer Sandstone Member of Logan Formation (Mississippian); Sciotoville, Scioto County, Ohio; OSU 46329.
4	*Conularia multicostata* Meek & Worthen. View of major face. Byer Sandstone Member of Logan Formation (Mississippian); Sciotoville, Scioto County, Ohio; OSU 46328.
5	*Paraconularia chagrinensis* Babcock & Feldmann. Two small specimens of a cluster preserved in a phosphatic concretion. Specimen at right preserves a stalk (arrow) attached to the apical end of the exoskeleton. Chagrin Shale Member of Ohio Shale (Devonian); Mill Creek, Lake County, Ohio; ClMNH 1788.
6	*Paraconularia subulata* (Hall). Specimen in advanced state of disarticulation showing rods coming free from the exoskeleton. Sunbury Shale (Mississippian); Bentleyville, Cuyahoga County, Ohio; USNM 395829.
7	*Paraconularia byblis* (White). Corner view of a large specimen showing infoldings of two faces near the aperture. The infoldings developed after the animal had died (see Babcock and Feldmann, 1986a). Cuyahoga Formation (Mississippian); London, Madison County, Ohio; OSU 7633.

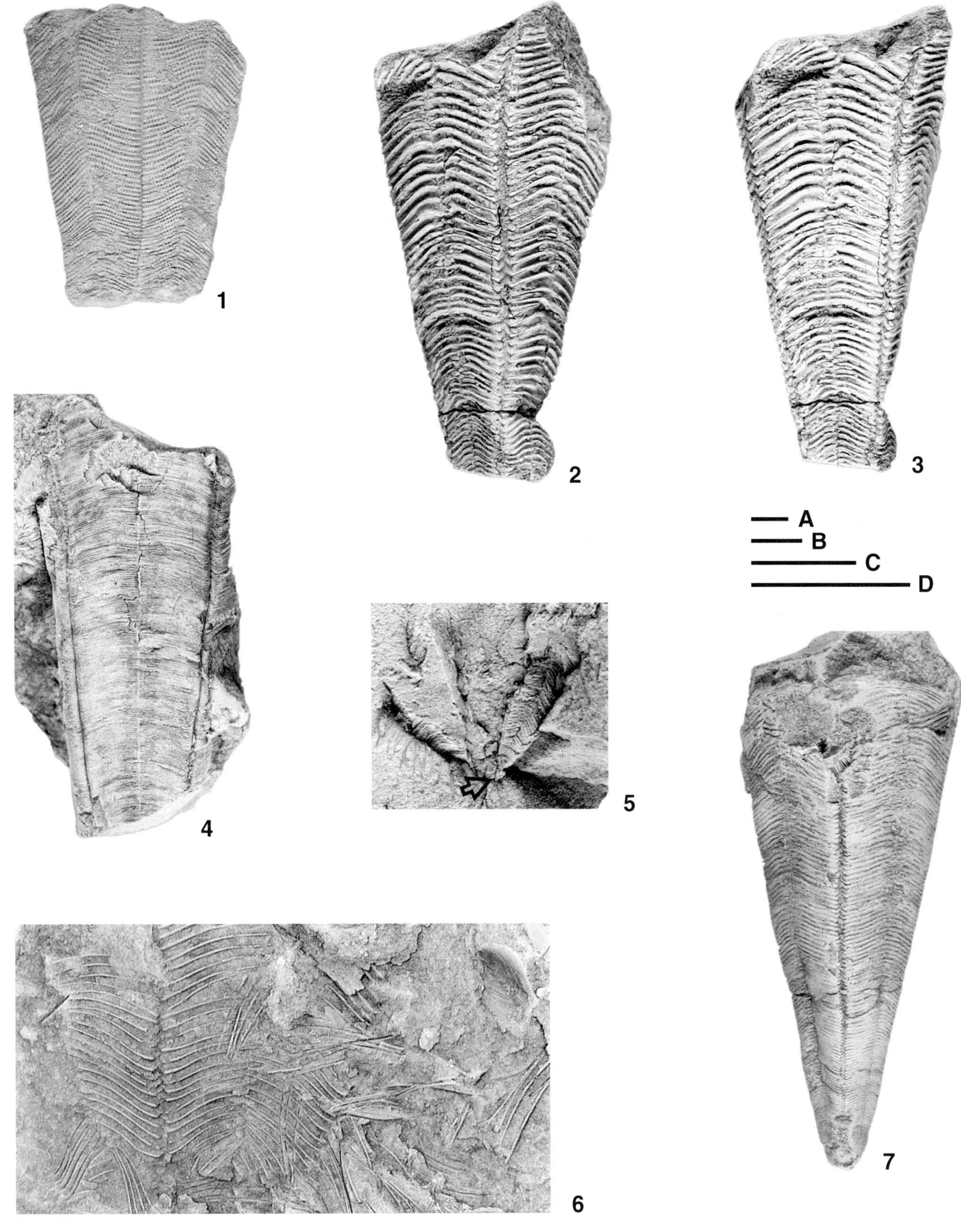
1
2
3
A
B
C
D
4
5
6
7

Chapter 7

PHYLUM CNIDARIA

by Loren E. Babcock

INTRODUCTION

The phylum Cnidaria (formerly part of the phylum called Coelenterata) comprises a large variety of both solitary and **colonial** invertebrates; it includes corals, anemones, jellyfishes, and hydrozoans. Cnidarians are characterized by a radial symmetry in gross aspect, two layers of soft tissue, a lack of organ systems, and tentacles. All cnidarians are aquatic, and most are marine. Cnidarians have a geologic record extending from the Late Precambrian to the present.

The phylum derives its name from the presence of stinging cells, called **cnidoblasts**, on the tentacles. The cnidoblasts contain **nematocysts**, which are stinging structures. Cnidarians gather food by the use of tentacles. They are typically carnivorous, at least in part, and immobilize their prey by stinging, which occurs by the firing of nematocysts from the cnidoblasts. Small fishes, crustaceans, and small **zooplankton** are typical prey of present-day cnidarians. The stings of some modern cnidarians, such as anemones, Portuguese man-of-war jellyfishes, and fire corals (milleporid hydrozoans), can be painful, and the stings of a few, such as the sea wasp, can be fatal, even to humans. In addition to capturing small animals, many corals also collect fine particles from the water on mucous films that are then moved by cilia to the mouth.

Important general features of the biology of cnidarians are **polymorphism**, coloniality, and **symbiosis** (Oliver and Coates, 1987). Polymorphism, which is most common in scyphozoans (jellyfishes), is exemplified by different body forms that occur in the same species. Different body forms may occur sequentially at different stages of the life cycle, or at the same time in a colony. Two body forms are recognized: a hollow, sacklike, tentacled **polyp**, and an umbrella-shaped, tentacled **medusa**. Polyps are adapted to a sessile lifestyle; medusae are free swimming.

Coloniality, the living together of physically united, genetically identical individuals, is present in some but not all cnidarians. Reproduction in a cnidarian colony typically occurs by the budding of daughter individuals that remain physically connected to the parent individuals; some corals also liberate eggs and sperm into water. Coloniality, which generally involves an integration of life functions that are performed by different individuals, also commonly provides for the protection of individuals (Coates and Oliver, 1973). In colonial corals, protection is provided in part by the buildup of rocky masses, including reefs. Colonial corals are the principal builders of large, spectacular reefs in warm tropical seas at the present time. Colonial corals also were largely responsible for the development of reefs during some intervals of ancient time, especially during the middle Paleozoic and Mesozoic Eras.

Symbiosis, which is the relationship of different organisms living in close and beneficial association, is characteristic of some cnidarians. In particular, present-day reef-building corals commonly contain photosynthetic algae, called zooxanthellae, in their soft tissues. The symbiotic relationship between corals and zooxanthellae is an example of mutualism, which means that both species derive benefit from the association. The nutritive needs of the coral are supplied in part by the planktonic animals on which it feeds and in part by its algal symbiont. Much of the carbon fixed by the algae is passed to the coral, and the food caught by the coral supplies both it and the algae with nitrogen and phosphorus. Algal photosynthesis increases the production of calcium carbonate by removing carbon dioxide and permits corals to build extensive skeletal material in a relatively short time. This carbonate buildup, in turn, leads to the development of modern reefs. It is likely that the buildup of some ancient reefs was partly related to the symbiosis of colonial corals and photosynthetic algae. Other examples of symbiosis from the fossil record include the intergrowth of some tabulate corals with stromatoporoid sponges.

Three living classes of cnidarians are recognized: the Anthozoa (including corals and anemones), the Hydrozoa (hydrozoans), and the Scyphozoa (jellyfishes). Only the corals have a significant fossil record (Bayer and others, 1956). Furthermore, they are the only undisputed fossil cnidarians known from multiple specimens collected in Ohio. Following recent study, representatives of other groups formerly thought to be cnidarians have been reassigned. Conulariids, which were commonly classified as scyphozoans, are here considered to represent a separate animal phylum (Chapter 6). Stromatoporoids, which were considered to be a class of cnidarians, are now widely classified as sponges (Chapter 5).

All present-day corals are colonial, but both colonial and solitary corals lived during ancient times. Corals have a rich fossil record because these animals secreted a carbonate **exoskeleton**, composed of either aragonite or calcite (see figs. 1-7, 1-8). The exoskeleton produced by either a solitary coral or the structure secreted by a colony is called a **corallum**. The structure secreted by an individual polyp of a colony is called a **corallite**. The exoskeleton is secreted by epidermal tissues at the base of a sessile polyp. The soft tissues of the polyp are almost never preserved as fossils. The **basal disk** of the coral polyp initially secretes a tiny **basal plate**. As the polyp grows, it develops a series of radial folds that increase the surface area available for digestion. Each of the folds results in the secretion by the basal disk of a vertical **septum** (see fig. 7-5.2) in the exoskeleton. During growth, the polyp rests in the **calice** (see fig. 7-5.9), which is the upper, cup-shaped depression in the exoskeleton. As the exoskeleton grows upward, a transverse plate called a **tabula** (see fig. 7-1.5) may be secreted by the basal disk across, or partly across, the corallite. In addition to tabulae, a series of small domed plates, called **dissepiments** (see fig. 7-6.1), may be secreted inside the exoskeleton. On the outside of the exoskeleton, which is called the **epitheca**, **growth lines** (see fig. 7-5.1) are developed. Growth lines may be secreted according to diurnal (daily), lunar monthly, or other cycles and thus provide an important record of periodicity in ancient environments. From data on growth lines in corals, paleontologists have been able to deduce that the number of days in the year at times during the geologic past was greater than it is today (Wells, 1963; Scrutton, 1965).

Corals are among the most diverse Paleozoic invertebrates known. It is estimated that more than 200 genera and 500 species are represented in the Paleozoic rocks of Ohio alone. The **taxa** listed in this chapter are merely representative of the great diversity of corals in the state. The principal groups of corals represented in Ohio belong to the orders Tabulata, Heliolitida, and Rugosa. All of these orders are now extinct, and their exact relationships to modern corals, including scleractinians and octocorals, is uncertain (see Oliver and Coates, 1987).

Tabulate corals (order Tabulata) are exclusively colonial and have relatively slender corallites connected by **mural pores** (see fig. 7-2.4) or tubes (see fig. 7-2.8). They commonly have either short septa, or rows of **septal spines** (see fig. 7-2.5) in place of septa. Tabulae are present in most taxa, and dissepiments may be present or absent. Skeletons of tabulate corals were originally calcitic. Coralla may be laminar to massive, moundlike, erect branching, palisadelike, or **encrusting**.

In Ohio, tabulate corals occur in rocks from Ordovician to Pennsylvanian age. They are most common in Silurian and Devonian rocks. In some localities they formed the framework of ancient reefs. By analogy with the present-day world, reefs represented in the rock record of Ohio were developed in warm, shallow, clear, and well-lit seas. Such environments would have been similar to those developed today in the Bahama Islands. Warm, clear, marine waters are generally required for the buildup of large carbonate bodies. Also, the likely presence of photosynthetic algae living in the tabulate corals places strict depth requirements on the development of Paleozoic reefs; they probably formed within the photic zone (the marine depth zone in which sunlight penetrates).

Heliolitid corals (order Heliolitida) (figs. 7-1.1, 7-1.2) are exclusively colonial and have slender corallites separated by extensive **coenosteum**, skeletal material located between corallites. Coenosteum is secreted by parts of the polyp that lie outside of each corallite. Heliolitids have spinose or laminar septa, commonly 12 in number. Their skeletons were originally calcitic. Because of their colonial habit, they are most similar to tabulate corals. Heliolitids can be distinguished from tabulates by the lack of pores or connecting tubes between adjacent corallites. Coralla may be laminar to massive, lenticular, hemispherical, or erect branching. Heliolitids are found in rocks of Ordovician to Devonian age but are not as common as representatives of other orders. In Ohio, occurrences are primarily in dolomitized carbonate rocks of Silurian age.

Rugose corals (order Rugosa) are either solitary or colonial and have major and minor septa (fig. 7-5.5). During upward growth, major septa were inserted (began development) at four positions around the circumference of the corallum. Shorter, minor septa may occur between major septa. Because of the presence of four positions for the initiation of growth of major septa, rugose corals are sometimes referred to as tetracorals. Large spaces, called **fossulae**, may remain between adjacent septa (figs. 7-5.2, 7-6.5, 7-6.9). Tabulae and dissepiments are present in most taxa, and **axial structures** such as **columellae** (fig. 7-5.7), formed of the inner edges of septa, are common. The exoskeletons were composed of calcium carbonate, probably calcite (Oliver and Coates, 1987; Sorauf, 1971). Solitary rugose corals can have many forms, from simple buttonlike shapes to various elongate horn shapes (figs. 7-5, 7-6). The common name horn coral is derived from the hornlike shape of many solitary rugose corals. Coralla of colonial forms commonly are either domal or erect branching. Rugose corals are found in rocks of Ordovician to Permian age. Because of the absence of marine Permian rocks in Ohio, corals in the state are known only from Ordovician to Pennsylvanian strata.

The literature pertaining to the Paleozoic corals of Ohio is voluminous. The references at the back of this book provide a brief list of some important published works. Modern **taxonomic** procedures commonly necessitate that corals be sectioned and examined microscopically for identification at the species level. Sectioning is also required for identification at the genus level in some groups. The genera illustrated in this chapter are generally recognizable from hand samples, and the characters listed below are mostly recognizable from unsectioned field samples. For a more complete list of characters, the interested reader should consult published works (particularly Bayer and others, 1956, and Hill, 1981) listed in the references at the back of this book or a paleontologist specializing in fossil cnidarians.

Many of the genera discussed in this chapter are long ranging, and some contain numerous species. Taxa are arranged according to the first (stratigraphically lowest) occurrence of common specimens in Ohio.

KEY TO REPRESENTATIVE CORAL GENERA FROM OHIO

The following key is intended to be used as a guide for identifying representative coral genera that are discussed in this chapter. The characters selected for use are commonly visible on hand samples.

1A. Coral solitary 2
1B. Coral colonial 16

2A. Corallum disk shaped .... *Hadrophyllum* (fig. 7-5.10)
2B. Corallum conical to elongate 3

3A. Corallum entirely filled with dissepiments .... *Cystiphylloides* (figs. 7-5.13, 7-6.1)
3B. Corallum not entirely filled with dissepiments 4

4A. Corallum has strong longitudinal ribbing 5
4B. Corallum without strong longitudinal ribbing 6

5A. Dissepiments absent and tabulae complete .... *Lophophyllidium* (fig. 7-6.4)
5B. Dissepiments present and/or tabulae incomplete .... *Zaphrenthis* (figs. 7-5.8, 7-5.9)

6A. Outline in calice (top) view subtriangular .... *Holophragma* (fig. 7-5.6)
6B. Outline in calice view ovoid to round 7

7A. Major septa extend to **axis** 8
7B. Major septa do not reach axis 13

8A. Septa converge toward fossula .... *Odontophyllum* (fig. 7-6.5)
8B. Septa do not converge toward fossula 9

9A. Septa twisted or whorled near center 10
9B. Septa not twisted or whorled near center 12

10A. Septa lack **carinae** .... *Rhegmaphyllum* (fig. 7-6.6)
10B. Septa have carinae 11

11A. Dissepiments numerous peripherally .... *Cyathophyllum* (fig. 7-6.7)
11B. Dissepiments not numerous peripherally .... *Heliophyllum* (figs. 7-6.8, 7-6.9)

12A. Minor septa have variable lengths .... *Grewingkia* (figs. 7-5.1 to 7-5.3)
12B. Minor septa are all short .... *Streptelasma* (figs. 7-5.4, 7-5.5)

13A. Minor septa generally not distinguishable .... *Amplexus* (fig. 7-5.7)
13B. Minor septa short but distinguishable 14

14A. Minor septa half the length of the major septa .... *Bethanyphyllum* (figs. 7-6.10, 7-6.11)
14B. Minor septa less than half the length of the major septa 15

15A. Inner edges of septa twisted together .... *Heterophrentis* (figs. 7-5.11, 7-5.12, 7-6.2, 7-6.3)
15B. Inner edges of major septa not twisted together .... *Siphonophrentis* (fig. 7-6.12)

16A. Corallum includes prismatic tubes with transverse walls .... *Heliolites* (figs. 7-1.1, 7-1.2)
16B. Corallum does not include prismatic tubes with transverse walls 17

17A. Corallites in contact with one another over most of their length 18
17B. Corallites not in contact over most of their length 29

18A. Corallum discoidal .... *Pleurodictyum* (fig. 7-3.6)
18B. Corallum not discoidal 19

19A. Corallum has constricted corallite **apertures** on cylindrical branches .... *Thamnoptychia* (fig. 7-3.2)
19B. Corallum without constricted corallite apertures on cylindrical branches 20

20A. Corallites all prismatic or polygonal 21
20B. Corallites not all prismatic or polygonal 27

21A. Mural pores present 22
21B. Mural pores absent 24

22A. Mural pores sparse .... *Foerstephyllum* (figs. 7-2.2, 7-2.3)
22B. Mural pores common 23

23A. Mural pores large and commonly triserial .... *Emmonsia* (fig. 7-3.1)
23B. Mural pores small and arranged in one to four rows .... *Favosites* (figs. 7-1.4 to 7-1.6, 7-2.4, 7-2.5)

24A. 12-15 septa present .... *Favistina* (fig. 7-1.7)
24B. More than 15 septa present 25

25A. Axial ends of septa coiled .... *Prismatophyllum* (fig. 7-4.2)
25B. Axial ends of septa not coiled 26

26A. Septa carinate .... *Hexagonaria* (fig. 7-4.3)
26B. Septa noncarinate .... *Arachnophyllum* (fig. 7-4.1)

27A. Some corallites polygonal .... *Calapoecia* (fig. 7-2.1)
27B. No corallites polygonal 28

28A. Corallites appear to be arranged in chainlike fashion in cross section .... *Halysites* (fig. 7-2.6)
28B. Corallites do not appear to be arranged in chainlike fashion in cross section .... *Coenites* (figs. 7-3.7, 7-3.8)

29A. Corallites narrow and trumpetlike or pipelike 30
29B. Corallites relatively wide and elongate 33

30A. Corallites connected by transverse tubular processes .... *Syringopora* (figs. 7-2.7, 7-2.8)
30B. Corallites not connected by transverse tubular processes 31

31A. Colonies prostrate or encrusting .... *Aulopora* (figs. 7-3.3, 7-5.13)
31B. Colonies branchlike 32

32A. Corallites oriented in same direction or alternating in direction .... *Cladochonus* (fig. 7-3.5)
32B. Corallites arranged irregularly .... *Aulocystis* (fig. 7-3.4)

33A. Corallites lack connecting processes .... *Fletcheria* (fig. 7-1.3)
33B. Corallites have connecting processes between them 34

34A. Septa strong, long, noncarinate .... *Synaptophyllum* (fig. 7-4.5)
34B. Septa thin, short, carinate .... *Eridophyllum* (fig. 7-4.4)

ORDOVICIAN CORALS

Corals are moderately common at some localities in Upper Ordovician rocks of the Cincinnati Arch region, including southwestern Ohio (Foerste, 1888, 1909b, 1909c, 1916; La Rocque and Marple, 1955; Elias, 1983, 1984; Davis, 1985). Only two genera of solitary rugose corals are known from the Upper Ordovician of Ohio: *Grewingkia* and *Streptelasma* (Elias, 1982, 1983). Colonial corals in the Ordovician of southwestern Ohio include the rugosan *Favistina*, the tabulates *Calapoecia* and *Foerstephyllum*, and the heliolitid *Heliolites*. Because *Heliolites* is rare in the Ordovician of Ohio, it is discussed in the section on Silurian corals.

Calapoecia Billings (fig. 7-2.1) is a tabulate coral having a massive, spheroidal, hemispheroidal, or encrusting corallum. Corallites are circular or polygonal in cross section; corallite walls are composed of fused septal elements and have pores alternating with the septa. Septa are short and typically 20 in number. Tabulae are present. Dissepiments are absent. Buds arise between the corallites. Representatives of *Calapoecia* have been reported from Ordovician rocks of the Cincinnati Arch region, including southwestern Ohio. They are most common in the upper part of the Richmondian Stage.

Favistina Flower (fig. 7-1.7) is a colonial rugose coral having a hemispherical or globose corallum composed of polygonal tubes that increase by lateral or interstitial budding. Septa are 12 to 15 in number and generally reach one-half to one-third the distance to the center of each corallite. Tabulae commonly have slightly downturned edges and median depressions. *Favistina* is locally common in Ordovician rocks of southwestern Ohio and looks superficially like the tabulate corals *Calapoecia* and *Favosites*. *Favistina* can be distinguished from those tabulate genera principally by the presence of strong septa and the lack of mural pores.

Foerstephyllum Bassler (figs. 7-2.2, 7-2.3) is a tabulate coral having a hemispherical or globose corallum composed of polygonal tubes that increase by lateral budding. Septa are short and inserted randomly. Mural pores are sparse. Tabulae are present. Representatives of *Foerstephyllum*, an Ordovician genus, are present in Cincinnatian Series rocks of southwestern Ohio.

Grewingkia Dybowski (figs. 7-5.1 to 7-5.3) is a solitary rugose coral having a simple, elongate, generally curved corallum. Septa are numerous. Major septa are long and weakly fused into a narrow axial structure in early stages; the axial structure is broad and spongy in later stages. Minor septa are of variable length. Tabulae are complete or incomplete. A single species of *Grewingkia*, *G. canadensis* (Billings), is present in Upper Ordovician strata of southwestern Ohio (figs. 7-5.1 to 7-5.3). It is the largest solitary rugose coral known from those rocks. Specimens may reach lengths in excess of 13 cm.

In older literature, *G. canadensis* was commonly referred to as *Streptelasma rusticum*. *Grewingkia* may be distinguished from *Streptelasma* by the presence of minor septa having variable lengths. In contrast, all the minor septa of *Streptelasma* are short.

Small borings into the epitheca (fig. 7-5.3) and remains of **epizoans** on the surface are common in *Grewingkia canadensis* (Elias, 1986). The solitary borings shown on figure 7-5.3 were possibly caused by polychaete worms; bryozoans are the most common epizoans. The distribution of borings and epizoans suggests that organisms became associated with the coral hosts during life or very shortly after death. The lack of extensive colonization by epizoans on corals in Cincinnatian strata suggests that most specimens were buried quickly after death.

Streptelasma Hall (figs. 7-5.4, 7-5.5) is a solitary rugose coral that characteristically has a curved corallum. The corallum has a funnel-shaped, deep calice. Septa are numerous. Major septa are fused into a weak axial structure in early stages; minor septa are short. A fossula is present in some species. Tabulae may be present. Dissepiments are absent. The epitheca is thin. *Streptelasma* is found in Ordovician and Silurian strata of Ohio. Ordovician representatives are commonly small, encrusting forms.

SILURIAN CORALS

The Silurian Period has been referred to as the Age of Corals because these organisms experienced great evolutionary diversification during this time. The great abundance and diversity of corals known from Ohio's rocks (see Hall, 1847, 1852; Nicholson, 1875, 1876; Foerste, 1917; La Rocque and Marple, 1955), particularly the carbonate lithofacies, exemplify the diversification of corals during the Silurian Period. Of particular importance is the Brassfield Formation of the Cincinnati Arch region, which documents an early stage in this evolutionary radiation (Laub, 1975, 1979). The Brassfield contains the earliest known, major Silurian coral fauna from North America.

Silurian corals were major components of both reef and muddy level-bottom communities that existed in warm, shallow, and clear marine waters at a time when Ohio was located in the tropics. Coral-dominated reefs were present during the Ordovician but did not become widespread until the Silurian. Ohio's Silurian reefs are located on the southern flank of a large reef tract that rimmed the Michigan Basin. The reefs contain a large variety of fossil organisms, but much of the framework was built by corals. There are exposed reefs and muddy level-bottom areas in the Cedarville and Springfield Dolomites of western Ohio. Some colonial corals in Silurian reefs have attained impressive dimensions; specimens may exceed 1 meter in diameter (La Rocque and Marple, 1955).

Representatives of the diverse coral faunas that are found in Silurian exposures of western Ohio are the solitary rugose genera *Amplexus*, *Cyathophyllum*, *Holophragma*, *Rhegmaphyllum*, *Streptelasma*, and *Zaphrenthis*; the colonial rugose genus *Arachnophyllum*; the tabulate genera *Halysites*, *Coenites*, *Favosites*, and *Syringopora*; and the heliolitid genus *Heliolites*. The genus *Fletcheria* is of uncertain phylogenetic affinities within the Anthozoa; it may be either a tabulate or rugose coral. *Streptelasma* is discussed in the section on Ordovician corals.

Amplexus Sowerby (fig. 7-5.7) is a solitary rugose coral that typially has a cylindrical or conico-cylindrical, thin-walled corallum. Major septa are short, thin, and subequally distributed; a fossula is well developed in later growth stages. Minor septa are commonly not distinguishable. Tabulae are well developed and flat except for downturned edges and a depression at the **cardinal fossula**. Dissepiments are absent. In Ohio, specimens referred to *Amplexus* have been found in rocks of Silurian and Devonian age. Elsewhere, the genus ranges into rocks of Mississippian age.

Arachnophyllum Dana (fig. 7-4.1) is a colonial rugose coral having a low, spreading corallum consisting mostly of dissepiments and secondary septal tissue; the **dissepimen-**

tarium is wide. Corallites are large and polygonal and have shallow calices. Septa are thickened and generally reach the axis. Tabulae are steeply domed and incomplete. *Arachnophyllum*, which is restricted to the Silurian, is moderately common in the Brassfield and Lilley Formations of Ohio.

Coenites Eichwald (figs. 7-3.7, 7-3.8) is a tabulate coral having a corallum composed of slender bifurcating branches. Corallites are small, thick walled, elongate, conical, and open obliquely to the surface. Septa may be represented by three processes in the calice. Mural pores and tabulae are sparse. *Coenites* has been found in Silurian (fig. 7-3.7) and Devonian (7-3.8) rocks of Ohio. The Silurian species *C. reticulata* (Hall) is fan shaped and superficially resembles a fenestrate bryozoan. The most obvious difference between *C. reticulata* and fenestrate bryozoans is the presence of openings (living chambers) on both sides of the branches in *C. reticulata*. Fenestrate bryozoans, in contrast, have openings on only one side of the branches, and the openings are commonly arranged in longitudinal rows. Another difference between *Coenites* and bryozoans is the presence of septa in some species. Great magnification is required, however, in order to observe the septa.

Cyathophyllum Goldfuss (fig. 7-6.7) is a solitary rugose coral having a conical corallum that becomes cylindrical in later growth stages. Septa are numerous and commonly are carinate; they extend to the center of the calice and become twisted. The fossula is indistinct or absent. Tabulae are present in the central area. Dissepiments are numerous in the **marginal area** (also called the peripheral zone). *Cyathophyllum* is characteristic of Devonian rocks, although Silurian representatives have been cited from Ohio. "*Cyathophyllum*" *roadsi* (fig. 7-6.7) from the Silurian of Ohio is tentatively referred to *Cyathophyllum* pending a modern restudy of the species.

Favosites Lamarck (figs. 7-1.4 to 7-1.6, 7-2.4, 7-2.5) is a tabulate coral having an expanded, massive, or branching corallum. Corallites are prismatic, thin walled, and in contact. Walls are perforated by one to four longitudinal rows of mural pores. Septa are absent or represented by ridges or rows of spines. Tabulae are present. *Favosites*, a so-called honeycomb coral, is nearly ubiquitous in Silurian (fig. 7-1.6) and Devonian (figs. 7-1.4, 7-1.5) carbonate-rich rocks of Ohio. *Favosites* is a common reef-dwelling genus, but isolated colonies that spread out on soft, muddy sea floors (fig. 7-1.6) also are known. Coralla of this genus typically form domal structures that may reach 1 meter or more in diameter.

Fletcheria Milne-Edwards & Haime (fig. 7-1.3) has a corallum composed of long, wide, cylindrical tubes that increase by calicular budding of three to four branches at widely spaced intervals. Mural pores or other connecting structures are absent. Septa form short vertical ridges. Tabulae are present and horizontal. At the present time, it is not certain whether this genus is a tabulate or rugose coral. Further study of the septa is needed to establish the affinities of this form within the Anthozoa. *Fletcheria* is common in Silurian carbonate deposits of Ohio. It is commonly preserved by dolomite replacement or as **molds** (fig. 7-1.3).

Halysites Fischer (fig. 7-2.6) is a tabulate coral having a corallum composed of a uniserial arrangement of cylindrical or elliptical corallites between which are **lacunae** of coenosteum. The corallum appears chainlike in cross section. Mural pores are absent. Septa or septal spines, if present, are weakly developed. Tabulae are present. *Halysites* is one of the most distinctive tabulates known from Ohio. Because of the chainlike arrangement of corallites, as seen in transverse cross section, it is commonly referred to as a chain coral. It is common in carbonate lithofacies of Silurian age (Buehler, 1955).

Heliolites Dana (figs. 7-1.1, 7-1.2) is a heliolitid coral having a laminar, domal, or spheroidal corallum. Corallites are slender tubes. If present, septa are 12 in number, laminar toward the outside, and spinose axially. Tabulae are present and horizontal. Coenosteum consists of small prismatic tubes with transverse walls. *Heliolites* is represented in rocks of Ordovician to Devonian age. In Ohio, it is best known from corallites poorly preserved as molds in which coenosteum is infilled and partly replaced with dolomite in Silurian rocks of the western part of the state.

Holophragma Lindström (fig. 7-5.6) is a solitary rugose coral having a corallum that is flattened on the **cardinal side**, giving the calice a subtriangular outline. Major septa extend to the center of the calice and are 25 to 30 in number; minor septa are short. Dissepiments are absent. In Ohio, *Holophragma* has been reported from only Silurian rocks. It is locally abundant in the Lilley Formation of Highland County.

Rhegmaphyllum Wedekind (fig. 7-6.6) is a solitary rugose coral that generally has a straight-conical corallum. Septa are radially arranged. Major septa extend to the axis and commonly have a counterclockwise whorl; minor septa are short. Dissepiments are absent. In Ohio, *Rhegmaphyllum* is known from only Silurian rocks. The counterclockwise twisting of the septa, which is characteristic of the genus, is a good example of a lateralized structure, or handedness. Although handedness has been rarely reported from the fossil record (see Babcock, 1993), examples seem to be common in the Anthozoa.

Syringopora Goldfuss (figs. 7-2.7, 7-2.8) is a tabulate coral having a corallum composed of numerous long, irregular, and cylindrical corallites. Corallites are separated but are commonly parallel; transverse tubular processes connect corallites at various intervals. Tabulae are funnel shaped. Septa, if present, are represented by spines. Because of its distinctive growth habit, *Syringopora* is sometimes referred to as the organ-pipe coral. This genus is known worldwide from rocks of Ordovician to Permian? age. In Ohio, it has been reported from only Silurian and Devonian rocks.

Zaphrenthis Rafinesque & Clifford (figs. 7-5.8, 7-5.9) is a solitary rugose coral having a simple, slightly curved, elongate corallum that has strong longitudinal ribbing (**septal grooves**). The calice is deep and has a single, well-developed fossula and no columella. Major septa are numerous, commonly serrate, and extend to the center; minor septa are short or immersed in the wall. Tabulae, if present, are incomplete. Dissepiments may be present. *Zaphrenthis* has been reported from rocks of Silurian, Devonian, and Mississippian age in Ohio. In Mississippian strata of Ohio, it is the only solitary rugose coral commonly encountered (La Rocque and Marple, 1955). Elsewhere in North America, *Zaphrenthis* ranges into Pennsylvanian strata.

DEVONIAN CORALS

During the Devonian Period, corals of the Great Lakes region attained a great diversity that was associated with the development of widespread carbonate environments in warm, shallow, and clear tropical waters (see Oliver, 1976). Reefs, which were commonly dominated by corals and stromatoporoids, were especially well developed during the

Early and Middle Devonian. Devonian-age reefs that are in the subsurface of Ohio today have economic importance, for some are petroleum traps.

The Columbus Limestone, which crops out in central and northwestern Ohio, contains a coral fauna consisting of more than 70 species (see Stewart, 1938), many of which lived in reef or muddy level-bottom communities. In places, corals of this formation have been **silicified** (replaced by silica), which permits them to weather free from limestone and allows easy examination of fine structural details.

Other Devonian units of Ohio, including the Lucas Dolomite, Delaware Limestone (Stewart, 1938), Olentangy Shale, Dundee Formation, and Tenmile Creek Dolomite (Stumm, 1968a), also contain numerous corals. In places, large assemblages of corals in some of these beds are associated with reef development.

The Silica Formation of Lucas County contains rich and well-preserved corals, among many other fossils (see Stewart, 1927; Stumm, 1967a, 1968b; Kesling and Chilman, 1975). The Silica Formation largely represents sedimentation in a muddy level-bottom environment. Corals tend to weather free from the soft shale and are easy to collect. More than 60 species have been reported from localities in northwestern Ohio and southeastern Michigan.

Devonian rocks of Ohio have long been famous for their abundant and well-preserved corals (see Goldfuss, 1826, 1829; Milne-Edwards and Haime, 1850; Milne-Edwards, 1851; Nicholson, 1875, 1876; Hall, 1876; Rominger, 1876; Hall and Simpson, 1887; Fenton and Fenton, 1936; Fenton, 1938; Stewart, 1938; Stumm, 1949, 1950, 1963, 1965a, 1968a; Ehlers and Stumm, 1949; Watkins, 1959; Kesling and Chilman, 1975). Characteristic representatives include the solitary rugose genera *Amplexus*, *Bethanyphyllum*, *Cyathophyllum*, *Cystiphylloides*, *Hadrophyllum*, *Heliophyllum*, *Heterophrentis*, *Odontophyllum*, *Prismatophyllum*, *Siphonophrentis*, and *Zaphrenthis*; the colonial rugose genera *Eridophyllum*, *Hexagonaria*, and *Synaptophyllum*; and the tabulate genera *Aulocystis*, *Aulopora*, *Cladochonus*, *Coenites*, *Emmonsia*, *Pleurodictyum*, *Syringopora*, and *Thamnoptychia*. *Amplexus*, *Coenites*, *Cyathophyllum*, *Favosites*, *Syringopora*, and *Zaphrenthis* are discussed in the section on Silurian corals.

Aulocystis Schlüter (fig. 7-3.4) is a tabulate coral having a corallum composed of moderately large, trumpetlike or tubelike corallites that are prostrate near their bases, but which become free branches farther along their length. Corallites are formed as lateral offsets through the walls near the bases of the calices below. Corallite walls have **cysts**, and the cysts have spines; walls are wrinkled externally. Tabulae, if present, are variably convex. *Aulocystis* is much like *Aulopora* in general morphology. The most obvious differences are in the branching pattern, the tendency for the corallites of *Aulocystis* to be larger, and the presence of cystose walls in *Aulocystis*. *Aulocystis* is most commonly encountered in Ohio in the Columbus and Delaware Limestones, the Olentangy Shale, and the Silica Formation.

Aulopora Goldfuss (fig. 7-3.3) is a tabulate coral having a corallum composed of small trumpetlike or tubelike corallites that are encrusting, prostrate, or prostrate basally with erect branches; branches are joined in linear chains or are **anastomosing**. Calices are slightly raised above the substrate. Corallite walls lack cysts, are smooth or wrinkled externally, and smooth or pustulose (having small bumps) internally. Septal spines may be present. Tabulae, if present, are variably convex. *Aulopora* is a cosmopolitan genus of Ordovician to Permian age. In Ohio, it is best known from Devonian rocks. It is particularly common in the Silica Formation (see Stewart, 1938; Kesling and Chilman, 1975), where it commonly encrusts the skeletons of other organisms (figs. 7-3.3, 7-5.13).

Bethanyphyllum Stumm (figs. 7-6.10, 7-6.11) is a moderately large, solitary, rugose coral having a curved corallum. The calice is bell shaped and has moderately steep walls that become flattened peripherally. Septa are numerous and noncarinate; major septa extend nearly to the axis; minor septa are half the length of the major septa. Tabulae are arched. Dissepiments are small and globose. *Bethanyphyllum*, which is restricted to the Devonian Period (see Stumm, 1963), is a common coral in the Silica Formation of Lucas County (see Kesling and Chilman, 1975). Superficially, it resembles *Heliophyllum*. It can be distinguished from that genus in hand sample principally by the septal pattern. In *Heliophyllum*, the minor septa are long, whereas in *Bethanyphyllum* the minor septa are half the length of the major septa. Also, in *Heliophyllum* the septa extend to the center of the calice and become slightly twisted.

Cladochonus M'Coy (fig. 7-3.5) is a tabulate coral having a corallum composed of small trumpetlike or pipelike corallites that are prostrate (attached or unattached) or free; the corallites are generally prostrate near their bases, although they are commonly ringlike if they are attached to crinoid stems. Corallites of the free-growing region either develop into zigzag branches (because of an alternation of the direction in which the apertures are oriented; see fig. 7-3.5), or have corallites all facing in the same direction. Dissepiments, mural pores, and septal spines are present. Tabulae are absent or sparse. *Cladochonus* is known from Devonian (Stewart, 1938) and Mississippian (Hyde, 1953) rocks of Ohio. Although *Cladochonus* bears some similarities to both *Aulopora* and *Aulocystis*, a zigzag or ringlike arrangement of the corallites commonly can be used to distinguish *Cladochonus* from either of those genera (Laub, 1972).

Cystiphylloides Chapman (fig. 7-5.13, 7-6.1) is a rugose coral that generally has a solitary growth habit. The corallum is of variable shape but commonly is cylindrical; the entire corallum is filled with dissepiments. The calice has spinelike **trabeculae** instead of septa. The epitheca is strongly wrinkled. *Cystiphylloides* is known from only Devonian rocks. Specimens from Ohio are common in both the Columbus Limestone (fig. 7-6.1) and the Silica Formation (fig. 7-5.13). In the Columbus Limestone, specimens may be silicified and preserve internal structures in exquisite detail (fig. 7-6.1) if the epitheca has been breached by weathering.

Emmonsia Milne-Edwards & Haime (fig. 7-3.1) is a tabulate coral having an expanded, massive, or branching corallum. Corallites are prismatic, thin walled, and in contact; walls are perforated by large mural pores that are commonly arranged triserially. Septa are absent or represented by ridges or rows of spines. Tabulae are present but reduced, being represented by discrete, flattened projections that appear as spines in longitudinal section. *Emmonsia* is restricted to Devonian rocks. In Ohio, it is known from carbonate lithofacies, primarily the Columbus Limestone of the central and northwestern parts of the state.

Eridophyllum Milne-Edwards & Haime (fig. 7-4.4) is a rugose coral having a variable growth form. The corallum commonly has cylindrical tubes and lateral connecting processes. Septa are thin, short, and carinate; axial edges of major septa are bent at right angles and fused to form a tube. Tabulae are horizontal and widely spaced. Dissepiments are numerous and globose. *Eridophyllum*, which is known from only Devonian rocks, is most common in the Columbus Limestone of central and northwestern Ohio. It is commonly found in reefs. The genus superficially resembles *Syringopora* in having cylindrical tubes that are connected by lateral processes. *Eridophyllum* is easily distinguished from *Syringopora* by its generally larger tubes and by its distinct, carinate septa.

Hadrophyllum Milne-Edwards & Haime (fig. 7-5.10) is a solitary rugose coral that is characteristically disk shaped or turbinate. The calice has four well-developed fossulae. The undersurface has concentric wrinkles and a conspicuous point of attachment. *Hadrophyllum*, a distinctive genus, is present in the Columbus Limestone and especially in the Delaware Limestone of central and north-central Ohio. It is sometimes referred to as a button coral because of its peculiar shape. The coral owes its distinctive shape to the lack of extensive secretion of a carbonate exoskeleton beyond the basal disk. It may be difficult to identify as a coral at first, but the strong septa reveal its relationship with corals.

Heliophyllum Hall (figs. 7-6.8, 7-6.9) is generally a solitary rugose coral. The corallum is conical, becoming cylindrical in later growth stages. Septa extend to the center of the calice and become twisted; the septa are thickened on their sides by opposite vertical carinae. Major and minor septa are both long, extending nearly to the center. The fossula is indistinct or absent. Tabulae are present in the central area and are weakly domed or concave and commonly incomplete. Dissepiments are small and globose and there is a strongly developed dissepimentarium. Representatives of *Heliophyllum*, a genus restricted to the Devonian Period, are present in various units in Ohio. They are most common in the Columbus Limestone, the Delaware Limestone, and the Silica Formation.

Heterophrentis Billings (figs. 7-5.11, 7-5.12, 7-6.2, 7-6.3) is a solitary rugose coral having a simple, elongated corallum. The calice is large and floored by a single flat tabula that has a low, rounded elevation centrally. Major septa are long and thick, and the inner edges commonly are twisted together; minor septa are short. Dissepiments are absent. *Heterophrentis* is a common genus in Devonian-age rocks, especially in the Columbus Limestone and the Silica Formation. Specimens of *Heterophrentis* illustrated here show a distinct handedness (see Babcock, 1993) in the twisting of the septa. Near the margin, the septa are twisted clockwise (figs. 7-5.11, 7-6.3); centrally, the direction of twisting is reversed (fig. 7-6.3). The functional significance of this handedness is unknown.

Hexagonaria Gürich (fig. 7-4.3) is a colonial rugose coral. Corallites are prismatic, in contact, and of nearly the same diameter for most of their length. Septa are radially arranged and in some species extend to the center of the calice; they are thickened on their sides by carinae. Tabulae are present and incomplete. Dissepiments are small, numerous, and globose. *Hexagonaria* is a distinctive and common genus in Devonian rocks through much of the world. Several species are known from Ohio. Most specimens have been collected from the Columbus Limestone and the Silica Formation. The genus is easily confused with *Prismatophyllum*; *Hexagonaria* differs from that genus primarily in having carinate septa.

Odontophyllum Simpson (fig. 7-6.5) is a solitary rugose coral having a simple, elongate corallum. The calice is deep and has a single, well-developed fossula and no columella. Septa are numerous and commonly serrated. Major septa extend to the axis; minor septa are short. Septa on each side of the fossula converge toward it. Tabulae are commonly domed and incomplete. Dissepiments are present. *Odontophyllum*, which is restricted to the Devonian, is present in various formations in Ohio. It is especially abundant in the Columbus Limestone.

Pleurodictyum Goldfuss (fig. 7-3.6) is a tabulate coral having a discoidal corallum, the lower surface of which is covered by concentric wrinkles. Corallites are small, prismatic, and funnel shaped. Septal ridges or spines are present. Tabulae typically are absent but, if present, may be incomplete; mural pores are irregularly distributed. In Ohio, *Pleurodictyum* is found in Devonian rocks and questionably in some Mississippian rocks. Discoidal colonies are moderately common in the Silica Formation of Lucas County. In the Columbus Limestone, representatives of this genus typically are preserved as molds (fig. 7-3.6). Such molds are easily identified if they are of the upper surface. *Pleurodictyum* evidently was adapted to life on a soft muddy substrate. The low, wide corallum provided a large surface area that would have increased friction against the mud. Commonly, the lower surface of a *Pleurodictyum* specimen bears the impression of a gastropod or other shell, to which the coral attached early in its life.

Prismatophyllum Simpson (fig. 7-4.2) is a colonial rugose coral. Corallites are thin walled, prismatic, in contact, and of nearly the same diameter for most of their length. Septa are long and characteristically have widely spaced carinae. Major septa may reach the center, and their axial ends may coil. Tabulae are present and incomplete. Dissepiments are small, numerous, and globose. *Prismatophyllum* is restricted to Devonian rocks. In Ohio, it occurs in the Columbus and Delaware Limestones. It resembles *Hexagonaria* but may be distinguished from that form by differences in the septal morphology, principally in the lack of carinate septa. In some species of *Prismatophyllum*, the major septa reach the center of the calice and coil, forming a distinct axial structure. This character is unknown in any species of *Hexagonaria*.

Siphonophrentis O'Connell (fig. 7-6.12) is a solitary rugose coral having a simple, elongated corallum. The calice may have a tabula at its base. Major septa are long but do not reach the axis; minor septa are short. Axial structures are not developed. The fossula is large and deep. Tabulae are flat, convex, or depressed axially. The epitheca may be strongly wrinkled. Dissepiments are absent. In Ohio, *Siphonophrentis*, which is restricted to the Devonian, has been reported from only the Columbus Limestone. Some specimens reached lengths of 75 cm, making this the largest solitary rugose coral from Ohio.

Synaptophyllum Simpson (fig. 7-4.5) is a rugose coral that commonly has long cylindrical tubes and lateral outgrowths on all sides. Septa are strong, noncarinate, and extend across the tabulate area to the central region. Axial edges of major septa are bent at right angles and fused to form a tube; minor septa are short. Tabulae are horizontal to arched and strongly deflected near the periphery. Dissepiments are absent. In Ohio, *Synaptophyllum* has been reported from only the Columbus Limestone of the central and northwestern parts of the state. It is a common genus in that unit.

Thamnoptychia Hall (fig. 7-3.2) is a tabulate coral having a corallum composed of bifurcating cylindrical branches. Corallites are prismatic; apertures appear to be far apart because the walls of the corallites are thick, causing a constriction of the rounded apertures. Tabulae are present. Mural pores are scattered. Rows of septal spines are present. In Ohio, *Thamnoptychia* is known from only rocks of Devonian age. It is most common in the Columbus Limestone, where it typically forms large colonies of fingerlike branches that grow along the margins of reefs. The branches probably extended mostly in the direction of the prevailing water current.

MISSISSIPPIAN CORALS

Corals are generally rare in Mississippian rocks of Ohio. Taxa identified (Hyde, 1953) include the rugose coral *Zaphrenthis*, which is discussed in the section on Silurian corals, and the tabulates *Cladochonus* and *Pleurodictyum*?, which are discussed in the section on Devonian corals.

PENNSYLVANIAN CORALS

Corals are rare in most Pennsylvanian-age localities of Ohio. One solitary rugose genus, *Lophophyllidium* Grabau (fig. 7-6.4), is locally abundant in some marine units. *Lophophyllidium* is a solitary rugose coral having a small to medium-sized, straight or curved corallum that has strong longitudinal ribbing. The calice is moderately deep and commonly has a central columella. Septa are 30 to 50 in number; major septa are long, and minor septa are short. Tabulae are present, and dissepiments are absent. *Lophophyllidium* ranges through rocks of Pennsylvanian and Permian age. In Ohio, however, it is known from only Pennsylvanian strata.

ACKNOWLEDGMENTS

For arranging loans of specimens used in the preparation of this chapter, I thank Dale M. Gnidovec (Orton Geological Museum of The Ohio State University) and Joe H. Marak (Department of Geology, Miami University). Daniel C. Fisher, Philip D. Gingerich, and Gregg F. Gunnell (University of Michigan Museum of Paleontology) arranged for the loan of negatives of corals previously illustrated by Kesling and Chilman (1975). Rodney M. Feldmann (Kent State University) provided access to some reference material. James St. John (The Ohio State University) provided information about borings preserved in Cincinnatian corals. Margaret T. Wilson (Columbus, Ohio) read an early version of the manuscript. Beth A. Daye (The Ohio State University) printed the photographs.

FIGURE 7-1.—Ordovician, Silurian, and Devonian heliolitid, tabulate, and rugose corals. Scale bars equal 1 cm. Scale bar A applies to figure 7-1.6; B applies to figure 7-1.7; C applies to figures 7-1.2 and 7-1.3; D applies to figure 7-1.1; E applies to figures 7-1.4 and 7-1.5.

1, 2 — *Heliolites* sp. Heliolitid coral. **1**, **external mold** of surface of corallum. Niagaran Series (Silurian), western Ohio; OSU 24347. **2**, small part of corallum, preserved as a mold in dolomite. Cedarville Dolomite (Silurian), Celina, Mercer County, Ohio; OSU 24280.

3 — *Fletcheria guelphensis* (Whiteaves). Tabulate or rugose coral. Several corallites replaced by dolomite or preserved as molds. Niagaran Series (Lower Silurian), Clay Center, Ottawa County, Ohio; OSU 20559.

4, 5 — *Favosites hemispherica minuta* Stewart. Tabulate coral. Natural cross sections of **holotype**. **4**, horizontal internal view showing corallites. **5**, lateral internal view showing tabulae. Columbus Limestone (Devonian), Columbus, Franklin County, Ohio; OSU 17754.

6 — *Favosites* sp. Tabulate coral. Underside of large weathered corallum showing internal structure. Cedarville Dolomite (Silurian), western Ohio; OSU 14875.

7 — *Favistina* sp. Colonial rugose coral. Surface view of corallum showing distinct septa; compare with tabulate corals. Cincinnatian Series (Ordovician), Cincinnati, Hamilton County, Ohio; OSU 8909.

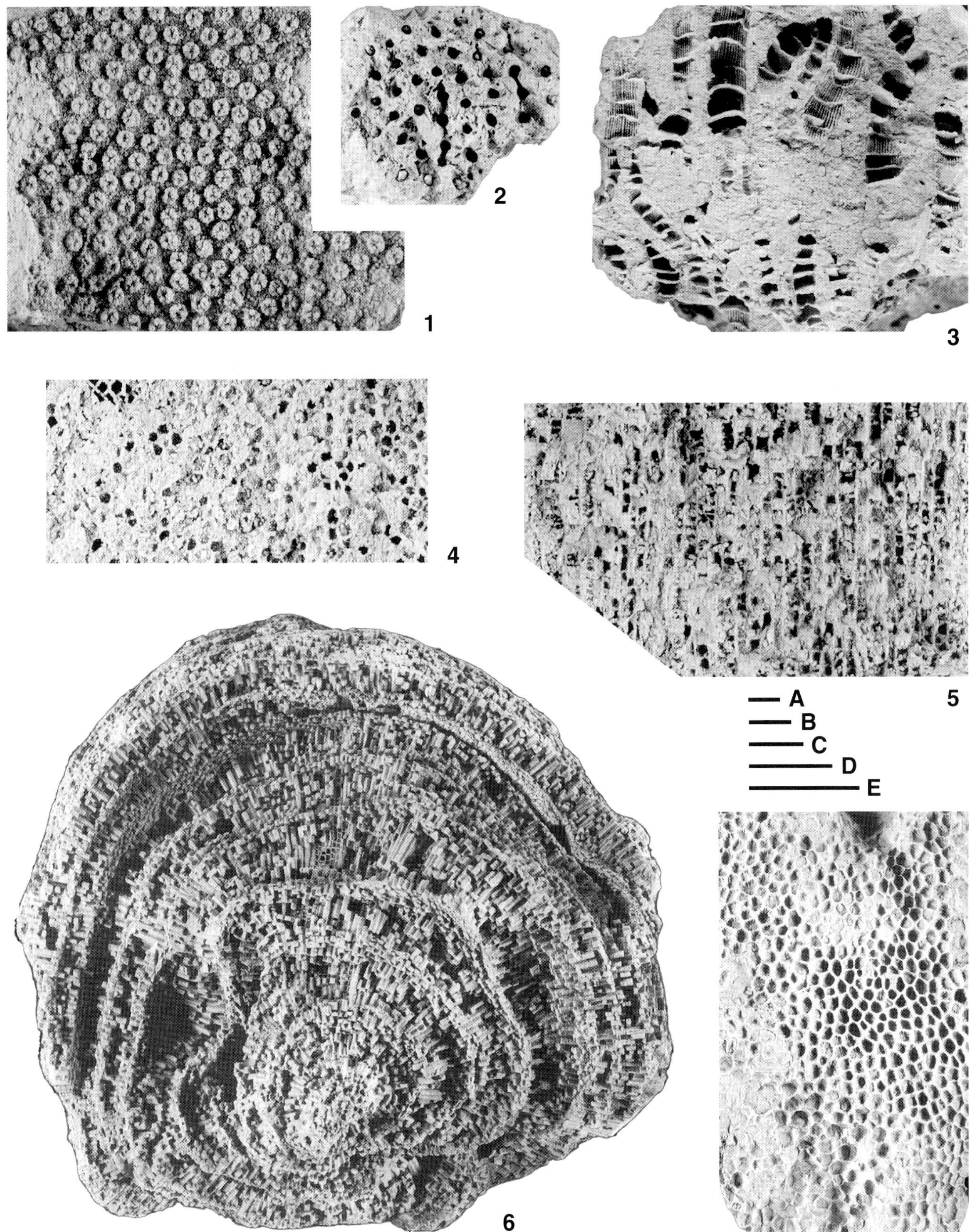
1
2
3
4
5
A
B
C
D
E
6
7

FIGURE 7-2.—Ordovician, Silurian, and Devonian tabulate corals. Scale bars equal 1 cm. Scale bar A applies to figure 7-2.1; B applies to figures 7-2.2 to 7-2.7; C applies to figure 7-2.8.

1	*Calapoecia* sp. Lateral view of external surface of corallum. Cincinnatian Series (Ordovician), southwestern Ohio; OSU 2878.
2, 3	*Foerstephyllum* sp. Lateral internal (**2**) and surface (**3**) views of corallum. Liberty Formation (Ordovician), near Oxford, Butler County, Ohio; MUGM 5438.
4, 5	*Favosites* sp. **4**, lateral internal view of colony showing mural pores. **5**, top view showing septal spines. Devonian?, central? Ohio; OSU 8817.
6	*Halysites* sp. Colony in transverse cross-sectional view showing uniserial arrangement of corallites between which are small lacunae of coenosteum. Niagaran Series (Lower Silurian), Preble County, Ohio; OSU 3240.
7, 8	*Syringopora tabulata* Milne-Edwards & Haime. **7**, silicified corallum in internal lateral view. **8**, enlargement of same specimen showing transverse processes connecting corallites. Columbus Limestone (Devonian), Marblehead, Ottawa County, Ohio; OSU 7009.

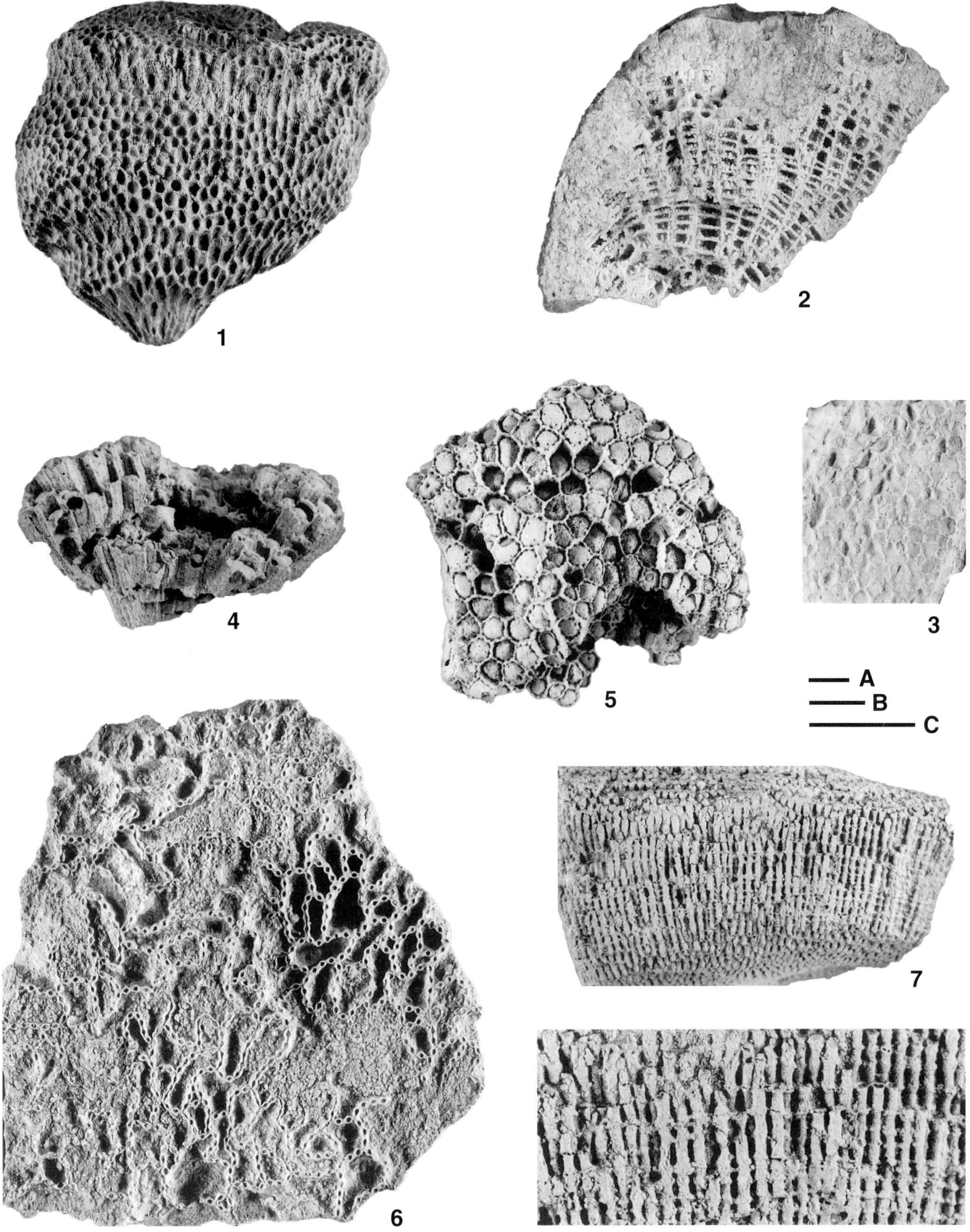
1
2
3
4
5
A
B
C
6
7
8

FIGURE 7-3.—Silurian, Devonian, and Mississippian tabulate corals. Scale bars equal 1 cm. Scale bar A applies to figures 7-3.1 and 7-3.7; B applies to figures 7-3.2 to 7-3.4, 7-3.6, and 7-3.8; C applies to figure 7-3.5. Figure 7-3.3 from Kesling and Chilman (1975), courtesy of the University of Michigan Museum of Paleontology.

1	*Emmonsia polymorpha* (Goldfuss). Silicified coralla showing internal and external surfaces. Columbus Limestone (Devonian), Columbus, Franklin County, Ohio; OSU 17762.
2	*Thamnoptychia alternans* (Rominger). External surface of colony. Columbus Limestone (Devonian), Sandusky, Erie County, Ohio; OSU 7399.
3	*Aulopora microbuccinata* (Watkins). Corallum encrusting a brachiopod, *Paraspirifer bownockeri* (Stewart). Silica Formation (Devonian), Silica, Lucas County, Ohio; UMMP 61055.
4	*Aulocystis flabellata* (Greene). Small part of colony. Silica Formation (Devonian), Silica, Lucas County, Ohio; OSU 16271.
5	*Cladochonus dumosus* Hyde. Branch of corallum showing zigzag appearance due to alternation of orientation of corallites. Wooster Shale Member of Cuyahoga Formation (Mississippian), Wayne County, Ohio; OSU 22313.
6	*Pleurodictyum* **cf.** *P. problematicum* Goldfuss. External molds of two coralla. Columbus Limestone (Devonian), Cable, Champaign County, Ohio; OSU 16128A (right) and 16128B (left).
7	*Coenites reticulata* (Hall). Sample of dolomite showing external mold of branching, fan-shaped corallum. Cedarville Dolomite (Silurian), Cedarville, Greene County, Ohio; OSU 20844.
8	*Coenites dublinensis* (Stewart). Holotype showing numerous branches of twiglike growth form. Coral zone of Columbus Limestone (Devonian), Dublin, Franklin County, Ohio; OSU 17768.

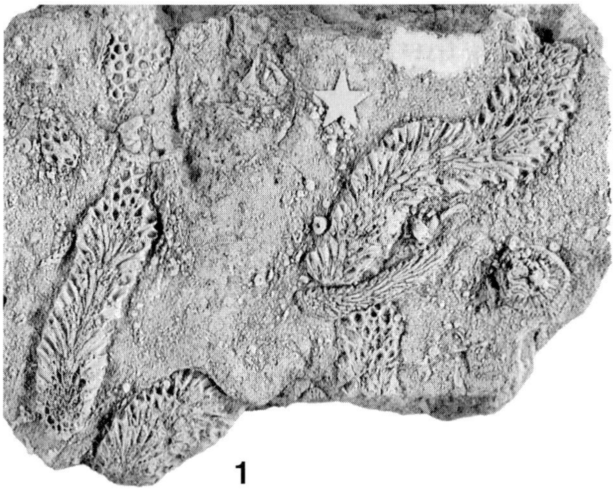

1

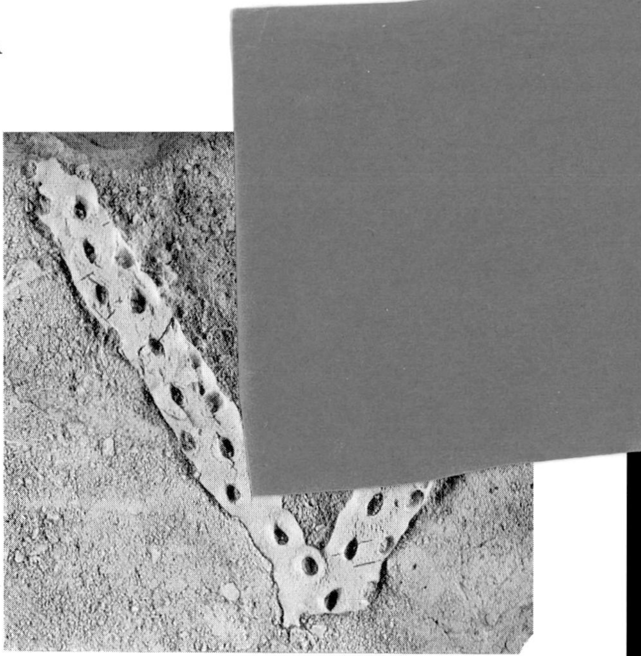

2

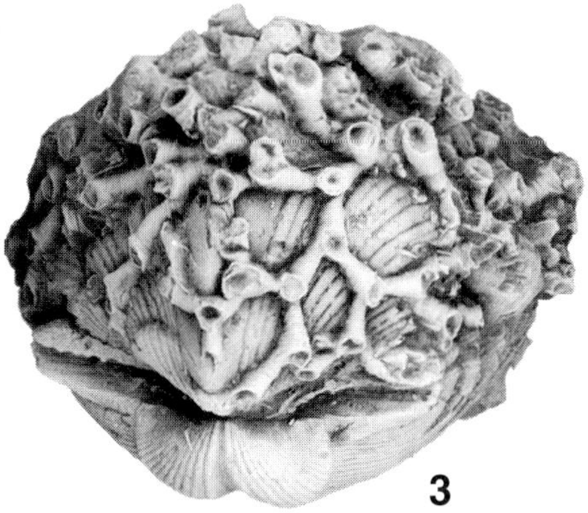

3

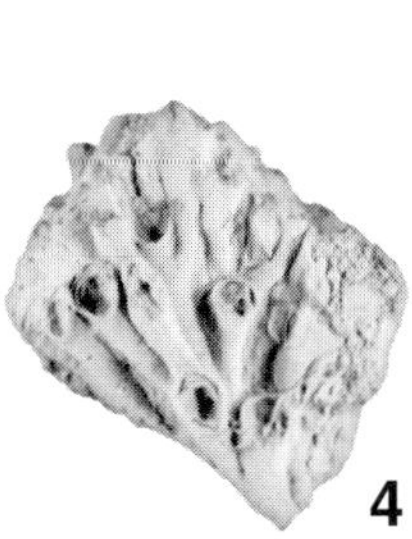

4

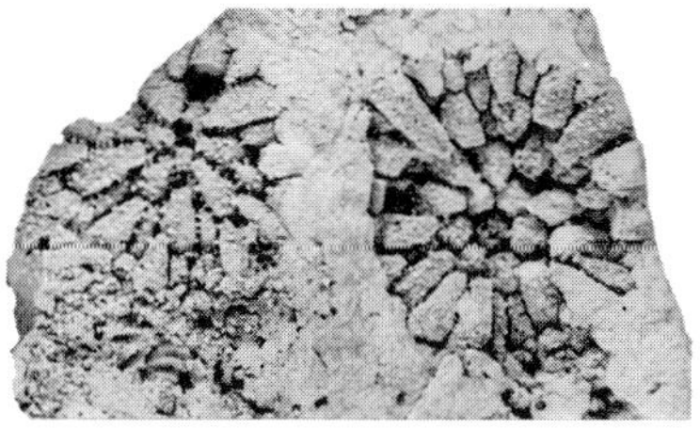

6

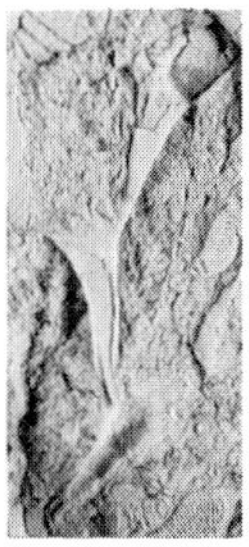

5

A

B

C

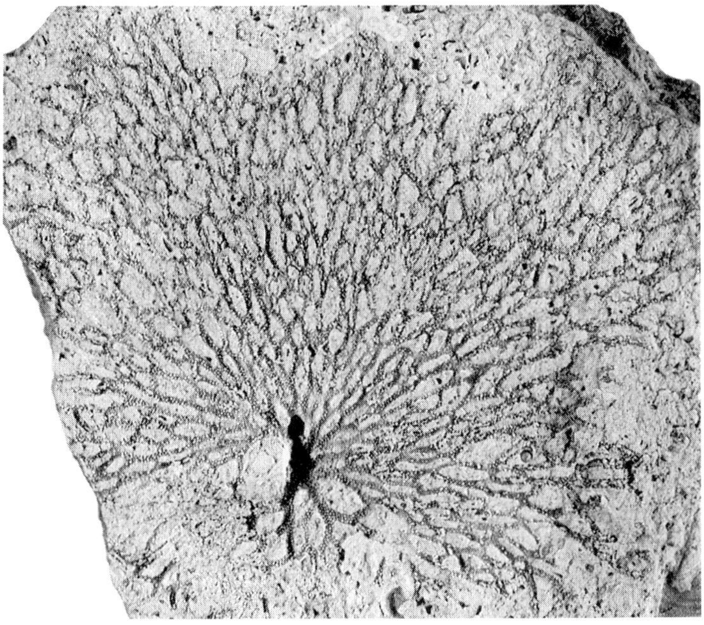

7

8

FIGURE 7-4.—Silurian and Devonian colonial rugose corals. Scale bar A equals 1 cm and applies to all figures. Specimen in figure 7-4.3 not coated with a whitening agent before photography.

1 *Arachnophyllum pentagonum* (Goldfuss). Surface view of corallum. Lilley Formation (Silurian), near Harriett, Highland County, Ohio; OSU 21095.

2 *Prismatophyllum rugosum* Simpson. Lateral internal view showing walls of prismatic corallites. Columbus Limestone (Devonian), Marblehead, Ottawa County, Ohio; OSU 17744.

3 *Hexagonaria anna* (Whitfield). Transverse cross section of colony. Columbus Limestone (Devonian), Antwerp, Paulding County, Ohio; OSU 3743A.

4 *Eridophyllum seriale* Milne-Edwards & Haime. Lateral view showing exteriors of widely separated corallites united by strong lateral outgrowths. Columbus Limestone (Devonian), Sandusky, Erie County, Ohio; OSU 3772.

5 *Synaptophyllum simcoense* (Billings). Lateral view of corallum showing internal structure. Columbus Limestone (Devonian), Bellepoint, Delaware County, Ohio; OSU 17735.

1
2
3
A
4
5

FIGURE 7-5.—Ordovician, Silurian, and Devonian solitary rugose corals. Individual specimens in calice view have **cardinal areas** oriented to the top of the figure. Scale bars equal 1 cm. Scale bar A applies to figures 7-6.1 to 7-6.3, 7-6.5, 7-6.6, and 7-6.8 to 7-6.13; B applies to figures 7-6.4 and 7-6.7. Figure 7-6.13 from Kesling and Chilman (1975), courtesy of the University of Michigan Museum of Paleontology.

1-3	*Grewingkia canadensis* (Billings). **1**, lateral view of corallum showing well-preserved growth lines on the epitheca. Liberty Formation (Ordovician), near Oxford, Butler County, Ohio; MUGM 29574A. **2**, calice view showing septa and distinct cardinal fossula (large gap between septa that is oriented vertically in this photograph). Liberty Formation (Ordovician), near Oxford, Butler County, Ohio; MUGM 29574B. **3**, lateral view of corallum showing numerous small solitary borings of the **ichnospecies** *Trypanites weisei* Mägdefrau (see Chapter 25). Cincinnatian Series, Richmondian Stage (Ordovician), near Fort Ancient, Warren County, Ohio; OSU 46327.
4	*Streptelasma pygmeum* Billings. Lateral view of corallum. Estill Shale (Silurian), near Leesburg, Highland County, Ohio; OSU 21123.
5	*Streptelasma* sp. View of **internal mold** from **apical** end showing impressions of major and minor septa. Springfield Dolomite? (Silurian), Eaton, Preble County, Ohio; MUGM 5275A.
6	*Holophragma calceoloides* Lindström. Lateral view of corallum. Lilley Formation (Silurian), Hillsboro, Highland County, Ohio; OSU 21088.
7	*Amplexus yandelli* (Milne-Edwards & Haime). Oblique calice view of silicified specimen showing deep calice and distinct axial structure. Columbus Limestone (Devonian), Columbus, Franklin County, Ohio; OSU 8178A.
8, 9	*Zaphrenthis perovalis* Stewart. **8**, lateral view of silicified corallum. OSU 8119A. **9**, Calice view of silicified specimen. OSU 8119B. Columbus Limestone (Devonian), Columbus, Franklin County, Ohio.
10	*Hadrophyllum orbignyi* Milne-Edwards & Haime. Slab with more than 20 silicified button corals. Delaware? Limestone (Devonian), Columbus, Franklin County, Ohio; OSU 3852.
11, 12	*Heterophrentis nitida* (Hall). Calice (**11**) and lateral (**12**) views of silicified corallum. Positions of the septa are well-expressed in lateral view. Columbus Limestone (Devonian), Columbus, Franklin County, Ohio; OSU 17714A.
13	*Cystiphylloides americanum* (Milne-Edwards & Haime). Oblique calice view of large broken specimen showing cystlike dissepiments in the calice. The epitheca has been overgrown in one area (arrow) by the tabulate coral *Aulopora* cf. *A. microbuccinata* (Watkins). Silica Formation (Devonian), Silica, Lucas County, Ohio; UMMP 52930.

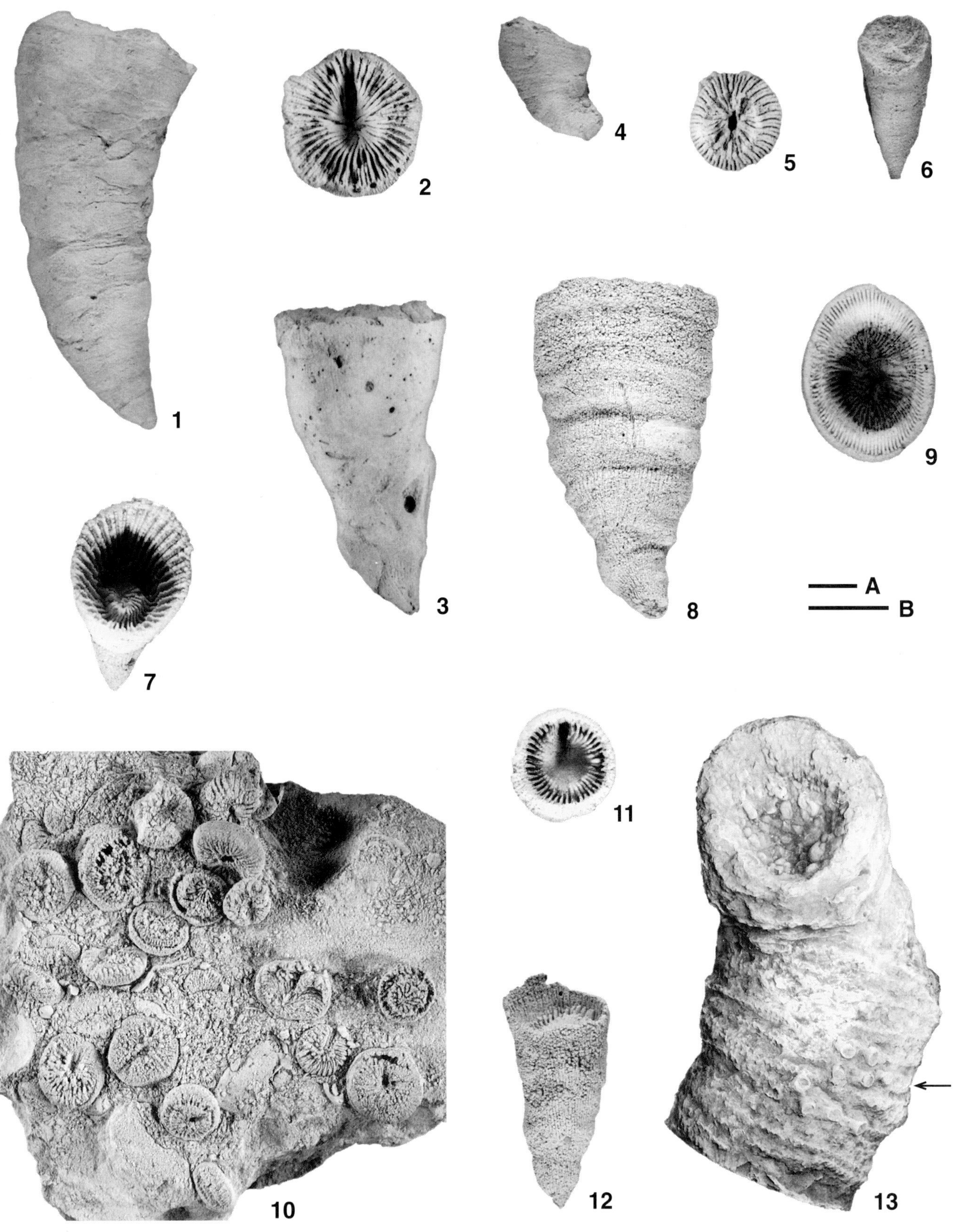
1
2
4
5
6
3
8
9
A
B
7
11
10
12
13

FIGURE 7-6.—Silurian, Devonian, and Pennsylvanian solitary rugose corals. Individual specimens in calice view have cardinal areas oriented to the top of the figure. Scale bars equal 1 cm. Scale bar A applies to figure 7-6.12; B applies to figures 7-6.1 to 7-6.11. Figures 7-6.2, 7-6.3, and 7-6.8 to 7-6.11 from Kesling and Chilman (1975), courtesy of the University of Michigan Museum of Paleontology.

1	*Cystiphylloides americanum* (Milne-Edwards & Haime). Lateral view of silicified specimen showing vesicular texture produced by dissepiments. Columbus Limestone (Devonian), Columbus, Franklin County, Ohio; OSU 17742A.
2, 3	*Heterophrentis inflata* (Hall). Lateral (**2**) and calice (**3**) views of corallum. Borings are evident in lateral view. Note the twisting of the septa, which is interpreted to be an example of handedness. Silica Formation (Devonian), Silica, Lucas County, Ohio; UMMP 52936.
4	*Lophophyllidium profundum* (Milne-Edwards & Haime). Lateral view showing characteristically grooved epitheca. Ames limestone (Conemaugh Group, Pennsylvanian), Quaker City, Guernsey County, Ohio; OSU 22035A.
5	*Odontophyllum convergens* (Hall). Oblique calice view of silicified specimen showing a well-developed fossula. Columbus Limestone (Devonian), Columbus, Franklin County, Ohio; OSU 8180A.
6	*Rhegmaphyllum charaxatum* (Foerste). Oblique calice view of corallum. Note the counterclockwise twisting of the septa, which is interpreted to be an example of handedness. Brassfield Formation (Silurian), Sharpsville, Highland County, Ohio; OSU 22600A.
7	*"Cyathophyllum" roadsi* Foerste. Oblique calice view of corallum. Lilley Formation (Silurian), near Harriett, Highland County, Ohio; OSU 21076.
8, 9	*Heliophyllum microcarinatum* Stumm. Lateral (**8**) and calice (**9**) views of corallum showing well-developed fossula. Silica Formation (Devonian), Silica, Lucas County, Ohio; UMMP 52919.
10, 11	*Bethanyphyllum robustum* (Hall). Lateral (**10**) and calice (**11**) views of corallum. In lateral view, septa show through parts of the epitheca that have been lost. Silica Formation (Devonian), Silica, Lucas County, Ohio; UMMP 52925.
12	*Siphonophrentis gigantea* (Lesueur). Lateral view of large specimen. Columbus Limestone (Devonian), Columbus, Franklin County, Ohio; OSU 17715.

1
2
3
4
5
6
7
A
B
8
9
10
11
12

Chapter 8

PHYLUM ARTHROPODA, CLASS TRILOBITA

by Loren E. Babcock

INTRODUCTION

The trilobites (pronounced try'-lo-bites) are a diverse group of marine arthropods known only from fossil remains. Worldwide, trilobites are the dominant group of arthropod **macrofossils** in Paleozoic marine strata. Their remains are among the most fascinating and sought-after fossils in Ohio, and several Ohio localities are world-renowned for their prolific and well-preserved specimens. The extraordinary fascination that Ohio's residents and visitors have with trilobites is reflected, in part, by the official designation in 1985 of a trilobite, *Isotelus*, as the State Invertebrate Fossil (Hansen, 1985b; see frontispiece of this book).

Trilobites are one of the most successful groups of organisms ever to have lived on Earth but, paradoxically, are now extinct. Their stratigraphic record spans more than 350 million years of Earth history. Trilobites have a rich fossil record owing primarily to heavy **calcification** of the **exoskeleton** (dorsal shield or upper surface), in most species, and periodic **molting** of the exoskeleton during growth. More than 4,000 genera and 20,000 species have been described, although these represent a small fraction of the taxa that have been preserved. Trilobites appeared abruptly during the early part of the Cambrian Period and radiated rapidly into various marine habitats (see Robison, 1987). The group reached its peak diversity in the Late Cambrian. A series of extinction events during the Late Cambrian significantly reduced the number of taxa that survived into the Ordovician. From the Ordovician to the Permian, trilobite diversity generally declined. During this long interval, trilobite families became more specialized than they were during the Cambrian, a fact that is evident in easily recognizable evolutionary groups called clades. Trilobites became extinct about the end of the Permian Period during a time of widespread extinction that affected numerous invertebrate animal groups. Several factors, including lowered sea level worldwide, may have been responsible for the ultimate demise of the trilobites (Robison, 1987).

The trilobite exoskeleton (see figs. 1-10 to 1-12) is divided lengthwise into a central **axial lobe** (commonly referred to simply as the **axis**) and two **pleural lobes** that flank the axial lobe. The division of the trilobite body into three lobes inspired the name of this group. The axial lobe contained most of the vital organs of the alimentary and nervous systems (Robison, 1987; Babcock, 1993). The pleural lobes provided cover for the ventral appendages (Schmalfuss, 1981; Robison, 1987) and contained some organs of the circulatory system (Jell, 1978). The exoskeleton is also divided transversely, from **anterior** to **posterior**, into a head region (the **cephalon**), an articulating, multisegmented **thorax**, and a tail region (the **pygidium**).

The cephalon is characteristically large and crescentic in outline. Characters of the cephalon evolved rapidly, and variations in those characters are therefore important in the identification of trilobites. The axial lobe of the cephalon, which is generally outlined by a distinct **axial furrow**, is composed of a long **glabella** and a short **occipital ring** at the posterior margin. Small **lateral glabellar furrows** commonly extend inward from the sides of the glabella, isolating the **lateral glabellar lobes**. The lateral glabellar furrows are expressed on the ventral surface as small knobs, called **apodemes**, which served as attachment sites for muscles, including those that operated the cephalic appendages. The pleural lobes of the cephalon are called **cheeks**. Many species bear a pair of raised, crescentic compound **eyes** on the cheeks. Narrow, symmetrical lines of weakness called **facial sutures** separate each cheek into an inner area, called the **fixigena** (fixed cheek), and an outer area, called the **librigena** (free cheek). In many trilobites the cephalon split along the facial sutures during molting, thereby enabling the growing animal to escape from its confining exoskeleton (Henningsmoen, 1975; Brandt, 1993). The part of the cephalon inside the facial sutures is referred to as the **cranidium**. The posterolateral (rear, side) corners of the cephalon are called **genal angles**. In many species, spines are developed at the posterolateral corners, on the occipital ring, or elsewhere on the cephalon. If present at the posterolateral corners, the spines are called **genal spines**.

The visual systems of trilobites were highly developed (Clarkson, 1975; Robison, 1987). Two types of compound eyes are recognized. Among sighted trilobites, the most common form is **holochroal eyes**, which are characterized by a close packing of biconvex lenses beneath a single cornea (see figs. 8-1.1, 8-1.13, 8-2.2). **Schizochroal eyes** are characterized by an aggregate of lenses each bearing a cornea and are present only in phacopid and dalmanitid trilobites (see figs. 8-5.2, 8-5.4, 8-5.7). A third type of eye, consisting of only a simple, light-sensitive eye spot, may have been present in a few taxa. Some forms lacked eyes altogether (see figs. 8-1.11, 8-1.12).

Facial sutures are useful for descriptive purposes in certain trilobites, although they are not of general utility for **taxonomic** purposes. Where facial sutures are present on the dorsal surface, they are defined according to whether the section behind the eye intersects the posterior cephalic margin (**opisthoparian**), the genal angle (**gonatoparian**), or the lateral cephalic margin (**proparian**) (see fig. 1-11). Examples of trilobites having opisthoparian sutures are *Proetidella* (fig. 8-1.13) and *Isotelus* (figs. 8-2.1, 8-2.2). Large adults of *Flexicalymene* (figs. 8-1.8 to 8-1.10) have gonatoparian sutures. Examples of trilobites having proparian sutures are *Phacops* (figs. 8-5.1, 8-5.2), *Greenops* (fig. 8-5.7), and *Trypaulites* (fig. 8-5.12). A few trilobites (for example, *Cryptolithus*, fig. 8-1.12) had marginal sutures.

All around the edge of the animal a recurved part of the **dorsal** exoskeleton, the **doublure**, extends inward a variable distance on the **ventral** side. An uncalcified **ventral membrane** stretched from the doublure on one side across to the other, covering the lower surface of the animal. The doublure at the anterior end of the cephalon may consist of one to three pieces. A large plate of variable shape, called the **labrum** or **hypostome** (fig. 8-2.3), covered the area beneath the trilobite's stomach and mouth regions.

The thorax is composed of articulating bandlike segments. The number of segments can range from two to more than 60, according to species. Axial furrows divide each **thoracic segment** into a medial **axial ring** and two lateral **pleurae**. Pleurae may be flat to moderately convex, and most are corrugated by an oblique **pleural furrow**. An **articulating half-ring** is present along the anterior edge of the axial ring. The articulating half-ring extends beneath the folded posterior margin of the preceding segment and functioned as an overlapping flange or flap during transverse bending of the body or enrollment. Articulation of the thoracic segments permitted most trilobites to enroll, thus providing protection for the ventral appendages and uncalcified areas of the ventral anatomy. The thoracic segments terminate distally in spines or rounded angles. These distal ends are commonly faceted so they could nest closely when the animals enrolled (compare specimens of *Phacops*, figs. 8-5.2, 8-5.4). Several styles of enrollment were developed in trilobites (Bergström, 1973).

The pygidium is a single plate composed of a series of fused segments. It varies considerably in size and morphology among taxa. It is connected to the posteriormost thoracic segment by an articulating half-ring. The axial lobe of the pygidium is generally outlined by a distinct axial furrow. The axis is long and divided into rings by **ring furrows**. The pleural lobes commonly have two types of furrows. The pleural furrows are long and oblique. These corrugated structures probably added strength to the exoskeleton, similar to the pleural furrows in the thorax. Shorter furrows, called **interpleural furrows**, mark the boundaries between fused segments. Marginal spines may be present medially or laterally.

The external surfaces of trilobites exhibit sculpturing related to sensory systems, organ systems, sediment gripping, or hydrodynamics (Robison, 1987). Minute pores may have been sites for the attachment of sensory hairs called **setae**. **Tubercles** of variable size (see figs. 8-5.1, 8-5.2) may have been related to sensory (John Miller, 1976) or other functions. Small, asymmetrical, scarplike ridges, called **terrace lines**, are present in most taxa. When confined to the doublure, the labrum, and lateral body margins (figs. 8-2.2, 8-2.3), they are thought to have aided burrowing by increasing friction between the exoskeleton and the sediment surface (Schmalfuss, 1981). When present primarily on the dorsal surface (fig. 8-1.13), they may have increased the hydrodynamic qualities of swimming trilobites (Babcock, 1994b). Fine, **anastomosing** ridges, which are most commonly expressed on the pleural lobes of the cephalon (fig. 8-1.1), probably reflect part of the underlying circulatory system (Jell, 1978).

Trilobite fossils rarely reveal details of the soft, or uncalcified, anatomy. Where they do, it is only because of exceptional preservational circumstances. One specimen of an Ohio trilobite (fig. 8-2.4) shows much of the uncalcified ventral anatomy. This specimen, and others that were found elsewhere (Harrington and others, 1959; Levi-Setti, 1993), show that the appendages of trilobites consisted of a series of bladelike bars, called **coxae**, that were located under the axial lobe. Emerging from each coxa are two leg branches. The appendages are therefore said to be **biramous**. The dorsal, featherlike (presumably gill-bearing) leg is called the **exite**, and the ventral walking or swimming leg is called the **telepod**. A pair of **antennae** extended from the interior surface of the labrum.

The growth history of trilobites, like that of other arthropods, is recorded in a series of molted exoskeletons that show progressive size increase and shape change (Harrrington and others, 1959; Speyer and Chatterton, 1989). The life history of a trilobite has four major phases. The first phase, during which time the animal is thought to have been encased in an egg, is not known to be represented in the fossil record. The earliest exoskeleton in most trilobite groups is a tiny, undivided, ovoid shield assigned to the **protaspid stage**. The beginning of the **meraspid stage** is defined by the appearance of a joint between the cephalon and the pygidium. During successive molts, thoracic segments were added to the thorax at the thoracic-pygidial joint. The beginning of the **holaspid stage** is defined as the molt stage (or **instar**) in which the full complement of thoracic segments is first attained. The animal continued to molt and undergo size and limited shape change through the holaspid stage, but additional segments were not added to the thorax.

Most trilobite fossils probably represent molted exoskeletons (see Henningsmoen, 1975) rather than carcasses. Unless there has been some displacement of **sclerites** (discrete exoskeletal pieces) associated with molting, it is difficult to determine whether an outstretched specimen is a molt or a carcass. During molting, the librigenae were commonly displaced (see fig. 8-6.10) or lost (see fig. 8-4.9), but this is not always the case (Brandt, 1993). In some trilobites, displacement of sclerites occurred at the joint between the cephalon and thorax. Specimens in figure 8-1.3 show disarticulation of sclerites along the facial sutures and at the joints between the cranidia and thoraxes. An individual trilobite could potentially leave as many complete fossils as it had molt stages. However, bottom currents and organisms that reworked sediment disarticulated and scattered molted exoskeletons. For this reason, most trilobite fossils are of individual sclerites such as cranidia, librigenae, labra, thoracic segments, or pygidia. The most commonly recognized remains are cranidia, cephala, and pygidia because these are generally larger and easier to identify than other sclerites.

Most trilobites were **benthic** (bottom dwelling) and vagrant inhabitants of relatively shallow, well-lit, marine waters (Brooks, 1957). Many benthic species were probably **epifaunal**, living on the sediment surface, or ploughing through the upper few millimeters of unconsolidated sediment (Schmalfuss, 1981). Some large, smooth forms having wide axial areas, such as *Bumastus* (figs. 8-4.7 to 8-4.9), may have been semi-**infaunal**, meaning that they lived partly submerged in the sediment. Some blind trilobites, such as *Cryptolithus* (figs. 8-1.11, 8-1.12), were probably burrowers (Campbell, 1975). Benthic trilobites may have been detritus-feeders, filter-feeders, scavengers, or possibly predators.

Benthic, epifaunal trilobites are commonly recognizable from a concentration of terrace lines on the lateral margins and doublure (see figs. 8-2.1 to 8-2.3). Many epifaunal species also have wide pleural lobes (see fig. 8-2.1). The terrace lines probably aided in sediment gripping, and the wide pleural areas would have provided a wide cover under which an area of circulating water (a feeding chamber) could have been established (Schmalfuss, 1981). Through rhythmic action of the legs under the cephalon, trilobites may have either stirred up bottom sediment and filtered food particles from it or directed water carrying food particles from outside the feeding chamber to inside the enclosure. Such activity is recorded in trace fossils known as *Rusophycus* (see Chapter 25, figs. 25-4.1, 25-4.3, 25-7.1, 25-7.2).

Some trilobites were almost certainly **pelagic**, or dwellers of the water column. A variety of morphological characters and independent geologic evidence are suggestive of a pelagic lifestyle (Fortey, 1985; Babcock, 1994b). Among characters thought to be indicative of a pelagic lifestyle are reduced pleural lobes, an **inflated** glabella, a dorsal surface that is either smooth or largely covered with terrace lines, and large or downwardly directed eyes. Although the presence of marginal spines (including genal spines) is not unambiguous evidence of lifestyle, long spines are present on some forms having an inferred pelagic habit. *Triarthrus* (figs. 8-1.2, 8-1.3), *Proetidella* (fig. 8-1.13), and *Sphaerexochus* (figs. 8-4.4, 8-4.5) are examples of presumed pelagic taxa that are found in Ohio. Pelagic trilobites may have been filter-feeders or perhaps predators that fed on small **planktonic** organisms.

More than 50 genera and 150 species of trilobites have been reported from the rocks of Ohio. At present, remains are known from rocks of Cambrian through Pennsylvanian age. The Cambrian trilobites of Ohio are known only from cores drilled into the subsurface (Babcock, 1994a) and have not been extensively studied to date. Marine rocks exposed at the surface in the state contain representatives of all major trilobite clades (groups related by a common ancestor) that lived from the Late Ordovician through the end of the Paleozoic. Information relating to the trilobites of Ohio is contained in hundreds of publications. The list of references at the end of this book provides a brief sampling of articles or books that describe aspects of the taxonomy or paleobiology of some trilobites that are found in Ohio.

KEY TO REPRESENTATIVE TRILOBITE GENERA FROM OHIO

The following key is intended to be used for adult (holaspid stage) specimens for which a cephalon and pygidium are available.

1A. Eyes absent .... *Cryptolithus* (figs. 8-1.11, 8-1.12)
1B. Eyes present 2

2A. Eyes schizochroal (showing large distinct facets) 3
2B. Eyes holochroal (individual facets not visible or covered by a single cornea) 9

3A. Glabella has a medial lobe and a pair of lateral lobes posteriorly .... *Phacops* (figs. 8-5.1 to 8-5.4)
3B. Glabella without a medial lobe at posterior 4

4A. Glabella has second and third lateral glabellar lobes circumscribed by furrows 5
4B. Glabella without furrow circumscribing second and third lateral glabellar lobes 7

5A. Pygidium has a smooth margin .... *Trypaulites* (fig. 8-5.12)
5B. Pygidium has a pair of marginal spines posteromedially 6

6A. Pygidial margin has numerous pairs of small spines .... *Coronura* (fig. 8-5.10)
6B. Pygidial margin without numerous pairs of small spines .... *Odontocephalus* (fig. 8-5.11)

7A. Pygidium has five pairs of broad marginal spines .... *Greenops* (figs. 8-5.7, 8-5.8)
7B. Pygidium without paired spines along margin 8

8A. Cephalon and pygidium both have single stout medial spine at margin .... *Dalmanites* (figs. 8-3.14, 8-3.15)
8B. Cephalon and pygidium both lack medial spine at margin .... *Tricopelta* (fig. 8-3.3)

9A. Facial sutures gonatoparian 10
9B. Facial sutures not gonatoparian 12

10A. Glabella globular, circular in outline, and composing most of cranidium .... *Sphaerexochus* (figs. 8-4.4, 8-4.5)
10B. Glabella tapering forward and has three pairs of deep lateral glabellar furrows 11

11A. Second lateral glabellar lobe has buttress extending into axial furrow .... *Calymene* (figs. 8-3.9, 8-3.10)
11B. Second lateral glabellar lobe lacks buttress extending into axial furrow .... *Flexicalymene* (figs. 8-1.8 to 8-1.10, 8-3.11, 8-4.1 to 8.4.3)

12A. Facial sutures proparian 13
12B. Facial sutures opisthoparian 17

13A. Cephalon and pygidium both elongate subtriangular in outline .... *Trimerus* (figs. 8-4.10, 8-4.11)
13B. Cephalon and pygidium not both elongate subtriangular in outline 14

14A. Glabella straight sided .... *Ceraurinus* (figs. 8-1.6, 8-1.7)
14B. Glabella expanding forward 15

15A. Pygidium without marginal spines .... *Encrinurus* (fig. 8-4.6)
15B. Pygidium has marginal spines 16

16A. Pygidium has a single pair of elongate spines .... *Ceraurus* (figs. 8-1.4, 8-1.5)
16B. Pygidium has three pairs of moderately long marginal spines .... *Cheirurus* (fig. 8-3.8)

17A. Glabella composed of three elongate lobes 18
17B. Glabella not composed of three elongate lobes 19

18A. Pygidium has three pairs of broad marginal spines and a long, pointed **terminal piece** in the axis ..... *Amphilichas* (fig. 8-3.6)
18B. Pygidium has two pairs of broad marginal spines and a long, posteriorly expanding terminal piece .... *Metopolichas* (figs. 8-3.12, 8-3.13)

19A. Cephalon and pygidium smooth (effaced) 20
19B. Cephalon and pygidium not smooth (have distinct furrows) 21

20A. Cephalon and pygidium subtriangular in outline .... *Isotelus* (figs. 8-2, 8-3.4, 8-3.5)
20B. Cephalon semicircular and pygidium subelliptical in outline .... *Bumastus* (figs. 8-4.7 to 8-4.9)

21A. Posterior pair of lateral glabellar lobes not isolated by furrows 22
21B. Posterior pair of lateral glabellar lobes isolated by furrows 24

22A. Marginal spines, other than genal spines, present on librigenae and pygidium .... *Acidaspis* (figs. 8-3.1, 8-3.2, 8-3.7)
22B. Marginal spines, other than genal spines, not present on librigenae and pygidium 23

23A. Glabella tapering forward and has indistinct lateral furrows .... *Cedaria* (fig. 8-1.1)
23B. Glabella straight sided and has distinct lateral furrows .... *Triarthrus* (figs. 8-1.2, 8-1.3)

24A. Posterior glabella has a pair of lateral lobes and a medial lobe 25
24B. Posterior glabella has a pair of lateral lobes only 26

25A. Pygidial axis has 6 to 8 rings .... *Ditomopyge* (figs. 8-6.6, 8-6.7)
25B. Pygidial axis has 17 to 19 rings .... *Sevillia* (fig. 8-6.10)

26A. Glabella hourglass shaped .... *Ameura* (figs. 8-6.8, 8-6.9)
26B. Glabella parallel sided, expanding forward, or tapering forward 27

27A. Glabella nearly as wide as long 28
27B. Glabella long (significantly longer than wide) 29

28A. Posterior lateral glabellar lobes large .... *Pudoproetus* (figs. 8-6.3, 8-6.4)
28B. Posterior lateral glabellar lobes small .... *Proetidella* (fig. 8-1.13)

29A. Pleural ribs of pygidium extend into short marginal spines .... *Australosutura* (fig. 8-6.5)
29B. Pleural ribs of pygidium do not extend beyond margin, margin smooth 30

30A. Pleural ribs of pygidium continue behind axis .... *Piltonia* (fig. 8-6.2)
30B. Pleural ribs of pygidium do not continue behind axis 31

31A. Pygidium much wider than long .... *Basidechenella* (figs. 8-5.5, 8-5.6)
31B. Pygidium longer than wide 32

32A. Pygidium semielliptical in outline .... *Paladin* (fig. 8-6.1)
32B. Pygidium elongate-subtriangular in outline .... *Crassiproetus* (fig. 8-5.9)

CAMBRIAN TRILOBITES

Several tens of isolated trilobite sclerites have been recovered from subsurface cores of Cambrian-age rocks in Ohio. Trilobite sclerites are by far the most common Cambrian-age **body fossils** recognized to date (Hansen, 1992c; Babcock, 1994a). Less common fossils known from those rocks are inarticulate brachiopods, a graptolite, and trace fossils (Babcock, 1994a). Although our knowledge of the Cambrian fossils of Ohio is meager at present, it is expected to increase in future years as more cores are drilled into rocks of that age in the state.

Cedaria Walcott (fig. 8-1.1) has an exoskeleton of up to 5 cm in length. The cephalon is semicircular in outline; pleural areas are much wider than the axis. The glabella is moderately convex, tapering forward, and commonly lacks or has indistinct lateral glabellar furrows. Eyes are small, low, and holochroal. Facial sutures are opisthoparian; librigenae are wide; genal angles commonly have spines. The thorax has about seven segments; pleural areas are much wider than the axis; each pleura is straight and terminates in a blunt spine. The pygidium is large and semicircular in outline. The axis has about two to eight distinct axial rings and a terminal piece. **Pleural fields** have about two to six pairs of distinct pleural furrows.

Cedaria is representative of Cambrian trilobites recognized from cores drilled into the upper part of the Eau Claire Formation. Other trilobite genera that have been recovered from Cambrian rocks of Ohio are not yet represented by good material.

ORDOVICIAN TRILOBITES

Upper Ordovician (Cincinnatian Series) shales and limestones in southwestern Ohio, particularly Hamilton, Warren, Montgomery, Highland, and Brown Counties, are rich in occurrences of trilobites, along with many other fossils (La Rocque and Marple, 1955). Adjacent areas of Kentucky and Indiana also yield abundant Cincinnatian fossils. At least 12 genera of Ordovician trilobites have been recognized from the Cincinnati Arch region (see Foerste, 1887, 1888, 1893, 1910, 1919a; Raymond and Barton, 1913; Evitt, 1953; Ross, 1967, 1979; Ludvigsen, 1977; Davis, 1985; Shrake, 1990). Genera that are represented by abundant remains through much of the Cincinnatian Series are *Cryptolithus*, *Flexicalymene*, and *Isotelus*. Some beds in the Cincinnatian Series are world famous for yielding large numbers of enrolled, articulated specimens of *Flexicalymene* (figs. 8-1.8, 8-1.9) that probably were episodically buried under conditions of rapid sedimentation (Osgood, 1970; Brandt Velbel, 1985; Babcock and Speyer, 1987). Other genera present in the Upper Ordovician of Ohio, generally in modest numbers, include *Acidaspis*, *Amphilichas*, *Ceraurinus*, *Ceraurus*, *Tricopelta*, and *Triarthrus*.

Acidaspis Murchison (figs. 8-3.1, 8-3.2, 8-3.7) has an exoskeleton up to 5 cm in length; it is small, spiny, and covered with numerous tubercles. The cephalon is short and wide; pleural areas are wider than the axis; a row of marginal spines extends downward from the anterior and lateral edges. The glabella is convex and overhangs the anterior margin of the cephalon; it has a large, isolated pair of lobes at the posterior end. The occipital ring has a thick, long medial spine. Eyes are small and holochroal. Facial sutures are opisthoparian; librigenae are narrow and have a row of short, blunt spines; genal spines are long, narrow, and bowed backward. The thorax has 10 segments; pleural areas are wider than the axis; each pleura is extended into a long, marginal spine that is directed posteriorly. The pygidium is small and has seven pairs of marginal spines; the fifth pair of marginal spines is longer and thicker than the others.

In Ohio, *Acidaspis* has been collected from Upper Ordovician (figs. 8-3.1, 8-3.2) and Silurian (fig. 8-3.7) strata in the southern part of the state. Elsewhere in North America, the genus is known from rocks of Middle Ordovician to Middle Devonian age.

Amphilichas Raymond (fig. 8-3.6) has an exoskeleton up to 4 cm in length. The cephalon is subtriangular in outline; pleural areas are approximately as wide as the axis. The glabella is convex and composed of three elongate lobes.

Eyes are moderately large and holochroal. Facial sutures are opisthoparian; librigenae are narrow; genal spines are moderately short. The thorax has 11 segments; pleural areas are wider than the axis; each pleura is curved, has a backward deflection near the middle, and terminates in a spine. The pygidium is large and subtriangular in outline and has three pairs of broad marginal spines. The axis has about three axial rings and a long, pointed terminal piece. Pleural fields have three pairs of pleural furrows and generally two distinct interpleural furrows. *Amphilichas* is present in Cincinnatian Series strata of southwestern Ohio. Most specimens have been collected from the Grant Lake Formation.

Ceraurinus Barton (figs. 8-1.6, 8-1.7) has an exoskeleton up to 6 cm in length. The cephalon is semicircular in outline; pleural areas are wider than the axis; border areas are flat. The glabella is low, straight sided, smooth, and has three pairs of nearly straight lateral glabellar furrows. Eyes are small and holochroal. Facial sutures are proparian; librigenae are narrow; genal spines are relatively short and stout. The thorax has 11 segments; pleural areas are wider than the axis; each pleura is curved and terminates in a long, blunt spine. The pygidium is small and has three pairs of marginal spines; each pair has a narrow medial ridge; the first pair is long, slightly curved, and blunt; the other two pairs are shorter and pointed. The axis has three axial rings. *Ceraurinus* is present in the Arnheim, Liberty, and Whitewater Formations of southwestern Ohio.

Ceraurus Green (figs. 8-1.4, 8-1.5) has an exoskeleton up to 5 cm in length. The cephalon is short, wide, rather semicircular in outline, and is covered with tubercles of various sizes; pleural areas are somewhat wider than the axis. The glabella is convex and slightly expanding forward; it slightly overhangs the anterior margin of the cephalon and has three pairs of deep lateral glabellar furrows. Eyes are small, holochroal, slightly elevated, and situated well away from the glabella. Facial sutures are proparian; librigenae are narrow; genal spines are moderately long, narrow, and directed posterolaterally. The thorax has 11 segments; pleural areas are wider than the axis; each pleura is nearly straight and terminates in a moderately long, stout, posteriorly curved marginal spine. The pygidium is small, semicircular in outline, and has a long, convex, slightly bowed pair of marginal spines extending posteriorly from the anterior segment. The axis has four axial rings and a short terminal piece. Sclerites of *Ceraurus* are locally common in the Kope, Grant Lake, Waynesville, and Whitewater Formations of southwestern Ohio. More complete specimens, however, are rare.

Cryptolithus Green (figs. 8-1.11, 8-1.12) has an exoskeleton up to 3 cm in length. The cephalon is short, wide, semielliptical in outline, and has a wide fringe that is ornamented by concentric and radiating rows of pits; pleural areas are nearly twice as wide as the axis. The glabella is convex, expanding forward, and has three short pairs of lateral glabellar furrows. The occipital ring has a moderately long medial spine. Eyes are absent. Facial sutures are marginal. Pleural areas of fixigenae, inside the fringe, are smooth and convex. Genal spines are long, narrow, and directed posteriorly. The thorax has six segments; pleural areas are wider than the axis; each pleura is nearly straight and terminates bluntly. The pygidium is short, wide, and rounded-subtriangular in outline. The axis has several axial rings and a terminal piece. Pleural fields have several pairs of shallow interpleural furrows.

Cryptolithus, which is sometimes called the lace-collar trilobite (Davis, 1985) because of its distinctive cephalic fringe, is present through much of the Cincinnatian Series strata of southwestern Ohio. Most specimens have been collected from the Kope, Fairview, and Grant Lake Formations. Only one species, *C. tessellatus* Green, seems to be present in the Cincinnatian of Ohio (Shaw and Lespérance, 1994). In some older literature, this species was identified as *C. bellulus* (Whittington, 1968).

Flexicalymene Shirley (figs. 8-1.8 to 8-1.10, 8-3.11, 8-4.1 to 8-4.3) has an exoskeleton up to 6 cm in length; it is **granulose** and penetrated by fine canals. The cephalon is rounded-subtriangular in outline; pleural areas are approximately as wide as thc axis. The glabella is convex, tapering forward, and has three pairs of deep lateral glabellar furrows separating rounded and convex lateral glabellar lobes; a distinct pair of glabellar pits is present at the anterior corners of the axial furrow. Eyes are small, holochroal, and moderately elevated. Facial sutures are gonatoparian; librigenae are narrow; genal angles are bluntly rounded or have a short spine. The thorax has 13 segments; pleural areas are wider than the axis; each pleura is slightly curved and has a rounded termination. The pygidium is small and lenticular in outline. The axis generally has six axial rings and a terminal piece. Pleural fields generally have four pairs of pleural furrows.

Flexicalymene is the most common trilobite in Upper Ordovician rocks of southwestern Ohio. It is present throughout the Cincinnatian Series. Several species have been reported from those rocks, although some may be synonyms. *Flexicalymene meeki* (Foerste) (figs. 8-1.8 to 8-1.10; also fig. 8-1.5) is by far the most abundant species of the genus in the Cincinnatian Series.

The generic name *Flexicalymene* refers to the trilobite's commonly enrolled (figs. 8-1.8, 8-1.9) or otherwise flexed posture. Enrolled specimens of *F. meeki* have been found in large numbers in certain thin beds (Osgood, 1970) that were probably deposited episodically by storms (Brandt Velbel, 1985; Babcock and Speyer, 1987). Many trilobites, including *Flexicalymene*, are thought to have enrolled (many of them after burrowing) in response to a number of stimuli, including changes in light, pressure, temperature, or oxygen conditions, and in response to the approach of predators. As discussed by Babcock and Speyer (1987), trilobites that have been preserved in large numbers in an enrolled posture must have been buried quickly. It is unlikely that most of the trilobites were killed directly by rapid sedimentation. Other environmental factors must have prevented them from digging their way back to the surface. One likely possibility is that the mud that buried them was oxygen deficient, and the trilobites remained enrolled until such time as the sediment became better oxygenated. On the basis of studies of present-day marine arthropods, the trilobites are inferred to have been capable of living without oxygen in an enrolled posture for a short length of time, probably one to two weeks. If the sediments that buried them were not reoxygenated within this critical length of time, the trilobites would have died in their enrolled posture.

Isotelus DeKay (figs. 8-2, 8-3.4, 8-3.5; frontispiece) is a large trilobite—its exoskeleton may exceed 50 cm in length. The cephalon is subtriangular in outline and smooth; pleural areas are narrower than the axis. The glabella is relatively low, poorly defined, tapering forward to the position of the eyes, then expanding forward; the lateral glabellar furrows are faint. Eyes are moderately long, holochroal, and slightly elevated. Facial sutures are opisthoparian; librigenae are moderately wide; genal angles are rounded, bluntly pointed, or have genal spines. The thorax has eight straplike segments; pleural areas are defined by broad, shallow axial furrows; pleural areas are narrower than the axis; each pleura is slightly curved and terminates bluntly. The pygidium is large, subequal in size to the cephalon, subtriangular in outline, and smooth. The axis is poorly defined and has many poorly defined axial rings and a terminal piece. Pleural fields have many poorly defined pairs of pleural furrows. The labrum is large and forked and has distinct terrace lines that parallel the margin. The doublure around the margin of the cephalon and pygidium is wide, flat, and covered with terrace lines that parallel the margin of the exoskeleton.

Isotelus, the State Invertebrate Fossil of Ohio (Hansen, 1985b), is abundant in Upper Ordovician (Cincinnatian) rocks of southwestern Ohio. It also has been found in drill cores that penetrate to Middle Ordovician strata. Separated sclerites are distinctive because of their large size and characteristic golden to dark-brown color. Cranidial fragments, pygidial fragments, and thoracic segments are generally flattened and rather smooth. Portions of the undersurface, including the doublure, labrum, and genal spines, bear conspicuous terrace lines that resemble a fingerprint pattern (figs. 8-2.1 to 8-2.3). In *Isotelus* and other benthic trilobites, terrace lines on the undersurface probably aided in stabilizing the animals during feeding by gripping the sediment at the margins of the exoskeleton (see Schmalfuss, 1981).

Isotelus is one of the largest trilobites known. Rare articulated specimens exceed 50 cm in length. Most large, outstretched specimens are flattened in shale. The specimens illustrated in figures 8-2.1, 8-2.2, and 8-3.5 are unusual in retaining their natural convexity, which is the result of their preservation in limestone.

One extraordinary specimen of *I. maximus* Locke from Butler County reveals some ventral appendages of the thorax (fig. 8-2.4). A series of slightly curved coxae are conspicuous. Attached to the coxae are multisegmented telepods. The exites are not discernible.

Several species of *Isotelus* have been reported from Ohio, although some are undoubtedly synonyms. A comprehensive revision of the genus is long overdue. Pending such revision, only two species from Upper Ordovician rocks of Ohio are recognized here: *I. maximus* Locke (fig. 8-2) and *I. gigas* DeKay (figs. 8-3.4, 8-3.5). *Isotelus gigas* may be distinguished from the much more common *I. maximus* by the lack of genal spines or the presence of short genal spines in adult (holaspid) specimens, and by the more triangulate cephalic and pygidial margins. Perceived differences between specimens commonly assigned to *I. maximus* and *I. brachycephalus* Foerste seem to be largely attributable to postdepositional compaction; *I. brachycephalus* is therefore tentatively considered to be synonymous with *I. maximus*.

Proetidella Bancroft (fig. 8-1.13) has an exoskeleton up to 5 cm in length. The cephalon is semielliptical to semicircular in outline; pleural areas are wider than the axis. The glabella is wide, convex, and tapering forward; it generally lacks lateral glabellar furrows and has an isolated pair of small lateral lobes posteriorly. Eyes are large, high, and holochroal. Facial sutures are opisthoparian; librigenae are moderately narrow; genal spines are narrow. The thorax has 10 segments that commonly have a row of small medial nodes on the axis; pleural areas are slightly wider than the axis; each pleura is slightly curved and terminates bluntly or in a spine. The pygidium is moderately large and semicircular in outline. The axis has six or more axial rings and a short terminal piece. Pleural fields have four or more pairs of pleural furrows.

A small species of this genus, *Proetidella parviusculus* (Hall), is present in the Upper Ordovician Kope Formation of southwestern Ohio. This species has terrace lines covering much of the dorsal surface, a greatly inflated glabella, and rather long genal spines. Such characteristics suggest that this species was pelagic (see Fortey, 1985; Babcock, 1994b). This interpretation is reinforced by the finding of this species in more than one lithofacies. Its remains are present in both medium-gray calcareous shales and in dark-gray shales. Some dark-gray shales yielding *P. parviusculus* seem to have been deposited where bottom waters were oxygen deficient and not conducive to sustaining benthic organisms. Therefore, fossils found in such settings may represent organisms that either lived in the oxygenated water column above or were washed in from neighboring areas.

Triarthrus Green (figs. 8-1.2, 8-1.3) has an exoskeleton up to 3 cm in length. The cephalon is semicircular in outline; pleural areas are slightly narrower than the axis. The glabella is low, parallel-sided, has three pairs of lateral glabellar furrows, and generally has a distinct pair of pits in the axial furrow at the anterolateral (front, side) corners of the glabella. Eyes are small and holochroal. Facial sutures are opisthoparian; librigenae are narrow and low; genal areas are developed into blunt angles or long, narrow spines. The thorax has 13 to 16 segments; pleural areas are narrower than the axis; each pleura is straight and terminates bluntly. The pygidium is small and lenticular in outline. The axis has three to five axial rings and a short terminal piece. Pleural fields have three to five pairs of pleural furrows.

Two species of *Triarthrus* have been identified from Middle and Upper Ordovician rocks of Ohio. The more common species, *T. eatoni* (Hall) (fig. 8-1.2), has rounded genal angles. The other species, *T. spinosus* Billings (fig. 8-1.3), has elongate genal spines that are covered with terrace lines. *Triarthrus* is known both from surface exposures of the Kope Formation and from subsurface rocks recovered through coring. The morphologies of *Triarthrus* species, their widespread distributions in North America (see Ludvigsen and Tuffnell, 1983), and their typical occurrence in black or dark-gray shales suggest that they were pelagic trilobites. In Ohio, *Triarthrus* commonly is found in association with *Proetidella parviusculus* in shales representing oxygen-deficient bottom conditions.

Some slabs bearing *Triarthrus* comprise mostly headless specimens (fig. 8-1.3). These are interpreted to represent molted exoskeletons. Whether such occurrences represent trilobites that molted in one small area at about the same time, or current-concentrated molts, is an open question.

Tricopelta Ludvigsen & Chatterton (fig. 8-3.3) has an exoskeleton up to 3 cm in length. The cephalon is semicircular in outline; pleural areas are approximately as wide as the axis. The glabella is convex, expanding forward, and has three pairs of lateral glabellar furrows; the anteriormost pair of furrows is directed anterolaterally. Eyes are large, kidney-bean shaped, and schizochroal. Facial sutures are proparian; librigenae are relatively narrow and have genal spines. The thorax has 11 segments; pleural areas are about the same width as the axis; each pleura is slightly curved and terminates bluntly. The pygidium is moderately large and subtriangular in outline. The axis has 6 to 20 axial rings and a terminal piece. Pleural fields have 5 to 19 pairs of pleural furrows. Specimens referable to *Tricopelta* have been found in the Liberty and Whitewater Formations of southwestern Ohio. Only one species, *T. breviceps* (Hall), has been reported from Ohio.

SILURIAN TRILOBITES

Silurian rocks of Ohio are dominated by carbonate deposits. However, most of Ohio's Silurian carbonate rocks have been dolomitized, so that preservation is poor and collecting generally is difficult. In these dolomitized rocks, the calcitic trilobite exoskeletons have been dissolved, and specimens are preserved as natural **internal** and **external molds** of the dorsal exoskeleton.

Representative genera in the Silurian rocks of Ohio are *Acidaspis*, *Bumastus*, *Calymene*, *Cheirurus*, *Dalmanites*, *Encrinurus*, *"Flexicalymene"*, *Metopolichas*, *Sphaerexochus*, and *Trimerus* (see Hall and Whitfield, 1875; Foerste, 1919a; La Rocque and Marple, 1955; Whittington, 1971; Ludvigsen, 1979; Mikulic, 1981; Gass and others, 1992). Many specimens have been collected, especially from quarries in Preble, Montgomery, and Highland Counties. *Acidaspis* (fig. 8-3.7) and *"Flexicalymene"* (figs. 8-3.11, 8-4.1 to 8-4.3) are discussed in the section on Ordovician trilobites. *"Flexicalymene" celebra* (Raymond) is present in Silurian dolomites of Ohio, particularly the Springfield and Cedarville Dolomites of the western part of the state. In older literature, this species commonly was identified as *Calymene celebra*. In 1971, Whittington placed the species in the genus *Flexicalymene*. He later (Whittington, 1992) placed the species in *Gravicalymene* Shirley. Because of uncertainty about the generic assignment of this species and about the morphological differences between *Flexicalymene* and *Gravicalymene*, the generic name of this species as used here is *"Flexicalymene,"* in quotation marks. Differences between *Calymene* and *Flexicalymene* are noted in the discussion of *Calymene* below (also see Whittington, 1971). *"Flexicalymene" celebra* typically is preserved in dolomite as internal and external molds. Internal molds commonly show infillings of the fine canals that penetrated the exoskeleton, especially along the marginal areas (fig. 8-4.3).

Bumastus Murchison (figs. 8-4.7 to 8-4.9) has an exoskeleton up to 15 cm in length. The cephalon is semicircular in outline, convex, and smooth; pleural areas are much narrower than the axis. The glabella is indistinctly defined, expanding forward, and lacks lateral glabellar furrows. Eyes are large and holochroal. Facial sutures are opisthoparian; librigenae are narrow; genal angles are rounded. The thorax has 10 smooth segments; each pleura is slightly curved and terminates bluntly. The pygidium is large, somewhat longer than the cephalon, subelliptical in outline, convex, and smooth. The doublure is wide.

Bumastus is moderately common in the Springfield Dolomite of southwestern Ohio but also is present in other carbonate strata. Specimens typically are disarticulated. The cephalon and pygidium are both quite smooth and in the past have been misidentified as the internal septa of cephalopods.

Bumastus may have been a semi-infaunal trilobite, meaning that it spent some time submerged in soft carbonate mud with little more than the large eyes penetrating the mud surface. The smooth dorsal surface would have left few hindrances to burrowing. Complementing this smooth surface is a wide doublure having terrace lines that parallel the margin. The terrace lines, which are commonly visible because of moldic preservation (fig. 8-4.9), would have facilitated sediment gripping (see Schmalfuss, 1981).

Calymene Brongniart (figs. 8-3.9, 8-3.10) has an exoskeleton up to 8 cm in length. The cephalon is rounded-subtriangular in outline; pleural areas are approximately as wide as the axis. The glabella is convex, tapering forward, and has three pairs of deep lateral glabellar furrows separating rounded and convex lateral glabellar lobes; a buttress extends into the axial furrow from the second lateral glabellar lobe opposite each eye. Eyes are small, holochroal, and moderately elevated. Facial sutures are gonatoparian; librigenae are narrow; genal angles are bluntly rounded. The thorax has 13 segments; pleural areas are wider than the axis; each pleura is slightly curved and has a rounded termination. The pygidium is small and lenticular in outline. The axis generally has six axial rings and a terminal piece. Pleural fields have four pairs of pleural furrows.

In the Silurian of Ohio, *Calymene* is best known from abundant disarticulated sclerites in the Brassfield Formation of western Ohio. It is quite similar in morphology to *"Flexicalymene"*, which also is common in some Ohio Silurian carbonate units. The most conspicuous difference between representatives of the two genera is the presence in *Calymene* of a buttress extending from the second lateral glabellar lobe into the axial furrow in a position opposite each eye (fig. 8-3.9).

Cheirurus Beyrich (fig. 8-3.8) has an exoskeleton up to 7 cm in length. The cephalon is semicircular in outline; pleural areas are narrower than the axis; cheeks are covered with large granules. The glabella is convex and expanding forward; it overhangs the anterior margin of the cephalon and has three pairs of deep lateral glabellar furrows; the first pair of furrows delineates a large, distinct lateral glabellar lobe at the posterior end of the glabella. Eyes are small and holochroal. Facial sutures are proparian; librigenae are narrow; genal spines are short and stout. The thorax has 11 segments; pleural areas are wider than the axis; each pleura is nearly straight and extends into a long, stout marginal spine. The pygidium is rather small, subtriangular in outline, and has three pairs of moderately long, stout, curved marginal spines plus a short, stout medial spine. The axis has about three axial rings and a short terminal piece. Pleural fields have two pairs of pleural furrows.

Cheirurus is present in Silurian carbonate units of Ohio. It is most common in the Springfield and Cedarville Dolomites, where it is typically associated with reef rocks. The morphology of *Cheirurus* suggests a pelagic lifestyle; perhaps it fed on zooplankton or suspended food particles that were present in the vicinity of coralline reefs. Evidence of a pelagic lifestyle includes an inflated glabella, reduced pleurae in the thorax, and distinct marginal spines.

Dalmanites Barrand (figs. 8-3.14, 8-3.15) has an exoskeleton that rarely exceeds 15 cm in length. The cephalon is subtriangular to semicircular in outline and has a wide, flat anteromedial margin that may be developed into a distinct, flat medial spine called a rostrum; pleural areas are wider than the axis. The glabella is moderately convex, expanding forward, and has three pairs of deep lateral glabellar furrows; the anteriormost pair is directed anterolaterally. Eyes are large, high, kidney-bean shaped, and schizochroal. Facial sutures are proparian; librigenae are wide; genal spines are long and stout. The thorax has 11 segments; pleural areas are much wider than the axis; each pleura is curved and terminates bluntly or in a spine. The pygidium is large, subtriangular in outline, and has a distinct medial spine at the margin. The axis has 11 to 16 axial rings and a short terminal piece. Pleural fields generally have six pairs of deep and wide pleural furrows. Sclerites of *Dalmanites* have been identified from various Silurian units in Ohio. Elsewhere, the genus ranges into the Lower Devonian.

Encrinurus Emmrich (fig. 8-4.6) has an exoskeleton up to 6 cm in length. The cephalon is semicircular in outline; pleural areas are approximately as wide as the axis; the surface of the cephalon is covered with large perforated tubercles. The glabella is convex, expanding forward, and has three pairs of short, faint lateral glabellar furrows. Eyes are small, holochroal, located well away from the glabella, and elevated or stalked. Facial sutures are proparian; librigenae are narrow; genal angles are rounded. The thorax has 11 or 12 segments; pleural areas are narrower than the axis; each pleura is slightly curved and terminates in a blunt spine. The pygidium is large, subtriangular in outline, and longer than wide. The axis has 5 to 10 axial rings and a terminal piece; it is ornamented with a medial row of tubercles. Pleural fields have about eight pairs of pleural furrows.

In Ohio, *Encrinurus* has been identified only from Silurian rocks. It is most common in the Brassfield and Bisher Formations of the western part of the state. Elsewhere in the world, the genus ranges through strata of Middle Ordovician to Silurian age.

Metopolichas Gürich (figs. 8-3.12, 8-3.13) has an exoskeleton up to 10 cm in length. The cranidium is relatively short and rounded anteriorly. The glabella is convex, expanding forward, and consists of three elongate lobes. Eyes are small and holochroal. Facial sutures are opisthoparian. The number of segments in the thorax is unknown; pleural areas are wider than the axis; each pleura terminates in a spine. The pygidium is large, semielliptical to subtriangular in outline, and has two pairs of broad marginal spines. The axis has about four axial rings and a long terminal piece that expands posteriorly. Pleural fields have two pairs of pleural furrows and three distinct interpleural furrows. All known specimens referable to *Metopolichas* from Ohio are incomplete. Most specimens are from the Brassfield Formation of the western part of the state.

Sphaerexochus Beyrich (figs. 8-4.4, 8-4.5) has an exoskeleton up to 5 cm in length; the surface is smooth. The cephalon is dominated by the glabella; pleural areas are much narrower than the axis. The glabella is highly convex, globular, nearly circular in outline, and has three pairs of lateral glabellar furrows; the posterior pair of furrows is deep and delineates a large ovoid pair of lateral glabellar lobes; the anterior two pairs of furrows are short and faint. Eyes are small and holochroal. Facial sutures are gonatoparian; librigenae are narrow; genal angles are rounded. The thorax has 10 segments; pleural areas are narrower than the axis; each pleura is **geniculate**, without a pleural furrow, and terminates in a blunt spine. The pygidium is large, subelliptical in outline, and has three pairs of short, blunt marginal spines. The axis has three axial rings and a long terminal piece. Pleural fields have two pairs of pleural furrows.

In Ohio, *Sphaerexochus* has been identified from such Silurian carbonate units as the Springfield and Cedarville Dolomites, where it is found primarily in reef-flank lithofacies. In these units, it is best known from the distinctive cranidium, which consists of little more than a round and greatly inflated glabella. Worldwide, the genus occurs in rocks of Middle Ordovician to Silurian age.

Sphaerexochus was probably a pelagic trilobite. The narrow pleural lobes, the inflated glabella, and the downwardly directed eyes (figs. 8-4.4, 8-4.5) are characteristics commonly associated with a pelagic lifestyle (see Fortey, 1985). The purpose of the large glabella is unknown; it may have served as a repository for food or fatty deposits. Because food tends to have a patchy distribution in the pelagic realm, a built-in storage receptacle would have been of tremendous adaptive value during lean times. Fatty deposits would have aided the trilobite in achieving neutral buoyancy, a necessary prerequisite for a pelagic animal.

Trimerus Green (figs. 8-4.10, 8-4.11) has an exoskeleton up to 20 cm in length. The cephalon is elongate-subtriangular in outline and without a border; pleural areas are approximately as wide as the axis. The glabella is low, subtrapezoidal in outline, slightly tapering forward, and commonly lacks lateral glabellar furrows. Eyes are small and holochroal. Facial sutures are proparian; librigenae are narrow; genal angles are rather narrowly rounded. The thorax has 13 straplike segments; pleural areas are narrower than the axis, defined by shallow and broad axial furrows; each pleura is slightly curved and has a rounded termination. The pygidium is large, convex, elongate-subtriangular in outline, and has a distinct, stout medial spine posteriorly. The axis has about 14 axial rings and a terminal piece. Pleural fields have about nine pairs of pleural furrows. *Trimerus* is the largest Silurian trilobite known from Ohio. Sclerites of *Trimerus* are locally common in Middle Silurian carbonate rocks of the Niagaran Series (see Thomas, 1977), particularly in Highland County.

DEVONIAN TRILOBITES

Devonian shales and limestones of Ohio contain about 15 genera of trilobites (see Delo, 1940; Stumm, 1953, 1954, 1965b, 1967b; Lespérance and Bourque, 1971; Eldredge, 1972, 1973; Lespérance, 1975). Specimens are most abundant in the Columbus Limestone of central and northwestern Ohio and the Silica Formation of Lucas County. Quarries in the Silica Formation (Stewart, 1927; Kesling and Chilman, 1975) are world-renowned for producing abundant and well-preserved specimens of *Phacops* (Eldredge, 1972; Babcock, 1992; Levi-Setti, 1993), many of which are complete. These quarries, which in most cases are no longer open to collectors, also have produced specimens of *Greenops* and *Basidechenella* in modest numbers. The Columbus Limestone contains the most diverse Devonian trilobite fauna known from Ohio. Remains of six genera—*Basidechenella*, *Coronura*, *Crassiproetus*, *Odontocephalus*, *Phacops*, and *Trypaulites*—are present in this formation. Of these genera, *Coronura* seems to be the most common. Articulated trilobite specimens are rare in the Columbus Limestone.

Basidechenella Richter (figs. 8-5.5, 8-5.6) has an exoskeleton up to 5 cm in length. The cephalon is semielliptical in outline; pleural areas are slightly wider than the axis. The glabella is long, convex, straight sided to slightly tapering forward, and has three pairs of lateral glabellar furrows; the first pair of furrows isolates a pair of lateral lobes posteriorly. The occipital ring is truncated at the anterolateral corners by a pair of small lateral lobes. Eyes are large, high, and holochroal. Facial sutures are opisthoparian; librigenae are wide and low; genal spines are long and narrow. The thorax has 10 segments, commonly with a row of small nodes medially on the axis; pleural areas are wider than the axis; each pleura is slightly curved and terminates in a blunt spine. The pygidium is large, much wider than long, and semielliptical in outline. The axis has 10 to 13 axial rings and a short terminal piece. Pleural fields have about seven pairs of pleural furrows. *Basidechenella* has been identified from the Columbus (fig. 8-5.6) and Delaware Limestones of central and northwestern Ohio and the Silica Formation (fig. 8-5.5) of northwestern Ohio.

Coronura Hall & Clarke (fig. 8-5.10) has an exoskeleton up to 30 cm in length; the surface is covered with large granules. The cephalon is semicircular in outline and has broad borders; pleural areas are wider than the axis. The glabella is moderately low, expanding forward, and has three pairs of deep lateral glabellar furrows; the anteriormost pair of furrows is directed anterolaterally; the second and third lateral glabellar lobes are circumscribed by furrows. Eyes are large, high, kidney-bean shaped, and schizochroal. Facial sutures are proparian; librigenae are wide; genal spines are present. The thorax has 11 segments; pleural areas are wider than the axis; each pleura is slightly curved and terminates in a spine. The pygidium is larger than the cephalon and semielliptical in outline; it has numerous pairs of short and narrow marginal spines and a pair of large posteriorly directed spines in the posteromedial area. The axis has 15 to 20 axial rings and a terminal piece. Pleural fields are much wider than the axis and have 15 to 20 pairs of pleural furrows.

Coronura is the largest Devonian trilobite known from Ohio; it is relatively common in the Columbus Limestone. Exposures yielding remains of *Coronura* are present in the central and northwestern parts of the state.

Crassiproetus Stumm (fig. 8-5.9) has an exoskeleton up to 8 cm in length. The cephalon is semicircular and convex; pleural areas are narrower than the axis. The glabella is long, parallel sided, and has one pair of lateral glabellar furrows that isolates a small pair of lateral glabellar lobes posteriorly. Eyes are large, high, and holochroal. Facial sutures are opisthoparian; librigenae are moderately wide; genal angles are rounded. The thorax has 10 segments; pleural areas are wider than the axis; each pleura is curved and terminates bluntly. The pygidium is large, longer than wide, elongate-subelliptical in outline, and convex. The axis has 12 to 15 axial rings and a terminal piece. Pleural fields have 8 to 11 pairs of pleural furrows. *Crassiproetus* is relatively common in some Devonian carbonate units, particularly the Columbus Limestone of central and northwestern Ohio.

Greenops Delo (figs. 8-5.7, 8-5.8) has an exoskeleton up to 6 cm in length. The cephalon is rounded-subtriangular in outline; pleural areas are wider than the axis. The glabella is moderately convex, expanding forward, and has three pairs of lateral glabellar furrows; the anteriormost pair is directed anterolaterally. The occipital ring has a small medial node. Eyes are large, high, kidney-bean shaped, and schizochroal. Facial sutures are proparian. Genal spines are long and vertically flattened. The thorax has 11 segments, commonly with a row of small nodes medially on the axis; pleural areas are wider than the axis; each pleura is slightly curved and terminates in a blunt spine. The pygidium is large, subelliptical in outline, and has five pairs of rather long and broad marginal spines plus a broad, triangular posteromedial spine. The axis has about 10 axial rings and a short terminal piece. Pleural fields have about five pairs of pleural furrows.

Greenops is present in the Silica Formation of northwestern Ohio. This distinctive Middle Devonian trilobite, which has stout genal spines on the cephalon and five stout pairs of marginal spines on the pygidium, is common at some localities in the Great Lakes region, but seems to be uncommon in Ohio.

Odontocephalus Conrad (fig. 8-5.11) has an exoskeleton up to 10 cm in length. The cephalon is rounded-subtriangular in outline and has a wide, ridged frill anteriorly; pleural areas are wider than the axis. The glabella is relatively low, expanding forward, and has three pairs of lateral glabellar furrows; the anteriormost pair of furrows is directed anterolaterally; the second and third lateral glabellar lobes are circumscribed by furrows. Eyes are moderately large, high, kidney-bean shaped, and schizochroal. Facial sutures are proparian; librigenae are wide; genal areas are rounded or have spines. The thorax has 11 segments. Pleural areas are wider than the axis; each pleura is slightly curved and terminates bluntly. The pygidium is large, semielliptical to subtriangular in outline, and has a distinct pair of marginal spines posteromedially. The axis has about 7 to 18 axial rings and a terminal piece. Pleural fields have about 7 to 12 pairs of pleural furrows.

Odontocephalus has been identified from the Columbus Limestone of central and northwestern Ohio. Because of the pair of marginal spines posteriorly, the pygidium of this genus resembles the pygidium of *Coronura*. The pygidium of *Coronura*, however, is generally larger, has more pleural furrows, and has numerous small lateral marginal spines.

Phacops Emmrich (figs. 8-5.1 to 8-5.4) has an exoskeleton up to 8 cm in length; its surface is largely covered with granules. The cephalon is semicircular and convex; pleural areas are narrower than the axis. The glabella is large and expanding forward; it has one pair of lateral glabellar furrows that extends across the posterior part of the glabella, isolating a medial lobe, and a pair of lateral glabellar lobes at the posterior; the anterior two pairs of lateral glabellar furrows are not visible except on an internal surface. Eyes are large, high, kidney-bean shaped, and schizochroal. Facial sutures are proparian. Genal angles are rounded. The thorax has 11 segments; pleural areas are wider than the axis; each pleura is slightly curved and has a rounded termination. The pygidium is large and lenticular. The axis generally has 7 to 10 axial rings and a terminal piece. Pleural fields have five to seven pairs of pleural furrows.

Phacops is the most common Devonian trilobite in Ohio. The Columbus Limestone has yielded numerous specimens of *P. cristata bombifrons* Hall (fig. 8-5.3) and fewer specimens of *P. cristata stummi* Eldredge (Eldredge, 1973). *Phacops rana milleri* Stewart (fig. 8-5.4) and *P. rana crassituberculata* Stumm (figs. 8-5.1, 8-5.2) are abundant in the Silica Formation (Stewart, 1927; Stumm, 1954; Eldredge, 1972; Babcock, 1992) and are among the best-known trilobites from anywhere in the world. The two subspecies commonly are confused. This confusion may be due in part to the inclusion of a specimen referable to *P. rana crassituberculata* in the suite of type specimens of *P. rana milleri*. The concepts of both subspecies were recently stabilized (Babcock, 1992), and consistent differences between *P. rana crassituberculata* and *P. rana milleri* have been established. *Phacops rana crassituberculata* has fewer lenses in each eye (average of 84 versus 104), fewer vertical rows of lenses in each eye (maximum of seven vs. nine), polygonal eye sockets, lenses that do not mostly protrude from the eye surface, and more strongly developed tubercles on the exoskeleton. The eye facets of *P. rana crassituberculata* alternate in vertical rows, giving them the appearance of a diagonal disposition (fig. 8-5.2) rather than an apparent vertical disposition as in *P. rana milleri* (fig. 8-5.4).

Trypaulites Delo (fig. 8-5.12) has an exoskeleton up to 8 cm in length. The cephalon is semicircular in outline; pleural areas are wider than the axis. The glabella is low, expanding forward, and has three pairs of moderately deep lateral glabellar furrows; the anteriormost pair of furrows is directed anterolaterally; the second and third lateral glabellar lobes are joined and circumscribed by furrows. Eyes are large, high, kidney-bean shaped, and schizochroal. Facial sutures are proparian; librigenae are wide; genal spines are short and wide. The thorax has 11 segments; pleural areas are wider than the axis; each pleura is slightly curved and angulate at its termination. The pygidium is subequal in size to the cephalon, rounded-subtriangular in outline, and has a smooth margin. The axis has 12 to 15 axial rings and a terminal piece. Pleural fields have about 12 pairs of pleural furrows. *Trypaulites* is present in Devonian carbonate units of Ohio and is known best from the Columbus Limestone of the central and northwestern parts of the state.

MISSISSIPPIAN TRILOBITES

Eight trilobite genera have been identified from Mississippian rocks of Ohio (Hyde, 1953; Brezinski, 1988). The most diverse faunas are in the Cuyahoga Formation of northeastern, central, and southern Ohio. Trilobites are not abundant in the Cuyahoga Formation, although diligent collecting is likely to result in the discovery of a few specimens. *Australosutura*, *Piltonia*, and *Pudoproetus* are the genera typically encountered in the Cuyahoga Formation. Trilobites are present at some localities in the Logan Formation of central and southern Ohio. *Paladin* is moderately common in the Maxville Formation of eastern Ohio.

The Mississippian and Pennsylvanian trilobites of Ohio that are illustrated in this chapter are all strikingly similar in appearance, which may reflect a common evolutionary origin. Phylogenetic or cladistic analysis (analysis of the evolutionary relationships among organisms) suggests that all or most of these taxa evolved from the same ancestral stock of trilobites and possibly a single species. This limited adaptive radiation occurred shortly after a Late Devonian extinction event that resulted in the elimination of many trilobites. Because differences between the Mississippian and Pennsylvanian genera are rather subtle, great care must be taken to distinguish one **taxon** from another.

Australosutura Amos, Campbell & Goldring (fig. 8-6.5) has an exoskeleton up to 3 cm in length; the surface is covered with coarse granules that on the thorax and pygidium are arranged in lengthwise rows. The cephalon is long and semielliptical in outline; pleural areas are wider than the axis. The glabella is convex, tapering forward, and has one distinct pair of lateral glabellar furrows that isolate a pair of lateral glabellar lobes posteriorly. Eyes are small and holochroal. Facial sutures are opisthoparian; librigenae are wide; genal spines are long. The thorax has nine segments; pleural areas are wider than the axis; each pleura is slightly curved and terminates bluntly. The pygidium is large and semielliptical in outline; pleural ribs are extended into eight or nine short, narrow marginal spines. The axis reaches the posterior border and has about 12 to 13 axial rings and a short terminal piece. Pleural fields have about eight or nine pairs of pleural furrows.

Australosutura is an uncommon fossil, but it is the trilobite most likely to be encountered in the Cuyahoga Formation. It has been found in the Meadville, Wooster, and Raccoon Shale Members of the Cuyahoga Formation in Ashland, Cuyahoga, Licking, Medina, Summit, and Wayne Counties.

Paladin Weller (fig. 8-6.1) has an exoskeleton up to 4 cm in length. The cephalon is semielliptical and convex; pleural areas are narrower than the axis. The glabella is long, convex, slightly expanding forward, and has three pairs of lateral glabellar furrows; the posterior pair of furrows isolates distinct lateral glabellar lobes, and the anterior pairs are faint. Eyes are large, holochroal, and elevated. Facial sutures are opisthoparian; librigenae are wide; genal spines are long and narrow. The thorax has nine segments; pleural areas are about the same width as the axis; each pleura is slightly curved and terminates in a spine. The pygidium is large, longer than wide, semielliptical in outline, and convex. The axis reaches the posterior border and has about 11 to 17 axial rings and a short terminal piece. Pleural fields have about 8 to 11 pairs of pleural furrows; pleural ribs continue behind the axis.

Paladin is probably the most common trilobite genus in Mississippian rocks of North America. In Ohio, the genus has been reported from the Byer Sandstone Member of the Logan Formation and the Maxville Formation. In the Maxville Formation, sclerites of *P. chesterensis* (Weller) (fig. 8-6.1) are moderately common. Outside Ohio, *Paladin* ranges into the Pennsylvanian.

Piltonia Goldring (fig. 8-6.2) has an exoskeleton up to 4 cm in length; the surface is covered with coarse granules. The cephalon is incompletely known. The glabella is long, moderately convex, tapering forward, and has three pairs of lateral glabellar furrows; the posterior pair of furrows isolates distinct lateral glabellar lobes. Eyes are holochroal. Facial sutures are opisthoparian. The number of segments in the thorax is unknown. The pygidium is large, parabolic in outline, and convex. The axis does not reach the posterior border and has about 13 or 14 axial rings and a short terminal piece. Pleural fields have about 11 or 12 pairs of pleural furrows. Pleural ribs continue behind the axis; surface granules form a row along the posterior side of each rib. *Piltonia* has been reported from the Meadville Shale Member of the Cuyahoga Formation in Medina County and the Byer Sandstone Member of the Logan Formation in Licking County.

Pudoproetus Steininger (figs. 8-6.3, 8-6.4) has an exoskeleton up to 6 cm in length. The cephalon is incompletely known. The glabella is wide, convex, tapering forward, and has three pairs of lateral glabellar furrows; the posterior pair of furrows isolates large, distinct lateral glabellar lobes. Eyes are large, high, and holochroal. Facial sutures are opisthoparian. The number of segments in the thorax is unknown. The pygidium is moderately large and parabolic in outline. The axis extends nearly to the posterior border and has about nine axial rings and a short terminal piece. Pleural fields have about seven pairs of pleural furrows. *Pudoproetus* has been reported from the Meadville Shale Member of the Cuyahoga Formation in Medina County and the Logan Formation in Licking and Scioto Counties.

PENNSYLVANIAN TRILOBITES

Three trilobite genera have been identified from Pennsylvanian strata of eastern Ohio (Herrick, 1887; Brezinski, 1988; Brezinski and others, 1989). *Sevillia* is present in the Pottsville and Allegheny Groups. *Ameura* and *Ditomopyge* are present in the Pottsville, Allegheny, and Conemaugh Groups.

Ameura Weller (figs. 8-6.8, 8-6.9) has an exoskeleton up to 7 cm in length. The cephalon is semicircular in outline; pleural areas are narrower than the axis. The glabella is wide, convex, hourglass shaped, and has three pairs of lateral glabellar furrows; the posterior pair of furrows isolates large, distinct lateral glabellar lobes. Eyes are large, high, and holochroal. Facial sutures are opisthoparian; librigenae are wide; genal spines are long and narrow. The thorax has nine segments; pleural areas are wider than the axis; each pleura is slightly curved and terminates in a blunt spine. The pygidium is large, rounded-subtriangular in outline, and has a wide, flat border. The axis extends to the posterior border and has 15 to 21 axial rings and a short terminal piece. Pleural fields have 9 to 11 pairs of pleural furrows. *Ameura* is the largest Pennsylvanian trilobite in Ohio and is present in marine units of the upper Pottsville, Allegheny, and Conemaugh Groups in the eastern part of the state.

Ditomopyge Newell (figs. 8-6.6, 8-6.7) has an exoskeleton up to 3 cm in length. The cephalon is semielliptical in outline; pleural areas are approximately as wide as the axis. The glabella is convex, expanding forward, and has three pairs of lateral glabellar furrows; the posterior pair of furrows extends across the posterior part of the glabella, isolating a medial lobe and a pair of lateral lobes; the anterior two pairs of furrows are faint. Eyes are large, high, and holochroal. Facial sutures are opisthoparian; librigenae are moderately wide; genal spines are long. The thorax has nine segments; pleural areas are slightly wider than the axis; each pleura is slightly curved and terminates bluntly. The pygidium is large, convex, and semicircular to subparabolic in outline. The axis extends nearly to the posterior border and has six to eight axial rings and a short terminal piece. Pleural fields have about 9 to 15 pairs of pleural furrows.

Two species of *Ditomopyge*, *D. scitula* (Meek & Worthen) and *D. decurtata* (Gheyselinck), are present in the Pennsylvanian of eastern Ohio. The species are distinguished by subtle differences in the cranidium and pygidium. In Ohio, *D. decurtata* has been reported from only the Ames limestone of the Conemaugh Group (Glenshaw Formation). *Ditomopyge scitula* is not known from the Ames, but has been reported from elsewhere in the Conemaugh Group, as well as in the Pottsville and Allegheny Groups (figs. 8-6.6, 8-6.7). Outside Ohio, *D. decurtata* has an observed stratigraphic range that extends into the Lower Permian.

Sevillia Weller (fig. 8-6.10) has an exoskeleton up to 3 cm in length. The cephalon is semielliptical in outline; pleural areas are approximately as wide as the axis. The glabella is convex, expanding forward, and has three pairs of lateral glabellar furrows; the posterior pair of furrows extends across the posterior part of the glabella, isolating a medial lobe and a pair of lateral lobes. Eyes are large, high, and holochroal. Facial sutures are opisthoparian; librigenae are moderately wide; genal spines are long. The thorax has nine segments; pleural areas are slightly wider than the axis; each pleura is slightly curved and terminates bluntly. The pygidium is large, convex, and rounded-subtriangular to subparabolic in outline. The axis extends to the posterior border and has about 17 to 19 axial rings and a short terminal piece. Pleural fields have about 8 to 10 pairs of pleural furrows. *Sevillia* is present in most marine units of the Pottsville Group through the lower part of the Allegheny Group in eastern Ohio, but it is relatively uncommon.

ACKNOWLEDGMENTS

For arranging loans of specimens used in the preparation of this chapter, I thank Thomas M. Berg, Gregory A. Schumacher, and Garry E. Yates (Ohio Department of Natural Resources, Division of Geological Survey), John L. Carter (Carnegie Museum of Natural History), Richard A. Davis (formerly of the Cincinnati Museum of Natural History, presently of the College of Mount St. Joseph), Daniel C. Fisher and Gregg F. Gunnell (Museum of Paleontology of the University of Michigan), Joseph T. Hannibal (Cleveland Museum of Natural History), Dale M. Gnidovec (Orton Geological Museum of The Ohio State University), Mark D. Izold (formerly of The Ohio State University), Ed Landing (New York State Museum and Science Service), Joe H. Marak (Department of Geology, Miami University), and David L. Meyer (Department of Geology, University of Cincinnati). Frederick J. Collier arranged for the loan of negatives of a U.S. National Museum specimen that was photographed by Donald Dean. Richard A. Robison (University of Kansas) and Allison R. Palmer (Institute for Cambrian Studies) provided some information on Cambrian trilobites. Douglas L. Shrake (Ohio Division of Geological Survey) and Robert E. Sloan (University of Minnesota) provided some information on Cincinnatian fossils. Information included here on Mississippian and Pennsylvanian trilobites is based in part on work supported by the Kansas Geological Survey. Margaret T. Wilson (Columbus, Ohio) read an early version of the manuscript. Beth A. Daye (The Ohio State University) printed the photographs.

FIGURE 8-1.—Cambrian and Ordovician trilobites. Scale bars equal 1 cm. Scale bar A applies to figure 8-1.4; B applies to figures 8-1.5 to 8-1.9; C applies to figures 8-1.1, 8-1.3, and 8-1.10 to 8-1.12; D applies to figure 8-1.2; E applies to figure 8-1.13.

1	*Cedaria* **cf.** *C. woosteri* (Whitfield). Latex cast of cephalon that has been cut by coring drill (left side of photograph). Upper part of Eau Claire Formation (Cambrian), Ohio Division of Geological Survey core number 2627, depth 860 meters, Warren County, Ohio; OSU 46323.
2	*Triarthrus eatoni* (Hall). Laterally compressed specimen lacking pygidium. Kope Formation (Upper Ordovician), Cincinnati, Hamilton County, Ohio; UCGM 25137A.
3	*Triarthrus spinosus* Billings. Slab with slightly disarticulated exoskeletons that are probably molts. Two long genal spines (arrows), which are characteristic of this species, are present on the slab. Cincinnatian Series (Kope Formation?) (Upper Ordovician), Cincinnati, Hamilton County, Ohio; OSU 14109.
4, 5	*Ceraurus milleranus* Miller & Gurley. **4**, cephalon and thorax. Waynesville Formation (Upper Ordovician), near Oxford, Butler County, Ohio; MUGM 29330. **5**, pygidium; fragmentary pygidia of *Flexicalymene meeki* (Foerste) also are present on this slab. Cincinnatian Series (Upper Ordovician), southwestern Ohio; OSU 3094.
6, 7	*Ceraurinus icarus* (Billings). Dorsal (**6**) and anterior (**7**) views of enrolled specimen. Upper part of Whitewater Formation (Upper Ordovician), near Oxford, Butler County, Ohio; MUGM 28998.
8-10	*Flexicalymene meeki* (Foerste). **8**, **9**, anterior and right-lateral views, respectively, of enrolled specimen. Cincinnatian Series (Upper Ordovician), southwestern Ohio; OSU 46324. **10**, outstretched specimen. Grant Lake For-mation? (Upper Ordovician), Stonelick Creek, Clermont County, Ohio; UCGM 39415A.
11, 12	*Cryptolithus tessellatus* Green. **11**, slab containing many disarticulated sclerites representing various molt stages (instars). Cincinnatian Series (Upper Ordovician), Cincinnati area, Hamilton County, Ohio; UCGM 46428. **12**, specimen lacking occipital spine and genal spines. Kope Formation (Upper Ordovician), Cincinnati area, Hamilton County, Ohio; MUGM 28928.
13	*Proetidella parviusculus* (Hall). Specimen in which glabella is crushed. Note terrace lines covering much of axis and lateral body margins. Cincinnatian Series (Kope Formation?) (Upper Ordovician), Cincinnati, Hamilton County, Ohio; UCGM 46429.

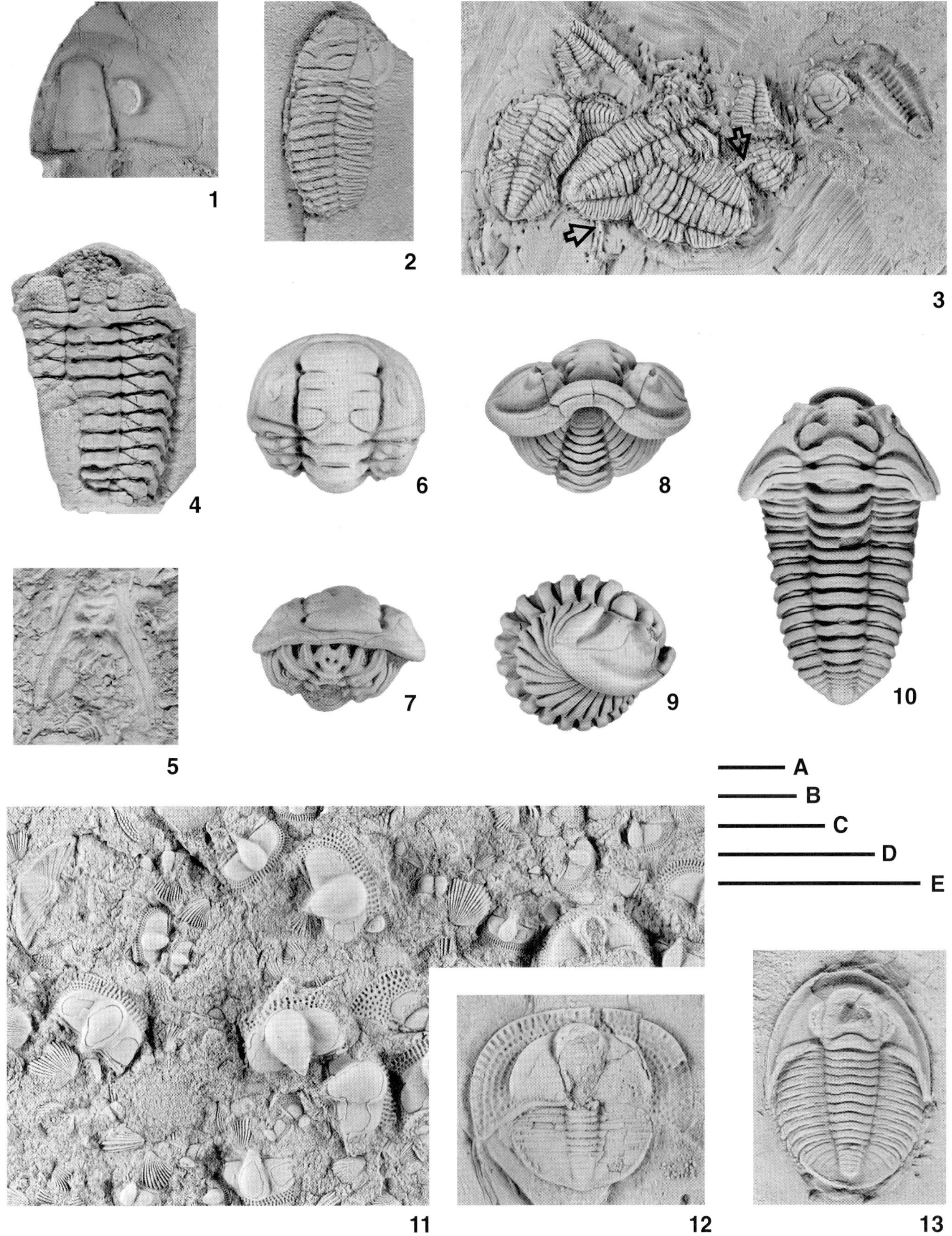
1
2
3
4
6
8
10
5
7
9
A
B
C
D
E
11
12
13

FIGURE 8-2.—Ordovician trilobite *Isotelus maximus* Locke. *Isotelus* is the State Invertebrate Fossil of Ohio. Scale bar A equals 1 cm and applies to all figures.

1, 2	Dorsal (**1**) and left-lateral (**2**) views of large specimen preserved in limestone and showing relief. Note terrace lines around lateral body margins. Tip of sixth thoracic segment on right side was broken and healed during the life of the animal (see Babcock and Robison, 1989; Babcock, 1993). Cincinnatian Series, Richmondian Stage, West Carrollton, Montgomery County, Ohio; OSU 32701.
3	Labrum (hypostome) showing strong terrace lines. Cincinnatian Series, Cincinnati, Hamilton County, Ohio; UCGM 24364A.
4	Ventral side of specimen preserving appendages. Cincinnatian Series, near Oxford, Butler County, Ohio; USNM 33458 (plaster cast, OSU 7018). Photograph by Donald Dean, courtesy of the U.S. National Museum of Natural History.

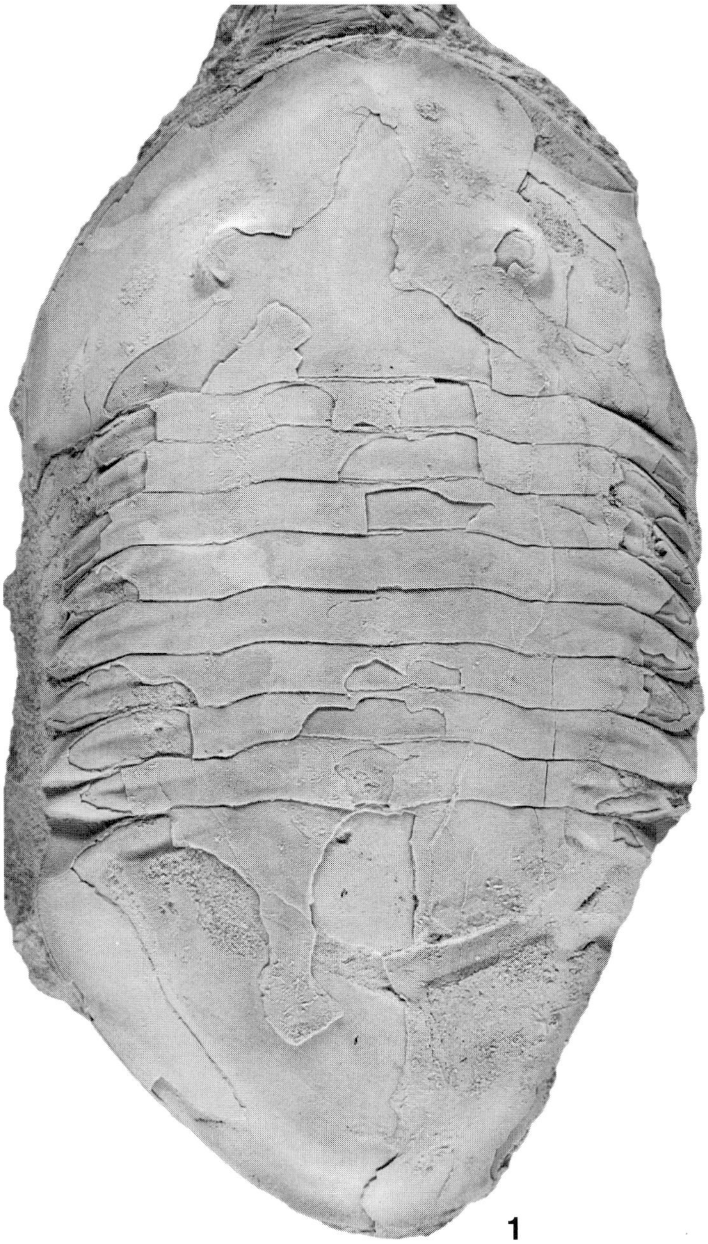

3

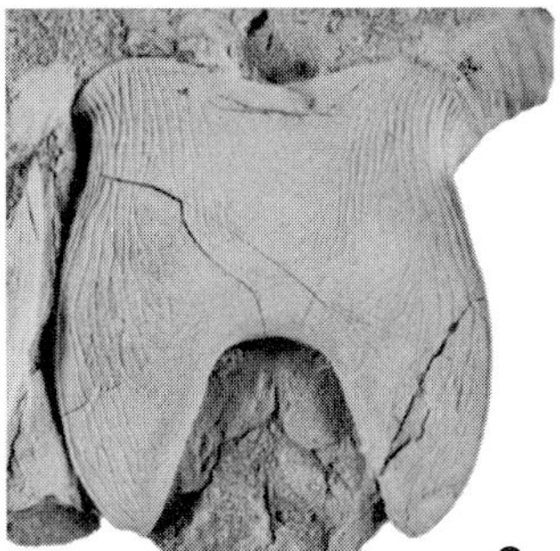

A

1

4

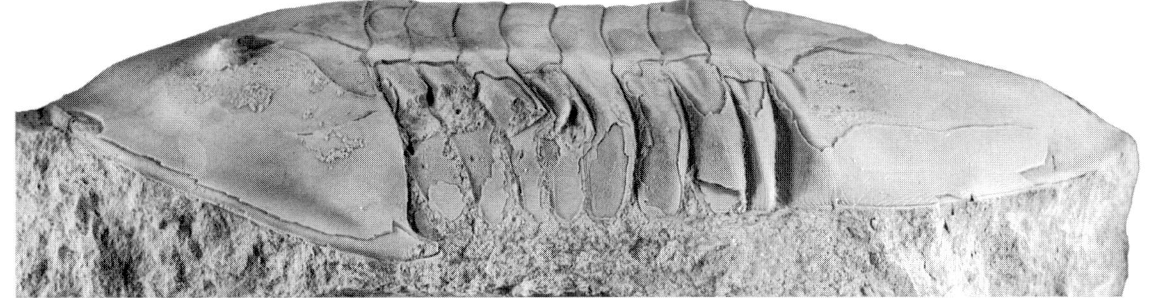

2

FIGURE 8-3.—Ordovician and Silurian trilobites. Scale bars equal 1 cm. Scale bar A applies to figures 8-3.8, 8-3.12, 8-3.13; B applies to figures 8-3.5, 8-3.9 to 8-3.11, 8-3.14, and 8-3.15; C applies to figure 8-3.2; D applies to figure 8-3.4; E applies to figures 8-3.1, 8-3.3, 8-3.6, and 8-3.7.

1, 2 *Acidaspis cincinnatiensis* Meek. Cincinnatian Series (Upper Ordovician), Cincinnati area, Hamilton County, Ohio. **1**, specimen preserved in limestone; the large occipital spine has been broken away. UCGM 43200. **2**, incomplete cephalon showing long spine extending from occipital lobe and marginal spines on librigena; marginal spines were directed downward in life. UCGM 24448.

3 *Tricopelta breviceps* (Hall). Small complete specimen. Waynesville Formation (Upper Ordovician), Butler County, Ohio; MUGM 29057.

4, 5 *Isotelus gigas* DeKay. **4**, right-lateral view of small enrolled specimen. Liberty Formation (Upper Ordovician), emergency spillway, Caesar Creek State Park, Warren County, Ohio; OSU 46325. **5**, outstretched specimen. Cincinnatian Series, Richmondian Stage (Upper Ordovician), Oxford, Butler County, Ohio; UCGM 39411.

6 *Amphilichas halli* (Foerste). Outstretched specimen. Marginal spines on left side of pygidium have been broken. Cincinnatian Series? (Upper Ordovician), probably southwestern Ohio; MUGM 29027.

7 *Acidaspis brevispinosa*? Foerste. Incomplete pygidium viewed from ventral surface. Brassfield Formation (Silurian), Centerville, Montgomery County, Ohio; UCGM 8503A.

8 *Cheirurus niagarensis* Hall. Internal mold of cranidium. Niagaran Series (Silurian), Pontiac, Preble County, Ohio; UCGM 12975.

9, 10 *Calymene vogdesi* Foerste. Brassfield Formation (Silurian), Centerville, Montgomery County, Ohio. **9**, incomplete cranidium showing buttress extending from second lateral glabellar lobe into axial furrow (arrow). UCGM 46430. **10**, pygidium. UCGM 46431.

11 *"Flexicalymene" celebra* (Raymond). Left-lateral view of slightly flexed specimen preserved as an internal mold. Cedarville Dolomite (Silurian), Eaton, Preble County, Ohio; OSU 11944.

12, 13 *Metopolichas breviceps* (Hall). Brassfield Formation (Silurian), New Carlisle, Clark County, Ohio. **12**, cranidium, mostly exfoliated. OSU 7029A. **13**, internal mold of incomplete pygidium. OSU 7029B.

14, 15 *Dalmanites brevicaudatus* Foerste. Bisher Formation (Silurian), near Danville, Highland County, Ohio. **14**, incomplete cephalon, mostly exfoliated, showing broken rostrum. OSU 20681. **15**, internal mold of pygidium. OSU 20678.

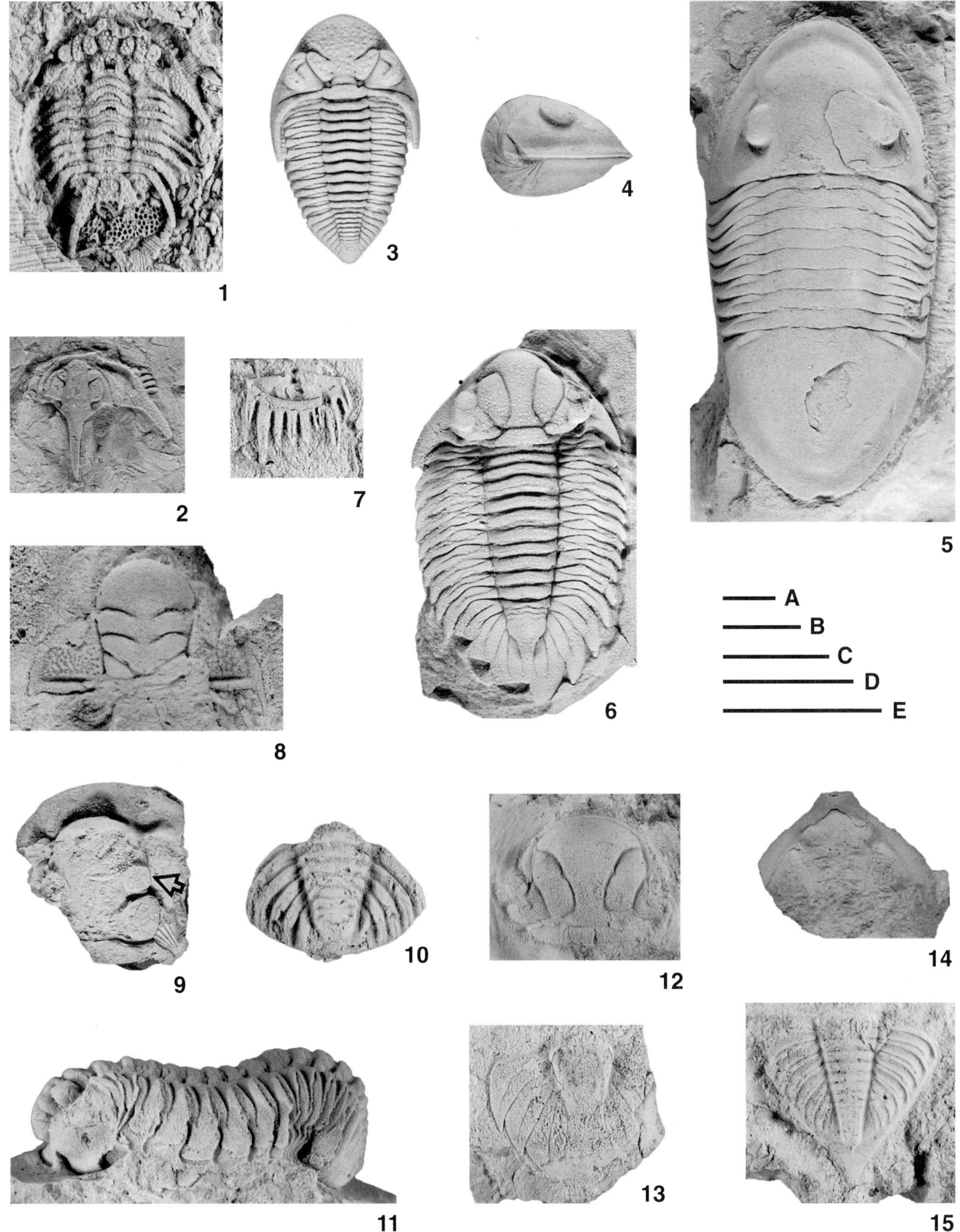

1
2
3
4
5
6
7
8
9
10
11
12
13
14
15
A
B
C
D
E

FIGURE 8-4.—Silurian trilobites. Scale bars equal 1 cm. Scale bar A applies to figures 8-4.7 and 8-4.8; B applies to figure 8-4.9; C applies to figures 8-4.1 to 8-4.3; D applies to figures 8-4.4, 8-4.5, 8-4.10, and 8-4.11; E applies to figure 8-4.6.

1-3 *"Flexicalymene" celebra* (Raymond). Dorsal (**1**), anterior (**2**), and left-lateral (**3**) views of outstretched specimen preserved as an internal mold. Fine, incomplete pillars that have filled in canals through the doublure (see Evitt and Whittington, 1953) are visible, especially near the faceted corners of the pleurae in **3**. Cedarville Dolomite, Lewisburg, Preble County, Ohio; UCGM 34570.

4, 5 *Sphaerexochus romingeri* Hall. Dorsal (**4**) and left-lateral (**5**) views of internal mold of cranidium. Niagaran Series, Wilmington, Clinton County, Ohio; OSU 7041.

6 *Encrinurus* cf. *E. ornatus* Hall & Whitfield. Pygidium. Lilley Formation, near Harriet, Highland County, Ohio; OSU 20677.

7-9 *Bumastus insignis* (Hall). Niagaran Series (Springfield Dolomite?). **7**, **8**, right-lateral and dorsal views, respectively, of internal mold of articulated specimen; central area of pygidium has been lost to weathering. Eaton, Preble County, Ohio; OSU 11943. **9**, internal mold of exoskeleton lacking librigenae; note wide doublure, which bears terrace lines paralleling margin, on pygidium. Displaced cranidium and lack of librigenae suggest than this is a molt (see Henningsmoen, 1975; Brandt, 1993). Springfield, Clark County, Ohio; OSU 3329A.

10, 11 *Trimerus delphinocephalus* Green. Bisher Formation, Highland County, Ohio. **10**, cephalon, mostly exfoliated, and a separate thoracic segment preserved at a high angle to bedding (lower left side of photograph). Near North Uniontown; OSU 20693. **11**, internal mold of incomplete pygidium. Near Harriett; OSU 20691.

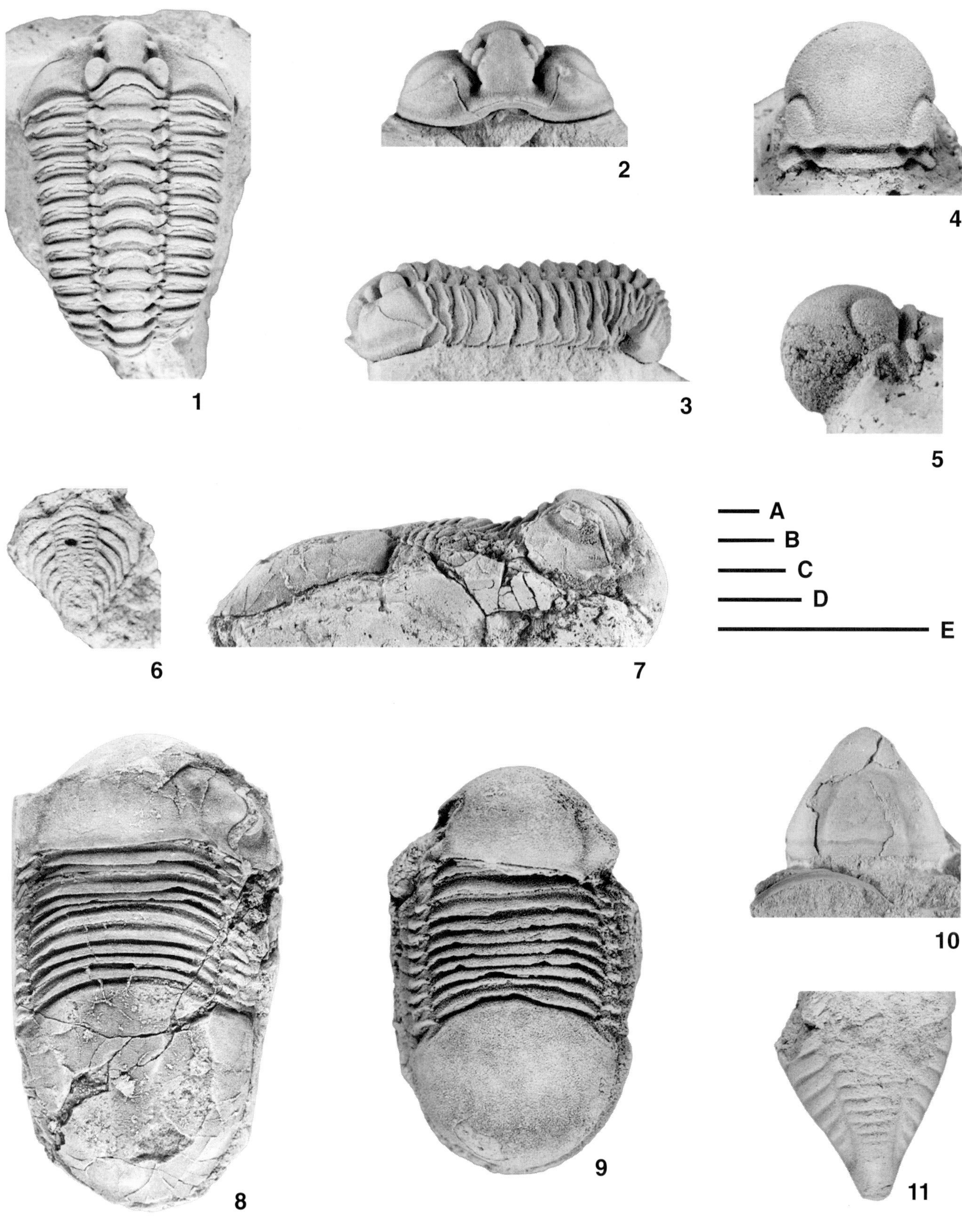
1
2
3
4
5
6
7
A
B
C
D
E
8
9
10
11

FIGURE 8-5.—Devonian trilobites. Scale bars equal 1 cm. Scale bar A applies to figures 8-5.1 to 8-5.3, 8-5.10, and 8-5.12; B applies to figures 8-5.5 and 8-5.9; C applies to figures 8-5.4, 8-5.6 to 8-5.8, and 8-5.11.

1, 2 *Phacops rana crassituberculata* Stumm. Dorsal (**1**) and right-lateral (**2**) views of outstretched specimen. Silica Formation, Sylvania, Lucas County, Ohio; OSU 17678.

3 *Phacops cristata bombifrons* (Hall). Internal mold of cephalon. Columbus Limestone, Columbus, Franklin County, Ohio; UCGM 24426.

4 *Phacops rana milleri* Stewart. Right-lateral view of **lectotype**. Specimen is incompletely enrolled, probably due to relaxation of muscles and ligaments following the death of the animal in a fully enrolled posture. Silica Formation, Silica, Lucas County, Ohio; OSU 16266A.

5 *Basidechenella lucasensis* Stumm. Complete specimen, crushed in shale. Silica Formation, Silica, Lucas County, Ohio; UMMP 61321.

6 *Basidechenella rowi* (Green). Pygidium, mostly exfoliated. Columbus Limestone, Columbus, Franklin County, Ohio; OSU 15734A.

7, 8 *Greenops chilmanae* Stumm. Silica Formation, Silica, Lucas County, Ohio. **7**, **holotype**; an incomplete cephalon. UMMP 49758. **8**, pygidium showing marginal spines. UMMP 54765.

9 *Crassiproetus crassimarginatus* Hall. Internal mold of weathered pygidium. Columbus Limestone?, Columbus, Franklin County, Ohio; OSU 11474.

10 *Coronura aspectans* (Conrad). Pygidium; paired spines at posterior end are broken, but most of small marginal spines are preserved. Columbus Limestone, Marblehead, Ottawa County, Ohio; ClMNH 4320.

11 *Odontocephalus bifidus* (Hall). Pygidium, mostly exfoliated, showing paired marginal spines at posterior margin. Columbus Limestone, Franklin County?, Ohio; OSU 3327A.

12 *Trypaulites calypso* (Hall & Clarke). Gutta-percha cast prepared for James Hall (see Hall and Clarke, 1888) from a natural external mold. Columbus Limestone, Sandusky, Erie County, Ohio; NYSM 4305.

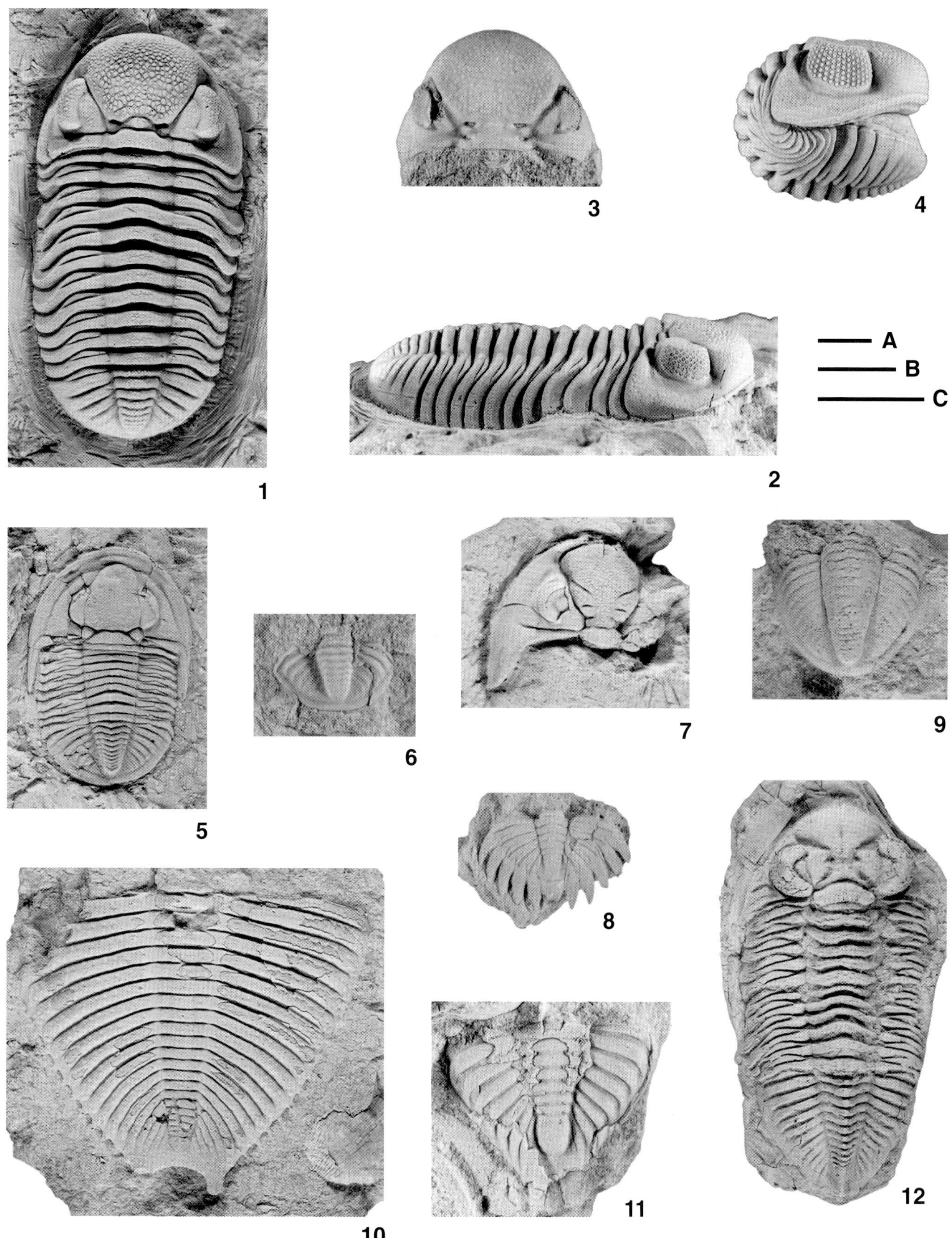
1
2
3
4
A
B
C
5
6
7
8
9
10
11
12

FIGURE 8-6.—Mississippian and Pennsylvanian trilobites. Scale bars equal 1 cm. Scale bar A applies to figure 8-6.3; B applies to figure 8-6.8; C applies to figures 8-6.4 and 8-6.9; D applies to figures 8-6.5 and 8-6.10; E applies to figures 8-6.2, 8-6.6, and 8-6.7; F applies to figure 8-6.1.

1 *Paladin chesterensis* (Weller). Pygidium. Maxville Formation (Mississippian), near Fultonham, Perry County, Ohio; OSU 14751.

2 *Piltonia eurybathrea* (Hessler). Internal mold of pygidium. Meadville Shale Member of the Cuyahoga Formation (Mississippian), Lodi, Medina County, Ohio; OSU 22532.

3, 4 *Pudoproetus missouriensis* (Shumard). Logan Formation (Mississippian), Sciotoville, Scioto County, Ohio. **3**, internal mold of broken cranidium. OSU 22807A. **4**, internal mold of weathered pygidium. OSU 22807C.

5 *Australosutura lodiensis* (Meek). Latex cast of external mold of articulated specimen. Wooster Shale Member of the Cuyahoga Formation (Mississippian), Loudonville, Ashland County, Ohio; OSU 46326.

6, 7 *Ditomopyge scitula* (Meek & Worthen). Washingtonville shale (Allegheny Group, Pennsylvanian), Sandy Township, Stark County, Ohio. **6**, cephalon, partially exfoliated. OSU 29170. **7**, pygidium. OSU 29176.

8, 9 *Ameura missouriensis* (Shumard). **8**, incomplete cephalon. Cambridge limestone (Conemaugh Group, Pennsylvanian), Aid Township, Lawrence County, Ohio; OSU 29169. **9**, pygidium. Brush Creek limestone, (Conemaugh Group, Pennsylvanian), Deerfield Township, Morgan County, Ohio; OSU 29168.

10 *Sevillia trinucleata* (Herrick). Exoskeleton that has displaced cranidium and librigenae, probably a molt ensemble (see Henningsmoen, 1975; Brandt, 1993). Putnam Hill limestone (Allegheny Group, Pennsylvanian), Lake Township, Stark County, Ohio; OSU 22234.

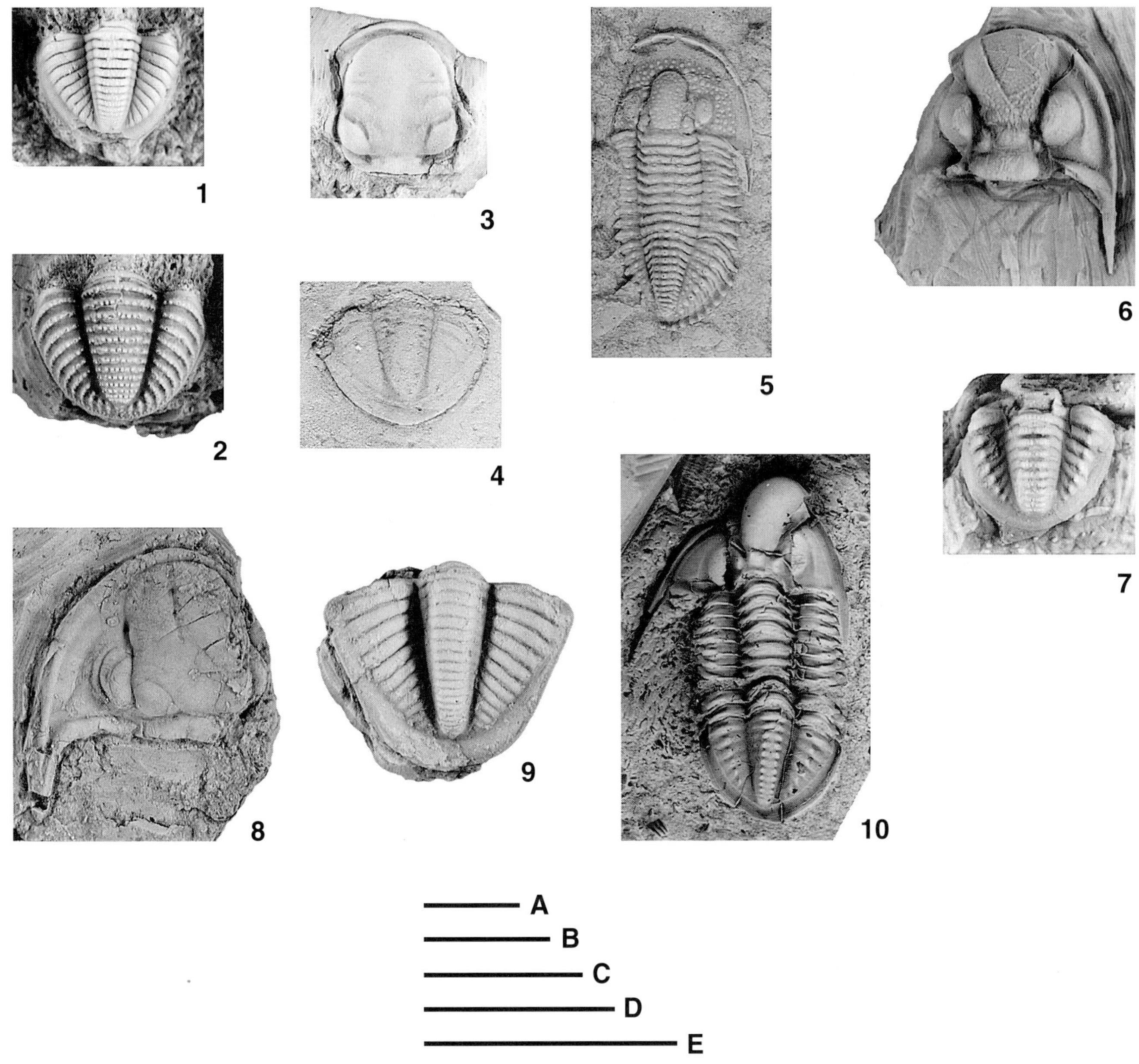
1
2
3
4
5
6
7
8
9
10
A
B
C
D
E

Chapter 9

PHYLUM ARTHROPODA, CLASS CRUSTACEA, SUBCLASS OSTRACODA

by Alison J. Smith and John R. Tillman

INTRODUCTION

Ostracodes are microscopic crustaceans that make a shell, called a **carapace**, composed of calcium carbonate. The carapace of an ostracode is made up of two parts, or **valves**, reminiscent of clam shells. Figure 1-13 in Chapter 1 illustrates the morphology of ostracodes. These tiny animals have a long geologic history that extends back to the Cambrian Period. In Ohio, it is possible to find ostracodes at both ends of this long history because many marine ostracode fossils can be found in Paleozoic rocks, and living freshwater ostracodes can be found in modern ponds, wetlands, lakes, and streams. Although some fossil ostracodes are greater than 4 mm in length, most are less than 1 mm long. To search for and study them, you need either a very good hand lens (at least 20X) or a reflected-light microscope. Ostracodes are easily overlooked in the marine Paleozoic fossil assemblages, but actually can be very abundant. Good fossil ostracode assemblages can be found in the Ordovician-age Waynesville, Liberty, and Whitewater Formations, as well as the Devonian-age Silica Formation, Columbus and Delaware Limestones, and Plum Brook and Olentangy Shales. The Mississippian-age Maxville Formation and the Pennsylvanian-age Lower Mercer, Putnam Hill, and Brush Creek units also are good sources of fossil ostracodes. Ostracodes also are found in Pleistocene lake sediments.

Fossil ostracodes are visible in outcrop, with the aid of a hand lens or pocket magnifier, as very tiny, rounded, bean-shaped objects lying on bedding planes or embedded in the rock. Their carapaces very commonly have **ornamentation** of **spines** and ridges, as well as "hills" and "valleys" referred to as **bulbs, lobes, nodes, pits**, and **sulci**. Most of the Paleozoic ostracodes that can be collected in Ohio have one straight edge, which is the **hinge**, which joins the two valves of the carapace together. In some specimens, the two valves may still be hinged together, but more commonly they became disarticulated after death and are therefore found as single valves. The task of distinguishing front (**anterior**) from back (**posterior**) and top (**dorsal**) from bottom (**ventral**) can be very difficult, even for a specialist. The muscles used by an ostracode to open and close the valves leave marks on the interior of the shell called **muscle scars**. These muscle scars commonly are preserved, especially in Cenozoic fossils, and can be used to distinguish shell anterior from posterior, as well as identify the family to which the ostracode belongs. Many ostracode species show variations that have been attributed to sex differences (see Guber, 1971). This sexual **dimorphism** (two forms) appears as differences in carapace shape and ornamentation for males and females.

COLLECTING OSTRACODES

FOSSIL OSTRACODES

There are several ways to separate marine Paleozoic ostracodes from the matrix of limestone and shale. These techniques are described in Chapter 2. The technique for extracting fossil ostracodes from Pleistocene lake deposits also is described in Chapter 2.

LIVING OSTRACODES

It is very easy to collect living ostracodes and study their behavior. Just take a turkey baster and a clean jam jar out to the nearest pond, from late April to October, and collect a bit of mud (not sand) from the shallow water, then add a bit of the pond water and some pond weed. When you return home, just pour a little of this mud and water into the jam-jar lid or a shallow dish and examine it with your hand lens or microscope. You will soon see ostracodes bustling around, some swimming, some scurrying through the mud, all looking for food. You will find some species living in streams, and still other species living in wetlands and springs. Compare these ostracodes with the fossil ostracodes that you find. It is fascinating to think that these tiny crustaceans have been around for hundreds of millions of years!

DESCRIPTIONS OF COMMON FOSSIL OSTRACODES IN OHIO

Many fossil ostracode genera are found in Ohio, and 26 genera from the Ordovician, Silurian, Devonian, Mississippian, Pennsylvanian, and Quaternary are briefly described here. The genera discussed are arranged in stratigraphic order, that is, the marine ostracodes of the Paleozoic periods are described first, followed by the Quaternary freshwater forms. Under each period, the genera are listed alphabetically.

These are, by no means, all of the genera that can be found in Ohio. Descriptions and illustrations of many others can be found in references at the end of this book. The volume by Benson and others (1961) in the *Treatise on Invertebrate Paleontology* provides an overview of most fossil ostracode genera. Paleozoic ostracodes from Ohio are described in Ulrich (1890-1891), Stewart (1936, 1950), Stewart and Hendrix (1945a, 1945b), Marple (1952), Kesling (1954), Tillman (1970, 1984), Tillman and Murphy (1978), Kesling and Chilman (1978), Warshauer and Berdan (1982), Burke (1985), Christopher and others (1990), Hoare (1991, 1993), and Hoare and others (1994). Quaternary forms in Ohio are described in Furtos (1933), Winkler (1962), Benson and MacDonald (1963), and Teeter (1970). The following key can be used to help identify the ostracodes described in this chapter.

KEY TO SOME OSTRACODE GENERA FROM OHIO

1A. Valves greater than 4 mm long, with or without **growth lines** 2
1B. Valves smaller than 4 mm long and without growth lines 3

2A. Valves have no growth lines and are smooth and unornamented .... *Leperditia* (fig.9-1.5)
2B Valves have growth lines and are smooth or ribbed .... see Pelecypoda (Chapter 12) or Brachiopoda (Chapter 16)

3A. Valves from lithified Paleozoic rocks and have ornamentation 4
3B. Valves from unlithified post-Paleozoic sediments, such as Quaternary silts and clays 22

4A. Valves have straight hinge 5
4B. Valves have curved hinge 20

5A. Ornamentation consists of faint curving ridges like a fingerprint .... *Quasillites* (fig.9-1.12)
5B. Ornamentation otherwise 6

6A. Valves smooth and each valve has a centrally located large spine .... *Aechmina* (fig. 9-1.6)
6B. Ornamentation otherwise 7

7A. Ornamentation includes one or more sulci but no prominent lobes or nodes 8
7B. Ornamentation includes prominent lobes and/or nodes 10

8A. Valves have three prominent sulci .... *Dizygopleura* (fig. 9-1.8)
8B. Valves have one sulcus 9

9A. Valves have one sulcus but no additional ornamentation .... *Milleratia* (fig. 9-1.4)
9B. Valves have one sulcus and several **costae** subparallel to dorsal and ventral margins .... *Glyptopleura* (figs. 9-2.6 to 9-2.9)

10A. Valves have one lobe and/or node .... *Amphissites* (fig. 9-2.4)
10B. Valves have more than one lobe and/or node 11

11A. Valves have two lobes and/or nodes 12
11B. Valves have more than two lobes and/or nodes 16

12A. Posterior lobe/node larger than anterior and **frills** present along anteroventral margins .... *Hollinella* (figs. 9-2.10, 9-2.11)
12B. Anterior lobe/node larger than posterior 13

13A. Valves have ventral lobe or a **carina** paralleling ventral margin 14
13B. Valves have semicircular ventral margin or both lobes and/or nodes project above dorsal margin 15

14A. Valves have a ventral lobe paralleling ventral margin and forming a U-shaped pattern .... *Bollia* (fig. 9-1.7)
14B. Valves have a carina paralleling ventral margin .... *Kegelites* (fig. 9-3.1)

15A. Valves semicircular and two lobes/nodes occupy about 40 percent of lateral valve surfaces .... *Kellettina* (fig. 9-3.2)
15B. Valves have nodes projecting above dorsal margin .... *Ulrichia* (fig. 9-1.11)

16A. Valves each have three lobes and/or nodes .... *Polytylites* (fig. 9-2.5)
16B. Valves each have four lobes and/or nodes 17

17A. All four lobes and/or nodes extend above hinge line 18
17B. All four lobes and/or nodes merge with ventral lobe 19

18A. Lobes have **granulae** .... *Ctenoloculina* (figs. 9-1.9, 9-1.10)
18B. Lobes and/or nodes smooth or slightly spinose .... *Drepanella* (fig. 9-1.1)

19A. Anterior lobe extends laterally as a mushroom-shaped process .... *Ceratopsis* (fig. 9-1.3)
19B. Some lobes divided by furrows .... *Tetradella* (fig. 9-1.2)

20A. Valves have **punctae** over most of lateral surface .... *Ponderodictya* (fig. 9-2.2)
20B. Valves have punctae only on posterior part of lateral surface 21

21A. Punctae number 5 to 15 .... *Thrallella* (fig. 9-2.3)
21B. Punctae very fine and number 40 or more .... *Bythocyproidea* (fig. 9-2.1)

22A. Valves elongate, cashew-nut shaped, translucent, white .... *Candona* (figs. 9-3.4, 9-3.5)
22B. Valves otherwise 23

23A. Valves wedge shaped, translucent, white .... *Darwinula* (fig. 9-3.3)
23B. Valves otherwise 24

24A. Valves round, brown, translucent and have faintly punctate to smooth surface and narrow **inner lamellae** .... *Cyclocypris* (figs. 9-3.7, 9-3.8)
24B. Valves otherwise 25

25A. Valves oval, brown, translucent and have high arch, punctate surface, and wide inner lamellae .... *Cypridopsis* (fig. 9-3.6)
25B. Valves otherwise 26

26A. Valves peanut shaped and have a waffle pattern, anterior end compressed, may have lateral spine .... *Limnocythere* (fig. 9-3.9)
26B. Valves rectangular and have a punctate surface, a deep sulcus in midsection, and may have **tubercles** along one edge .... *Ilyocypris* (fig. 9-3.10)

ORDOVICIAN OSTRACODES

Ceratopsis Ulrich (fig. 9-1.3) is characterized by four elongate vertical lobes, all of which merge with a ventral lobe. The anterior lobe is large and ornate, projecting as a spine above the hinge or extending laterally in a mushroom shape. *Ceratopsis* has been reported from several formations in the Upper Ordovician of the Cincinnati area. In other regions it also occurs in Middle Ordovician rocks.

Drepanella Ulrich (fig. 9-1.1) has a straight hinge and elongate ridges, nodes, and spines. It may be one of the most ornate ostracodes that you will find in the early Paleozoic rocks. It is restricted to Upper Ordovician rocks, such as the Whitewater Formation, in Ohio. Elsewhere this genus ranges from Middle Ordovician to Lower Silurian.

Milleratia Swartz (fig. 9-1.4) can be identified by its straight hinge and inflated shell that has a single, centrally located, deep, pitlike sulcus. *Milleratia* is found only in Upper Ordovician rocks, such as the Waynesville Formation, in Ohio, although it has been reported from Middle Ordovician rocks elsewhere.

Tetradella Ulrich (fig. 9-1.2) has four elongate lobes separated by deep sulci that are arranged roughly perpendicular to the straight hinge. **Loculi** are present along the **free margin** of the female. *Tetradella* is found in the Upper Ordovician Waynesville Formation in Ohio but is reported in both Middle and Upper Ordovician rocks elsewhere.

SILURIAN OSTRACODES

Leperditia Rouault (fig. 9-1.5) is easily spotted because of its large size; typical lengths of this fossil range from 4 to 9 mm, but they can be larger (lengths up to 18 mm have been recorded). The carapace is very smooth, has a straight hinge, and may have a single **eye tubercle** on each valve of the carapace. In Ohio, this genus has been collected from the Middle Silurian Euphemia Dolomite. Elsewhere, it occurs in rocks of Early Silurian to Late Devonian age. The ostracode fauna of Silurian rocks in Ohio is not well known.

DEVONIAN OSTRACODES

Aechmina Jones & Holl (fig. 9-1.6) is very distinctive, if specimens are unbroken, because it has a single large lateral spine extending dorsally from the central region of each valve. The free margin may have some small tubercles. *Aechmina* occurs in several Upper Ordovician and Middle Devonian formations in Ohio. In other areas, it is found in rocks ranging from Middle Ordovician to Middle Mississippian in age.

Bollia Jones & Holl (fig. 9.1-7) is easily identified by the pronounced U-shaped pattern of lobes that extend very slightly beyond the dorsal margin on each valve. This genus has been found in Upper Ordovician and Middle Devonian rocks in Ohio and is reported from Middle Ordovician and Silurian rocks elsewhere.

Bythocyproidea Stewart & Hendrix (fig. 9-2.1) has a curved hinge and an oval carapace that is smooth except for a narrow, curved ridge at the posterior end of the smaller valve. Just anterior to the ridge is a cluster of many (40 or more) small punctae. The genus is restricted to rocks of Middle Devonian age such as the Silica Formation and the Plum Brook and lower Olentangy Shales.

Ctenoloculina Bassler (figs. 9-1.9, 9-1.10) has three wide, deep sulci and four flattened lobes. The lobes have surface granulae. The free margins of female shells have a loculate frill. *Ctenoloculina* is confined to rocks of Middle Devonian age such as the Silica Formation and the Plum Brook and lower Olentangy Shales.

Dizygopleura Ulrich & Bassler (fig. 9-1.8) is identified by three narrow, deep sulci that are roughly perpendicular to the straight hinge. The four lobes have a swollen appearance but are otherwise smooth. The genus occurs in several Middle Devonian formations in Ohio. Elsewhere its range is Silurian through Devonian.

Ponderodictya Coryell & Malkin (fig. 9-2.2) is a relatively large ostracode that has an oval carapace. It has a curved hinge and punctate valve surfaces. One or both valves may have a short spine at the posterior end, and the smaller valve may have a short curved ridge at the anterior end. *Ponderodictya* is restricted to the Middle Devonian but occurs in several formations in Ohio and elsewhere.

Quasillites Coryell & Malkin (fig. 9-1.12) is characterized by its surface ornamentation, which consists of whorls of faint ridges and grooves like a fingerprint. There is a small lateral spine on the posteroventral part of each valve. *Quasillites* has been reported only from Middle Devonian rocks in Ohio but occurs in rocks of Early Devonian through Mississippian age elsewhere.

Thrallella Stewart & Hendrix (fig. 9-2.3) is characterized by a narrow ridge subparallel to the posterior margin on both valves. Valves are otherwise smooth except for a group of 5 to 15 relatively large punctae just anterior to the ridge on the posterior third of the valves. In Ohio, *Thrallella* occurs in Middle and Upper Devonian rocks such as the lower and upper Olentangy Shale.

Ulrichia Jones (fig. 9-1.11) has two almost equally prominent nodes close to the hinge on each valve. Other ornamentation includes many tiny punctae on the surface of the valves and a prominent ridge along the free margin of the valves. *Ulrichia* has been reported from several Upper Ordovician and Middle Devonian formations in Ohio. The genus also occurs in Middle Ordovician rocks in other regions.

MISSISSIPPIAN OSTRACODES

Amphissites Girty (fig. 9-2.4) is distinguished by a prominent node in the middle of each valve. Two carinae extend around the free margin and may merge dorsally to form a single carina paralleling the dorsal margin of the valves. The lateral surfaces of the valves are **reticulate**. *Amphissites* has been found in many rock units in Ohio from Late Devonian through Pennsylvanian age. Its range is reported as being Middle Devonian through Middle Permian in other localities.

Glyptopleura Girty (figs. 9-2.6 to 9-2.9) is characterized by valve surfaces that have numerous costae subparallel to the dorsal and ventral margins. In the central part of each valve the costae may be interrupted by a pit. Female carapaces are thicker posteriorly than males. *Glyptopleura* occurs in the Maxville Formation in central Ohio. Elsewhere it occurs in rocks from Middle Mississippian to Middle Permian in age.

Polytylites Cooper (fig. 9-2.5) has three nodes on the dorsal half of the valves and one or two carinae paralleling the ventral margin. The posterior and central nodes are more prominent. In Ohio, *Polytylites* has been found in the Maxville Formation. It occurs in rocks from Early Mississsippian to Middle Permian age in other places.

PENNSYLVANIAN OSTRACODES

Hollinella Coryell (figs. 9-2.10, 9-2.11) has two prominent lobes in the central part of the valves near the dorsal margin. The posterior lobe is bulblike and large. The anterior lobe is smaller and more nodelike. Some species also have a ventral lobe. Both males and females have a frill; the female frill is generally wider than that of the male. In Ohio, *Hollinella* has been reported from rocks dating from Middle Devonian through Pennsylvanian in age. In other places, it also occurs in Permian rocks.

Kegelites Coryell & Booth (fig. 9-3.1) has two prominent nodes. The more prominent of the two is located in the posterodorsal corner of each valve and projects slightly above the hinge. The second, larger node is located in the central region of each valve. *Kegelites* has one carina that parallels the ventral border. There is no dorsal carina. The lateral surfaces of the valves are reticulate. This genus occurs throughout the Pennsylvanian rocks in Ohio. It is found in Middle Mississippian through Middle Permian rocks in other regions.

Kellettina Swartz (fig. 9-3.2) can be distinguished by its semicircular outline and two unequally prominent nodes located close to each other and toward the middle of the valve length. The two nodes occupy the valve surface from midheight of the valve to or above the hinge. It has reticulate valve surfaces and a well-developed marginal ridge. *Kellettina* has been reported from the Boggs, Putnam Hill, and Vanport units in Ohio. In other places it has been reported from rocks of Early Pennsylvanian through Middle Permian age.

QUATERNARY OSTRACODES

Candona Baird (figs. 9-3.4, 9-3.5) is a relatively large ostracode (1 to 2 mm long) that can be collected from Pleistocene lake sediments and collected live in Ohio today. *Candona* is identified by its distinctive elongate cashew-nut shape. The shell has a smooth, white surface, which may appear yellow when the animal is alive. The genus ranges from Pleistocene to Recent in Ohio and Tertiary to Recent elsewhere. Today, species of *Candona* live on the bottom of freshwater lakes (including Lake Erie) and ponds.

Cyclocypris Brady & Norman (figs. 9-3.7, 9-3.8) has a small, round, brown shell that has tiny punctae. The inner lamellae are very narrow. The carapace in dorsal view is egg shaped. Shells of *Cyclocypris* can be found in Pleistocene lake sediments in Ohio. The living animal can be found swimming among the plants in the nearshore areas of modern ponds and lakes. The genus ranges from Tertiary to Recent.

Cypridopsis Brady (fig. 9-3.6) has a small, oval, brown shell that has a high arch and many distinct punctae. To distinguish *Cypridopsis* from *Cyclocypris*, look at the inner lamellae; *Cypridopsis* has wide inner lamellae, whereas *Cyclocypris* has very narrow inner lamellae. Also, the carapace of *Cypridopsis* in dorsal view is football shaped, whereas that of *Cyclocypris* is egg shaped. Shells of *Cypridopsis* can be found in Pleistocene lake deposits in Ohio, and the genus lives today in ponds and lakes, swimming among the plants in the nearshore area. *Cypridopsis* ranges from Pleistocene to Recent in Ohio and Upper Cretaceous to Recent elsewhere.

Darwinula Brady & Robertson (fig. 9-3.3) has a smooth, unornamented, wedge-shaped, white shell. The unusual wedge shape distinguishes it from other ostracodes. This small ostracode is a common fossil in Pleistocene lake sediments and lives today on the bottom of lakes and ponds. Its shell is somewhat yellow when the animal is alive. In Ohio this genus ranges from Pleistocene to Recent but has been reported from rocks as old as Pennsylvanian elsewhere.

Ilyocypris Brady & Norman (fig. 9-3.10) has a carapace that is compressed and rectangular. The surface is covered with tiny punctae and there is one deep, centrally located sulcus. Small tubercles may be observed along the free margin. This genus is found as fossils in Pleistocene lake sediments and lives today in lakes, springs, and streams in Ohio. *Ilyocypris* ranges from Pleistocene to Recent in Ohio and has been questionably reported from rocks as old as Triassic elsewhere.

Limnocythere Brady (fig. 9-3.9) has a carapace shaped like a peanut shell and has a waffle pattern on the surface. The anterior end is compressed, whereas the posterior end is inflated and rounded. *Limnocythere* is found in Pleistocene lake sediments in Ohio and lives today on the bottom of freshwater lakes and ponds. This genus ranges from Pleistocene to Recent in Ohio and from Jurassic to Recent elsewhere.

ACKNOWLEDGMENTS

Valuable comments and advice were provided by I. G. Sohn and Jean Berdan (National Museum of Natural History), Richard M. Forester (U.S. Geological Survey), and Christopher Dewey (Department of Geology, Mississippi State University). Some of the illustrations were provided by Jean Berdan and Richard D. Hoare (Department of Geology, Bowling Green State University). Technical assistance was provided by Cathy L. Simpkins (Ohio Wesleyan University).

FIGURE 9-1.—Ordovician, Silurian, and Devonian ostracodes. All scale bars equal 0.1 mm, except that for figure 9-1.5, which equals 1 mm. Arrows point toward the anterior of the specimen.

1 *Drepanella crassinoda* Ulrich. Lateral view of left valve. Tyrone Limestone (Middle Ordovician), High Bridge, Kentucky; USNM 41,377. Photograph courtesy of J. M. Berdan.

2 *Tetradella quadrilirata* (Hall & Whitfield). Lateral view of right valve of male. Richmondian (Upper Ordovician), southwestern Ohio. From Benson and others (1961, fig. 92, 1e).

3 *Ceratopsis oculifera* (Hall). Lateral view of right valve of carapace. Upper Ordovician, southwestern Ohio. From Benson and others (1961, fig. 82, 2c).

4 *Milleratia cincinnatiensis* (Miller). Lateral view of left valve. Upper Ordovician, southwestern Ohio; UCGM 8789. Photograph courtesy of J. M. Berdan.

5 *Leperditia* sp. Lateral view of left valve. Upper Silurian of Gotland, Sweden. From Benson and others (1961, fig. 43).

6 *Aechmina longioroidea* Stewart. Lateral view of left valve. Delaware Limestone (Middle Devonian), north of Hyatts, Delaware County, Ohio; OSU 34754. From Tillman (1984, fig. 1-S).

7 *Bollia stewartae* Tillman. Lateral view of left valve. Columbus Limestone (Middle Devonian), near Warrensburg, Delaware County, Ohio; OSU 34765. From Tillman (1984, fig. 2-O).

8 *Dizygopleura compsa* Kesling. Lateral view of right valve of carapace. Delaware Limestone (Middle Devonian), north of Hyatts, Delaware County, Ohio.

9, 10 *Ctenoloculina elongata* Stewart. **9**, lateral view of left valve of female. OSU 31449. **10**, lateral view of right valve of male. OSU 31450. Delaware Limestone (Middle Devonian), Upper Arlington, Franklin County, Ohio. From Tillman and Murphy (1978, pl. 2, figs. 1 and 3).

11 *Ulrichia conradi* Jones. Lateral view of right valve. Bell Shale (Middle Devonian), Michigan. From Benson and others (1961, fig. 62, 5a).

12 *Quasillites obliquus* Coryell & Malkin. Lateral view of right valve of carapace of **holotype**. Hungry Hollow Formation (Middle Devonian), near Thedford, Lambton County, Ontario. From Benson and others (1961, fig. 297, 1a).

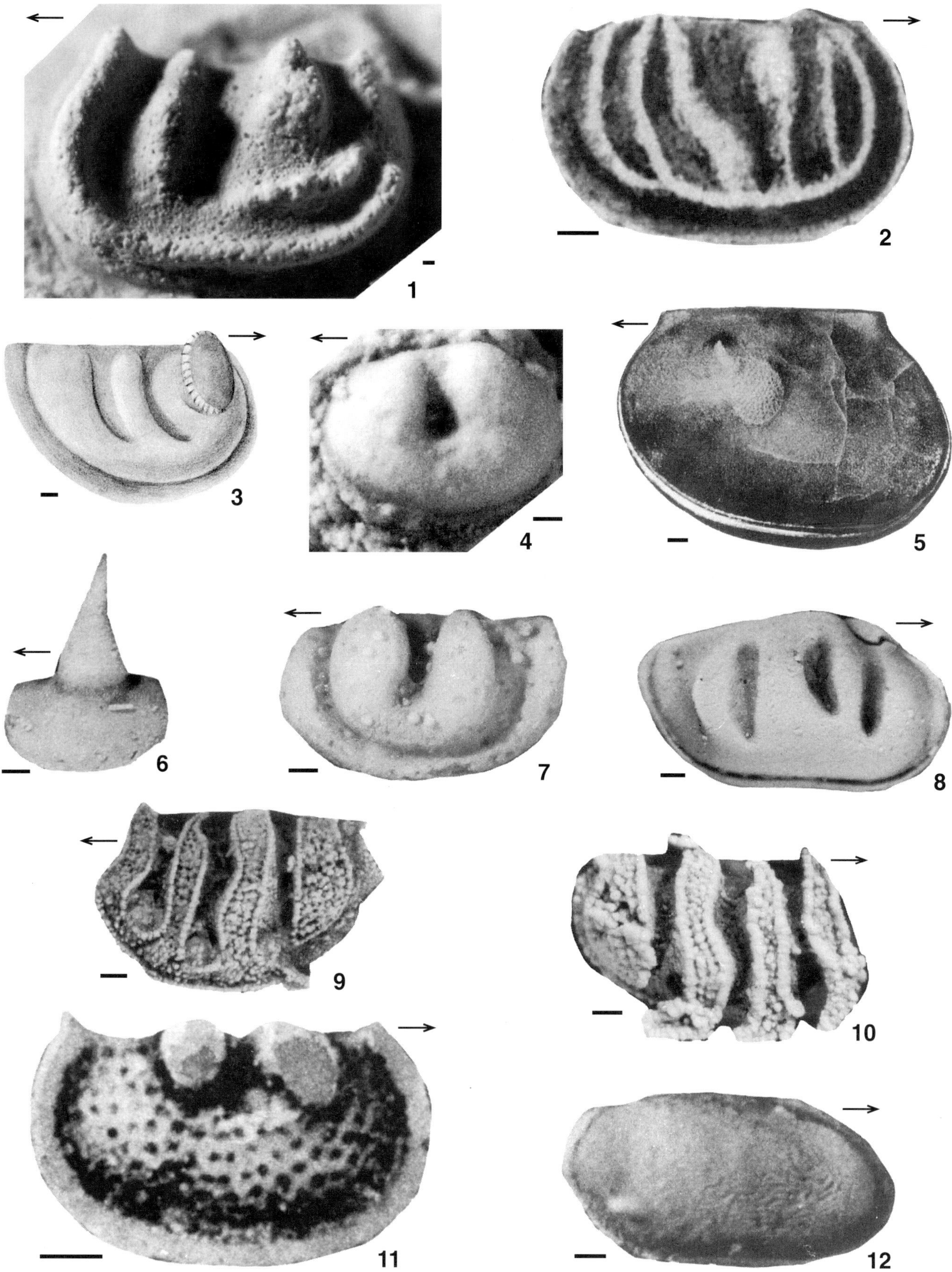
1
2
3
4
5
6
7
8
9
10
11
12

FIGURE 9-2.—Devonian, Mississippian, and Pennsylvanian ostracodes. All scale bars equal 0.1 mm. Arrows point toward the anterior of the specimen.

1 *Bythocyproidea eriensis* Stewart & Hendrix. Right-lateral view of carapace. Lower Olentangy Shale (Middle Devonian), northeast of Hyatts, Delaware County, Ohio; OSU 28664. From Tillman (1970, fig. 4-4).

2 *Ponderodictya unicornis* (Van Pelt). Right-lateral view of complete carapace. Lower Olentangy Shale (Middle Devonian), northeast of Hyatts, Delaware County, Ohio; OSU 28674. From Tillman (1970, fig. 4-14).

3 *Thrallella phaseolina* Stewart & Hendrix. Right-lateral view of complete carapace. Plum Brook Shale (Middle Devonian), north of Bloomingville, Erie County, Ohio; OSU 28682. From Tillman (1970, fig. 4-23).

4 *Amphissites rugosus* Girty. Left-lateral view of carapace. Mississippian, Arkansas. From Benson and others (1961, fig. 98, 3a).

5 *Polytylites wilsoni* (Croneis & Gutke). Right-lateral view of carapace. Maxville Formation (Upper Mississippian), Perry County, Ohio; OSU 46735. From Hoare (1993, fig. 3-13).

6-9 *Glyptopleura costata* (McCoy). **6**, **7**, left-lateral and dorsal views, respectively, of male. OSU 46434 and OSU 46437. **8**, **9**, right-lateral and dorsal views, respectively, of female. OSU 46438 and OSU 46440. Maxville Formation (Upper Mississippian), southwestern Perry County, Ohio. From Hoare (1993, figs. 3-27 to 3-30).

10, 11 *Hollinella warthini* Cooper. **10**, lateral view of left valve of female. OSU 34986. **11**, lateral view of left valve of male. OSU 34988. Ames shale (Conemaugh Group, Pennsylvanian), Athens County, Ohio.

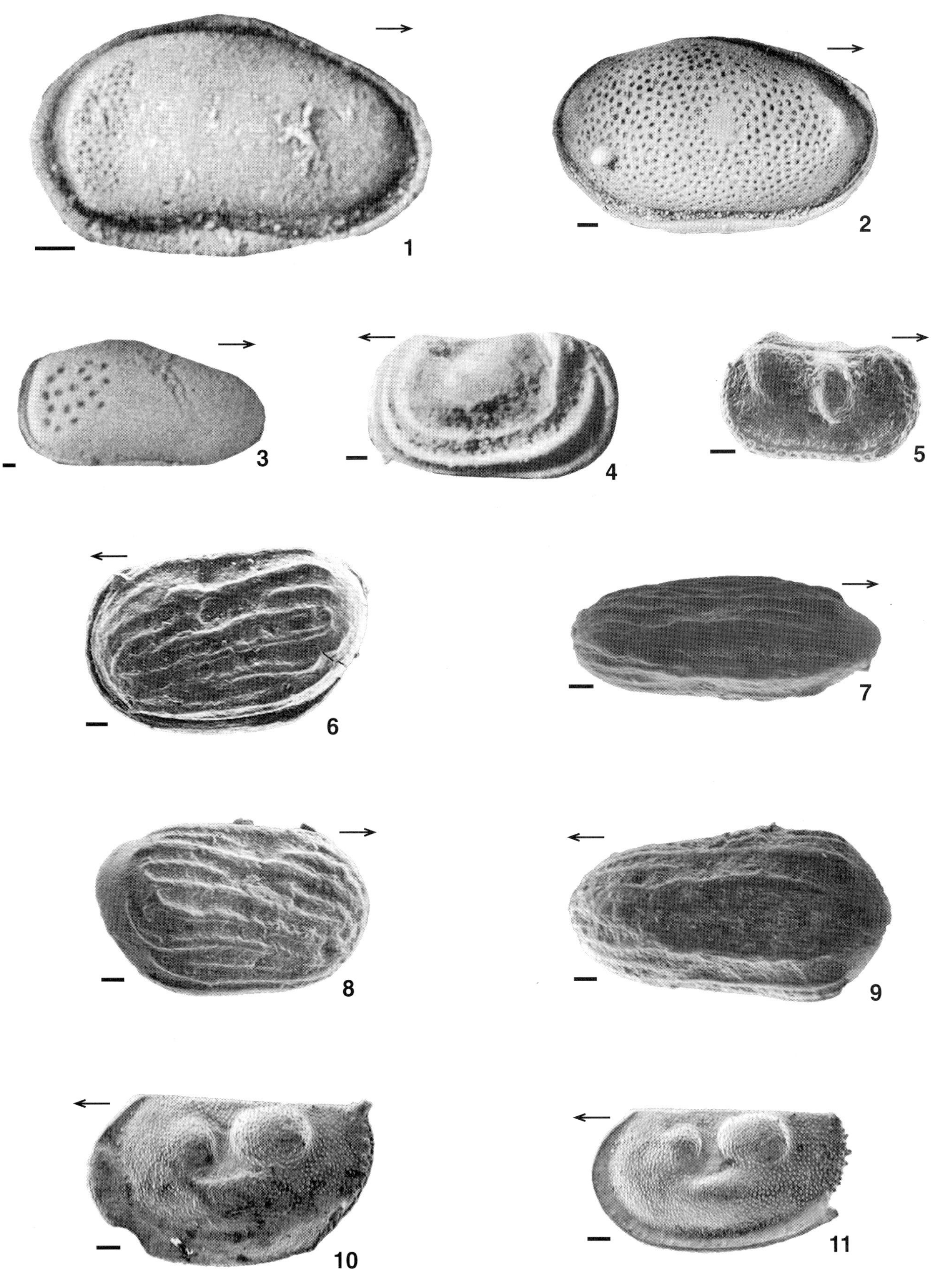
1
2
3
4
5
6
7
8
9
10
11

FIGURE 9-3.—Pennsylvanian and Quaternary ostracodes. All scale bars equal 0.1 mm. Arrows point toward the anterior of the specimen.

1 *Kegelites cooperi* Christopher, Hoare & Sturgeon. Lateral view of right valve of holotype. Putnam Hill shale (Allegheny Group, Pennsylvanian), Tuscarawas County, Ohio; OSU 37153. From Christopher and others (1990, fig. 5-1).

2 *Kellettina prolata* Hoare, Hansen & Merrill. Lateral view of right valve. Boggs shale (Pottsville Group, Pennsylvanian), Muskingum County, Ohio; OSU 45662. From Hoare and others (1994, fig. 6-10).

3 *Darwinula stephensoni* (Brady & Robertson). Lateral view of left valve. Recent, East Twin Lake, Portage County, Ohio.

4, 5 *Candona ohioensis* Furtos. **4**, lateral view of right valve of male. **5**, lateral view of right valve of female. Recent, Mud Lake, Williams County, Ohio.

6 *Cypridopsis vidua* (Müller). Lateral view of right valve. Recent, East Twin Lake, Portage County, Ohio.

7, 8 *Cyclocypris ampla* Furtos. **7**, lateral view of right valve. **8**, dorsal view of carapace. Recent, Pickerel Lake, Day County, South Dakota.

9 *Limnocythere* (*Limnocytherina*) *itasca* Cole. Lateral view of left valve of male. Recent, East Twin Lake, Portage County, Ohio.

10 *Ilyocypris gibba* (Ramdohr). Lateral view of right valve. Recent, Kiser Lake, Champaign County, Ohio.

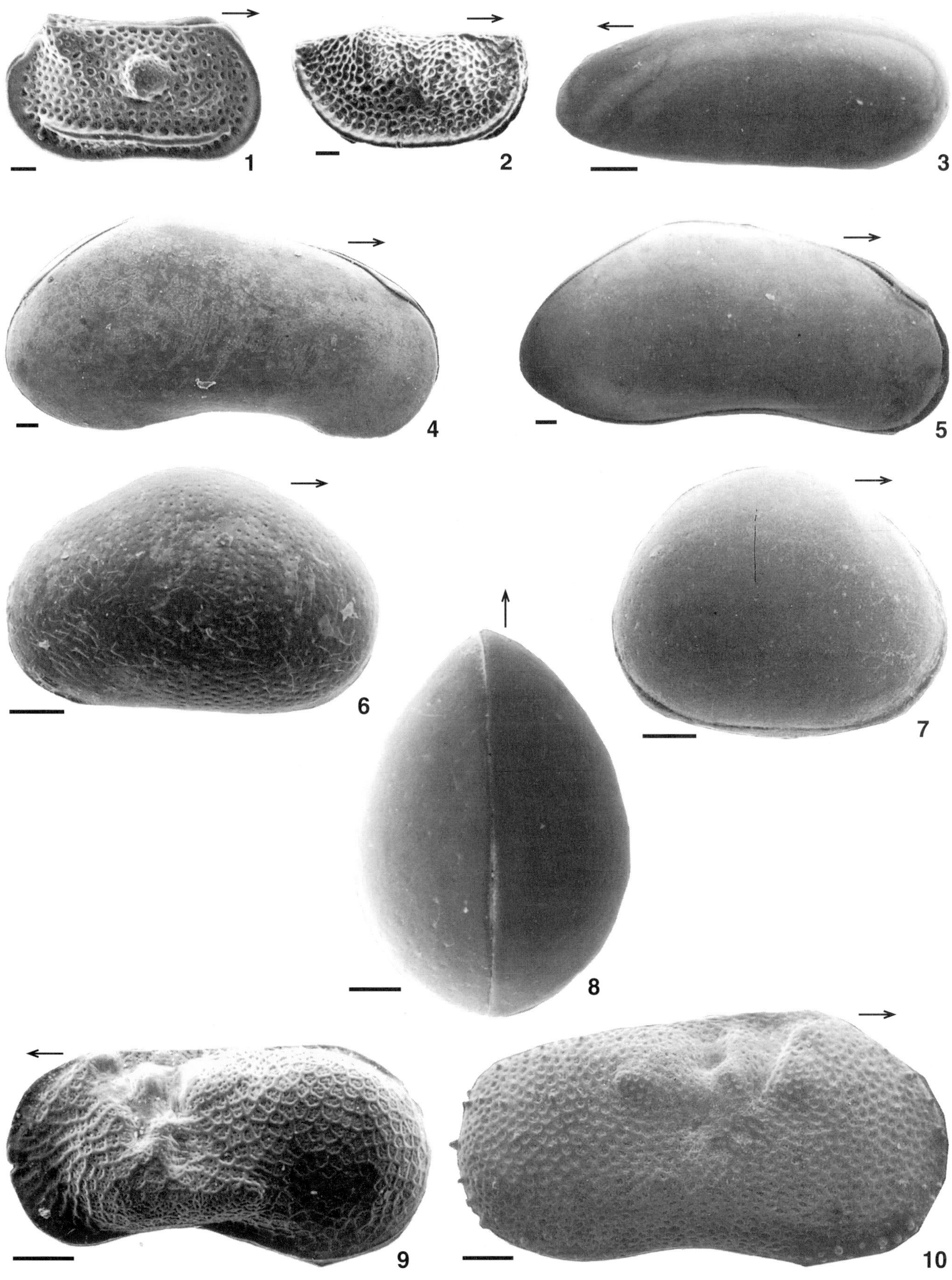
1
2
3
4
5
6
7
8
9
10

Chapter 10

PHYLUM ARTHROPODA: PHYLLOCARIDS, MILLIPEDES, INSECTS, AND OTHER LESS COMMON FORMS

by Joseph T. Hannibal

INTRODUCTION

Arthropods, other than trilobites and ostracodes, generally are not abundant in Ohio. A number of forms, however, are described and illustrated in classic paleontological works such as those by Hall and Clarke (1888), Whitfield (1893), and Scudder (1895). Additional forms have been described by subsequent workers. The less common fossil arthropods can be found in a number of Ohio rock units, including rocks of the Ordovician, Silurian, Devonian, Mississippian, Pennsylvanian, and Permian Systems. They also may be found in Pleistocene sediments.

One is most likely to find these less common arthropods in Ohio in rocks of Devonian and Pennsylvanian age. Some of these arthropods are relatively common in some rock units. For example, phyllocarid crustaceans are found in some abundance in the Middle Devonian Silica Formation and in the Upper Devonian Chagrin Shale Member of the Ohio Shale and are important components of the faunas of those rock units. Millipedes and insects may be found in some Pennsylvanian rocks in Ohio. Selected examples of such forms are illustrated and described in this chapter.

IDENTIFYING FOSSIL ARTHROPODS

The types of fossils discussed in this chapter usually can be recognized as arthropods by their general similarity to modern shrimp, cockroaches, and the like. Fragmentary specimens may be problematical. Arthropod parts generally can be identified as such, in part, by color. Some parts of fossil arthropods may be gray blue to brown to black owing to their phosphate content. Care must be taken, however, not to confuse such arthropods with other organisms having phosphatic remains, such as tube worms and fish (see Chapter 21). Portions of arthropods, particularly those in Pennsylvanian rocks, may be **carbonized**. Care must be taken not to confuse such specimens with fossil leaves (see Chapters 22-24), which they resemble. Some arthropod fossils may be pyritized.

The following key was designed as an aid in identifying the arthropods discussed in this chapter. For further information one should turn to additional works, including those listed in the references at the end of this book. The sections on arthropods in the *Treatise on Invertebrate Paleontology*, such as those by Hoffman (1969), Rolfe (1969), Tasch (1969), and Carpenter (1992), are especially recommended.

KEY TO SOME MISCELLANEOUS FOSSIL ARTHROPODS FROM OHIO

1A. Fossil has wings .... insect (figs. 10-3.1, 10-3.3)
1B. Fossil lacks wings 2

2A. Fossil composed of 11 or more similar segments and lacks a **carapace** .... millipede (fig. 10-3.2)
2B. Fossil has fewer than 11 similar visible segments, has a carapace, and has toothed **mandibles** (all these features rarely preserved together) 3

3A. Fossil is a toothed mandible (complete mandibles have about eight teeth) .... phyllocarid (fig. 10-2.6)
3B. Fossil consists of carapace and **abdomen** 4

4A. Carapace has several prominent **nodes** and at least one prominent ridge on each well-preserved **valve** .... *Echinocaris* (fig. 10-1)
4B. Carapace lacks prominent nodes, may or may not have ridges 5

5A. **Posterior** of each side of carapace concave, edge of carapace has a series of very fine grooves .... *Rhinocaris* (fig. 10-2.4)
5B. Posterior of each side of carapace convex 6

6A. Each valve of carapace has prominent Y-shaped groove toward the **anterior**, tail end has broad spatulalike plates .... *Palaeopalaemon* (figs. 10-2.1 to 10-2.3)
6B. Each valve of carapace broadly rounded; carapace has broad, rectangular medial plate .... *Ohiocaris* (fig. 10-2.5)

PHYLLOCARIDS

Phyllocarids are crustaceans that resemble a clam with a shrimp's tail. They are characterized by a bivalved carapace covering the head and **thoracic** region and a multisegmented abdomen. Various genera are distinguished primarily by the overall shape of the carapace and the presence or absence of various nodes, ridges, **tubercles**, and fine sculpturing. Three Devonian genera are described here: *Echinocaris*, *Ohiocaris*, and *Rhinocaris*. *Dithyrocaris*, a genus resembling *Rhinocaris*, occurs in rocks of Devonian through Pennsylvanian age in Ohio. Although entire specimens of *Echinocaris* and other phyllocarids can be found in Ohio, more commonly the carapace, abdomen, **telson**, or mandibles are found as isolated elements. Trace fossils assigned to the ichnogenus *Chagrinichnites* have been ascribed to *Echinocaris* (see Chapter 25). Additional information on phyllocarids can be found in Rolfe (1969) and Kesling and Chilman (1975).

Echinocaris (figs. 1-14, 10-1) is the most common genus of nontrilobite arthropod **macrofossil** found in Ohio. Entire specimens typically range in length from 2 to 15 cm. The carapace of this phyllocarid bears well-developed nodes separated by grooves. There are tubercles on the nodes and commonly on other parts of the carapace as well. The number and placement of tubercles vary—some species are especially tuberculate. There is also at least one pair of prominent ridges on the carapace of well-preserved specimens. *Echinocaris* has at least six abdominal segments and a telson that has three slender prongs, known as axial and lateral telson **spines**. Specimens of this genus are known in Ohio from the Middle Devonian Silica Formation in northwestern Ohio and from the Upper Devonian Chagrin Shale Member of the Ohio Shale in northeastern Ohio. More information on *Echinocaris* can be found in Hannibal and Feldmann (1987).

Ohiocaris (fig. 10-2.5) has a carapace that consists of two wide valves separated by a broad, rectangular medial plate, which distinguishes this crustacean from other forms described in this chapter. Each valve is marked by a fold that extends backward at about a 45° angle from its origin near the center of the front of the carapace. The posterior of each valve is convex. The carapace is up to 3.5 cm in length. *Ohiocaris* is known only from the Upper Devonian Ohio Shale in northern Ohio.

The carapace of *Rhinocaris* (fig. 10-2.4) may exceed 5 cm in length and has two thin dorsal plates, one anterior and the other posterior. The dorsal plates are not always preserved or evident, however. The posterior margin of each valve of the carapace is concave. The carapace is longer than wide and lacks the prominent ridges and grooves that characterize *Echinocaris*. Well-preserved specimens also have finely sculptured grooves paralleling the outer margin of the carapace. In Ohio, *Rhinocaris* is most common in the Middle Devonian Silica Formation of northwestern Ohio. The carapaces of the Silica specimens may be opalescent (pearly).

Phyllocarid mandibles (fig. 10-2.6) are thick, slightly to strongly curved, jawlike fossils having a number of "teeth" projecting from their gnathal (biting) surface. Such mandibles have been confused with jaws of Paleozoic fishes, which they superficially resemble. The mandible illustrated in figure 10-2.6 is moderately arcuate and bears eight teeth. The teeth on one end are longer and more incisorlike; those on the other end are flatter and more molarlike. Because phyllocarid mandibles are thick and well mineralized, they are more robust than other body parts and commonly are found as isolated fossils. Phyllocarid mandibles are most common in the Middle Devonian Silica Formation in northwestern Ohio.

PALAEOPALAEMON

Palaeopalaemon (figs. 10-2.1 to 10-2.3) is a decapod crustacean, distantly related to modern shrimps and lobsters (see Schram and others, 1978). The carapace of this crustacean has a distinctive, thin median ridge and a distinct Y-shaped groove toward the anterior. Its tail fan consists of wide, spatulalike elements called uropods flanking a central, pointed telson. Complete specimens typically range up to 6 cm in length.

The carapace of *Palaeopalaemon* is somewhat similar to that of various phyllocarids, but it is commonly preserved with a great deal of three-dimensional relief, wrapped around the top and sides of the crustacean (see figs. 10-2.1 to 10-2.3), whereas the carapaces of phyllocarids are typically preserved with their valves splayed outward (fig. 10-2.5) or flattened (fig. 10-2.4). *Palaeopalaemon* is found in the Chagrin Shale Member of the Ohio Shale in northeastern Ohio.

MILLIPEDES

Millipedes (fig. 10-3.2) are many-legged arthropods, popularly known as "thousand-leggers." They have a more or less cylindrical body consisting primarily of a large number (11 or more) of similar body segments, each with two pairs of legs. Care must be taken in identifying a specimen as a millipede. They may be easily confused with centipedes ("hundred-leggers"), which have only one pair of legs per body segment. However, one is less likely to find a fossil centipede. Partial specimens may be easily confused with the abdominal portion of crustaceans. Specimens lacking legs are particularly difficult to identify. Fossil millipedes have been found in coals and shales of the Pennsylvanian System in eastern Ohio. More information on Paleozoic millipedes can be found in Hoffman (1969) and Shear and Kukalovà-Peck (1990).

INSECTS

Insects (figs. 1-9, 10-3.1, 10-3.3) are arthropods with three main body parts: head, **thorax**, and abdomen. The head has one pair of antennae. Insects have six legs and commonly have wings. There may be one or two pairs of wings. Fossil insects found in Paleozoic rocks may resemble living forms but are only distantly related. Insects can be identified generally by shape, but precise identification is based on the pattern of the veins of the wings (see Cloudsley-Thompson, 1988, p. 44-53; Shear and Kukalovà-Peck, 1990; and Carpenter, 1992).

Fossil insect wings may be confused with plant parts, such as **pinnules** of Pennsylvanian ferns. The main veins of insect wings are typically curved, at least in part, and commonly are located toward the leading edge of the wing, whereas the midribs of fern pinnules are typically straight. However, it may require an expert to distinguish some insect wings from plant parts.

Insect remains have been found in shales of the Pennsylvanian System in eastern Ohio (see McComas and Mapes,

1988). Fragments of cockroaches (see figs. 1-9, 10-3.1) are among the most common insect fossils found in these deposits. Remains of beetles, especially their elytra, the hardened first pair of wings, are found in Pleistocene deposits (see Morgan and Morgan, 1990).

OTHER FORMS

Fossils of chelicerates, a class of arthropods characterized by one pair of limbs with pincers located in front of their mouths, have been found in Ohio. Eurypterids, one type of chelicerate, have long been known from Ohio (Whitfield, 1893, p. 416; Kjellesvig-Waering, 1961), but specimens are typically fragmentary. Eurypterid remains have been found in Ordovician, Silurian, and Devonian rocks in Ohio. Remains of spiderlike arachnids, another type of chelicerate, have been found in Pennsylvanian and Permian rocks (see McComas and Mapes, 1988). Fossils of conchostracan branchiopods also have been found in Pennsylvanian rocks of Ohio. These generally small (2 cm or less) crustaceans have carapaces resembling clam shells (see Tasch, 1969).

COLLECTING LOCALITIES

The major types of fossil arthropods discussed in this chapter have been found in quarry exposures of the Silica Formation in northwestern Ohio; in natural outcrops of the Chagrin Shale Member of the Ohio Shale in northeastern Ohio, where they are most common in concretions; or in Pennsylvanian-age shales and coals in old, unreclaimed strip mines and old mine dumps in eastern Ohio. The quarries are generally inaccessible. With permission of the landowner, specimens may be collected along outcrops of the Chagrin Member located on private property. Collecting is <u>not</u> permitted in most of the metropolitan and county park systems of northeastern Ohio where the Chagrin crops out. Mine sites in eastern Ohio are on private property and permission must be obtained from the property owner before collecting.

ACKNOWLEDGMENTS

Bruce Frumker and Dan Flocke (The Cleveland Museum of Natural History) and Rodney M. Feldmann (Kent State University) took several of the photographs on figures 10-1 and 10-2.

FIGURE 10-1.—Devonian phyllocarid crustacean *Echinocaris*. All scale bars equal 1 cm.

1, 2 — *Echinocaris sublevis* Whitfield preserved in concretions. Chagrin Shale Member of the Ohio Shale, northeastern Ohio. **1**, an almost complete carapace of a rather tuberculate specimen from Lake or Geauga County. ClMNH 3722. **2**, dorsal view of the last four abdominal segments and the telson of the **lectotype**. The three prongs of the telson of *Echinocaris*, as seen on this specimen, are more slender than those of other Paleozoic phyllocarids found in Ohio. AMNH 12281.

3, 4 — *Echinocaris multinodosa* Whitfield preserved in concretions. Chagrin Shale Member of the Ohio Shale, northeastern Ohio. **3**, carapace of lectotype; the specimen is slightly worn. AMNH 5511G. **4**, lateral view of a poorly preserved but fairly complete carapace, plus abdomen and telson. ClMNH 1809.

5 — *Echinocaris punctata* (Hall). Almost complete specimen. Hamilton Group, Pratt's Falls, New York; NYSM 4401 (old # 13442/4). This species is found in the Silica Formation at Sylvania, Lucas County, Ohio.

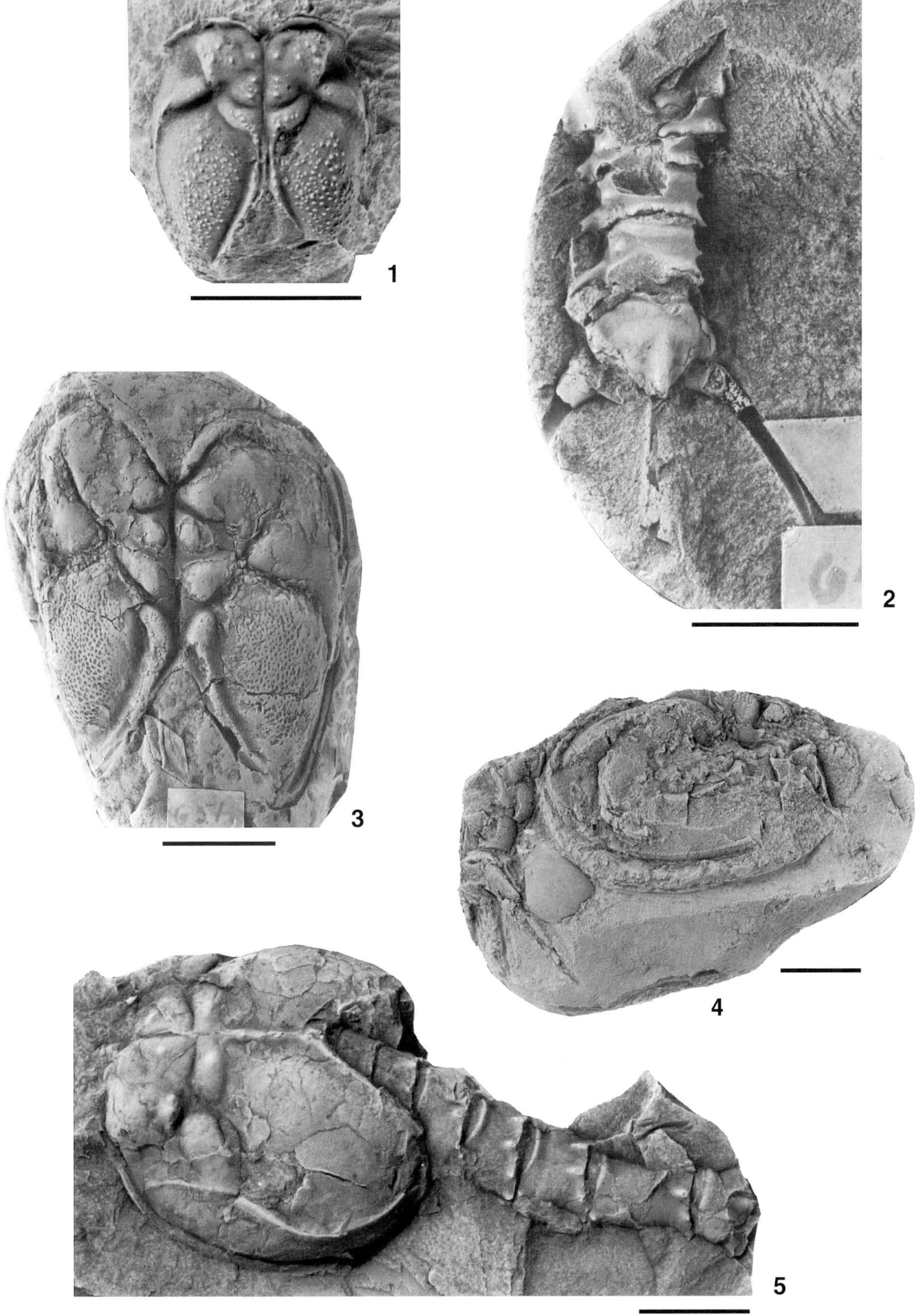
1
2
3
4
5

FIGURE 10-2.—Devonian marine arthropods. All scale bars equal 1 cm.

1-3 *Palaeopalaemon newberryi* Whitfield. Chagrin Shale Member of the Ohio Shale, northeastern Ohio. This species is named after John Strong Newberry, one of Ohio's preeminent early geologists (see Dedication at front of this volume). **1**, reproduction of a drawing of the **holotype** of *P. newberryi* in Hall and Clarke (1888). Note that portions of two stout appendages extend from the front (on the right) of the fossil. Also note the broad spatulalike plate (the right uropod) at the tail end (on the left). **2**, dorsal view of carapace and portions of front appendages. KSU 3083. **3**, lateral view of carapace (top middle) and abdomen (left). Note the prominent Y-shaped groove toward the front of the carapace and the convexity of the posterior of the side of the carapace. ClMNH 4106.

4 *Rhinocaris ehlersi* Stewart. Right valve of carapace. The distinctive, concave posterior of the valve can be seen to the left; the anterior portion (on the right) of the specimen has been broken off. There are also cracks in the carapace. Note the finely sculptured grooves paralleling the outer (lower) margin of the carapace. Silica Formation, Sylvania, Lucas County, Ohio; ClMNH 3920.

5 *Ohiocaris wycoffi* Rolfe. Holotype preserved in a concretion. The large rounded area is the carapace. The fine, irregular polygons on the surface of the carapace are not original but were acquired during the process of fossilization. A portion of the abdomen is seen below the carapace. Ohio Shale, western Cuyahoga County, Ohio; ClMNH 33241.

6 Gnathal (biting) lobe of a phyllocarid mandible. The molar end of the mandible is on the left; the incisor area, which has longer teeth, is on the right. This specimen probably belongs to the genus *Dithyrocaris*. Silica Formation, Sylvania, Lucas County, Ohio; ClMNH 3927a.

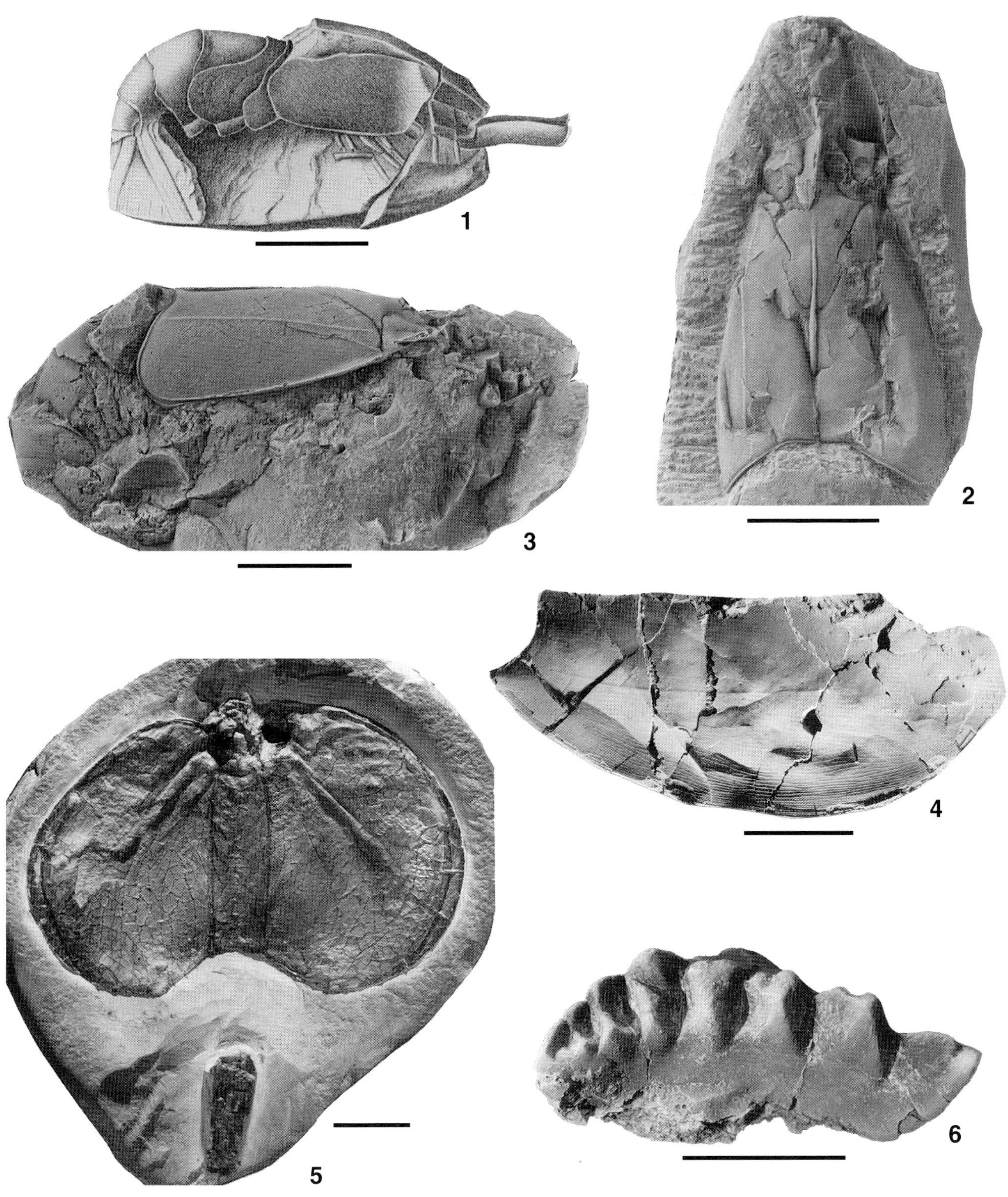
1
2
3
4
5
6

FIGURE 10-3.—Pennsylvanian terrestrial arthropods from rocks of the Conemaugh Group exposed in a strip mine, called the 7-11 mine by paleontologists, in Madison Township, Columbiana County, Ohio. All scale bars equal 1 cm. Photos courtesy of Gregory and Melissa McComas and reproduced from McComas and Mapes (1988) with permission.

1 One of the largest known fossil cockroaches, distantly related to modern cockroaches.

2 Millipede. Note the large number of segments.

3 Long-legged, winged insect.

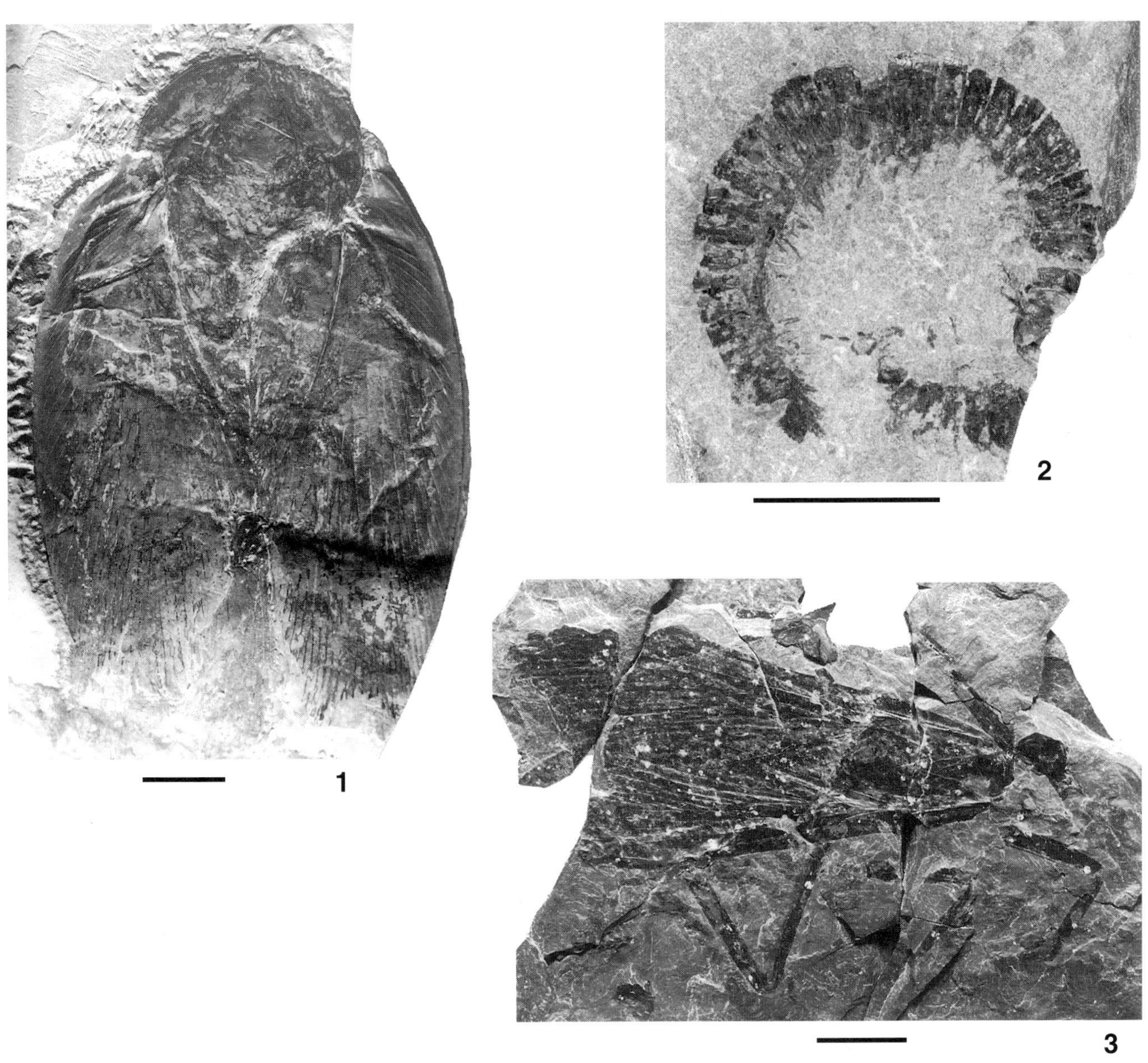
1
2
3

Chapter 11

PHYLUM MOLLUSCA, CLASS ROSTROCONCHIA

by Richard D. Hoare

INTRODUCTION

The rostroconchs are an extinct class of mollusks found in rocks of Cambrian to Permian age. Their morphology is shown in figure 1-16 in Chapter 1. Rostroconchs were marine organisms that inhabited limy and clayey sea floors. They lived partially buried in the sediment so that the **gape** at the **anterior** end was down in the sediment and the **rostrum** at the **posterior** end was at or near the sediment surface. They fed on organic debris within the sediment. Rostroconchs were placed in the class Pelecypoda until 1972, when they were recognized as a separate class.

Rostroconchs are not overly common in Ohio. They have been found in Ordovician, Devonian, Mississippian, and Pennsylvanian strata. Although the paleoenvironmental settings of some Silurian units in Ohio are such that rostroconchs could have been present, they have not been reported. Continued collecting from rocks of Silurian age may reveal the presence of rostroconchs.

Rostroconchs are relatively rare in Ordovician rocks in Ohio. They are most common in Devonian rocks, particularly the Dundee Formation in northwestern Ohio and the Columbus Limestone in central Ohio. Mississippian rostroconchs have been reported from the Cuyahoga and Logan Formations in central and south-central Ohio. Most Pennsylvanian species are very small and are not easily found without extensive sample preparation and use of a microscope. However, some larger specimens are present, although rare, and more are likely to be found in the future.

In the key and the descriptions of Ohio rostroconchs that follow, size ranges are: small, 0.2-0.4 cm; medium, 1-3 cm; and large, 7-10 cm. Additional information on Ohio rostroconchs can be found in Pojeta and Runnegar (1976), Hoare and others (1979), and Hoare (1989, 1990).

KEY TO SOME ROSTROCONCHS FROM OHIO

1A. No **hood** present .... *Pseudomulceodens* (figs. 11-1.10 to 11-1.13)
1B. One hood present .... *Hippocardia* (figs. 11-1.1 to 11-1.4, 11-1.14 to 11-1.18)
1C. Two hoods present 2

2A. Shell of medium size .... *Bigalea* (figs. 11-1.5 to 11-1.7)
2B. Shell very small .... *Pseudobigalea* (figs. 11-1.8, 11-1.9)

DEVONIAN ROSTROCONCHS

In Devonian rocks, the most common genus is *Hippocardia*, and the most common species is *H. cunea* (Conrad) (figs. 11-1.14 to 11-1.18). This large species is found in the Dundee Formation and the Columbus Limestone. The presence of a single large hood, an extension of shell material along the **ventral** margin pointing posteriorly from the **rostral face**, is diagnostic of the genus. The outer shell layer, including the hood, is commonly missing or lost when the specimen is extracted from limestone so that the **costate** inner shell layer is exposed.

Two less common Devonian species are *Hippocardia curta* Hoare (figs. 11-1.2 to 11-1.4) and *Bigalea yangi* Pojeta & Runnegar (figs. 11-1.5 to 11-1.7). Both are of medium size. *Hippocardia curta* has a single hood, a swollen posterior or body region, and a narrowed anterior or **snout** region. *Bigalea yangi* has two short hoods associated with the rostral face. The genus *Hippocardia* has a worldwide range of Middle Ordovician to Mississippian. *Bigalea* has a range of Middle Silurian to Middle Devonian.

MISSISSIPPIAN ROSTROCONCHS

Mississippian rostroconchs include *Hippocardia herricki* Hoare (fig. 11-1.1), which is of medium size and has an obliquely truncate rostral face. Another Mississippian species, *Pseudomulceodens cancellatus* (Hyde) (figs. 11-1.10 to 11-1.13), is also of medium size, has a narrow, ovately shaped gape bordered by **denticles**, and lacks a hood. The genus *Pseudomulceodens* is restricted to Lower Mississippian rocks.

PENNSYLVANIAN ROSTROCONCHS

Pseudobigalea crista Hoare, Mapes & Brown (= *Pseudoconocardium parrishi* Hoare, Sturgeon & Kindt) (figs. 11-1.8, 11-1.9) is a small Pennsylvanian species found in Ohio. Specimens, which are commonly distorted in shape, may have the cap-shaped larval shell preserved in the area of the **beaks**. This genus is restricted to the Pennsylvanian.

COLLECTING LOCALITIES

Rostroconchs have been found at the following localities in Ohio. All are on private property and require permission from the landowner for access.

Devonian localities include the Dundee Formation in the quarry on the east edge of Whitehouse, Lucas County, just south of Ohio Route 64; the Columbus Limestone exposed in Eversole Run in Concord Township, Delaware County, approximately 3.2 km (2 miles) north of the county line on the west side of the Scioto River; and the Columbus Limestone in quarries on Kelleys Island, Erie County.

Mississippian localities include the Logan Formation exposed along the C & O railroad cut approximately 3.2 km (2 miles) northwest of Sciotoville, Harrison Township, Scioto County; and the Cuyahoga Formation exposed in the bed of West Fork Black River approximately 3.2 km (2 miles) west of Lodi and south of U.S. Route 224, Harrisville Township, Medina County.

FIGURE 11-1.—Rostroconchs. Scale bars equal 1 cm except scale bar B, which equals 1 mm. Scale bar A applies to figures 11-1.1 to 11-1.7; B applies to figures 11-1.8 and 11-1.9; C applies to figures 11-1.10 to 11-1.13; D applies to figures 11-1.14 to 11-1.18.

1	*Hippocardia herricki* Hoare. Ventral view, hood and outer shell layer missing. Cuyahoga Formation (Mississippian), near Lodi, Medina County, Ohio; ClMNH 5275.1. Reprinted from Hoare (1990) with permission.
2-4	*Hippocardia curta* Hoare. Ventroanterior (**2**), dorsal (**3**), and right-lateral (**4**) views, most of outer shell layer missing. Dundee Formation (Devonian), quarry at Whitehouse, Lucas County, Ohio; OSU 30688. Reprinted from Hoare (1989) with permission.
5-7	*Bigalea yangi* Pojeta & Runnegar. Silica Formation (Devonian), quarry west of Sylvania, Lucas County. **5**, **6**, right-lateral and posterior views; OSU 46652. **7**, ventral view; OSU 46653.
8, 9	*Pseudobigalea crista* Hoare, Mapes & Brown. **8,** ventral view showing gape. **9**, dorsoposterior view showing larval shell at beaks. Vanport shale (Allegheny Group, Pennsylvanian), abandoned strip mine north of U.S. Route 50 east of McArthur, Vinton County, Ohio; OSU 29271. Reprinted from Hoare and others (1979).
10-13	*Pseudomulceodens cancellatus* (Hyde). Logan Formation (Mississippian), railroad cut northwest of Sciotoville, Scioto County, Ohio. **10**, **11**, right-lateral and dorsal views of internal mold; OSU 19874.3. **12**, **13**, anterior and right-lateral views of cast of external mold; OSU 19874.8. Reprinted from Hoare (1990) with permission.
14-18	*Hippocardia cunea* (Conrad). Dundee Formation (Devonian), quarry at Whitehouse, Lucas County, Ohio. **14**, ventral view showing part of hood, outer shell layer missing; OSU 30684. **15**, posterior view, outer shell layer missing; OSU 30679. **16**, **17**, dorsal and right-lateral views showing filling of ventral posterior opening; OSU 30675. **18**, ventral view, hood and partial outer shell layer present; OSU 30683. Reprinted from Hoare (1989) with permission.

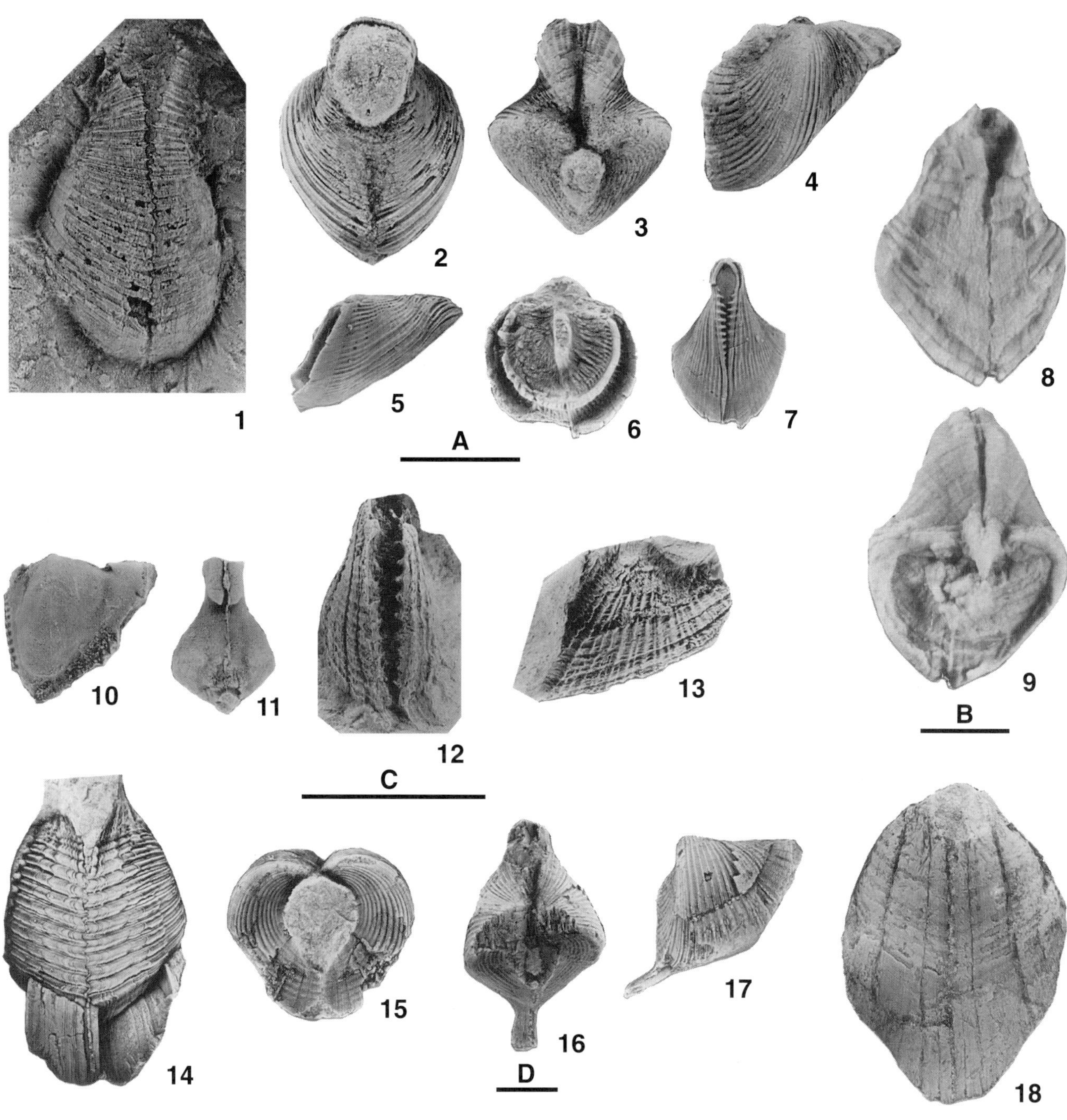
1
2
3
4
5
6
7
8
9
10
11
12
13
14
15
16
17
18
A
B
C
D

Chapter 12

PHYLUM MOLLUSCA, CLASS PELECYPODA

by Richard D. Hoare and Barry B. Miller

INTRODUCTION

Pelecypods, commonly referred to as clams, have a long geologic history ranging from Cambrian to modern-day forms. They inhabit marine, brackish-water, and freshwater environments. Pelecypods have adapted to a wide range of life modes. Some pelecypods burrow into sediment and rock (**infaunal**); others crawl at or very near the sediment surface or are attached to the surface by an organic structure (byssus) or are cemented down (**epifaunal**); still others are swimming forms. They feed on organic debris in the sediment or the water column. The classification of fossil pelecypods is based on shell shape, shell microstructure, **hinge** structure, **muscle scars**, and **ornamentation**. The morphology of pelecypods is illustrated in figure 1-15 in Chapter 1. The Pelecypoda have also been called Bivalvia (bivalves) and Lamellibranchiata (lamellibranchs).

In Ohio, pelecypods are fairly common in rocks of Ordovician to Pennsylvanian age. The sparse exposures of Permian rocks in the state yield a few pelecypods. In Pleistocene lake and stream deposits pelecypods can be quite abundant. Many genera and species have long stratigraphic ranges. Because the shell material is easily destroyed during **diagenesis**, pelecypods are most commonly preserved as **internal molds**, making them more difficult to identify to species. If an **external mold** is found, it is possible to make a cast from the mold to show better the original shape, size, and ornamentation of the specimen.

In the following key and descriptions of Ohio pelecypods, size ranges are: small, 2 cm or less in length; medium, 3-5 cm in length; large, 6 cm or more in length. Sizes apply to average, mature specimens; juvenile specimens may be smaller.

Additional information on Ohio bivalves can be found in Meek (1873, 1875); Hall and Whitfield (1875); Foerste (1893); Ulrich (1893); Whitfield (1893); Stauffer (1909); Mark (1912); Morningstar (1922); Hyde (1953); Pojeta (1966); La Rocque (1966, 1967); Cox and others (1969, 1971); Kesling and Chilman (1975); Hoare and others (1979); and Davis (1985).

KEY TO SOME PALEOZOIC PELECYPODS FROM OHIO

1A. Shell **valves** of equal size 2
1B. Shell valves not of equal size 30

2A. Shell small 3
2B. Shell of medium size 7
2C. Shell large 24

3A. Shell has coarse **comarginal** ornamentation (including **growth lines**) .... *Astartella* (figs. 12-4.14, 12-4.15)
3B. Shell has fine comarginal ornamentation 4
3C. Shell smooth 5

4A. **Posterior** area narrowly tapered .... *Phestia* (figs. 12-4.3 to 12-4.5)
4B. Posterior area truncate to rounded .... *Anthraconaia* (figs. 4-3.19 to 4-3.21)
4C. Posterior area rounded 6

5A. Shell subequidimensional .... *Nuculopsis* (figs. 12-4.1, 12-4.2)
5B. Shell elongate .... *Ctenodonta* (fig. 12-1.6)

6A. Internal ridges in **umbonal** area .... *Nuculites* (figs. 12-2.4, 12-2.5)
6B. No internal ridges in umbonal area .... *Palaeoneilo* (figs. 12-3.2, 12-4.6, 12-4.7)

7A. **Beaks** near **anterior** margin 8
7B. Beaks not near anterior margin 14

8A. Shell has **radial** ornamentation .... *Amphicoelia* (fig. 12-1.11)
8B. Shell smooth 9

9A. Shell elongate 10
9B. Shell short 11

10A. Posterior area **spatulate** 12
10B. Posterior area not spatulate 13

11A. Posterior area broadly rounded .... *Mytilarca* (figs. 12-1.9, 12-1.10)
11B. Posterior area narrowly rounded .... *Promytilus* (fig. 12-4.9)

12A. Strong umbonal ridge present .... *Modiomorpha* (figs. 12-1.12, 12-1.13)
12B. No umbonal ridge .... *Lithophaga* (fig. 12-3.12)

13A. Shell has anterior flap .... *Prothyris* (figs. 12-3.17, 12-3.18)
13B. Shell without anterior flap .... *Ischyrodonta* (fig. 12-1.8)

14A. Shell subequidimensional 15
14B. Shell elongate 21

15A. Shell has weak comarginal ridges 16
15B. Shell has coarse comarginal ridges 19

16A. Posterior margin truncate 17
16B. Posterior margin rounded 18

17A. Strong umbonal ridge present .... *Cyrtodontula* (fig. 12-1.7)
17B. No umbonal ridge .... *Schizodus* (figs. 12-3.3, 12-4.22, 12-4.23)

18A. Beak at midlength .... *Paracyclas* (fig. 12-2.12)
18B. Beak anterior to midlength .... *Modiolus* (figs. 12-3.15, 12-3.16)

19A. Shell has one or more distinct radial **sulci** .... *Grammysia* (figs. 12-2.7, 12-2.8)
19B. Shell has weak radial sulcus 20

20A. Posterior margin truncate .... *Ectogrammysia* (fig. 12-3.5)
20B. Posterior margin rounded .... *Edmondia* (figs. 12-3.6, 12-4.26)

21A. Shell has radial ornamentation 22
21B. Shell without radial ornamentation 23

22A. Posterior margin rounded .... *Permophorus* (fig. 12-4.10)
22B. Posterior margin truncate .... *Parallelodon* (fig. 12-4.19)

23A. Shell smooth .... *Sphenotus* (fig. 12-3.9)
23B. Shell has strong comarginal **plications** .... *Orthonota* (fig. 12-2.6)

24A. Shell has radial ornamentation 25
24B. Shell without radial ornamentation 26

25A. Radial ornamentation is broad plications .... *Anomalodonta* (fig. 12-1.2)
25B. Radial ornamentation is narrow plications .... *Ambonychia* (figs. 12-1.3 to 12-1.5)

26A. Shell smooth 27
26B. Shell has comarginal ornamentation 28

27A. Shell thick, subequidimensional .... *Megalomoidea* (figs. 12-1.14, 12-1.15)
27B. Shell elongate .... *Sanguinolites* (fig. 12-3.13)

28A. Beaks subcentral .... *Promacrus* (fig. 12-3.14)
28B. Beaks nearly terminal (at anterior end of shell) 29

29A. Shell narrowly V shaped .... *Pteronites* (fig. 12-4.18)
29B. Shell elongate .... *Wilkingia* (figs. 12-3.10, 12-3.11, 12-4.27)

30A. Shell small 31
30B. Shell of medium size 36
30C. Shell large 39

31A. Shell smooth or nearly so .... *Leptodesma* (figs. 12-2.10, 12-3.4, 12-4.8)
31B. Shell has ornamentation 32

32A. Ornamentation radial and comarginal .... *Streblochondria* (figs. 12-3.1, 12-4.11, 12-4.17)
32B. Ornamentation only radial 33

33A. **Auricles** subequal in size 34
33B. Auricles unequal in size 35

34A. Auricles large .... *Pseudaviculopecten* (fig. 12-2.3)
34B. Auricles small .... *Palaeolima* (fig. 12-4.13)

35A. Shell **opisthocline** .... *Ptychopteria* (figs. 12-2.1, 12-2.2, 12-2.11)
35B. Shell **acline** to **prosocline** .... *Dunbarella* (fig. 12-4.12)

36A. Beaks nearly terminal 37
36B. Beaks not terminal 38

37A. Comarginal ornamentation widely spaced .... *Septimyalina* (fig. 12-4.21)
37B. Comarginal ornamentation closely spaced .... *Posidonia* (fig. 12-4.25)

38A. Ornamentation radial only .... *Aviculopecten* (figs. 12-3.7, 12-3.8, 12-4.16)
38B. Ornamentation radial and comarginal .... *Acanthopecten* (fig. 12-4.20)

39A. Ornamentation comarginal only .... *Caritodens* (fig. 12-1.1)
39B. Ornamentation radial only 40

40A. Radial **costae** bundled or grouped .... *Fasciculiconcha* (fig. 12-4.24)
40B. Radial costae not bundled .... *Limoptera* (fig. 12-2.9)

ORDOVICIAN PELECYPODS

A number of genera may commonly be encountered in Ordovician rocks. The Upper Ordovician genus *Caritodens* is represented in Cincinnatian rocks by *C. demissa* (Conrad) (fig. 12-1.1), a large species distinguished by auricles (large winglike extensions of the hinge), strongly developed comarginal ridges, and the lack of any radial ornamentation. The Upper Ordovician genus *Anomalodonta* is represented by *A. gigantea* Miller (fig. 12-1.2), a large species that lacks auricles and has broad, radial plications. The genus *Ambonychia*, which ranges from Middle to Upper Ordovician, is represented in the Ordovician of Ohio by *A. robusta* Hall (figs. 12-1.3 to 12-1.5). This medium-sized species has narrow, radial plications. The Ordovician genus *Cyrtodontula* is represented by *C. umbonata* (Ulrich) (fig. 12-1.7), which is medium sized and has prominent beaks and a truncate posterior margin. The Upper Ordovician genus *Ischyrodonta* is represented by *I. elongata* Ulrich (fig. 12-1.8), a medium-sized, narrowly elongate species having a distinct anterior muscle scar evident on internal molds. The Middle Ordovician genus *Ctenodonta* is represented by *C. perminuta* Foerste (fig. 12-1.6), a small, ovate species that has the beaks near the anterior margin and numerous subequal **teeth** in the hinge.

SILURIAN PELECYPODS

Silurian pelecypods are less common than Ordovician forms in Ohio. In the dolomitic rocks in the northwestern portion of the state, the Middle Silurian genus *Megalomoidea*, formerly called *Megalomus*, is represented by *M. canadensis* (Hall), a very large (±25 cm) species. It is most commonly preserved as an internal mold (fig. 12-1.14) that shows prominent beaks and distinct muscle scars. The outer shell surface is smooth except for growth lines (fig. 12-1.15) and has a much different shape than the internal mold (fig. 12-1.14). The genus *Modiomorpha* ranges from Middle Silurian to Upper Permian and is represented in the Silurian of Ohio by *Modiomorpha* sp. (figs. 12-1.12, 12-1.13), which is medium sized and has an elongate shape and a prominent ridge running from the umbones to the posteroventral margin. The Middle-Upper Silurian genus *Amphicoelia* is represented by *A. costata* Hall & Whitfield (fig. 12-1.11), a medium-sized species that has pronounced terminal beaks and a subquadrangular shape. The internal mold reflects the costate shell ornamentation. The genus *Mytilarca* ranges from Lower Silurian to Upper Devonian and is represented in the Silurian of Ohio by *M. acutirostris* (Ulrich) (figs. 12-1.9, 12-1.10). This medium-sized species also has terminal beaks, but has a smoother, narrower, more elongate shell than *Amphicoelia*.

DEVONIAN PELECYPODS

Numerous pelecypods are found in the Devonian shales and limestones. The genus *Nuculites*, which ranges from Ordovician to Devonian, is represented by *N. oblongatus* Conrad (figs. 12-2.4, 12-2.5), a small, smooth (except for growth lines), elongate species. The internal mold shows prominent muscle scars, an internal ridge, a **pallial line**, and **dentition**. The Devonian genus *Paracyclas* is represented by *P. elliptica* Hall (fig. 12-2.12), a medium-sized, subcircular species that has rather coarse comarginal ridges. The Devonian genus *Grammysia* is represented by *G. bisulcata* Conrad (figs. 12-2.7, 12-2.8), a medium-sized, robust form that has prominent beaks, two sulci radiating from the beak area to the **ventral** margin, and numerous comarginal ridges. *Orthonota*, which ranges from Middle Ordovician to Middle Devonian, is represented by *O. undulata* Conrad (fig. 12-2.6), a large, elongate form that has a ridge radiating from the beak to the posteroventral margin and prominent comarginal plications that are reflected on internal molds.

Many Devonian species are **pectiniform**, that is, shaped like the modern scallop or the Shell Oil Company symbol, and have variable development of auricles on either side of the beak. The genus *Leptodesma* ranges from Middle Silurian to Upper Permian and is represented in the Devonian of Ohio by *L. ausablensis* Ehlers & Wright (fig. 12-2.10). This medium-sized species has a small anterior auricle and a large posterior auricle set off from the body of the shell by a distinct, broad sulcus. The surface is ornamented by low, indistict, comarginal plications. The genus *Ptychopteria* ranges from Silurian to Lower Permian, and there are several Devonian species from Ohio. *Ptychopteria boydi* (Conrad) (fig. 12-2.2) is small and has auricles that are somewhat similar to those of *Leptodesma ausablensis*, but the shell bears numerous radial plications that are crossed by comarginal ridges to form a **reticulate** pattern. *Ptychopteria decussata* (Hall) (fig. 12-2.1) also is small, but the anterior auricle is less prominent than that of *P. boydi*, and the numerous radiating costae are crossed by growth lines to form a finer reticulate pattern on the shell surface. *Ptychopteria flabella* (Conrad) (fig. 12-2.11) is medium sized and has several widely spaced, coarse costae interspersed with three to four finer costae. The costae are crossed by fine ridges to form a very distinct ornamentation. The genus *Limoptera* ranges from Upper Silurian to Middle Devonian and is represented by *L. macoptera* (Conrad) (fig. 12-2.9), a thick, large species that has a large posterior auricle set off slightly from the shell body and numerous narrow, radiating costae. The genus *Pseudaviculopecten*, which ranges from Middle Devonian to Lower Mississippian, is represented by *P. scabridus* (Hall) (fig. 12-2.3), which is small, subcircular in shape, and has a large anterior auricle set off from the shell body by a broad, U-shaped indentation. The posterior auricle is smaller and numerous costae ornament the shell.

MISSISSIPPIAN PELECYPODS

Mississippian pelecypods are commonly preserved as internal molds. The genus *Palaeoneilo*, which ranges from Ordovician to Mesozoic, is represented in the Mississippian of Ohio by *P. truncata* Hall (fig. 12-3.2). This species is small, elongate, and has numerous small, subequal teeth and a muscle scar near the anterior margin. *Lithophaga*, a genus that ranges from Mississippian to Recent, is represented by *L. jessicae* (Miller & Gurley) (fig. 12-3.12), a medium-sized, narrowly elongate, spatulate form that has the beaks located at the anterior extremity. *Leptodesma* is represented in the Mississippian of Ohio by *L. scutella* Herrick (fig.

12-3.4), a small, smooth form that has a broadly developed posterior wing. The genus *Modiolus*, which ranges from Devonian to Recent, is represented by *M. missouriensis* (Weller) (figs. 12-3.15, 12-3.16), a medium-sized species having nearly terminal beaks. The internal mold of this species shows a distinct muscle scar just below the beaks and low, irregularly spaced, comarginal undulations of the shell.

Four Mississippian species are elongate forms that have a distinct ridge radiating from the beak area. *Promacrus andrewsi* Meek (fig. 12-3.14) is quite large (±12 cm) and has coarse, comarginal ridges ornamenting the shell; the beaks are located near midlength. The genus is restricted to the Lower Mississippian. *Sanguinolites naiadiformis* Winchell (fig. 12-3.13) is large, narrowly elongate, and has a smooth shell in which the beaks are nearer the anterior margin than in *P. andrewsi*. The genus *Sanguinolites* ranges from Upper Devonian to Permian. *Sphenotus aeolus* Hall (fig. 12-3.9) is medium sized and has a smooth shell. The genus ranges from Devonian to Mississippian. *Prothyris meeki* Winchell (figs. 12-3.17, 12-3.18) is medium sized, narrow, and has the beaks near the anterior margin. It has a truncate posterior margin and a small flap at the anterior margin separated from the rest of the shell by a notch.

The genus *Aviculopecten* ranges from Lower Mississippian to Upper Permian. *Aviculopecten winchelli* Meek (fig. 12-3.8) and *A. subcardiformis* (Herrick) (fig. 12-3.7) are representative medium-sized Mississippian pectiniform species in Ohio. *Aviculopecten winchelli* has larger auricles and more broadly rounded shell margins than *A. subcardiformis*. Both are ornamented by numerous radiating costae of at least two sizes. The genus *Streblochondria* ranges from Mississippian to Permian and is represented by *Streblochondria* sp. (fig. 12-3.1), a small species that has fine, subequal, radiating costae crossed by fine, comarginal ridges to form a reticulate pattern.

Edmondia depressa Hall (fig. 12-3.6) is a medium-sized species ornamented with comarginal ridges. The genus ranges from Upper Devonian to Upper Permian. *Wilkingia winchelli* (Meek) (figs. 12-3.10, 12-3.11) also is medium sized but becomes larger than *E. depressa*, has coarser comarginal ridges, and commonly has a posterior **gape** between the two valves. The genus ranges from Mississippian to Permian. The genus *Schizodus* also ranges from Mississippian to Permian and is represented in the Mississippian of Ohio by *S. medenaensis* Meek (fig. 12-3.3). The medium-sized, ovate shell of this species has the beaks near midlength and an abruptly truncate posterior margin. *Ectogrammysia plena* (Hall) (fig. 12-3.5) is somewhat similar in shape and size to *S. medenaensis*, but has coarse comarginal ridges, some of which split in the anterior portion of the shell. It also has a weak sulcus radiating from the beak area to the ventral margin. The genus is restricted to the Mississippian.

PENNSYLVANIAN PELECYPODS

Pennsylvanian pelecypods are common and are more likely to have the shell material preserved than specimens from older rocks in Ohio. Although they are found in limestones, shales yield a much greater number of specimens.

The most abundant forms are small and have numerous small, subequal teeth. *Nuculopsis anodontoides* (Meek) (figs. 12-4.1, 12-4.2) is suboval and has a smooth shell. It differs from another, very common, similar species, *N. girtyi* Schenck (not illustrated), in having a more produced (elongated in one direction) posterior margin. The genus ranges from Mississippian to Permian. *Phestia arata* (Hall) (figs. 12-4.3 to 12-4.5) is an elongate form that has conspicuous comarginal ridges. The genus ranges from Devonian to Lower Triassic. A Pennsylvanian species of *Palaeoneilo*, *P. oweni* (McChesney) (figs. 12-4.6, 12-4.7), also is elongate in shape but has a smooth shell except for fine growth lines.

Less common are forms such as *Parallelodon carbonarius* (Cox) (fig. 12-4.19), a medium-sized species that has a subrectangular form and is ornamented by numerous radiating costae. The genus ranges from Lower Ordovician to Upper Jurassic. *Promytilus pottsvillensis* Hoare, Sturgeon & Kindt, *Septimyalina perattenuata* (Meek & Hayden), *Pteronites peracuta* (Shumard), and *Leptodesma ohioense* (Herrick) are all subtriangular forms in which the beaks are located very close to the anterior margin of the shell. *Promytilus pottsvillensis* (fig. 12-4.9) is small, has a pronounced ridge extending from the beak to the posteroventral margin, and has a spatulate posterior. *Septimyalina perattenuata* (fig. 12-4.21) is medium sized and commonly has coarse, **lamellose** growth lines. *Pteronites peracuta* (fig. 12-4.18) becomes quite large (±12 cm) and has a narrowly triangular shape. *Promytilus, Septimyalina*, and *Pteronites* all range from Mississippian to Permian. *Leptodesma ohioense* (fig. 12-4.8) is small and has a large, sharply pointed posterior auricle.

Pennsylvanian taxa that are pectiniform are common. *Dunbarella knighti* Newell (fig. 12-4.12) is small, has a small anterior auricle and a large posterior auricle not set off from the shell body, and is ornamented with numerous radiating costae. The genus ranges from Mississippian to Pennsylvanian. *Aviculopecten sorer* Herrick (fig. 12-4.16) also is small and has distinct posterior and anterior auricles and radiating costae of two different sizes. Numerous other species of *Aviculopecten* are present. Some reach a much larger size (up to 14 cm) and differ in shape and the development of costae. *Fasciculiconcha scalaris* (Herrick) (fig. 12-4.24) is medium sized and has pronounced auricles and radiating costae grouped in bundles. This genus ranges from Middle Pennsylvanian to Upper Permian. *Acanthopecten bellosum* Hoare, Sturgeon & Kindt (fig. 12-4.20) is medium sized and has distinct auricles and broadly rounded, radiating plications crossed by lamellose, comarginal ridges on the **left valve**. Figure 12-4.20 shows the differences in the radiating costae on the left valve and **right valve**, which is typical of many pectiniform bivalves. The genus *Acanthopecten* ranges from Mississippian to Upper Permian. *Streblochondria stantonensis* Newell (fig. 12-4.17) is small and has fine radiating costae crossed by nearly equal sized, comarginal ridges to form a reticulate pattern. *Streblochondria tenuilineata* (Meek & Worthen) (fig. 12.4.11) is small and has a smooth shell, in contrast to most species of this genus, which have radial and comarginal ornamentation. *Posidonia fracta* (Meek) (fig. 12-4.25) is medium sized, lacks distinct auricles, and is ornamented only by comarginal ridges. The genus ranges from Mississippian to Upper Jurassic. *Palaeolima triplistriata* (Stevens) (fig. 12-4.13) is small and has small auricles and numerous fine, radiating costae. The genus ranges from Mississippian to Upper Triassic.

Schizodus wheeleri (Swallow) (figs. 12-4.22, 12-4.23) is medium sized and has a smooth shell that has a truncate posterior margin. *Permophorus spinulosa* (Morningstar) (fig. 12-4.10) is medium sized, narrowly elongate, and has four ridges radiating from the beak area to the posterior margin. The genus ranges from Mississippian to Permian.

Astartella varica McChesney (figs. 12-4.14, 12-4.15) is small and has coarse, widely spaced, comarginal ridges. Other species of *Astartella* have finer and more closely spaced ridges. The genus ranges from Pennsylvanian to Permian. *Edmondia ovata* Meek & Worthen (fig. 12-4.26) is medium sized, has nearly evenly rounded anterior and posterior margins, and is ornamented with low, comarginal wrinkles. *Wilkingia terminale* (Hall) (fig. 12-4.27) is large, has beaks near the anterior margin, and is ornamented with coarse, comarginal wrinkles. Some specimens may show the posterior shell gape typical of this genus.

PENNSYLVANIAN AND PERMIAN PELECYPODS

A number of freshwater pelecypods occur in shales associated with coal beds, particularly in the Upper Pennsylvanian and Permian rocks in Ohio. Specimens are small, thin shelled, and commonly distorted by compaction. *Anthraconaia* **aff.** *A. minuta* (Stauffer & Schroyer) (figs. 12-3.19, 12-3.20) has beaks near the anterior margin and a somewhat truncate posterior margin. *Anthraconaia* aff. *A. belmontensis* (Stauffer & Schroyer) (fig. 12-3.21) is more elongate and has a long, rounded, posterior margin. The beaks are not as close to the anterior margin as in *A. minuta*. The genus ranges from Pennsylvanian to Permian.

QUATERNARY PELECYPODS

Climatic changes during the past 2 million years (the approximate time span represented by the Quaternary Epoch) were responsible for the development of a series of ice sheets that waxed and waned over large areas of North America. These climatic oscillations caused numerous changes in the distributions of animals and plants in Ohio.

Quaternary-age sediments can be found in all parts of Ohio. The fossils preserved in these deposits, for the most part, are represented by living species, although their modern geographic distributions may no longer include Ohio. It is this aspect of the Quaternary fossil record that is so fascinating. The fossils indirectly are proxy records of the climatic changes that controlled their distributions.

Quaternary mollusks occur in a variety of habitats, including sediments deposited in lakes, ponds, river floodplains, and marshes. The sediments commonly contain mixtures of both land and freshwater pelecypods. La Rocque (1966, 1967) published detailed information on the Quaternary pelecypods of Ohio.

KEY TO SOME QUATERNARY PELECYPODS FROM OHIO

1A.	Beaks terminal of center; shell typically less than 10 mm long	*Pisidium* (fig. 12-5.1)
1B.	Beaks central or subcentral; shell typically less than 25 mm long; valves relatively smooth	2
2A.	Beak typically separated from main body of valve by distinct groove (caused by break in growth)	*Musculium* (fig. 12-5.2)
2B.	Beak not separated from main body of valve by groove	*Sphaerium* (fig. 12-5.3)

Pelecypods most commonly encountered in Quaternary deposits are members of the genera *Pisidium* Pfeiffer, *Sphaerium* Scopoli, or *Musculium* Link. These genera are represented by small, smooth shells, generally less than 25 mm in length, that belong to the family Pisidiidae, or fingernail clams. The genus *Pisidium* (fig. 12-5.1) can generally be distinguished from the other genera of fingernail clams by its small size (typically less than 10 mm in length) and the location of the beaks posterior to the center of the shell. *Sphaerium* (fig. 12-5.3) can generally be recognized by the central to subcentral position of the beaks. *Musculium* (fig. 12-5.2) is similar to *Sphaerium* but the beaks are generally separated from the remainder of the valve by a groove.

Members of a second family, the Unionidae (freshwater mussels) may also be encountered at some localities, but they are rare and commonly too poorly preserved to collect and identify.

COLLECTING LOCALITIES

Pelecypods have been collected from the localities listed below. Collecting at Caesar Creek State Park requires a permit, available at the park Visitor Center. All other localities are on private property and are not accessible without permission of the landowner.

Ordovician localities include exposures of the Waynesville, Liberty, and Whitewater Formations at the emergency spillway in Caesar Creek State Park, approximately 8 km (5 miles) southeast of Waynesville, Warren County, and the Waynesville Formation below the dam on Twin Creek, approximately 1.6 km (1 mile) west of Germantown, just north of Ohio Route 725, Montgomery County.

Silurian localities include an exposure of the Lockport Formation in the limestone quarry on the southwest side of Woodville, west of U.S. Route 20, Sandusky County.

Devonian localities include exposures of the Columbus Limestone at Hayden Run Falls, where Hayden Run Road crosses Hayden Run west of the Scioto River in Columbus, Franklin County, and in old quarries just south of Sandusky, Erie County.

Mississippian localities include exposures of the Cuyahoga Formation on the east side of Little Rush Creek below the railroad station at the old dam at Rushville, Fairfield County, and along Healey Creek, 2.6 km (1.6 miles) east of Bennetts Corners, above the bridge on Boston Road, in Hinkley Township, Medina County.

Pennsylvanian localities include exposures of the Putnam Hill shale and limestone in a borrow pit and abandoned coal mine on the east side of Interstate 77, south of U.S. Route 250, approximately 1.6 km (1 mile) southwest of New Philadelphia, Tuscarawas County, and the Lower Mercer limestone along Muskingum County Route 117 approximately 4.8 km (3 miles) southeast of Frazeyburg, Muskingum County.

Quaternary pelecypods have been collected from the marl pits just west of Castalia, Erie County.

FIGURE 12-1.—Ordovician and Silurian pelecypods. Scale bars equal 1 cm. Scale bar A applies to figures 12-1.1 and 12-1.2; B applies to figures 12-1.3 and 12-1.4; C applies to figure 12-1.6; D applies to figures 12-1.5 and 12-1.7 to 12-1.15.

1	*Caritodens demissa* (Conrad). Left-valve view. Whitewater Formation (Upper Ordovician), exposure below dam at Germantown, Montgomery County, Ohio; OSU 46654.
2	*Anomalodonta gigantea* Miller. Left-valve view of **composite** internal mold. Whitewater Formation (Upper Ordovician), road cut on U.S. Route 27 south of Richmond, Wayne County, Indiana; OSU 46655.
3-5	*Ambonychia robusta* Hall. **3**, **4**, dorsal and right-valve views of composite internal mold. Same unit and location as **2**; OSU 46656. **5**, crushed right-lateral view showing external ornamentation; Waynesville Formation (Upper Ordovician), emergency spillway, Caesar Creek State Park, Warren County, Ohio; OSU 46657.
6	*Ctenodonta perminuta* Foerste. Left-valve view of composite internal mold. Upper Ordovician, unknown locality in Cincinnati area; OSU 46658.
7	*Cyrtodontula umbonata* (Ulrich). Left-valve view of internal mold. Same unit and location as **5**; OSU 46659.
8	*Ischyrodonta elongata* Ulrich. Left-valve view of composite internal mold. Same unit and location as **5**; OSU 46660.
9, 10	*Mytilarca acutirostris* (Ulrich). Dorsal (**9**) and left-valve (**10**) views of composite internal mold. Cedarville Dolomite (Silurian), Cedarville, Greene County, Ohio; OSU 5904.
11	*Amphicoelia costata* Hall & Whitfield. Left-valve view of composite internal mold. Same unit and location as **9**, **10**; OSU 3333.
12, 13	*Modiomorpha* sp. Dorsal (**12**) and left-valve (**13**) views of composite internal mold. Lockport Dolomite (Silurian), quarry at Woodville, Sandusky County, Ohio; OSU 46661.
14, 15	*Megalomoidea canadensis* (Hall). **14**, left-valve view of composite internal mold. Internal molds of *Megalomoidea* commonly are referred to as "beef hearts." Same unit and location as **12**, **13**; OSU 46662. **15**, right-valve view showing shell; Lockport Dolomite (Silurian), quarry at Genoa, Ottawa County, Ohio; OSU 46663.

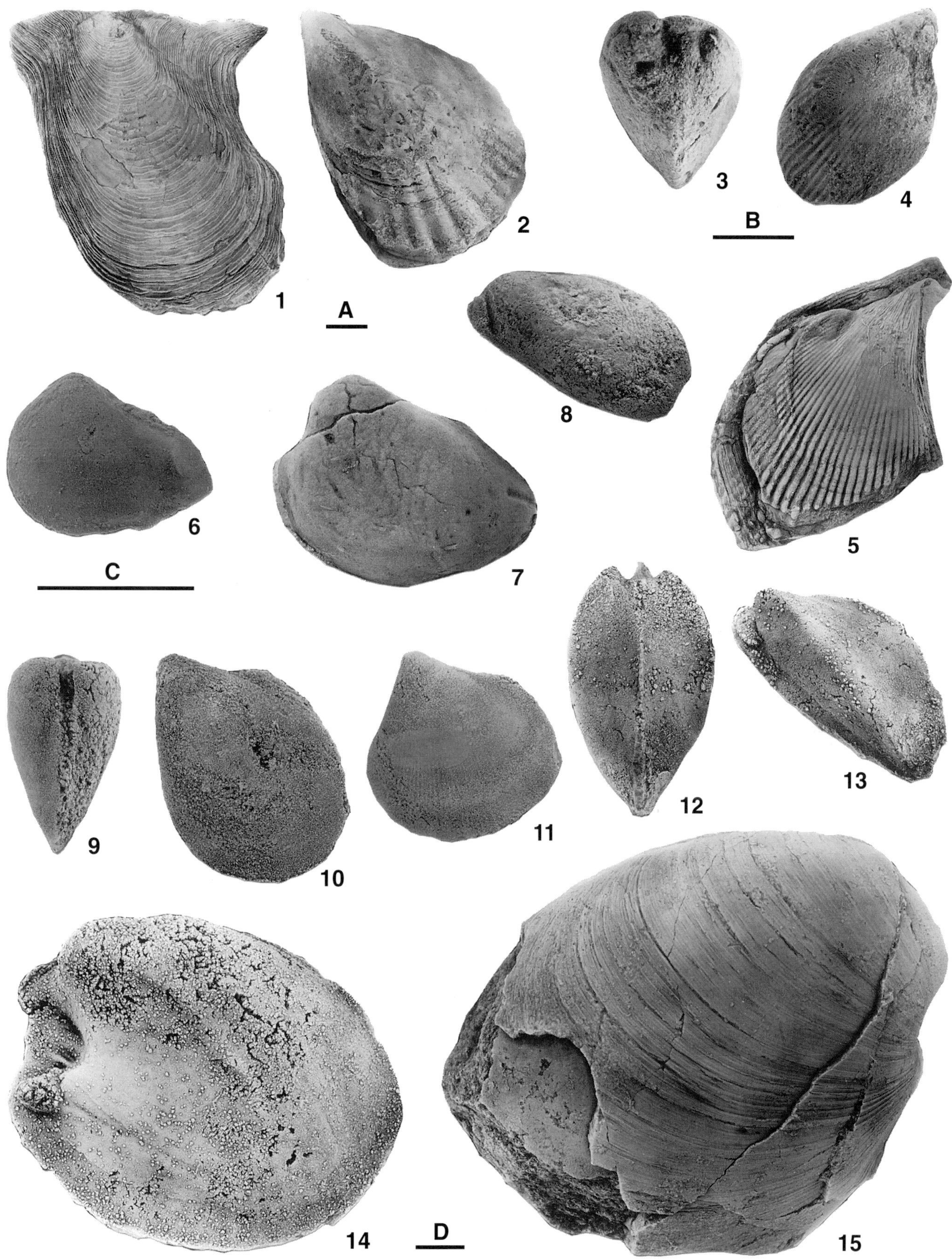

1
2
3
4
B
A
5
6
7
8
C
9
10
11
12
13
14
D
15

FIGURE 12-2.—Devonian pelecypods. Scale bars equal 1 cm. Scale bar A applies to figures 12-2.1 to 12-2.5; B applies to figure 12-2.6; C applies to figures 12-2.7 to 12-2.9; D applies to figures 12-2.10 to 12-2.12.

1	*Ptychopteria decussata* (Hall). Left-valve view of internal mold. Amherstburg Dolomite, exposure south of bridge over Sandusky River, Pitt Township, Wyandot County, Ohio; OSU 46664.
2	*Ptychopteria boydi* (Conrad). View of left-valve interior. Silica Formation, quarry west of Sylvania, Lucas County, Ohio; OSU 46665.
3	*Pseudaviculopecten scabridus* (Hall). View of left-valve interior. Same unit and location as **2**; OSU 46666.
4, 5	*Nuculites oblongatus* Conrad. Left-lateral (**4**) and dorsal (**5**) views of composite internal mold showing muscle scars, pallial line, and dentition. Plum Brook Shale, exposure in NASA Reservation, Erie County, Ohio; OSU 46667.
6	*Orthonota undulata* Conrad. Left-valve view of internal mold. Same unit and location as **2**; UMMP 61377.
7, 8	*Grammysia bisulcata* Conrad. Right-valve (**7**) and dorsal (**8**) views. Same unit and location as **2**; UMMP 61376.
9	*Limoptera macoptera* (Conrad). Left-valve view. Same unit and location as **2**; OSU 46668.
10	*Leptodesma ausablensis* Ehlers & Wright. Left-valve view. Same unit and location as **2**; UMMP 38201.
11	*Ptychopteria flabella* (Conrad). Left-valve view, auricles missing. Same unit and location as **2**; OSU 46669.
12	*Paracyclas elliptica* Hall. Right-valve view of composite internal mold. Dundee Formation, quarry at Whitehouse, Lucas County, Ohio; OSU 46670.

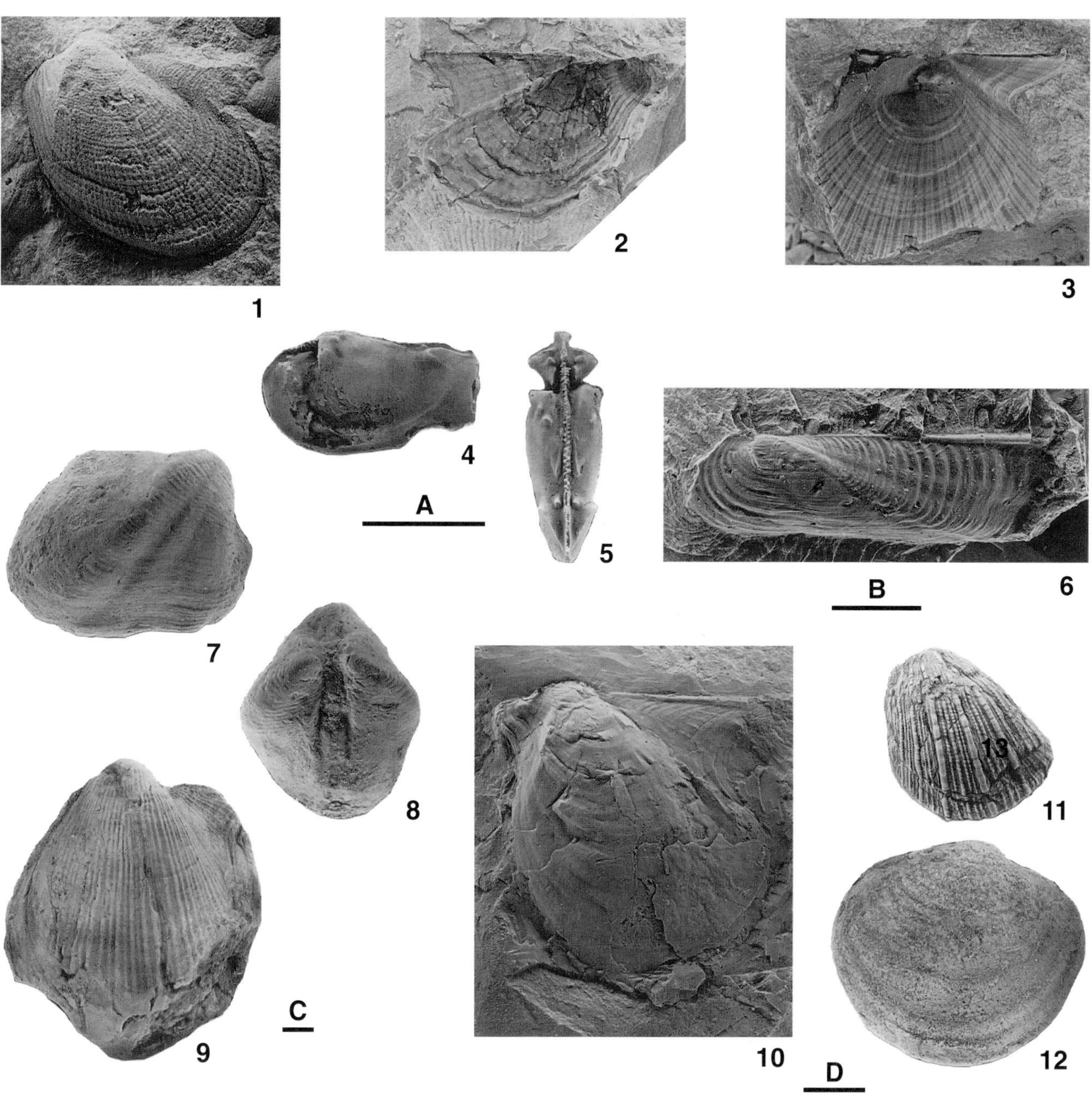
1
2
3
4
5
6
7
8
9
10
11
12
13
A
B
C
D

FIGURE 12-3.—Mississippian and Pennsylvanian pelecypods. Scale bars equal 1 cm. Scale bar A applies to figures 12-3.1 and 12-3.2; B applies to figures 12-3.3 to 12-3.5; C applies to figures 12-3.6 to 12-3.13; D applies to figure 12-3.14; E applies to figures 12-3.15 to 12-3.18; F applies to figures 12-3.19 to 12-3.21.

1 — *Streblochondria* sp. Right-valve view of internal mold. Cuyahoga Formation (Mississippian), unknown locality in Cuyahoga County, Ohio; OSU 22480.

2 — *Palaeoneilo truncata* Hall. Left-valve view of internal mold. Cuyahoga Formation (Mississippian), unknown locality in Wayne County, Ohio; OSU 22442.

3 — *Schizodus medenaensis* Meek. Left-valve view of composite internal mold. Same unit and location as **2**; OSU 22465.

4 — *Leptodesma scutella* Herrick. Right-valve view of internal mold. Logan Formation (Mississippian), unknown locality in Licking County, Ohio; OSU 20266.

5 — *Ectogrammysia plena* (Hall). Right-valve view of internal mold. Cuyahoga Formation (Mississippian), unknown locality in Medina County, Ohio; OSU 22436.

6 — *Edmondia depressa* Hall. Left-valve view of internal mold. Same unit and location as **1**; OSU 22497.

7 — *Aviculopecten subcardiformis* (Herrick). Left-valve view of internal mold. Same unit and location as **4**; OSU 7478.

8 — *Aviculopecten winchelli* Meek. Left-valve view of internal mold. Same unit and location as **4**; OSU 20393.

9 — *Sphenotus aeolus* Hall. Left-valve view of internal mold. Mississippian, unit and locality unknown; OSU 23831.

10, 11 — *Wilkingia winchelli* (Meek). Right-valve (**10**) and dorsal (**11**) views of composite internal mold. Logan Formation (Mississippian), unknown locality in Hocking County, Ohio; OSU 20402.

12 — *Lithophaga jessicae* (Miller & Gurley). Left-valve view of internal mold. Same unit and location as **5**; OSU 22492.

13 — *Sanguinolites naiadiformis* Winchell. Left-valve view of internal mold. Same unit and location as **4**; OSU 7484.

14 — *Promacrus andrewsi* Meek. Left-valve view of composite internal mold. Logan Formation (Mississippian), unknown locality in Scioto County, Ohio; OSU 13753.

15, 16 — *Modiolus missouriensis* (Weller). Dorsal (**15**) and left-valve (**16**) views of composite internal mold. Logan Formation (Mississippian), railroad cut northwest of Sciotoville, Scioto County, Ohio; OSU 19865.

17, 18 — *Prothyris meeki* Winchell. Left-valve (**17**) and dorsal (**18**) views of composite internal mold. Logan Formation (Mississippian), exposure at Rushville, Fairfield County, Ohio; OSU 13779.

19, 20 — *Anthraconaia* aff. *A. minuta* (Stauffer & Schroyer). Left-valve (**19**) and right-valve (**20**) views of two internal molds. Upper Pittsburgh pelecypod zone (Monongahela Group, Pennsylvanian), exposure near Calais, Monroe County, Ohio; OSU 46671, 46672.

21 — *Anthraconaia* aff. *A. belmontensis* (Stauffer & Schroyer). Articulated internal mold. Same unit and location as **19**, **20**; OSU 46673.

1
2
A
3
4
B
5
6
7
8
9
10
11
C
12
13
15
16
19865
18
14
D
E
17
19
20
F
21

FIGURE 12-4.—Pennsylvanian pelecypods. Scale bars equal 1 cm. Scale bar A applies to figures 12-4.1 to 12-4.16; B applies to figure 12-4.17; C applies to figures 12-4.18 to 12-4.27.

1, 2 *Nuculopsis anodontoides* (Meek). Right-valve (**1**) and dorsal (**2**) views. Brush Creek shale (Conemaugh Group), road cut on Appalachian Highway (Ohio Route 32) southwest of Athens, Athens County, Ohio; OSU 46674.

3-5 *Phestia arata* (Hall). **3**, **4**, left-valve and dorsal views. OSU 46675. **5**, interior of right valve showing dentition and muscle scars. OSU 27187. All specimens from same unit and location as **1**, **2**.

6, 7 *Palaeoneilo oweni* (McChesney). **6**, left-valve view. Washingtonville shale (Allegheny Group), strip mine southwest of New Philadelphia, Tuscarawas County, Ohio; OSU 27178. **7**, dorsal view. Columbiana shale (Allegheny Group), strip mine near Waynesburg, Stark County, Ohio; OSU 27175.

8 *Leptodesma ohioense* (Herrick). Right-valve view. Lower Mercer limestone (Pottsville Group), road cut on county road southeast of Newark, Licking County, Ohio; OSU 27234.

9 *Promytilus pottsvillensis* Hoare, Sturgeon & Kindt. Left-valve view. Lower Mercer limestone (Pottsville Group), exposure near Millersburg, Holmes County, Ohio; OSU 4587-1.

10 *Permophorus spinulosa* (Morningstar). Right-valve view. Lower Mercer limestone (Pottsville Group), exposure on Bald Knob, Licking County, Ohio; OSU 15248.

11 *Streblochondria tenuilineata* (Meek & Worthen). Right-valve view. Lower Mercer limestone (Pottsville Group), road cut on County Route 117 southeast of Frazeyburg, Muskingum County, Ohio; OSU 15289-2.

12 *Dunbarella knighti* Newell. Left-valve view. Putnam Hill shale (Allegheny Group), borrow pit on west side of Interstate 77 south of New Philadelphia, Tuscarawas County, Ohio; OSU 27245.

13 *Palaeolima triplistriata* (Stevens). Articulated internal mold. Brush Creek shale (Conemaugh Group), railroad cut at south edge of Summitville, Columbiana County, Ohio; OSU 27348.

14, 15 *Astartella varica* McChesney. Right-valve (**14**) and dorsal (**15**) views. Putnam Hill shale (Conemaugh Group), abandoned strip mine north of U.S. Route 50 east of McArthur, Vinton County, Ohio; OSU 27379.

16 *Aviculopecten sorer* Herrick. Left-valve view of internal mold. Lower Mercer limestone (Pottsville Group), exposure in Big Run near Dresden, Muskingum County, Ohio; OSU 27259.

17 *Streblochondria stantonensis* Newell. Left-valve view of internal mold. Portersville limestone (Conemaugh Group), abandoned railroad cut south of Portersville, Perry County, Ohio; OSU 14033.

18 *Pteronites peracuta* (Shumard). Left-valve view. Ames limestone (Conemaugh Group), exposure on Crooked Creek south of New Concord, Muskingum County, Ohio; OSU 27217.

19 *Parallelodon carbonarius* (Cox). Right-valve view. Putnam Hill shale (Allegheny Group), strip mine northeast of Alliance, Mahoning County, Ohio; OSU 27222.

20 *Acanthopecten bellosum* Hoare, Sturgeon & Kindt. Articulated internal mold. Putnam Hill shale (Allegheny Group), abandoned strip mine northeast of Logan, Hocking County, Ohio; OSU 27284.

21 *Septimyalina perattenuata* (Meek & Hayden). Left-valve view. Same unit and location as **16**; OSU 27226.

22, 23 *Schizodus wheeleri* (Swallow). Dorsal (**22**) and left-valve (**23**) views of internal mold. Same unit and location as **1**, **2**; OSU 27352.

24 *Fasciculiconcha scalaris* (Herrick). Left-valve view of internal mold. Lower Mercer limestone (Pottsville Group), road cut south of Lyra, Scioto County, Ohio; OSU 15287.

25 *Posidonia fracta* (Meek). Right-valve view of internal mold. Lower Mercer shale (Pottsville Group), exposure in Rock Hollow near McArthur, Vinton County, Ohio; OSU 27333.

26 *Edmondia ovata* Meek & Worthen. Left-valve view. Same unit and location as **1**, **2**; OSU 27390.

27 *Wilkingia terminale* (Hall). Right-valve view of internal mold. Ames limestone (Conemaugh Group), exposure in ravine near Jacksonville, Athens County, Ohio; OSU 28986.

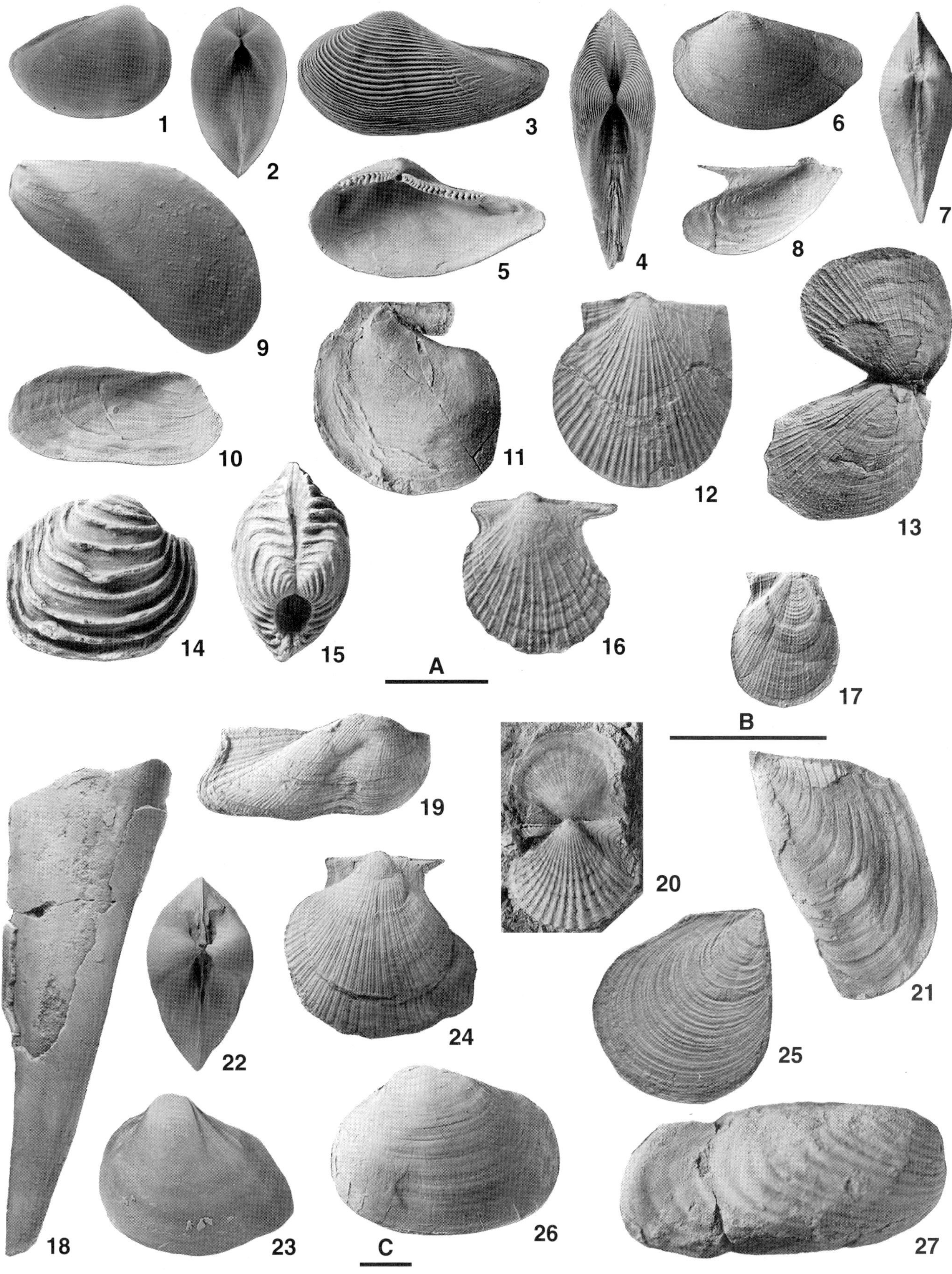
1
2
3
4
5
6
7
8
9
10
11
12
13
14
15
16
17
A
B
18
19
20
21
22
23
24
25
26
27
C

FIGURE 12-5.—Quaternary pelecypods. Scale bars for figures 12-5.1 and 12-5.2 equal 1 mm; scale bar for figure 12-5.3 equals 1 cm. All figures redrawn from Burch (1975).

1 *Pisidium* sp. Left valve, showing beak posterior of center.

2 *Musculium* sp. Left valve, showing beak anterior of center and separated from remainder of the valve by a groove.

3 *Sphaerium* sp. Left valve, showing beak slightly anterior of center.

Chapter 13

PHYLUM MOLLUSCA, CLASS GASTROPODA

by Richard D. Hoare and Barry B. Miller

INTRODUCTION

Gastropods, commonly called snails, inhabit marine, freshwater, and land environments. They are common in modern-day streams, lakes, and oceans. Those that live in marine habitats breath by the use of gills. Those living in freshwater have gills or a lunglike structure. Terrestrial gastropods have a lunglike structure. Gastropods are mobile organisms, crawling slowly over the surface (**epifaunal**), although a few forms live below the surface (**infaunal**).

In Ohio, gastropods are relatively common as fossils, especially in Pennsylvanian rocks. Specimens from Ordovician and Silurian rocks are commonly preserved as **internal molds**, called **steinkerns**, which lack the external **ornamentation** and which typically have a much different shape than specimens in which the shell is preserved. It is generally difficult to impossible to determine the correct species on the basis of internal molds.

Gastropods have a coiled shell that is **conispiral**, **planispiral**, or **pseudoplanispiral** in form (see fig. 1-17). A number of the planispiral forms, particularly those from lower Paleozoic rocks, have recently been placed in the class Monoplacophora, a primitive group of the Mollusca, but are included here in the gastropods for convenience.

In the following key and descriptions of Ohio gastropods, size ranges are: small, 1 cm or less in height; medium, 1.5-4 cm in height; large, 5 cm or more in height. Sizes apply to average, mature specimens; juvenile specimens may be smaller.

Additional information on Ohio gastropods can be found in Meek (1873, 1875), Hall and Whitfield (1875), Foerste (1893), Whitfield (1893), Stauffer (1909), Mark (1912), Morningstar (1922), Hyde (1953), Knight and others (1960), La Rocque (1968, 1970), Nave (1969), Solem and Yochelson (1979), and Davis (1985).

KEY TO SOME PALEOZOIC GASTROPODS FROM OHIO

1A. Shell planispiral 2
1B. Shell pseudoplanispiral 8
1C. Shell conispiral 9

2A. **Selenizone** absent 3
2B. Selenizone present 5

3A. Expanded **aperture** ..... *Tremanotus* (figs. 13-1.14, 13-1.15)
3B. Narrow aperture 4

4A. Shell loosely coiled ..... *Cyrtolites* (figs. 13-1.5, 13-1.6)
4B. Shell tightly coiled ..... *Sinuites* (figs. 13-1.1, 13-1.2)

5A. Expanded aperture 6
5B. Narrow aperture 7

6A. Shell has **transverse** ornamentation ..... *Bellerophon* (figs. 13-2.16, 13-3.6 to 13-3.8, 13-3.15, 13-3.16)
6B. Shell has transverse and spiral ornamentation ..... *Knightites* (figs. 13-3.1, 13-3.2)

7A. Shell narrow ..... *Tropidodiscus* (figs. 13-2.17, 13-2.18)
7B. Shell broad ..... *Euphemites* (figs. 13-3.3 to 13-3.5)

8A. Selenizone absent ..... *Straparollus* (figs. 13-2.11, 13-2.12, 13-3.11, 13-3.12)
8B. Selenizone present ..... *Pleuronotus* (fig. 13-2.3)

9A. Selenizone absent 10
9B. Selenizone present 18
9C. **Pseudoselenizone** present .... *Platyschisma* (figs. 13-2.19, 13-2.20)

10A. Shell has ornamentation 11
10B. Shell smooth except for **growth lines** 15

11A. Shell typically has **spines** .... *Platyceras* (figs. 13-1.12, 13-1.13, 13-2.7, 13-2.9, 13-2.10)
11B. Shell without spines 12

12A. Transverse and spiral ornamentation present .... *Cyclonema* (figs. 13-1.3, 13-1.10)
12B. Transverse ornamentation only present 13

13A. Shell low **spired** .... *Isonema* (fig. 13-2.8)
13B. Shell moderately spired .... *Elasmonema* (fig. 13-2.4)
13C. Shell high spired 14

14A. Ornamentation coarse .... *Palaeozygopleura* (fig. 13-3.19)
14B. Ornamentation fine .... *Loxonema* (figs. 13-2.2, 13-2.15)

15A. Shell relatively narrow 16
15B. Shell relatively broad 17

16A. **Whorl profile** flat .... *Meekospira* (fig. 13-3.22)
16B. Whorl profile rounded .... *Bulimorpha* (fig. 13-2.14)

17A. Whorls rapidly expanding .... *Strobeus* (figs. 13-3.17, 13-3.21, 13-3.24)
17B. Whorls slowly expanding .... *Holopea* (fig. 13-1.4)

18A. Shell smooth 19
18B. Shell ornamented 23

19A. Shell high spired 20
19B. Shell moderately spired .... *Clathrospira* (fig. 13-1.11)
19C. Shell low spired 21

20A. Whorl profile angular .... *Loxoplocus* (fig. 13-1.7)
20B. Whorl profile rounded or angular .... *Murchisonia* (figs. 13-1.19, 13-1.20, 13-2.1)

21A. Whorl profile angular 22
21B. Whorl profile rounded .... *Euryzone* (figs. 13-2.5, 13-2.6)

22A. Shell small .... *Liospira* (figs. 13-1.8, 13-1.9)
22B. Shell large .... *Rhombella* (figs. 13-1.17, 13-1.18)

23A. Transverse and spiral ornamentation present 24
23B. Spiral ornamentation only present 27

24A. Whorl profile rounded 25
24B. Whorl profile angular 26

25A. Final whorl expanded .... *Phanerotrema* (fig. 13-1.16)
25B. Final whorl not expanded .... *Mourlonia* (fig. 13-2.13)

26A. Selenizone marked by row of **nodes** .... *Worthenia* (fig. 13-3.9)
26B. Selenizone a deep groove .... *Spiroscala* (fig. 13-3.20)
26C. Selenizone a shallow groove .... *Phymatopleura* (fig. 13-3.10)

27A. Whorl profile angular .... *Trepospira* (figs. 13-3.13, 13-3.14)
27B. Whorl profile convex or concave 28

28A. Shell narrow, whorl profile concave .... *Stegocoelia* (fig. 13-3.18)
28B. Shell broad, whorl profile convex .... *Shansiella* (fig. 13-3.23)

ORDOVICIAN GASTROPODS

Ordovician conispiral forms are illustrated by *Loxoplocus bowdeni* (Safford) (fig. 13-1.7), which is a medium-sized, relatively high-**turreted** form that has a **keel** or angulation running around the shell. Internal molds of this species are common and do not show the keel. The genus ranges from Ordovician to Silurian. *Clathrospira subconica* (Hall) (fig. 13-1.11) is a medium-sized, broadly turreted species. The genus ranges from Middle Ordovician to Silurian. The genus *Cyclonema* ranges from Middle Ordovician to Upper Silurian and is represented by several medium-sized species in Ordovician rocks of Ohio. The shell commonly is well preserved. *Cyclonema bilix* (Conrad) (fig. 13-1.3) is the most common species and has numerous fine, spiral **costae** of three different sizes on the whorls. *Cyclonema varicosa* Hall (fig. 13-1.10) also has three sizes of spiral costae, but they are more prominent and the shell becomes larger than other species of the genus. *Holopea obliqua* Hall (fig. 13-1.4) is medium sized and moderately low spired and has strongly rounded whorls ornamented only with growth lines. The genus ranges from Middle Ordovician to Devonian. *Liospira vitruvia* (Billings) (figs. 13-1.8, 13-1.9) is small, very low spired, and has a sharp angulation at midwhorl. The genus ranges from Lower Ordovician to Silurian.

Planispiral species, termed bellerophontaceans, are an extinct group of organisms ranging from Cambrian to Triassic in age. Planispiral Ordovician forms such as the medium-sized *Sinuites cancellatus* (Hall) (figs. 13-1.1, 13-1.2) are classified by many paleontologists as monoplacophorans on the basis of the presence of multiple, bilaterally arranged **muscle scars**. Because these shells commonly are preserved as internal molds, the muscle scars may or may not be preserved. *Cyrtolites ornatus* Conrad (figs. 13-1.5, 13-1.6) also is classified as a monoplacophoran. It is medium sized, its keeled shell is narrower than that of *Sinuites*, and it has broad, transverse undulations and a more loosely coiled shell. The genus ranges from Middle Ordovician to Lower Silurian. These forms are included here with the gastropods because they are so difficult to distinguish from them and they may indeed be gastropods.

SILURIAN GASTROPODS

Internal molds of Silurian gastropods are especially difficult to identify because they do not show the type and position of the **slit** or the selenizone. The specimen illustrated in figure 13-1.19 probably represents a large species of *Murchisonia*, a genus that ranges from Ordovician to Triassic; the specimen in figure 13-1.20 may be a different species of the same genus. Both are tall, narrow, conispiral forms that have deeply incised **sutures** and the selenizone at midwhorl. Whether the specimens have a narrow, deep slit in the aperture or a shallow notch, which would distinguish the species, is unknown, because neither feature is preserved on internal molds. *Rhombella* sp. (figs. 13-1.17, 13-1.18) is a large, very broad, low-spired form that has a distinct angulation near the bottom of the whorls marking the position of the selenizone. The genus ranges from Ordovician to Silurian. *Phanerotrema* sp. (fig. 13-1.16) is medium sized and narrower and more highly spired than *Rhombella*. Internal molds do not show the transverse and spiral ornamentation of the shell. The genus *Phanerotrema* ranges from Lower Silurian to Lower Devonian. *Platyceras niagarensis* (Hall) (fig. 13-1.13) is a medium-sized, very low spired form ornamented by numerous low, sinuous growth lines. Its final whorl tends to separate from the rest of the shell. The genus ranges from Silurian to Middle Permian. Another, unidentified species of *Platyceras* (fig. 13-1.12) differs by having numerous fine, widely spaced, spiraling ridges. *Tremanotus alpheus* (Hall) (figs. 13-1.14, 13-1.15) is a large, narrow, loosely coiled, planispiral form that has a ridge or row of nodes along the bilateral plane of symmetry. This genus ranges from Middle Ordovician to Middle Silurian and may or may not be a monoplacophoran.

DEVONIAN GASTROPODS

High-spired Devonian gastropods are illustrated by *Loxonema pexatum* Hall (fig. 13-2.2). This large species has incised sutures and is ornamented with fine, closely spaced, curving, transverse costae. The genus ranges from Middle Ordovician to Mississippian. *Murchisonia* sp. (fig. 13-2.1) is large, high turreted, and has a sharp angle at midwhorl. *Elasmonema bellatum* (Hall) (fig. 13-2.4) is a small, conical species that has fine, closely spaced, transverse costae. *Isonema humile* Meek (fig. 13-2.8) is a medium-sized, low-spired, conical species ornamented with fine, closely spaced, transverse costae. *Elasmonema* and *Isonema* are both restricted to the Lower Devonian. *Mourlonia lucina* (Hall) (fig. 13-2.13) is medium sized, has strongly rounded whorls, and is ornamented with numerous fine, transverse and spiraling costae forming a **reticulate** pattern. The selenizone is at midwhorl. The genus ranges from Middle Ordovician to Lower Permian. *Euryzone arata* Hall (figs. 13-2.5, 13-2.6) is a medium-sized, low-spired, conical form most commonly preserved as an internal mold in Ohio. The mold does not show the prominent slit and selenizone present in the shell of this species. The genus ranges from Upper Ordovician to Middle Devonian. *Pleuronotus decewi* Billings (fig. 13-2.3) is a large, pseudoplanispirally coiled form that has sharp angulations forming the upper and lower margins of the whorls. It is also commonly preserved as an internal mold, which does not show the selenizone. The genus is restricted to the Devonian.

Numerous species of the genus *Platyceras* are present in the Devonian rocks of Ohio. These species differ in terms of tightness of coiling of the shell and the development of spines and radial **plications** of the shell material, among other features. Many, if not all, species of this genus are considered to be **coprophagous**, that is they eat the waste products of other organisms. They have been found attached directly over the anal opening of crinoids (see fig. 17-6.2). *Platyceras rarispinum* Hall (fig. 13-2.7) has a medium-sized, loosely coiled shell that has radiating plications and a scattering of spines. *Platyceras multispinosum* Hall (fig. 13-2.9) is also loosely coiled but is larger than *P. rarispinum* and has many more spines. It is commonly found as an internal mold, but specimens preserving the spinose shell are not uncommon.

MISSISSIPPIAN GASTROPODS

Mississippian gastropods include *Loxonema pikensis* Hyde (fig. 13-2.15), a medium-sized, high-spired species having numerous closely spaced, sinuous, transverse costae. *Platyschisma* sp. (figs. 13-2.19, 13-2.20) has strongly rounded whorls, is relatively low spired, and has a pseudoselenizone. *Bulimorpha melanoides* (Whitfield) (fig. 13-2.14) is higher spired than *Platyschisma*, smooth, and has rounded whorls. *Platyschisma* and *Bulimorpha* are both medium sized and restricted to the Mississippian. *Straparollus similis* Meek & Worthen (figs. 13-2.11, 13-2.12) is a small, very low spired (pseudoplanispiral) species that has a sharp angulation at the top of the whorl, a spiraling ridge at midwhorl, and a ridge at the edge of the depression on the bottom of the whorl. The genus ranges from Silurian to Middle Permian. *Platyceras lodiensis* Meek (fig. 13-2.10) is medium sized, almost conical in shape, and has very little curvature to the shell, which is ornamented by coarse growth lines.

Planispiral forms of Mississippian age are illustrated by *Bellerophon sublaevis* Hall (fig. 13-2.16), which is small, has a broadly rounded shell, a narrow selenizone, and fine growth lines. The genus ranges from Silurian to Lower Triassic. *Tropidodiscus cyrtolites* (Hall) (figs. 13-2.17, 13-2.18) is slightly larger than *B. sublaevis* and has a narrower, more sharply curved shell. It also has a narrow selenizone and fine growth lines. *Tropidodiscus* ranges from Lower Ordovician to Devonian. These genera are classified as monoplacophorans by some specialists, as gastropods by others.

PENNSYLVANIAN GASTROPODS

Pennsylvanian gastropods are more common and generally better preserved than those from older rocks in Ohio. Although internal molds may be found, many species are commonly preserved with the shell intact.

Medium-sized to large, high-spired forms include several species of the genus *Strobeus*, which ranges from Middle Devonian to Middle Permian. *Strobeus regularis* (Cox) (fig. 13-3.21) is large and has a narrowly triangular shape and only slightly rounded whorl profiles. Medium-sized *Strobeus paludinaeformis* (Hall) (fig. 13-3.17) is relatively broader and has more strongly rounded whorl profiles than *S. regularis*. *Strobeus klipparti* (Meek) (fig. 13-3.24) is large and has an overall suboval shape. *Meekospira peracuta* (Meek & Worthen) (fig. 13-3.22) has a medium-sized, narrow, triangular shell and flat-sided whorl profiles. The genus ranges from Mississippian to Lower Permian. *Stegocoelia copei* (White) (fig. 13-3.18) has a medium-sized, narrow, turreted shell that has a prominent angulation near the base of the whorls and three fine, spiraling ridges on the whorl face. This genus ranges from Mississippian to Middle Permian. *Palaeozygopleura*? *scitula* (Meek & Worthen) (fig. 13-3.19) is medium sized and has prominent, closely spaced, transverse costae on the whorls. This genus ranges from Devonian to Middle Pennsylvanian.

A number of small, broadly turreted forms are present in Pennsylvanian rocks. *Spiroscala pagoda* Knight (fig. 13-3.20) has two prominent ridges bordering the selenizone on the lower portion of the whorl and fine transverse and spiraling ridges forming a reticulate pattern on the whorl surface. The genus ranges from Mississippian to Middle Permian. *Worthenia tabulata* (Conrad) (fig. 13-3.9) has a row of nodes marking the selenizone at the angulation just below midwhorl. The spiraling ridges are more prominent than the fine, transverse ridges. This genus ranges from Mississippian to Lower Triassic. *Phymatopleura nodosus* (Girty) (fig. 13-3.10) is less turreted in appearance than *Worthenia tabulata* and has a row of small, spiraling nodes at the top of the whorl, fine ridges bordering the selenizone, and subequal, fine, transverse and spiraling ridges overall. This genus is restricted to the Pennsylvanian.

Shansiella carbonaria (Norwood & Pratten) (fig. 13-3.23) is medium sized, low spired, has strongly rounded whorls, and is ornamented by numerous, coarse, spiraling ridges. The genus ranges from Mississippian to Lower Permian. *Trepospira illinoiensis* (Worthen) (figs. 13-3.13, 13-3.14) is small, very low spired, and has a distinct row of nodes at the upper border of the angulated whorl. This genus ranges from Devonian to Middle Permian. *Straparollus cattiloides* (Conrad) (figs. 13-3.11, 13-3.12) is a small pseudoplanispiral form that has sharp angulations separating the upper and lower whorl surfaces.

Small planispiral forms are common in Pennsylvanian rocks in Ohio. *Bellerophon graphicus* Moore (figs. 13-3.6 to 13-3.8) is smooth except for growth lines and a narrow, slightly raised selenizone. *Bellerophon tricarinatus*

(Shumard) (figs. 13-3.15, 13-3.16) has a pronounced ridge forming the selenizone, coarse transverse ridges partially raised as nodes, and a more expanded aperture than *B. graphicus*. *Knightites montfortianus* (Norwood & Pratten) (figs. 13-3.1, 13-3.2) has much the same shape as *B. tricarinatus*, but the selenizone is not raised into a ridge and there are numerous fine, spiraling ridges crossing the coarse, transverse ridges. The genus *Knightites* ranges from Devonian to Middle Permian. *Euphemites enodis* Sturgeon (figs. 13-3.3 to 13-3.5) has a relatively wide selenizone bordered by two low ridges and a number of spiraling ridges that extend out of the aperture and onto the nearby portion of the whorl. This genus ranges from Mississippian to Permian.

PENNSYLVANIAN AND PERMIAN GASTROPODS

Several freshwater gastropods occur in the Upper Paleozoic rocks in Ohio. All are small but may be seen on the weathered surfaces of limestone beds. *Anthracopupa? dunkardana* Stauffer & Schroyer (fig. 13-3.26) has very fine, transverse ridges on the shell. *Anthracopupa? parva* (Stauffer & Schroyer) (fig. 13-3.25) has coarser, more prominent, transverse ridges than *A.? dunkardana*. The genus is restricted to the Lower Permian.

QUATERNARY GASTROPODS

Terrestrial gastropods generally are the most commonly encountered and abundant fossils in Quaternary wind-transported silt (loess) deposits. Thin beds of this type of fine-grained sediment, which has the texture of flour, can be found in areas of the state that were glaciated. The abundance of fossils in these deposits may be deceiving. To the naked eye the sediments may appear to have few shells exposed at the surface because most of the shells are small, generally less than 5 mm in length. But a small 50-mm-square block of silt soaked in a pail of water will come apart and dozens of individuals of *Pupilla*, *Columella*, and *Vertigo* may float to the surface when released from the sediment!

Gastropods representing former freshwater marsh, pond, lake, and stream habitats also may be found in Quaternary-age sediments throughout the state. These deposits commonly accumulated in the poorly drained depressions that pock-marked the surface as the ice sheets melted. The freshwater gastropods typically occur in association with fingernail clams (see Chapter 12) and in some cases with land snails that may have washed into these basins.

KEY TO SOME QUATERNARY GASTROPODS FROM OHIO

1A. Shell has prominent transverse costae 2
1B. Shell without prominent transverse costae 3

2A. Shell less than 5 mm wide, has ribbonlike **lamellae** in roof of aperture .... *Strobilops* (figs. 13-4.2, 13-4.3)
2B. Shell more than 5 mm wide, no **teeth** in aperture 4

3A. Aperture on left side .... *Physa* (fig. 13-4.13)
3B. Aperture on right side 5

4A. Adult shell less than 10 mm in diameter .... *Discus* (fig. 13-4.14)
4B. Adult shell greater than 10 mm in diameter .... *Anguispira* (fig. 13-4.1)

5A. Spire height clearly greater than aperture height 6
5B. Spire height equal to or less than aperture height 9

6A. Spire narrow relative to last whorl 7
6B. Spire wide relative to last whorl 8

7A. Spiral ornamentation indistinct or absent .... *Lymnaea* (fig. 13-4.7)
7B. Spiral ornamentation distinct on early whorls .... *Goniobasis* (fig. 13-4.12)

8A. Shell less than 5 mm high 10
8B. Shell greater than 5 mm high 15

9A. Aperture has one long lamella extending to center of shell .... *Stenotrema* (figs. 13-4.8 to 13-4.10)
9B. Aperture has no teeth or lamellae .... *Succinea* (fig. 13-4.19)

10A. Aperture toothless or has small **tubercular** teeth 11
10B. Aperture teeth well developed 12

11A. **Apertural lip** not flared, shell 2.5-3.0 mm high .... *Columella* (fig. 13-4.16)
11B. Apertural lip flared, shell 3-4 mm high .... *Pupilla* (fig. 13-4.15)

12A. Tooth or teeth on roof of aperture reach outer margin .... *Gastrocopta* (figs. 13-4.5, 13-4.18)
12B. Tooth or teeth on roof of aperture do not reach outer margin .... *Vertigo* (figs. 13-4.4, 13-4.17)

13A. Shell has spiral ornamentation .... *Stagnicola* (fig. 13-4.11)
13B. Shell without spiral ornamentation .... *Campeloma* (fig. 13-4.6)

Terrestrial gastropods include *Columella alticola* (Ingersoll) (fig. 13-4.16), a small (2.5-3 mm high), high-spired, cylindrical shell that has more than six whorls. *Pupilla muscorum* (Linnaeus) (fig. 13-4.15) is similar in shape to *C. alticola* but is larger (3-4 mm high) and the apertural lip is slightly flared outward. *Discus cronkhitei* (Newcomb) (fig. 13-4.14) has a low spire and coarse, transverse costae. *Anguispira alternata* (Say) (fig. 13-4.1) is similar to *Discus cronkhitei* but is larger and may preserved a color pattern of light brown, curving, transverse, color patches. *Gastrocopta contracta* (Say) (fig. 13-4.18) has a high, cone-shaped spire and four toothlike structures that almost completely block the aperture. A closely related species is *Gastrocopta armifera* (Say) (fig. 13-4.5), which is larger and has smaller teeth in the aperture. *Vertigo elatior* Sterki (fig. 13-4.4), a common loess fossil, is quite small and has a tapering spire and typically five teeth in the aperture. *Vertigo modesta* (Say) (fig. 13-4.17) is a common associate of *V. elatior*, from which it generally can be distinguished by its slightly longer shell and the presence of four apertural teeth arranged in the shape of a cross. *Strobilops labyrinthica* (Say) (figs. 13-4.2, 13-4.3) has a small, radially ribbed, beehive-shaped shell. *Stenotrema hirsutum* (Say) (figs. 13-4.8 to 13-4.10) is a low-spired species that may be recognized by its long toothlike lamella that parallels the basal lip of the aperture. *Succinea ovalis* Say (fig. 13-4.19) has an ovate aperture that is about three-fourths the total height of the shell.

Freshwater species are illustrated by *Lymnaea stagnalis jugularis* Say (fig. 13-4.7), which has an attenuate, high-spired shell that has several low, widely spaced, spiraling ridges. *Stagnicola elodes* (Say) (fig. 13-4.11) is smaller than *L. stagnalis jugularis*, the spire is not as narrow, and the spiraling ridges are more prominent. *Campeloma decisum* (Say) (fig. 13-4.6) has a spire that is equal to or shorter than the **last whorl** and does not have spiral ornamentation. *Goniobasis livescens* (Menke) (fig. 13-4.12) has three spiraling ridges on the early whorls; later whorls are marked only by growth lines. *Physa gyrina* Say (fig. 13-4.13) has a disproportionately large aperture that is on the left (sinistral) side when viewed with the spire pointed up.

COLLECTING LOCALITIES

Gastropod fossils have been found at the following localities, all of which are on private property and require permission of the landowner before collecting.

Ordovician localities include exposures of the Whitewater Formation in road cuts along U.S. Route 27, 3.2-6.4 km (2-4 miles) south of Richmond, Wayne County, Indiana, and the Arnheim Formation at Dent, on U.S. Route 52 approximately 4.8 km (3 miles) west of Cincinnati, Hamilton County, Ohio.

Silurian localities include exposures of the Brassfield Formation in road cuts on Ohio Route 41 just south of the bridge over Ohio Brush Creek, south of Jacksonville, Adams County.

Devonian localities include exposures of the Silica and Dundee Formations in quarries approximately 3.2 km (2 miles) west of Sylvania on Brint Road, Lucas County, and the Columbus Limestone in a quarry at Flat Rock, Seneca County.

Mississippian localities include exposures of the Logan Formation in the C & O railroad cut approximately 3.2 km (2 miles) northwest of Sciotoville, Scioto County, and the Maxville Formation in a quarry on the west side of Ohio Route 668 approximately 1.6 km (1 mile) north of Maxville, Perry County.

Pennsylvanian localities include exposures of the Brush Creek shale in a road cut along Ohio Route 56 west of the intersection with Ohio Route 682, on the west side of Athens, Athens County, and the Cambridge shale and limestone and Portersville shale in a quarry approximately 1.6 km (1 mile) northeast of New Concord, Guernsey County.

Quaternary localities include the marl pits just west of Castalia, Erie County; loess deposits in old gravel pits southwest of Mill Creek and north of McCracken Road, Garfield Heights, Cuyahoga County (see B. B. Miller and Szabo, 1987); and a cut bank along the east side of Four Mile Creek about 0.4 km (0.25 mile) south of the dam in Hueston Woods State Park, Butler County (see Stewart and Miller, 1987).

FIGURES 13-1 TO 13-4 FOLLOW

FIGURE 13-1.—Ordovician and Silurian gastropods. Scale bars equal 1 cm. Scale bar A applies to figures 13-1.1 and 13-1.2; B applies to figures 13-1.3, 13-1.4, 13-1.8, 13-1.9, 13-1.12, and 13-1.13; C applies to figures 13-1.5 to 13-1.7, 13-1.10, 13-1.11, and 13-1.14 to 13-1.20.

1, 2 — *Sinuites cancellatus* (Hall). Dorsal (**1**) and lateral (**2**) views of internal mold. Whitewater Formation (Upper Ordovician), road cut on U.S. Route 27 south of Richmond, Wayne County, Indiana; OSU 46676.

3 — *Cyclonema bilix* (Conrad). Apertural view. Waynesville Formation (Upper Ordovician), emergency spillway, Caesar Creek State Park, Warren County, Ohio; OSU 46677.

4 — *Holopea obliqua* Hall. **Adapertural** view; Cincinnatian Series (Upper Ordovician), unknown locality in Cincinnati area; CiMNH PT628.

5, 6 — *Cyrtolites ornatus* Conrad. Lateral (**5**) and dorsal (**6**) views of internal mold. Same unit and location as **4**; CiMNH PT651.

7 — *Loxoplocus bowdeni* (Safford). Adapertural view. Same unit and location as **3**; OSU 46678.

8, 9 — *Liospira vitruvia* (Billings). **Apical** (**8**) and apertural (**9**) views of internal mold. Same unit and location as **4**; CiMNH P214.

10 — *Cyclonema varicosa* Hall. Adapertural view. Cincinnatian Series (Upper Ordovician), unknown locality in Oxford area, Butler County, Ohio; OSU 46679.

11 — *Clathrospira subconica* (Hall). Adapertural view of internal mold. Same unit and location as **3**; OSU 46680.

12 — *Platyceras* sp. Adapertural view. Brassfield Formation (Silurian), road cut on Ohio Route 41 south of bridge over Ohio Brush Creek, south of Jacksonville, Adams County, Ohio; OSU 46681.

13 — *Platyceras niagarensis* (Hall). Adapertural view. Same unit and location as **12**; OSU 46682.

14, 15 — *Tremanotus alpheus* (Hall). Dorsal (**14**) and lateral (**15**) views of internal mold. Lockport Dolomite (Silurian), quarry at Genoa, Ottawa County, Ohio; OSU 14901.

16 — *Phanerotrema* sp. Adapertural view of internal mold. Lockport Dolomite (Silurian), quarry at Woodville, Sandusky County, Ohio; OSU 46683.

17, 18 — *Rhombella* sp. Adapertural (**17**) and apical (**18**) views of internal mold. Lockport Dolomite (Silurian), quarry at Clay Center, Ottawa County, Ohio; OSU 46684.

19 — ?*Murchisonia* sp. Adapertural view of internal mold. Same unit and location as **16**; OSU 46685.

20 — ?*Murchisonia* sp. Adapertural view of internal mold. Same unit and location as **17**, **18**; OSU 46686.

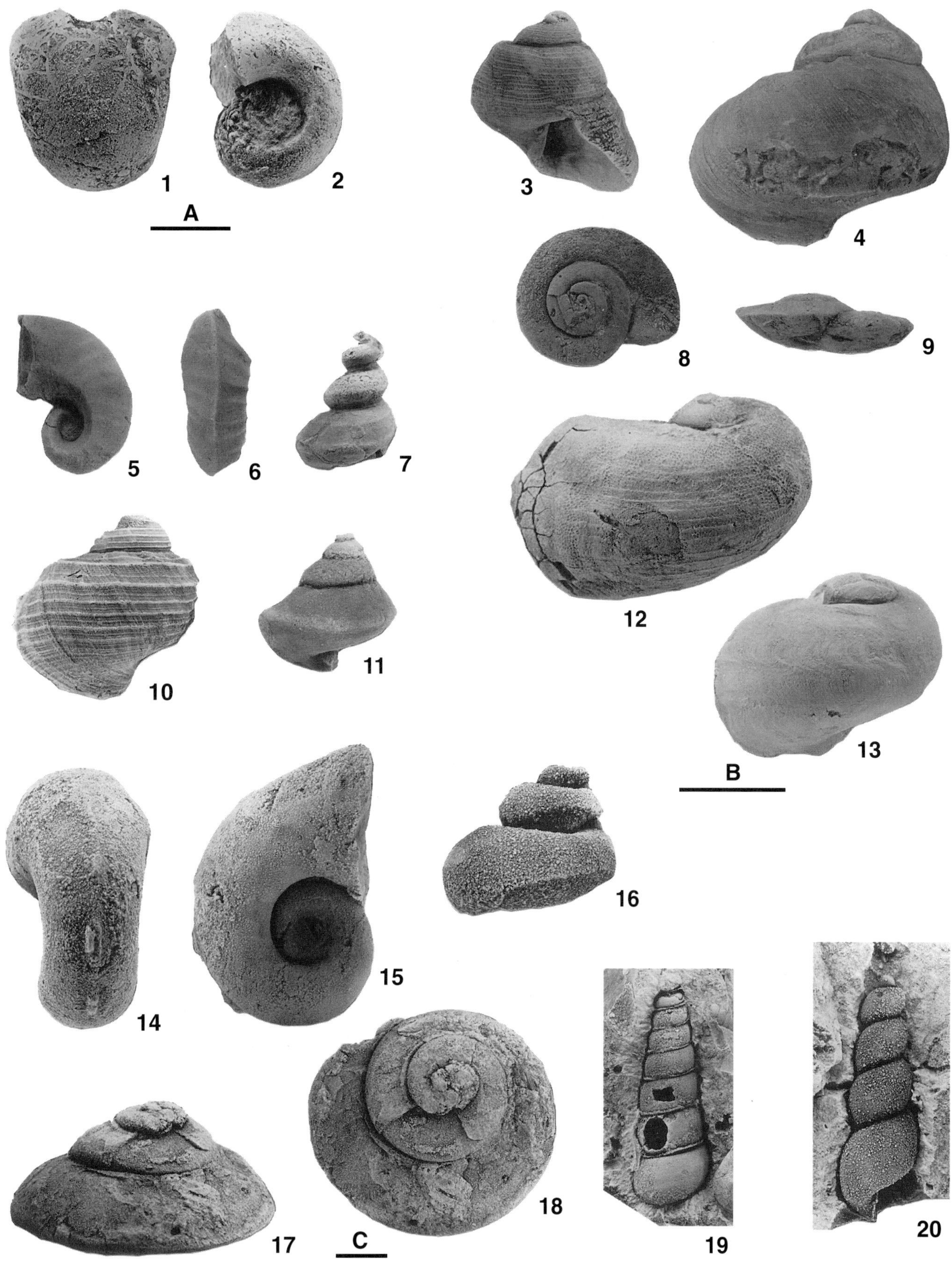
1
2
A
3
4
8
9
5
6
7
12
10
11
13
B
16
14
15
17
C
18
19
20

FIGURE 13-2.—Devonian and Mississippian gastropods. Scale bar A equals 1 mm and applies to figure 13-2.4. Scale bars B-E equal 1 cm. Scale bar B applies to figures 13-2.1 to 13-2.3, 13-2.5 to 13-2.7, 13-2.9, and 13-2.10; C applies to figures 13-2.8, 13-2.11, and 13-2.12; D applies to figures 13-2.15 and 13-2.16; E applies to figures 13-2.13, 13-2.14, and 13-2.17 to 13-2.20.

1 *Murchisonia* sp. Apertural view of internal mold. Dundee Formation (Devonian), quarry at Whitehouse, Lucas County, Ohio; OSU 46687.

2 *Loxonema pexatum* Hall. Adapertural view. Columbus Limestone (Devonian), exposure at Dublin, Franklin County, Ohio; OSU 3618.

3 *Pleuronotus decewi* Billings. Apical view of internal mold. Columbus Limestone (Devonian), unknown locality in Franklin County, Ohio; OSU 46688.

4 *Elasmonema bellatum* (Hall). Adapertural view. Columbus Limestone (Devonian), exposure in Eversole Run, Delaware County, Ohio; OSU 11937.

5, 6 *Euryzone arata* Hall. Apical (**5**) and adapertural (**6**) views of internal mold. Same unit and location as **1**; OSU 46689.

7 *Platyceras rarispinum* Hall. Adapertural view. Silica Formation (Devonian), quarry west of Sylvania, Lucas County, Ohio; OSU 46690.

8 *Isonema humile* Meek. Adapertural view. Same unit and location as **1**; OSU 11932.

9 *Platyceras multispinosum* Hall. Adapertural view of internal mold. Same unit and location as **3**; OSU 3626.

10 *Platyceras lodiensis* Meek. Adapertural view. Cuyahoga Formation (Mississippian), unknown locality in Wayne County, Ohio; OSU 22521.

11, 12 *Straparollus similis* Meek & Worthen. Apical (**11**) and apertural (**12**) views. Maxville Formation (Mississippian), abandoned quarry northwest of Somerset, Perry County, Ohio; OSU 46691.

13 *Mourlonia lucina* (Hall). Adapertural view. Same unit and location as **2**; OSU 27921.

14 *Bulimorpha melanoides* (Whitfield). Adapertural view of internal mold. Same unit and location as **11, 12**; OSU 46692.

15 *Loxonema pikensis* Hyde. Adapertural view of cast of external mold. Logan Formation (Mississippian), railroad cut northwest of Sciotoville, Scioto County, Ohio; OSU 19892.

16 *Bellerophon sublaevis* Hall. Dorsal view. Same unit and location as **11, 12**; OSU 46693.

17, 18 *Tropidodiscus cyrtolites* (Hall). Dorsal (**17**) and lateral (**18**) views of internal mold. Cuyahoga Formation (Mississippian), unknown locality in Trumbull County, Ohio; OSU 22503.

19, 20 *Platyschisma* sp. Apical (**19**) and adapertural (**20**) views. Same unit and location as **10**; OSU 22514.

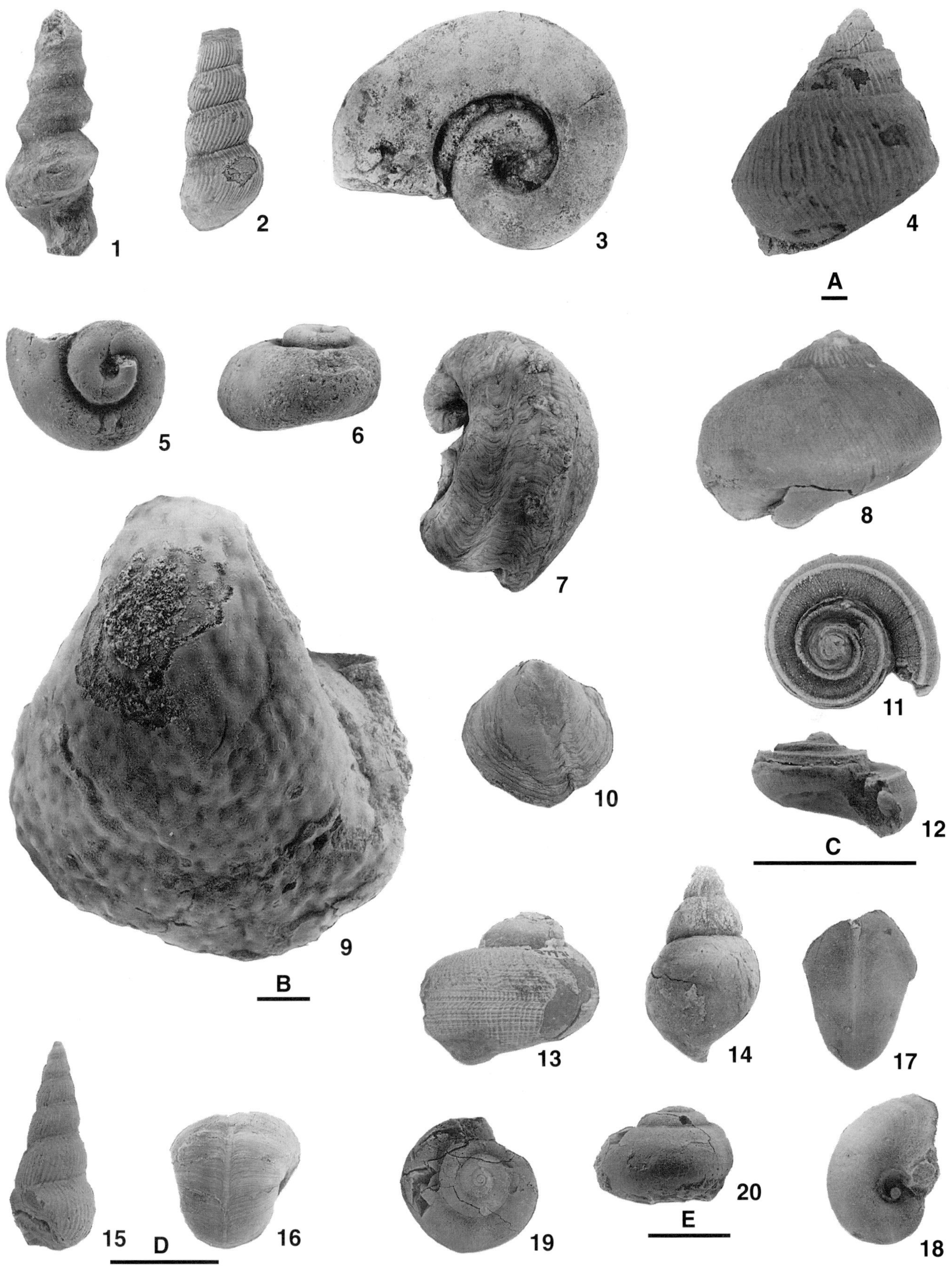
1
2
3
4
A
5
6
7
8
9
B
10
11
12
C
13
14
17
15
D
16
19
20
E
18

FIGURE 13-3.—Pennsylvanian and Permian gastropods. Scale bars A-E equal 1 cm. Scale bar A applies to figures 13-3.1 and 13-3.2; B applies to figures 13-3.3 to 13-3.5; C applies to figures 13-3.6 to 13-3.14; D applies to figures 13-3.15 to 13-3.20; E applies to figures 13-3.21 to 13-3.24. Scale bar F equals 1 mm and applies to figures 13-3.25 and 13-3.26.

1, 2 *Knightites montfortianus* (Norwood & Pratten). Dorsal (**1**) and apertural (**2**) views. Ames shale (Conemaugh Group, Pennsylvanian), abandoned quarry just north of Dent, on west side of West Virginia Route 92, Preston County, West Virginia; OSU 46722.

3-5 *Euphemites enodis* Sturgeon. Lateral (**3**), apertural (**4**), and dorsal (**5**) views. Putnam Hill shale (Allegheny Group, Pennsylvanian), abandoned strip mine northeast of Alliance, Mahoning County, Ohio; OSU 46721.

6-8 *Bellerophon graphicus* Moore. Apertural (**6**), dorsal (**7**), and lateral (**8**) views. Putnam Hill shale (Allegheny Group, Pennsylvanian), borrow pit on east side of Interstate 77, south of New Philadelphia, Tuscarawas County, Ohio; OSU 46720.

9 *Worthenia tabulata* (Conrad). Adapertural view. Washingtonville shale (Allegheny Group, Pennsylvanian), strip mine east of Mineral City, Carroll County, Ohio; OSU 46695.

10 *Phymatopleura nodosus* (Girty). Adapertural view. Cambridge shale (Conemaugh Group, Pennsylvanian), abandoned quarry north of U.S. Route 40 just east of New Concord, Guernsey County, Ohio; OSU 46696.

11, 12 *Straparollus cattiloides* (Conrad). Apical (**11**) and apertural (**12**) views. Putnam Hill shale (Allegheny Group), abandoned strip mine north of U.S. Route 50, east of McArthur, Vinton County, Ohio; OSU 46702.

13, 14 *Trepospira illinoiensis* (Worthen). Apical (**13**) and apertural (**14**) views. Same unit and location as **6-8**; OSU 46698.

15, 16 *Bellerophon tricarinatus* (Shumard). Lateral (**15**) and dorsal (**16**) views. Same unit and location as **10**; OSU 46719.

17 *Strobeus paludinaeformis* (Hall). Adapertural view. Same unit and location as **10**; OSU 46700.

18 *Stegocoelia copei* (White). Adapertural view. Same unit and location as **9**; OSU 46704.

19 *Palaeozygopleura? scitula* (Meek & Worthen). Adapertural view. Same unit and location as **10**; OSU 46705.

20 *Spiroscala pagoda* Knight. Adapertural view. Same unit and location as **11, 12**; OSU 46694.

21 *Strobeus regularis* (Cox). Adapertural view. Same unit and location as **6-8**; OSU 46699.

22 *Meekospira peracuta* (Meek & Worthen). Adapertural view. Same unit and location as **10**; OSU 46703.

23 *Shansiella carbonaria* (Norwood & Pratten). Adapertural view. Same unit and location as **11, 12**; OSU 46697.

24 *Strobeus klipparti* (Meek). Section through the coiling axis to show the **columella**. Same unit and location as **11, 12**; OSU 46701.

25 *Anthracopupa? parva* (Stauffer & Schroyer). Adapertural view. Lower Washington limestone (Washington Formation, Permian), exposure just south of Pleasant Grove, Belmont County, Ohio; OSU 15165.

26 *Anthracopupa? dunkardana* Stauffer & Schroyer. Adapertural view. Same unit and location as **25**; OSU 15161.

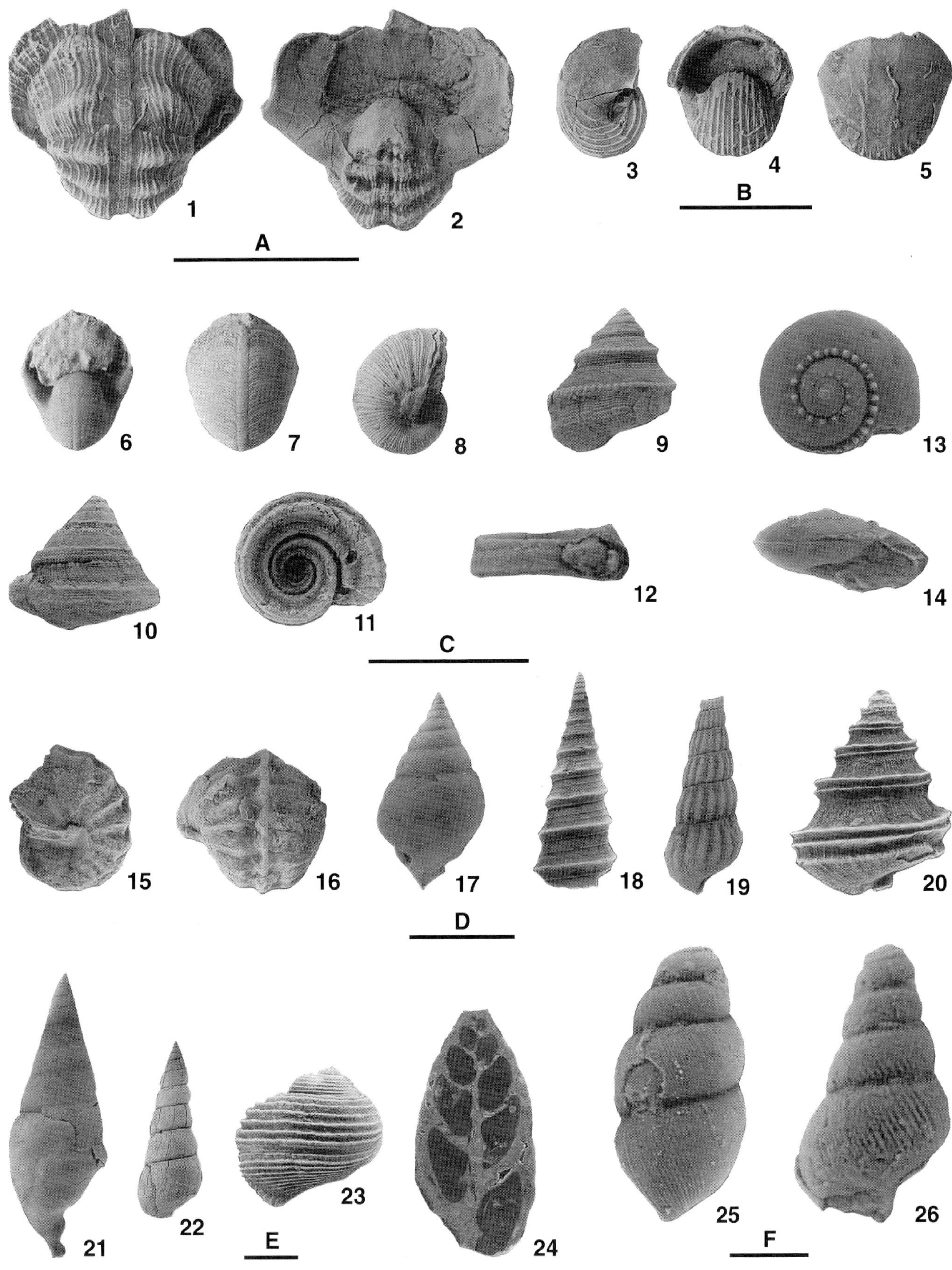
1
2
A
3
4
5
B
6
7
8
9
13
10
11
12
14
C
15
16
17
18
19
20
D
21
22
23
E
24
25
26
F

FIGURE 13-4.—Quaternary gastropods. Scale bars A (fig. 13-4.1), E (figs. 13-4.6 and 13-4.7), F (figs. 13-4.8 to 13-4.10), and G (figs. 13-4.11 to 13-4.13) equal 1 cm. Scale bar M (fig. 13-4.19) equals 5 mm. Scale bars C (fig. 13-4.4), D (fig. 13-4.5), H (fig. 13-4.14), I (fig. 13-4.15), and K (fig. 13-4.17) equal 1 mm. Scale bars B (figs. 13-4.2 and 13-4.3), J (fig. 13-4.16), and L (fig. 13-4.18) equal 0.5 mm. Figures 13-4.14 to 13-4.19 are redrawn from Burch (1962).

1	*Anguispira alternata* (Say). Apical view showing preserved radial color pattern. Marl pit just west of Castalia, Erie County, Ohio; OSU 46707.
2, 3	*Strobilops labyrinthica* (Say). Apertural (**2**) and basal (**3**) views. Some of the internal lamellae that extend beyond the aperture can be seen in **2**. Mt. Scott local fauna, southwest of Meade, Meade County, Kansas; UMMZ 200640.
4	*Vertigo elatior* Sterki. Apertural view showing constriction of outer lip. Doby Springs local fauna, Harper County, Oklahoma; UMMZ 213770.
5	*Gastrocopta armifera* (Say). Apertural view showing prominent apertural teeth. Little Sioux local fauna, Iowa; UMMZ 220316.
6	*Campeloma decisum* (Say). Apertural view of modern specimen. Lake Erie shore at Crane Creek State Park, Ottawa County, Ohio; OSU 46709.
7	*Lymnaea stagnalis jugularis* Say. Apertural view. Same age and location as **6**; OSU 46710.
8-10	*Stenotrema hirsutum* (Say). Apical (**8**), apertural (**9**), and basal (**10**) views. Same location as **1**; OSU 46711-46713.
11	*Stagnicola elodes* (Say). Apertural view. Same location as **1**; OSU 46714.
12	*Goniobasis livescens* (Menke). Apertural view. Same location as **1**; OSU 46715.
13	*Physa gyrina* Say. Apertural view. Same location as **1**; OSU 46716.
14	*Discus cronkhitei* (Newcomb). Apertural view.
15	*Pupilla muscorum* (Linnaeus). Apertural view.
16	*Columella alticola* (Ingersoll). Apertural view.
17	*Vertigo modesta* (Say). Apertural view.
18	*Gastrocopta contracta* (Say). Apertural view.
19	*Succinea ovalis* Say. Apertural view.

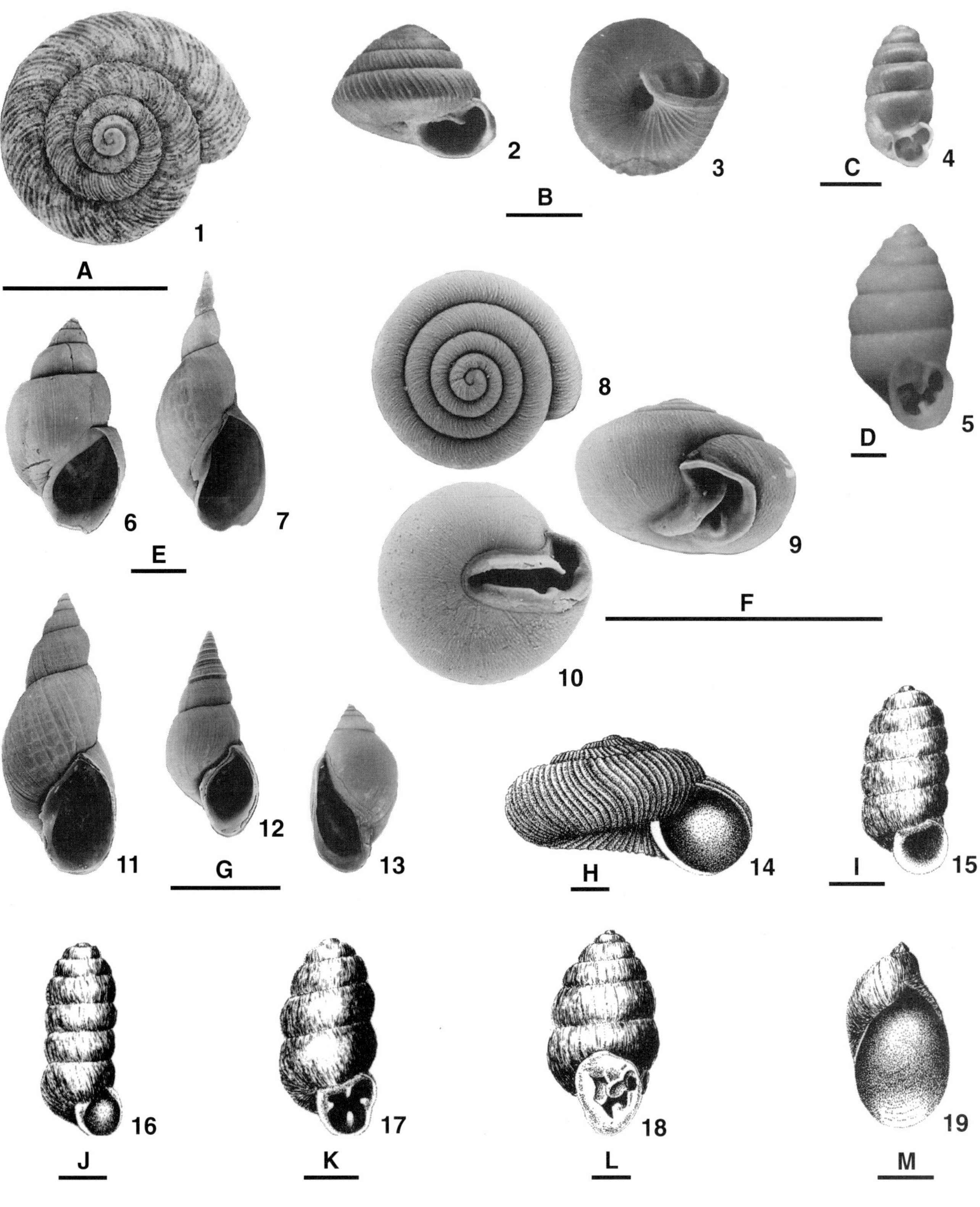
1
A
2
3
B
C
4
D
5
6
7
E
8
9
10
F
11
12
G
13
H
14
I
15
16
J
17
K
18
L
19
M

Chapter 14

PHYLUM MOLLUSCA, CLASS CEPHALOPODA

by Richard Arnold Davis and Royal H. Mapes

INTRODUCTION

Cephalopods are common fossils in Ohio and are relatively easy to identify as cephalopods. They occur in many marine rock units of Ordovician through Pennsylvanian age. No fossil cephalopods have been recovered from Permian rocks of the state because all rocks in Ohio considered to be Permian are nonmarine.

The basic structure of the fossil cephalopods of Ohio is that of a cone divided by **transverse** partitions, or **septa** (see figs. 1-18, 1-21). The septa divide the cone of the shell into **chambers** or **camerae**. Extending lengthwise in the shell, through the camerae, is a tube called the **siphuncle**.

The cone may be straight (**orthoconic**), curved (**cyrtoconic**), or coiled (see fig. 1-19). An orthoconic shell may be short and stout (**breviconic**) or long and narrow (**longiconic**). Each individual coil in a coiled form is called a **whorl** (or volution). If the coiling is loose, so that the whorls do not touch one another, the shell is said to be **gyroconic**. If the coiling is tight enough that the whorls do touch one another, the shell is said to be **evolute**. If the shell is so tightly coiled that each whorl overlaps the previously formed one, it is said to be **involute**.

If a cephalopod shell were to be cut perpendicular to its length, the result is a transverse cross section. In the case of a coiled shell, the result would be a series of whorl cross sections (see figs. 1-19.5, 1-19.6, and 1-19.7). If the transverse cross section of the tube is wider than tall, it is said to be **depressed**; if, on the other hand, the tube is taller than wide, it is said to be **compressed**.

The present-day *Nautilus* (fig. 1-18) is the only living cephalopod that has an external shell similar to the shell of most fossil cephalopods. In *Nautilus,* the camerae contain gas, so that the animal, shell and all, is just about the same weight as an equal volume of water. Thus, the animal does not have to spend energy swimming upward or downward to maintain a particular level in the water. Presumably, in life, the cephalopods we find as fossils functioned the same way.

Although the camerae were empty during life, the chambers in a fossil generally are filled with rock. In such cases, what is seen is the **internal mold** of the shell and the edges of the septa. The line that marks the intersection of a septum and the interior of the shell wall is called a **suture**. In some fossil cephalopods each septum is more-or-less smooth, so that the suture is a straight line (see fig. 1-21), is gently curved, or is slightly sinuous. In other fossil cephalopods each septum is corrugated, near the shell wall at least, and the suture is a decidedly wiggly line (see fig. 1-22.3).

Of the fossil cephalopods found in Ohio, those with straight, curved, or slightly sinuous sutures are called **nautiloid** cephalopods, or nautiloids, and belong to several subclasses (see table 14-1). Those with decidedly wiggly sutures are called **ammonoid** cephalopods, or ammonoids, and belong in the subclass Ammonoidea.

ECOLOGY AND LIFE HISTORY OF CEPHALOPODS

All present-day cephalopods are marine creatures, that is, they are found only in the oceans. There is no evidence that the myriad extinct cephalopods known only as fossils were any different in that respect. Thus, fossil cephalopods in Ohio are found only in rocks originally deposited under marine conditions.

Most living cephalopods are active predators. Like many predators, however, they will scavenge, if the suitable occasion presents itself. In either case, they live their lives hunting for a meal. Each animal is equipped with a pair of jaws that, together, look rather like the beak of a bird (although, unlike the beak of a bird, the lower jaw of a cephalopod overlaps the upper). The **beak** of some present-day cephalopods is strong enough to shear flesh and break shell and bone.

On the other hand, cephalopods can be a convenient and tasty source of protein for other active predators in today's oceans. The largest hunter of cephalopods probably is the sperm whale, which actively seeks giant squids in the ocean deeps. However, beginning at least as early as the Devonian Period, fishes, including sharks, almost certainly have been the consumers of the largest amount of cephalopod flesh (see fig. 21-6.3). Direct fossil evidence of attacks by sharks and other fishes is rare (Mapes and Hansen, 1984; Hansen and Mapes, 1990). Most such events probably resulted in the destruction of the shell of the cephalopod victim (Boston and Mapes, 1991). However, on rare occasions, shells of Ohio cephalopods are found that bear evidence of these attacks in the form of tooth punctures (see fig. 14-5.7).

Present-day octopuses crawl about on the sea floor by means of their tentacles, and cuttlefishes lie partially buried in the sand of the sea floor. However, it is unknown just how much time the cephalopods now found as fossils spent on the sea floor. Flower (1955) interpreted impressions in some Ordovician rock layers of southwestern Ohio as having been made by orthoconic nautiloids; however, Osgood (1970) strongly argued that those markings were not made by cephalopod tentacles.

Although some cephalopods do spend much time on the sea floor, either at rest or crawling by means of their tentacles, most cephalopods can swim effectively, should the occasion demand. Cephalopods swim by "jet propulsion." Water is taken into the **mantle cavity** and squirted out a muscular tube called the **hyponome** (see fig. 1-18). In general, this action results in the animal's being propelled backward. However, the hyponome is very flexible and can be bent to squirt in a variety of directions. The hyponome in the body of a living cephalopod is located in a **ventral** position. In cephalopods that have external shells, there is the potential problem of the shell margin being in the way of the hyponome. The margin of the **aperture** of *Nautilus* has a broad, shallow indentation, called the **hyponomic sinus** (see fig. 1-22), that permits the hyponome to flex. The **growth lines** on many specimens of fossil cephalopods indicate these specimens each had a hyponomic sinus and, hence, almost certainly possessed a hyponome. Thus, it is almost certain that they were active swimmers.

In fossil specimens in which the shell wall is preserved, some individuals show darker markings on the lighter background of the shell exterior. For example, in specimens of the Ordovician species *Treptoceras duseri*, there may be **longitudinal** dark lines (fig. 14-1.1). These lines are the remains of color bands on the living animal. It is not known what the actual colors were, but the pattern of those colors is clear. Such color patterns commonly are interpreted as having served as camouflage, although they may have had a function in mating.

The sexes are separate in present-day cephalopods. Moreover, in many species, male and female cephalopods differ from one another morphologically, in some cases strikingly so. Sexual **dimorphism** has been postulated for a number of kinds of cephalopods known only as fossils. For example, two forms of *Manitoulinoceras* occur together in the Waynesville Formation (Ordovician) of southwestern Ohio; these have been named *Manitoulinoceras tenuiseptum* and *Manitoulinoceras williamsae,* but actually may be the male and female of the same biological species.

When the time for reproduction comes, males and females mate, and eggs are laid. Complete life cycles are known for only relatively few present-day species (see, for example, Mangold, 1987). In most of these species, the male generally dies shortly after mating, and the female ordinarily does not survive long after the eggs hatch. Most of the kinds of cephalopods that lack external shells live from six months to two years, although some have been known to live as long as six years. On the other hand, it has been estimated that individuals of *Nautilus* may take over five years to reach maturity and then may live for an additional several years (Landman and Cochran, 1987). In present-day cephalopods the babies are basically miniature adults. In other words, there is no free-living larval stage in which the baby looks strikingly different from its parents.

As a cephalopod grows, a record of that growth is preserved in the growth lines (see fig. 1-22), which mark the former positions of the aperture of the shell. By examining the growth lines, one can determine what happened to that aperture throughout the life of the animal. For example, many cephalopod shells show irregularities in the growth lines that record that the edge of the shell had been damaged, perhaps by a would-be predator, and subsequently repaired by the cephalopod.

The life history of an organism—everything that happens to it from conception to death—is called its **ontogeny**. Examination of fossils of many kinds of long-extinct cephalopods reveals that, as the animal proceeded through its life, there were striking changes in the shape of the shell. In particular, when the animal approached sexual maturity, commonly there were changes in coiling, or the **living chamber** became broader, or the aperture became constricted, and so on. These changes are called **mature modifications**. The shell of an adult cephalopod may be strikingly different in appearance from that of a younger animal of the same species. Thus, it is important to examine specimens in all stages of ontogeny to be able to identify them. Similarly, it is crucial to compare different kinds of cephalopods at the same stage of ontogeny in order to identify them correctly.

ENCRUSTATION OF CEPHALOPOD SHELLS

Almost all shelled aquatic organisms are subject to what is called fouling or **encrusting**, that is, the growth of other organisms on the shell surface. In certain beds of the Waynesville Formation (Ordovician), a significant number of specimens of the orthoconic cephalopod *Treptoceras* are encrusted with bryozoans (see fig. 14-1.4; also see Chapter 15 on the Bryozoa). These encrustations generally cover the full circumference of the shell. In some encrustations, the **monticules** of the bryozoan are aligned with the length of the shell, as though for "streamlining" in swimming (Baird and others, 1989). In those specimens in which the bryozoan colony encircles the shell and apparently exhibits a preferred orientation, it might be concluded that the colony grew on a live, swimming animal, rather than on a dead shell lying on the sea floor. However, an empty shell that had **cameral deposits** or **siphuncular deposits** in its **apical** part might have floated vertically in the water; this circumstance also might have resulted in the growth of a bryozoan colony completely around the shell and with a preferred orientation.

In other instances, bryozoans are encrusted on what were internal structures in life, for example, the siphuncle and septa. In those cases, larval bryozoans must have settled on the remains of broken shells lying on the sea floor. In addition to bryozoans, other organisms have been found attached to fossil cephalopods in Ohio, including cornulitid worm tubes and inarticulate brachiopods (see fig. 14-1.3).

USEFULNESS OF FOSSIL CEPHALOPODS

For paleontologists and other geologists, cephalopods are very useful because they help to determine the age of the rocks containing them. The ammonoid cephalopods, for example, evolved rapidly. Thus, any one **taxon** existed on Earth for only a relatively short time. If one finds a given taxon of ammonoid in a rock layer, then one knows that the layer was deposited during the short period of time during which that particular taxon of ammonoid lived. In addition to having evolved rapidly, ammonoids are relatively common around the world and are moderately easy to recognize. Given these characteristics, ammonoids are among the most important **index fossils**—they allow the sedimentary rocks in which they occur to be dated precisely over a broad geographic area. Such dating, in turn, allows a more accurate reconstruction of the history of Earth.

NAUTILOID CEPHALOPODS

The sutures of nautiloid cephalopods found in Ohio may be straight, curved, or slightly sinuous and are less diagnostic than the decidedly wiggly sutures of ammonoid cephalopods. Partly because the suture is much less diagnostic, identification of many nautiloids is much more difficult than is that of most ammonoids.

In this chapter, the word "nautiloid" is used for any externally shelled cephalopod in which the suture is straight, curved, or gently sinuous. The word was used this way for many years in a scientific context and is the way the word is used to this day in a nontechnical sense. However, the

TABLE 14-1.—SUBCLASSES, ORDERS, AND GENERA OF FOSSIL CEPHALOPODS INCLUDED IN THIS CHAPTER

The **taxonomic** subclasses are in the order they are listed in Teichert and others (1964, p. K12). The taxonomic orders and the genera are listed alphabetically. Geologic occurrence in Ohio is noted in parentheses for each genus. Commonly, members of the subclasses Actinoceratoidea, Endoceratoidea, and Nautiloidea collectively are called nautiloid cephalopods.

Subclass Nautiloidea
- Order Barrandeocerida
  - *Charactoceras* (Ordovician)
  - *Heracloceras* (Devonian)
  - *Lechritrochoceras* (Silurian)
- Order Discosorida
  - *Phragmoceras* (Silurian)
- Order Nautilida
  - *Domatoceras* (Pennsylvanian)
  - *Goldringia* (Devonian)
  - *Latitemnocheilus* (Pennsylvanian)
  - *Metacoceras* (Pennsylvanian)
  - *Parametacoceras* (Pennsylvanian)
  - *Stenodomatoceras* (Pennsylvanian)
  - *Tainoceras* (Pennsylvanian)
  - *Temnocheilus* (Pennsylvanian)
  - *Wellsoceras* (Devonian)
- Order Oncocerida
  - *Acleistoceras* (Devonian)
  - *Amphicyrtoceras* (Silurian)
  - *Manitoulinoceras* (Ordovician)
- Order Orthocerida
  - *Dawsonoceras* (Silurian)
  - *Kionoceras* (Silurian, Devonian)
  - *Mooreoceras* (Pennsylvanian)
  - *Pseudorthoceras* (Pennsylvanian)
  - *Spyroceras* (Devonian)
  - *Treptoceras* (Ordovician)
- Order Tarphycerida
  - *Graftonoceras* (Silurian)

Subclass Endoceratoidea
- Order Endocerida
  - *Cameroceras* (Ordovician)

Subclass Actinoceratoidea
- Order Actinocerida
  - *Orthonybyoceras* (Ordovician)

Subclass Bactritoidea
- Order Bactritida
  - *Bactrites* (Devonian)

Subclass Ammonoidea
- Order Anarcestida
  - *Foordites* (Devonian)
- Order Goniatitida
  - *Aktubites* (Pennsylvanian)
  - *Eoschistoceras* (Pennsylvanian)
  - *Glaphyrites* (Pennsylvanian)
  - *Gonioglyphioceras* (Pennsylvanian)
  - *Gonioloboceras* (Pennsylvanian)
  - *Mangeroceras* (Pennsylvanian)
  - *Neoaganides* (Pennsylvanian)
  - *Pennoceras* (Pennsylvanian)
  - *Schistoceras* (Pennsylvanian)
  - *Somoholites* (Pennsylvanian)
  - *Tornoceras* (Devonian)
  - *Wellerites* (Pennsylvanian)

Subclass uncertain (almost certainly Ammonoidea)
- *Sidetes* (Devonian)

animals lumped together as "nautiloids" actually belong in several distinct groups (table 14-1) that may well not be very closely related biologically. Members of four subclasses commonly are called "nautiloids"; these groups are as different from one another as the "nautiloids" as a whole are different from animals of the subclass Ammonoidea. A potential source of confusion is the fact that one of the subclasses of "nautiloids" has the technical name Nautiloidea (the others are the Endoceratoidea, the Actinoceratoidea, and the Bactritoidea). All these groups are treated as "nautiloids" in this chapter because, in some instances, a shell can be assigned to the proper subclass only after careful study of the internal structure of the **conch**. In other words, specimens of certain genera of all four subclasses can look confusingly alike externally.

The main problem is that nautiloids that look alike externally may differ markedly on the interior. Much of the identification of nautiloids is based on details of the siphuncle and of the interior of the camerae. For example, in some cephalopods the siphuncle is basically a tube of uniform **diameter**; in others, the siphuncle is expanded between septa (see fig. 1-20.2), so that it resembles a string of beads.

In present-day *Nautilus,* the camerae are filled with gas; in the chambers nearest the body of the animal, liquid also may be present. The siphuncle of a living *Nautilus* is occupied by a strand of soft tissue, so that, in a shell that no longer contains the animal, the siphuncle is an empty tube.

However, in many fossil nautiloids, especially orthocones, the camerae and the siphuncle may contain mineral matter that was deposited by the animal during life (see fig. 1-20). These cameral and siphuncular deposits are concentrated toward the apex of the shell and on the **venter** of the animal (the bottom side in life) and apparently served to help orient and balance the animal in the water. For example, mineral matter deposited in the apical end of the shell would make that part of the conch heavier and tend to bring an orthoconic shell into a horizontal position during life (see figs. 1-20.1 to 1-20.3). The presence and nature of the cameral and siphuncular deposits are important features in the identification of fossil cephalopods, especially orthoconic nautiloids. They also are important for interpreting the environmental needs and way of life of the animals.

Because internal features of orthoconic nautiloids are the basis for identification, to identify many nautiloids it is necessary to cut them open to see internal details. Not only does this require special equipment, but it means that one has to damage beautiful specimens.

As one generation of scientists after another studies a group of animals, we reach an ever-better understanding of these organisms. From the point of view of the amateur paleontologist or fossil collector, however, this evolution of understanding can have a confusing side effect—the names of the animals may be changed.

Consider, for example, the cephalopod genus *Orthoceras.*

In former years, virtually any small- to medium-sized nautiloid found in Ohio probably would have been identified as a member of the genus *Orthoceras* (the name means "straight horn"). Paleontologists have been studying the fossils of Ohio for more than a century and a half. In that time, they discovered that the name *Orthoceras* had been used for a wide variety of orthoconic nautiloids—for animals whose great diversity of features indicates that they belong in a number of different genera. The most common Ordovician cephalopod in Ohio originally was named *Orthoceras duseri*, but it was discovered that the shell of this animal is so different from that of true *Orthoceras* that paleontologists considered that the species called *Orthoceras duseri* belongs in a genus different from *Orthoceras*. Hence, it now is called *Treptoceras duseri*. (There do not seem to be any true *Orthoceras* in any of the rocks of Ohio.)

The message here is not to be frustrated when the names of genera in older literature do not match those in more recent publications. This is not a mean trick on the part of paleontologists. Rather, it is a reflection of progress in our understanding of the fossils.

Another problem involves the preservation of the animal. **Taphonomy** is the technical term for everything that happens to an organism from the time it dies until the time it is collected. Every cephalopod that is found as a fossil in the rocks of Ohio lived many millions of years ago. In those millions of years many destructive things can have happened to the remains of that cephalopod. If one is to understand just what the animal looked like in life and how it lived, one must be able to reconstruct the organism—in effect, to undo the taphonomy.

Unfortunately, cephalopods that underwent different taphonomic histories may look very different as fossils, even though they are the same kind of animal and originally looked very similar to one another. Consider, for example, the siphuncle. Each septum has a hole in it that is incorporated into the siphuncle. In many orthocones the siphuncle is more-or-less central in position—essentially equidistant from the top, bottom, and sides of the shell. The camerae through which the siphuncle extends may have been mostly filled with gas during life. Upon the death of the animal, the empty shell rests on the sea floor, and sediment slowly piles on top of it. Eventually the shell may break under the weight of the overlying sediment, and the siphuncle may collapse to the bottom of the shell. A problem for the paleontologist millions of years later is to determine whether the siphuncle was central in position during life, or whether it originally was ventral, or even **dorsal**. Thus, the remains of the same animal could look strikingly different, depending upon how the animal was preserved. Moreover, remains of animals that were different in life could look strikingly similar, depending on taphonomy.

AMMONOID CEPHALOPODS

The ammonoid cephalopods in the rocks of Ohio are all coiled forms that have decidedly wiggly sutures. The geologically earliest known ammonoids in Ohio are rare specimens from Devonian rocks in northeastern and central Ohio. Mississippian-age ammonoids also are very rare; only relatively few occurrences are known. Pennsylvanian-age ammonoids are more numerous, although in a collection of over 70,000 specimens of Pennsylvanian-age fossil invertebrates, fewer than 300 were ammonoids (Mapes and others, in press).

Because ammonoid cephalopods changed shape and appearance as they grew, a baby specimen of a particular ammonoid species commonly looks remarkably different from a specimen of the same species that has reached a juvenile growth stage, and mature specimens can be so different in appearance from juveniles that even professional paleontologists have been confounded. In short, the inexperienced investigator may have considerable difficulty in identifying material. In general, baby ammonoids are rare or, at least, are not collected commonly; hence, most collections will contain the larger specimens of a species, those that were sexually mature or nearly so.

To identify an ammonoid there are three major morphological features that must be examined closely. These are, in order of importance: (1) the suture, (2) the **ornament** on the conch, and (3) the conch shape.

The suture, with its **lobes** and **saddles** (see figs. 1-22.3, 14-10), is extremely important to identification. Although sutures did change gradually as an individual animal grew, for the purposes of this guide to fossil identification, only the sutures of larger individuals of a species are diagrammed because juvenile ammonoids generally are not common in collections. Most identifications are based on the **external suture**, that part of the suture that is visible outside the **umbilical seam**.

The ornament is visible only if shell material is preserved. There may be fine to coarse **lirae** confined to the outside shell layer. In some forms, both transverse and longitudinal lirae are present; these lines result in a cross-hatched pattern referred to as **reticulate** or cancellate. **Nodes** or ribs that affect both the interior and the exterior of the shell may be present.

Conch shape (see figs. 1-19 and 1-22) includes the size and shape of the **umbilicus**, **whorl height**, **whorl width**, overall diameter, and the relationship of these to one another (for example, a conch with a large diameter relative to the whorl width is said to be narrow). It is important to understand that, in individuals of some taxa, these features changed profoundly as the animal grew.

ADDITIONAL READING

Alas! There is no one book one can turn to in order to look up the characteristics of all the fossil cephalopods of Ohio, be they nautiloids or ammonoids. There have been literally dozens of scientific papers that deal entirely or in part with Ohio cephalopods. There are far too many to list in a work such as this one.

The bulk of the papers dealing with Ohio nautiloid cephalopods were written by two paleontologists, August F. Foerste (1862-1936) and Rousseau H. Flower (1913-1988). Bassler (1937) compiled a bibliography of Dr. Foerste's publications, and Wolberg and Gil (1988) compiled a bibliography of Dr. Flower's publications. Both bibliographies are listed in the references section of this volume.

The Pennsylvanian cephalopods of Ohio are an exception to the rule of no up-to-date, thorough studies. Both the nautiloids and the ammonoids are dealt with in a comprehensive manner in a Division of Geological Survey bulletin that will be published soon after this bulletin (Sturgeon and others, in press; Mapes and others, in press).

The best single source of information on fossil cephalopods in general is the *Treatise on Invertebrate Paleontology*; the sections on cephalopods were compiled by Arkell and others (1957) and Teichert and others (1964). Although Ohio cephalopods are not dealt with in any single place in those volumes, most of the genera that occur in the state are individually described and figured in the *Treatise*.

KEY TO THE COMMON CEPHALOPODS OF OHIO

The following key is based purely on the morphology of relatively well-preserved specimens. The key includes only those genera mentioned in this chapter and will not work for taxa not included in this chapter. Even for the genera included, the key may not work for species not reported from Ohio.

In order to identify some specimens, one may need to use equipment, such as microscopes and rock saws, not ordinarily available to the amateur fossil collector. Moreover, well-preserved specimens of various ontogenetic ages may need to be studied. If such situations arise, identification by a professional paleontologist may be required.

1A. Suture essentially straight, gently curved, or gently sinuous 2
1B. Suture decidedly wiggly .... ammonoid cephalopod
Because of the great importance of the suture in recognizing ammonoid genera, they do not lend themselves to identification by means of a dichotomous key such as this one. Once you have determined that a given specimen is an ammonoid, look at figure 14-10 and find the suture that best matches that on the specimen; then, go to the description of that genus and similar forms to confirm your identification.

2A. Conch orthoconic 3
2B. Conch definitely curved or coiled 8

3A. Siphuncle ventral in position 4
3B. Siphuncle not ventral in position 5

4A. Conch large (may exceed a diameter of 20 cm); siphuncle large (up to half the diameter of the conch) .... *Cameroceras* (figs. 14-1.5 to 14-1.7)
4B. Conch and siphuncle both small .... *Bactrites* (not illustrated)

5A. Conch has **annulations** .... *Dawsonoceras* (fig. 14-2.7) or *Spyroceras* (fig. 14-2.8)
5B. Conch has no annulations 6

6A. Conch has well-developed, longitudinal ridges .... *Kionoceras* (fig. 14-2.2)
6B. Conch does not have well-developed, longitudinal ridges 7

7A. Conch longiconic .... *"Orthoceras"*
Includes forms such as *Treptoceras* (figs. 14-1.1, 14-1.2, 14-1.4), *Pseudorthoceras* (figs. 14-5.1, 14-5.2), and *Mooreoceras* (figs. 14-5.3 to 14-5.5), which cannot be differentiated without careful study of internal details.
7B. Conch breviconic .... *Acleistoceras* (figs. 14-2.3, 14-2.5)

8A. Conch cyrtoconic 9
8B. Conch coiled 10

9A. Conch breviconic .... *Acleistoceras* (figs. 14-2.3, 14-2.5), *Amphicyrtoceras* (fig. 14-2.4), or *Phragmoceras* (figs. 14-2.6, 14-2.9)
These genera differ especially in the shape of the living chamber and the aperture of the mature individual.

9B. Conch longiconic .... *Manitoulinoceras* (fig. 14-2.1)

10A. Coiling gyroconic 11
10B. Coiling evolute 12

11A. Whorls almost touch one another; conch has no transverse frills .... *Heracloceras* (fig. 14-3.6)
11B. Whorls separated from one another; conch has transverse frills (frills may be broken off so that only their bases are evident on the wall of the conch) .... *Goldringia* (fig. 14-3.2)

12A. Whorl compressed .... *Domatoceras* (figs. 14-7.2 to 14-7.5) or *Stenodomatoceras* (figs. 14-7.6, 14-7.7)

Stenodomatoceras is narrower than *Domatoceras*.

12B. Whorl not compressed 13

13A. Siphuncle dorsal or nearly so .... *Graftonoceras* (figs. 14-3.3, 14-3.4)

13B. Siphuncle central or between the venter and the center .... numerous genera

Includes *Charactoceras* (fig. 14-3.1), *Latitemnocheilus* (figs. 14-6.1, 14-6.2), *Metacoceras* (figs. 14-5.6 to 14-5.10), *Parametacoceras* (fig. 14-6.3), *Tainoceras* (fig. 14-5.11), *Temnocheilus* (fig. 14-7.1), and *Wellsoceras* (fig. 14-3.5). In order to differentiate them, one needs specimens suitably preserved to show the nature of the siphuncle, growth lines, nodes, **tubercles**, whorl cross section, and sutures at various stages in the life of the animal.

ORDOVICIAN CEPHALOPODS

Next to brachiopods and bryozoans, cephalopods well may be the most abundant fossils in the Ordovician rocks of Ohio. Numerous genera have been reported over the years, but specimens of most of these are rare in most rock units. Only orthoconic forms up to about 5 cm in diameter are really common. All the cephalopods found in the Ordovician rocks of Ohio are nautiloids (in the general sense of that word).

There is no single comprehensive work on Ordovician cephalopods of the state. However, several papers on some of them have been published (Aronoff, 1979; Frey, 1981, 1985, 1988, 1989, 1995).

The genus *Cameroceras* Conrad (figs. 14-1.5 to 14-1.7) includes the largest orthoconic cephalopods known from the state. Individual shells can exceed 210 cm in length and 20 cm in diameter. Of course, only very rarely are more-or-less complete specimens found. More common are fragments less than 25 cm long.

The siphuncle of *Cameroceras* also is very large—it may be half the diameter of the shell. In most specimens the siphuncle is at or near the shell wall and ventral in position. The suture is essentially a straight line and extends straight across the shell.

Specimens in limestone may be preserved in their original shape (fig. 14-1.7); the cross section is round or a bit depressed. Specimens in shale, on the other hand, may be crushed so that the shell is nearly flat.

Cameroceras belongs to a group of cephalopods technically called endoceroids or endocerids, after the order Endocerida, to which they belong. (In some publications, they are called endoceratoids, after their subclass, Endoceratoidea.) These animals have siphuncular deposits called **endocones** (see fig. 1-20.3). When the animal was alive, each endocone was hollow at the larger end, and the siphuncle contained a series of endocones, each with its point nestled in the base of the next cone toward the apex of the shell. In some cases the endocones are the only part of the shell preserved.

In some specimens only part of the internal mold of the siphuncle remains (fig. 14-1.5). It may be difficult to differentiate these internal molds from individuals of other genera in which the entire shell is of a diameter similar to that of the siphuncle of *Cameroceras*. In specimens in which camerae are preserved, the sutures generally are perpendicular to the length of the shell, and septa extend through the specimen. However, on internal molds of the siphuncles of *Cameroceras*, the lines that mark the intersections of the siphuncle and the septa are inclined, and there are no septa within the mold.

Another relatively common kind of preservation is the internal mold of the base of an endocone (fig. 14-1.6). Such an internal mold has no internal structure, except for the particles of the rock of which it is composed, and it can be a very sharp-pointed object.

According to Frey (1989), *Cameroceras inaequabile* (Miller) is the species of the genus most commonly found in the Ordovician rocks of the state. In former years, specimens of *Cameroceras* generally were identified as *Endoceras* Hall (hence the label on the specimen in fig. 14-1.6), and *Endoceras proteiforme* Hall was the most commonly cited species.

Treptoceras Flower (figs. 14-1.1, 14-1.2, 14-1.4) is the most common cephalopod in the Ordovician rocks of Ohio. *Treptoceras* is orthoconic and reaches a maximum length of about 60 cm. The shell is circular in cross section, or nearly so. The sutures are straight and extend directly across the length of the shell. There are well-developed cameral deposits in the apical part of the shell; they are best developed ventrally. The siphuncle is nearly central in small specimens and somewhat ventral of the center in larger individuals. The siphuncle is broader within camerae and narrower where it passes through each septum, thus giving the appearance of a string of beads (see fig. 1-20.2). The apical portion of the shell also contains siphuncular deposits.

Teichert and others (1964) included in the genus *Orthonybyoceras* Shimizu & Obata those specimens others (for example, Aronoff, 1979) had referred to *Treptoceras*. Hence, the name *Orthonybyoceras* commonly has been used for specimens here included in *Treptoceras*. To differentiate specimens of the two genera, one must carefully examine internal features of the shells.

Specimens of *Treptoceras* are very abundant in certain rock layers. For example, Frey (1989) referred to the "*Treptoceras duseri* shale" layer within the Waynesville Formation of southwestern Ohio. This layer includes three species of the genus, one of which is a new species, as yet unnamed.

Manitoulinoceras Foerste (fig. 14-2.1) is a slender cyrtocone; in other words, it is a curved (but not coiled) longicone. When the animal was alive, the shell was oriented with the convex side of the curve down. The shell is depressed in cross section; the venter is rounded or subangular, and the **dorsum** is somewhat flattened. The siphuncle is close to the ventral (convex) side of the shell. Siphuncular deposits may be present in the apical portion of large shells, but there are no cameral deposits. Sutures are straight and transverse in small individuals, but slant in the **adapertural** portions of larger individuals, where the suture is closer to the aperture on the venter. Maximum length in Ohio specimens is about 9 cm. A number of species of *Manitoulinoceras* have been recorded from Ohio. Not uncommonly, specimens of the genus have been referred to *Cyrtoceras*.

Charactoceras Foerste (fig. 14-3.1) is the only well-known coiled cephalopod in the Ordovician rocks of Ohio. Average specimens are 10-15 cm across the coil. The first-named species in the genus, and the one that has been found in Ohio, is *Charactoceras baeri* (Meek & Worthen). It originally was called *Trochoceras? baeri* and also has been called *Gyroceras baeri* in older works.

SILURIAN CEPHALOPODS

All of the Silurian cephalopods from Ohio are nautiloids. A large number of different kinds have been reported, particularly in works of August F. Foerste (see, for example, Davis and Troike, 1990). That many of these have been reported only once or twice may be a function of the fact that there has been no modern study of the Silurian cephalopods of the state.

Although fossil cephalopods are not especially uncommon in some units (for example, the Brassfield Formation and the Cedarville Dolomite), they generally are preserved only as internal molds. Hence, details of the exterior of the shell tend to be poorly known, and ordinarily there are few or no internal details preserved.

An assortment of mostly smooth, orthoconic nautiloids have been found in the Silurian rocks of Ohio. All of these forms would have been called *Orthoceras* at one time—for example, fossils that have been identified as *Orthoceras simulator* Hall. Unfortunately, such fossils have not been studied seriously in half a century, so their generic identification is uncertain. It is virtually certain, however, that they are not true *Orthoceras*. Specimens properly assigned to that genus are known only from the Middle Ordovician of Europe.

Dawsonoceras Hyatt (fig. 14-2.7) is a longiconic nautiloid that is orthoconic or slightly curved. It is characterized by conspicuous transverse ridges called annulations. Several genera of orthoconic nautiloids are characterized by annulations, including *Dawsonoceras*, *Spyroceras*, and others. These genera can be differentiated only after careful study of the internal features of the shells. A number of species of *Dawsonoceras* have been reported from Ohio. In some cases, these forms have been identified erroneously as belonging in the genus *Cycloceras*.

Kionoceras Hyatt (fig. 14-2.2) is an orthoconic or slightly curved longicone characterized by longitudinal ridges and grooves. Several species of *Kionoceras* have been reported from the Silurian rocks of Ohio.

Phragmoceras Broderip (figs. 14-2.6, 14-2.9) is one of a number of breviconic cyrtocones reported from the Silurian of Ohio, each of which has a highly constricted aperture at maturity (fig. 14-2.9). In representatives of this genus, the aperture is a narrow slit that broadens ventrally and dorsally (fig. 14-2.6). Several species of *Phragmoceras* have been reported from the Silurian rocks of the state.

Amphicyrtoceras Foerste (fig. 14-2.4), like a number of other breviconic cyrtocones reported from the Silurian of Ohio, has a constricted aperture at maturity, but not as constricted as that in *Phragmoceras*. Formerly, specimens of this genus probably would have been identified as belonging in the genus *Oncoceras*.

Graftonoceras Foerste (figs. 14-3.3, 14-3.4) is a **planispirally** coiled nautiloid that has been reported from the Silurian rocks of Ohio. The coiling is basically evolute, such that each whorl is just barely impressed into the next whorl toward the outside of the coil. There is a tendency for uncoiling in the outermost whorl in the vicinity of the aperture of the shell. The siphuncle is dorsal in position, or nearly so, and the hyponomic sinus is just a simple reentrant. In older publications, specimens of this genus have been referred to the genera *Lituites* and *Discoceras*.

Specimens of another genus that has been reported from the Silurian rocks of Ohio, *Lechritrochoceras*, potentially might be confused with those of *Graftonoceras*. However, the coiling in *Lechritrochoceras* is slightly **trochospiral**.

DEVONIAN CEPHALOPODS

It is in Devonian rocks that the oldest ammonoid cephalopods in the state have been found. A variety of nautiloids also occur in these rocks, but not as many different genera as in the older rocks of Ohio.

One kind of cephalopod fossil deserves special mention here. In the aperture of the shell of some ammonoids, there may be a pair of plates that together just fill up the aperture. These plates, called **aptychi**, apparently served the same function as does an operculum in some snails, namely, a "trap door" to close the aperture.

In other ammonoids, instead of a pair of aptychi, there is a structure in the living chamber that is much thinner than aptychi but commonly about the same shape as a pair of aptychi together. This single structure is called an **anaptychus**. Because ammonoids long have been extinct, there has been some disagreement among paleontologists as to just how an anaptychus functioned in life. Some specialists have argued that it was an operculum—closing the aperture, if the occasion demanded it. Others are convinced that anaptychi are the lower jaws of ammonoids; presumably, the upper jaws of such animals were of a different composition that was not preserved as readily as were the lower jaws.

Aptychi and anaptychi deserve special mention because specimens of anaptychi have been found in the Cleveland and Chagrin Shale Members of the Ohio Shale in the northeastern part of the state (Frye and Feldmann, 1991). Unfortunately, no anaptychi have been found in place in shells, so it is not known to which ammonoid they may have belonged. The name applied to the Ohio anaptychi is *Sidetes* Giebel (fig. 14-4).

In the above discussion of apytchi and anaptychi, only ammonoid cephalopods are mentioned. It should be pointed out that specimens of nautiloids have been found with plate-like structures preserved in their apertures. These structures have some similarities to the aptychi considered characteristic of some ammonoids, and it may be that some aptychi and anaptychi belonged to nautiloids. In any case, no nautiloids have been found in Ohio that have any such plates in place in the aperture or living chamber.

The conchs of Devonian cephalopods of Ohio have not been studied comprehensively in recent times, so they are not as well known as might be desired. The majority of taxa have been reported from the Columbus Limestone, the Delaware Limestone, and the Plum Brook Shale (Stauffer, 1909); some have been reported from the Silica Formation (Kesling and Chilman, 1975).

NAUTILOIDS

A number of species referred to *Orthoceras* were reported from Devonian rocks of Ohio by Stauffer (1909). These species were re-assigned to other genera by Kindle and Miller

(1939), but the Devonian "*Orthoceras*" of Ohio have not been studied in recent years, and the generic identifications are uncertain. It is virtually certain, however, that they are not true *Orthoceras,* because, as mentioned previously, specimens properly assigned to that genus are known only from the Middle Ordovician of Europe.

Spyroceras Hyatt (fig. 14-2.8) is one of the orthoconic longicones that originally was called *Orthoceras*. In this genus, however, the shell bears transverse annulations. *Spyroceras* is one of several genera of orthoconic nautiloids that are characterized by annulations; they can be differentiated only after careful study of the internal features of the shells. The apex of the cone of *Spyroceras* is faintly cyrtoconic, and there may be longitudinal lirae, but these characteristics are only rarely preserved. Two species of *Spyroceras* have been reported from the Columbus Limestone in central Ohio.

Acleistoceras Hyatt (figs. 14-2.3, 14-2.5) is a straight to slightly curved brevicone. A mature specimen of *Acleistoceras* has a well-developed hyponomic sinus and a constricted aperture that is subtriangular in shape. In the past, species of this genus have been referred to *Gomphoceras* and *Poterioceras*.

Heracloceras Teichert (fig. 14-3.6) is a gyroconically coiled shell that consists of two to three whorls that almost touch one another. Each whorl is compressed in cross section. In earlier works, specimens of this genus were referred to *Gigantoceras*. The species reported from Ohio is *Heracloceras inelegans* (Meek).

Goldringia Flower (fig. 14-3.2) is a gyrocone consisting of one or two whorls so loosely coiled as not to touch at all. In life this animal must have been one of the most spectacular nautiloids in the Devonian seas. The shell is unusual in that it has a series of regularly spaced, transverse frills. Each frill is crenulate and extends completely around the whorl and out from it to a distance equal to half the width of the whorl or more. For example, in an animal that has a diameter of 25 cm and a whorl width of about 5 cm, the frill extends out more than 2.5 cm all the way around the whorl. These frills are delicate and virtually always break off when a specimen is removed from the enclosing rock. Hence, only their bases show in figure 14-3.2.

Goldringia cyclops (Hall), a species found in the Columbus Limestone, originally was assigned to the genus *Gyroceras* and has been referred to *Rhyticeras* in some older works. *Goldringia trivolve* (Conrad), also from the Columbus Limestone, first was assigned to *Cyrtoceras* and also has been referred to *Gyroceras* or *Rhyticeras* in some publications.

Wellsoceras Flower (fig. 14-3.5) is an evolutely coiled form that is probably the most common nautiloid in the Columbus Limestone. The whorls touch one another, although the living chamber is free from the preceding volution. In cross section, each whorl has a tendency to be quadrangular. *Wellsoceras columbiense* (Whitfield), the **type species** of the genus, originally was placed in the genus *Gyroceras* and has been referred to *Rhyticeras* in some older literature.

At first glance, a specimen of *Bactrites* Sandberger looks like an ordinary smooth, orthoconic longicone. However, instead of having a straight, transverse suture, the shell has sutures that each have a ventral lobe, and the siphuncle is ventral in position. Many paleontologists are convinced that the evolutionary lineage that gave rise to all the ammonoid cephalopods had its origin in animals like *Bactrites*. *Bactrites arkonensis* Whiteaves occurs in the Columbus Limestone and in the Plum Brook Shale. No specimen of *Bactrites* is illustrated in this chapter because it would look like any other smooth orthocone. This resemblance is a problem. *Bactrites* is considered to be quite rare in Ohio, but this may well be because specimens of this genus look so much like ordinary orthoconic nautiloids that they are not recognized as anything special by most collectors.

AMMONOIDS

Ammonoids are not common fossils in the Devonian rocks of Ohio. Although the total number of specimens that have been collected is unknown, a count of those reported in Sweet and Miller (1956), Kesling and Chilman (1975), House (1978), and House and others (1986) suggests that fewer than 70 individuals are known (not counting the anaptychi reported by Frye and Feldmann, 1991).

Tornoceras Hyatt (figs. 14-8.1 to 14-8.3, 14-10.1) is the least uncommon genus of Devonian ammonoids known from Ohio. The conch has a small umbilicus. The simple suture has relatively shallow lobes. Specimens of the genus have been recovered from the Columbus Limestone near Columbus, Franklin County (Sweet and Miller, 1956), although House (1962) suggested that these may belong in the genus *Foordites* Wedekind. *Tornoceras uniangulare* (Conrad) (figs. 14-8.1 to 14-8.3) has been recovered from the Silica Formation in quarries at Silica, Lucas County (Kesling and Chilman, 1975).

MISSISSIPPIAN CEPHALOPODS

The Mississippian nautiloids of the state are poorly known. Ammonoids are extremely rare in these rocks, and those that have been discovered have received relatively little study. Hyde (1953) and Manger (1971) did describe several specimens of ammonoids recovered from isolated exposures along the outcrop belt in central and southern Ohio.

PENNSYLVANIAN CEPHALOPODS

The Pennsylvanian cephalopods of Ohio, both the ammonoids and the nautiloids, recently have been studied thoroughly (Sturgeon and others, in press; Mapes and others, in press). Once these publications appear in print, the Pennsylvanian cephalopods will be the best documented in the state.

NAUTILOIDS

Pseudorthoceras Girty (figs. 14-5.1, 14-5.2), a longicone, is orthoconic for virtually all of its length, but near the apex of the shell it is slightly cyrtoconic. In cross section the shell is circular, and the siphuncle is central in position, or nearly so. Maximum length of the shell may exceed 70 cm, and the diameter may be over 8 cm. Both cameral and siphuncular deposits are present in the apical portion of the shell. Because of these deposits, the apical portion of the shell may be preserved in its proper shape; however, the adapertural portion of the conch commonly is crushed. In Ohio, *Pseudorthoceras knoxense* (McChesney) has been identified only from Pennsylvanian rocks. In other regions this species has been reported to range from rocks as old as Devonian and as young as Permian.

Mooreoceras Miller, Dunbar & Condra (figs. 14-5.3 to

14-5.5) is very similar to *Pseudorthoceras*. In fact, a number of paleontologists have suggested that perhaps individuals of the two genera are members of a single genus. The differences that have been noted are that in larger specimens of *Mooreoceras* the cross section commonly is somewhat depressed and the siphuncle is between the center of the shell and the venter. Otherwise, the two genera are closely similar, if not identical. In Ohio, *Mooreoceras normale* Miller, Dunbar & Condra has been reported only from Pennsylvanian rocks. Elsewhere this species has been reported to range from the Devonian into the Permian.

Shells identified as belonging in the genus *Metacoceras* Hyatt (figs. 14-5.6 to 14-5.10) are evolutely coiled. In cross section, a whorl generally is subquadrate (that is, like a rectangle with rounded corners). There may be ribs on the flanks. In addition, there may be a row of nodes on each "corner" of the venter, or there may be a row on each **umbilical shoulder**, or there may be rows of nodes in all four positions. Several species have been reported from the Pennsylvanian rocks of Ohio. *Metacoceras latum* Sturgeon, Windle, Mapes & Hoare has both **ventrolateral** and **dorsolateral** nodes (figs. 14-5.6, 14-5.7); these nodes are connected by irregular ridges in smaller specimens. *Metacoceras mcchesneyi* Murphy, on the other hand, has only ventrolateral nodes (figs. 14-5.8, 14-5.9). *Metacoceras mutabile* Miller & Owen also has ventrolateral nodes (fig.14-5.10), and some individuals have dorsolateral nodes.

Tainoceras Hyatt (fig. 14-5.11) is similar in appearance to *Metacoceras* but has two longitudinal rows of nodes on the venter. *Tainoceras* is not a common genus in Ohio. Only a few specimens of several species, including *Tainoceras collinsi* Sturgeon, Windle, Mapes & Hoare, have been reported from the Ames limestone (Conemaugh Group).

Parametacoceras Miller & Owen (fig. 14-6.3) also is similar to *Metacoceras*. However, *Parametacoceras* has neither conspicuous ventrolateral nodes nor ribs on the **flanks**. Specimens of *Parametacoceras bellatulum* Miller & Owen can exceed a diameter of 3 cm. Specimens tentatively referred to this species have been found in the Putnam Hill unit (Allegheny Group) in Ohio.

The genus *Temnocheilus* M'Coy (fig. 14-7.1) includes evolutely coiled shells that have longitudinal ridges and grooves in small individuals and on the innermost whorls of large ones. Larger specimens have pronounced ventrolateral nodes, and the whorls are elliptical in cross section; the shorter diameter of the ellipse is the dorsoventral one. Individuals of *Temnocheilus annulonodosus* Sturgeon, Windle, Mapes & Hoare can exceed 10 cm in diameter and have been found in rocks of the Allegheny Group in Ohio.

The evolute shells of *Latitemnocheilus* Sturgeon, Windle, Mapes & Hoare (figs. 14-6.1, 14-6.2) reach a maximum diameter of 20 cm and, thus, are distinctly larger than individuals referred to *Temnocheilus*. The whorls in *Latitemnocheilus* are depressed, but the whorl cross section is subrectangular, rather than subelliptical, as in *Temnocheilus*. Individuals of several species of *Latitemnocheilus* have been reported from rocks of the Pottsville and Allegheny Groups of Ohio.

The evolute shells of *Domatoceras* Hyatt (figs. 14-7.2 to 14-7.5) have a compressed whorl cross section and are discoidal in shape. The venter is flattened or even concave. The flanks are flattened on the sides of the shell, but converge somewhat toward the venter. The umbilical shoulder may be rounded or subangular and may bear nodes. There also may be ventrolateral nodes. Specimens of a number of species of *Domatoceras* have been reported from rocks of the Pottsville, Allegheny, and Conemaugh Groups of Ohio. They can exceed 15 cm in maximum diameter.

Stenodomatoceras Ruzhencev & Shimansky (figs. 14-7.6, 14-7.7) is similar to *Domatoceras*, only narrower. (The prefix "steno" means "narrow.") Specimens of *Stenodomatoceras gardi* (Murphy) have been reported from the Conemaugh Group of Ohio (Sturgeon and others, in press). The maximum diameter of the shell can exceed 11 cm.

AMMONOIDS

The largest collections of ammonoids in Ohio have come from a variety of Pennsylvanian localities in eastern and southeastern Ohio. Most specimens have been recovered from rock exposures uncovered during coal-mining activities. All of the known specimens have been described in detail by Mapes and others (in press). No ammonoids have been reported from uppermost Pennsylvanian rocks (nor from Permian rocks) of the state.

Of the more than 50 Pennsylvanian ammonoid genera that are known to exist in North America, 20 have been recovered from Ohio. Of the 273 specimens analyzed by Mapes and others (in press), most genera are represented by one to five poorly preserved specimens. In fact, specimens of three genera, *Neoaganides*, *Mangeroceras*, and *Pennoceras*, make up 46 percent of the entire Pennsylvanian ammonoid collection analyzed.

Of the 20 genera of ammonoids recovered from Pennsylvanian rocks of Ohio, the 11 illustrated here are characteristic in terms of sutural variation and conch form. For some taxa, specimens collected in other states are better preserved than known Ohio specimens and, hence, have been illustrated here. Detailed information about the Pennsylvanian ammonoids from Ohio is provided in Mapes and others (in press). A general world overview, including an in-depth bibliography, is contained in Boardman and others (1994).

The genus *Gonioloboceras* Hyatt is represented by *G. goniolobum* (Meek) (figs. 14-8.4, 14-10.2). Juvenile specimens from Ohio have ribs, an open umbilicus, and a diameter of less than 10 mm. Adult forms have a discoidal conch up to 70 mm in diameter, a pinpoint umbilicus, and a rounded venter.

The genus *Pennoceras* Miller & Unklesbay is represented by *P. seamani* Miller & Unklesbay (figs. 14-8.5, 14-8.6, 14-10.3). This small, **inflated** ammonoid has coarse transverse ornament and a simple suture. The maximum diameter of this species is less than 30 mm.

The genus *Neoaganides* Plummer & Scott is represented by *N. grahamensis* Plummer & Scott (figs. 14-8.7 to 14-8.9, 14-10.4). This ammonoid is very small at maturity; maximum diameter is less than 10 mm. It has a smooth shell, a small umbilicus, and a unique, tongue-shaped ventral lobe in the suture (fig. 14-10.4).

The genus *Gonioglyphioceras* Plummer & Scott is represented by *G. gracile* (Girty) (figs. 14-8.10, 14-8.11, 14-10.5). The growth pattern and suture of this species are similar to those of *Gonioloboceras goniolobum*, but the venter has a distinct groove, and the overall conch at maturity is narrower.

The genus *Mangeroceras* Sturgeon, Windle, Mapes & Hoare is represented by *M. canfieldense* Sturgeon, Windle, Mapes & Hoare (figs. 14-8.14 to 14-8.17, 14-10.6), an intermediate-sized ammonoid. Its diameter is about 45 mm when nearing maturity. It has a moderately rounded conch and a moderately open, ribbed umbilicus. The ornament is sinuous, and the ventral prongs of the suture are wide and parallel sided.

Individuals of *Schistoceras* Hyatt (figs. 14-8.12, 14-8.13, 14-9.11, 14-10.7) developed into relatively large ammonoids, 80 to 100 mm in diameter. Mature sutures are characterized by a series of spear-point-shaped lobes. It is possible that several species are represented in Ohio, but these have not been differentiated owing to lack of a sufficient number of specimens.

The genus *Glaphyrites* Ruzhencev is represented by *G. jonesi* (Miller & Owen) (figs. 14-9.1, 14-9.2, 14-10.8). Individuals of this widely umbilicate ammonoid can attain diameters greater than 100 mm. In youthful individuals the suture is relatively simple and the lobes are blunt; in mature and nearly mature specimens, the lobes are long and spear-point shaped.

The genus *Aktubites* Ruzhencev is represented by *A. trifidus* Ruzhencev (figs. 14-9.3, 14-9.4, 14-10.9), which characteristically has a relatively small conch (diameter less than 40 mm) and a moderately wide umbilicus. The distinctive suture has a three-part lateral lobe; this subdivision of the lobes is present on the internal part of the suture as well.

The genus *Wellerites* Plummer & Scott is represented by *Wellerites* **cf.** *W. mohri* Plummer & Scott (figs. 14-9.6 to 14-9.10, 14-10.10), which has a moderate-sized umbilicus. The conch is relatively narrow and attains comparatively large diameters (greater than 50 mm). The internal suture exhibited on some specimens (figs. 14-9.6 to 14-9.9) is relatively undiagnostic; however, the multiple-lobed external suture (figs. 14-9.10, 14-10.10) is characteristic of this taxon.

The genus *Eoschistoceras* Ruzhencev is represented by *E. postvenatum* (Plummer & Scott) (fig. 14-9.5). *Eoschistoceras* has the same conch form as *Schistoceras* (compare figs. 14-9.5 and 14-9.11); however, the suture of *Eoschistoceras* lacks the well-developed lobe that occurs near the umbilical shoulder of *Schistoceras* (compare figs. 14-10.11 and 14-10.7).

The genus *Somoholites* Ruzhencev is represented by *S. sagittarius* Saunders (figs. 14-9.12 to 14-9.14, 14-10.12). Its conch is similar to that of *Glaphyrites* (compare figs. 14-9.1 and 14-9.2 to 14-9.14). However, the suture of *Somoholites* has inflated lobes, whereas the lobes of *Glaphyrites* are always narrower (compare figs. 14-10.8 to 14-10.12).

COLLECTING FOSSIL CEPHALOPODS IN OHIO

Fossil cephalopods have been recovered from most Ohio counties. Places that are especially good are Ordovician, Silurian, and Devonian limestone quarries in the central and western portions of the state. Other good potential collecting sites are exposures of marine beds exposed in coal mines in eastern Ohio. However, please remember that owners and operators of mines and quarries are very concerned about their legal liabilities. Hence, for both amateur and professional paleontologists, the best such localities almost always are closed to collecting. It is imperative that persons wanting to collect fossils obtain permission from the landowner before looking for any fossils. And it isn't just lawyers, government officials, and insurance companies that are the problem; quarries and mines can be very dangerous. No fossil on Earth is worth getting killed or maimed for—ALWAYS obey safety regulations and ALWAYS "use your head" when endeavoring to collect fossils.

Road cuts also can be good collecting sites. But here the danger isn't limited just to loose rocks and potential falls. After all, it would be a shame to find a nice fossil and then get struck by a truck when you step out into the roadway in your excitement. (Of course, a good way to avoid automobile traffic is to look for fossils in stream cuts! But even these are someone's property, so always get permission.)

ACKNOWLEDGMENTS

With unfailing courtesy and professionalism, Dale M. Gnidovec (Orton Museum, The Ohio State University), David L. Meyer (University of Cincinnati), Joe H. Marak (Miami University), and Elizabeth Merritt (The Cincinnati Museum of Natural History) allowed the authors access to the collections of cephalopods at their respective institutions. We are most grateful to all these people for their help and kindnesses.

FIGURE 14-1.—Ordovician orthoconic nautiloid cephalopods. Scale bars equal 1 cm, except those for figures 14-1.3 and 14-1.7, which equal 5 cm.

1, 2, 4	*Treptoceras duseri* (Hall & Whitfield). Ordovician, Cincinnati area. **1**, dark longitudinal lines are remains of what, in life, were color bands. OSU 47417. **2**, internal mold of part of **phragmocone** and living chamber. OSU 47422. **4**, specimen encrusted by a bryozoan colony. OSU 47418.
3	An orthoconic cephalopod encrusted by numerous individuals of the inarticulate brachiopod *Schizocrania filosa* (Hall). Ordovician, Clermont County, Ohio; OSU 9675.
5-7	*Cameroceras inaequabile* (Miller). Ordovician, Cincinnati area. **5**, internal mold of portion of siphuncle. OSU 47420. **6**, internal mold of an endocone; the tip of the cone is not preserved. The label indicates the specimen was previously assigned to the genus *Endoceras*. OSU 47421. **7**, internal mold of portion of phragmocone and part of living chamber. OSU 47419.

1
2
3
4
5
Endoceras
6
7

FIGURE 14-2.—Ordovician, Silurian, and Devonian nautiloid cephalopods. Scale bars equal 1 cm, except those for figures 14-2.3, 14-2.5, and 14-2.9, which equal 5 cm.

1	*Manitoulinoceras ultimum* Flower. **Holotype**. Internal mold of part of phragmocone. Elkhorn Formation (Ordovician), 3.2 km (2 miles) west of Hamburg, Indiana; MUGM T426.
2	*Kionoceras* sp. Niagaran Series (Silurian), Yellow Springs, Ohio; OSU 14802 (3431A). Specimen figured in Foerste (1928).
3, 5	*Acleistoceras eximium* Hall. **3**, Columbus Limestone (Devonian), Sandusky, Ohio; OSU 3673. **5**, Delaware Limestone (Devonian), Wagner Quarry #1, Sandusky, Ohio; OSU 34032.
4	*Amphicyrtoceras welchi* Foerste. Holotype. Internal mold of living chamber and part of phragmocone. Cedarville Dolomite (Silurian), Moodie (or Moody) Quarry, Wilmington, Ohio; CiMNH P315.
6	*Phragmoceras wilmingtonense* Foerste. **Paratype**. Apertural view of internal mold of living chamber. Niagaran Series (Silurian), Bowling Green, Ohio; OSU 9441.
7	*Dawsonoceras annulatum* (Sowerby). Niagaran Series (Silurian), Yellow Springs, Ohio; OSU 3428.
8	*Spyroceras thoas* (Hall). Columbus Limestone (Devonian), Columbus, Ohio; OSU 3657.
9	*Phragmoceras carmani* Foerste. Holotype. Lateral view of internal mold of most of phragmocone and living chamber. Niagaran Series (Silurian), Greene County, Ohio; OSU 14912. (Specimen number was cited incorrectly as 10912 in Foerste, 1930.)

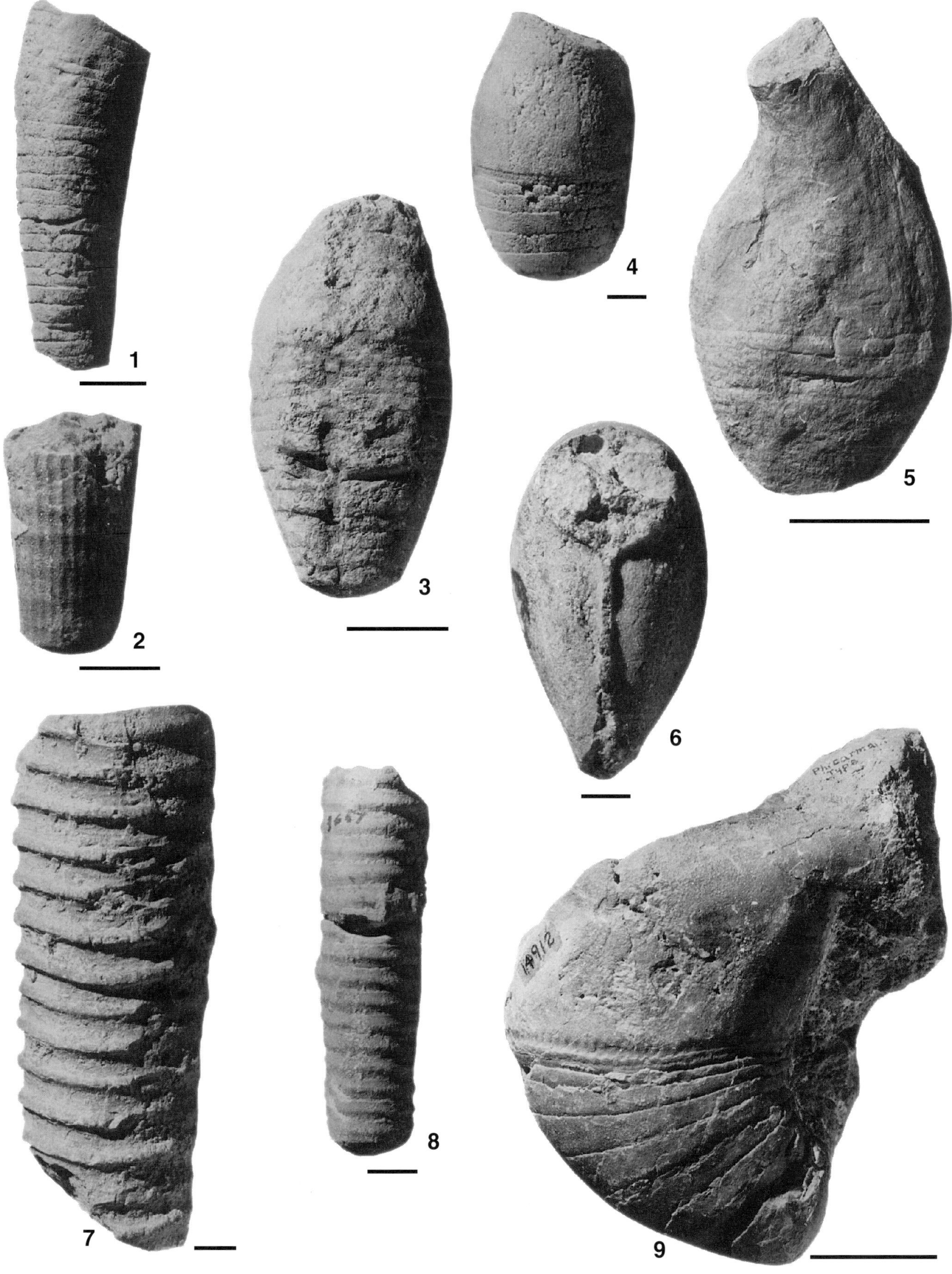

FIGURE 14-3.—Ordovician, Silurian, and Devonian coiled nautiloid cephalopods. Scale bars for figures 14-3.1, 14-3.3, and 14-3.4 equal 1 cm; scale bars for remaining figures equal 5 cm.

1	*Charactoceras baeri* (Meek & Worthen). "Lower Whitewater member," Whitewater Formation (Ordovician), Preble County, Ohio; MUGM 29591.
2	*Goldringia cyclops* (Hall). The frills that characterize specimens of this genus are not preserved. Columbus Limestone (Devonian), Columbus, Ohio; OSU 8999.
3, 4	*Graftonoceras ortoni* (Meek). Niagaran Series (Silurian), Greenville, Ohio. **3**, specimen on which someone has inked in growth increments. OSU 7057. **4**, holotype, on which someone has inked in the sutures. OSU 3404. Both specimens figured in Foerste (1925).
5	*Wellsoceras columbiense* (Whitfield). Columbus Limestone (Devonian), Delaware, Ohio; OSU 9297.
6	*Heracloceras inelegans* (Meek). Columbus Limestone (Devonian), Columbus, Ohio; OSU 3905.

1
2
3
4
5
6

FIGURE 14-4.—An anaptychus of *Sidetes chagrinensis* from the Cleveland Shale Member of the Ohio Shale (Devonian), Chance Creek, Lorain County, Ohio; ClMNH 3746. Photograph courtesy of Rodney M. Feldmann. Scale bar equals 1 cm.

FIGURE 14-5.—Pennsylvanian nautiloid cephalopods. All scale bars equal 1 cm. All figures from Sturgeon and others (in press).

1, 2	*Pseudorthoceras knoxense* (McChesney). **1**, Putnam Hill limestone-Vanport limestone undifferentiated (Allegheny Group), Muskingum County, Ohio; OSU 29425. **2**, Putnam Hill limestone (Allegheny Group), Tuscarawas County, Ohio; OSU 29368.
3-5	*Mooreoceras normale* Miller, Dunbar & Condra. **3**, Brush Creek limestone (Conemaugh Group), Meigs County, Ohio; OSU 29311. **4**, end view. Brush Creek limestone (Conemaugh Group), Athens County, Ohio; OSU 29422. **5**, Putnam Hill limestone (Allegheny Group), Mahoning County, Ohio; OSU 19556.
6, 7	*Metacoceras latum* Sturgeon, Windle, Mapes & Hoare. **6**, lateral view of incomplete specimen. Washingtonville shale (Allegheny Group), Coshocton County, Ohio; OSU 28896. **7**, ventral view of incomplete specimen; the holes in the specimen are tooth marks of a predator that attacked the live animal. Washingtonville shale (Allegheny Group), Muskingum County, Ohio; OSU 28897.
8, 9	*Metacoceras mcchesneyi* Murphy. Brush Creek limestone (Conemaugh Group), Columbiana County, Ohio. **8**, ventral view of incomplete specimen. OSU 28921. **9**, lateral view. OSU 28929.
10	*Metacoceras mutabile* Miller & Owen. Lateral view. Putnam Hill limestone (Allegheny Group), Mahoning County, Ohio; OSU 28893.
11	*Tainoceras collinsi* Sturgeon, Windle, Mapes & Hoare. Ventral view of incomplete specimen (holotype). Ames limestone (Conemaugh Group), Monongalia County, West Virginia; OSU 28826.

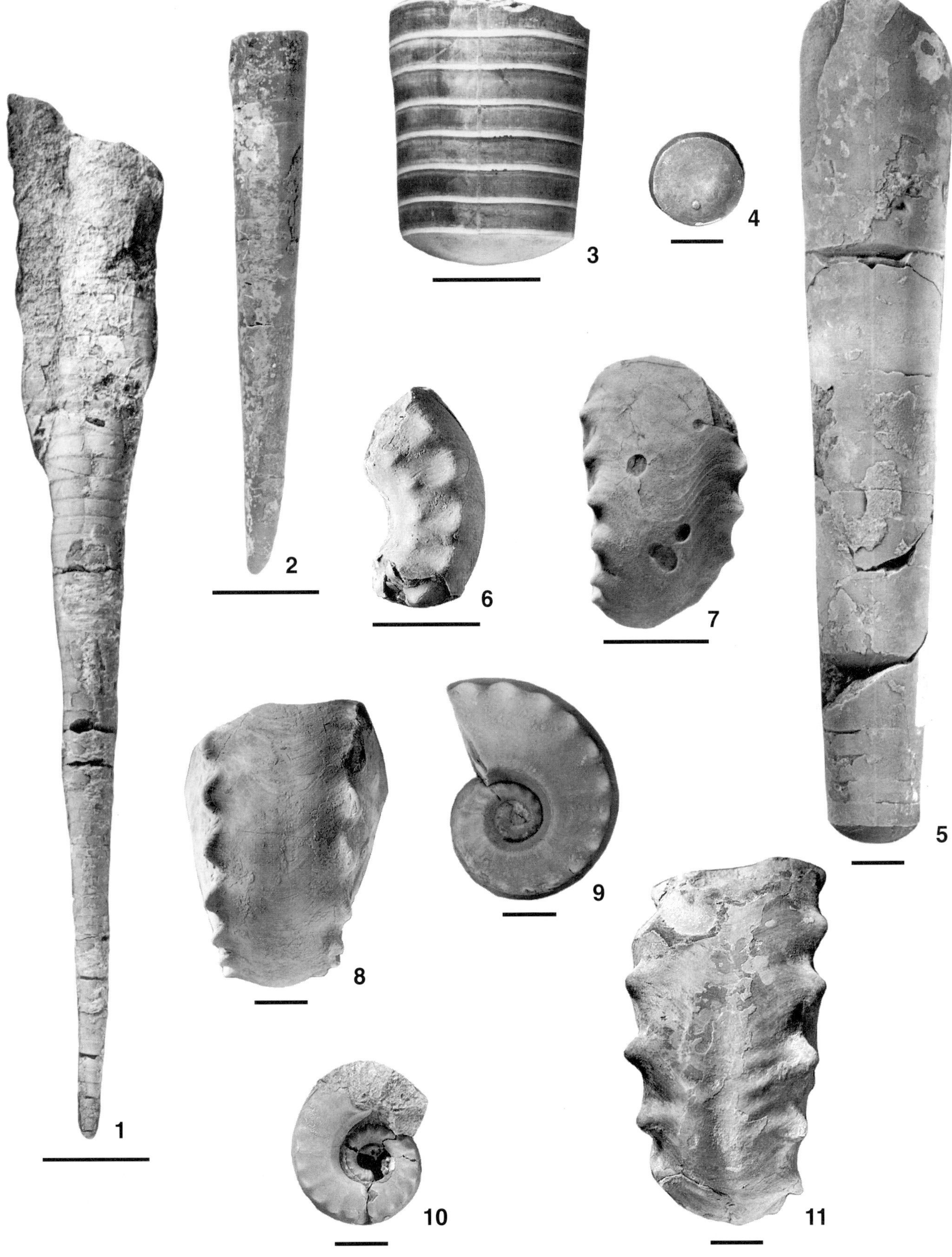
1
2
3
4
5
6
7
8
9
10
11

FIGURE 14-6.—Pennsylvanian nautiloid cephalopods. All scale bars equal 1 cm. All figures from Sturgeon and others (in press).

1, 2	*Latitemnocheilus latus* (Meek & Worthen). Lateral (**1**) and oblique ventrolateral (**2**) views of holotype. Seville Limestone, Rock Island County, Illinois; UI X 438A.
3	*Parametacoceras bellatulum* Miller & Owen. Lateral view of holotype. Cherokee Formation, Henry County, Missouri; SUI 13408.

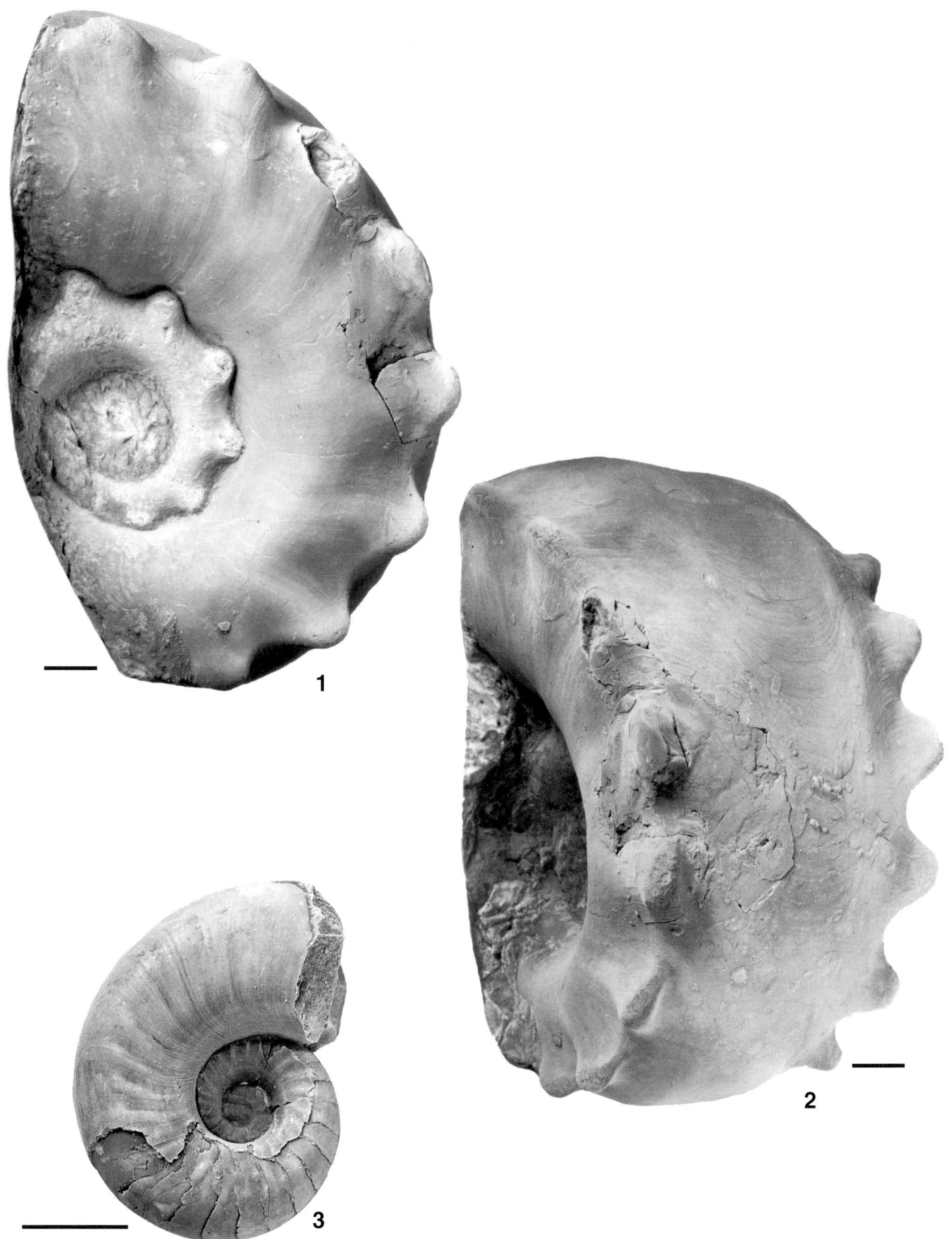
1
2
3

FIGURE 14-7.—Pennsylvanian nautiloid cephalopods. Scale bar equals 1 cm and applies to all figures. All figures from Sturgeon and others (in press).

1	*Temnocheilus annulonodosus* Sturgeon, Windle, Mapes & Hoare. Ventral view of incomplete specimen (paratype). Note the tooth mark (lower center) and the attached inarticulate brachiopod (lower left). Columbiana shale (Allegheny Group), Columbiana County, Ohio; OSU 19547.
2, 3	*Domatoceras obsoletum* Sturgeon. Lateral (**2**) and ventral (**3**) views of holotype. Columbiana shale (Allegheny Group), Mahoning County, Ohio; OSU 18726.
4, 5	*Domatoceras oreskovichi* Sturgeon, Windle, Mapes & Hoare. Lateral (**4**) and ventral (**5**) views of incomplete specimen (paratype). Putnam Hill limestone (Allegheny Group), Mahoning County, Ohio; OSU 29139.
6, 7	*Stenodomatoceras gardi* (Murphy). Brush Creek limestone (Conemaugh Group), Columbiana County, Ohio. **6**, lateral view of incomplete specimen. OSU 28945. **7**, ventral view of incomplete specimen. OSU 28947.

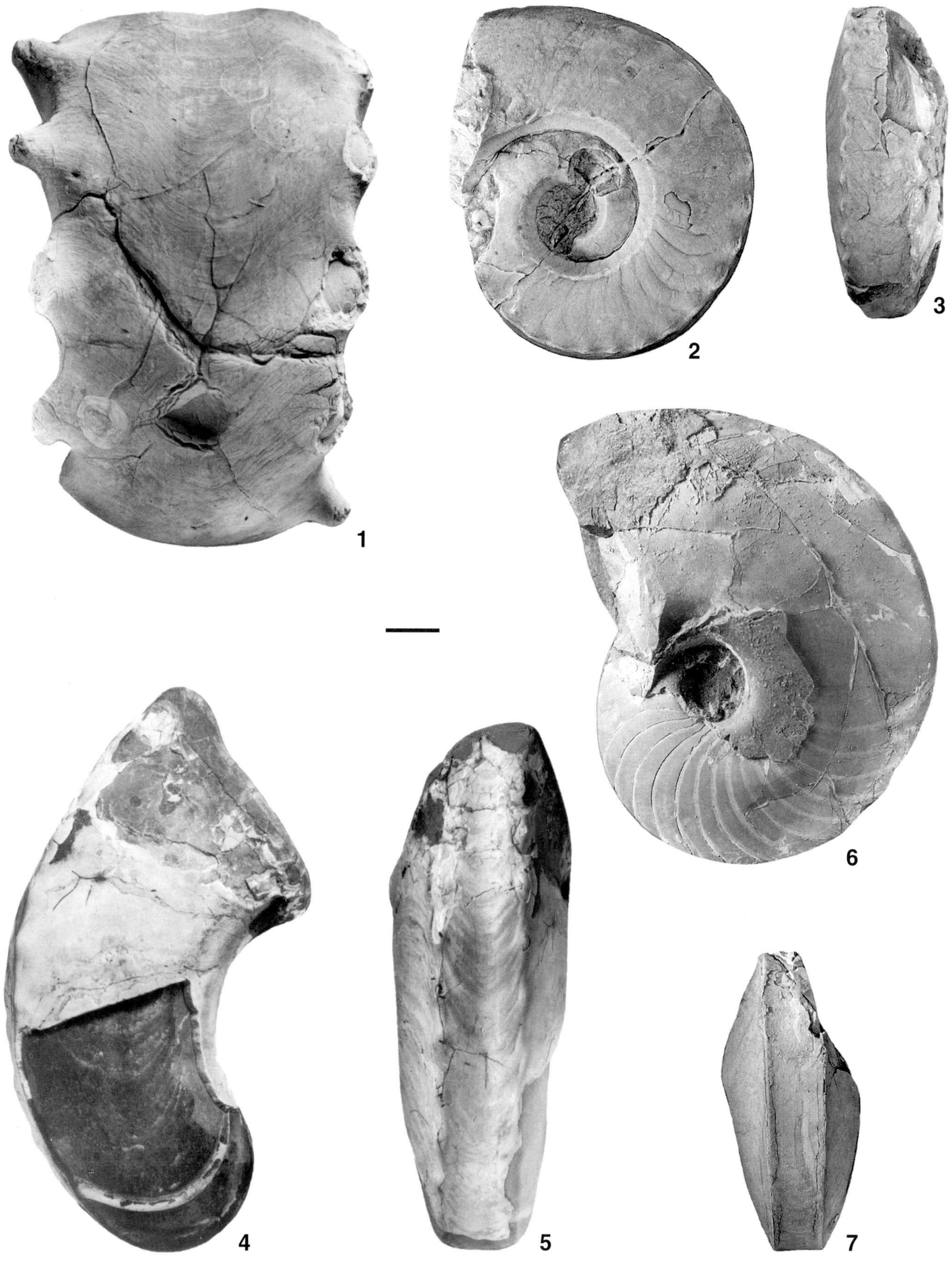
1
2
3
4
5
6
7

FIGURE 14-8.—Devonian and Pennsylvanian ammonoid cephalopods. Scale bars equal 1 cm, except those for figures 14-8.7 to 14-8.9 and 14-8.15 to 14-8.17, which equal 0.25 cm. Figures 14-8.1 to 14-8.3 are from Kesling and Chilman (1975). Remaining figures are from Mapes and others (in press).

1-3 *Tornoceras uniangulare* (Conrad). Ventral (**1**), dorsal (**2**), and right-lateral (**3**) views, respectively, showing the suture on the internal mold. Silica Formation (Devonian), Medusa North Quarry, Silica, Ohio; UMMP 61330.

4 *Gonioloboceras goniolobum* (Meek). Left-lateral view of a large specimen. Juveniles less than 10 mm in diameter have a ribbed, open umbilicus. Finis Shale Member of Graham Formation (Pennsylvanian), Texas; SUI 17035. Specimens of this taxon occur in the Brush Creek shale (Conemaugh Group, Pennsylvanian) in Ohio.

5, 6 *Pennoceras seamani* Miller & Unklesbay. Ventral (**5**) and left-lateral (**6**) views. Brush Creek shale (Conemaugh Group, Pennsylvanian), Athens County, Ohio; OSU 30707.

7-9 *Neoaganides grahamensis* Plummer & Scott. Brush Creek shale (Conemaugh Group, Pennsylvanian), Athens County, Ohio. **7**, **8**, dorsal views. OSU 30787. **9**, left-lateral view of **body chamber**. OSU 30788.

10, 11 *Gonioglyphioceras gracile* (Girty). Ventral (**10**) and right-lateral (**11**) views of holotype showing **bicarinate keel** and suture, respectively. Washingtonville shale (Allegheny Group, Pennsylvanian), Carroll County, Ohio; OSU 30712.

12, 13 *Schistoceras* sp. Left-lateral (**12**) and right-lateral (**13**) views showing spear-head-shaped lobes of external suture on phragmocone. Cambridge limestone (Conemaugh Group, Pennsylvanian), Ohio; SUI 1437.

14-17 *Mangeroceras canfieldense* Sturgeon, Windle, Mapes & Hoare. Paratypes. Putnam Hill shale (Allegheny Group, Pennsylvanian), Mahoning County, Ohio. **14**, right-lateral view of internal mold of phragmocone showing suture. OSU 30713. **15**, **16**, **17**, dorsal, ventral, and right-lateral views, respectively, showing sinuous ornament and ribbed umbilicus of body chamber. OSU 30739.

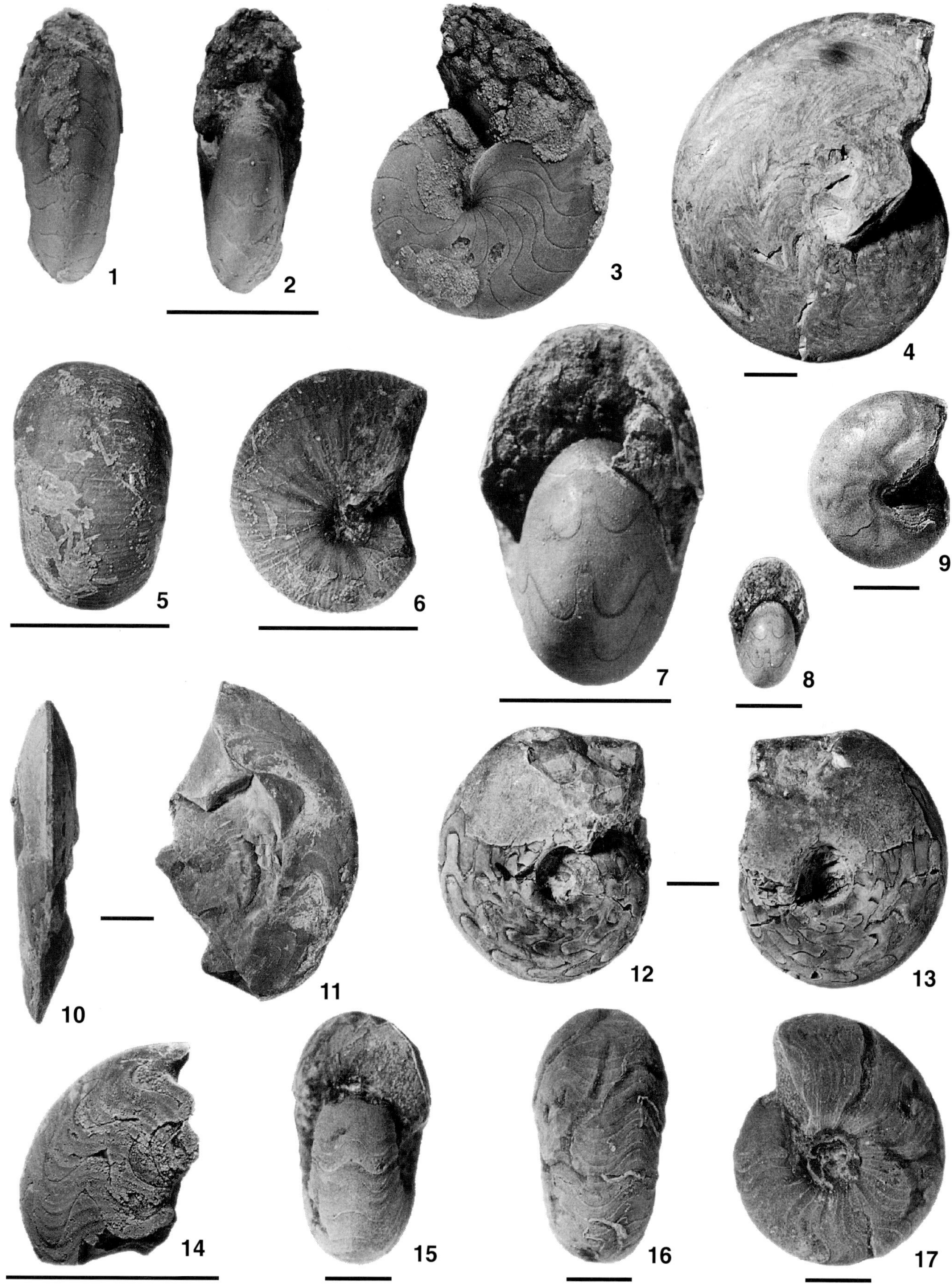
1
2
3
4
5
6
7
8
9
10
11
12
13
14
15
16
17

FIGURE 14-9.—Pennsylvanian ammonoid cephalopods. All scale bars equal 1 cm. All figures from Mapes and others (in press).

1, 2	*Glaphyrites jonesi* (Miller & Owen). Washingtonville shale (Allegheny Group), Carroll County, Ohio. **1**, left-lateral view showing ornament on umbilical shoulder of wide umbilicus. OSU 30790. **2**, dorsal view. OSU 30800.
3, 4	*Aktubites trifidus* Ruzhencev. Putnam Hill shale (Allegheny Group), Mahoning County, Ohio; OSU 30723. **3**, ventral view showing complex and inflated lobes of external suture. **4**, left-lateral view showing relatively wide umbilicus.
5	*Eoschistoceras postvenatum* (Plummer & Scott). Right-lateral view. Wewoka Formation, Oklahoma; SUI 9672. The single known Ohio specimen is from the Putnam Hill shale (Allegheny Group) and is crushed.
6-10	*Wellerites* cf. *W. mohri* Plummer & Scott. **6**, **7**, ventral and right-lateral views of OSU 30731; **8**, **9**, left-lateral and ventral views of OSU 30728. Both specimens are from the Washingtonville shale (Allegheny Group), Carroll County, Ohio, and show internal suture and part of body chamber. **10**, Right-lateral view of phragmocone showing complex external suture. Columbiana shale (Allegheny Group), Columbiana County, Ohio; OSU 30726.
11	*Schistoceras* sp. Right-lateral view showing suture and size of umbilicus. Cambridge limestone (Allegheny Group), Guernsey County, Ohio; OSU 48921.
12-14	*Somoholites sagittarius* Saunders. Dorsal (**12**), ventral (**13**), and right-lateral (**14**) views of holotype showing wide umbilicus and part of suture. Columbiana shale (Allegheny Group), Columbiana County, Ohio; OSU 18736.

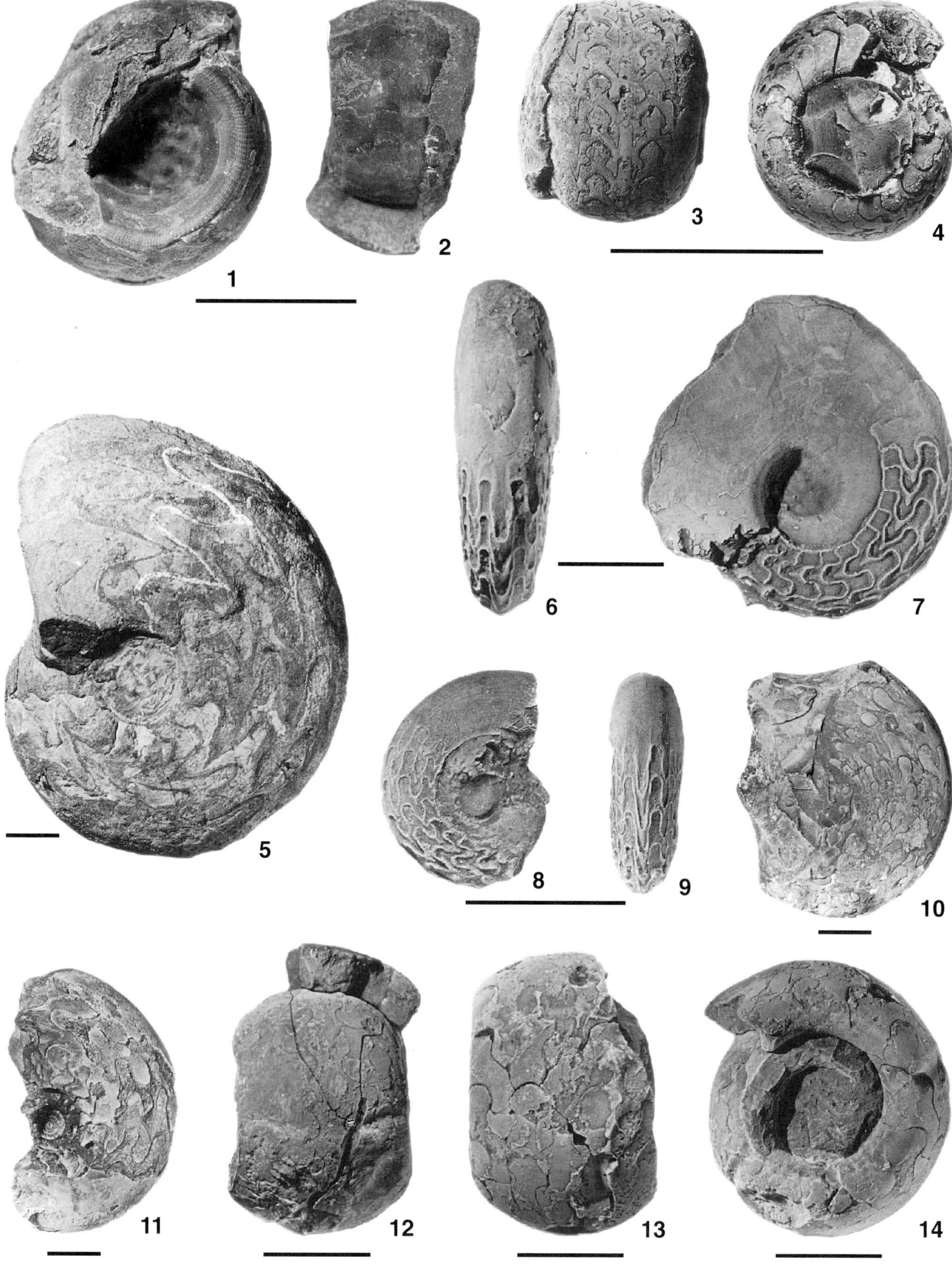
1
2
3
4
5
6
7
8
9
10
11
12
13
14

FIGURE 14-10.—Suture diagrams of Devonian and Pennsylvanian ammonoid cephalopods. For each suture diagram, the arrow points toward the aperture and lies on the plane of bilateral symmetry of the conch. The marks at the opposite end of the suture from the arrow define the umbilical region of the conch. Note: the arrow in figure 14-10.11 is correctly placed; it does not bisect the saddle, perhaps because the specimen, in life, had some disease or other pathological condition that led to a slight departure from bilateral symmetry. Figure 14-10.1 is from Arkell and others (1957, fig. 48); remaining figures are from Mapes and others (in press).

1 *Tornoceras crebriseptum* Raymond. The suture of *T. uniangulare* from the Silica Formation (Devonian) of northwestern Ohio is very similar.

2 *Gonioloboceras goniolobum*, at diameter of 65 mm. Finis Shale Member of Graham Formation (Pennsylvanian), Texas; SUI 17035.

3 *Pennoceras seamani*, at diameter of 7.5 mm. Brush Creek Shale (Pennsylvanian), Glassmere, Pennsylvania; CM 25801.

4 *Neoaganides grahamensis*, at estimated diameter of 4.5 mm. Brush Creek shale (Conemaugh Group, Pennsylvanian), Athens County, Ohio; OSU 30788.

5 *Gonioglyphioceras gracile*, at diameter of 54 mm. Washingtonville shale (Allegheny Group, Pennsylvanian), Carroll County, Ohio; OSU 30712.

6 *Mangeroceras canfieldense*, at estimated diameter of 35 mm. Putnam Hill shale (Allegheny Group, Pennsylvanian), Mahoning County, Ohio; OSU 30713.

7 *Schistoceras* sp., at diameter of 36.0 mm. Cambridge limestone (Conemaugh Group, Pennsylvanian), Ohio; SUI 1437.

8 *Glaphyrites jonesi*, at estimated diameter of 19.8 mm. Washingtonville shale (Allegheny Group, Pennsylvanian), Carroll County, Ohio; OSU 30808.

9 *Aktubites trifidus*, at estimated diameter of 10.2 mm. Putnam Hill shale (Allegheny Group, Pennsylvanian), Mahoning County, Ohio; OSU 30723.

10 *Wellerites* cf. *W. mohri*, at diameter of 28.8 mm. Putnam Hill shale (Allegheny Group, Pennsylvanian), Columbiana County, Ohio; OSU 30781.

11 *Eoschistoceras* sp., at estimated diameter of 100 mm. Putnam Hill shale (Allegheny Group, Pennsylvanian), Mahoning County, Ohio; OSU 30725.

12 *Somoholites sagittarius*, at estimated diameter of 27 mm. Holotype. Columbiana shale (Allegheny Group, Pennsylvanian), Columbiana County, Ohio; OSU 18736.

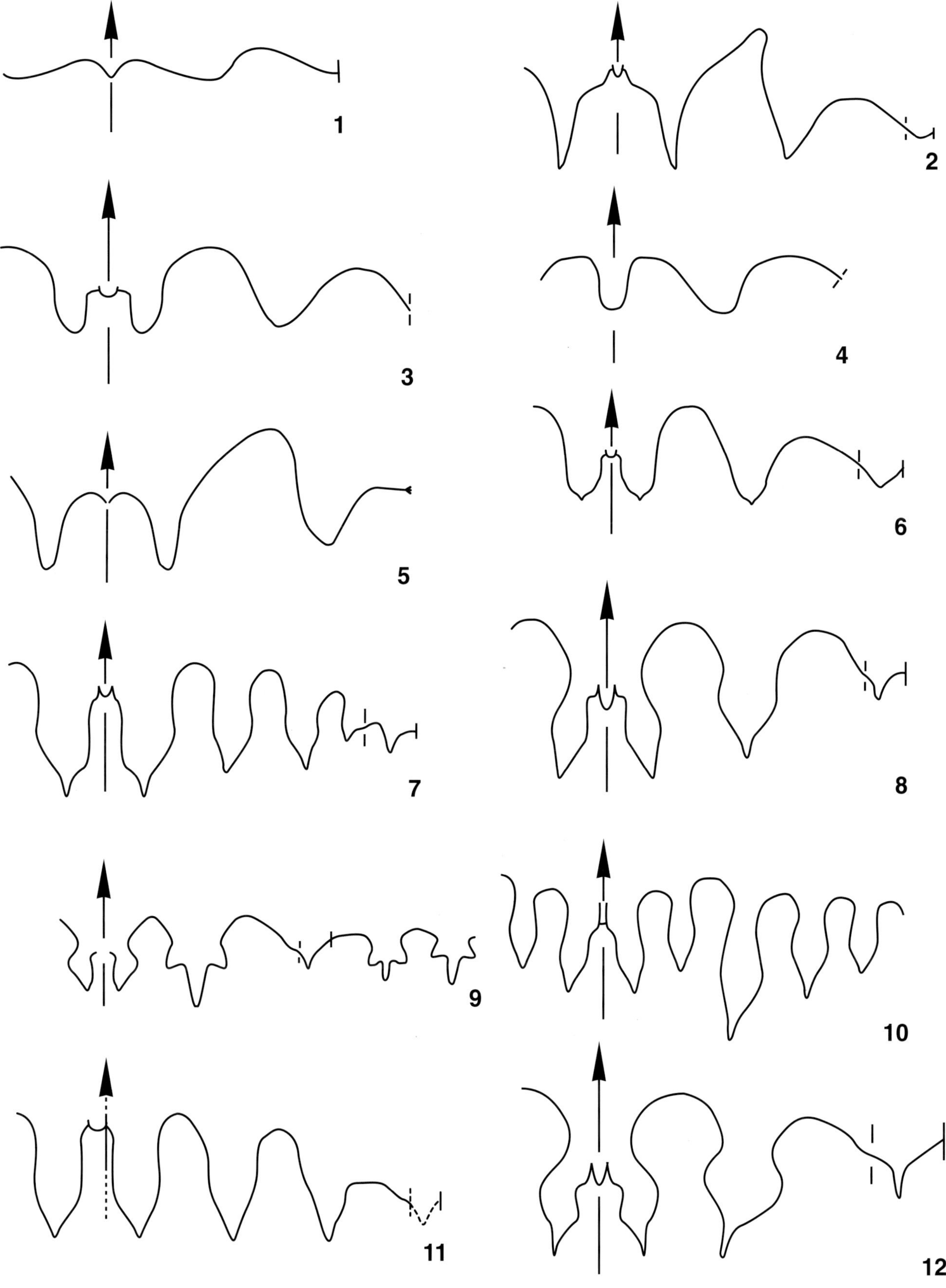
1
2
3
4
5
6
7
8
9
10
11
12

Chapter 15

PHYLUM BRYOZOA

by Robert L. Anstey and Mark A. Wilson

INTRODUCTION

Representatives of the phylum Bryozoa are among the most common marine fossils found in the Ordovician rocks in the southwestern corner of Ohio. The vast majority of these **colonial** animals resemble broken twigs that are honeycombed with small pinholelike openings, each no more than 0.2 mm in diameter. Some of the pioneering scientists who studied fossil bryozoans grew up in the vicinity of Cincinnati and collected bryozoan fossils as children. These early workers include R. S. Bassler, J. F. James, U. P. James, S. A. Miller, J. M. Nickles, and E. O. Ulrich. Some of these scientists used only a 10-power magnifying lens to study their specimens. Although they are best studied with a low-power binocular microscope, one can still learn a great deal about fossil bryozoans using nothing more than a hand lens. In Ohio, bryozoans are most commonly found in the Cincinnatian Series (Upper Ordovician), the Brassfield Formation (Silurian), and the Silica Formation (Devonian). Bryozoans also are found in many other marine limestones and shales of the Ordovician, Silurian, Devonian, Mississippian, and Pennsylvanian Systems. A list of the fossil bryozoan genera known from Ohio is provided in table 15-1, arranged by geologic system and taxonomic suborder.

Modern paleontologists use thin sections or acetate peels to obtain conclusive identifications of most bryozoans. Tentative or preliminary identifications, however, can be made by studying features of the outer surfaces of the fossil colony. Such features will be emphasized in this chapter. For more definitive work, **acetate peels** should be prepared; the techniques of preparation are given in Chapter 2 and described in detail by Wilson and Palmer (1989). Peels adequate for most identifications can be made using materials available in most homes. To make the peel, grind the specimen on 400 grit (or finer) wet-or-dry sandpaper with water, etch the polished surface in dilute acetic acid (such as white vinegar), wet the etched surface with acetone, and press it into a sheet of acetate plastic. The dried acetate can be peeled off the specimen and provides a near-perfect replica of the bryozoan's microstructure. Further information on bryozoan microstructure can be found in almost any invertebrate paleontology textbook, but Chapter 17 of Boardman and others (1987) is highly recommended. The morphological features of most fossil bryozoan genera are briefly described in the volumes by Bassler (1953) and Boardman and others (1983) in the *Treatise on Invertebrate Paleontology*.

To see the surface features of a bryozoan colony, the specimen must be clean. To remove imbedded mud from the surface, soak specimens overnight in a strong detergent and water solution. Ultrasonic cleaners, such as those for cleaning jewelry or silver, can be very effective in removing mud or other sediment from a fossil bryozoan. Caution is recommended because this technique may break delicate specimens. Specimens with hardened or caked-on mud can be soaked overnight in kerosene before being treated with detergent and water. The action of the detergent on the kerosene helps to break up the muddy coatings.

MORPHOLOGY OF BRYOZOAN COLONIES

All bryozoans are colonial animals; the basic unit of a bryozoan colony is a **zooid** (see fig. 1-23), a capsule-shaped body containing a tentacular apparatus for feeding and a complete digestive tract. All the zooids in a colony are produced by budding from a single parent zooid, and all remain physically connected during life. In one group of bryozoans, the stoloniferous ctenostomes (bryozoans in the order Ctenostomata and suborder Stolonifera), the zooids bore holes into calcareous shells, and the preserved colony is only a linear series of pits connected by grooves (fig. 15-1.1). In all the other fossilizable suborders, each zooid is encased in a calcareous skeleton that has an opening or **aperture** at one end. The individual zooid skeleton is a **zooecium**, and the colonial skeleton is a **zoarium**.

The simplest bryozoans that have hard skeletons are **uniserial** colonies made up of linear chains of connected zooids that encrust a hard surface. The chains branch at intervals to spread out over the available surface. Individual zooids in uniserial colonies are generally flanked by open space on the lateral sides of each chain. Only hard skeletons of uniserial colonies in the suborder Paleotubuliporina are found in Paleozoic rocks (figs. 15-1.2, 15-1.3).

Multiserial colonies have zooids filling all available space for budding; no empty space exists on the sides of zooids. In most multiserial colonies, skeletal material fills in all the space between the apertures, so the colony surface is a honeycombed structure of zooecial openings. The simplest multiserial colonies are flat sheets that encrust hard surfaces (fig. 15-2.1). **Encrusting** colonies are flat and develop no vertical or upward growth. Encrusting colonies that grew on the stems of algae may result in fossils that look outwardly like branching or **ramose** colonies, but they are hollow in the center because the alga was not preserved (fig. 15-1.5).

Erect or elevated colonies have continuous growth of the individual or colonial skeleton. The zooids occupy living chambers in the uppermost part of the skeleton, and the lower parts represent previously occupied and abandoned chambers. The erect bryozoans have evolved a wide variety of colony shapes and architectures.

Simple erect colonies may be shaped like domes or hemispheres (fig. 15-2.9). Others may grow upward as solid vertical sheets or fronds, with zooids facing outward on both sides of the sheet (only one side shown in fig. 15-2.3). Still others have developed cylindrical stems that frequently branch to form shrublike colonies (figs. 15-2.2, 15-2.4, 15-2.8). In some branching colonies, the stems are elliptical in cross section rather than circular and have a solid wall of calcite dividing each stem through its long axis. Colonies that have such a dividing wall are **bifoliate**, meaning zooids face outward in both directions from the central wall.

In some branching colonies, the stems are very thin and the zooids open on only one side of the branch. In a few of these one-sided colonies, the branches regularly split and rejoin, forming an **anastomosing** or **cribrate** zoarium (fig. 15-4.5). In others, the thin branches are joined by cross-struts or **dissepiments**, forming a **fenestrate** or "windowed" zoarium (figs. 15-4.6, 15-4.7). Zooecial apertures are observable only on the obverse (front) side of fenestrate colonies, and not on the reverse (basal) side; unfortunately, most fenestrate bryozoans lying on bedding surfaces are preserved with the reverse side up. Differences in the forms of erect colonies are important keys to identifying the orders and suborders of Paleozoic bryozoans.

Both encrusting and erect colonies may have regularly spaced, small mounds or flat, dark-looking patches on the colony surface that are termed **monticules**. Monticules are generally spaced from 1/2 to 1 cm apart. They are absent in very thin branching colonies, as well as in uniserial colonies. The center of a monticule may be a dark patch of solid-appearing skeleton (fig. 15-2.3) and may be surrounded by zooecial apertures that are larger than those away from the monticule. Monticules may be strongly or weakly star shaped (fig. 15-1.7), simple circular or oval mounds (fig. 15-2.1), or bar-shaped ridges on the colony surface.

MORPHOLOGY OF BRYOZOAN ZOOECIA

In all but the uniserial colonies, only the zooecial apertures are visible on the colony surface. Apertures may differ in terms of size, shape, and alignment. Some apertures are perfectly circular, whereas others are five- or six-sided polygons. In the order Cystoporata, apertures commonly have a crescent-shaped rim or hood, called a **lunarium**, on one side. Apertures may be patterned like a honeycomb, or may show strong alignment as long straight rows or as diagonal rows that spiral up the colony's vertical axis.

Smaller apertures, one-tenth to one-third the size of zooecial apertures, may be found between the zooecial apertures, or may be clustered in the centers of monticules. These either represent variant zooids termed **polymorphs**, or may just be space fillers that economize on carbonate secretion by the colony. When split open along their long axis, the skeletons of small polymorphs may be simple hollow tubes or may be internally partitioned by closely spaced transverse plates, or **tabulae**.

Spinelike structures, **acanthostyles**, are commonly embedded in the skeletal wall between zooecial apertures. In well-preserved colonies, they may be externally visible as spines that project above the colony surface. Both acanthostyles and small polymorphs may be difficult to observe on external surfaces but are easily seen in sections or peels.

In most erect and branching multiserial colonies, two distinct regions or zones of zooecia are present. In the central or **axial zone** (also termed the **endozone**), zooecia are typically thin walled and polygonal in cross section. Small polymorphs and acanthostyles are normally absent. Axial zooecia may be observable in the core of a broken branch or at the very tip of an unbroken branch. Surrounding the axial zone is an **outer zone** (also called the **exozone**) of thicker walled zooecia that have more rounded apertures; they generally are associated with small polymorphs, acanthostyles, and monticules.

BRYOZOAN SUBORDERS

Marine rocks younger than those deposited during the Paleozoic Era have not been preserved in Ohio, so only bryozoans of Paleozoic age are described in this chapter. They are assigned to two classes, six orders, and 12 suborders. Their **taxonomy** and the geologic range of the suborders are given below. Representatives of all suborders except the Esthonioporina and the Timanodictyina have been found in Ohio (table 15-1).

Phylum Bryozoa
- Class Gymnolaemata
  - Order Ctenostomata
    - Suborder Stoloniferina (Ordovician to Recent)
- Class Stenolaemata
  - Order Cyclostomata
    - Suborder Paleotubuliporina (Ordovician to Permian)
  - Order Cystoporata
    - Suborder Ceramoporina (Ordovician to Silurian)
    - Suborder Fistuliporina (Ordovician to Permian)
  - Order Trepostomata
    - Suborder Esthonioporina (Ordovician to Mississippian)
    - Suborder Halloporina (Ordovician to Pennsylvanian)
    - Suborder Amplexoporina (Ordovician to Triassic)
  - Order Cryptostomata
    - Suborder Ptilodictyina (Ordovician to Pennsylvanian)
    - Suborder Timanodictyina (Devonian to Permian)
    - Suborder Rhabdomesina (Ordovician to Permian)
  - Order Fenestrata
    - Suborder Phylloporinina (Ordovician to Permian)
    - Suborder Fenestellina (Ordovician to Permian)

Specimens may be identified to suborder using the simplified key that follows. The key is based on externally observable features. Identifications may be tentative because the key feature that defines most members of a suborder might be missing in one or more of its taxa. For example, the lunarium is missing in *Constellaria* Dana, which otherwise has all the features of a fistuliporine cystoporate. An apparent ancestor of *Constellaria*, known from fossils from Oklahoma, has a lunarium. This feature was lost when *Constellaria* diverged from its ancestral lineage. Another example is the bifoliate genus *Peronopora* Nicholson. This genus is a halloporine trepostome, but it has independently evolved a bifoliate zoarium, which is a characteristic of the ptilodictyines. Therefore, the key must be used with caution.

TABLE 15-1.—FOSSIL BRYOZOAN GENERA RECORDED FROM LOCALITIES IN OHIO, BY GEOLOGIC SYSTEM AND TAXONOMIC SUBORDER

ORDOVICIAN
- Stoloniferina: *Ropalonaria* Ulrich
- Paleotubuliporina: *Corynotrypa* Bassler, *"Proboscina,"* *Sagenella* Hall
- Ceramoporina: *Acanthoceramoporella* Utgaard, *Ceramophylla* Ulrich, *Ceramoporella* Ulrich, *Crepipora* Ulrich
- Fistuliporina: *Constellaria* Dana
- Halloporina: *Aspidopora* Ulrich, *Atactoporella* Ulrich, *Balticoporella* Vinassa de Regny, *Batostoma* Ulrich, *Bythopora* Miller & Dyer, *Calloporella* Ulrich, *Dekayia* Milne-Edwards & Haime, *Eridotrypa* Ulrich, *Gortanipora* Vinassa de Regny, *Heterotrypa* Nicholson, *Homotrypa* Ulrich, *Homotrypella* Ulrich, *Lioclemella* Foerste, *Mesotrypa* Ulrich, *Monticulipora* D'Orbigny, *Nicholsonella* Ulrich, *Parvohallopora* Singh, *Peronopora* Nicholson, *Prasopora* Nicholson, *Stigmatella* Ulrich & Bassler
- Amplexoporina: *Amplexopora* Ulrich, *Atactopora* Ulrich, *Cyphotrypa* Ulrich & Bassler, *Discotrypa* Ulrich, *Leptotrypa* Ulrich, *Monotrypa* Nicholson, *Paleschara* Hall, *Rhombotrypa* Ulrich & Bassler, *Spatiopora* Ulrich, *Tetratoechus* Boardman &McKinney
- Ptilodictyina: *Escharopora* Hall, *Graptodictya* Ulrich, *Phaenopora* Hall, *Ptilodictya* Lonsdale, *Stictopora* Hall, *Stictoporella* Ulrich, *Trigonodictya* Ulrich
- Rhabdomesina: *Arthrostylus* Ulrich, *Helopora* Hall
- Phylloporinina: *Chasmatopora* Eichwald, *Phylloporina* Ulrich
- Fenestellina: *Fenestella* Lonsdale

SILURIAN
- Paleotubuliporina: *Corynotrypa* Bassler
- Ceramoporina: *Ceramopora* Hall
- Fistuliporina: *Cheilotrypa* Ulrich, *Diamesopora* Hall, *Fistulipora* McCoy, *Rhinopora* Hall
- Halloporina: *Aspidopora* Ulrich, *Eridotrypa* Ulrich, *Hallopora* Bassler, *Homotrypa* Ulrich, *Lioclemella* Foerste, *Trematopora* Hall
- Amplexoporina: *Monotrypella* Ulrich
- Ptilodictyina: *Clathropora* Hall, *Pachydictya* Ulrich, *Phaenopora* Hall, *Ptilodictya* Lonsdale, *Trigonodictya* Ulrich
- Phylloporinina: *Chasmatopora* Eichwald, *Phylloporina* Ulrich
- Fenestellina: *Fenestrellina* D'Orbigny, *Helicopora* Claypole, *Hemitrypa* Phillips, *Ptiloporella* Hall, *Semicoscinium* Prout

DEVONIAN
- Stoloniferina: *Ropalonaria* Ulrich
- Paleotubuliporina: *Corynotrypa* Bassler
- Fistuliporina: *Botryllopora* Nicholson, *Coscinium* Keyserling, *Fistulipora* McCoy, *Lichenalia* Hall, *Prismopora* Hall, *Semiopora* Hall, *Sulcoretepora* D'Orbigny
- Halloporina: *Leioclema* Ulrich, *Trematella* Hall
- Amplexoporina: *Anomalotoechus* Duncan, *Atactotoechus* Duncan, *Leptotrypella* Vinassa de Regny, *Monotrypa* Nicholson, *Paleschara* Hall, *Stereotoechus* Duncan
- Ptilodictyina: *Intrapora* Hall, *Stictopora* Hall, *Stictoporina* Hall & Simpson
- Rhabdomesina: *Acanthoclema* Hall, *Helopora* Hall, *Nemataxis* Hall, *Orthopora* Hall, *Streblotrypa* Vine
- Fenestellina: *Anastomopora* Simpson, *Fenestella* Lonsdale, *Fenestrellina* D'Orbigny, *Fenestrapora* Hall, *Loculipora* Hall, *Lyropora* Hall, *Penniretepora* D'Orbigny, *Polypora* McCoy, *Reteporina* D'Orbigny, *Semicoscinium* Prout, *Unitrypa* Hall

MISSISSIPPIAN
- Fistuliporina: *Sulcoretepora* D'Orbigny
- Rhabdomesina: *Acanthoclema* Hall, *Rhombopora* Meek, *Streblotrypa* Vine
- Fenestellina: *Fenestella* Lonsdale, *Fenestrellina* D'Orbigny, *Penniretepora* D'Orbigny, *Septopora* Prout

PENNSYLVANIAN
- Fistuliporina: *Cystodictya* Ulrich, *Fistulipora* McCoy, *Prismopora* Hall
- Amplexoporina: *Tabulipora* Young
- Rhabdomesina: *Rhombopora* Meek, *Streblotrypa* Vine
- Phylloporinina: *Chainodictyon* Foerste
- Fenestellina: *Fenestella* Lonsdale, *Fenestrellina* D'Orbigny, *Pinnatopora* Vine, *Polypora* McCoy, *Septopora* Prout

SIMPLIFIED KEY TO PALEOZOIC BRYOZOAN SUBORDERS USING EXTERNALLY OBSERVABLE FEATURES

1A. Colony a linear series of pits or borings .... Stoloniferina
1B. Colony calcified 2

2A. Colony a linear series of teardrop-shaped zooids .... Paleotubuliporina
2B. Colony multiserial, made up of close-packed tubular zooids 3

3A. Massive colonies of polygonal zooids, no small polymorphs, and no axial zone .... Esthonioporina
3B. Colonies of variable shape, predominantly three-dimensional and having vertical growth; rounded zooids, small polymorphs and axial zones 4

4A. Lunaria present 5
4B. Lunaria absent, axial zones distinct 6

5A. Monticules radiating or star shaped .... Fistuliporina
5B. Monticules circular, low, flat, and have a central cluster of small polymorphs; polymorphs are simple, open tubes .... Ceramoporina

6A. Moundlike monticules present 7
6B. Moundlike monticules absent 10

7A. Colonies not bifoliate 8
7B. Colonies bifoliate 9

8A. Small polymorphs common, divided by closely spaced transverse partitions .... Halloporina
8B. Small polymorphs rare, present as simple, open tubes .... Amplexoporina

9A. Zooids hexagonally arranged .... Timanodictyina
9B. Zooids form a linear-rhombic pattern .... Ptilodictyina

10A. Colonies thin, sticklike, nonfenestrate; zooids form a linear-rhombic pattern .... Rhabdomesina
10B. Colonies fenestrate, zooids on one face only 11

11A. Branches anastomosing .... Phylloporinina
11B. Branches joined by crossbars .... Fenestellina

BRIEF DESCRIPTIONS OF BRYOZOAN GENERA FROM OHIO

This section provides brief descriptions of the most common fossil bryozoans found in Ohio. Genera are listed in stratigraphic order under each suborder. The brief descriptions listed may not lead to conclusive identifications, which may require thin sections or acetate peels. Geologists commonly make preliminary or tentative identifications of fossils in the field and follow them up with lab-based identifications later. The reader should consider identifications based on external features as preliminary or tentative. In particular, identifications of the numerous genera of branching trepostomes from southwestern Ohio are especially difficult without internal sections. One publication that illustrates numerous Ordovician bryozoans externally, but which might not be readily available in local libraries, is Cumings (1908); see especially his plates XXVI through XXXII. Excellent illustrations of the external features of Devonian bryozoans from the Silica Formation are available in Kesling and Chilman (1975).

SUBORDER STOLONIFERINA

Ropalonaria Ulrich (fig. 15-1.1) is characterized by a linear series of pits and bilateral branching of the **stolon** at regular intervals. Its borings typically are etched into a brachiopod shell. *Ropalonaria* has been found in Ordovician and Devonian rocks in Ohio.

SUBORDER PALEOTUBULIPORINA

Corynotrypa Bassler (fig. 15-1.2) consists of uniserial branching chains of teardrop-shaped zooecia that have circular apertures. It typically is encrusting a brachiopod shell or other bryozoans. *Corynotrypa* has been found in Ordovician, Silurian, and Devonian rocks in Ohio.

"*Proboscina*" (not *Proboscina* Audouin; revised and renamed *Cuffeyella* in Taylor and Wilson, 1996) (fig. 15-1.3) forms uniserial or multiserial, branching and anastomosing chains of tubular zooecia that have circular apertures and porous walls. It typically is encrusting shells or other bryozoans. "*Proboscina*" has been found in Ordovician rocks in Ohio.

SUBORDER ESTHONIOPORINA

Chondraulus Duncan (fig. 15-1.4) forms massive colonies of polygonal zooids. There are no small polymorphs and no axial zone. *Chondraulus* has been found in Devonian rocks in Indiana and Kentucky, and very likely will be found in Ohio.

SUBORDER CERAMOPORINA

Ceramophylla Ulrich (fig. 15-1.5) forms hollow-ramose colonies. Lunaria are present, as well as low, flat monticules. *Ceramophylla* has been found in Ordovician rocks in Ohio.

SUBORDER FISTULIPORINA

Constellaria Dana (fig. 15-1.7) forms branching colonies. Unlike other genera in this suborder, *Constellaria* lacks lunaria. Monticules are strongly star shaped. *Constellaria* has been found in Ordovician rocks in Ohio.

Diamesopora Hall (not illustrated) forms hollow-ramose colonies. Lunaria are present, monticules are absent, and zooecia have a rhombic arrangement. *Diamesopora* has been found in Silurian rocks in Ohio.

Fistulipora McCoy (fig. 15-1.6) forms colonies that are encrusting to massive. Lunaria are present. Zooecial apertures are circular and well separated. *Fistulipora* has been found in rocks of Silurian, Devonian, and Pennsylvanian age in Ohio.

Sulcoretepora D'Orbigny (fig. 15-1.8) forms bifoliate colonies that have thin straplike or ribbonlike branches. Lunaria are present. *Sulcoretepora* has been found in Devonian and Mississippian rocks in Ohio.

Prismopora Hall (not illustrated) forms trifoliate colonies. Lunaria are present. *Prismopora* has been found in Devonian and Pennsylvanian rocks in Ohio.

SUBORDER HALLOPORINA

Peronopora Nicholson (fig. 15-2.3) forms colonies of flat, bifoliate sheets. Zooecial apertures are rounded. *Peronopora* has been found in Ordovician rocks in Ohio.

Homotrypella Ulrich (not illustrated) forms hemispherical, gumdrop-shaped colonies. Apertures are rounded. *Homotrypella* has been found in Ordovician rocks in Ohio.

Prasopora Nicholson (fig. 15-2.9) forms hemispherical, dome-shaped colonies. Apertures are subpolygonal. *Prasopora* has been found in Ordovician rocks in Ohio.

Stigmatella Ulrich & Bassler (not illustrated) forms encrusting to massive colonies. It has polygonal zooids and acanthostyles. *Stigmatella* has been found in Ordovician rocks in Ohio.

Eridotrypa Ulrich (fig. 15-2.2) forms branching colonies that have tapered bases. Apertures are elongate. *Eridotrypa* has been found in Ordovician and Silurian rocks in Ohio.

Bythopora Miller & Dyer (not illustrated) forms colonies of very thin sticklike branches. Apertures are elongate oval. *Bythopora* has been found in Ordovician rocks in Ohio.

Parvohallopora Singh (fig. 15-2.8) forms branching colonies. Apertures are smoothly oval, very uniform in shape, and well separated. There are no acanthostyles, but there are numerous small polymorphs. Monticules are prominent and regularly spaced. *Parvohallopora* has been found in Ordovician rocks in Ohio.

Batostoma Ulrich (figs. 15-2.4, 15-2.7) forms branching colonies. Apertures are elongate but irregularly shaped. Monticules are sparse and not uniformly spaced. There are large acanthostyles. *Batostoma* has been found in Ordovician rocks in Ohio.

Dekayia Milne-Edwards & Haime (fig. 15-2.5) forms branching colonies; branch diameters are large (up to 1 cm). Apertures are subpolygonal. Monticules are not prominent. There are large acanthostyles. *Dekayia* has been found in Ordovician rocks in Ohio.

Heterotrypa Nicholson (fig. 15-2.6) forms branching colonies. Apertures are subpolygonal. Monticules are prominent and regularly spaced. There are large acanthostyles and numerous small polymorphs. *Heterotrypa* has been found in Ordovician rocks in Ohio.

Homotrypa Ulrich (not illustrated) forms branching colonies. Apertures are subpolygonal. Monticules are prominent and regularly spaced. There are large acanthostyles but few or no small polymorphs. *Homotrypa* has been found in Ordovician and Silurian rocks in Ohio.

SUBORDER AMPLEXOPORINA

Rhombotrypa Ulrich & Bassler (not illustrated) forms branching colonies. Zooecia in the axial zone have square outlines in branch cross sections; zooecial apertures are subpolygonal on branch surfaces. There are no small polymorphs or acanthostyles. *Rhombotrypa* has been found in Ordovician rocks in Ohio.

Amplexopora Ulrich (fig. 15-3.1) forms branching colonies. Apertures are polygonal on branch surfaces and in axial-zone cross sections. There are no small polymorphs, except in monticules. Acanthostyles are numerous. *Amplexopora* has been found in Ordovician rocks in Ohio.

Atactotoechus Duncan (fig. 15-2.1) forms encrusting colonies. Apertures are polygonal. There are no small polymorphs. Monticules are prominent. *Atactotoechus* has been found in Devonian rocks in Ohio.

Tabulipora Young (fig. 15-3.2) forms branching colonies. Apertures are large and subpolygonal. There are no small polymorphs. *Tabulipora* has been found in Pennsylvanian rocks in Ohio.

SUBORDER PTILODICTYINA

Escharopora Hall (not illustrated) forms colonies of bifoliate, unbranched, lance-shaped, narrow sheets that taper to a point at the base. *Escharopora* has been found in Ordovician rocks in Ohio.

Phaenopora Hall (figs. 15-3.5, 15-3.6) forms colonies of bifoliate, flat sheets. Zooecial apertures are strongly aligned in longitudinal rows. *Phaenopora* has been found in Ordovician and Silurian rocks in Ohio.

Stictopora Hall (not illustrated) forms colonies of thin, ribbonlike, bifoliate sheets. *Stictopora* has been found in Ordovician and Devonian rocks in Ohio.

Clathropora Hall (fig. 15-3.3) forms bifoliate and anastomosing (cribrate) colonies. *Clathropora* has been found in Silurian rocks in Ohio.

Intrapora Hall (fig. 15-3.4) forms colonies of bifoliate, flat sheets. Apertures are rounded. There are numerous small polymorphs. *Intrapora* has been found in Devonian rocks in Ohio.

SUBORDER RHABDOMESINA

Arthrostylus Ulrich (not illustrated) forms very thin, sticklike branches that have apertures on only one side of the branch. *Arthrostylus* has been found in Ordovician rocks in Ohio.

Helopora Hall (not illustrated) forms thin, sticklike colonies that have apertures on all sides, forming a rhombic pattern. Colony segments do not branch. *Helopora* has been found in Ordovician and Devonian rocks in Ohio.

Streblotrypa Vine (fig. 15-4.1) forms thin, sticklike colonies that have apertures on all sides. Apertures are strongly aligned in longitudinal rows separated by long ridges. *Streblotrypa* has been found in Devonian, Mississippian, and Pennsylvanian rocks in Ohio.

Acanthoclema Hall (fig. 15-4.2) forms thin, sticklike colonies that have apertures in longitudinal rows on all sides. There are one or two small polymorphs between apertures. *Acanthoclema* has been found in Devonian and Mississippian rocks in Ohio.

Rhombopora Meek (figs. 15-4.3, 15-4.4) forms thin, sticklike colonies that have apertures on all sides, forming a rhombic pattern. Branches bifurcate. *Rhombopora* has been found in Mississippian and Pennsylvanian rocks in Ohio.

SUBORDER PHYLLOPORININA

Chasmatopora Eichwald (fig. 15-4.5) forms meshwork colonies of anastomosing branches. There are two or more zooid rows per branch. Apertures are not strongly aligned. *Chasmatopora* has been found in Ordovician and Silurian rocks in Ohio.

SUBORDER FENESTELLINA

Fenestella Lonsdale (figs. 15-4.6, 15-4.7) forms meshwork colonies of branches joined by crossbars. There are two rows of zooids per branch. *Fenestella* has been found in Ordovician, Devonian, Mississippian, and Pennsylvanian rocks in Ohio.

Semicoscinium Prout (not illustrated) forms meshwork colonies of anastomosing branches. Zooids are in two rows along each branch, separated by a strong ridge. *Semicoscinium* has been found in Silurian and Devonian rocks in Ohio.

Polypora McCoy (not illustrated) forms meshwork colonies of branches joined by crossbars. There are three to eight rows of zooids per branch. *Polypora* has been found in Devonian, Mississippian, and Pennsylvanian rocks in Ohio.

Pinnatopora Vine (not illustrated) forms feather-shaped colonies. Branches are not laterally joined. *Pinnatopora* has been found in Pennsylvanian rocks in Ohio.

COLLECTING LOCALITIES

Bryozoans are so abundant in the Ordovician rocks of southwestern Ohio that a stop at virtually any road cut or stream exposure will provide specimens. They are less abundant and more difficult to find in younger strata. Localities for Silurian- and Devonian-age bryozoans are predominantly quarries, to which public access is restricted. Mississippian bryozoans have been found in stream beds which expose the dark shales of the Cuyahoga Formation in northeastern Ohio. Most Pennsylvanian bryozoans are recovered from thin limestone units in the eastern part of the state. Please remember that road cuts can be dangerous places, and access to streams is generally across private property.

ACKNOWLEDGMENTS

We thank Rodney M. Feldmann and Tim Miller (Kent State University) for photographic assistance, and Paul Taylor (Natural History Museum, London) and Robert Whitmoyer (Ohio Agricultural Research and Development Center), who kindly provided the scanning electron micrographs. We also thank The Cleveland Museum of Natural History, the U.S. National Museum, The Ohio State University, Michigan State University, Indiana University, Miami University, and the College of Wooster for loaning specimens.

FIGURE 15-1.—Ordovician, Devonian, and Pennsylvanian bryozoans of the suborders Stoloniferina, Paleotubuliporina, Esthonioporina, Ceramoporina, and Fistuliporina. Scale bars adjacent to figures 15-1.1 to 15-1.3 equal 1 mm. Scale bar A equals 1 cm and applies to figures 15-1.4 to 15-4.8.

STOLONIFERINA

1 *Ropalonaria venosa* Ulrich. Boring in a strophomenid brachiopod valve. Richmondian Stage (Upper Ordovician), Warren County, Ohio; MSU 210335-00001.

PALEOTUBULIPORINA

2 *Corynotrypa inflata* (Hall). Encrustation on a strophomenid brachiopod valve. Bellevue beds (Upper Ordovician), Cincinnati; USNM 40113.

3 *"Proboscina" auloporoides* (Nicholson) (recently redefined as *Cuffeyella arachnoidea* (Hall) by Taylor and Wilson, 1996). Encrustation on a strophomenid brachiopod valve. Grant Lake Formation (Upper Ordovician), Washington, Kentucky; BMNH PD-9888.

ESTHONIOPORINA

4 *Chondraulus ponderosus* (Rominger). Side view of broken colony. Jeffersonville Limestone (Middle Devonian), Charlestown, Indiana; IU 5199-281.15.

CERAMOPORINA

5 *Ceramophylla* sp. Zoarial fragments. Kope Formation (Upper Ordovician), Miamitown, Hamilton County, Ohio; MSU 220335-00289.

FISTULIPORINA

6 *Fistulipora carbonaria* Ulrich. External view of zoarium. Ames limestone (Conemaugh Group, Pennsylvanian), Carrollton, Carroll County, Ohio; ClMNH 5255.

7 *Constellaria* sp. External view of zoarium. Cincinnati Group (Upper Ordovician), Cincinnati, Ohio; CW 131-1.

8 *Sulcoretepora* sp. External view of zoarium. Silica Formation (Devonian), Sylvania, Wood County, Ohio; MSU 220535-00001.

1
2
3
4
5
6
7
8
A

FIGURE 15-2.—Ordovician and Devonian bryozoans of the suborders Halloporina and Amplexoporina. Scale bars equal 1 cm. Scale bar A applies to figures 15-2.4 and 15-2.9; scale bar B applies to remaining figures.

AMPLEXOPORINA

1 *Atactotoechus* sp. Encrustation on a spiriferid brachiopod valve. Silica Formation (Devonian), Sylvania, Wood County, Ohio; MSU 220535-00003.

HALLOPORINA

2 *Eridotrypa mutabilis* Ulrich. External view of zoarium. Kope Formation (Upper Ordovician), Gallatin County, Kentucky; IU 8974-3003.

3 *Peronopora vera* Ulrich. External view of zoarium. Kope Formation (Upper Ordovician), Miamitown, Hamilton County, Ohio; IU 8976-29007.

4, 7 *Batostoma jamesi* (Nicholson). **4**, external view of zoarium. **7**, magnified view of **4**. Kope Formation (Upper Ordovician), Miamitown, Hamilton County, Ohio; IU 8976-21012.

5 *Dekayia aspera* Milne-Edwards & Haime. External view of zoarium. Kope Formation (Upper Ordovician), Miamitown, Hamilton County, Ohio; IU 8976-21025.

6 *Heterotrypa ulrichi* Nicholson. External view of zoarium. Kope Formation (Upper Ordovician), Miamitown, Hamilton County, Ohio; IU 8976-17002.

8 *Parvohallopora* sp. External view of zoarium. Kope Formation (Upper Ordovician), Miamitown, Hamilton County, Ohio; IU 8976-3003.

9 *Prasopora* sp. External view of specimen broken longitudinally. Cincinnati Group (Upper Ordovician), Cincinnati, Ohio; CW 131-2.

1
2
3
4
5
6
7
8
9
A
B

FIGURE 15-3.—Ordovician, Silurian, Devonian, and Pennsylvanian bryozoans of the suborders Amplexoporina and Ptilodictyina. Scale bar A equals 1 mm and applies to figure 15-3.6; scale bar B equals 1 cm and applies to remaining figures.

AMPLEXOPORINA

1 *Amplexopora septosa* (Ulrich). External view of zoarium. Kope Formation (Upper Ordovician), Miamitown, Hamilton County, Ohio; IU 8976-16001.

2 *Tabulipora ohioensis* (Foerste). External view of zoarium. Cambridge limestone (Conemaugh Group, Pennsylvanian), New Concord, Muskingum County, Ohio; ClMNH 5345.

PTILODICTYINA

3 *Clathropora frondosa* Hall. External view of zoarium. Brassfield Formation (Silurian), Highland County, Ohio; OSU 22643.

4 *Intrapora* sp. External view of zoarium. Silica Formation (Devonian), Lucas County, Ohio; MSU 220535-00002.

5, 6 *Phaenopora* sp. **5**, external view of zoarium. **6**, magnified view of **5**. Brassfield Formation (Silurian), Fairborn, Greene County, Ohio; MSU 220435-00001.

1
2
3
4
5
6
A
B

FIGURE 15-4.—Silurian, Devonian, and Mississippian bryozoans of the suborders Rhabdomesina, Phylloporinina, and Fenestellina. Scale bar A equals 1 mm and applies to figures 15-4.1 and 15-4.2; scale bar B equals 1 cm and applies to remaining figures.

RHABDOMESINA

1 *Streblotrypa* sp. External view of zoarium. Silica Formation (Devonian), Washtenaw County, Michigan; MSU 220522-00027.

2 *Acanthoclema* sp. External view of zoarium. Silica Formation (Devonian), Washtenaw County, Michigan; MSU 220522-00026.

3 *Rhombopora incrassata* Ulrich. External view of zoarium. Cuyahoga Formation (Mississippian), New London, Huron County, Ohio; ClMNH 5231.

4 *Rhombopora vesiculosa* (Winchell). External view of zoarium. Cuyahoga Formation (Mississippian), Lodi, Medina County, Ohio; OSU 4353.

PHYLLOPORININA

5 *Chasmatopora* sp. External view of zoaria. Brassfield Formation (Silurian), Fairborn, Greene County, Ohio; MSU 220435-00001.

FENESTELLINA

6 *Fenestella albida* Hall. External view of reverse side of zoarium. Cuyahoga Formation (Mississippian), Lodi, Medina County, Ohio; ClMNH 5857.

7 *Fenestella erectipora* Hall. External view of reverse side of zoarium. Columbus Limestone (Devonian), Marblehead, Ottawa County, Ohio; ClMNH 6062.

1
2
3
4
5
6
7
A
B

Chapter 16

PHYLUM BRACHIOPODA

by Barbara A. Schwimmer and Michael R. Sandy

INTRODUCTION

Brachiopods are an important component of Paleozoic faunas in Ohio. The group reached its greatest diversity during the Devonian, and this diversity is reflected in Ohio's rocks. Typically, fossils are preserved as **external molds** or **internal molds**, yet in many cases original shell material can be recovered that is only slightly altered by infiltration of minerals deposited from ground water. In some cases, shell material is replaced by other minerals such as quartz or pyrite. If **replacement** has occurred, external **ornamentation** and internal features may be obscured. Samples commonly are crushed, broken, or otherwise distorted; this state may affect overall appearance and hinder identification.

Brachiopod shells consist of a **brachial valve** and a **pedicle valve**. Fossil shells display a wide range of shapes and structures. The external and internal features and the shapes of brachiopods are illustrated in figures 1-24 to 1-26 in Chapter 1.

Some brachiopods may look very similar to each other externally, and are termed **homeomorphic**. However, they have been put in separate genera by paleontologists. Examples of homeomorphic brachiopods include *Rafinesquina* and *Strophomena* (fig. 16-1); *Dalmanella, Sowerbyella*, and *Plectorthis* (fig. 16-2); and *Glyptorthis, Eoplectodonta*, and *Holtedahlina* (fig. 16-2). Details of the valve interiors and of microscopic shell structure are used to distinguish between similarly shaped, but distantly related brachiopods. Adaptation to living in similar environments, or ecologic niches, is commonly cited as the reason that some brachiopods may have almost identical external morphologies or shapes, but different shell structure and interior details.

Brachiopods are divided into two classes—the Inarticulata, or **inarticulates**, and the Articulata, or **articulates**. The valves of inarticulate brachiopods may be **calcareous** but most are chitinophosphatic, that is, composed of alternating layers of organic **chitin** and the phosphate mineral apatite. Inarticulates lack **teeth** and **sockets**, instead employing various muscles for opening and closing the shells. They do possess a complete digestive tract. The valves of articulate brachiopods are composed of calcium carbonate and possess pedicle-valve teeth and brachial-valve sockets (referred to as the **dentition**), which together act as a pivoting mechanism for shell closure. There is great variety in the morphology of the articulate brachiopods. There is also great variety in how many genera may be found in one single unit or locality, ranging from many genera to perhaps only one. The diversity and kind of brachiopods help to interpret ancient environments.

The two classes of brachiopods are further subdivided into orders. Each class and order is characterized by specific details of morphology that aid in classification and in detailing relationships and origins of the group. The orders of brachiopods found in Ohio's fossil record are listed below.

Class Inarticulata

- Order Lingulida
  - Valves typically chitino-phosphatic, **biconvex** in **profile**, elliptical in **outline**.
- Order Acrotretida
  - Valves either phosphatic or calcareous, conical, **convexi-plane** or **convexi-concave** in profile, circular or subcircular in outline; **pedicle opening** (pedicle foramen) opens through the pedicle valve.

Class Articulata

- Order Strophomenida
  - Valves typically **concavo-convex**, convexi-concave, or **resupinate** in profile, semicircular in outline; **hinge line** straight; fine **ribs** radiate toward the **commissure**; may have **spines** along hinge line and/or on the pedicle-valve surface.
- Order Orthida
  - Valves unequally biconvex in profile, subquadrate in outline; hinge line straight; fine to coarse ribs on both valves.
- Order Atrypida
  - Valves typically biconvex in profile (brachial valve **inflated**, pedicle valve nearly plane), rounded in outline; hinge line short; ribs across both valves.
- Order Rhynchonellida
  - Valves biconvex in profile, rounded to triangular in outline; hinge short; ribs typically across both valves.
- Order Pentamerida
  - Valves biconvex in profile, commonly elongate in outline; strong **median septum** in the brachial valve and a **spondylium** in the pedicle valve.
- Order Spiriferida
  - Valves typically biconvex in profile; hinge line long and straight; well-developed **fold** and **sulcus** at the **anterior** commissure; width commonly greater than length; may be **mucronate** (winged); ribs radiate across both valves; characteristic is a pair of spirally coiled, calcareous **brachidia**, which act as supports for the feeding organ, the **lophophore**.

For further details of brachiopod classification refer to books on paleontology such as the brachiopod volume by Williams and others (1965) in the *Treatise on Invertebrate Paleontology* and those by Boardman and others (1987) and Murray (1985).

In Ohio, Ordovician brachiopods are generally abundant in the thinly bedded dark-blue to gray Upper Ordovician limestones and shales that are exposed in many places in the tri-state area of Ohio, Kentucky, and Indiana, especially in the triangle defined by Cincinnati and Dayton, Ohio, and Richmond, Indiana. Ordovician brachiopods have played an important role in the biostratigraphic subdivision of the Cincinnatian Series. They are typically well preserved, and shell material is commonly intact. For more information on Ordovician brachiopods see Richards (1972), Pope (1976, 1982), Hay and others (1981), Meyer and others (1981, 1985), Walker (1982) and Davis (1985).

Silurian brachiopods are found in several formations over a large geographic area in the western part of the state. They are generally not as abundant or conspicuous as Ordovician brachiopods, although in certain units *Pentamerus* (Springfield Dolomite) and *Cryptothyrella* (Bisher Formation) are abundant. Many Silurian limestones have been dolomitized, resulting in the dissolution and replacement of calcite, the mineral that most brachiopod shells are made of. Brachiopod shell material may be dissolved and the brachiopods preserved as molds in the tan dolomitic rocks. If the rock is strong enough and not crumbly, it can be filled with a casting material such as latex to make a reproduction or **cast** of the original fossil (see Parsley, 1989).

Middle Devonian brachiopods are found in northwestern Ohio in the Columbus Limestone, the Dundee Formation, and the Silica Formation. Through the central part of the state from the Lake Erie islands to Franklin and Pickaway Counties in south-central Ohio, brachiopods are found in the Lucas Dolomite; the Columbus, Delaware, and Prout Limestones; and the Plum Brook Shale. For more information on Middle Devonian brachiopods see Stauffer (1909), Stumm (1942), Stewart (1955), Fagerstrom (1971), and Kesling and Chilman (1975).

Upper Devonian brachiopods are found in the Olentangy Shale in central Ohio and in the Ohio Shale along the southern shore of Lake Erie in northeastern Ohio and southward through the central part of the state into Kentucky. Of the three members of the Ohio Shale, the Chagrin Shale Member appears to bear the most diverse and abundant assemblage of brachiopods; however, the Chagrin is not very fossiliferous when compared with the Middle Devonian limestones in Ohio. For more information on Upper Devonian brachiopods see Baker (1942), Szmuc (1970a), and Schwimmer and Feldmann (1990).

Mississippian brachiopods are found in the Bedford Shale and in many of the units of the Cuyahoga Formation, notably the Sharpsville, Meadville, and Wooster Members. The fossiliferous units in the Logan Formation include the Byer and Vinton Members. For more information on Mississippian brachiopods see Fagadau (1952), Hyde (1953), Szmuc (1957, 1970b), and Coogan and others (1981).

Pennsylvanian brachiopods are abundant and diverse in the marine units in eastern Ohio. Three of the four Pennsylvanian groups in Ohio have many fossiliferous beds within them. The Pottsville Group has brachiopods in the Boggs, Lower Mercer, and Upper Mercer units. The Allegheny Group has three fossiliferous shales, the Columbiana, the Washingtonville, and the Dorr Run, as well as several marine limestones, including the Putnam Hill and the Vanport. Several brachiopod-rich units are present in the Conemaugh Group, notably the limestones and shales of the Brush Creek and the Ames. The Monongahela Group, as well as the Dunkard Group of Pennsylvanian-Permian age, are nonmarine and have no recorded occurrences of brachiopods. For more information on Pennsylvanian brachiopods see Sturgeon and Hoare (1968) and Rau (1970).

The following key includes the more common genera of brachiopods found in Ohio. Not all Ohio taxa are described or illustrated. When you are comparing fossil brachiopods with those illustrated here, remember that broken, crushed, or slightly distorted shells will affect the appearance of the fossil. Although some specimens may attain a length or width of several centimeters when fully grown, they enlarge incrementally by addition of shell material to the margins of the valves, from very small sizes when young. Therefore, specimens may be smaller, or perhaps larger, than those illustrated here. With careful collecting it is possible to find examples of such smaller specimens and develop a whole growth series for your collection.

In the key and the descriptions, the approximate dimensions for length or width are: small, 1 cm or less; medium, 1 to 2 cm; large, greater than 2 cm. Unless otherwise noted, anterior and **posterior** views are oriented with the brachial valve above the pedicle valve.

KEY TO SOME BRACHIOPOD GENERA FROM OHIO, BASED PRIMARILY ON EXTERNAL CHARACTERISTICS

Some genera can be distinguished from each other only on the basis of internal characteristics, which are discussed in the text.

1A. Shell without radial ornamentation of ribs 2
1B. Shell has radial ornamentation of coarse or fine ribs 16

2A. Shell smooth or has concentric ornamentation only 3
2B. Shell smooth or has concentric ornamentation and spines 13

3A. Shell without fold or sulcus 4
3B. Shell has fold and/or sulcus 15

4A. Outline elongate (length greater than width) 5
4B. Outline circular or triangular 8

5A. Shell narrow, **spatulate**; sides parallel .... *Lingula* (figs. 16-6.1, 16-6.2)
5B. Outline broader, more elongate or oval 6

6A. Shell small to medium sized .... *Pseudolingula* (fig. 16-2.31)
6B. Shell large 7

7A. Spondylium in pedicle-valve interior .... *Pentamerus* (figs. 16-3.14 to 16-3.18)
7B. No spondylium .... *Cryptothyrella* (figs. 16-4.7 to 16-4.9)

8A. Outline triangular to subtriangular 9
8B. Outline circular 10

9A. Shell small to medium sized .... *Trigonoglossa* (fig. 16-8.6)
9B. Shell large, generally preserved as an internal mold; traces of **septa** in both valves .... *Trimerella* (figs. 16-4.1, 16-4.2, 16-5.1 to 16-5.4)

10A. **Beak** near center of valve .... *Orbiculoidea* (figs. 16-6.3, 16-6.4)
10B. Beak on or near margin of valve 11

11A. Ornamentation of small surficial pits .... *Trematis* (figs. 16-2.32, 16-2.33)
11B. Ornamentation of concentric lines 12

12A. Concentric markings regular .... *Oehlertella* (figs. 16-8.9, 16-8.10)
12B. Shell thin, concentric markings irregular, reflecting the markings of the surface to which it is attached .... *Petrocrania* (figs. 16-1.16, 16-2.38)

13A. Fold and sulcus present .... *Mesolobus* (figs. 16-9.20, 16-9.21)
13B. No fold or sulcus 14

14A. Both valves have concentrically arranged spines on ridges .... *Juresania* (figs. 16-9.15, 16-9.16)
14B. Only pedicle valve has very fine, concentrically arranged spines, which are not on ridges .... *Acanthatia* (figs. 16-6.20 to 16-6.22)

15A. Outline **transverse** (width greater than length) .... *Athyris* (figs. 16-8.17, 16-8.18)
15B. Outline elongate (length greater than width) .... *Composita* (fig. 16-9.19)

16A. Profile biconvex 17
16B. Profile otherwise (combination of convex, concave, or plane) 53

17A. Outline circular, subcircular, or semicircular 18
17B. Outline triangular or subtriangular, elliptical or subquadrate (width greater than length), elongate or subrectangular (length greater than width), or equidimensional (width and length approximately equal) 28

18A. Beak in center of valve and ribs radiate outward .... *Philhedra* (fig. 16-2.37)
18B. Beak at or near posterior margin of valve 19

19A. Fold and/or sulcus strong 20
19B. Fold and/or sulcus weak or absent 23

20A. Deep sulcus in pedicle valve .... *Holtedahlina* (figs. 16-2.14 to 16-2.16)
20B. Fold and sulcus both present 21

21A. Ribs fine .... *Zygospira* (figs. 16-2.34 to 16-2.36)
21B. Ribs coarse 22

22A. Ribs crests angular .... *Centrorhynchus* (figs. 16-7.11 to 16-7.15)
22B. Ribs crests rounded .... "*Camarotoechia*" (figs. 16-7.7, 16-7.8)

23A. Ribs coarse 24
23B. Ribs medium to fine 25

24A. Hinge line rounded .... *Sphaerirhynchia* (figs. 16-4.19 to 16-4.21)
24B. Hinge line straight .... *Plectorthis* (figs. 16-2.21 to 16-2.24)

25A. **Pseudodeltidium** present .... *Schellwienella* (fig. 16-8.11)
25B. No pseudodeltidium 26

26A. **Growth lines** prominent .... *Rhipidomella* (figs. 16-6.11 to 16-6.13)
26B. Growth lines faint or absent 27

27A. Ribs fine; low pedicle-valve fold and brachial-valve sulcus .... *Aulacella* (figs. 16-6.7 to 16-6.10)
27B. Ribs slightly coarser; shallow brachial-valve sulcus only .... *Dalmanella* (figs. 16-2.25 to 16-2.30)

28A. Outline subtriangular to subcircular 29
28B. Outline elliptical or subquadrate (width greater than length), elongate or subrectangular (length greater than width), or equidimensional (width and length approximately equal) 34

29A. Valves unequally convex 30
29B. Valves equally or almost equally convex 32

30A. Pedicle valve more convex than brachial valve .... *Ambocoelia* (figs. 16-7.19 to 16-7.22)
30B. Brachial valve more convex that pedicle valve 31

31A. Pedicle-valve beak and opening extended .... *Rhynchotreta* (figs. 16-4.25 to 16-4.27)
31B. Pedicle-valve beak curves over triangular **delthyrium** .... *Rhynchopora* (figs. 16-8.15, 16-8.16)

32A. Prominent growth lines and ribs form distinctive pattern .... *Lepidocyclus* (figs. 16-3.1 to 16-3.8)
32B. Growth lines less prominent 33

33A. One rib in pedicle-valve sulcus .... *Rhynchotrema* (figs. 16-3.10 to 16-3.13)
33B. Multiple ribs in pedicle-valve sulcus .... *Stegerhynchus* (figs. 16-4.22 to 16-4.24)

34A. Outline elongate (length greater than width) .... *Kirkidium* (figs. 16-4.5, 16-4.6, 16-5.5)
34B. Outline elliptical or subquadrate (width greater than length) or equidimensional (width and length approximately equal) 35

35A. Fold and sulcus weak or absent 36
35B. Fold and sulcus strong 38

36A. Ribs prominent in area of fold and sulcus, weak or absent on flanks .... *Leiorhynchus* (figs. 16-7.9, 16-7.10)
36B. Ribs consistent across both valves 37

37A. Delthyrium covered .... *Derbyia* (figs. 16-9.10, 16-9.11)
37B. Delthyrium open .... *Glyptorthis* (figs. 16-2.17 to 16-2.20)

38A. Fold and sulcus not ribbed 39
38B. Fold and sulcus ribbed 45

39A. Fewer than 20 ribs on flanks 40
39B. More than 20 ribs on flanks 41

40A. **Spinules** present on both valves .... *Punctospirifer* (figs. 16-9.1 to 16-9.4)
40B. No spinules present .... *Brevispirifer* (fig. 16-7.24)

41A. **Interarea** pyramid shaped 42
41B. Interarea linear 43

42A. Shell large .... *Syringothyris* (figs. 16-9.5, 16-9.6)
42B. Shell small to medium sized .... *Cyrtina* (figs. 16-7.25, 16-7.26)

43A. Tiny granules on summits of ribs .... *Spinocyrtia* (fig. 16-7.23)
43B. Chevron pattern on valves 44

44A. Shell large, quadrate, equidimensional .... *Paraspirifer* (figs. 16-8.7, 16-8.8)
44B. Shell medium sized, highly elliptical .... *Mucrospirifer* (figs. 16-8.1 to 16-8.3)

45A. Ribs on fold and sulcus only .... *Gypidula* (figs. 16-4.16 to 16-4.18)
45B. Ribs consistent across both valves 46

46A. Ribs fine 47
46B. Ribs medium to coarse 49

47A. Delthyrium partially closed by **deltidial plates** .... *Eospirifer* (figs. 16-4.10 to 16-4.12)
47B. Delthyrium open 48

48A. Outline subquadrate .... *Hebertella* (figs. 16-1.24 to 16-1.26)
48B. Outline elliptical .... *Schizophoria* (figs. 16-6.16 to 16-6.19)

49A. Interarea pyramid shaped .... *Sphenospira* (figs. 16-8.4, 16-8.5)
49B. Interarea linear 50

50A. Rib crests angular .... *Platystrophia* (figs. 16-1.1 to 16-1.12)
50B. Rib crests rounded 51

51A. Ribs on flanks simple, not branched .... *Cyrtospirifer* (figs. 16-7.27 to 16-7.30)
51B. Ribs on flanks branching at anterior ends or in bundles 52

52A. Shell large, ribs of various diameters and in bundles .... *Neospirifer* (figs. 16-9.24, 16-9.25)
52B. Shell small to medium sized, ribs fewer, stronger .... *Anthracospirifer* (figs. 16-9.22, 16-9.23)

53A. Profile has one planar or nearly planar valve 54
53B. Profile has concave and convex valves 57

54A. Profile convexi-plane to unequally biconvex 55
54B. Profile **plano-convex** to very slightly concavo-convex 56

55A. Outline subcircular .... *Atrypa* (figs. 16-4.13 to 16-4.15)
55B. Outline more subtriangular to subrectangular .... *Pseudoatrypa* (figs. 16-7.16 to 16-7.18)

56A. Shell small; spine row on hinge only .... *Chonetes* (fig. 16-8.12)
56B. Shell medium sized; scattered spines on pedicle valve and one to two spine rows on hinge .... *Linoproductus* (figs. 16-9.17, 16-9.18)

57A. Profile resupinate .... *Strophomena* (figs. 16-1.18 to 16-1.23, 16-3.9) or *Strophonella* (figs. 16-4.3, 16-4.4)
57B. Profile concavo-convex or convexi-concave 58

58A. Profile concavo-convex 59
58B. Profile convexi-concave .... *Plaesiomys* (figs. 16-2.11 to 16-2.13)

59A. Outline subcircular or semicircular 60
59B. Outline elliptical or subquadrate, or elongate or subrectangular 65

60A. Shell has spines 61
60B. Shell without spines 63

61A. Fold and sulcus prominent; bilobed appearance .... *Chonetinella* (figs. 16-9.13, 16-9.14)
61B. Fold and sulcus weak or absent 62

62A. Ornamentation of fine ribs, few spinules, spine row on hinge .... *Devonochonetes* (figs. 16-6.14, 16-6.15)
62B. Ornamentation of long curved spines on pedicle valve, in groups on flanks, and near hinge .... *Spinulicosta* (figs. 16-7.1, 16-7.2)

63A. Shell has **rugae** .... *Leptaena* (figs. 16-2.1 to 16-2.4, 16-5.6)
63B. Shell without rugae 64

64A. Shell large .... *Rafinesquina* (figs. 16-1.13 to 16-1.17, 16-2.37, 16-2.38)
64B. Shell small to medium sized .... *Eoplectodonta* (fig. 16-2.10) or *Sowerbyella* (figs. 16-2.5 to 16-2.9)

65A. Shell without spines 66
65B. Shell has spines 67

66A. Ribs coarse; open delthyrium .... *Tropidoleptus* (figs. 16-6.5, 16-6.6)
66B. Ribs fine; complete pseudodeltidium .... *Megastrophia* (figs. 16-6.23, 16-6.24) or *Strophodonta* (figs. 16-7.3 to 16-7.6)

67A. Shell has rugae in irregular pattern .... *Desmoinesia* (fig. 16-9.12)
67B. Shell has concentric rugae that form a **reticulate** pattern with ribs 68

68A. Fine spines in patch on flanks .... *Dictyoclostus* (figs. 16-8.13, 16-8.14)
68B. Coarse spine row on ridge running up flanks .... *Antiquatonia* (figs. 16-9.7 to 16-9.9)

ORDOVICIAN BRACHIOPODS

Dalmanella Hall & Clarke (figs. 16-2.25 to 16-2.30) is a small to medium-sized orthid brachiopod. It has a gently biconvex profile, and the oval to subcircular outline is truncated by a straight hinge line. Width is greater than length, although it may be only just so. The brachial valve has a shallow sulcus. Ribs radiate from the beaks toward the commissure. The ribbing may be finer than that of *Plaesiomys* and *Glyptorthis* and is certainly finer than that of *Plectorthis*. Species of *Dalmanella* have been referred to *Onniella* by some workers (see, for example, discussion in Walker, 1982, p. M10). *Dalmanella* has been recorded from much of the Cincinnatian Series.

Eoplectodonta Kozlowski (fig. 16-2.10) is a small to medium-sized strophomenid brachiopod. It has a concavo-convex profile and a semicircular outline truncated by a wide, straight hinge line. Numerous very fine ribs radiate from the **umbones** to the commissure. *Eoplectodonta* and *Sowerbyella* are difficult to distinguish by external appearance alone. Distinguishing internal characteristics of *Eoplectodonta* include a **denticulate** hinge line and septa (platelike structures) in the brachial valve. Some authors have referred brachiopods from the Waynesville and Liberty Formations to the genus *Thaerodonta*. However, Williams and others (1965) referred *Thaerodonta* to *Eoplectodonta*, considering them to be the same genus.

Glyptorthis Foerste (figs. 16-2.17 to 16-2.20) is a medium-sized orthid brachiopod that has an unequally biconvex profile and an elliptical outline truncated by a straight hinge line. The width is greater than the length. The more inflated brachial valve has a sulcus. Numerous branching ribs radiate from the beaks of both valves. The intersection of radiating ribs and concentric growth lines results in a reticulate ornamentation on the exterior surface of the valves. The delthyrium is open. The interior of the pedicle valve has a **muscle scar** consisting of two deep grooves, made by the **diductor muscles**; this muscle scar is separated by a ridge from the **adductor muscle** scars. **Pallial markings** are present beyond the muscle scar (see fig. 16-2.20). *Glyptorthis* occurs in the Waynesville and basal Liberty Formations.

Hebertella Hall & Clarke (figs. 16-1.24 to 16-1.26) is a large, subquadrate orthid brachiopod that is biconvex in profile. The pedicle valve may be flatter than the brachial valve. The width is markedly greater than the length, and the hinge line is straight. Many fine ribs radiate from the umbones. The beak of the brachial valve may be incurved. The brachial valve has a well-developed fold at the anterior commissure, and the pedicle valve has a corresponding sulcus. The pedicle valve has a raised beak with a triangular interarea and a triangular delthyrium. Muscle scars on the interior of the pedicle valve have three lobes. The two larger outer muscle scars are from the diductor muscles, and the central scar is from the adductor muscles (see fig. 16-1.26). *Hebertella* is recorded from the Cincinnatian Series.

Holtedahlina Foerste (figs. 16-2.14 to 16-2.16) is a small to medium-sized strophomenid brachiopod that has an unequally biconvex profile. Its semicircular outline is truncated by a straight hinge line. Fine ribs radiate from the umbones of both valves. One of the characteristics that helps to distinguish this genus from others is the deep sulcus of the pedicle valve. *Holtedahlina* is recorded from the Waynesville Formation to the Drakes Formation.

Lepidocyclus Wang (figs. 16-3.1 to 16-3.8) is a small to large rhynchonellid brachiopod. Its profile ranges from moderately biconvex, especially when small, to strongly biconvex when large. The outline ranges from subtriangular to subcircular. The hinge line is rounded. Coarse ribs radiate from the beaks across both valves. The ribs do not branch. A distinct fold is present in the brachial valve, and a corresponding sulcus in the pedicle valve. The pedicle opening is small and rounded. In large specimens the pedicle umbo may be incurved and obscure the pedicle opening. The intersection of numerous, closely spaced, concentric growth lines with the coarse, radiating ribs results in a highly distinctive ornament. *Lepidocyclus* has been recorded from the Arnheim to the Drakes Formations. Some paleontologists (for example, Amsden, 1983) have referred specimens to the genus *Hiscobeccus* Amsden, but it has only minor differences from *Lepidocyclus*. A very similar looking rhynchonellid has been recorded from the Fairview Formation and has been referred to the genus *Orthorhynchula* Hall & Clarke (not described or illustrated here). A detailed discussion of Ordovician rhynchonellids is given in Jin (1989).

Leptaena Dalman (figs. 16-2.1 to 16-2.4) is a medium-sized to large, concavo-convex strophomenid brachiopod. Its semicircular outline is truncated by a straight hinge line. *Leptaena* is characteristically wider than long and has concentric ridges or rugae. It also has numerous fine ribs radiating across each valve from the umbones. *Leptaena* is recorded from the Cincinnatian Series and ranges into the Devonian of Ohio.

Petrocrania Raymond (figs. 16-1.16, 16-2.38) is a small to medium-sized acrotretid brachiopod. It has a circular outline and a calcareous shell. This brachiopod commonly is found attached to other types of shells, such as that of the articulate brachiopod *Rafinesquina*. Because the shell of *Petrocrania* is very thin, the ornament of the underlying surface to which this brachiopod has attached is commonly visible (see figs. 16-1.16, 16-2.38). *Petrocrania* is recorded from the entire Cincinnatian Series and also is found in Silurian and Devonian rocks of Ohio.

Philhedra Koken (fig. 16-2.37) is a small acrotretid brachiopod that has a circular to subcircular outline and a biconvex profile. The upper, brachial valve is conical. The beak is in the center of the valve. Characteristic is the presence of numerous fine ribs radiating from the **apex** of the brachial valve. *Philhedra* is known from the Cincinnatian Series.

Plaesiomys Hall & Clarke (figs. 16-2.11 to 16-2.13) is a medium-sized orthid brachiopod that ranges in profile from convexi-concave to unequally biconvex. It has a subquadrate outline and a straight hinge line. Width is greater than length. The delthyrium is open. Numerous branching ribs radiate from the umbones of both valves. The interior of the pedicle valve shows the teeth and a muscle-scar area that has two broad diductor muscle scars enclosing a smaller, central adductor muscle scar (see fig. 16-2.13). *Plaesiomys* has a more rectangular outline than *Glyptorthis*. Both have irregularly branching ribs, but in *Plaesiomys* the ribs curve noticeably toward the commissure. *Plaesiomys* has been recorded from the Liberty and Whitewater Formations.

Platystrophia King (figs. 16-1.1 to 16-1.12) is a large orthid brachiopod whose width is significantly greater than its length. The valves are commonly strongly biconvex in profile. The outline is variable, from quadrate or rectangular to subtriangular and mucronate. The hinge line is straight. Coarse ribs radiate from the umbones; rib crests are angular. The brachial valve has a well-developed fold at the anterior commissure, and the pedicle valve has a corresponding sulcus. A number of species have been identified on the basis of differences in outline and the number of ribs on the valves. The interior of the pedicle valve has a broad muscle scar toward the posterior (see fig. 16-1.5). Externally, *Platystrophia* resembles a spiriferid brachiopod, but the lack of a spiral brachidium and details of shell structure indicate that it is an orthid. *Platystrophia* is recorded from the Cincinnatian Series and also from the Silurian rocks of Ohio.

Plectorthis Hall & Clarke (figs. 16-2.21 to 16-2.24) is a small to medium-sized orthid brachiopod that has a gently biconvex profile. The rectangular to subcircular outline is truncated by a straight hinge line. Width is greater than length. Ribs radiate from the umbones toward the commissure. The ribs are coarser than those of *Plaesiomys* and *Glyptorthis*. *Plectorthis* is recorded from the Fairview Formation.

Pseudolingula Mickwitz (fig. 16-2.31) is a small to medium-sized lingulid brachiopod that has an elongate outline. The anterior margin of the outline may be flat or truncated. The phosphatic shell may be white. Concentric growth lines may be well preserved. This genus is recorded from the entire Cincinnatian Series.

Rafinesquina Hall & Clarke (figs. 16-1.13 to 16-1.17, 16-2.37, 16-2.38) is a large, concavo-convex strophomenid brachiopod. The outline is semicircular and is truncated by a straight hinge line. Width and length are approximately equal. Ornamentation consists of numerous fine ribs that radiate from the umbones of both valves toward the commissure. The brachial valve is concave and the pedicle valve is convex, in contrast to *Strophomena*, which, for most of its length, has the brachial valve convex and the pedicle valve concave. The brachial-valve interior of *Rafinesquina* has a massive, bilobed **cardinal process** adjacent to the hinge line (fig. 16-1.14). The interior of the pedicle valve has broad, poorly defined muscle scars (fig. 16-1.15). *Rafinesquina* has been recorded from the Cincinnatian Series.

Rhynchotrema Hall (figs. 16-3.10 to 16-3.13) is a small rhynchonellid brachiopod that has a biconvex profile and a subtriangular outline. Ribs radiate from the umbones of both valves. A small pedicle opening is present. Specimens of *Rhynchotrema* may resemble small specimens of *Lepidocyclus*, but *Rhynchotrema* tends to have a more pointed beak on the pedicle valve, a more pronounced fold of the commissure, and one rib within the sulcus of the pedicle valve. *Rhynchotrema* has been recorded from the Waynesville to the Whitewater Formations.

Sowerbyella Jones (figs. 16-2.5 to 16-2.9) is a small to medium-sized strophomenid brachiopod that has a concavo-convex profile and a semicircular outline truncated by a wide, straight hinge line. Numerous very fine ribs radiate from each umbo to the commissure. The interior of the pedicle valve has a small median septum at the posterior end, and the brachial valve has two divergent septa. The concavo-convex profile of *Sowerbyella* helps to distinguish it from the biconvex genus *Holtedahlina*. *Sowerbyella* is recorded from the Cincinnatian Series.

Strophomena Rafinesque (figs. 16-1.18 to 16-1.23, 16-3.9) is a medium-sized to large, resupinate, strophomenid brachiopod. It has a semicircular outline truncated by a straight hinge line. Width and length are approximately equal. Ornamentation consists of numerous fine ribs radiating from the umbones of both valves toward the commissure. If a triangular calcareous plate, the **symphytium**, can be distinguished along the flat interarea of the concave (pedicle) valve, then the specimen is *Strophomena*, not *Rafinesquina*. The brachial-valve interior of *Strophomena* has a bilobed cardinal process, typically smaller than that in *Rafinesquina*, and low septa that may be traced for more than half the length of the valve interior (fig. 16-3.9). The pedicle-valve interior has wedge-shaped teeth and a subcircular muscle scar that may be bordered by a ridge (figs. 16-1.19, 16-1.21). *Strophomena* is recorded from the Cincinnatian Series.

There are other strophomenid brachiopods that are homeomorphic with *Strophomena* and *Rafinesquina*. See the works of Pope (1976, 1982) for a more detailed discussion of these brachiopods.

Trematis Sharpe (figs. 16-2.32, 16-2.33) is a medium-sized acrotretid brachiopod that has a biconvex profile and a circular outline. The pedicle valve has a large, elongate pedicle opening that extends to the valve margin. Small pits are characteristic on the surface of both valves. This genus is known from the Cincinnatian Series.

Zygospira Hall (figs. 16-2.34 to 16-2.36) is a small atrypid brachiopod, generally less than 5 mm in length. It has a biconvex profile and a circular to subcircular outline. Length and width are nearly equal in dimensions, although in some individuals width may be slightly greater than length. The valves are characterized by their small size and fine ribs that radiate from the beaks across both valves. There is a minute, circular pedicle opening in the beak region of the pedicle valve. The anterior commissure of the brachial valve may be sulcate to very gently sulcate. The central rib of the brachial valve may be slightly wider than adjacent ribs at the anterior commissure. Care must be taken to distinguish

Zygospira from small specimens of other ribbed brachiopod genera, such as *Lepidocyclus*. Specimens of *Zygospira* have been found in association with bryozoans, indicating that some may have attached to these colonial organisms (Richards, 1972). *Zygospira* is the smallest adult articulate brachiopod known from Ohio and has been recorded from the entire Cincinnatian Series.

SILURIAN BRACHIOPODS

Atrypa Dalman (figs. 16-4.13 to 16-4.15) is a small to medium-sized atrypid brachiopod that is convexi-plane to unequally biconvex in profile; the brachial valve is more inflated. It has a circular to subcircular outline. Ribs radiate from the beaks of both valves and intersect the growth lines to produce rugae. The brachial valve may have a gentle fold and the pedicle valve a slight sulcus at the anterior commissure. *Atrypa* is recorded from the Niagaran Series in Ohio.

Cryptothyrella Cooper (figs. 16-4.7 to 16-4.9) is a large, elongate spiriferid brachiopod that has a biconvex profile. Valves are smooth, although growth lines may be visible. *Cryptothyrella* resembles small specimens of *Pentamerus*, but can be distinguished from *Pentamerus* by the incurved pedicle beak and the lack of a spondylium in the pedicle valve. *Cryptothyrella* has **dental plates** in the pedicle valve and a short median septum in the brachial valve. *Cryptothyrella* is common in places in the Silurian. A *Cryptothyrella* "zone" or biofacies has been recognized near the base of the Bisher Formation in Adams County (Schmidt and others, 1961; Horvath, 1969; Kleffner and Ausich, 1988).

Eospirifer Schuchert (figs. 16-4.10 to 16-4.12) is a large spiriferid brachiopod that is biconvex in profile. The elliptical outline is truncated by a straight hinge line. Width is greater than length. The valves have fine ribbing that radiates from the beaks and crosses the distinct fold and sulcus. The delthyrium is partly closed by deltidial plates. The pedicle-valve interior has two divergent dental plates. *Eospirifer* is recorded from the Niagaran Series.

Gypidula Hall (figs. 16-4.16 to 16-4.18) is a medium-sized to large pentamerid brachiopod that is biconvex in profile. The outline is elliptical, and width is greater than length. The shell is generally smooth, although a few ribs may develop in the brachial-valve fold and corresponding pedicle-valve sulcus. This genus is common in the Niagaran Series.

Kirkidium Amsden, Boucot & Johnson (figs. 16-4.5, 16-4.6, 16-5.5) is a large, elongate pentamerid brachiopod that has a strongly biconvex, inflated profile. Length is greater than width. It may reach proportions similar to *Pentamerus*, but distinguishing features of *Kirkidium* include the presence of ribs and the incurved beak of the pedicle valve. *Kirkidium* is recorded from the upper part of the Niagaran Series.

Leptaena (fig. 16-5.6) is known from the Brassfield Formation and the Springfield Dolomite. This genus is described in the section on Ordovician brachiopods.

Pentamerus Sowerby (figs. 16-3.14 to 16-3.18) is a very large pentamerid brachiopod, commonly attaining lengths of 10 cm or more. The biconvex profile may be inflated. The oval to subpentagonal outline is pointed toward the posterior. Length is greater than width. Growth lines may be easily distinguished on shell material, but commonly are obscured by dolomitization. The shell in many cases has been dissolved away and the internal mold displays a characteristic deep, narrow slit, the former site of the spondylium, in the posterior of the pedicle valve (figs. 16-3.14, 16-3.18). Two long, rodlike blades of shell material (septa) are present in the brachial valve and may have supported part of the lophophore. In internal molds they appear as two parallel grooves (figs. 16-3.14, 16-3.15, 16-3.17, 16-3.18). *Pentamerus* is the largest fossil brachiopod in Ohio. It is abundant in distinct layers or "zones" in Silurian rocks, such as the Springfield Dolomite close to the contact with the overlying Cedarville Dolomite in Greene and Montgomery Counties. The brachiopods commonly are preserved in their former living position, beaks pointing downward (fig. 16-3.18). Where they occur in abundance, these brachiopods have been popularly referred to as "turtle heads" or "fossil pig's feet" because of their resemblance to turtle heads peeping above water or to the impression of cloven pigs' hooves in mud. *Pentamerus* has been recorded from the Niagaran Series and is common to abundant in certain layers in the Euphemia, Springfield, and Cedarville Dolomites.

Platystrophia has been recorded from the Brassfield and Dayton Formations. This genus is described in the section on Ordovician brachiopods.

Rhynchotreta Hall (figs. 16-4.25 to 16-4.27) is a small to medium-sized rhynchonellid brachiopod that is unequally biconvex in profile; the brachial valve is more inflated. It has a distinctive triangular to subtriangular outline due to the extension of the beak region. The hinge is narrow and rounded. There is a pedicle opening on the posterior extension of the pedicle valve. Coarse ribs radiate from the beaks to the commissure. A low fold in the brachial valve corresponds to a sulcus in the pedicle valve. The brachial valve interior has a median septum. This genus is recorded from the Niagaran Series of Ohio.

Sphaerirhynchia Cooper & Muir-Wood (figs. 16-4.19 to 16-4.21) is a small to medium-sized rhynchonellid brachiopod that has a circular, biconvex profile, a circular outline, and a rounded hinge line. Coarse ribs radiate from the beaks to the commissure. A weak fold in the brachial valve and a corresponding sulcus in the pedicle valve are indicated by a deflection of the anterior commissure. The **tongue** of the sulcus is weak. The brachial-valve interior has a median septum. *Sphaerirhynchia* is recorded from the Niagaran Series.

Stegerhynchus Foerste (figs. 16-4.22 to 16-4.24) is a small to medium-sized rhynchonellid brachiopod that has a biconvex profile and a triangular to subtriangular outline. The hinge is short and rounded. The beak of the pedicle valve is pointed. Coarse ribs radiate from both beaks to the commissure. A well-developed fold in the brachial valve corresponds to a sulcus in the pedicle valve. Internal structures include dental plates in the pedicle valve and a median septum in the brachial valve. *Stegerhynchus* is recorded from the Niagaran Series.

Strophonella Hall (figs. 16-4.3, 16-4.4) is a large strophomenid brachiopod that has a resupinate profile. The semicircular outline is truncated by a straight hinge line. Fine ribbing radiates from the beaks of both valves. The denticulate hinge line and large, elongate muscle scars on the interior of the pedicle valve (fig. 16-4.4) help to distinguish this genus from *Rafinesquina* and from *Strophomena*. *Strophonella* has been recorded from the Silurian of Ohio.

Trimerella Billings (figs. 16-4.1, 16-4.2, 16-5.1 to 16-5.4) is a large lingulid brachiopod that has a biconvex profile. The pedicle valve has a triangular to subtriangular outline and a pedicle opening; the brachial valve has a more subcircular outline. Specimens of *Trimerella* generally are found as internal molds. Both valves have traces of a median septum and two flanking septa (platelike structures), preserved as grooves where shell material is lost; these structures divide the valve interiors into four lobes (fig 16-4.1). *Trimerella* is recorded from the Brassfield Formation and the Guelph Dolomite (Lockport Group).

DEVONIAN BRACHIOPODS

Acanthatia Muir-Wood & Cooper (figs. 16-6.20 to 16-6.22) is a small to medium-sized strophomenid brachiopod that has a concavo-convex profile. The outline is subcircular. Width is greater than length. The pedicle valve has an evenly spaced, concentric arrangement of spines, as well as a spine row at the hinge. The pedicle-valve interior has fine perforations, which are evidence of internal spines. The brachial-valve interior has a thin **breviseptum** that is not fused to the bilobed cardinal process but is separated from it by a small pit or **alveolus**. *Acanthatia* is found in the Chagrin Shale Member of the Ohio Shale.

Ambocoelia Hall (figs. 16-7.19 to 16-7.22) is a small spiriferid brachiopod that has an unequally biconvex profile. The triangular to subtriangular pedicle valve is strongly convex and has a narrow sulcus, a prominent incurved beak, and a large interarea that has an open delthyrium. The shell is commonly thin. The brachial valve is semicircular and weakly convex and there is no fold. Ornament consists of concentric growth lines and very weak radial lines. The pedicle-valve interior lacks dental plates. The brachial-valve interior has a large, bilobed cardinal process and distinct **crural plates**. *Ambocoelia* is found in the Lucas Dolomite, Delaware Limestone, Plum Brook Shale, Silica Formation, and Chagrin Shale Member. This genus ranges into the Mississippian in Ohio.

Athyris M'Coy is a medium-sized, biconvex spiriferid brachiopod that has a transverse outline and a short hinge line. The shell may have a slight fold and sulcus, as well as **lamellae** (expansions at the growth lines), which give the effect of frills. These frills may bear very fine, radially arranged spines. *Athyris* is found in the Silica Formation and the Chagrin Shale Member and ranges into the Mississippian rocks of Ohio. A Mississippian specimen is illustrated in figures 16-8.17 and 16-8.18.

Aulacella Schuchert & Cooper (figs. 16-6.7 to 16-6.10) is a small orthid brachiopod that is unequally biconvex in profile and has a subcircular outline. Very fine, hollow ribs radiate from the umbones of both valves. A low fold in the pedicle valve corresponds to a sulcus in the brachial valve. The delthyrium is open. Muscle scars in the interior of the pedicle valve are long and bilobed. *Aulacella* has been found in the Chagrin Shale Member.

Brevispirifer Cooper (fig. 16-7.24) is a medium-sized, biconvex spiriferid brachiopod that has an equidimensional outline. A few heavy lateral ribs are present, but the fold and sulcus are without ribbing or have a median ridge in the sulcus and a median groove in the fold. *Brevispirifer* is found in the Dundee Formation, Columbus Limestone, and Delaware Limestone.

"Camarotoechia" Hall & Clarke (figs. 16-7.7, 16-7.8) is a small to medium-sized rhynchonellid brachiopod. It has a biconvex profile, which is slightly inflated at the umbones. The outline is subcircular. Coarse, rounded ribs ornament both valves. A well-defined fold and sulcus are present. The pedicle-valve interior has short, strong dental plates. The brachial-valve interior has a high median septum or ridge, but no cardinal process. Over the years, several similar genera have been given the name *"Camarotoechia."* As a result, there is much confusion concerning identification of this **taxon**, and work is still in progress to resolve the problem (Sartenaer, 1961a, 1961b). For this reason, the name *"Camarotoechia"* commonly appears in quotation marks to signify uncertainty over the identification. This genus occurs in the Lucas Dolomite, Columbus Limestone, Delaware Limestone, and Prout Limestone.

Centrorhynchus Sartenaer (figs. 16-7.11 to 16-7.15) is a small biconvex rhynchonellid brachiopod that has a subcircular outline. Ornament consists of coarse ribs that have angular crests. There is a strong pedicle-valve sulcus and a well-developed tongue. The pedicle-valve beak is slightly incurved over the interarea. The pedicle-valve interior has short dental plates, and the brachial-valve interior has deep sockets and a stout septum extending half the length of the valve. The angular peaks on the ribs help to distinguish *Centrorhynchus* from *"Camarotoechia,"* which has rounded ribs. Other differences involve examination of internal structures. *Centrorhynchus* is found in the Chagrin Shale Member.

Composita Brown is a medium-sized biconvex spiriferid brachiopod that has an elongate outline and a short hinge line. There is a brachial-valve fold and pedicle-valve sulcus. The fold may have a furrow in the middle. The pedicle-valve interior has short dental plates. *Composita* is found in the Chagrin Shale Member and in the Mississippian and Pennsylvanian rocks of Ohio. A Pennsylvanian specimen is illustrated in figure 16-9.19.

Cyrtina Davidson (figs. 16-7.25, 16-7.26) is a small to medium-sized, almost equidimensional spiriferid brachiopod. It has a pyramid-shaped pedicle valve and high interarea. The brachial valve is weakly convex. Lateral slopes show distinct ribs. The fold and sulcus are smooth except for growth lines. A large delthyrium is present in the pedicle valve, covered by a convex pseudodeltidium. *Cyrtina* is found in the Dundee Formation, Delaware Limestone, Prout Limestone, Plum Brook Shale, and Silica Formation. This genus ranges into the Mississippian rocks of Ohio.

Cyrtospirifer Nalivkin (figs. 16-7.27 to 16-7.30) is a medium-sized, biconvex, gently elliptical spiriferid brachiopod. The hinge line is equal to the maximum width. The strong fold and sulcus have numerous ribs, which are rounded at their crests. Simple ribs—ribs that do not bifurcate or split—continue across the flanks. The delthyrium is open. The pedicle-valve interior shows well-developed but short dental plates. *Cyrtospirifer* is found in the Columbus Limestone, Silica Formation, and Chagrin Shale Member.

Devonochonetes Muir-Wood (figs. 16-6.14, 16-6.15) is a small to medium-sized strophomenid brachiopod that has a moderately concavo-convex profile. The semicircular outline is truncated by a straight hinge line. Ornamentation consists of numerous fine ribs bearing a few spinules and short, low-angle hinge spines. The hinge line almost equals the greatest width. A pseudodeltidium and a **chilidium** are present. Many taxa of chonetid brachiopods have been identified, and externally it is difficult to tell them apart. For example, *Chonetes* (described in the section on Mississippian brachiopods) has a bilobed cardinal process, and, instead of a prominent median septum, three to five ridges diverging anterior to an alveolus in the brachial-valve interior. These characteristics distinguish *Chonetes* from *Devonochonetes*, which has a trilobed cardinal process, no alveolus, a long median septum, and prominent lateral septa in the brachial valve. *Devonochonetes* is found in the Columbus Limestone, Prout Limestone, Plum Brook Shale, and Silica Formation.

Leiorhynchus Hall (figs. 16-7.9, 16-7.10) is a medium-sized, thin-shelled, globose, biconvex rhynchonellid brachiopod. The outline is subquadrate. A weak fold and sulcus begin near the midlength of the valve. Ribs are strong on the fold and sulcus but weak or absent on the flanks. *Leiorhynchus* has an undulating commissure and curved beak. The pedicle-valve interior has well-developed dental plates. The brachial-valve interior has a high, long median septum and curving **crura**. *Leiorhynchus* is found in the Delaware Limestone, Prout Limestone, Plum Brook Shale, and Chagrin Shale Member.

Leptaena is found in the Columbus and Delaware Limestones. It is described in the section on Ordovician brachiopods.

Lingula Bruguière (figs. 16-6.1, 16-6.2) is a small to medium-sized, biconvex lingulid brachiopod. The shell is spatula shaped and has an elongate outline. The lateral edges are parallel or gently rounded. The valves are approximately equal in size and convexity. Length is generally greater than width. The pedicle-valve beak is slightly elevated and pointed. Ornament consists only of concentric growth lines. Many species of *Lingula* are found throughout the Paleozoic and are distinguished from each other by size, outline, length-to-width ratios, and the spacing of growth rings. *Lingula* is found in the Delaware Limestone, Prout Limestone, Silica Formation, and Chagrin and Cleveland Shale Members of the Ohio Shale. This genus ranges to the present and is found in Mississippian and Pennsylvanian rocks in Ohio.

Megastrophia Caster (figs. 16-6.23, 16-6.24) is a large, concavo-convex strophomenid brachiopod. The outline is subrectangular. Ornament consists of many fine ribs radiating from the beaks of both valves. The pseudodeltidium is entire and may have a median fold. There is no functional pedicle. The interior of the pedicle valve has a transversely oval muscle field and strong denticles along the wide hinge line. The interior of the brachial valve has a prominent bilobed cardinal process. *Megastrophia* differs from *Strophodonta* in the positioning of the diductor and adductor muscle scars in the pedicle-valve interior. In *Megastrophia*, the adductor scars are lateral to the diductors; in *Strophodonta*, the adductor scars are slightly in front and to the sides of the diductors. This difference is very difficult to see in all specimens, and erroneous identifications may occur. *Megastrophia* is found in the Lucas Dolomite, Columbus Limestone, and Silica Formation.

Mucrospirifer Grabau (figs. 16-8.1 to 16-8.3) is a medium-sized, biconvex, highly elliptical or transverse spiriferid brachiopod. The hinge line is very long, and the **cardinal extremities** are commonly mucronate. Ornament consists of numerous lateral ribs; the fold and sulcus are smooth. Strong growth lines crossing the ribs form a distinctive chevron-shaped ornamentation. The pedicle-valve interior has short dental plates. *Mucrospirifer* is found in the Columbus Limestone and in the Silica Formation.

Orbiculoidea D'Orbigny (figs. 16-6.3, 16-6.4) is a small to large acrotretid brachiopod that has a circular outline, a convex brachial valve, and a concave pedicle valve. The brachial-valve apex is near the center of the valve and pointed. Ornament consists of strong, evenly spaced, concentric growth lines. Very faint radial ornament may be visible. Fossils of this genus are commonly dark brown to black and flattened to a thin film. Species are distinguished by the amount of convexity, position of the apex, location and shape of the pedicle opening, and size. *Orbiculoidea* resembles *Oehlertella* (described in the section on Mississippian brachiopods). In *Orbiculoidea*, the pedicle opening is narrow and does not extend all the way to the posterior margin; in *Oehlertella* this opening is wider and does extend to the posterior margin of the valve. *Orbiculoidea* is found in the Delaware Limestone, Silica Formation, and Chagrin and Cleveland Shale Members. This genus ranges into the Mississippian and Pennsylvanian rocks of Ohio.

Paraspirifer Wedekind (figs. 16-8.7, 16-8.8) is a large, quadrate, equidimensional spiriferid brachiopod. The brachial valve is highly convex, the pedicle valve less so. Maximum width is at midlength. Ornament consists of numerous lateral ribs crossed by light growth lines, forming an indistinct chevron pattern. The fold is smooth, high, and broad, and the sulcus is smooth, wide, and deep. *Paraspirifer* is found in the Columbus Limestone and Silica Formation.

Petrocrania is found in the Silica Formation. This inarticulate brachiopod is described in the section on Ordovician brachiopods.

Pseudoatrypa Copper (figs. 16-7.16 to 16-7.18) is a medium-sized, biconvex or convexi-plane atrypid brachiopod. It has a flattened pedicle valve and subtriangular to subrectangular outline. Tubelike ribs ornament both valves. *Pseudoatrypa* also has a small pedicle beak, a tiny interarea, and deltidial plates. The brachial-valve interior has small dental sockets. *Pseudoatrypa* is found in the Silica Formation.

Rhipidomella Oehlert (figs. 16-6.11 to 16-6.13) is a medium-sized, biconvex to convexi-plane orthid brachiopod. It has a subcircular to subtriangular outline and an open delthyrium. Numerous strong ribs ornament both valves. Weak concentric growth lines are present and may be especially prominent near the anterior margin. A fold and sulcus are very rare, although, in some cases, a sulcus occurs in each valve. The interior of the pedicle valve has broad muscle scars, which are scalloped on the edges and completely enclose the adductor muscle scars. *Rhipidomella* is found in the Lucas Dolomite, Columbus Limestone, Delaware Limestone, Prout Limestone, Plum Brook Shale, and Silica Formation. This genus also is found in Mississippian and Pennsylvanian rocks of Ohio.

Schellwienella Thomas is a medium-sized, biconvex to resupinate strophomenid brachiopod. The semicircular outline is truncated by a straight hinge line. The pedicle valve is commonly less convex than the brachial valve. The valves are finely ribbed, and the pseudodeltidium is well-developed. The pedicle-valve interior has short dental plates, and the brachial-valve interior has a low cardinal process. *Schellwienella* is found in the Chagrin Shale Member and ranges into the Mississippian rocks of Ohio. A Mississippian specimen is illustrated in figure 16-8.11.

Schizophoria King (figs. 16-6.16 to 16-6.19) is a medium-sized to large orthid brachiopod. Its profile is biconvex in early growth stages, but alters to an inflated brachial valve and less convex or even resupinate pedicle valve in adult forms. The outline is elliptical and the straight hinge line is less than half the maximum width. There is a low brachial-valve fold and pedicle-valve sulcus. Ornament consists of radial ribs and concentric markings. The pedicle-valve interior has strong teeth and a heart-shaped muscle field. *Schizophoria* is homeomorphic with the Ordovician genera *Hebertella* (figs. 16-1.24 to 16-1.26) and *Schizophorella* Reed (not described), differing from them on the basis of internal structures in the brachial valve. *Schizophoria* is found in the Lucas Dolomite, Columbus Limestone, Plum Brook Shale, and Silica Formation and also in Mississippian and Pennsylvanian rocks in Ohio.

Sphenospira Cooper (figs. 16-8.4, 16-8.5) is a large, elliptical spiriferid brachiopod. The pedicle valve and interarea are pyramid shaped. The lateral slopes, fold, and sulcus have very fine ribs crossed by concentric growth lines. The pedicle-valve interior has long, divergent dental plates and a well-defined muscle scar between them. A prominent **delthyrial plate** and **stegidium** also are evident. *Sphenospira* is found in the Chagrin Shale Member.

Spinocyrtia Frederiks (fig. 16-7.23) is a large, biconvex spiriferid brachiopod that has an elliptical or transverse outline. The hinge line is equal to the maximum width. This genus has a high, linear interarea and a wide delthyrium. The pedicle-valve interarea has both horizontal and vertical striations (fine parallel lines) in the central area. Horizontal striations are present only in the marginal areas of the interarea. Numerous ribs ornament the flanks of both valves; the brachial-valve fold and pedicle-valve sulcus are smooth. There are very weak growth lines as well as very fine ribs, called capillae, that radiate from the beak areas. Small, teardrop-shaped granules appear at the summits of the capillae. These granules are very difficult to see and may be easily destroyed by rough handling of the specimens. *Spinocyrtia* is found in the Lucas Dolomite, Dundee Limestone, Columbus Limestone, Delaware Limestone, and Silica Formation. A similar Devonian brachiopod, *Mediospirifer* Bublichenko (not illustrated), also is known from the Silica Formation and is distinguished by the presence of globose granules at the ends of very fine, radial "threads."

Spinulicosta Nalivkin (figs. 16-7.1, 16-7.2), known as *Productella spinulicosta* in the older literature, is a small to medium-sized, concavo-convex strophomenid brachiopod that has a subcircular to elongate outline. The interareas are linear or absent. The pedicle-valve exterior has concentric growth lamellae, long curved spines on the flank and near the hinge, **spine ridges**, and faint ribbing. The brachial valve is dimpled and has concentric ornamentation and rare spines. *Spinulicosta* is found in the Lucas Dolomite, Dundee Limestone, Columbus Limestone, Delaware Limestone, Prout Limestone, and Silica Formation.

Strophodonta Hall (figs. 16-7.3 to 16-7.6), identified as *Stropheodonta* in the older literature, is a medium-sized to large, concavo-convex strophomenid brachiopod. The quadrate outline is truncated by a straight hinge line. It has a complete pseudodeltidium and fine ribbing on both valves. There are no dental plates. Strong muscle scars are present, as well as a bilobed cardinal process. *Strophodonta* may be confused with *Megastrophia* (figs. 16-6.23, 16-6.24) because of external similarities. Differences are discussed under the description of *Megastrophia*. *Strophodonta* is found in the Columbus Limestone, Delaware Limestone, Prout Limestone, Plum Brook Shale, and Silica Formation.

Trigonoglossa Dunbar & Condra is a small to medium-sized lingulid brachiopod that has a slightly convex profile and a triangular outline. Length is greater than width; greatest width is at the anterior third of the valve. *Trigonoglossa* has a pointed posterior end, rounded margins, and ornamentation of strong concentric growth lines. A Mississippian specimen of *Trigonoglossa* is illustrated in figure 16-8.6. This genus is distinguished from *Lingula* (figs. 16-6.1, 16-6.2) by its triangular outline and especially by the prominence of the growth lines. *Trigonoglossa* occurs in the Chagrin Shale Member and in Mississippian and Pennsylvanian rocks in Ohio.

Tropidoleptus Hall (figs. 16-6.5, 16-6.6) is a medium-sized orthid brachiopod that has a concavo-convex profile and subquadrate outline. Broad, rounded ribs radiate from the beaks of both valves. A narrow fold and sulcus are present. The delthyrium is open. The pedicle-valve interior has massive teeth, and the outer sides are strongly crenulated or notched, supported by strong dental plates. *Tropidoleptus* is found in the Dundee Formation, Plum Brook Shale, and Silica Formation.

MISSISSIPPIAN BRACHIOPODS

Ambocoelia is found in the Cuyahoga Formation and is described in the section on Devonian brachiopods.

Athyris (figs. 16-8.17, 16-8.18) is found in the Cuyahoga Formation. It is described in the section on Devonian brachiopods.

Chonetes Fischer de Waldheim (fig. 16-8.12) is a small, plano-convex or slightly concavo-convex strophomenid brachiopod. The semicircular outline is truncated by a wide, straight hinge line. Spines extend outward from the hinge line but commonly are not preserved. Very fine ribs ornament the shell surface. A pseudodeltidium is present. The brachial-valve interior has a bilobed cardinal process, an alveolus, and three or more septa diverging anteriorly from the alveolus. Many genera of chonetid brachiopods have been identified. Exteriors are similar, so they are commonly distinguished by internal characteristics such as the prominence of the median septum and alveolus and the size and number of septa in the brachial valve. *Chonetes* is found in the Logan Formation.

Composita is found in the Cuyahoga and Logan Formations and is described in the section on Devonian brachiopods.

Cyrtina is found in the Cuyahoga Formation and is described in the section on Devonian brachiopods.

Dictyoclostus Muir-Wood (figs. 16-8.13, 16-8.14) is a large strophomenid brachiopod that has a concavo-convex profile and a quadrate to subquadrate outline. The brachial valve is small and nestled inside a humped pedicle valve. The shell surface has concentric rugae and radiating ribs that form a reticulate pattern. The patch of fine, erect spines on the flanks distinguishes this genus from *Linoproductus*, which also is found in Mississippian rocks in Ohio, and *Antiquatonia*, a Pennsylvanian genus. A spine row is present near the hinge but may not be preserved. The brachial-valve interior has a massive cardinal process attached to the valve floor by a short **shaft**. *Dictyoclostus* is found in the Cuyahoga and Logan Formations.

Lingula is found in the Bedford Shale, Berea Sandstone, Sunbury Shale, and the Cuyahoga Formation. It is described in the section on Devonian brachiopods.

Linoproductus Chao is a medium-sized **geniculated** strophomenid brachiopod. The profile is plano-convex to slightly concavo-convex and the outline is subquadrate to subpentagonal. There is ribbing on both valves but it may be irregular. Rugae appear as broad wrinkles on the flanks and the **ears**. Scattered spines are present on the pedicle valve; one to two spine rows are at a high angle to the hinge. Spines are rare on the small brachial valve. The brachial-valve interior has a trilobed cardinal process, an alveolus, and short lateral ridges diverging from the hinge. Ribs on this genus are finer than those on *Dictyoclostus*, which also has a spine patch on the flanks. *Linoproductus* is found in the Cuyahoga and Logan Formations. This genus ranges into the Pennsylvanian rocks in Ohio. A Pennsylvanian specimen is illustrated in figures 16-9.17 and 16-9.18.

Oehlertella Hall & Clarke (figs. 16-8.9, 16-8.10) is a small, circular acrotretid brachiopod. The brachial valve is convex and the apex is located near the posterior margin. The pedicle valve is concave to slightly convex and has a large depressed area around the nearly parallel-sided pedicle opening, which extends to the posterior margin. The shell has regular concentric markings, which distinguish it from *Petrocrania*. The brachial-valve interior has lateral ridges diverging from an area near the apex; this feature, along with the nature of the pedicle opening, differentiates it from *Orbiculoidea*. *Oehlertella* is recorded from the Cuyahoga and Logan Formations. It also has been reported from Pennsylvanian rocks of Ohio.

Orbiculoidea is found in the Sunbury Shale, Cuyahoga Formation, and Logan Formation. It is described in the section on Devonian brachiopods.

Punctospirifer North (figs. 16-9.1 to 16-9.4) is a small to medium-sized, biconvex spiriferid brachiopod. It has an elliptical outline and a well-defined, nonribbed brachial-valve fold and pedicle-valve sulcus. The ribs on the flanks are strong and broad. Other features include strong growth lines and very small spinules. The shell itself has **punctae**; the perforations extend from the outer surface to the inner surface. *Punctospirifer* is found in the Cuyahoga and Logan Formations.

Rhipidomella is found in the Bedford Shale, Cuyahoga Formation, and Logan Formation. It is described in the section on Devonian brachiopods.

Rhynchopora King (figs. 16-8.15, 16-8.16) is a small to large, subpentagonal to subtriangular rhynchonellid brachiopod. It has a gently biconvex profile; the brachial valve is more convex than the pedicle valve. Angular ribs radiate across both valves. A brachial-valve fold and pedicle-valve sulcus originate at about midlength and end in a long tongue at the anterior margin. The greatest width is at midvalve. The prominent pedicle-valve beak incurves over a triangular delthyrium. The pedicle-valve interior has small teeth and short dental plates. The different species of *Rhynchopora* are distinguished on the basis of size, the number of ribs in the fold and sulcus, and the number of ribs on the lateral slopes. In comparison to other, similar genera, *Rhynchopora* generally has five to eight ribs in the sulcus. The Ordovician genus *Rhynchotrema* has fewer lateral ribs than *Rhynchopora* and only one rib in the pedicle-valve sulcus. *Rhynchopora* differs from the Devonian genus "*Camarotoechia*" by having an undivided **hinge plate** in the brachial-valve interior and angular, rather than rounded, ribs. *Rhynchopora* is found in the Cuyahoga and Logan Formations.

Schellwienella (fig. 16-8.11) is found in the Cuyahoga and Logan Formations. It is described in the section on Devonian brachiopods.

Schizophoria is found in the Cuyahoga Formation and is described in the section on Devonian brachiopods.

Spinulicosta is recorded from the Bedford Shale, Cuyahoga Formation, and Logan Formation. It is described in the section on Devonian brachiopods.

Syringothyris Winchell (figs. 16-9.5, 16-9.6) is a large, biconvex spiriferid brachiopod that has an elliptical outline. Ribs radiate across the lateral slopes of both valves; the fold and sulcus are not ribbed. The high, pyramid-shaped pedicle-valve interarea has fine horizontal and vertical surface markings. Very small pustules or bumps and very fine ribs intersect concentric growth lines, giving a textured appearance. The pedicle-valve interior has long dental plates, a delthyrial plate, and a **syrinx**. The brachial valve lacks a median septum. *Syringothyris* is similar to the Devonian genus *Sphenospira*, but is distinguished by the lack of ribs in the fold and sulcus. *Syringothyris* is found in the Bedford Shale, Cuyahoga Formation, and Logan Formation.

Trigonoglossa (fig. 16-8.6) is recorded from the Berea Sandstone and the Cuyahoga Formation. It is described in the section on Devonian brachiopods.

PENNSYLVANIAN BRACHIOPODS

Anthracospirifer Lane (figs. 16-9.22, 16-9.23) is a small to medium-sized spiriferid that has a biconvex profile and an elliptical outline. The hinge line is denticulate and equal to the greatest width. Strong, bifurcating lateral ribs are present, and the brachial-valve fold and pedicle-valve sulcus are ribbed. The pedicle-valve interior has dental plates. *Anthracospirifer* is found in the Poverty Run, Boggs, Lower Mercer, and Upper Mercer units of the Pottsville Group and in the Putnam Hill, Zaleski, and Vanport units of the Allegheny Group.

Antiquatonia Miloradovich (figs. 16-9.7 to 16-9.9) is a medium-sized strophomenid brachiopod that has a concavo-convex profile and an elongate, subrectangular outline. Both valves are geniculated. The greatest width is at the hinge. Ribs and rugae give a reticulate appearance at the posterior umbo. There are scattered spines on the valves and a spine row on the hinge. *Antiquatonia* also has a thick spine ridge on the lateral flanks of the pedicle valve, a feature which distinguishes it from the Mississippian genus *Dictyoclostus* and from *Linoproductus*. *Antiquatonia* is found in the Lowellville, Boggs, Lower Mercer, and Upper Mercer units of the Pottsville Group; in the Putnam Hill and Washingtonville units of the Allegheny Group; and in the Brush Creek, Cambridge, Ames, and Gaysport units of the Conemaugh Group.

Chonetinella Ramsbottom (figs. 16-9.13, 16-9.14) is a small, highly concavo-convex strophomenid brachiopod. A deep median pedicle-valve sulcus and a high brachial-valve fold give it a semicircular, bilobed outline. The greatest width is at the hinge. Ornament consists of numerous fine ribs bearing very fine spines. A row of spines extends at a low angle from the hinge. The brachial-valve interior has a small bilobed cardinal process, an alveolus, and prominent **brachial ridges**. *Chonetinella* is found in the Putnam Hill, Vanport, and Columbiana units of the Allegheny Group and in the Brush Creek, Cambridge, Portersville, and Ames units of the Conemaugh Group.

Composita (fig. 16-9.19) is found in the Boggs, Lower Mercer, and Upper Mercer units of the Pottsville Group; in the Putnam Hill, Zaleski, Vanport, Columbiana, and Washingtonville units of the Allegheny Group; and in the Brush Creek, Portersville, Ames, Gaysport, and Skelley units of the Conemaugh Group. It is described in the section on Devonian brachiopods.

Derbyia Waagen (figs. 16-9.10, 16-9.11) is a small to medium-sized, biconvex strophomenid brachiopod. The outline is subquadrate to subrectangular depending on the species. It has fine ribs and fine, closely spaced, concentric growth lines that cross the ribs. The pedicle valve is of variable depth. The delthyrium is closed off by a slightly convex plate of shell material. The pedicle-valve interior has a strong median septum, and the brachial-valve interior has a high, bilobed cardinal process. *Derbyia* is found in the Boggs and Lower Mercer units of the Pottsville Group; in the Putnam Hill, Zaleski, Vanport, Columbiana, and Washingtonville units of the Allegheny Group; and in the Portersville, Ames, and Skelley units of the Conemaugh Group.

Desmoinesia Hoare (fig. 16-9.12) is a small, moderately concavo-convex strophomenid brachiopod. The outline is subrectangular to subquadrate depending upon the species. The pedicle valve is ribbed and spines are scattered over the valve on the ribs, along the hinge, and on the flanks. The posterior of the pedicle valve is rugose. The brachial valve is more rugose than the pedicle valve but the ribbing is more obscure and there are fewer spines. *Desmoinesia* is found in the Lowellville, Boggs, Lower Mercer, and Upper Mercer units of the Pottsville Group and in the Putnam Hill, Vanport, Columbiana, and Washingtonville units of the Allegheny Group.

Juresania Frederiks (figs. 16-9.15, 16-9.16) is a medium-sized, concavo-convex strophomenid brachiopod that has a subquadrate outline and geniculated valves. The greatest width is toward the anterior margin. Both valves are rugose posteriorly and have concentric spine ridges as well as spines in rows over most of their surfaces. An attachment scar appears on the posterior end of the brachial valve. The brachial-valve interior has a bilobed cardinal process, an alveolus, and a breviseptum. *Juresania* is found in the Putnam Hill, Vanport, Columbiana, and Washingtonville units of the Allegheny Group and in the Brush Creek, Cambridge, Portersville, Ames, Gaysport, and Skelley units of the Conemaugh Group.

Lingula is found in the Lower Mercer unit of the Pottsville Group; in the Putnam Hill, Vanport, and Columbiana units of the Allegheny Group; and in the Brush Creek unit of the Conemaugh Group. It is described in the section on Devonian brachiopods.

Linoproductus (figs. 16-9.17, 16-9.18) is found in the Lowellville, Boggs, Lower Mercer, and Upper Mercer units of the Pottsville Group; in the Putnam Hill and Washingtonville units of the Allegheny Group; and in the Brush Creek, Cambridge, Portersville, Ames, Gaysport, and Skelley units of the Conemaugh Group. This genus is described in the section on Mississippian brachiopods.

Mesolobus Dunbar & Condra (figs. 16-9.20, 16-9.21) is a small, moderately concavo-convex strophomenid brachiopod that has a quadrate outline. The pedicle valve has a broad sulcus that has a fold within it. The exterior of both valves is generally smooth and covered with many spinules. The greatest width is at the hinge, where fine spines extend at a 30°-45° angle. A pseudodeltidium and a chilidium are present. The brachial-valve interior has a long median septum elevated and serrated toward the front and separated from the lobed cardinal process by an alveolus. Curved ridges or septa are present on either side of the median septum. *Mesolobus* is found in the Boggs, Lower Mercer, and Upper Mercer units of the Pottsville Group and in the Putnam Hill, Vanport, Columbiana, and Washingtonville units of the Allegheny Group.

Neospirifer Frederiks (figs. 16-9.24, 16-9.25) is a large, biconvex spiriferid brachiopod that has an elliptical outline. The greatest width is at the hinge line, which is denticulate. The lateral slopes have numerous ribs that are in bundles. There is a distinct, ribbed brachial-valve fold and pedicle-valve sulcus. The pedicle-valve interior has short dental plates. Adults of this genus are larger and have finer ribs than adults of *Anthracospirifer*. *Neospirifer* is found in the Lower Mercer and Upper Mercer units of the Pottsville Group; in the Putnam Hill, Vanport, and Columbiana units of the Allegheny Group; and in the Brush Creek, Cambridge, Portersville, Ames, Gaysport, and Skelley units of the Conemaugh Group.

Oehlertella is found in the Harrison and Sharon units of the Pottsville Group. It is described in the section on Mississippian brachiopods.

Orbiculoidea is recorded from the Quakertown and Lower Mercer units of the Pottsville Group; the Zaleski, Vanport, and Dorr Run units of the Allegheny Group; and the Brush Creek unit of the Conemaugh Group. It is described in the section on Devonian brachiopods.

Rhipidomella is found in the Poverty Run, Boggs, and Lower Mercer units of the Pottsville Group; in the Putnam Hill unit of the Allegheny Group; and in the Brush Creek, Cambridge, Ames, and Skelley units of the Conemaugh Group. It is described in the section on Devonian brachiopods.

Schizophoria is found in the Lower Mercer and Upper Mercer units of the Pottsville Group and in the Ames unit of the Conemaugh Group. This genus is described in the section on Devonian brachiopods.

Trigonoglossa is reported from the Lower Mercer unit of the Pottsville Group and from the Vanport and Columbiana units of the Allegheny Group. It is described in the section on Devonian brachiopods.

COLLECTING LOCALITIES

Permission must be obtained from the landowner before looking for fossils or collecting. Be especially careful if stopping on a highway to look at a road cut. It is illegal to stop along interstate highways.

Ordovician brachiopods are likely to be found wherever fossil-bearing Ordovician limestones or shales are exposed in southwestern Ohio and adjacent Indiana and Kentucky. Space does not permit a listing of many localities here. Only a few will be mentioned. Some of the references, particularly the Ohio Academy of Science and Ohio Intercollegiate field guides, may be difficult to locate.

A variety of Ordovician brachiopods can be collected from the emergency spillway of the dam at Caesar Creek State Park near Waynesville, Warren County. A permit must be obtained from the Visitors' Center before any specimens are collected. No tools are allowed, and any rock and fossil specimens that you collect must be smaller than the palm of your hand. There are recommended localities for collecting in Hueston Woods State Park in Butler and Preble Counties. Collecting is permitted at certain localities in the Miami Conservancy District, adjacent to the dams at Germantown, Taylorsville, and Englewood Reserves. No tools are allowed, or needed. Rangers are available to advise on where collecting is allowed. The railroad cut below the Wright Brothers' Memorial in Dayton, adjacent to Ohio Route 444 (Frank, 1969, p. 17-1 to 17-7) exposes a section through the Whitewater and Drakes Formations, capped by basal Silurian strata. A number of Ordovician localities are mentioned in Davis (1985) and in the booklet by Sisson and Sisson (1988). Meyer and others (1981) and Hay and others (1981) describe Ordovician localities in the Cincinnati and Ohio-Indiana area, respectively. A guidebook by Schumacher and others (1987) includes the Caesar Creek emergency spillway, and a guidebook by Shrake (1992) describes the rocks and fossils at Caesar Creek. An Ordovician section in Clermont County was described by Meyer and others (1985).

Finding localities in the Silurian from which to collect brachiopods may be more problematic. Road cuts, sections along creeks, abandoned quarries, and temporary exposures during excavation are likely to be the most accessible exposures. Road cuts through the Silurian are present in Adams County (see Kleffner and Ausich, 1988). In Greene County, Silurian rocks are exposed in John Bryan State Park (Horvath and Sparling, 1967; Ausich, 1987) and adjacent Glen Helen (Bernhagen and others, 1960; Anderson and others, 1989; Richard and Evers, 1990). However, both sites are protected and collecting is not permitted. A number of quarries in southwestern Ohio may grant permission to collect from loose blocks but not from high quarry faces, which can be extremely dangerous. See the Ohio Division of Geological Survey annual *Report on Ohio mineral industries* for a list of the active quarries in Ohio, including addresses, telephone numbers, geologic formations, and production. Again, permission must be obtained before entering private property, including active or abandoned quarries. Silurian and Ordovician localities are briefly discussed in La Rocque and Marple (1955).

Devonian localities in Ohio open to collecting are rare. Many of the rock units, including the Chagrin Shale Member, are exposed on private property or in city, state, or national parks and collecting is prohibited.

Mississippian brachiopods can be freely collected at Lodi City Park, in Lodi, Medina County. Pennsylvanian brachiopods can be collected from the Ames limestone at several road cuts on Ohio Route 78 in Noble County, just east of Caldwell. Another Ames limestone locality is Reed's Mill Hill in Jefferson County, at a road cut on U.S. Route 22 approximately 7 km (4.4 miles) west of the west corporation boundary of Steubenville. Again, be mindful of traffic when collecting along roadways and obtain permission before entering private property.

ACKNOWLEDGMENTS

The authors thank Richard A. Davis (College of Mount St. Joseph, Cincinnati) for permission to copy plates from *Cincinnati fossils*, L. R. M. Cocks (Natural History Museum, London) and John W. Murray (Department of Geology, University of Southampton, England) for assistance in obtaining permission to use photographs from the *Atlas of invertebrate macrofossils*, and to the Longman Group Limited for granting permission for their use. Dr. Davis (while Curator of Invertebrate Paleontology at the Cincinnati Museum of Natural History) and Erika Elswick (while Associate Director and Curator of Geology, Dayton Museum of Natural History) kindly assisted with access to collections in their care. We are grateful to Joseph T. Hannibal, who made the invertebrate paleontology collections at The Cleveland Museum of Natural History available; to Rodney M. Feldmann, who arranged access to the darkroom facilities of the Kent State University Department of Geology; and to Dan Flocke (Photography Department, The Cleveland Museum of Natural History), who printed photographs.

FIGURE 16-1.—Ordovician articulate brachiopods. Scale bars equal 1 cm. Scale bar A applies to figures 16-1.1 to 16-1.21 and 16-1.24 to 16-1.26; scale bar B applies to figures 16-1.22 and 16-1.23. All figures from Davis (1985) except figures 16-1.22 and 16-1.23. Information on stratigraphic occurrence for figures from Davis (1985) is as given in that publication; no locality or repository information is available.

1-5 *Platystrophia ponderosa* Foerste. **1**, brachial valve; **2**, pedicle valve; **3**, anterior view; **4**, posterior view; **5**, interior of pedicle valve. Fairview and Oregonia (= Arnheim) Formations.

6-9 *Platystrophia clarksvillensis* Foerste. **6**, brachial valve; **7**, pedicle valve; **8**, posterior view; **9**, anterior view. Waynesville and Liberty Formations.

10-12 *Platystrophia cypha* James. **10**, brachial valve; **11**, pedicle valve; **12**, anterior view. Grant Lake to Liberty Formations.

13-17 *Rafinesquina ponderosa* Hall. **13**, pedicle valve; **14**, interior of brachial valve showing bilobed cardinal process and muscle scars; **15**, interior of pedicle valve showing teeth and muscle scars; **16**, brachial valve on which the **epifaunal** inarticulate brachiopod *Petrocrania* is attached; **17**, pedicle valve. Cincinnatian Series.

18, 19 *Strophomena planoconvexa* Hall. **18**, brachial valve; **19**, interior of pedicle valve, showing muscle scars. Cincinnatian Series.

20, 21 *Strophomena concordensis* Foerste. **20**, brachial valve; **21**, interior of pedicle valve, showing muscle scars. Cincinnatian Series.

22, 23 *Strophomena planumbona* (Hall). **22**, brachial valve; **23**, pedicle valve. Liberty Formation, emergency spillway, Caesar Creek State Park, Warren County, Ohio; MS 1606.

24-26 *Hebertella occidentalis* (Hall). **24**, brachial valve; **25**, pedicle valve; **26**, pedicle-valve interior showing teeth and muscle scars. Cincinnatian Series.

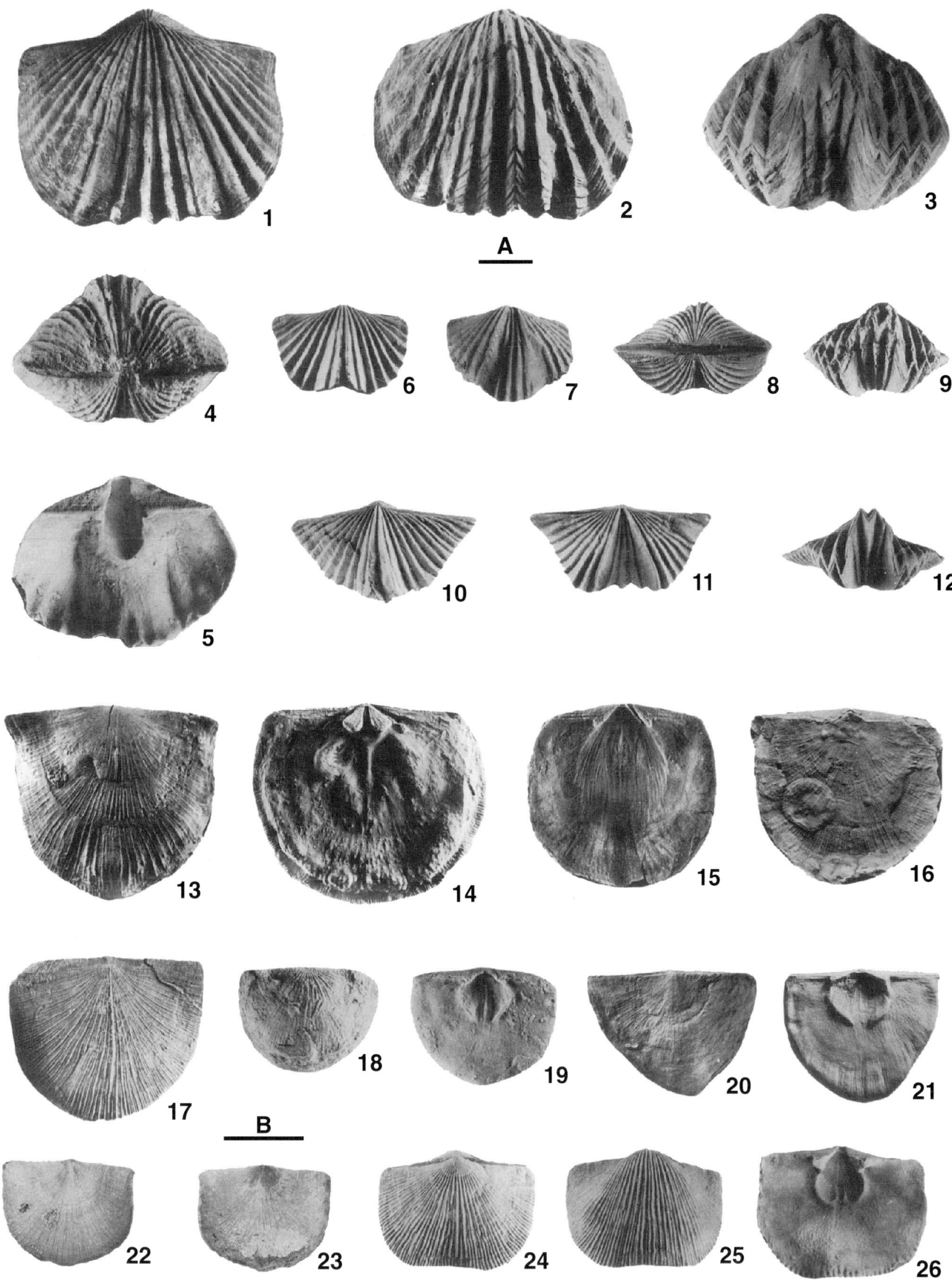
1
2
3
A
4
6
7
8
9
5
10
11
12
13
14
15
16
17
18
19
20
21
B
22
23
24
25
26

FIGURE 16-2.—Ordovician articulate and inarticulate brachiopods. Scale bars equal 1 cm. Scale bar A applies to figures 16-2.1 to 16-2.4 and 16-2.7 to 16-2.31; scale bar B applies to figures 16-2.5, 16-2.6, and 16-2.32 to 16-2.38. All figures from Davis (1985) except figures 16-2.5, 16-2.6, 16-2.14 to 16-2.16, and 16-2.32 to 16-2.38. Information on stratigraphic occurrence for figures from Davis (1985) is as given in that publication; no locality or repository information is available.

1-4 *Leptaena richmondensis* Foerste. Pedicle valves. Grant Lake to Drakes Formations.

5, 6 *Sowerbyella* sp. **5**, pedicle valve; **6**, brachial valve. Liberty Formation, emergency spillway, Caesar Creek State Park, Warren County, Ohio; MS 1607.

7-9 *Sowerbyella rugosa* (Meek). **7**, brachial valve; **8**, **9**, pedicle valves. Cincinnatian Series.

10 *Eoplectodonta clarksvillensis* (Foerste) (*Thaerodonta clarksvillensis* in Davis, 1985). Brachial valve. Waynesville and Liberty Formations.

11-13 *Plaesiomys subquadrata* (Hall). **11**, brachial valve; **12**, pedicle valve; **13**, interior of pedicle valve showing teeth and muscle scars. Cincinnatian Series.

14-16 *Holtedahlina sulcata* (de Verneuil). **14**, brachial valve; **15**, pedicle valve; **16**, anterior view. Liberty Formation, emergency spillway, Caesar Creek State Park, Warren County, Ohio; MS 1608.

17-20 *Glyptorthis insculpta* (Hall). **17**, brachial valve; **18**, pedicle valve; **19**, interior of brachial valve showing sockets, muscle scars, and ridgelike cardinal process along hinge line; **20**, interior of pedicle valve showing teeth, muscle scars, and pallial markings. Waynesville and basal Liberty Formations.

21, 22 *Plectorthis fissicosta* (Hall). **21**, brachial valve; **22**, pedicle valve. Cincinnatian Series.

23, 24 *Plectorthis plicatella* (Hall). **23**, pedicle valve; **24**, brachial valve. Cincinnatian Series.

25-28 *Dalmanella meeki* (Miller) (*Onniella meeki* in Davis, 1985). **25**, **28**, brachial valves; **26**, **27**, pedicle valves. Cincinnatian Series.

29, 30 *Dalmanella emacerata* Hall (*Onniella emacerata* in Davis, 1985). **29**, pedicle valve; **30**, brachial valve. Cincinnatian Series.

31 *Pseudolingula* sp. Cincinnatian Series.

32, 33 *Trematis millipunctata* Hall. **32**, brachial valve; **33**, pedicle valve showing pedicle opening. Cincinnatian Series, Morrow, Warren County, Ohio; CiMNH P227A (specimen has been renumbered).

34-36 *Zygospira modesta* (Say). **34**, brachial valve; **35**, pedicle valve; **36**, anterior view. Liberty Formation, emergency spillway, Caesar Creek State Park, Warren County, Ohio; MS 1609.

37 *Philhedra laelia* (Hall). On pedicle valve of *Rafinesquina* (photograph trimmed). Cincinnatian Series, Weisburg, Indiana; CiMNH P226.

38 *Petrocrania scabiosa* (Hall). On brachial valve of *Rafinesquina*. Cincinnatian Series, Weisburg, Indiana; CiMNH P225 (specimen has been renumbered).

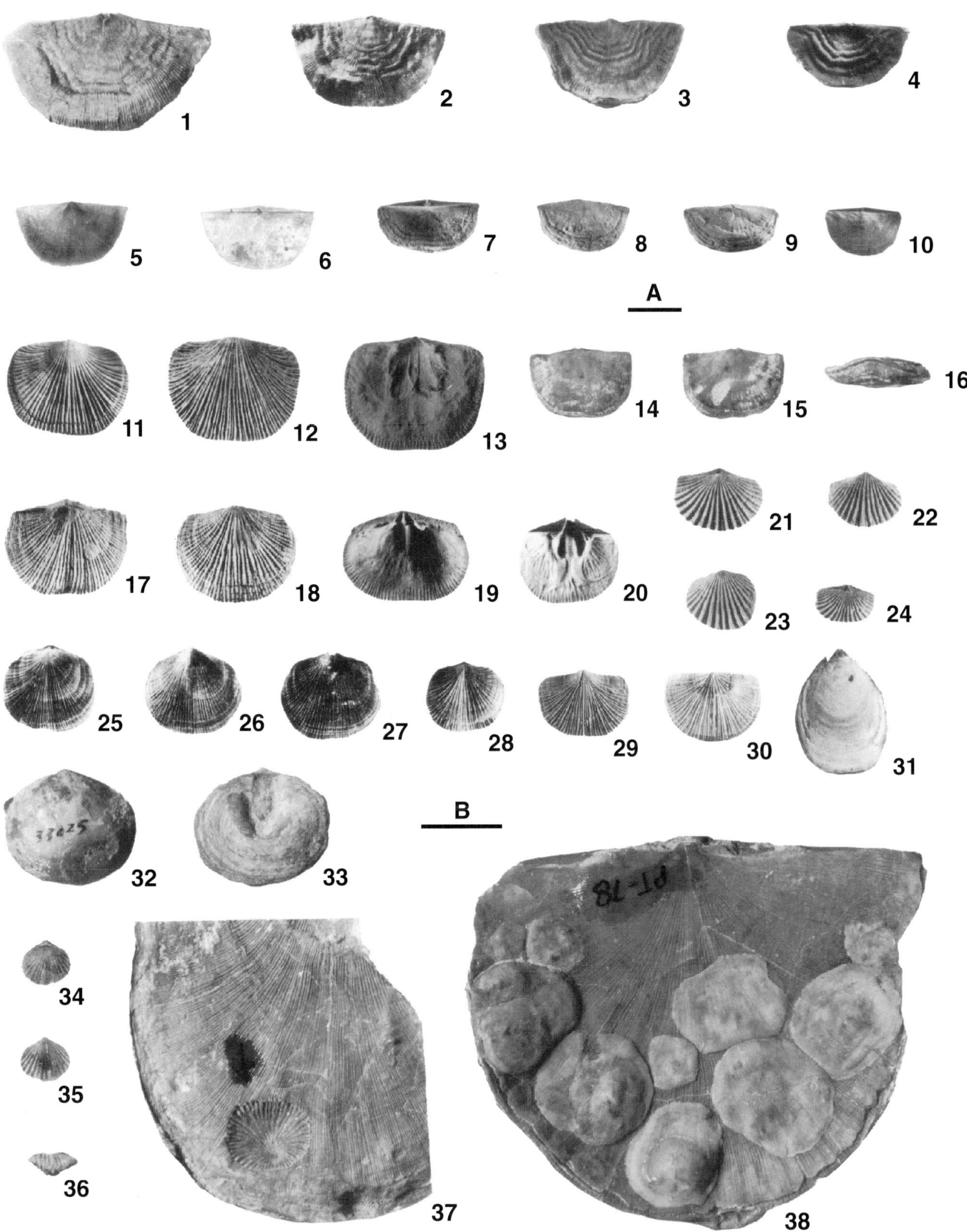
A
B

FIGURE 16-3.—Ordovician and Silurian brachiopods. Scale bars equal 1 cm. Scale bar A applies to figures 16-3.1 to 16-3.9; scale bar B applies to figures 16-3.10 to 16-3.17; scale bar C applies to figure 16-3.18. Figures 16-3.10 to 16-3.13 are from Davis (1985).

1-8 *Lepidocyclus capax* (Conrad). **1**, brachial valve; **2**, pedicle valve; **3**, profile; **4**, anterior view. MS 1611. **5**, brachial valve; **6**, pedicle valve; **7**, profile; **8**, anterior view. MS 1612. (Specimen numbers have been changed.) Whitewater Formation (Ordovician), emergency spillway, Caesar Creek State Park, Warren County, Ohio.

9 *Strophomena* sp. Interior of brachial valve showing bilobed cardinal process along hinge line and low septa perpendicular to hinge line. Valve is fractured. Waynesville-Liberty Formations (Ordovician), downstream from dam spillway at Cowan Lake, by Ohio Route 730, Clinton County, Ohio; MS 1613.

10-13 *Rhynchotrema dentatum* Hall. **10**, brachial valve; **11**, pedicle valve; **12**, profile; **13**, anterior view. Waynesville through Whitewater Formations (Ordovician). No locality or repository information available.

14-18 *Pentamerus oblongus* (Sowerby). **14**, posterior view, pedicle valve uppermost, showing trace of spondylium; brachial valve shows double septa; **15**, brachial valve; **16**, profile. *Pentamerus* zone near top of Springfield Dolomite (Silurian), 90 cm below base of Cedarville Dolomite, temporary exposure on Shiloh Springs Road, Dayton, Montgomery County, Ohio; MS 1610. **17**, growth lines and double septa visible on brachial valve; sediment is adhering to anterior commissure. Same unit and location as **14-16**; MS 1614. **18**, underside of a slab with several specimens in life position, posteriors embedded in sediment. Slab probably from a *Pentamerus* zone in the Springfield or Cedarville Dolomite (Silurian), Dayton area; University of Dayton collection, MS 1644.

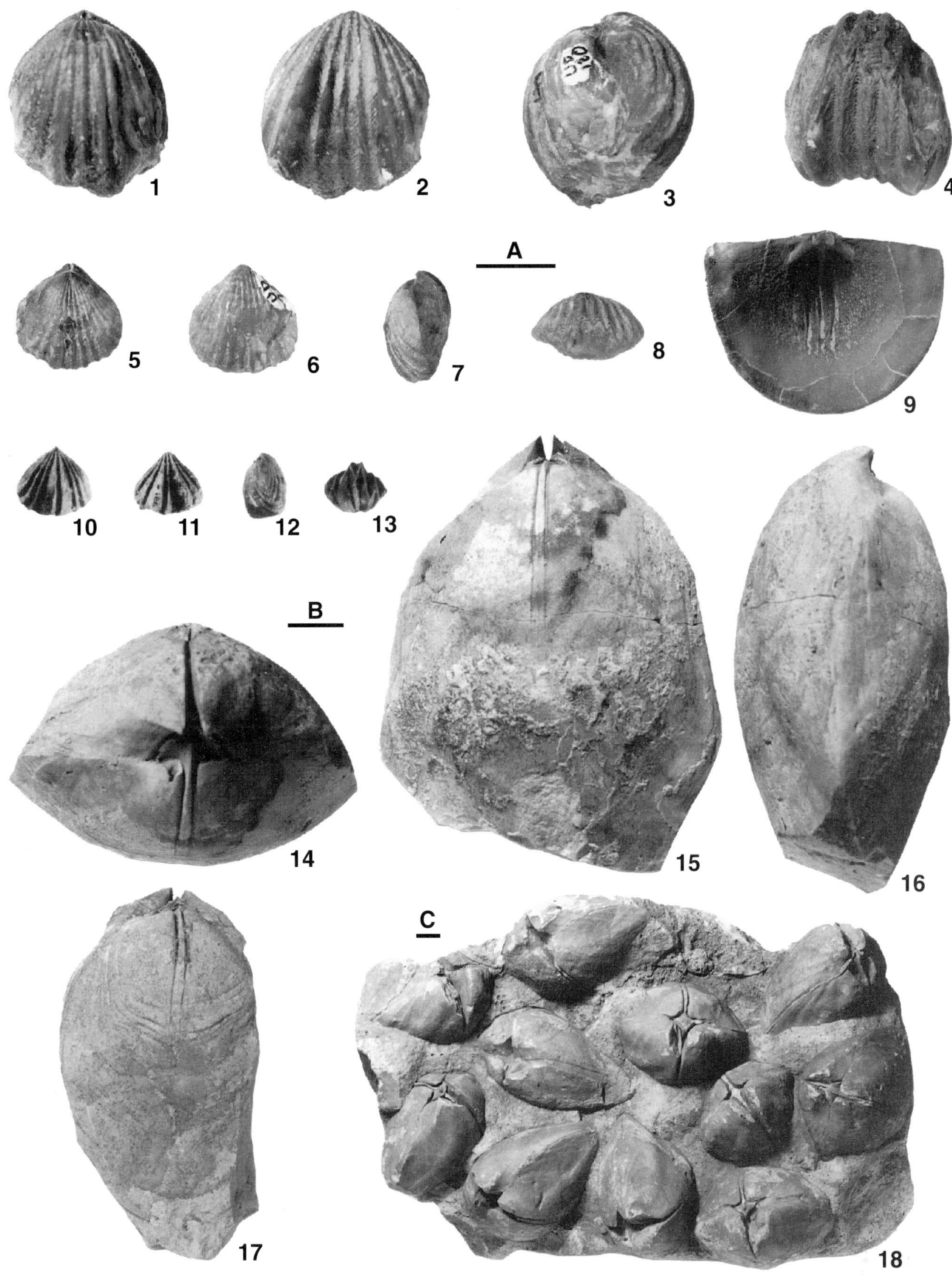
1
2
3
4
A
5
6
7
8
9
10
11
12
13
B
14
15
16
17
C
18

FIGURE 16-4.—Silurian brachiopods. Scale bar A equals 1 cm and applies to all figures. All figures from Murray (1985). No repository information available.

1	*Trimerella ohioensis* Meek. Mold of brachial-valve interior. Ottawa County, Ohio. No stratigraphic unit given.
2	*Trimerella lindstroemi* (Dall). Exterior of brachial valve. Interarea of pedicle valve showing pedicle opening at top. Klinteberg Limestone, Gotland, Sweden.
3, 4	*Strophonella euglypha* (Dalman). **3**, brachial-valve exterior; **4**, pedicle-valve interior. Wenlock Limestone, Dudley, West Midlands, England.
5, 6	*Kirkidium knighti* (Sowerby). **5**, brachial valve; **6**, profile. Aymestry Limestone, England.
7-9	*Cryptothyrella quadrangularis* (Foerste). **7**, brachial valve; **8**, profile; **9**, anterior view. "Indian Fields Formation," as given in Murray (probably Brassfield Formation), Dunkinsville, Adams County, Ohio.
10-12	*Eospirifer radiatus* (Sowerby). **10**, brachial valve; **11**, profile; **12**, anterior view. Wenlock Limestone, Dudley, West Midlands, England.
13-15	*Atrypa reticularis* (Linnaeus). **13**, brachial valve; **14**, profile; **15**, pedicle valve. Wenlock Limestone, Wenlock Edge, Shropshire, England.
16-18	*Gypidula galeata* (Dalman). **16**, brachial valve; **17**, pedicle valve; **18**, profile. Wenlock Limestone, Dudley, West Midlands, England.
19-21	*Sphaerirhynchia davidsoni* (M'Coy). **19**, brachial valve; **20**, anterior view; **21**, profile. Wenlock Limestone, Dudley, West Midlands, England.
22-24	*Stegerhynchus borealis* (Schlotheim). **22**, brachial valve; **23**, profile; **24**, anterior view. Wenlock Limestone, Wenlock Edge, Shropshire, England.
25-27	*Rhynchotreta cuneata* (Dalman). **25**, brachial valve; **26**, pedicle valve; **27**, profile. Wenlock Limestone, Dudley, West Midlands, England.

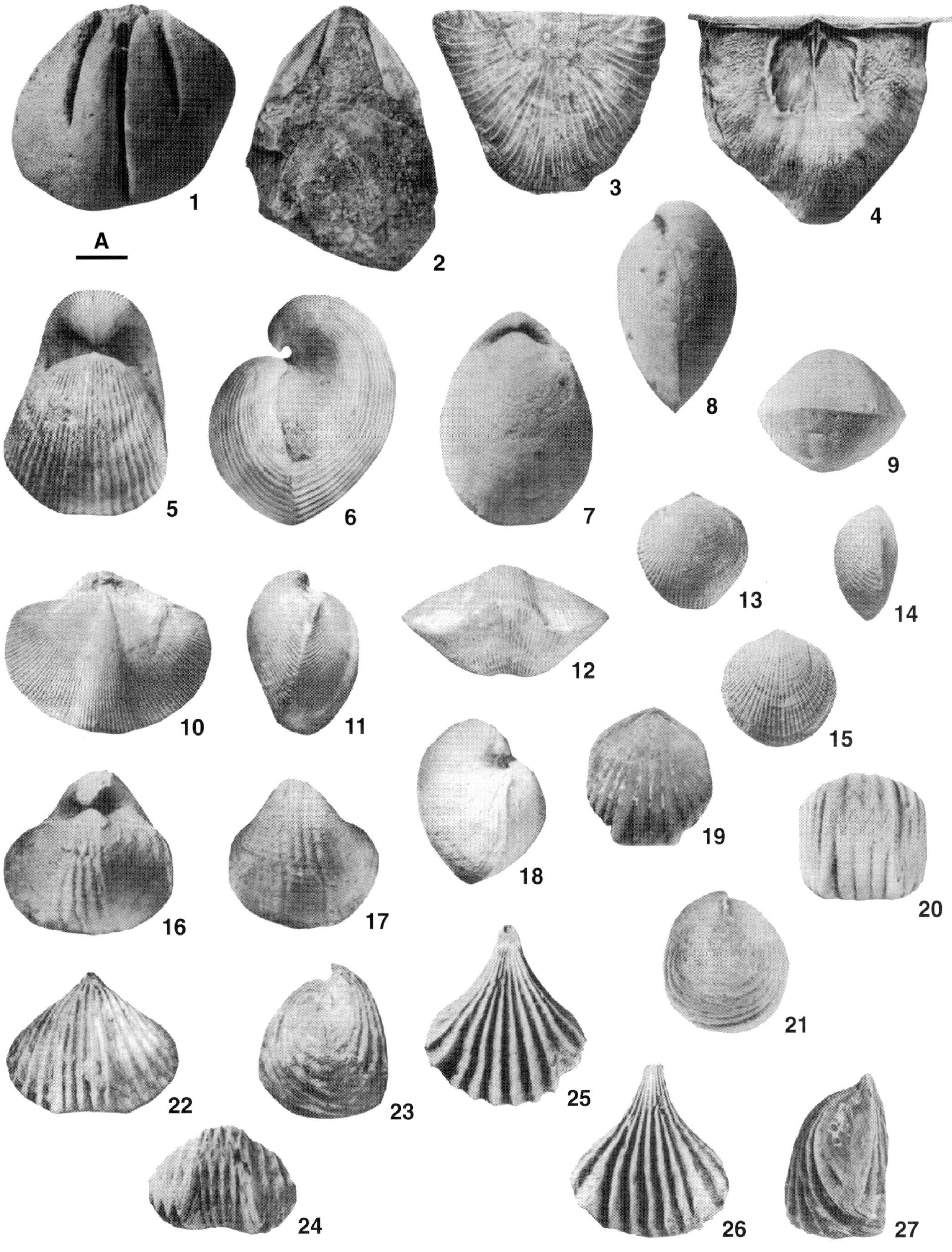
A
1
2
3
4
5
6
7
8
9
10
11
12
13
14
15
16
17
18
19
20
21
22
23
24
25
26
27

FIGURE 16-5.—Silurian brachiopods. Scale bars equal 1 cm. Scale bar A applies to figures 16-5.1 to 16-5.5; scale bar B applies to figure 16-5.6.

1-4 *Trimerella ohioensis* Meek. Internal mold. **1**, brachial valve; **2**, pedicle valve; **3**, profile (brachial valve on right); **4**, posterior view (pedicle valve on top). Niagaran Series, Woodville, Sandusky County, Ohio; CiMNH P223.

5 *Kirkidium* sp. Pedicle valve. Niagaran Series, Louisville, Kentucky; CiMNH P1708.

6 *Leptaena* sp. Pedicle valve showing concentric rugae and very fine ribbing; some sediment is adhering to anterior commissure. Springfield Dolomite, 11 cm below base of Cedarville Dolomite, temporary exposure on Shiloh Springs Road, Dayton, Montgomery County, Ohio; MS 1615.

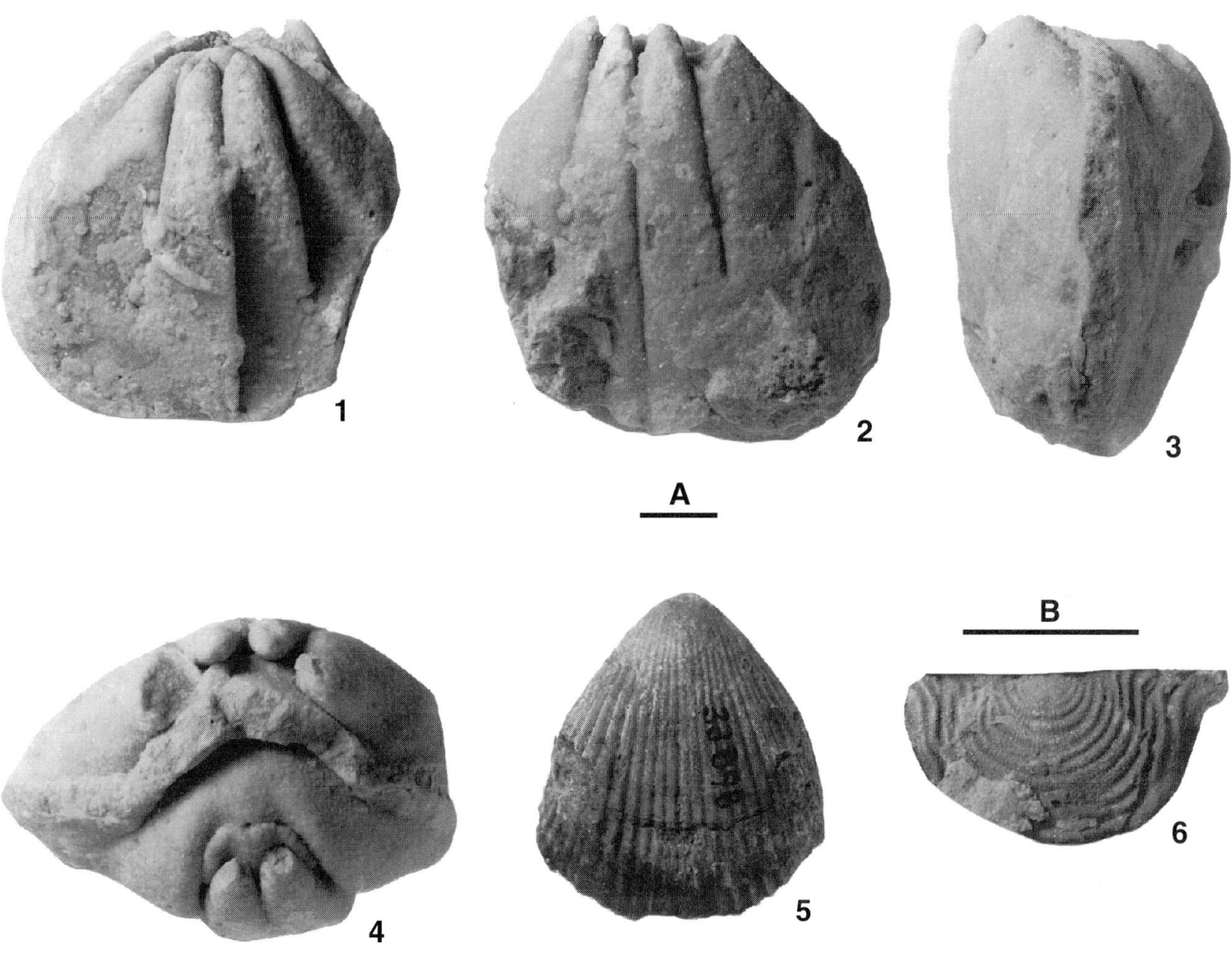
1
2
3
A
B
4
5
6

FIGURE 16-6.—Devonian brachiopods. Scale bars equal 1 cm. Scale bar A applies to figures 16-6.1, 16-6.2, 16-6.7 to 16-6.10, 16-6.13 to 16-6.15, 16-6.18, 16-6.19, 16-6.21, and 16-6.22; scale bar B applies to figures 16-6.3 to 16-6.6, 16-6.11, 16-6.12, 16-6.23, and 16-6.24; scale bar C applies to figures 16-6.16, 16-6.17, and 16-6.20.

1, 2	*Lingula arcta* Girty. Partially exfoliated pedicle valve in a concretion. Chagrin Shale Member of the Ohio Shale, Cleveland, Ohio; ClMNH 8402.
3, 4	*Orbiculoidea* sp. **3**, pedicle-valve interior. Mill Creek, Ohio; KSU 4899. **4**, internal mold of brachial valve. Cleveland, Ohio; ClMNH 8401. Both specimens from Chagrin Shale Member.
5, 6	*Tropidoleptus carinatus* (Conrad). Pedicle-valve (**5**) and brachial-valve (**6**) exteriors. Plum Brook Shale, Bloomingville, Erie County, Ohio; ClMNH 5375.
7-10	*Aulacella* sp. **7**, pedicle-valve interior; ClMNH 8406. **8**, brachial-valve interior; ClMNH 8409. **9**, **10**, brachial-valve exterior and posterior view of interarea; ClMNH 8408. All specimens from Chagrin Shale Member, Cleveland Ohio.
11, 12	*Rhipidomella vanuxemi* Hall. **11**, pedicle-valve exterior. Plum Brook Shale, Bloomingville, Erie County, Ohio; ClMNH 5402. **12**, profile. Silica Formation, Sylvania, Lucas County, Ohio; ClMNH 2853.
13	*Rhipidomella* sp. Brachial-valve interior. Silica Formation, Sylvania, Lucas County, Ohio; ClMNH 2963.
14, 15	*Devonochonetes scitulus* (Hall). Pedicle-valve (**14**) and brachial-valve (**15**) exteriors. Silica Formation, Sylvania, Lucas County, Ohio; ClMNH 8921.
16-19	*Schizophoria ferronensis* Imbrie. **16**, **17**, brachial-valve and pedicle-valve exteriors; ClMNH 4581. **18**, **19**, posterior view and profile; ClMNH 2974. Both specimens from Silica Formation, Sylvania, Lucas County, Ohio.
20-22	*Acanthatia* sp. **20**, internal mold of brachial valve showing elongate cleft representing breviseptum. Summit County, Ohio; ClMNH 8437. **21**, mold of pedicle-valve exterior and spines. Summit County, Ohio; ClMNH 8433. **22**, pedicle-valve exterior showing elongate hinge spines (arrow) and body spines. Cleveland, Ohio; ClMNH 8432. All specimens from Chagrin Shale Member.
23, 24	*Megastrophia concava* (Hall). **23**, pedicle-valve exterior; **24**, internal mold of brachial valve showing prominent cardinal process, muscle scars on a raised platform, and denticles on hinge line. Silica Formation, Sylvania, Lucas County, Ohio; ClMNH 5651.

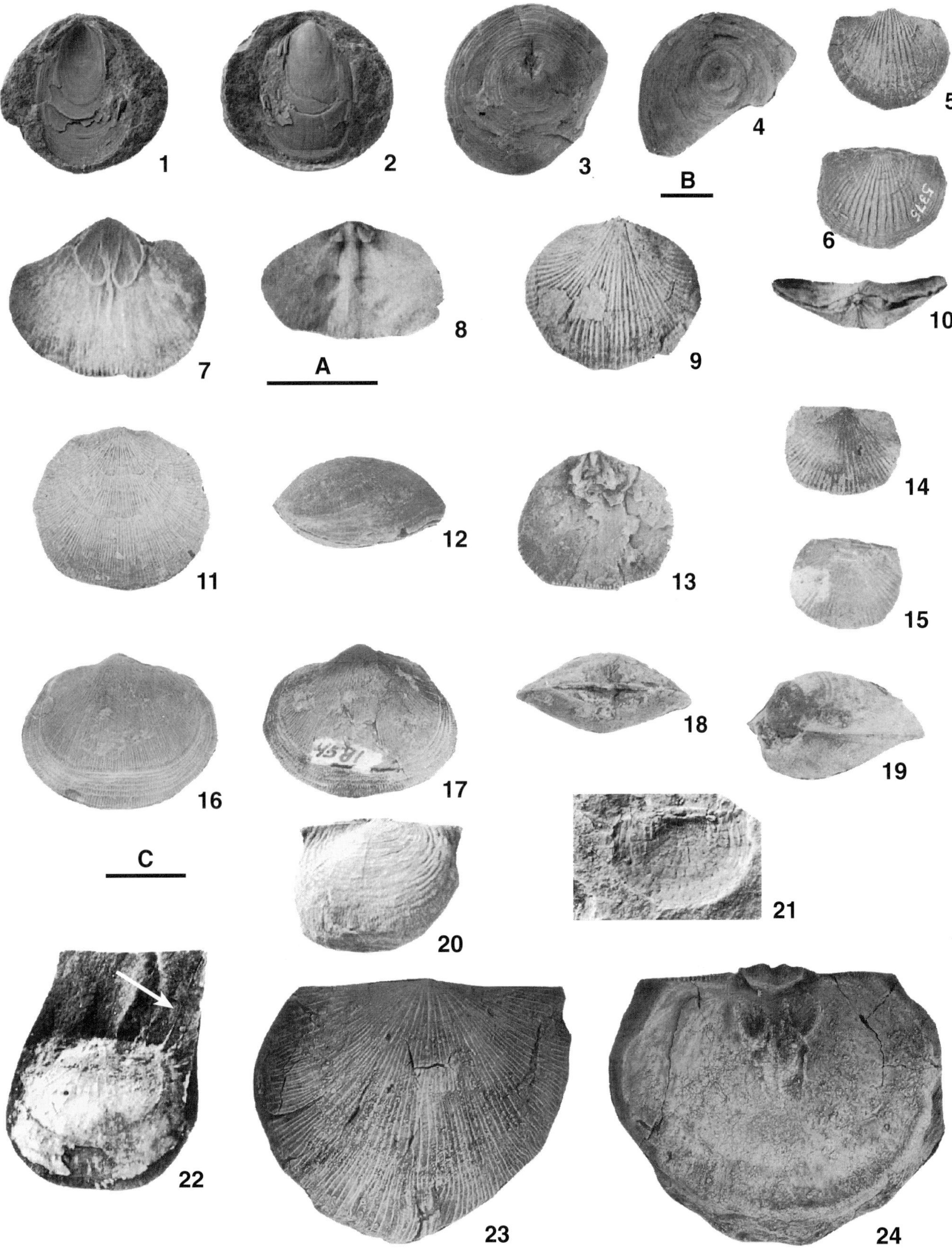
1
2
3
4
5
B
6
7
8
A
9
10
11
12
13
14
15
16
17
18
19
C
20
21
22
23
24

FIGURE 16-7.—Devonian brachiopods. Scale bars equal 1 cm. Scale bar A applies to figures 16-7.1 to 16-7.10, 16-7.16 to 16-7.18, 16-7.23, and 16-7.27 to 16-7.29; scale bar B applies to figures 16-7.11 to 16-7.15, 16-7.19 to 16-7.22, 16-7.24 to 16-7.26, and 16-7.30.

1, 2	*Spinulicosta spinulicosta* (Hall). Internal mold of brachial valve (**1**) and profile (**2**). Columbus Limestone, Sandusky, Erie County, Ohio; ClMNH 4191.
3-6	*Strophodonta "demissa"* (Conrad). **3**, Pedicle-valve exterior with epibionts (attached organisms). Plum Brook Shale, Bloomingville, Erie County, Ohio; ClMNH 5365. **4**, profile, and **5**, brachial-valve exterior showing pedicle-valve interarea. Silica Formation, Sylvania, Lucas County, Ohio; ClMNH 2849. **6**, brachial-valve interior showing bilobed cardinal process and muscle scars. Silica Formation, Sylvania, Lucas County, Ohio; ClMNH 2458.
7, 8	*"Camarotoechia"* sp. **7**, pedicle-valve exterior; **8**, anterior view. Columbus Limestone, Marblehead, Ottawa County, Ohio; ClMNH 5112.
9, 10	*Leiorhynchus kelloggi* Hall. **9**, brachial-valve exterior; **10**, anterior view. Prout Limestone, Bloomingville, Erie County, Ohio; ClMNH 5384.
11-15	*Centrorhynchus* sp. Internal molds of brachial valve (**11**) and pedicle valve (**12**), profile (**13**), and posterior (**14**) and anterior (**15**) views. Chagrin Shale Member of the Ohio Shale, Cleveland, Ohio; ClMNH 8441.
16-18	*Pseudoatrypa* **cf.** *P. devoniana* (Webster). **16**, **17**, brachial-valve and pedicle-valve exteriors; ClMNH 5662. **18**, pedicle-valve interior; ClMNH 8840. Both specimens from Silica Formation, Sylvania, Lucas County, Ohio.
19-22	*Ambocoelia "umbonata"* (Conrad). Pedicle-valve (**19**) and brachial-valve (**20**) exteriors, profile (**21**), and anterior view (**22**). Silica Formation, Sylvania, Lucas County, Ohio; ClMNH 5663.
23	*Spinocyrtia "euryteines"* (Owen). Pedicle-valve exterior. Silica Formation, Sylvania, Lucas County, Ohio; ClMNH 4559.
24	*Brevispirifer gregarius* (Clapp). Pedicle-valve exterior. Columbus Limestone, Delaware, Delaware County, Ohio; ClMNH 4601.
25, 26	*Cyrtina hamiltonensis* (Hall). **25**, anterior view; **26**, posterior view. Silica Formation, Sylvania, Lucas County, Ohio; ClMNH 5664.
27-30	*Cyrtospirifer leboeufensis* Greiner. **27**, pedicle-valve exterior. Summit County, Ohio; ClMNH 8481. **28**, mold of pedicle-valve interior. Cleveland, Ohio; ClMNH 8482. **29**, posterior view showing pedicle-valve interarea and a partially covered delthyrium. Summit County, Ohio; ClMNH 8184. **30**, pedicle-valve interior showing diverging dental plates. Summit County, Ohio; ClMNH 8487. All specimens from Chagrin Shale Member.

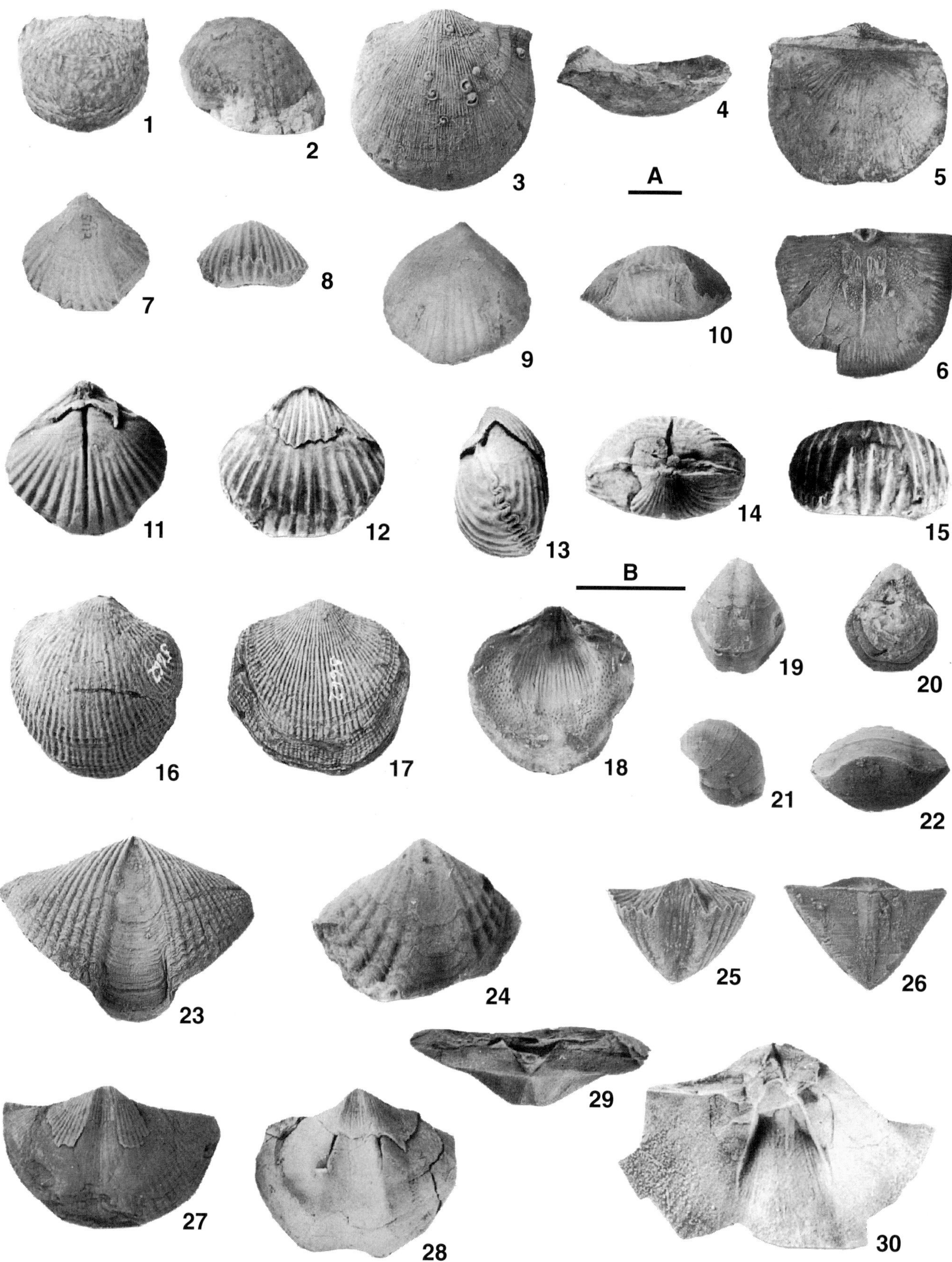
1
2
3
4
5
A
7
8
9
10
6
11
12
13
14
15
B
19
20
16
17
18
21
22
23
24
25
26
29
27
28
30

FIGURE 16-8.—Devonian and Mississippian brachiopods. Scale bars equal 1 cm. Scale bar A applies to figures 16-8.1 to 16-8.5, 16-8.7, 16-8.8, 16-8.11, and 16-8.13 to 16-8.18; scale bar B applies to figures 16-8.9 and 16-8.10; scale bar C applies to figures 16-8.6 and 16-8.12.

1-3 *Mucrospirifer mucronatus* (Conrad). Brachial-valve (**1**) and pedicle-valve (**2**) exteriors and posterior view (**3**). Silica Formation (Devonian), Sylvania, Lucas County, Ohio; ClMNH 2772.

4, 5 *Sphenospira alta* (Hall). **4**, brachial-valve exterior; ClMNH 8496. **5**, internal mold of pedicle-valve interarea and stegidium; ClMNH 8497. Both specimens from Chagrin Shale Member of the Ohio Shale (Devonian), Cleveland, Ohio.

6 *Trigonoglossa meeki* (Herrick). Sharpsville Sandstone Member of the Cuyahoga Formation (Mississippian), Parkman, Geauga County, Ohio; ClMNH 4712.

7, 8 *Paraspirifer bownockeri* (Stewart). **7**, brachial-valve exterior; **8**, anterior view. Silica Formation (Devonian), Sylvania, Lucas County, Ohio; ClMNH 5640.

9, 10 *Oehlertella pleurites* (Meek). **9**, brachial valve; **10**, pedicle valve. Meadville Shale Member of the Cuyahoga Formation (Mississippian), Kinsman, Trumbull County, Ohio; ClMNH 5915.

11 *Schellwienella inflata* (White & Whitfield). Mold of pedicle valve. Logan Formation (Mississippian), Bellville, Richland County, Ohio; ClMNH 6269.

12 *Chonetes tumidus* Herrick. Slab showing several specimens. Meadville Shale Member of the Cuyahoga Formation (Mississippian), Burbank, Wayne County, Ohio; ClMNH 5872.

13, 14 *Dictyoclostus sedaliensis* (Weller). **13**, pedicle-valve exterior; **14**, profile. Wooster Shale Member of the Cuyahoga Formation (Mississippian), Wooster, Wayne County, Ohio; ClMNH 5272.

15, 16 *Rhynchopora cuyahoga* Szmuc. **15**, internal mold of brachial valve showing a cleft representing median septum. **16**, internal mold of pedicle valve showing impressions of short dental plates around a distinct muscle scar. Meadville Shale Member of the Cuyahoga Formation (Mississippian), Lodi, Medina County, Ohio; ClMNH 5923.

17, 18 *Athyris lamellosa* (L'Éveillé). Internal molds of pedicle valve (**17**) and brachial valve (**18**). Portsmouth Shale Member of the Cuyahoga Formation (Mississippian), Sciotoville, Scioto County, Ohio; ClMNH 4872.

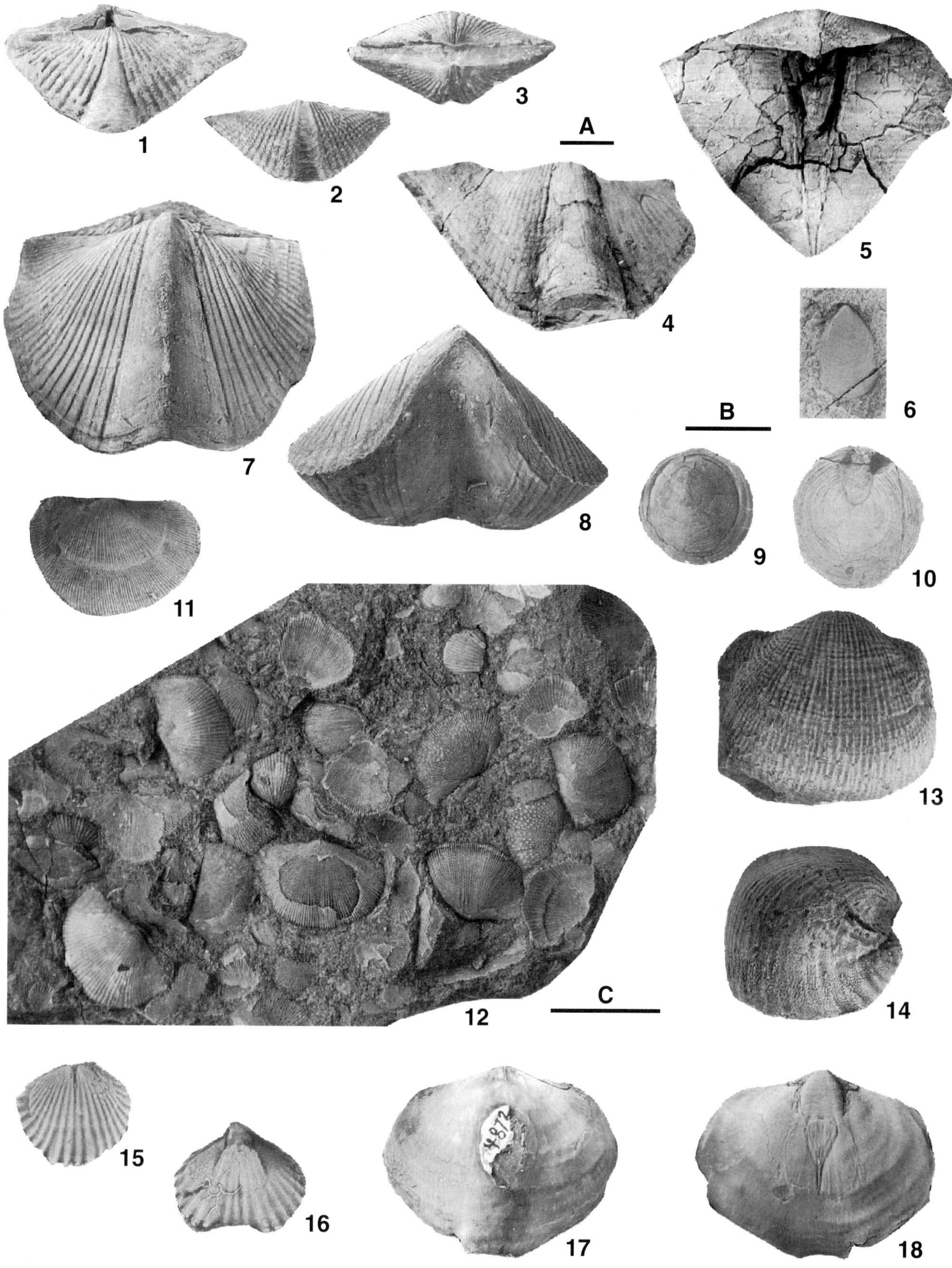
1
2
3
A
4
5
6
7
8
B
9
10
11
12
C
13
14
15
16
17
18

FIGURE 16-9.—Mississippian and Pennsylvanian brachiopods. Scale bars equal 1 cm. Scale bar A applies to figures 16-9.1 to 16-9.4; scale bar B applies to figures 16-9.5 to 16-9.12, 16-9.17 to 16-9.19, 16-9.24, and 16-9.25; scale bar C applies to figures 16-9.13, 16-9.14, 16-9.20, and 16-9.21; scale bar D applies to figures 16-9.15, 16-9.16, 16-9.22, and 16-9.23.

1-4 *Punctospirifer depressus* (Herrick). **1**, pedicle valve; **2**, brachial valve; **3**, posterior view; **4**, anterior view. Wooster Shale Member of the Cuyahoga Formation (Mississippian), Canaan, Wayne County, Ohio; ClMNH 4922.

5, 6 *Syringothyris typus* (Winchell). **5**, internal mold of brachial and pedicle valves. **6**, internal mold showing interarea, delthyrium, and delthyrial plate. Wooster Shale Member of the Cuyahoga Formation (Mississippian), Loudonville, Ashland County, Ohio; ClMNH 5945.

7 *Antiquatonia portlockiana quadratia* Sturgeon & Hoare. Brachial-valve interior showing brachial ridges. Lower Mercer limestone (Pottsville Group, Pennsylvanian), Mt. Pleasant, Hocking County, Ohio; ClMNH 4281.

8, 9 *Antiquatonia portlockiana* (Norwood & Pratten). **8**, pedicle-valve exterior; **9**, posterior view. Putnam Hill limestone (Allegheny Group, Pennsylvanian), North Canton, Stark County, Ohio; ClMNH 5023.

10, 11 *Derbyia crassa* (Meek & Hayden). Pedicle-valve (**10**) and brachial-valve (**11**) exteriors. Putnam Hill limestone (Allegheny Group, Pennsylvanian), Dover, Tuscarawas County, Ohio; ClMNH 4454.

12 *Desmoinesia muricatina* (Dunbar & Condra). Pedicle-valve exterior. Lowellville limestone (Pottsville Group, Pennsylvanian), Navarre, Stark County, Ohio; ClMNH 4968.

13, 14 *Chonetinella verneuiliana* (Norwood & Pratten). Pedicle-valve (**13**) and brachial-valve (**14**) exteriors. Cambridge limestone (Conemaugh Group, Pennsylvanian), Waterloo, Lawrence County, Ohio; ClMNH 5356.

15, 16 *Juresania nebrascensis* (Owen). **15**, pedicle-valve exterior; **16**, brachial-valve interior. Ames limestone (Conemaugh Group, Pennsylvanian), Middlebourne, Guernsey County, Ohio; ClMNH 4132.

17, 18 *Linoproductus echinatus* Hoare. Pedicle-valve (**17**) and brachial-valve (**18**) exteriors. Cambridge limestone (Conemaugh Group, Pennsylvanian), New Concord, Muskingum County, Ohio; ClMNH 5264.

19 *Composita subtilita* (Hall). Pedicle-valve exterior. Putnam Hill limestone (Allegheny Group, Pennsylvanian), North Canton, Stark County, Ohio; ClMNH 5022.

20 *Mesolobus mesolobus* (Norwood & Pratten). Pedicle-valve exterior showing hinge spines. Putnam Hill limestone (Allegheny Group, Pennsylvanian), Alliance, Stark County, Ohio; ClMNH 5137.

21 *Mesolobus striatus* Weller & McGehee. Brachial-valve interior. Note hinge spines. Putnam Hill limestone (Allegheny Group, Pennsylvanian), Alliance, Stark County, Ohio; ClMNH 5143.

22, 23 *Anthracospirifer occiduus* (Sadlick). Pedicle-valve (**22**) and brachial-valve (**23**) exteriors. Putnam Hill limestone (Allegheny Group, Pennsylvanian), North Canton, Stark County, Ohio; ClMNH 5461.

24, 25 *Neospirifer cameratus* (Morton). **24**, pedicle valve; **25**, posterior view. Putnam Hill limestone (Allegheny Group, Pennsylvanian), North Canton, Stark County, Ohio; ClMNH 4160.

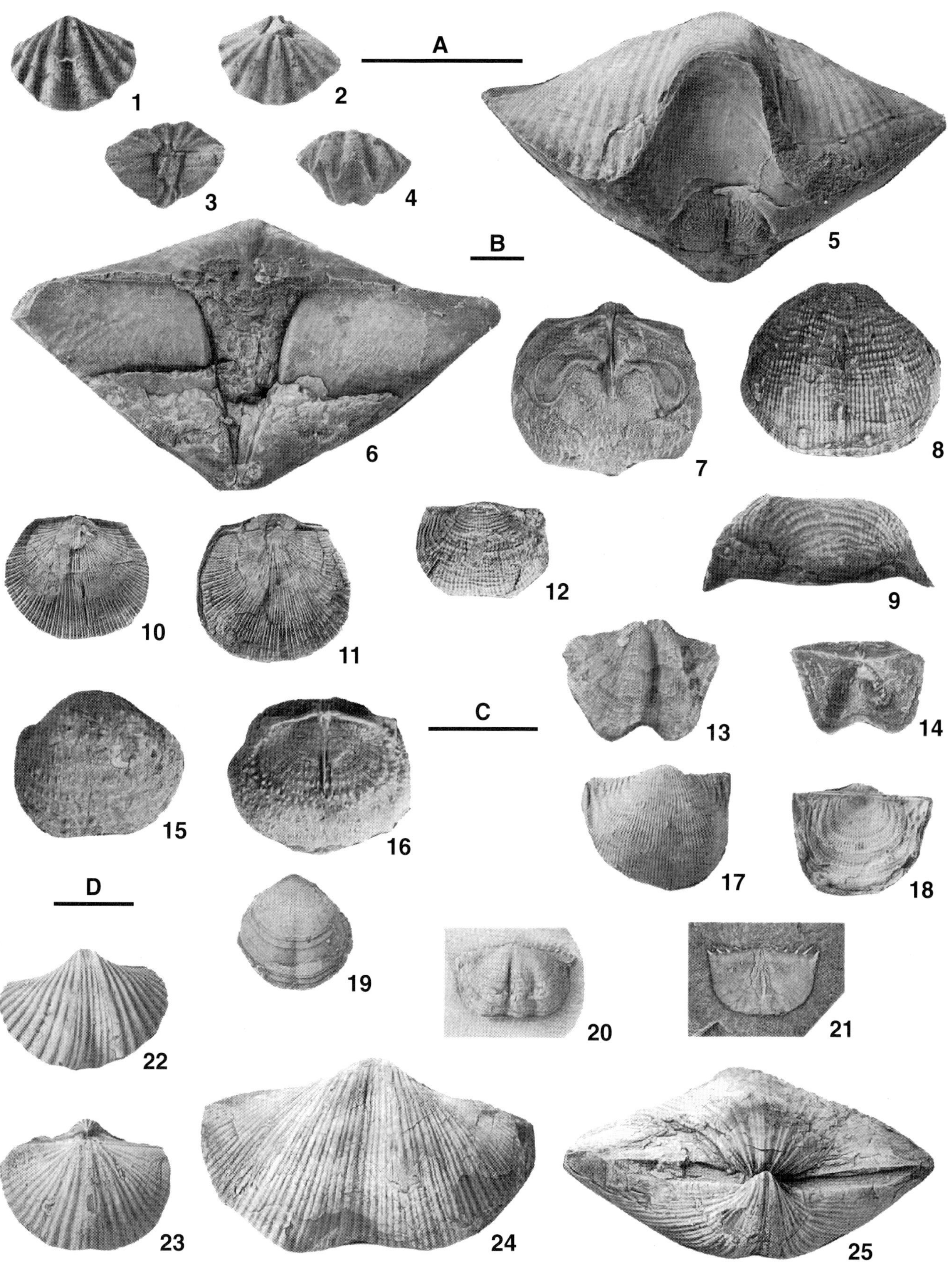
A
B
C
D
1
2
3
4
5
6
7
8
9
10
11
12
13
14
15
16
17
18
19
20
21
22
23
24
25

Chapter 17

PHYLUM ECHINODERMATA

by William I. Ausich

INTRODUCTION

The Echinodermata is a group of exclusively marine organisms that are represented by five living classes. The multiplated echinoderm skeleton is a body plan that has allowed for considerable architectural experimentation, accounting for the considerable class-level diversity of Paleozoic echinoderms (table 17-1). Many of these echinoderm classes are present in the Paleozoic strata of Ohio (table 17-2).

Although echinoderms may be very abundant fossils in Paleozoic rocks—fragments form the bulk of many limestones—they are only rarely preserved as complete fossil specimens, which is particularly frustrating when trying to collect them. Poor preservation results because each echinoderm individual is composed of tens to thousands of individual calcite plates in which each plate is a single crystal. These plates are cemented together or bound by muscular or ligamentary tissue on a live echinoderm. After death, the muscular and ligamentary tissue decomposes quickly, and an individual echinoderm disarticulates into component plates. For these reasons, nearly every completely preserved echinoderm specimen was buried alive as the result of a rapid burial event, such as a storm. Consequently, preservation of a complete echinoderm is a random event, and the likelihood of collecting a complete echinoderm is unpredictable.

TABLE 17-1.—SUBPHYLA AND CLASSES OF THE PHYLUM ECHINODERMATA

(* indicates classes discussed and illustrated)

Subphylum Homalozoa
- Class Stylophora
- Class Homoiostelea
- Class Homostelea
- Class Ctenocystoidea

Subphylum Blastozoa
- * Class Blastoidea
- * Class Rhombifera
- * Class Diploporita
- Class Eocrinoidea
- Class Parablastoidea
- Class Coronoidea

Subphylum Crinozoa
- * Class Crinoidea
- Class Paracrinoidea

Subphylum Asterozoa
- * Class Asteroidea
- * Class Ophiuroidea

Subphylum Echinozoa
- * Class Echinoidea
- Class Holothuroidea
- * Class Edrioasteroidea
- Class Ophiocistioidea
- Class Helicoplacoidea
- Class Cyclocystoidea
- Class Edrioblastoidea

Complete or nearly complete echinoderms are typically necessary for species identification. However, in some instances, single plates may be distinctive enough for identification. Although complete fossils are the principal interest in this chapter, distinctive echinoderm plates that are commonly encountered in Ohio also are treated.

The only common echinoderms in Ohio are crinoids, and crinoid **columnals** (pieces of the **column**) are the most abundant recognizable remains. Other echinoderms are typically rare in Ohio, but the more common of these rare fossils also will be discussed, including blastoids, rhombiferans, diploporans, asteroids, ophiuroids, echinoids, and edrioasteroids. Figures 1-27 to 1-32 in Chapter 1 illustrate the morphology of some echinoderms. General references on echinoderms include the *Treatise on Invertebrate Paleontology* volumes on echinoderms (Durham and others, 1966; Ubaghs and others, 1966, 1978; Beaver and others, 1967) and the summaries by Fay (1961) and Bell (1976). References on Ohio echinoderms include Kesling and Chilman (1975), Bell (1976), Warn and Strimple (1977), Schumacher and Ausich (1983), Davis (1985), Ausich (1985, 1986a, 1986b), and Meyer (1990).

CLASS CRINOIDEA

CRINOID MORPHOLOGY

Crinoids are composed of three basic parts: the column, the **aboral cup** or **calyx**, and the **arms** (figs. 17-1, 17-2). A paradox for the fossil collector is that crinoid identification is based nearly exclusively on the calyx and arms, but columnals are most commonly collected. As with all echinoderms, the complete terminology of the numerous plates is complex. However, general knowledge of the basic calyx and arm plates is sufficient to understand the primary crinoid types and to identify most common specimens.

Crinoids are generally regarded as having **pentameral symmetry**, which is a distinctive type of **bilateral symmetry**. The five **rays** (sets of repeating plates leading to the arms) are designated by letters; A is in the **anterior**, the **CD interray** (commonly visible as the widest space between rays) is in the **posterior**, and rays are lettered A through E counter-clockwise with the calyx viewed from the bottom at the column attachment.

The calyx is the portion of the crinoid animal above the column and below the position where the arms become freely moving appendages. The calyx may consist of only the aboral cup or the aboral cup and **fixed brachials** (arm plates joined together and incorporated into the calyx). The aboral cup is composed of two or three circlets of plates. All crinoids

TABLE 17-2.—STRATIGRAPHIC DISTRIBUTION[1] OF FOSSIL ECHINODERMS FROM OHIO

	Crinoidea	Paracrinoidea	Blastoidea	Rhombifera	Diploporita	Eocrinoidea	Parablastoidea	Coronoidea	Asteroidea	Ophiuroidea	Echinoidea	Holothuroidea	Edrioasteroidea	Ophiocistioidea	Helicoplacoidea	Cyclocystoidea	Edrioblastoidea	Stylophora	Homoiostelea	Homostelea	Ctenocystoidea
Permian	O	-	O	-	-	-	-	-	O	O	O	O	-	-	-	-	-	-	-	-	-
Pennsylvanian	X	-	O	-	-	-	-	-	O	O	X	O	O	-	-	-	-	O	-	-	-
Mississippian	X	-	X	-	-	-	-	-	O	X	O	O	O	O	-	-	-	O	-	-	-
Devonian	X	-	X	O	O	-	-	-	X	X	O	O	X	O	-	O	-	O	-	O	-
Silurian	X	O	X	X	X	O	-	X	X	O	O	O	O	O	-	O	-	O	-	O	-
Ordovician	X	O	O	X	O	O	O	O	X	X	O	O	X	?	-	X	O	X	-	O	-
Cambrian	-	-	-	-	-	O	-	O	-	-	-	-	O	-	O	O	-	O	O	O	O

[1]X, reported from Ohio; ?, questionably reported from Ohio; O, known elsewhere but not reported from Ohio; -, class not yet evolved or already extinct.

possess **radial plates** and **basal plates**. Crinoids with only radial and basal plates are called **monocyclic**, and in these crinoids the basal plates articulate to the column and the radial plates support the arms (figs. 17-1.1, 17-2.2). Other crinoids have three circlets of plates in the aboral cup—radial plates, basal plates, and a lower circlet of **infrabasal plates** (figs. 17-1.2, 17-2.1) situated between the column and the basal plates. Crinoids with two plate circlets beneath the radials are called **dicyclic**.

Where the arms are free-moving appendages above the radials, only the radials, basals (and infrabasals if present), and any extra plates in the CD interray form the plates of the aboral cup (fig. 17-1). Alternatively, where fixed brachials are present, the calyx is composed of more plates, including fixed brachials, extra plates (**interradials**) in all interrays (fig. 17-2), and a CD interray that typically has more plates than other interrays (fig. 17-2). A crinoid calyx typically has five radial plates, three or five basal plates, three or five infrabasal plates (if present), and a few to numerous fixed brachials and interradials (if present).

The **free arms** of crinoids are composed of a series of arm plates or **brachials**, which are either **uniserial** (a single row of brachials along the arm) or **biserial** (a double row of brachials along the arm). Free arms may be branched or unbranched.

The column or stalk of a crinoid is composed of a series of individual columnals, which may be identical or differentiated along the column length. Columnals have characteristic outlines, distinctive shapes of the **lumen** (central cavity), and other morphological details. The distal end of the column typically has a **holdfast**, which was used to anchor the animal to the substrate.

To identify a crinoid, the first thing to do is identify the plates. The key plates are the radial plates. Once these plates are identified, it is easy to determine whether the cup is monocyclic or dicyclic and whether there are fixed brachials or free arms directly above the radials. The radial plate can be identified as the last (lowest) plate in line with the arm plates (ray). Practically, it can be found by tracing down the ray beginning on a brachial. The radial plate is below the last horizontal suture crossed as you follow down a ray. The basal plates beneath the radial plates are offset laterally so that the suture between two basal plates is directly beneath a radial plate (figs. 17-1.2, 17-2.1). In drawings of crinoid plates, the radial plates are blackened to highlight these important plates.

CRINOID CLASSIFICATION

Common crinoids from Ohio belong to three subclasses, Camerata, Inadunata, and Flexibilia (table 17-3). The Camerata and Inadunata each have two common orders, which can be easily distinguished because for both subclasses one order is monocyclic and the other is dicyclic.

Camerate crinoids typically have many plates in a rigidly cemented calyx. A few to numerous fixed brachials and interradials are incorporated into the calyx between the radial plates and the position where the free arms begin (fig. 17-2). The **tegmen**, which covers the oral side of the calyx, also is rigidly sutured in most camerates.

Nearly all camerate crinoids have biserial brachials on the arms. Although uniserial arms are unusual among camerate crinoids in general, camerates with uniserial brachials are relatively common in Ordovician strata of Ohio and include *Gaurocrinus*, *Pycnocrinus*, and *Xenocrinus*. The subclass Camerata is subdivided into the order Diplobathrida, which has dicyclic cups, and the order Monobathrida, which has monocyclic cups (fig. 17-2).

The inadunates are a diverse group of crinoids that typically have a small aboral cup, compared with the calyx of camerates, because they lack fixed brachials and interradial plates (fig. 17-1). The free arms arise directly from the radial plates. Also in contrast to the camerates, the plates of the aboral cup of inadunates are less firmly joined, a rigid tegmen is lacking, and the arms are uniserial except for some Late Mississippian to Permian forms. The two primary orders of the subclass Inadunata are the monocyclic Disparida and the dicyclic Cladida (fig. 17-1).

The subclass Flexibilia can be difficult to identify because one type lacks interradial plates and fixed brachials and appears similar to cladid crinoids, and the other type has interradial plates and fixed brachials and may be easily confused with the camerates. Unifying features among flexible crinoids include the fact that all flexibles are dicyclic and have only three infrabasal plates. Also, calyx plates tend to be loosely sutured, the top portion of the arms curls inward, and sutures between brachials are commonly sinuous.

A key has been constructed only for Ordovician crinoid species. Crinoids of other ages and other types of echinoderms are described in the text.

TABLE 17-3.—CLASSIFICATION OF COMMON PALEOZOIC CRINOIDS

Class Crinoidea

- Subclass Camerata
  - Calyx typically composed of fixed brachials and interradials as well as plates of the aboral cup, so free arms begin at a position above the radial plates. Arms typically biserial (uniserial in some Ordovician forms). Tegmen forms rigid covering over the oral side of the organism. Calyx and tegmen rigidly cemented together.
  - Order Diplobathrida
    - Dicyclic aboral cup—radial, basal, and infrabasal plates.
  - Order Monobathrida
    - Monocyclic aboral cup—only radial and basal plates.
- Subclass Inadunata
  - Calyx typically composed of only the aboral cup, so free arms begin on the radial plates. Arms typically uniserial but may be biserial in Late Mississippian to Permian forms. Lacks a rigid tegmen. Aboral cup plates well cemented together.
  - Order Disparida
    - Monocyclic aboral cup—only radial and basal plates.
  - Order Cladida
    - Dicyclic aboral cup—radial, basal, and infrabasal plates.
- Subclass Flexibilia
  - Dicyclic aboral cup. Arms are free above the radial plates or numerous fixed brachials. Calyx plates loosely cemented together, and arms curl inward at the top. Three infrabasal plates.

KEY TO SOME ORDOVICIAN CRINOID SPECIES FROM OHIO

1A. Calyx (= aboral cup) small, no fixed brachials or interradials, arms free immediately above radial plates, not **pinnulate** (subclass Inadunata) 2

1B. Calyx large, fixed brachials and interradials, arms pinnulate and not free immediately above radial plates (subclass Camerata) 7

2A. Aboral cup composed of radial and basal plates only (order Disparida) 3

2B. Aboral cup composed of radial, basal, and infrabasal plates (order Cladida) 6

3A. Aboral cup has dominant sculpturing on plates, raised folds on plate centers, and depressions at triple plate junctions; arms have many branches, arm width gradually decreases with successive branching; columnals pentalobate (five lobed) .... *Iocrinus subcrassus* (figs. 17-3.5, 17-3.6, 17-4.8, 17-4.9)

3B. Aboral cup plates smooth, no sculpturing 4

4A. Aboral cup extremely small, cylindrical, very short, only slightly wider (if at all) than column; arms very slender; columnals distinctively circular and edges highly rounded .... *Cincinnaticrinus pentagonus* (figs. 17-3.3, 17-3.4, 17-4.7)

4B. Aboral cup small, conical shape gradually expands to be wider than column 5

5A. Ten primary arms have numerous very thin branches on every second brachial; columnals circular .... *Ectenocrinus simplex* (figs. 17-3.9, 17-3.10)

5B. Numerous arm branches, arm width gradually decreases with successive branching; **anal sac** spirally coiled; columnals subpentagonal .... *Ohiocrinus laxus* (fig. 17-3.11)

6A. Aboral cup has stellate (star-shaped) ridges on plates; arms separated laterally and have many branches, arm width decreases gradually with successive branching; brachials as wide as high; anal sac long, individual plates have fine stellate pattern of ridges; columnals pentalobate .... *Plicodendrocrinus casei* (figs. 17-3.7, 17-3.8)

6B. Aboral cup plates prominent, smooth, convex; arms abut laterally and have many branches, arm width decreases gradually with successive branching; brachials much wider than high; anal sac plates smooth; columnals circular .... *Cupulocrinus polydactylus* (figs. 17-3.1, 17-3.2)

7A. Calyx composed of fixed brachials, interradials, radials, and basals only (order Monobathrida) 8

7B. Calyx composed of fixed brachials, interradials, radials, basals, and infrabasals (order Diplobathrida); radials and fixed brachials dominant plates on calyx and much larger than interradial plates; interradial areas depressed; radial-plate circlet interrupted by extra plate in posterior; free arms branched; brachials uniserial; columnals pentagonal .... *Gaurocrinus nealli* (fig. 17-4.2)

8A. Radials and fixed brachials dominant plates on calyx and much larger than interradials; radial-plate circlet interrupted by extra plate in posterior; free arms not branched; columnals quadrangular .... *Xenocrinus baeri* (figs. 17-4.1, 17-4.10, 17-4.11)

8B. Radials, fixed brachials, and interradials approximately same size; prominent stellate ridges on all calyx plates; radial-plate circlet not interrupted (all plates in contact); free arms branched; columnals circular .... *Pycnocrinus dyeri* (fig. 17-4.3)

ORDOVICIAN ECHINODERMS

At least fragments of echinoderms are encountered at most Ordovician outcrops in southwestern Ohio. Crinoid columnals or **pluricolumnals** are most common, but crinoid **crowns** and edrioasteroids are found with regularity. Echinoderms commonly are preserved on the upper surface of limestone beds but also are present in shales. Because complete echinoderms are not readily preserved, where conditions were suitable for preservation of one individual, several may be present.

CRINOIDS

More than 25 species of crinoids are recognized from the Ordovician of Ohio; disparid inadunates and camerates are most commonly encountered. Important characteristics for distinguishing different Ordovician crinoids are the presence of fixed brachials and interradials, presence or absence of infrabasals, size and shape of the aboral cup, plating of the arms, plate sculpturing, and column shape.

Common Ordovician crinoids illustrated here include the diplobathrid *Gaurocrinus nealli* (Hall); the monobathrids *Pycnocrinus dyeri* (Meek) and *Xenocrinus baeri* (Meek); the disparids *Cincinnaticrinus pentagonus* (Ulrich), *Ectenocrinus simplex* (Hall), *Iocrinus subcrassus* (Meek & Worthen), and *Ohiocrinus laxus* (Hall); and the cladids *Cupulocrinus polydactylus* (Shumard) and *Plicodendrocrinus casei* (Meek).

In the diplobathrid *Gaurocrinus nealli* (fig. 17-4.2), the radials and fixed brachials are the dominant plates of the calyx, and the interradial plates are much smaller. Other distinguishing features of *Gaurocrinus nealli* include characteristic diplobathrid infrabasal plates, depressed interradial areas, a radial-plate circlet interrupted by an extra plate in the posterior (CD interray), branching free arms, and pentagonal columnals. The genus *Gaurocrinus* is known from the Late Ordovician of North America; in southwestern Ohio, *G. nealli* is present in the Waynesville and Liberty Formations.

The two illustrated monobathrids contrast in the size of the plates in the rays versus the interradial areas of the calyx. The calyx of *Pycnocrinus dyeri* (fig. 17-4.3) has plates of subequal size both in the rays and in the interradial areas. Stellate ridges characterize all calyx plates, and the circlet of radial plates is not interrupted in the posterior. Free arms branch and have uniserial brachials. Columnals are circular. This species typically has been assigned to the genus *Glyptocrinus* (for example, see Davis, 1985). However, because this species has 10 free arms that branch once immediately after the arms become free, it is more properly assigned to *Pycnocrinus* (see Ubaghs and others, 1978, p. T487). The genus *Pycnocrinus* is known from the Middle and Late Ordovician of North America. *Pycnocrinus dyeri* is present in the Grant Lake, Arnheim, and Waynesville Formations of southwestern Ohio.

Like *Gaurocrinus* and in contrast to *Pycnocrinus*, *Xenocrinus baeri* (fig. 17-4.1) has a bimodal size distribution between the radial plates and fixed brachials (large) and the interradial plates (much smaller); also the radial-plate circlet is interrupted by an extra plate in the posterior (CD interray). The free arms of *Xenocrinus* are uniserial and do not branch. The column (fig. 17-4.10) is composed of very distinctive quadrangular columnals (fig. 17-4.11). The genus *Xenocrinus* is present in both North America and Europe in Upper Ordovician strata. In southwestern Ohio, *Xenocrinus baeri* is present in the Liberty and Whitewater Formations.

Of the illustrated disparids, *Cincinnaticrinus pentagonus* (figs. 17-3.3, 17-3.4) is characterized by an extremely small, very short, cylindrical aboral cup that is typically not wider than the column. It has very slender arms. The column of *C. pentagonus* is quite distinctive; columnals are circular and have highly rounded edges (fig. 17-4.7). The genus *Cincinnaticrinus* is recognized throughout the Late Ordovician in eastern North America. *Cincinnaticrinus pentagonus* is known from Maysvillian and Richmondian strata of southwestern Ohio, including the Fairview, Grant Lake, Waynesville, and Liberty Formations. Another species of *Cincinnaticrinus*, *C. varibrachialis* Warn & Strimple, which is not illustrated here, is common in the Kope and Fairview Formations. The cemented holdfast for several disparids, including *Cincinnaticrinus*, has been called "*Lichenocrinus*" (figs. 17-4.4 to 17-4.6; discussed below).

Ectenocrinus simplex (figs. 17-3.9, 17-3.10) has a small, smooth, conical aboral cup and only 10 primary arms. The 10 arms bear very slender branches (ramules) on every second brachial. Columnals are circular. The genus *Ectenocrinus* is recognized throughout the Middle and Late Ordovician of North America; *E. simplex* is known from the Kope and Fairview Formations of southwestern Ohio. The cemented holdfast called "*Lichenocrinus*" (figs. 17-4.4 to 17-4.6) also belongs to *Ectenocrinus*.

Iocrinus subcrassus (figs. 17-3.5, 17-3.6) is characterized by a conical aboral cup and dominant ridges and depressions on the cup plates. The arms branch many times and arm width decreases gradually. A distinctively plated anal sac is present. The column is composed of pentalobate (five-lobed) columnals that have a strongly pentalobate pattern on the facets of adjoining columnals (figs. 17-4.8, 17-4.9). The genus *Iocrinus* is recognized throughout Middle and Upper Ordovician strata from North America and in western Europe. *Iocrinus subcrassus* is known from nearly every formation in the Late Ordovician of southwestern Ohio.

Ohiocrinus laxus (fig. 17-3.11) is an extremely rare crinoid characterized by a spirally coiled anal sac. It has a small, smooth, conical aboral cup and arms that branch many times; arm width decreases gradually. Columnals are subpentagonal. The genus *Ohiocrinus* is recognized throughout Maysvillian strata of Ohio and Indiana. In southwestern Ohio, *O. laxus* is known from the Fairview Formation.

Of the illustrated cladids, *Cupulocrinus polydactylus* (figs. 17-3.1, 17-3.2) has large, prominent infrabasals and basals. Radials are smooth and convex. The arms abut laterally and have very short brachials, which decrease gradually in width with successive branching. The anal sac has smooth plates. Columnals are circular. The genus *Cupulocrinus* is recognized throughout Middle and Upper Ordovician strata of North America. *Cupulocrinus polydactylus* is recognized from the Waynesville, Liberty, and Whitewater Formations of southwestern Ohio.

Plicodendrocrinus casei (formerly *Dendrocrinus casei*; see Brower, 1995) is characterized by a conical aboral cup and dominant plate sculpturing. Aboral cup plates have a distinctive stellate (star-shaped) pattern of ridges (figs. 17-3.7, 17-3.8). *Plicodendrocrinus casei* has a large, multiplated anal sac (fig. 17-3.8); each sac plate has fine stellate ridges. Although inflated during life, the fossilized anal sac commonly is flattened and may be detached from the cup. The arms of *P. casei* are laterally separated, branch many times, and decrease in width gradually with successive branching. Brachials are as high as wide. Columnals are pentalobate. *Plicodendrocrinus* is known from the Middle to Late Ordovician of North America and Europe. *Plicodendrocrinus casei* has been reported from the Waynesville and Liberty Formations of southwestern Ohio.

As mentioned above, disarticulated crinoid columnals are quite common, and a few Ordovician crinoid columnals are distinctive. These include the strongly pentalobate columnals of *Iocrinus subcrassus* (figs. 17-4.8, 17-4.9); the circular, laterally rounded columnals of *Cincinnaticrinus* that have a strongly pentalobate pattern on the facet (fig. 17-4.7); and the quadrangular columnals of *Xenocrinus* (fig. 17-4.10, 17-4.11). The four-sided columnal of *Xenocrinus* is very unusual for echinoderms, which as a group are typified by pentameral symmetry.

The unique multiplated holdfast given the name "*Lichenocrinus*" in the older literature is another relatively common crinoid fossil (figs. 17-4.4 to 17-4.6). Despite the fact that generic and specific names have been assigned to these structures, the name is properly placed in quotations because it is not a valid biological name. Rather, it is a name for a type of holdfast belonging to several crinoids, including *Ectenocrinus* and *Cincinnaticrinus*. "*Lichenocrinus*" structures range in size from a few millimeters to more than 10 mm and may be either smooth or very **nodose**. They are found either on shells or on **hardgrounds** (limestone beds that lithified soon after deposition).

OTHER ECHINODERMS

Under normal circumstances, edrioasteroids are quite rare; however, they are common locally in southwestern Ohio, especially in Maysvillian strata. Edrioasteroid fossils typically are cemented to a hard surface, such as a *Rafinesquina* brachiopod shell. The most spectacular occurrences of Ordovician edrioasteroids are on buried, in situ sea floors. In such cases, edrioasteroids typically are attached to brachiopods and occur in densities as high as 30 per square meter. Approximately nine species of Late Ordovician edrioasteroids are present in Ohio, but only two are illustrated here. *Isorophus cincinnatiensis* (Roemer) (fig. 17-5.4) can be distinguished by having a double biseries of plates along the **ambulacra** and four primary **oral plates**. The genus *Isorophus* is known from Middle and Upper Ordovician strata in Ohio and adjacent states; in Ohio, *I. cincinnatiensis* has been reported from the Fairview, Grant Lake, and Arnheim Formations. *Carneyella pilea* (Hall) (figs. 17-5.1, 17-5.2) is characterized by a single biseries of plates along the ambulacra and three primary orals. The genus *Carneyella* is known from Middle and Upper Ordovician strata of eastern North America. In southwestern Ohio, *Carneyella pilea* is present in the Fairview, Grant Lake, Waynesville, and Whitewater Formations.

Although asteroids (starfishes) are extremely rare, several species have been described. Paleozoic asteroids look superficially similar to living asteroids, but the plating of the arms is very different from their modern counterparts. Asteroids are known from throughout the Late Ordovician in Ohio; two are illustrated here. *Salteraster grandis* (Meek) (fig. 17-4.13) is characterized by long arms and a very small central **disk**. The arms are narrow and are composed of numerous large plates. The genus *Salteraster* is known from the Middle and Late Ordovician and Silurian worldwide. In Ohio, *Salteraster grandis* is present in Richmondian strata. *Petraster speciosus* (Miller & Dyer) (fig. 17-4.12) is characterized by a very broad disk that is poorly differentiated from the relatively short arms and by a marginal rim of large plates. The genus *Petraster* is known from the Late Ordovician and Silurian worldwide. In Ohio, *Petraster speciosus* is present in both Maysvillian and Richmondian strata.

Very rare Ordovician echinoderms also known from Ohio but not described here include rhombiferans, cyclocystoids, stylophorans, and, questionably, ophiocistioids (table 17-2). Several classes of echinoderms, such as the echinoids and paracrinoids, are known from Ordovician strata elsewhere but have not been recognized from Ohio (table 17-2).

SILURIAN ECHINODERMS

Echinoderms form the bulk of many Silurian limestones and dolomites in Ohio. Unfortunately, echinoderm remains are principally disarticulated columnals of crinoids and blastozoans. For example, at many outcrops of the Brassfield Formation, the rock is composed entirely of disarticulated crinoid columnals, but no complete aboral cups or crowns are found. In limestones and shales of the Osgood Shale and the Brassfield Formation, echinoderms may be preserved with good calcite preservation. However, in Silurian dolomites, echinoderms (including crinoids, blastoids, diploporans, and rhombiferans) are typically preserved as **internal** and **external molds** that may be difficult to identify.

Echinoderm molds and **casts** in Silurian dolomites are difficult to collect and identify, but they are as valuable scientifically as more perfectly preserved specimens. Because of this preservational problem, the very important role of echinoderms on the vast reefs that grew throughout the

Great Lakes region during the Silurian has not been fully appreciated.

CRINOIDS

The Lower Silurian Brassfield Formation in Greene, Montgomery, and Adams Counties has yielded an important crinoid fauna that contains more than 35 species. The most abundant Brassfield crinoid is the diplobathrid camerate *Stereoaster squamosus* Foerste (figs. 17-5.3, 17-5.5, 17-5.10), which has a large, multiplated, bowl-shaped calyx. The calyx plates have a series of fine stellate ridges. *Stereoaster squamosus* has branched free arms (fig. 17-5.3) and a complexly plated, dendritic (branching) holdfast (fig. 17-5.10). Holdfasts of *S. squamosus* commonly occur in clusters of six or more. *Stereoaster* is known only from the Brassfield Formation of Greene County, Ohio.

Phrygilocrinus batheri Ausich (fig. 17-5.13) is the most common monobathrid camerate in the Brassfield. It has a cone-shaped calyx that has no more than 14 fixed brachials per ray and typically one or two fixed plates in the interrays. *Phrygilocrinus* also is known only from the Brassfield Formation of Greene County, Ohio.

Two inadunate crinoids from the Brassfield Formation are illustrated. The disparid *Stibarocrinus centervillensis* (Foerste) (fig. 17-5.12) is a member of a unique group of crinoids, the calceocrinids. Instead of being erect and having pentameral symmetry, calceocrinids lived with the column lying along the sea floor and had a strongly bilaterally symmetrical crown. The crescent-shaped basal-plate circlet was attached along a movable hinge to the trapezoidal-shaped radial-plate circlet. *Stibarocrinus centervillensis* has a subcylindrical aboral cup, four basal plates, and three robust arms with robust branches. *Stibarocrinus* is known only from the Brassfield Formation of Montgomery and Greene Counties, Ohio.

The cladid *Euspirocrinus heliktos* Ausich (fig. 17-5.8) has convex, nodose cup plates; infrabasal, basal, and radial plates are clearly visible. The genus *Euspirocrinus* is known from the Middle Ordovician to Late Silurian of North America and Europe, but *E. heliktos* has only been reported from the Brassfield Formation of Greene County, Ohio.

Crinoids in the Silurian dolomites of Ohio are preserved as molds. Monobathrid camerate crinoids are most common; four are illustrated here.

Calliocrinus primibrachialis Busch (fig. 17-5.6) has a medium-sized, bowl-shaped calyx, few fixed interradials, few fixed brachials, and a central **anal tube**. The genus *Calliocrinus* is known from Devonian and Silurian strata of North America, Europe, and Asia; *C. primibrachialis* is known from the Cedarville Dolomite in Clark County, Ohio.

Eucalyptocrinites proboscidialis (Miller) (fig. 17-5.15) has a high, conical calyx, only a few fixed brachials and fixed interradials, a central anal tube, and unusual partition plates separating the free arms. The anal tube of *E. proboscidialis* is extremely long, distinguishing it from other species of *Eucalyptocrinites* that occur in Ohio. The genus *Eucalyptocrinites* is known worldwide from the Silurian to the Middle Devonian and is present throughout the Silurian outcrop belt in Ohio. *Eucalyptocrinites proboscidialis* is reported from the Cedarville Dolomite in Miami County.

Marsupiocrinus praematurus (Hall & Whitfield) (fig. 17-5.9) has a relatively small, nearly globular calyx, which is composed of only a few small fixed plates other than basal and radial plates. The genus *Marsupiocrinus* is known from the Middle Silurian to Early Devonian of Europe and North America; *M. praematurus* has been reported from the Cedarville Dolomite in southwestern and western Ohio.

Periechocrinus ornatus (Hall & Whitfield) (fig. 17-5.7) also has a high, conical calyx, similar in shape to that of *Eucalyptocrinites*, but it is composed of numerous plates, has an eccentric (off-center) anal tube, and lacks partition plates. The genus *Periechocrinus* is recognized from the Middle Silurian throughout North America and Europe; *P. ornatus* is reported from the Cedarville Dolomite and equivalent units in southwestern and western Ohio.

Most Silurian crinoid columns and columnals are nondescript (fig. 17-5.14). Although the "cog-wheel" type of columnal (fig. 17-5.11) from the uppermost Brassfield Formation "bead bed" is very distinctive, it cannot be associated with a specific crinoid crown.

OTHER ECHINODERMS

Blastozoan echinoderms also are well known from the Silurian dolomites of Ohio. The blastoid *Troosticrinus subcylindricus* (Hall & Whitfield) (fig. 17-5.16) has a large, high, conical **theca** in which the ambulacra project only a short distance down from the summit. The genus *Troosticrinus* is known only from North America in Middle and Upper Silurian strata; *T. subcylindricus* is reported from the Cedarville Dolomite in southwestern and western Ohio.

The rhombiferan *Caryocrinites ornatus* Say (fig. 17-5.17; see also fig. 1-31.2) has a subellipsoidal theca composed of 18 major plates that have a distinctive stellate sculpturing on the outer surface and a complex set of **pore rhombs** (system of pores and tubes that connect across adjacent plates) on the inner surface. The moldic preservation in Silurian dolomites can preserve either surface of the thecal plates. The genus *Caryocrinites* is recognized from the Middle Ordovician to Late Silurian worldwide. *Caryocrinites ornatus* is widespread in the North American Silurian and occurs in the Cedarville Dolomite in southwestern and western Ohio.

Two representative diploporans are illustrated, *Holocystites greenvillensis* Foerste and *Gomphocystites bownockeri* Foerste. Diploporans are characterized by numerous, randomly positioned, paired pores (**diplopores**) that penetrate thecal plates. *Holocystites greenvillensis* (fig. 17-5.19) has a cigar-shaped theca that has a regular arrangement of alternating large (primary) and small (secondary) plates along its length (see fig. 1-31.1). Three very short ambulacra are present on the summit but are rarely preserved. The genus *Holocystites* is known from the Late Ordovician to Late Silurian of North America and Europe; *H. greenvillensis* is reported from the Cedarville Dolomite in western Ohio. *Gomphocystites bownockeri* (fig. 17-5.18) has a teardrop-shaped theca composed of numerous irregularly arranged plates and five long ambulacra that spiral down along the theca from the summit (bulbous end). The genus *Gomphocystites* is known from throughout North America and Europe in Middle Silurian strata; *G. bownockeri* is reported from the Cedarville Dolomite of southwestern Ohio.

Rare Silurian echinoderms known from Ohio but not described here include members of the Coronoidea and the Asteroidea (table 17-2). Several classes of echinoderms, such as the Cyclocystoidea, are known from Silurian strata elsewhere but have not been recognized from Ohio.

DEVONIAN ECHINODERMS

Devonian echinoderms are relatively common from two contrasting areas in Ohio. In central Ohio, crinoids and blastoids are present in the Columbus and Delaware Limestones. Disarticulated echinoderm remains form much of these limestones, but complete cups are rare. Typically, echinoderms are partially replaced by silica in the Columbus and Delaware Limestones, so these fossils tend to stand out in slight relief on weathered rock surfaces. Many of the collections from the nineteenth and early twentieth centuries consisted of loose silicified specimens collected from the terra rossa soils above the limestone. "Terra rossa" refers to the red soil that develops on limestone. In northwestern Ohio, a variety of echinoderms is known from the Silica Formation. Here, crinoids, blastoids, asteroids, and other echinoderms are preserved either partially or completely replaced by pyrite and are present either on thin limestone bedding surfaces or in the shales.

CRINOIDS

Two monobathrid camerate crinoids are illustrated from the Devonian of central Ohio. *Dolatocrinus lacus* Lyon (figs. 17-6.10, 17-6.11) is characterized by a low, broad, bowl-shaped calyx that has stellate ridges on the plates. *Dolatocrinus* specimens possess a distinctive column in which three vertically oriented flanges or spines and an annular flange are secreted periodically along the outside of otherwise circular columnals (figs. 17-6.7, 17-6.8). Several columnals may be bound by these flanges, and these pluricolumnals make it possible to recognize *Dolatocrinus* even where parts of the calyx are not found. These columnals contrast with a typical Devonian crinoid pluricolumnal (fig. 17-6.9), which cannot be assigned to a genus. The genus *Dolatocrinus* is represented in the Lower and Middle Devonian of North America; *D. lacus* is reported from the Columbus Limestone of central Ohio.

Melocrinites bainbridgensis (Hall & Whitfield) (fig. 17-6.4) has a conical calyx that has nearly smooth, convex plates and depressed sutures between adjacent plates. *Melocrinites bainbridgensis* is a typical camerate, having many brachials and interradials fixed into the calyx. The genus *Melocrinites* is known from the Middle to Late Devonian of North America, Europe, and northern Asia. *Melocrinites bainbridgensis* is reported from the lower part of the Ohio Shale in Ross County.

Four representative crinoids from the Silica Formation are illustrated here. The monobathrid *Arthroacantha carpenteri* (Hinde) (figs. 17-6.1 to 17-6.3) is the most common crinoid in the Silica Formation. It is unusual because it is a camerate with only a few plates in the calyx and it has spines (fig. 17-6.3) on its calyx plates, similar to an echinoid. *Arthroacantha carpenteri* has a conical calyx composed primarily of large basal and radial plates. Only a few small fixed brachials and interradial plates are present. Although spines are diagnostic for this crinoid, they are rarely preserved. Instead, small nodes, which are the attachment bosses of the spines, are scattered over the calyx surface (figs. 17-6.1, 17-6.2). The arms of *A. carpenteri* branch many times and have spines at the arm bifurcations. A platyceratid gastropod is commonly attached to the tegmen directly over the anus (see fig. 17-6.2), where this gastropod engaged in a parasitic or commensal lifestyle. The genus *Arthroacantha* is recognized in the Early to Late Devonian of North America and Europe, and *A. carpenteri* is known from the Silica Formation of northwestern Ohio.

The diplobathrid *Gilbertsocrinus ohioensis* Stewart (figs. 17-6.16, 17-6.17; also fig. 17-6.1) is relatively small and has a boxlike calyx that is widest at the base, a deep basal concavity, spinose radial plates, and ridges along the fixed brachials. *Gilbertsocrinus* is one of the few diplobathrid camerate genera that survived into the late Paleozoic. It is known from the Middle Devonian through the Early Mississippian of North America and Europe; *G. ohioensis* is known from the Silica Formation of northwestern Ohio.

Poteriocrinites duluki Kesling (figs. 17-6.12, 17-6.13) is one of several cladids from the Silica Formation. Its conical aboral cup has dominant stellate ridges. *Poteriocrinites duluki* is distinct because it has very small infrabasal plates, **arm facets** that are not the full width of the radial plates, and three extra plates in the posterior (CD interray). This genus is known from the Devonian and Mississippian of North America, Europe, and Australia; *P. duluki* is reported from the Silica Formation of northwestern Ohio.

Euryocrinus? laddi Stewart (figs. 17-6.5, 17-6.6) is a well-known flexible crinoid from the Silica Formation in northwestern Ohio, but assignment of this species to a genus has always been problematic. It is characterized by a small aboral cup, arms that branch many times, a ridge along the arm axis, nodes common on branching points, and wide, short brachials. The genus *Euryocrinus* is known from Middle Devonian to Early Mississippian in North America and Europe; *E.? laddi* is reported from the Silica Formation of northwestern Ohio.

OTHER ECHINODERMS

In central Ohio, both crinoids and blastoids are common, but blastoid thecae are more common. The two blastoids that are present in the Devonian Columbus Limestone typify the two basic blastoid designs (see fig. 1-29). In *Heteroschisma pyramidatus* (Shumard) (fig. 17-6.15), the ambulacra are very short and confined nearly to the summit, the radial plates are the largest plates in the theca, and the theca is conical and has a rounded summit. In contrast, *Eleacrinus verneuili* (Troost) (fig. 17-6.14) has very long ambulacra that span nearly the entire height of the theca, the **deltoid plates** are the largest plates of the theca, and the theca is subellipsoidal. Both genera are represented in the Middle Devonian of North America, and both *H. pyramidatus* and *E. verneuili* are reported from the Columbus Limestone in central Ohio.

Rare Devonian echinoderms known from Ohio but not described here include edrioasteroids, asteroids, and ophiuroids (table 17-2). Several classes of echinoderms, such as the echinoids and the holothurians, are known from Devonian strata elsewhere but have not been recognized from Ohio.

MISSISSIPPIAN ECHINODERMS

In general, echinoderms are rare in Mississippian strata of Ohio, but where they are present they may be very abundant (see fig. 17-7.4). In northeastern Ohio, small, rare pockets preserve abundant, exceptionally complete crinoids. These pockets represent diverse, once-living colonies that were smothered by a sudden burial event, such as a storm. In other parts of the Mississippian strata in Ohio, crinoid remains are typically preserved as molds in siltstones and fine-grained sandstones.

CRINOIDS

More than 20 crinoid species have been reported from the Cuyahoga Formation of northeastern Ohio. Three species are illustrated here.

Aorocrinus helice (Hall) (fig. 17-7.5) is a relatively small but typical Lower Mississippian monobathrid camerate crinoid; it has fixed brachials, interradial plates, and biserial brachials on the free arms. *Aorocrinus helice* is characterized by a relatively small, conical calyx that is wider than high; only three interrays and fewer than 10 fixed brachials; variable sculpturing on plates from smooth to nodose to ridged; and 12 to 18 biserial free arms. The genus *Aorocrinus* is known in eastern North America from Middle Devonian through Lower Mississippian strata; *A. helice* is known from the Cuyahoga Formation in northeastern Ohio.

Platycrinites looks superficially like an inadunate crinoid because the arms are typically free above the radial plates; however, this crinoid is an unusual monobathrid camerate. Two circlets of plates, a plated tegmen, and biserial brachials indicate the camerate affinities of this crinoid. The genus *Platycrinites* is further distinguished by having elliptical columnals that form a helically spiraled column. *Platycrinites lodiensis* (Hall & Whitfield) (figs. 17-7.2, 17-7.3) is characterized by a small crown; a bowl-shaped aboral cup composed only of basal plates, radial plates, and the first brachial (where arms divide); and 20 biserial arms. This unusual crinoid genus was highly successful, being reported from Lower Devonian to Permian strata in North America, Europe, Japan, Africa, and Indonesia. *Platycrinites lodiensis* is known from the Cuyahoga Formation in Medina County, Ohio. The natural sandstone mold of *P. lodiensis* in figure 17-7.3 is typical of its preservation in Mississippian rocks of Ohio.

Pachylocrinus subtortuosus (Hall) (fig. 17-7.1) is a representative Mississippian cladid inadunate. Its aboral cup is small in relation to the arms and has a medium cone shape, robust stellate ridges on cup and anal-sac plates, and a keel along the arms. *Pachylocrinus subtortuosus* has more than 20 arms. The first branch is on the second brachial, and there are three extra plates in the posterior (CD interray). *Pachylocrinus* is a widespread Lower Mississippian crinoid genus in North America, but *P. subtortuosus* is reported from only the Cuyahoga Formation in Summit County.

OTHER ECHINODERMS

A spectacular occurrence of the ophiuroid *Strataster ohioensis* Kesling & LeVasseur (fig. 17-7.4) was collected from the Cuyahoga Formation in Cuyahoga County (see Kesling, 1971). A single bed exposed for about 18 feet along the outcrop (other horizontal dimension unknown) and averaging only 1 cm in thickness contained an average of 4,500 *S. ohioensis* individuals per square meter. These densely packed ophiuroids show both the oral and aboral surfaces of *S. ohioensis*. The small disk that is clearly distinct from the narrow arms distinguishes *Strataster* as an ophiuroid, rather than an asteroid.

Mississippian echinoderms known from Ohio but not described here include the blastoid *Pentremites*, which is rare in Ohio but very abundant in eastern North America (table 17-2). Several other types of echinoderms, such as edrioasteroids and echinoids, are known from Mississippian strata elsewhere but have not been recognized from Ohio.

PENNSYLVANIAN ECHINODERMS

Echinoderm remains are uncommon in Pennsylvanian strata of Ohio. They are principally confined to marine units that represent peak transgressions, such as the Lower Mercer limestone in the Pottsville Group and the Brush Creek, Cambridge, and Ames limestones in the Conemaugh Group. The Ames limestone contains abundant echinoderm remains, but in the remainder of the Ohio Pennsylvanian, even disarticulated echinoderm material is rare.

CRINOIDS

The most distinctive echinoderm remains from the Pennsylvanian of Ohio are various spine plates, either from the arms or anal sac of crinoids. Characteristic spines, such as the first arm plate of *Plaxocrinus mooresi* (Whitfield) (fig. 17-7.7), can be identified to species. Crinoid columnals from Pennsylvanian strata cannot be assigned to crowns (figs. 17-7.15, 17-7.16).

All crinoids known from the Ohio Pennsylvanian are cladid inadunates, whose aboral cups may look very similar—a small, bowl-shaped calyx and arm facets the full width of the radial plates. Useful characteristics to distinguish these crinoids are presence or absence of a basal concavity, relative size of cup plates, sculpturing on cup plates and arms, extra plates in the posterior, and nature of the arms.

Plaxocrinus mooresi (figs. 17-7.6, 17-7.7, 17-7.9, 17-7.10, 17-7.17) is characterized by a flat, bowl-shaped aboral cup that has smooth sculpturing, infrabasal plates in the basal concavity, radial plates as the largest cup plates, three extra plates in the posterior, large spinose first brachials, and as many as 20 free arms. *Plaxocrinus* is a common crinoid in Middle and Upper Pennsylvanian rocks throughout North America; *P. mooresi* is reported from Pottsville, Allegheny, and Conemaugh strata in southeastern Ohio.

Delocrinus sp. (figs. 17-7.8, 17-7.11) is characterized by a medium-sized, bowl-shaped aboral cup that has smooth sculpturing, infrabasal plates in the basal concavity, basal plates a little smaller than radial plates, one small extra plate in the posterior, large but not spinose first brachials, and 20 free arms. *Delocrinus* is known from the Pennsylvanian of North America, including southeastern Ohio.

OTHER ECHINODERMS

Echinoids, along with asteroids, are the most familiar living echinoderms. They are well represented in the fossil record, especially in the Mesozoic and Cenozoic, but are virtually unreported from Ohio. Only disarticulated parts, such as echinoid spines and spine boss plates, have been reported from the Pennsylvanian of Ohio. Numerous echinoid spines are present in certain units. Illustrated here are long, nodose spines assigned to *Archaeocidaris* sp. (figs. 17-7.12, 17-7.13) and spine boss plates (fig. 17-7.14). Echinoid remains have been reported from the Lower Mercer limestone (Pottsville Group), the Vanport limestone (Allegheny Group), and the Cambridge limestone (Conemaugh Group) in eastern and southeastern Ohio.

Only crinoids and echinoids are known from the Pennsylvanian of Ohio (table 17-2). Several classes of echinoderms, such as the blastoids and holothurians, are known from

Pennsylvanian strata elsewhere but have not been recognized from Ohio.

ACKNOWLEDGMENTS

The following individuals allowed access to specimens: Stig M. Bergström and Dale M. Gnidovec (The Ohio State University), David L. Meyer (University of Cincinnati), John K. Pope and Joe H. Marak (Miami University), and Frederick J. Collier and Jann W. Thompson (U.S. National Museum of Natural History). Daniel C. Fisher, Phillip D. Gingerich, and Gregg F. Gunnell (University of Michigan) provided access to negatives of photographs in Kesling and Chilman (1975). Gregory A. Schumacher (Ohio Division of Geological Survey) donated specimens illustrated herein. Beth A. Daye (The Ohio State University) aided with photography. Helen H. Hayes (The Ohio State University) typed the manuscript. David L. Meyer, John K. Pope, and Gregory A. Schumacher offered important advice, and Rodney M. Feldmann and Merrianne Hackathorn improved earlier drafts of parts of the manuscript.

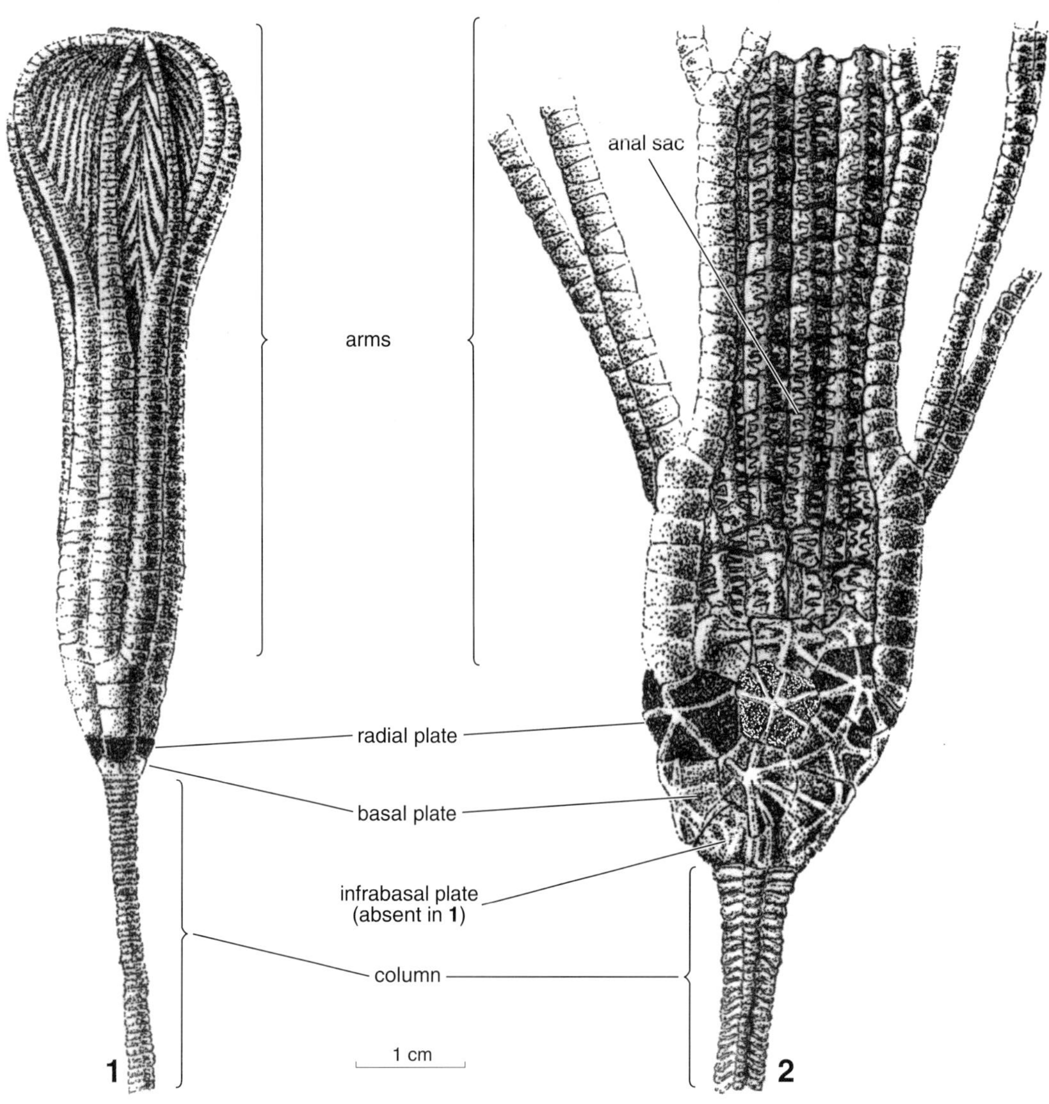

FIGURE 17-1.—Contrasting constructions of inadunate crinoid orders. **1,** Disparida, monocyclic aboral cup (infrabasal plates lacking) of *Ectenocrinus*; **2,** Cladida, dicyclic aboral cup of *Dendrocrinus*. Radial plates are blackened.

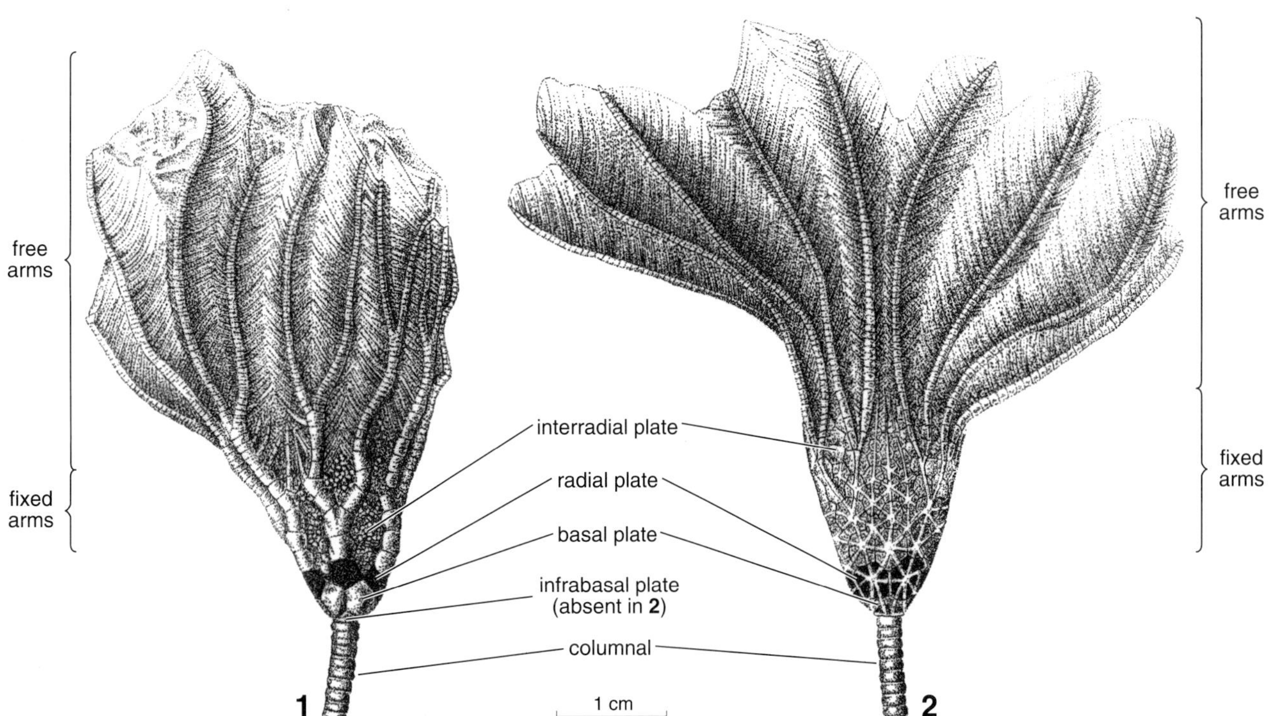

FIGURE 17-2.—Contrasting constructions of camerate crinoid orders. **1,** Diplobathrida, dicyclic calyx (infrabasal plates present) of *Gaurocrinus*; **2,** Monobathrida, monocyclic calyx of *Glyptocrinus*. Radial plates are blackened.

FIGURE 17-3.—Ordovician inadunate crinoids. Scale bars equal 1 cm. Scale bar A applies to figures 17-3.1, 17-3.3, 17-3.6, and 17-3.7; B applies to figures 17-3.2, 17-3.5, and 17-3.8 to 17-3.11; C applies to figure 17-3.4.

1, 2 *Cupulocrinus polydactylus* (Shumard). **1**, six crowns. **2**, enlargement of specimen illustrated in **1**. Richmondian strata, Butler County, Ohio; MUGM 28344.

3, 4 *Cincinnaticrinus pentagonus* (Ulrich). **3**, crown and column. **4**, enlargement of specimen illustrated in **3**. Richmondian strata, Warren County, Ohio; OSU 10420.

5, 6 *Iocrinus subcrassus* (Meek & Worthen). **5**, enlargement of aboral cup illustrated in **6**. **6**, crown and distal column. Unknown stratigraphic unit and geographic location in Ohio; MUGM 28048.

7, 8 *Plicodendrocrinus casei* (Meek). **7**, lateral view of crown with part of column attached. Richmondian strata, Warren County, Ohio; MUGM 28343. **8**, specimen with aboral cup and anal sac. Note ornate ridge pattern of anal sac. Whitewater Formation, Warren County, Ohio; MUGM 7851.

9, 10 *Ectenocrinus simplex* (Hall). **9**, crown with arms slightly opened. UCGM 35436. **10**, crown with arms closed. UCGM 39079a. Both specimens from unknown stratigraphic unit in Hamilton County, Ohio.

11 *Ohiocrinus laxus* (Hall). Note the unusual coiled anal sac (arrow). Fairview Formation, Hamilton County, Ohio; USNM 42304a.

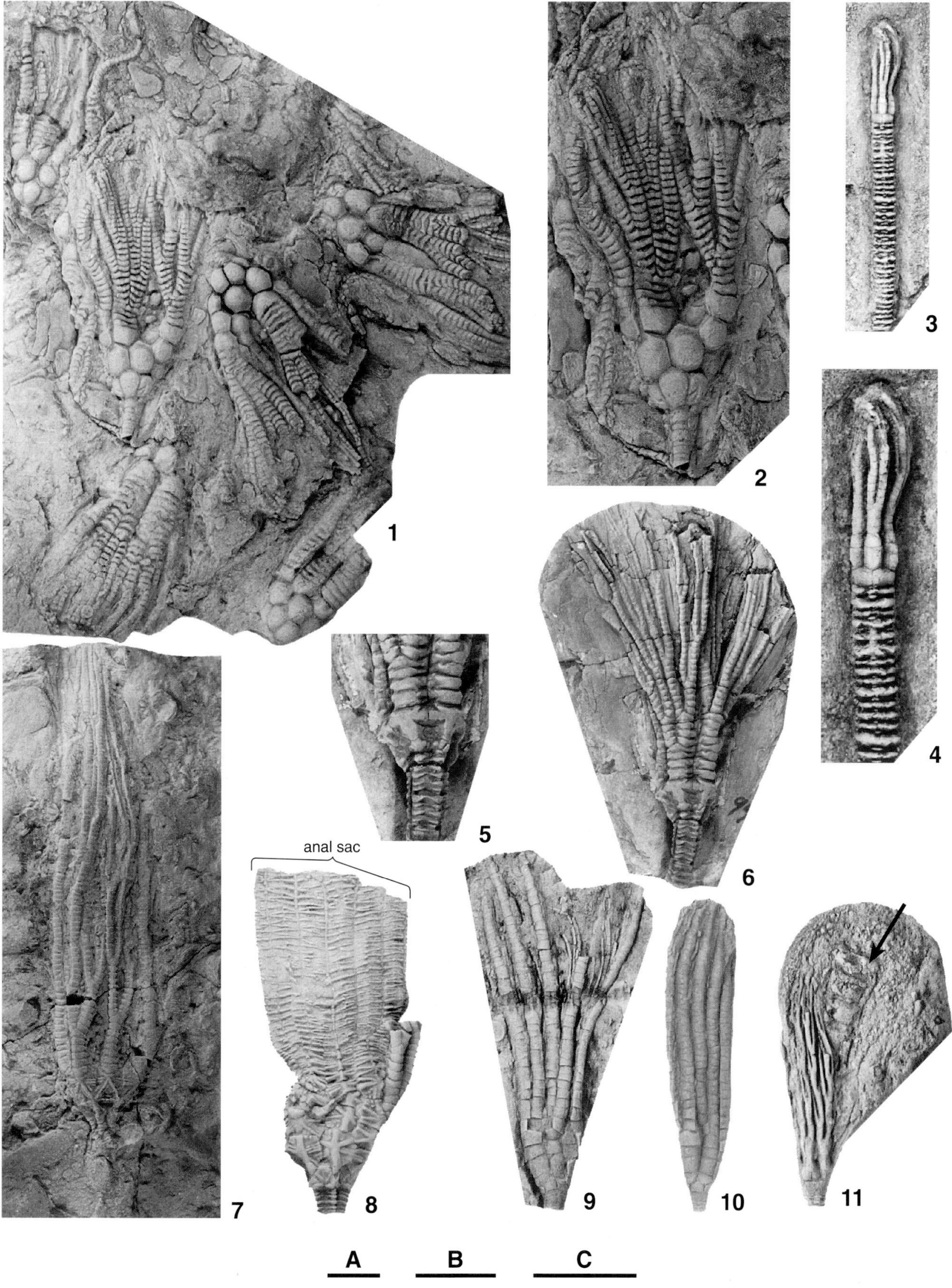
1
2
3
4
5
6
anal sac
7
8
9
10
11
A
B
C

FIGURE 17-4.—Ordovician camerate crinoids, crinoid parts (holdfasts and columns), and asteroids. Scale bars equal 1 cm. Scale bar A applies to figures 17-4.3, 17-4.12, and 17-4.13; B applies to figures 17-4.1, 17-4.2, 17-4.4 to 17-4.6, 17-4.8, and 17-4.10; C applies to figures 17-4.7 and 17-4.9; D applies to figure 17-4.11.

1 *Xenocrinus baeri* (Meek). Two nearly complete crowns. Liberty Formation, Warren County, Ohio; UCGM 17621.

2 *Gaurocrinus nealli* (Hall). Posterior side of crown. Waynesville? Formation, southwestern Ohio; MUGM 27726.

3 *Pycnocrinus dyeri* (Meek). Four nearly complete crowns or calyces. Fairview Formation, Hamilton County, Ohio; UCGM 31526.

4-6 *"Lichenocrinus"* holdfasts. **4**, isolated specimen. Unknown stratigraphic unit, southwestern Ohio; UCGM 11061a. **5**, holdfast attached to a bryozoan colony. Drakes Formation, Preble County, Ohio; MUGM 7842. **6**, isolated specimen. Unknown stratigraphic unit, southwestern Ohio; UCGM 11061b.

7 *Cincinnaticrinus* column. Unknown stratigraphic unit, Hamilton County, Ohio; UCGM 39079a.

8 *Iocrinus subcrassus* column. Liberty Formation, Warren County, Ohio; OSU 46931.

9 *Iocrinus subcrassus* columnal **articular facet**. Liberty Formation, Warren County, Ohio; OSU 46932.

10 *Xenocrinus baeri* column. Liberty Formation, Warren County, Ohio; OSU 46933.

11 *Xenocrinus* columnal articular facet. Note quadrangular outline. Unknown stratigraphic unit, southwestern Ohio; UCGM 43200.

12 *Petraster speciosus* (Miller & Dyer). Unknown stratigraphic unit, Adams County, Ohio; OSU 28747.

13 *Salteraster grandis* (Meek). Unknown stratigraphic unit, southwestern Ohio; MUGM T-240.

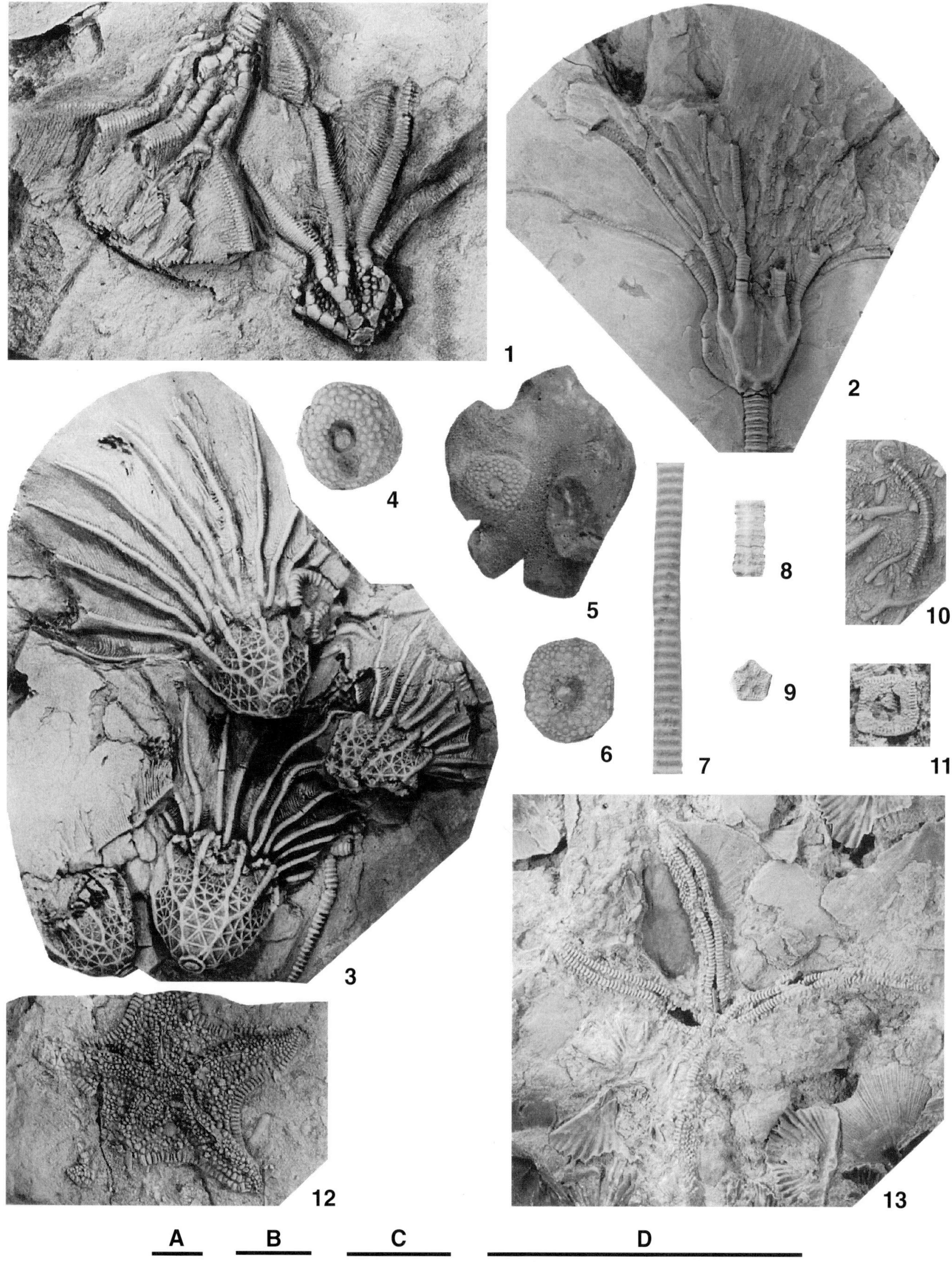
1
2
3
4
5
6
7
8
9
10
11
12
13
A
B
C
D

FIGURE 17-5.—Ordovician edrioasteroids and Silurian echinoderms. Silurian specimens are crinoids unless otherwise noted. Scale bars equal 1 cm. Scale bar A applies to figures 17-5.1, 17-5.3, 17-5.6, 17-5.7, 17-5.14 to 17-5.16, 17-5.18, and 17-5.19; B applies figures 17-5.2, 17-5.4, 17-5.5, 17-5.8 to 17-5.11, and 17-5.17; C applies to figure 17-5.13; D applies to 17-5.12.

1, 2	*Carneyella pilea* (Hall) attached to a *Rafinesquina* brachiopod. **2** is an enlargement of **1**. Note ambulacra constructed of a single biseries of plates. Grant Lake Formation (Ordovician), Hamilton County, Ohio; UCGM 34537.
3, 5, 10	*Stereoaster squamosus* (Foerste). **3**, lateral view of incomplete, partially crushed crown. Note branched arms. USNM 358227. **5**, basal view of calyx. USNM 358225. **10**, part of a holdfast. Note bricklike plating of **cirrus** (arrow) and **pentameres** in column. USNM 358230. Brassfield Formation (Silurian), Greene County, Ohio.
4	*Isorophus cincinnatiensis* (Roemer). Note ambulacra constructed of a double biseries of plates. Grant Lake Formation (Ordovician), Hamilton County, Ohio; UCGM 7781.
6	*Calliocrinus primibrachialis* Busch. Internal mold of calyx, anal tube is broken. Cedarville Dolomite (Silurian), Clark County, Ohio; OSU 19259.
7	*Periechocrinus ornatus* (Hall & Whitfield). Internal mold of calyx, short anal tube preserved. Cedarville Dolomite (Silurian), Greene County, Ohio; OSU 3298.
8	*Euspirocrinus heliktos* Ausich. Upper part of arms, disarticulated. Brassfield Formation (Silurian), Greene County, Ohio; USNM 369297.
9	*Marsupiocrinus praematurus* (Hall & Whitfield). Internal mold of calyx. Cedarville Dolomite (Silurian), Greene County, Ohio; OSU 3316.
11	Distinctive "cog-wheel" crinoid columnal, not identifiable to genus or species. Uppermost Brassfield Formation "bead bed" (Silurian), Montgomery County, Ohio; OSU 46935.
12	*Stibarocrinus centervillensis* (Foerste), a calceocrinid crinoid. Brassfield Formation (Silurian), Montgomery County, Ohio; USNM 91093.
13	*Phrygilocrinus batheri* Ausich. Calyx, arms not preserved. Brassfield Formation (Silurian), Greene County, Ohio; USNM 375777.
14	Crinoid column segment, not identifiable to genus or species. Brassfield Formation (Silurian), Greene County, Ohio; OSU 46934.
15	*Eucalyptocrinites proboscidialis* (Miller). Internal mold of calyx. Note long anal tube and distinctive partition plates. Cedarville Dolomite (Silurian), Miami County, Ohio; OSU 13867.
16	*Troosticrinus subcylindricus* (Hall & Whitfield), a blastoid. Internal mold. Cedarville Dolomite (Silurian), Miami County, Ohio; MUGM 6981.
17	*Caryocrinites ornatus* Say, a rhombiferan. Internal mold. Cedarville Dolomite (Silurian), Miami County, Ohio; OSU 24077.
18	*Gomphocystites bownockeri* Foerste, a diploporan. Cedarville Dolomite (Silurian), Greene County, Ohio; OSU 8736.
19	*Holocystites greenvillensis* Foerste, a diploporan. Internal mold. Cedarville Dolomite (Silurian), Mercer County, Ohio; OSU 19252.

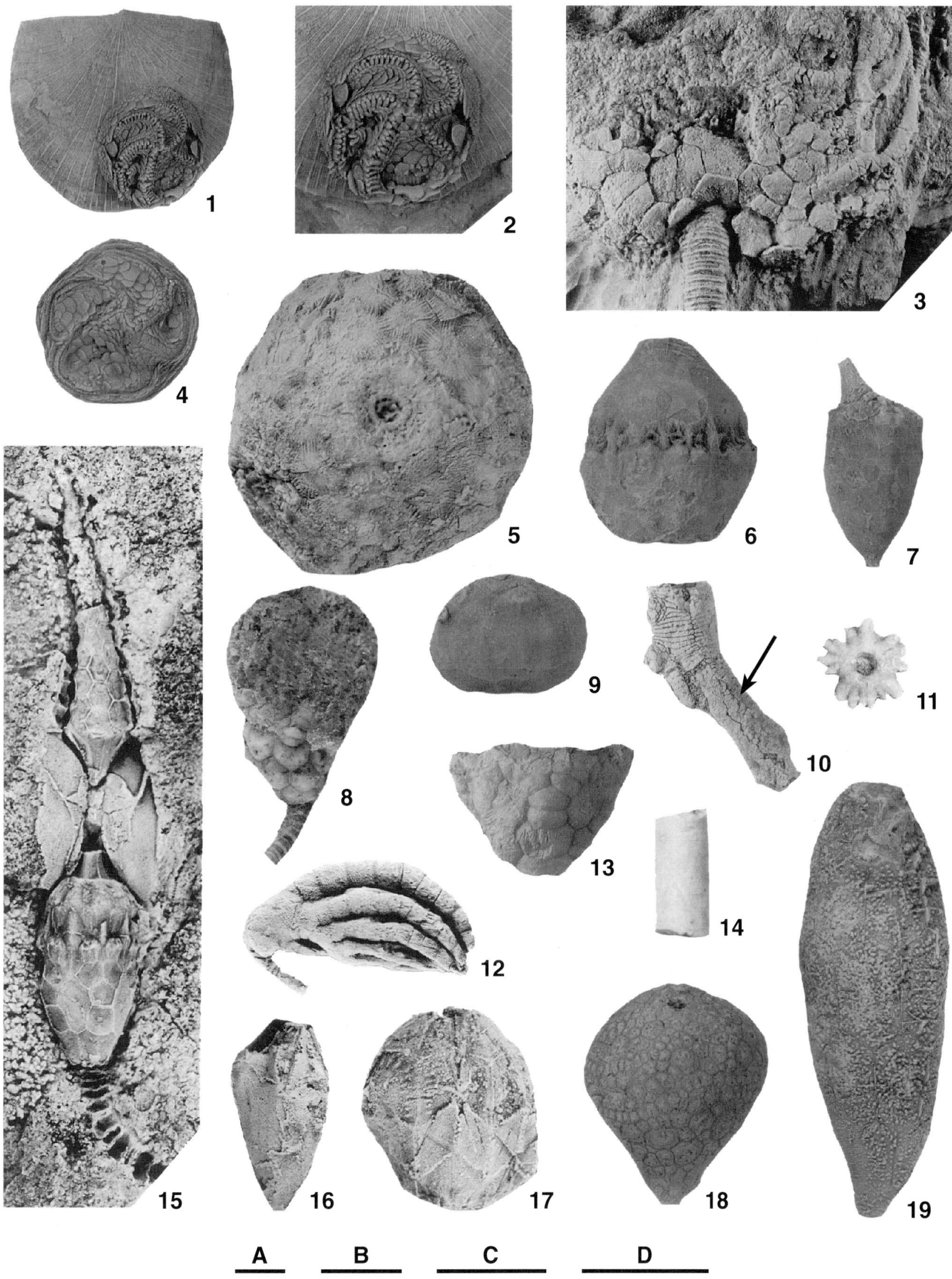
1
2
3
4
5
6
7
8
9
10
11
12
13
14
15
16
17
18
19
A
B
C
D

FIGURE 17-6.—Devonian echinoderms. Figures 17-6.14 and 17-6.15 are blastoids; all others are crinoids. Scale bars equal 1 cm. Scale bar A applies to figures 17-6.1 to 17-6.4; B applies to figures 17-6.7 to 17-6.11 and 17-6.14; C applies to figures 17-6.5, 17-6.6, 17-6.12, 17-6.13, and 17-6.15 to 17-6.17. Figures 17-6.1, 17-6.3, 17-6.5, 17-6.6, 17-6.12, 17-6.13, and 17-6.16 are reproduced from Kesling and Chilman (1975).

1-3	*Arthroacantha carpenteri* (Hinde). **1**, crown with column attached. Note spine bosses on calyx plates, spinose brachials, and partial *Gilbertsocrinus ohioensis* at lower right. UMMP 61328. **2**, specimen with arms not preserved and *Platyceras* sp. preserved on tegmen. OSU 16281. **3**, specimen with spines still present on calyx. UMMP 61327. All specimens from the Silica Formation, Lucas County, Ohio.
4	*Melocrinites bainbridgensis* (Hall & Whitfield). Calyx, arms not preserved. Ohio Shale, Ross County, Ohio; OSU 3965.
5, 6	*Euryocrinus*? *laddi* Stewart. Basal (**5**) and lateral (**6**) views of crown. Silica Formation, Lucas County, Ohio; UMMP 61322.
7, 8	*Dolatocrinus* sp. Column. **7**, articular facet of columnal. **8**, lateral view of column. Probably from the Columbus Limestone, Franklin County, Ohio; OSU 46936.
9	Crinoid column, not identifiable to genus or species. Probably from the Columbus Limestone, Franklin County, Ohio; OSU 46938.
10, 11	*Dolatocrinus lacus* Lyon. **10**, calyx, arms not preserved. **11**, basal view of specimen in **10**. Columbus Limestone, Franklin County, Ohio; OSU 19397.
12, 13	*Poteriocrinites duluki* Kesling. **12**, aboral cup with a few columnals attached. **13**, basal view of specimen in **12**. Silica Formation, Lucas County, Ohio; UMMP 57350.
14	*Eleacrinus verneuili* (Troost). Columbus Limestone, Franklin County, Ohio; OSU 29057.
15	*Heteroschisma pyramidatus* (Shumard). Columbus Limestone, Franklin County, Ohio; OSU 19853.
16, 17	*Gilbertsocrinus ohioensis* Stewart. **16**, specimen with arms missing and spines broken from the bottom. USNM 102170. **17**, specimen with arms preserved. OSU 19037. Silica Formation, Lucas County, Ohio.

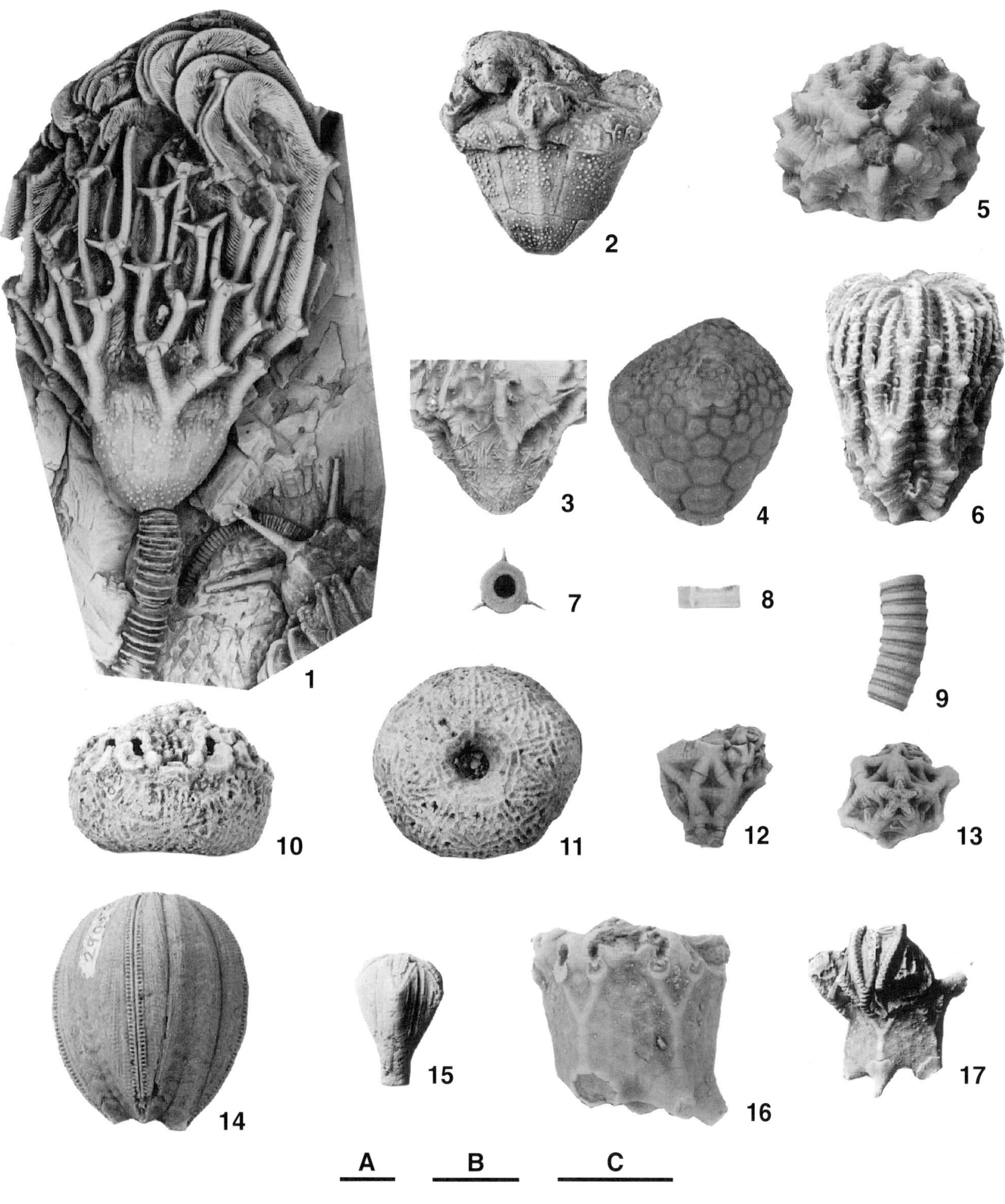
1
2
3
4
5
6
7
8
9
10
11
12
13
14
15
16
17
A
B
C

FIGURE 17-7.—Mississippian and Pennsylvanian echinoderms. Figure 17-7.4 is an ophuiroid; all others are crinoids. Scale bars equal 1 cm. Scale bar A applies to figures 17-7.1, 17-7.5, 17-7.13, and 17-7.16; B applies to figures 17-7.2 to 17-7.4, 17-7.6 to 17-7.12, 17-7.14, 17-7.15, and 17-7.17.

1	*Pachylocrinus subtortuosus* (Hall). Cuyahoga Formation (Mississippian), Summit County, Ohio; UCGM 46183.
2, 3	*Platycrinites lodiensis* (Hall & Whitfield). **2**, latex cast of external mold in fine-grained sandstone illustrated in **3**. Cuyahoga Formation (Mississippian), Medina County, Ohio; OSU 4310.
4	*Strataster ohioensis* Kesling & LeVasseur. Numerous specimens. Cuyahoga Formation (Mississippian), Cuyahoga County, Ohio; OSU 37312.
5	*Aorocrinus helice* (Hall). Cuyahoga Formation (Mississippian), Summit County, Ohio; UCGM 46055.
6, 7, 9, 10, 17	*Plaxocrinus mooresi* (Whitfield). **6**, basal view of aboral cup with four spinose first brachials attached. OSU 9787. **7**, spinose first brachial. OSU 15205. **9**, A-ray view of aboral cup illustrated in **6**; cup is complete except A ray and spinose first arm plate are missing. OSU 9787. **10**, lateral view, and **17**, basal view, of aboral cup with arms not preserved. OSU 15205. All specimens from Putnam Hill limestone (Allegheny Group, Pennsylvanian), Hocking County, Ohio.
8, 11	*Delocrinus* sp. **8**, basal view of aboral cup. **11**, lateral view of crown. Note two arms per ray and biserial brachials. Brush Creek limestone (Conemaugh Group, Pennsylvanian), Athens County, Ohio; OSU 35041.
12, 13	*Archaeocidaris* sp. **12**, spine. Cambridge limestone (Conemaugh Group, Pennsylvanian), Lawrence County, Ohio; OSU 46941. **13**, latex cast of spine. Lower Mercer limestone (Pottsville Group, Pennsylvanian), Scioto County, Ohio; OSU 15211.
14	*Archaeocidaris* sp. Spine base plates from body. Note central boss for spine attachment. Cambridge limestone (Conemaugh Group, Pennsylvanian), Lawrence County, Ohio; OSU 46942.
15, 16	Crinoid columnal, not identifiable to genus or species. **15**, articular surface. **16**, lateral view. Cambridge limestone (Conemaugh Group, Pennsylvanian), Guernsey County, Ohio; OSU 46940.

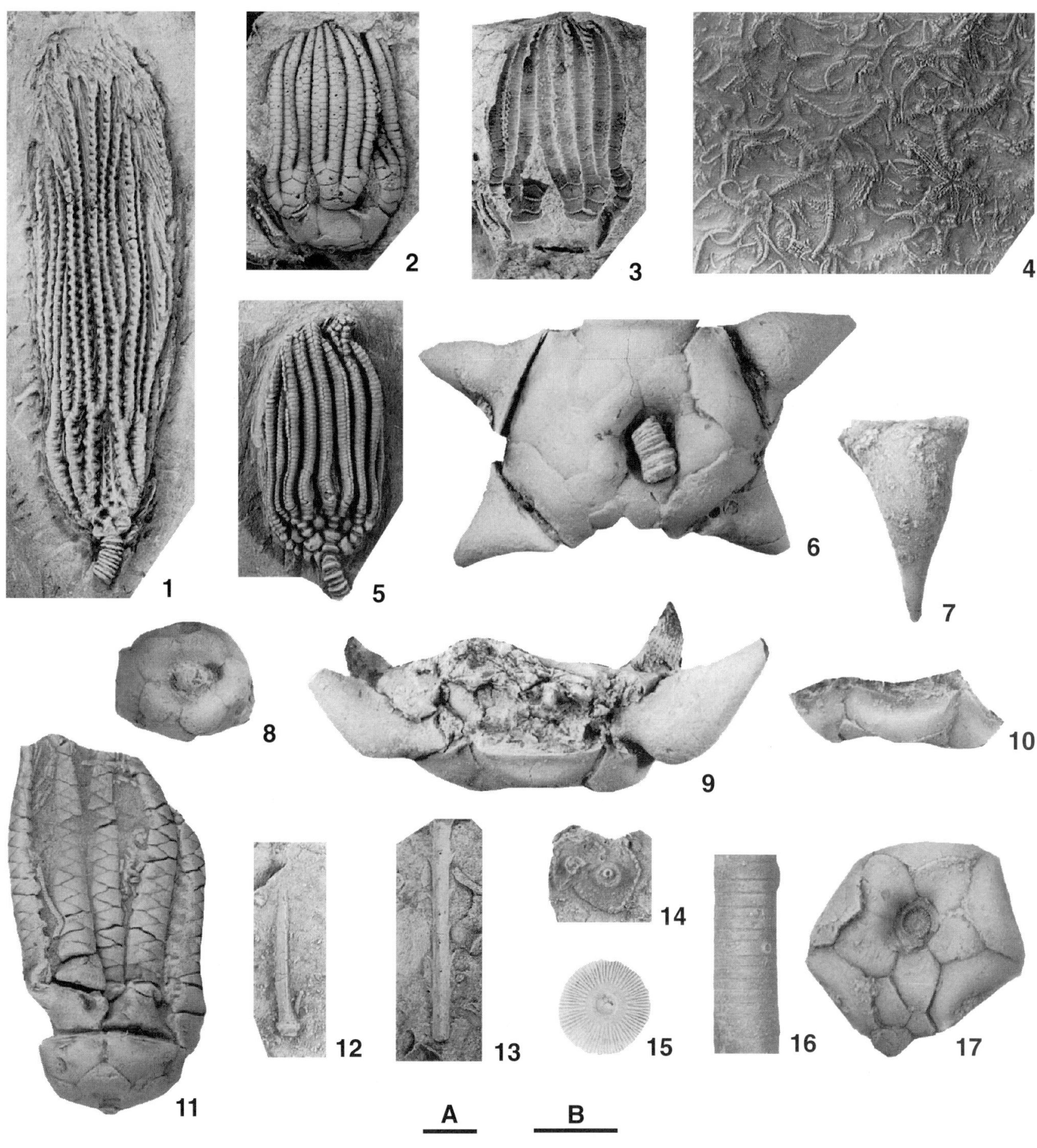
1
2
3
4
5
6
7
8
9
10
11
12
13
14
15
16
17
A
B

Chapter 18

PHYLUM CONODONTA

by Walter C. Sweet

INTRODUCTION

Conodonts are an extinct phylum of marine animals that were worldwide in their distribution from late in the Cambrian Period to the end of the Triassic Period. Only a few complete conodonts have ever been found, but from those specimens it has been learned that they were wormlike animals whose only hard parts were tiny phosphatic toothlike and jawlike **elements**, mostly less than a millimeter long. These elements were clustered together in the head and probably served to capture, shred, and prepare food for digestion.

Because conodonts were largely soft-bodied animals, their fossil record is composed almost entirely of the toothlike and jawlike elements that formed the cephalic **apparatus**. After death the soft tissues of conodonts probably decayed rapidly (or were eaten by other animals) and only the hard elements remained. However, because those elements are formed of calcium phosphate, which is heavier than most common sedimentary materials and is also quite resistant chemically, these tiny components of the skeleton accumulated on the sea floor in considerable numbers. They are to be found today in almost every rock in Ohio that formed from sediment originally deposited in the sea.

The very widespread geographic distribution of many conodont species, coupled with their common occurrence in rocks like black shales, which represent sea-floor environments that were hostile to most bottom-living animals, suggest that most conodonts were swimmers. Also, elements of many groups exhibit considerable change in morphology from bed to bed, indicating that the animals they represent evolved rapidly. Because of their broad geographic distribution and rapid evolutionary development, conodonts are commonly used today to demonstrate that rocks in widely separated parts of the Earth were deposited at the same time.

ORGANIZATION AND TERMINOLOGY OF CONODONT APPARATUSES

Because conodonts have been extinct since the end of the Triassic Period, there is nothing quite like them in modern marine faunas. And, because their tiny skeletons tended to come apart upon death, when soft tissues that originally held them together decayed, a collection of conodont elements is likely to be a mixture of elements belonging to several different species. Reconstruction of original apparatuses from such a collection requires a good deal of care. Fortunately, a few conodont apparatuses have been preserved intact and these serve as very useful models in the reconstruction of others.

The apparatuses of conodonts that are preserved intact include elements of several different shapes, just as the human skeleton does. Most complete apparatuses are composed of elements of six or seven different shapes. Just as many skeletal elements in our bodies are duplicated on opposite sides of our midline, so were elements of the conodont apparatus. Thus, not only are apparatuses made up of elements of six or seven different shapes, they also include at least twice that number of elements. The only elements that were not paired are ones that are themselves **bilaterally symmetrical**—evidently they occupied the body's midline, just as our backbone does. Thus, a complete conodont apparatus included at least 12 or 14 elements. Study of complete specimens indicates most of them had a few more than this because certain types of elements were represented by several (rather than just one) pairs (like our ribs, for example).

Long before it was learned that the cephalic apparatus of conodonts was made up of elements of several different shapes, paleontologists who studied conodonts sorted large collections of elements into three general shape categories. In recent years these have been termed **coniform**, **ramiform**, and **pectiniform elements**. Several different types of these shapes are illustrated in figure 1-33 of Chapter 1. Later discovery of complete specimens showed that apparatuses could also be divided into three distinct regions, which we now term **S**, **M**, and **P regions**. Figure 1-34 is a general plan of a typical conodont apparatus showing these regions. In the majority of conodonts found in Ohio, the S region was occupied by fragile ramiform elements of several different types. One, which was itself bilaterally symmetrical, apparently occupied the midline of the head, and two or three other types were represented by several pairs of elements. The M region in the cephalic apparatus was occupied by a single pair of pick-shaped ramiform elements, and the P region was made up of two pairs of pectiniform elements. In Devonian, Mississippian, and Pennsylvanian conodonts (and in a few earlier ones), one position in the P region commonly was occupied by pectiniform elements that had a broad platformlike expansion at one end. Figure 1-33 illustrates a number of different types of pectiniform elements—some with platforms, some without—because these elements are commonly the ones that are most diagnostic of different conodont genera. Each type of ramiform and pectiniform element has been given a different name. More information on the morphology of conodonts can be found in Clark and others (1981) and Sweet (1988).

Very early in the history of conodonts, cephalic apparatuses were made up entirely of simple, fang-shaped coniform elements (fig. 1-33). And, because the first conodonts found were almost all coniform types, this gave rise to the name for the entire phylum—conodont, or cone-teeth. In Ohio, specimens representing the earliest phases of conodont history are in very deeply buried rocks, which are nowhere exposed at the surface. The oldest exposed rocks, the Ordovician rocks in southwestern Ohio, yield conodonts that represent a much later stage of development—one in which most positions in the cephalic apparatus were occupied by ramiform or pectiniform elements.

COLLECTION AND PREPARATION OF CONODONTS FROM OHIO

Conodonts may be collected from almost any of Ohio's Paleozoic rocks that formed from sediment originally deposited on the sea floor. However, specimens are most abundant (and best preserved) in limestones—particularly in ones that also contain many larger fossils—and in formations such as the Estill Shale (Silurian) and the Olentangy Shale (Devonian), which are composed primarily of soft shale. Unfortunately, it is rarely possible to determine in the field if a particular limestone or shale bed contains conodont elements because specimens are quite small and difficult to see with the unaided eye. Consequently, in the field, one collects large chunks of limestone or shale, and, at home or in the laboratory, uses various simple procedures to dissolve (or remove) the rock matrix and concentrate the conodont elements that may remain.

Conodont elements may be collected from Estill Shale or Olentangy Shale samples by first soaking to ½ to 1 kg of shale thoroughly in water to form a thick gooey mud, then washing the mud through a fine-mesh screen (one with about 100 openings per square inch is satisfactory). Most of the mud will pass through the screen, but conodonts and other small fossils will remain. This residue may then be washed off the screen, dried, and examined under a binocular microscope for conodonts.

Preparation of limestone samples is somewhat more involved, but still fairly simple. Place a ½- to 1-kg chunk of limestone, broken first into fragments no more than 2 to 3 cm in diameter, in a plastic bucket and soak for several days in a 10 to 15% solution of glacial acetic acid until all evidence of activity ceases. The insoluble residue that remains on the bottom of the bucket will contain any conodonts in the sample. It should be washed out of the bucket onto a filter paper (or paper towel), dried, and examined under a binocular microscope for conodonts. If large chunks remain after the first acid bath is spent, additional charges of acid may be required to reduce the sample entirely. If care is taken to insure that the acid has been used up in dissolving the limestone, small amounts of spent acid, which is likely to be dark reddish brown in color, may be discharged into a regular drain without damaging the plumbing. If a large project is contemplated, however, arrangements should be made to use a laboratory that is equipped to neutralize wastewater before discharging it into a drainage system. All of this work, of course, should be done in space that is well ventilated, and care should be taken to protect hands and clothing from the acid, which is mildly corrosive and has a very strong vinegary odor.

ORDOVICIAN CONODONTS

Phragmodus Branson & Mehl (fig. 18-1) has a skeletal apparatus composed of six differently shaped elements. The cockscomblike ramiform elements (fig. 18-1.1) that occupied all three S positions are the most distinctive. Both P elements (figs. 18-1.3, 18-1.4) are **pastinate** pectiniform structures, and the M element of *Phragmodus undatus* Branson & Mehl (fig. 18-1.2), the only species represented in Ohio, is a **geniculate** coniform element. Elements of *P. undatus* are especially common in limestones interbedded in the thick bluish-green shales of the Kope Formation, but may be found in samples from almost any level in the famous Cincinnatian section of southwestern Ohio.

The apparatus of *Plectodina* Stauffer (figs. 18-2.13 to 18-2.18) also includes elements of six different shapes. P positions in the apparatus of *Plectodina tenuis* (Branson & Mehl), the most abundant species of *Plectodina* in Ohio, are occupied by distinctive **angulate** pectiniform elements (figs. 18-2.17, 18-2.18). The M element (fig. 18-2.16) is a pick-shaped ramiform element, and the three S positions (figs. 18-2.13 to 18-2.15) include elements that are quite unlike those in similar positions in the *Phragmodus* apparatus. Elements of *Plectodina tenuis* occur by the hundreds in Upper Ordovician limestones collected from almost any roadside exposure in southwestern Ohio. In samples containing numerous specimens of *Phragmodus undatus*, elements of *Plectodina tenuis* are commonly few in number, and in samples dominated by *Plectodina tenuis*, there tend to be few representatives of *Phragmodus undatus*. This situation suggests that these two conodonts had somewhat different ecologic preferences, although their living spaces probably overlapped a good deal.

Samples from the Upper Ordovician Fairview Formation yield elements of *Oulodus* Branson & Mehl (figs. 18-2.7 to 18-2.12), which are commonly robust, larger than other specimens in the same sample, and distinguished by the fact that most **denticles** are circular in cross section and separated from other denticles by spaces. The diagnostic element of the *Oulodus* apparatus, however, is an elongate, stout, curiously twisted, ramiform element (fig. 18-2.12) that probably occupied one of the P positions. Species of *Oulodus*, including *O. velicuspis* (Pulse & Sweet), illustrated in figures 18-2.7 to 18-2.12, seem to have been most at home in relatively shallow-water environments in Ordovician seas. Thus, samples that contain many specimens of *Oulodus* rarely have many representatives of *Phragmodus* or *Plectodina*.

More information on Ordovician conodonts can be found in Sweet and others (1959), Pulse and Sweet (1960), Bergström and Sweet (1966), Kohut and Sweet (1968), and Sweet (1979).

SILURIAN CONODONTS

Panderodus Ethington (fig. 18-3.10) is represented by thousands of distinctive coniform elements in the Brassfield Formation (Lower Silurian) in southwestern Ohio. These elements are slender, sharply pointed, and have a deep, longitudinal furrow on one side and one or several sharp-edged ridges parallel to it on the other sides. Careful study of a collection of *Panderodus* elements from the same limestone sample will show that these superficially similar specimens can be sorted into six categories, on the basis of slight differences in symmetry and the arrangement of longitudinal ridges. There were species of *Panderodus* around before the Silurian, but their elements are far less common in Ordovician rocks of Ohio than in the Brassfield Formation.

Like *Panderodus, Ozarkodina* Branson & Mehl (figs. 18-2.1 to 18-2.6) first appeared in the Ordovician, but is first common in Silurian rocks in Ohio; it ranges upward into Devonian strata. The skeleton of *Ozarkodina* was quite similar to that of its probable ancestor, *Plectodina*; that is, it included elements of six different shapes. Positions in the P region were occupied by distinctive angulate and **carminate** pectiniform elements (figs. 18-2.5, 18-2.6). The M region included a pair of **dolabrate** ramiform elements (fig. 18-2.4). Positions in the S region were occupied by an array of ramiform types (figs. 18-2.1 to 18-2.3). If one compares the S-position elements of *Ozarkodina* with those of *Plectodina* (figs. 18-2.13 to 18-2.15), a number of similarities are immediately apparent, but differences also are obvious—and these help to distinguish the two conodont genera. *Ozarkodina* was very important in that it was ancestral to a majority of the more specialized genera of conodonts that became widespread later in Silurian and Devonian seas.

Unfortunately, it is difficult (and expensive) to collect conodonts from many of the Silurian rocks in Ohio younger than the Brassfield Formation because most of these rocks are dolomite. Dolomite dissolves slowly in acetic acid and yields very large insoluble residues in which conodont elements tend to be rare. At several localities in the Ohio Brush Creek valley of northern Adams County, however, the Brassfield Formation is overlain by about 40 meters of Estill Shale, which disaggregates easily and will yield 6 to 10 well-preserved conodont elements per kilogram of shale. Kleffner (1987) has described and illustrated these conodonts. Other references on Silurian conodonts include Rexroad (1967), Cooper (1975), and Kleffner (1990).

DEVONIAN CONODONTS

Icriodus Branson & Mehl (figs. 18-3.17, 18-3.18) is an exclusively Devonian conodont genus that is common in the Columbus and Delaware Limestones of Ohio. It had an apparatus composed of tiny coniform elements in what amount to S and M positions, and paired **segminiscaphate** elements in P positions. The P elements are the most diagnostic of the many species included in this genus. Insoluble residues from 2- to 3-kg samples of Columbus Limestone, collected from just about any roadside exposure in central or north-central Ohio, ought to yield several of the P elements typical of *Icriodus*.

The same Columbus Limestone samples that yield elements of *Icriodus* should also contain numerous representatives of *Polygnathus* Hinde (figs. 18-3.15, 18-3.16), which first appeared in Devonian seas and persisted into the early part of the Mississippian. *Polygnathus* had a skeletal apparatus composed of six different types of elements. Five of these are similar to those in S, M, and one of the P positions in the apparatus of *Ozarkodina*, but the other P position includes a distinctive **anguliplanate** element (figs. 18-3.15, 18-3.16), which is diagnostic of the genus. Elements of *Polygnathus* from the Columbus Limestone are mostly quite large (up to 2 mm long) and represent *Polygnathus linguiformis* Hinde, a species that apparently flourished in shallow, warm, well-oxygenated seas any place in the world that such an environment existed in the Devonian.

Collections from the upper part of the Olentangy Shale will almost certainly include a few of the distinctive leaflike pectiniform elements that occupied one of the positions in the P region of *Palmatolepis* Ulrich & Bassler (fig. 18-3.11). *Palmatolepis* species also formed complex skeletal apparatuses that included at least six morphologically different types of elements. However, because the leaflike P elements of these apparatuses are the ones most diagnostic of the many species assigned to this genus, this type is the only one illustrated.

More information on Devonian conodonts can be found in Stauffer (1938), Stewart and Sweet (1956), and Sparling (1981, 1983, 1984, 1988).

MISSISSIPPIAN CONODONTS

In Ohio, much of the record of Mississippian time is made up of siliciclastic rocks (conglomerate, sandstone, siltstone, and shale) in which conodonts have not been found. However, surfaces of certain thin black shale beds in the Sunbury Shale, near the base of the Mississippian section in central Ohio, display large numbers of elements. These specimens cannot be removed from the rock, but small, flat chips may include many elements, which may be examined easily under a microscope. Insoluble residues of limestone samples from the Rushville and Maxville Formations, at the top of the Mississippian succession, will yield conodonts to the patient collector. Unfortunately, the Rushville Formation is known to contain limestone at only one place in southwestern Perry County (Thompson and others, 1971). This location is on private property and difficult to find. Most Maxville localities are the sites of mines or active quarries, which may be hazardous and generally do not welcome fossil collectors.

One conodont genus known from the Ohio Mississippian is *Gnathodus* Pander, whose species had skeletal apparatuses composed of six differently shaped elements, of which a **carminiscaphate** form in a P position (fig. 18-3.7) is most distinctive. Both the Rushville and Maxville Formations are known to contain specimens of *Gnathodus*, but they are not common in either unit. Species of *Gnathodus* are very useful in international correlation of Mississippian rocks, so every specimen that is found is important. However, neither the Rushville nor the Maxville was apparently deposited in the environment favored by most species of *Gnathodus*, so specimens are rare.

Hindeodus Rexroad & Furnish (figs. 18-3.1 to 18-3.6) is another Mississippian genus that had an apparatus composed of six different types of elements. *Hindeodus* has not been found in the Sunbury Shale or the Rushville Formation, but it is represented in some abundance in the Maxville Formation at several localities and continues into the Pennsylvanian. As with many other conodonts, *Hindeodus* is best identified from one of its very characteristic P elements (fig. 18-3.1); this carminate pectiniform element has a tall cusp at one end and a single row of denticles atop the broadly expanded **base**.

Cavusgnathus Harris & Hollingsworth (figs. 18-3.8, 18-3.9) is represented by numerous specimens in the Maxville Formation and in marine limestone beds in younger Pennsylvanian formations. Elements of Mississippian and Pennsylvanian species differ from one another in several subtle aspects, but all are similar in representing apparatuses composed of six differently shaped element types. Only one of these types is illustrated—a carminiscaphate pectiniform element that has a distinct bladelike extension at one end and a platform at the other. Denticles of the blade are continuous with a low row of denticles along one side of the platform. This row is separated by a deep trough from a similar denticle row on the opposite margin of the platform. In both Mississippian and Pennsylvanian times, *Cavusgnathus* seems to have been most abundant in warm, relatively shallow, marine environments.

PENNSYLVANIAN CONODONTS

Many of the Pennsylvanian rocks in Ohio were deposited in nonmarine environments, hence they lack fossils of conodonts and other marine organisms. Here and there in the lower two-thirds of the Pennsylvanian sequence, however, are thin marine limestones, which evidently formed in very shallow water but may nevertheless yield the skeletal elements of conodonts in considerable abundance. It has already been mentioned that *Hindeodus* and *Cavusgnathus* continue from the Mississippian into the Pennsylvanian, and specimens representing species of both genera are common in Ohio Pennsylvanian limestones. *Gnathodus* is limited to the Mississippian; however, species of the closely related genera *Neognathodus* Dunn, *Idiognathodus* Gunnell, and *Streptognathodus* Stauffer & Plummer are well represented in Pennsylvanian limestones in Ohio.

Neognathodus had a six-member skeletal apparatus, but its species are especially distinguished by carminiscaphate P elements (fig. 18-3.14), which have a long, comblike blade at one end and a broadly expanded platform at the other. The upper side of the platform bears three parallel rows of low denticles, the central one of which is a continuation of the blade onto the platform. The central denticle row extends almost to the end of the platform in early Pennsylvanian species of *Neognathodus*, but fuses with one of the marginal rows of denticles at points closer and closer to the blade in younger species.

Idiognathodus (fig. 18-3.12) and *Streptognathodus* (fig. 18-3.13), like *Neognathodus*, had six-member skeletal apparatuses in which one of the P elements is the most distinctive. In both genera those elements are carminiscaphate or **anguliscaphate** pectiniform elements that have a long comblike blade (which commonly breaks off) and a broadly expanded platform at the opposite end. The platform surmounts a broadly scoop-shaped base and bears a variety of different types of ridges and denticles on its upper surface. In P elements of *Streptognathodus* the comblike blade is replaced on the platform by a deep axial furrow, or trough, which extends down the center of the platform to, or almost to, its tip. In P elements of *Idiognathodus*, however, the platform surface is ornamented by prominent transverse ridges and clusters of denticles and there is no axial trough.

For more information on Pennsylvanian conodonts and conodont localities, see Sturgeon and Youngquist (1949) and Merrill (1972, 1973, 1974).

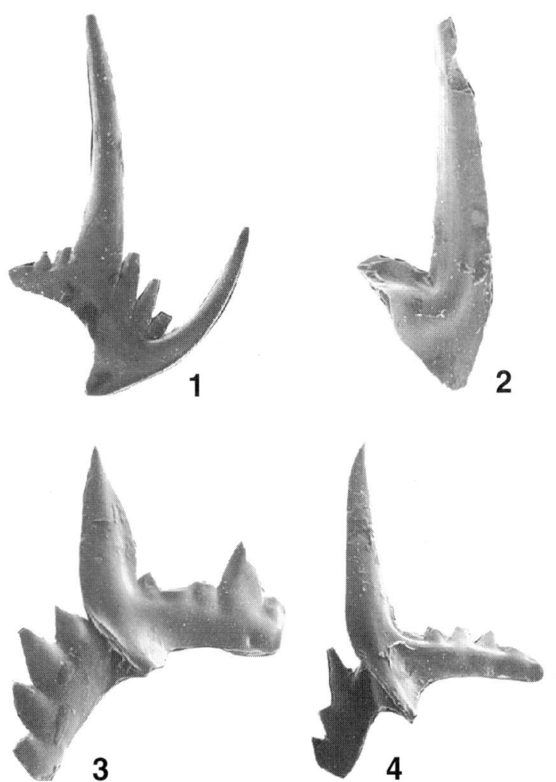

FIGURE 18-1.—The elements of the apparatus of *Phragmodus undatus* Branson & Mehl, a common conodont in Ordovician rocks in Ohio. All elements are 130 times natural size. **1**, typical S-region element. **2**, M-region element. **3**, **4**, P-region elements. Point Pleasant Formation, old quarry at junction of U.S. Route 52 and Bear Creek Road, Washington Township, Clermont County, Ohio. SEM (scanning electron microscope) stub OSU 47263.

FIGURE 18-2.—Ordovician and Silurian conodonts. All specimens on SEM stubs OSU 47263 and OSU 47264.

1-6 *Ozarkodina* Branson & Mehl. **1-3**, S-region elements, 230 times natural size. **4**, M-region element, 350 times natural size. **5**, **6**, P-region elements, 190 times natural size. Brassfield Formation (Silurian), road cut on Ohio Route 41 northeast of West Union, Adams County, Ohio.

7-12 *Oulodus velicuspis* (Pulse & Sweet). **7-9**, S-region elements, 75 to 200 times natural size. **10**, M-region element, 110 times natural size. **11**, **12**, P-region elements, 90 times natural size. Fairview Formation (Ordovician), Stonelick Creek north of Owensville, Stonelick Township, Clermont County, Ohio.

13-18 *Plectodina tenuis* (Branson & Mehl). **13-15**, S-region elements, about 115 times natural size. **16**, M-region element, 130 times natural size. **17**, **18**, P-region elements, 150 and 85 times natural size, respectively. Point Pleasant Formation (Ordovician), old quarry at junction of U.S. Route 52 and Bear Creek Road, Washington Township, Clermont County, Ohio.

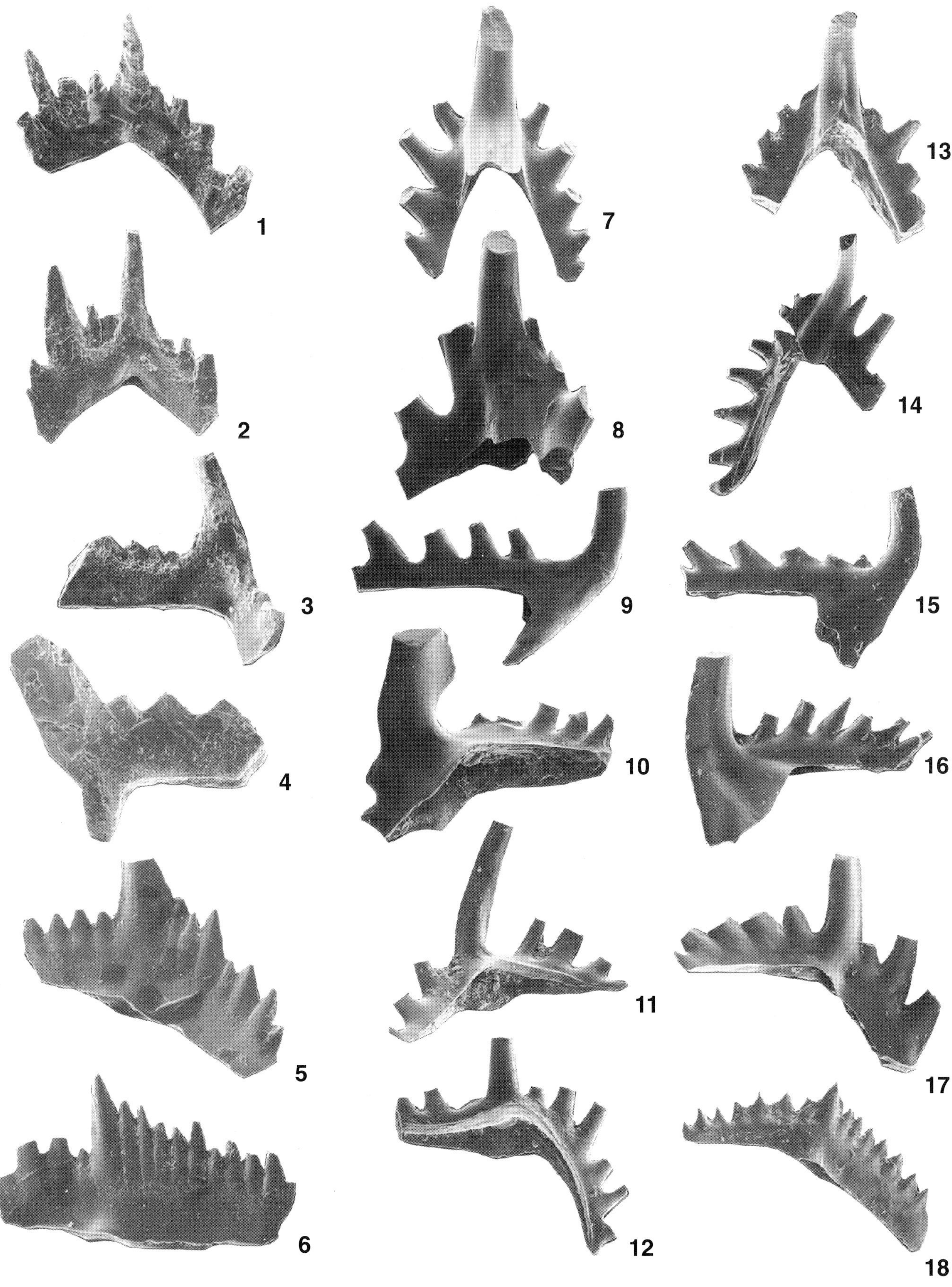
1
2
3
4
5
6
7
8
9
10
11
12
13
14
15
16
17
18

FIGURE 18-3.—Silurian, Devonian, Mississippian, and Pennsylvanian conodonts. All specimens on SEM stubs OSU 47263 and OSU 47264.

1-6	*Hindeodus cristulus* (Youngquist & Miller). **1**, **2**, P-region elements, 180 times natural size. **3**, M-region element, 160 times natural size. **4-6**, S-region elements, 140 to 190 times natural size. Maxville Formation (Mississippian), mine at East Fultonham, Newton Township, Muskingum County, Ohio.
7	*Gnathodus* Pander. P-region element, 120 times natural size. Maxville Formation (Mississippian), quarry on Jonathan Creek, between Fultonham and East Fultonham, Newton Township, Muskingum County, Ohio.
8, 9	*Cavusgnathus* Harris & Hollingsworth. **8**, typical P-region element viewed from above, 170 times natural size. **9**, another P-region element of same species viewed from the side, 140 times natural size. Same unit and location as **1-6**.
10	*Panderodus* Ethington. One of six subtly different coniform elements in the apparatus, 140 times natural size. Brassfield Formation (Silurian), road cut on Ohio Route 41 northeast of West Union, Adams County, Ohio.
11	*Palmatolepis* Ulrich & Bassler. Leaflike P-region element viewed from above, 80 times natural size. Olentangy Shale (Devonian), east bank of Olentangy River downstream from mouth of Mill Run, city of Delaware, Delaware County, Ohio (type section of unit).
12	*Idiognathodus* Gunnell. P-region element viewed from above, 55 times natural size. Lower Mercer limestone (Pottsville Group, Pennsylvanian), Grindstone Run, southeast corner of Lowellville, Poland Township, Mahoning County, Ohio.
13	*Streptognathodus* Stauffer & Plummer. P-region element viewed from above, 65 times natural size. Brush Creek limestone (Conemaugh Group, Pennsylvanian), along East Liverpool Road (old U.S. Route 30) northwest of Cannons Mills, Madison Township, Columbiana County, Ohio.
14	*Neognathodus* Dunn. P-region element viewed from above, 85 times natural size. Lower Mercer limestone (Pottsville Group, Pennsylvanian), bed of Yellow Creek, north edge of Poland, Poland Township, Mahoning County, Ohio.
15, 16	*Polygnathus linguiformis* Hinde. Two P-region elements characteristic of *Polygnathus*. **15**, view from above, 60 times natural size. **16**, view from below, 65 times natural size. Columbus Limestone (Devonian), quarry southeast of White Sulphur, Scioto Township, Delaware County, Ohio.
17, 18	*Icriodus* Branson & Mehl. P-region elements. **17**, view from above, and **18**, view from below, both 130 times natural size. Same unit and location as **15**, **16**.

1
2
3
4
5
6
7
8
9
10
11
12
13
14
15
16
17
18

Chapter 19

PHYLUM HEMICHORDATA, CLASS GRAPTOLITHINA

by Stig M. Bergström

INTRODUCTION

Graptolites are an extinct group of **colonial** animals that were common in the seas from the Middle Cambrian (525 million years ago) to the Pennsylvanian (320 million years ago). Most species were **planktic** (order Graptoloidea) and presumably lived within a few tens of meters of the water surface. These forms, which represent the Earth's first large zooplankton, are most commonly present in deeper water shales and mudstones, particularly in areas along the continental borders such as in the Appalachian Mountains, the Ouachita Mountains, and the Great Basin. Other graptolites were bottom dwelling (**benthic**) and attached to the bottom like a small shrub. These forms (order Dendroidea and some smaller orders) typically are found in shallow-water sediments deposited in the vast epicontinental seas that covered large parts of the interior of North America during most of the Paleozoic Era.

Most graptolite species are between 5 and 50 mm long when fully developed. However, some species reached only a couple of millimeters in size at maturity, and there are also giant colonies that exceed 1 meter in largest dimension.

Very little is known about the soft parts of graptolites because such tissues were not preserved during the fossilization process. However, the individuals (**zooids**) in the colony constructed a colonial skeleton (**rhabdosome**) that consists of a fibrous protein known as collagen. This substance is relatively resistant, and the rhabdosomes were readily preserved in the fossil record. Accordingly, morphological studies of graptolites, and their **taxonomy**, are based solely on features of the rhabdosome.

PRESERVATION AND PREPARATION

The most common mode of preservation of graptolites is as a black or silver-gray film on bedding planes; they generally look like tiny saw blades or pencil scribbles. The distinctive appearance of these structures gave rise to the term "graptolith," which is derived from the Greek "graphein" (to write) and "lithos" (stone). Despite deformation during the fossilization process, such specimens may preserve a surprising amount of morphological detail and, in most cases, they are identifiable to species. More rarely, rhabdosomes retain their original three-dimensional shape (fig. 19-3.4) because of infilling by pyrite, glauconite, hematite, or some other mineral during an early stage of fossilization. Graptolites preserved in this way provide a maximum amount of morphological information and can be subjected to very detailed study. Such specimens preserved in limestone can be isolated from the rock by dissolving limestone pieces in dilute acetic or hydrochloric acid. If this procedure is attempted, it should be carried out only in a well-ventilated area. This treatment does not affect the rhabdosome collagen, which is quite resistant to chemicals. Isolation of graptolites by acid treatment also has the advantage that it commonly produces numerous growth stages of the rhabdosomes (figs. 19-3.5 to 19-3.7) that make it possible to reconstruct the development of the colony.

Graptolites preserved on bedding planes can be prepared mechanically using fine needles and great care. In most cases, a low-powered binocular microscope is needed for this delicate procedure. It is important to remember that cleaning graptolite specimens with a brush and water will generally result in destruction of the specimens because the wall of the rhabdosome, the **periderm**, tends to flake off during such treatment. If a specimen needs cleaning, it should be washed in water but never use a brush!

MORPHOLOGY AND TERMINOLOGY

Figure 1-37 in Chapter 1 illustrates the morphological terms used for graptolites. The first portion of the rhabdosome that was secreted was a small conical or cylindrical structure known as the **sicula** (fig. 19-3.5), which apparently served as the **exoskeleton** of the larva, the first zooid in the colony. From this zooid were budded new zooids that each constructed a cuplike living chamber, called a **theca**. Benthic graptolites (order Dendroidea) were multibranched and had two types of theca (fig. 19-3.11), and many species had a stem for attachment. Most floating, or planktic, graptolites (order Graptoloidea) had a morphologically simple rhabdosome and only one type of theca. In these rhabdosomes the thecae may be arranged in one row (**monoserial**) (fig. 19-4.1), two rows (**biserial**) (fig. 19-2.1), or, less commonly, three (**triserial**) or four (**quadriserial**) rows. The graptoloid graptolites are taxonomically more diverse and geographically more widespread than the dendroid graptolites and include virtually all graptolites useful for determining stratigraphic position. More than half of the graptolites known from Ohio are graptoloids, including all the common forms.

In the absence of preserved soft parts, graptolites have to be classified solely on the basis of the morphology of the rhabdosome. Important characteristics used for discrimination of genera and species include the arrangement of thecae (monoserial, biserial, etc.); the shape and number of thecae per 10 mm; the presence of spines and other distinctive **ornamentation** on the thecae and on the proximal end of the rhabdosome; the size and shape of the rhabdosome (simple or branched); and the growth pattern of the thecae, especially in the proximal portion of the colony.

GRAPTOLITES IN OHIO

Except in the Kope Formation of early Cincinnatian (early Late Ordovician) age, graptolites are relatively uncommon fossils in Ohio's marine sedimentary rocks. Among the approximately 35 species currently recorded from the state, about 80 percent are known from the Upper Ordovician, and about 15 percent from the Silurian. Cambrian and Devonian graptolites are very rare in Ohio and are known only from single occurrences. Elsewhere in the world, graptolites are most abundant and taxonomically diverse in Ordovician and Silurian deeper water shales and mudstones, in which they are the most common **macrofossils** at many localities. Most graptoloid species appear to have preferred an offshore oceanic environment, and relatively few species were adapted to the shallow seas that covered much of the continental interior of North America during Paleozoic time. This environmental preference is a likely explanation of why graptolites are far less common and diverse in Ohio than in the Appalachian Mountains or the Great Basin.

The literature on Ohio graptolites is not extensive and much of it is out of date or not readily accessible except in major university libraries. The references at the end of the book include handbooks (Ruedemann, 1947; Bulman, 1970; Palmer and Rickards, 1991) and some significant papers (Berry, 1966; Erdtmann and Moor, 1973; Mitchell and Bergström, 1977, 1991; Crowther and Bergström, 1980; Bergström and Mitchell, 1986, 1990, 1992; Mitchell, 1986, 1987) that provide useful information about graptolites.

KEY TO REPRESENTATIVE GENERA AND SPECIES OF GRAPTOLITES IN OHIO

This key is intended to be used for identification of reasonably complete specimens showing well-preserved thecae and the proximal end. Very fragmentary specimens, especially if they are flattened, may be indeterminate to species, even for the graptolite specialist. This key should be used for classification of graptolites only from Ohio and adjacent parts of Indiana and Kentucky; its application to specimens from other regions may result in erroneous identification at the species level.

1A. Rhabdosome has many branches that may form a complex network; may have an attachment stem (order Dendroidea) .... *Dictyonema* (figs. 19-4.8 to 19-4.13) or *Mastigograptus* (figs. 19-3.9 to 19-3.11, 19-4.2 to 19-4.5)
1B. Rhabdosome unbranched, or has only two branches; no attachment stem (order Graptoloidea) 2

2A. Rhabdosome Y shaped, consists of a biserial portion and two monoserial branches .... *Dicranograptus nicholsoni* (figs. 19-2.12, 19-2.13)
2B. Rhabdosome not Y shaped 3

3A. Rhabdosome broadly V shaped to U shaped, consists of two monoserial branches .... *Dicellograptus flexuosus* (fig. 19-2.9) or *Dicellograptus* **aff.** *D. forchammeri* (figs. 19-2.10, 19-2.11)
3B. Rhabdosome not broadly V shaped to U shaped 4

4A. Rhabdosome monoserial, in most species nearly straight and without branches .... *Monograptus* (figs. 19-4.1, 19-4.6, 19-4.7)
4B. Rhabdosome biserial 5

5A. Thecae nearly parallel with rhabdosome axis; margin of theca opening perpendicular to rhabdosome axis 6
5B. Thecae inclined 20°-30° to rhabdosome axis; margin of theca opening forms an angle of about 45° with rhabdosome axis 7

6A. Proximal end of rhabdosome has three small spines directed more or less downward .... *Geniculograptus* (figs. 19-2.1 to 19-2.7)
6B. Proximal end of rhabdosome has two prominent spines of subequal size and directed more or less outward .... *Climacograptus spiniferus* (fig. 19-2.8)

7A. Thecae have distinct spines, particularly those in middle to upper part of rhabdosome .... *Orthograptus quadrimucronatus* (figs. 19-2.14 to 19-2.16)
7B. Thecae without distinct spines in middle to upper portion of rhabdosome .... *Arnheimograptus anacanthus* (figs. 19-3.1 to 19-3.8)

ORDOVICIAN GRAPTOLITES

Without any doubt, the best collecting sites for graptolites in Ohio are in the Upper Ordovician (Cincinnatian) rocks exposed in natural outcrops and road cuts in the Cincinnati region and near the Ohio River upstream to near Ripley in Brown County. Virtually every outcrop of the Kope Formation produces specimens, and at some localities literally thousands of specimens can be found in the shales of this stratigraphic unit. However, the species diversity is low and only two species are common—*Geniculograptus typicalis* (Hall) and *G. pygmaeus* (Ruedemann). Another stratigraphic interval yielding rather abundant graptolites, particularly in Butler and adjacent counties, is the Arnheim Formation, from which *Arnheimograptus anacanthus* (Mitchell & Bergström) and *Orthograptus quadrimucronatus* (Hall) can be collected. In both the Kope Formation and the Arnheim Formation, some limestone interbeds produce specimens preserved in three dimensions that can be isolated from the rock by acid treatment.

The most diverse Ordovician graptolite faunas in Ohio occur in Middle to Upper Ordovician rocks equivalent to the Utica Shale of New York. Unfortunately, this unit, which can be traced in the subsurface from New York to Ohio, is nowhere exposed at the surface in Ohio, and its interesting graptolites are available for study only in drill cores. The Utica Shale graptolite faunas were discovered only a few years ago, but study of the many cores obtained during the last decade by the Ohio Division of Geological Survey in its extensive drilling program in southwestern Ohio has more than doubled the list of graptoloid species previously known from the state. Figure 19-1 gives a summary of the known stratigraphic distribution, both in surface exposures and in the subsurface, of some of the common and widespread graptolites in the Middle and Upper Ordovician of Ohio.

The most abundant Ohio graptolite is doubtless *Geniculograptus typicalis typicalis* (figs. 19-2.1 to 19-2.3). Although its rhabdosome may reach a length of 60 mm, most specimens are 20-30 mm long. The rhabdosome is unbranched and biserial, widens gradually from 0.3-0.4 mm near the proximal end to about 2.5 mm in its middle-distal portion, and is essentially straight. The thecae, which number 11-15 in 10 mm, are nearly parallel with the rhabdosome axis and lack spines. In lateral view, the aperture margin of the thecae makes an perpendicular angle with the rhabdosome axis. Three short spines, which are clearly visible only in well-preserved specimens (fig. 19-2.3), extend more or less downward from the sicula at the proximal end of the rhabdosome. Specimens of this subspecies are very common in the Kope Formation, especially in the lower two-thirds of the unit.

Another subspecies, *G. typicalis posterus* (Ruedemann) (not illustrated), has been found in the upper Fairview Formation near Williamsburg in Clermont County. It is distinguished from *G. typicalis typicalis* by its smaller size (13-14 mm long and up to 2 mm wide) and by its somewhat more closely spaced thecae (12-15 thecae in 10 mm). A third subspecies, *G. typicalis magnificus* (Twenhofel) (fig. 19-2.4), which is both wider (up to 4 mm) and longer (up to 70 mm) than *G. typicalis typicalis*, has been found in strata of Maysvillian age (Utica Shale) in a core in Seneca County.

A species closely related to *Geniculograptus typicalis typicalis* is *G. pygmaeus* (figs. 19-2.5 to 19-2.7), which is distinguished from *G. typicalis typicalis* by its smaller size (rhabdosome length less than 10 mm, rhabdosome width less than 1 mm) and smaller and more closely spaced thecae (14-16 in 10 mm). Also, the rhabdosome of *G. pygmaeus* tends to be more parallel sided and less gradually widening than that of *G. typicalis typicalis*. In southwestern Ohio, specimens of *G. pygmaeus* appear about 20-25 meters above the base of the Kope Formation and at the corresponding stratigraphic level in the Utica Shale in the subsurface. *Geniculograptus pygmaeus* is locally extremely common in the middle and upper parts of the Kope Formation. Abundant specimens may be collected from this interval in two road cuts near I-275 just west of the Ohio River at Brent, Kentucky, about 13 km (8 miles) southeast of the center of Cincinnati. *Geniculograptus pygmaeus* ranges into the Fairview Formation, although it is rare in that formation.

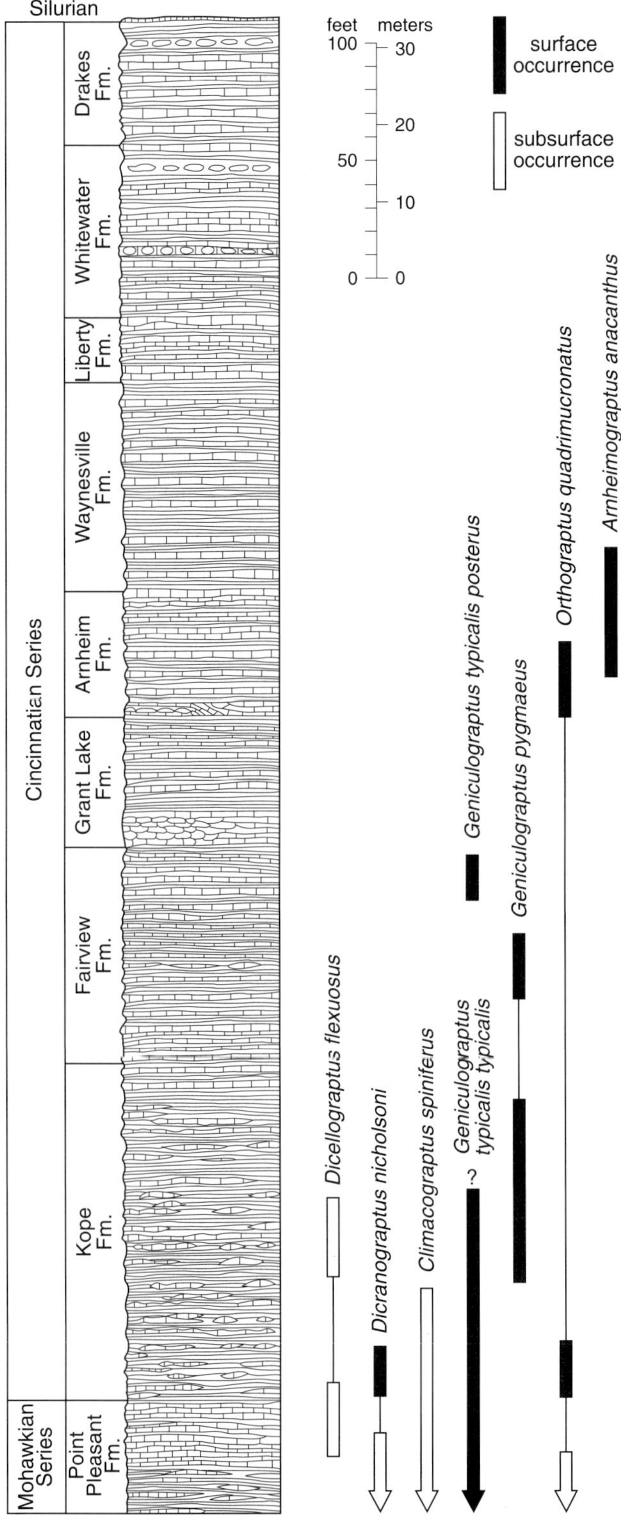

FIGURE 19-1.—Known stratigraphic distribution of some important graptolites in the upper Middle Ordovician (Mohawkian Series) and Upper Ordovician (Cincinnatian Series) in Ohio. Surface occurrences are from the outcrop area in southwestern Ohio and subsurface occurrences are from southwestern and north-central Ohio. All records are projected into the stratigraphic column of the Cincinnati area published by Davis (1985), whose lithostratigraphic terminology has been somewhat modified to conform with that currently adopted by the Ohio Division of Geological Survey. Note that the thickness of the various formations is not to scale; for approximate formation thicknesses, see Davis (1985).

A highly characteristic, and biostratigraphically important, graptolite in the upper Mohawkian and lowermost Cincinnatian is *Climacograptus spiniferus* Ruedemann (fig. 19-2.8). Although not yet found in surface exposures in Ohio, this species is relatively common in several cores from southwestern and northern Ohio. The straight rhabdosome of *C. spiniferus* is generally 20-40 mm long but may reach a length of 70 mm. It widens from 0.7-0.8 mm near the proximal end to a maximum of 2.8 mm distally. There are 9-13 thecae in 10 mm. The proximal end has two nearly symmetrically arranged prominent spines of about equal size that tend to be directed more or less laterally. This species is a very widespread **guide fossil** elsewhere in the world. In Ohio it occurs in the lower Kope Formation and slightly older strata, and in the corresponding interval in the Utica Shale in the subsurface.

Among the other graptolites in the Kope Formation, two distinctive but not common species of two genera deserve mention. *Dicellograptus flexuosus* Lapworth (fig. 19-2.9) has a broadly U-shaped to V-shaped rhabdosome that consists of two monoserial branches that may reach a length of more than 10 cm. These branches are 0.5-1 mm wide, almost straight, and form an angle of 60°-150°. There are 8-10 thecae in 10 mm and many thecae have spinelike extensions. In Ohio, *D. flexuosus* has been found in the Utica Shale in a core from Seneca County and in the lower part of the Kope Formation in several cores from Butler County. Specimens similar to another *Dicellograptus* species, *D. forchammeri* (Geinitz) (figs. 19-2.10, 19-2.11), which differ from *D. flexuosus* in having slightly wider branches and a less conspicuous sicula, have been collected from the lowermost Kope Formation in an outcrop that is now flooded along the Ohio River in Cincinnati.

Specimens of *Dicranograptus nicholsoni* Hopkinson (figs. 19-2.12, 19-2.13), the other noteworthy species in the Kope, have a Y-shaped rhabdosome that consists of a short, straight, biserial proximal part from which diverge two monoserial branches that form an angle of 40°-70° with each other. The biserial portion of the rhabdosome is about 5 mm long and 0.7-1.7 mm wide and has 5-8 thecae along each side. The monoserial branches, which are incomplete in most specimens, are straight or gently curved and may reach a length of more than 100 mm, although they are only about 1 mm wide. There are 9-13 thecae in 10 mm, and those in the biserial portion of the rhabdosome bear distinct spines. This species has been found in the lowermost Kope Formation in the same flooded outcrop along the Ohio River in Cincinnati as *Dicellograptus* aff. *D. forchammeri*, and in the Utica Shale in several cores from southwestern Ohio.

As noted above, two distinctive biserial graptolites are present in the Upper Cincinnatian Arnheim Formation in southwestern Ohio. The rhabdosome of *Orthograptus quadrimucronatus* (figs. 19-2.14 to 19-2.16) is up to 60 mm long, almost parallel sided for most of its length, and up to 3 mm wide. The thecae are about three times as long as wide and form an angle of about 30° with the axis of the rhabdosome. There are about 10 thecae in 10 mm, and, in well-preserved specimens, the thecae may have conspicuous spines. Specimens of this species have been collected at several localities in southwestern Ohio (particularly in Butler County), and the species also is present in cores from southwestern and northern Ohio. As shown in figure 19.1, in Ohio *O. quadrimucronatus* is not restricted to the Arnheim Formation but has a rather long range from the upper Middle Ordovician to the upper Upper Ordovician.

The rhabdosome of *Arnheimograptus anacanthus* (figs. 19-3.1 to 19-3.4, 19-3.8) is up to 10 mm long and widens rather gradually but rapidly from about 0.7 mm at the proximal end to a maximum of about 1.8 mm. In some specimens, the distal part of the rhabdosome is narrower than the middle part (fig. 19-3.3). The thecae form an angle of 20°-30° to the axis of the rhabdosome, number 14-18 in 10 mm, and lack spines. There are three short, spinelike projections extending from the sicula at the proximal end (fig. 19-3.3), but these are visible only in well-preserved specimens. This species was originally described from excellent three-dimensionally preserved specimens isolated from limestone nodules from a now-covered outcrop of the Arnheim Formation in Stonelick State Park in Clermont County. Subsequently, it has been found in the same stratigraphic interval at several localities in Butler County and also is present in a core from Seneca County. It appears to be characteristic of, and relatively common in, a rather narrow interval in the Arnheim Formation and lower Waynesville Formation.

Dendroid graptolites are not uncommon locally in the Upper Ordovician of southwestern Ohio, and at least seven species are known. Several species belong to the genus *Mastigograptus* Ruedemann, which includes bushlike multibranched rhabdosomes that may be several centimeters across. Individual rhabdosome branches are slender, less than 1 mm wide, and branch in a dichotomous or irregular fashion. The thecae are of two types (fig. 19-3.11) but are difficult to see in flattened specimens.

The original species description of *Mastigograptus perexilis* Ruedemann (fig. 19-4.3) is based on specimens collected from the Waynesville Formation just west of Clarksville in Clinton County. The rhabdosome branches of this species are very thin (0.05-0.1 mm). Specimens from the Arnheim Formation at Russellville in Brown County were used to distinguish *M. strictus* Ruedemann (figs. 19-4.4, 19-4.5), which have wider (0.1-0.6 mm) rhabdosome branches. Another species, *M. tenuiramosus* (Walcott) (fig. 19-4.2), has been collected from the Kope Formation at several localities in the Cincinnati region, and a similar form (figs. 19-3.9 to 19-3.11) occurs in the Arnheim Formation at Stonelick State Park in Clermont County. The rhabdosome of these forms may reach a size of 200 mm and exhibits a simpler (mostly dichotomous) type of branching than the two former species.

SILURIAN GRAPTOLITES

In comparison to Ordovician graptolites, Silurian graptolites are far less common and of lower taxonomic diversity in Ohio. Only five species of dendroid graptolites are recorded, and graptoloid graptolites are known only from a single locality that yields a single species. Because taxonomically quite diverse dendroid graptolite faunas are described from eastern Indiana (especially from the middle Silurian Mississinewa Shale at Yorktown in Delaware County), it is surprising that Ohio's Silurian graptolite record is so poor. The scarcity and low diversity of Silurian graptolites in Ohio may be partly due to the fact that the shallow-water depositional environments in which the Silurian carbonates in Ohio were laid down were not suitable for the preservation of these fossils. Also, the recent find of graptolites in the Estill Shale in southern Ohio might be taken as indication that graptolites may have been overlooked in the Silurian succession of the state.

The only record of a Silurian graptoloid graptolite from Ohio is the recent find of monoserial rhabdosome fragments provisionally identified as *Monograptus* sp. (figs. 19-4.6, 19-4.7) in the Lower Silurian Estill Shale. These fragments were discovered by Mark A. Kleffner (The Ohio State University—Lima) in a road cut along Ohio Route 41 south-southwest of Jacksonville in Adams County. Monograptids, which have an unbranched monoserial rhabdosome (fig. 19-4.1), are a biostratigraphically important and taxonomically diverse group of Silurian and early Devonian graptolites that have a virtually global distribution.

Two representative species of the few dendroid graptolites known from the Silurian of Ohio are *Dictyonema scalariforme* Foerste and *D. pertenue* Foerste, both originally described on the basis of specimens from the Brassfield Formation at Dayton. The rhabdosome of *D. scalariforme* (figs. 19-4.8, 19-4.9), which may be several centimeters across in complete specimens, consists of a complex network that developed by dichotomous branching from the proximal portion of the colony. The individual branches are connected by irregularly placed transverse bars referred to as **dissepiments**. The branches are 0.50-0.65 mm wide, and, measured across the colony, there are 10-12 branches in 10 mm. Dissepiments are distributed along the colony at a density of 10-15 dissepiments in 10 mm. Along the middle of each branch there is a series of slender thecae, but their detailed morphology is poorly known. They number 11-26 in 10 mm.

The rhabdosome of *Dictyonema pertenue* (figs. 19-4.10, 19-4.11) is similar to that of *D. scalariforme* but is distinguished by having slightly finer branches (about 0.2 mm wide) that are located closer to each other (about 18 branches in 10 mm, measured across the colony). Along the branches there are about 24 thecae in 10 mm.

DEVONIAN GRAPTOLITES

Although more than a dozen graptolite species are recorded from the Devonian of North America, graptolites of that age are, by and large, rare and have been collected from only a few localities. There appears to be no published record of Devonian graptolites from Ohio, but a sample of Columbus Limestone collected long ago at Sandusky in Erie County contains several specimens identified as *Dictyonema hamiltoniae* Hall (figs. 19-4.12, 19-4.13). The rhabdosome of this species is 5-10 cm across and has numerous branches that are 0.5-0.6 mm wide. Between the branches are well-developed dissepiments that are about the same width as the branches. Along the branches there are about 10 thecae per 10 mm. Previously, this species has been found in the Devonian Onondaga Limestone and Hamilton Group at a few localities in New York.

ACKNOWLEDGMENTS

Many thanks are extended to Charles E. Mitchell (State University of New York at Buffalo) for 20 years of enjoyable cooperation in graptolite studies in Ohio and elsewhere, which produced much of the data used in the present compilation. Helen H. Hayes, Karen S. Tyler, and Beth A. Daye of the technical staff of the Department of Geological Sciences, The Ohio State University, provided much appreciated assistance during the course of the preparation of the manuscript.

FIGURES 19-2 TO 19-4 FOLLOW

FIGURE 19-2.—Ordovician graptoloid graptolites. All specimens in lateral view. All scale bars equal 1 mm. Figures 19-2.1 and 19-2.2 are from Bulman (1932); figures 19-2.3 to 19-2.5 and 19-2.15 are from Bergström and Mitchell (1992); figures 19-2.6, 19-2.7, and 19-2.10 to 19-2.13 are from Bergström and Mitchell (1986); figures 19-2.8, 19-2.9 and 19-2.14 are from Bergström and Mitchell (1990); figure 19-2.16 is from Goldman and Mitchell (1991).

1-3 *Geniculograptus typicalis typicalis* (Hall). **1**, 16-theca stage of three-dimensionally preserved rhabdosome. Cincinnati, Ohio; specimen 573 in the Holm graptolite collection, Swedish Museum of Natural History, Stockholm. **2**, 13-theca stage of three-dimensionally preserved rhabdosome. Cincinnati, Ohio; specimen 565 in the Holm graptolite collection. **3**, outline drawing of mature rhabdosome. Utica Shale, lower *G. pygmaeus* Zone, Ohio Division of Geological Survey core 2580, depth 425 meters (1417 feet), Seneca County, Ohio.

4 *Geniculograptus typicalis magnificus* (Twenhofel). Outline drawing of mature rhabdosome. Utica Shale, upper *G. pygmaeus* Zone, Ohio Division of Geological Survey core 2580, depth 351 meters (1170 feet), Seneca County, Ohio.

5-7 *Geniculograptus pygmaeus* (Ruedemann). **5**, outline drawing of rhabdosome. Utica Shale, lower *G. pygmaeus* Zone, Ohio Division of Geological Survey core 2974, depth 343 meters (1143 feet 2 inches), Wyandot County, Ohio. **6**, outline drawing of mature rhabdosome. Cincinnati region; specimen in lot 9448/2 in the Dyer collection, Harvard University. **7**, outline drawing of 12-theca stage rhabdosome. Cincinnati region; specimen in lot 9448/2 in the Dyer collection.

8 *Climacograptus spiniferus* Ruedemann. Outline drawing of incomplete rhabdosome. Utica Shale, *C. spiniferus* Zone, 37.8 meters above the top of the Trenton Limestone in the Cook Farm well (Indiana Geological Survey well 57), Wayne County, Indiana.

9 *Dicellograptus flexuosus* Lapworth. Outline drawing of virtually complete rhabdosome. Utica Shale, *C. spiniferus* Zone, 48.7 meters above the top of the Trenton Limestone in the New Point well (Indiana Geological Survey well 124), Decatur County, Indiana.

10, 11 *Dicellograptus* aff. *D. forchammeri* (Geinitz). Outline drawings of incomplete rhabdosomes. Lowermost Kope Formation, Cincinnati, Ohio; USNM 54274.

12, 13 *Dicranograptus nicholsoni* Hopkinson. Outline drawings of incomplete rhabdosomes. Lowermost Kope Formation, Cincinnati, Ohio; USNM 54269e (**12**) and 54269d (**13**).

14-16 *Orthograptus quadrimucronatus* (Hall). **14**, outline drawing of rhabdosome with well-developed spines. Utica Shale, *C. spiniferus* Zone, 34 meters above the top of the Trenton Limestone in the Cook Farm well (Indiana Geological Survey well 57), Wayne County, Indiana. In a recent study of the *O. quadrimucronatus* group, Goldman (1995) referred specimens that have one or two pairs of extraordinary long spines between the sixth and thirteenth theca pair, as this specimen does, to a separate species, *O. spinigerus* Lapworth. **15**, outline drawing of mature rhabdosome. Utica Shale, *Amplexograptus manitoulinensis* Zone, Ohio Division of Geological Survey core 2580, depth 257 meters (856 feet 10 inches), Seneca County, Ohio. **16**, acid-isolated, distally incomplete rhabdosome. Arnheim Formation, near Oxford, Butler County, Ohio; no. 1L in the Shideler collection, Miami University.

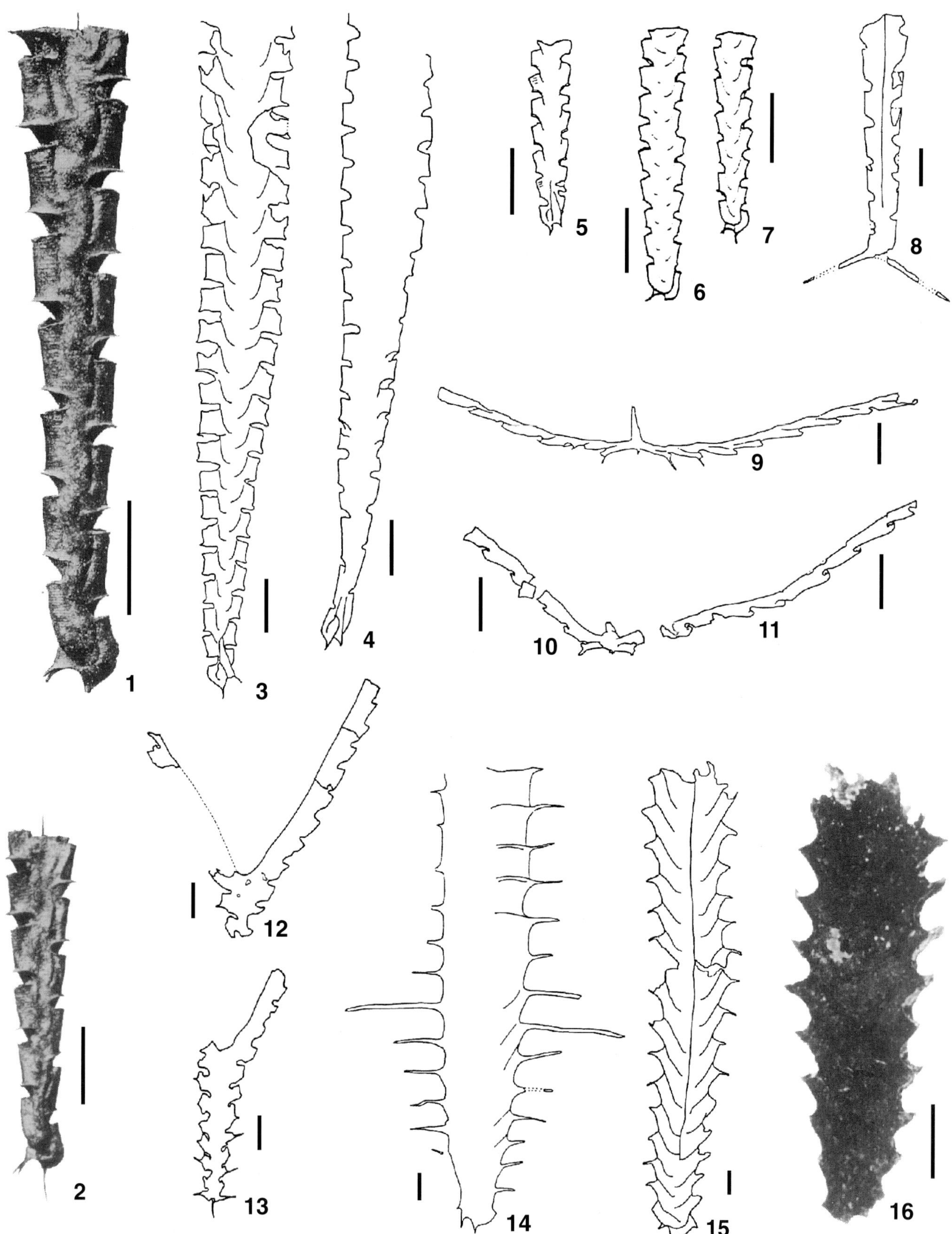
1
2
3
4
5
6
7
8
9
10
11
12
13
14
15
16

FIGURE 19-3.—Ordovician graptolites from the Arnheim Formation at Stonelick State Park, Clermont County, Ohio. All scale bars equal 1 mm except those for figures 19-3.5 to 19-3.7, which equal 0.1 mm, and those for figures 19-3.8 and 19-3.10, which equal 10 mm. Figures 19-3.1 to 19-3.8 are from Mitchell and Bergström (1977); figures 19-3.9 to 19-3.11 are from Mitchell (1975).

1-8 *Arnheimograptus anacanthus* (Mitchell & Bergström). **1**, **2**, lateral views of three-dimensionally preserved rhabdosomes. OSU 31651 (**1**) and OSU 31653 (**2**). **3**, outline drawing of fully developed rhabdosome. OSU 31663. **4**, inclined view of part of rhabdosome showing appearance of thecae. OSU 31655. **5-7**, growth stages representing sicula and development of first theca of rhabdosome. **8**, Numerous well-preserved, randomly oriented rhabdosomes partially dissolved out of a limestone nodule using acetic acid. OSU 26659.

9-11 *Mastigograptus* **cf.** *M. tenuiramosus* (Walcott). **10**, incomplete rhabdosomes. **9**, upper left portion of **10** at higher magnification. **11**, drawing of upper central portion of **9** at higher magnification showing appearance of two types of thecae (**a**, autotheca; **b**, bitheca).

1
2
3
4
5
6
7
8
9
10
11
a
b

FIGURE 19-4.—Ordovician, Silurian, and Devonian graptolites. All specimens except figures 19-4.1, 19-4.6, and 19-4.7 are dendroid graptolites. All scale bars equal 10 mm except those for figures 19-4.7 and 19-4.9 to 19-4.11, which equal 1 mm. All figures from Ruedemann (1947) except figures 19-4.1, 19-4.6, 19-4.7, 19-4.12, 19-4.13.

1, 6, 7	*Monograptus* sp. **1**, schematic drawing showing appearance of typical monograptid graptolite. After Bulman (1970, fig. 99, 1b). **6**, **7**, two views of three-dimensionally preserved rhabdosome fragment including sicula and spinose thecae. Estill Shale (Silurian), road cut along Ohio Route 41 south-southwest of Jacksonville, Adams County, Ohio; OSU 47299.
2	*Mastigograptus tenuiramosus* (Walcott). Incomplete rhabdosome. Kope Formation (Ordovician), Covington, Kentucky.
3	*Mastigograptus perexilis* Ruedemann. Incomplete rhabdosome. Waynesville Formation (Ordovician), Clarksville, Clinton County, Ohio; USNM 66721.
4, 5	*Mastigograptus strictus* Ruedemann. **4**, incomplete rhabdosome. **5**, upper portion of same specimen at higher magnification. Arnheim Formation (Ordovician), Russellville, Brown County, Ohio; no. 148A9 in the Shideler collection, Miami University.
8, 9	*Dictyonema scalariforme* Foerste. **8**, relatively complete rhabdosome. **9**, portion of same specimen at higher magnification. Note dissepiments. Brassfield Formation (Silurian), Dayton, Ohio.
10, 11	*Dictyonema pertenue* Foerste. **10**, relatively complete rhabdosome. **11**, portion of same rhabdosome at higher magnification. Note dissepiments. Brassfield Formation (Silurian), Dayton, Ohio.
12, 13	*Dictyonema hamiltoniae* Hall. **12**, several fragmentary specimens preserved on limestone bedding plane. **13**, portion of rhabdosome at higher magnification. Columbus Limestone (Devonian), Sandusky, Erie County, Ohio; OSU 3849.

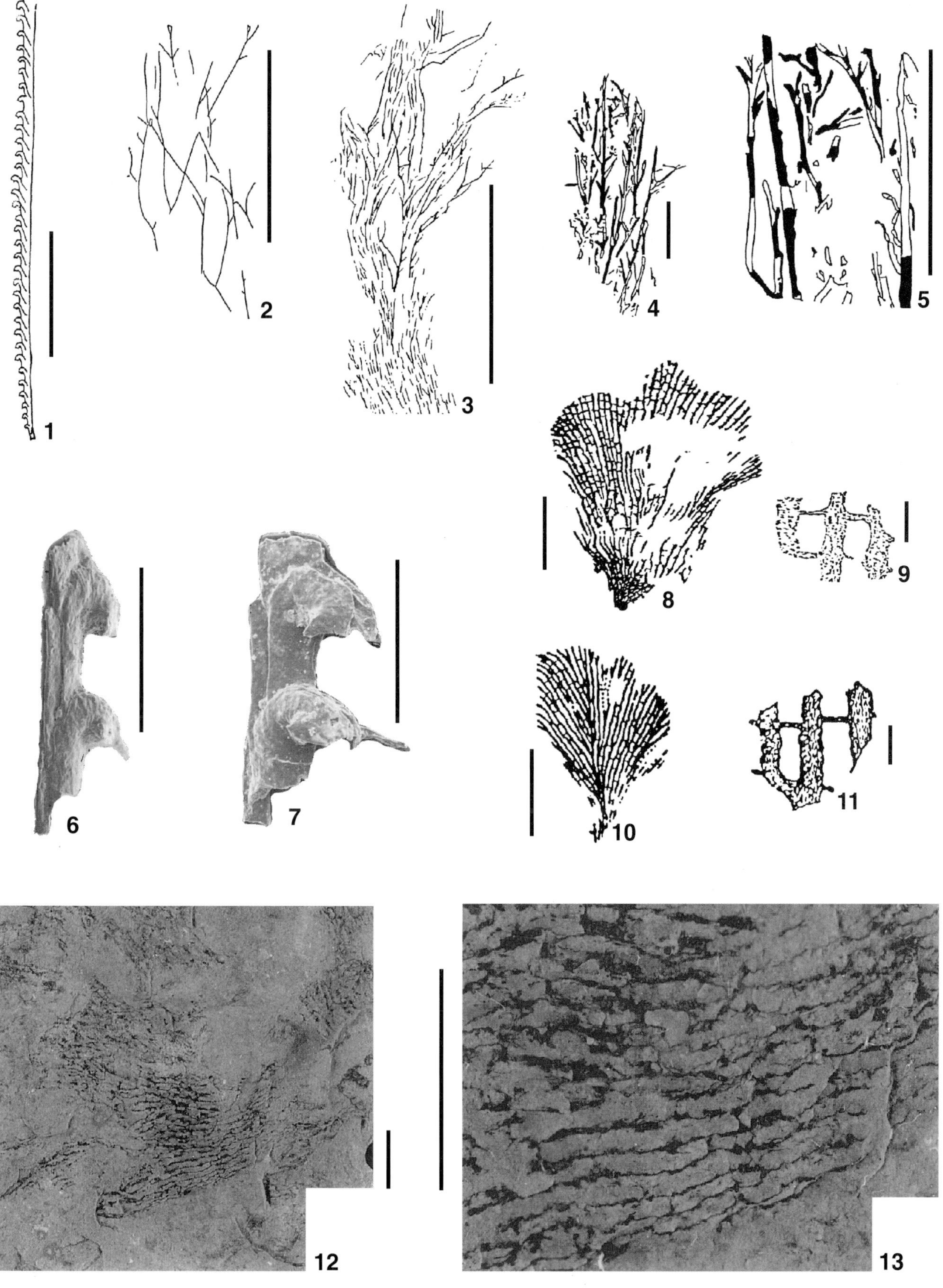
1
2
3
4
5
6
7
8
9
10
11
12
13

Chapter 20

TENTACULITOIDS

by Stig M. Bergström

INTRODUCTION

Tentaculitoids are a group of extinct marine animals whose conical shells (**conchs**) are quite common in some intervals in Ohio's Lower Paleozoic stratigraphic succession. The conchs are 1-40 mm (rarely up to 80 mm) long and consist of calcium carbonate. In most cases they are straight or slightly bent, circular in cross section (unless flattened during the fossilization process), and **bilaterally symmetrical**. The first-formed part of the conch, the **initial chamber**, is pointed; it developed as a droplike structure that has an **apical end**. The opposite end of the conch has a circular opening (**aperture**) without a cover or other lid structure. Figure 1-35 in Chapter 1 illustrates the morphology of tentaculitoids.

In the proximal portion of the conch, the interior cavity is partitioned into a series of chambers (**camerae**) by **septa**, which are not perforated, or penetrated by a siphuncle as in cephalopods. The distal part of the conch lacks septa and other internal structures, and the conch cavity forms a **living chamber**, where the soft parts of the animal are likely to have been located. In many, but not all, species the exterior wall of the conch has transverse rings and other types of **ornamentation**. As seen in **thin sections** at high magnification, the wall of the conch consists of two or three separate layers that are composed of many thin **lamellae** of calcite crystals and organic material. The septa are built up of many thin lamellae of uniform appearance.

Very little is known about the soft parts in these animals. X-ray photographs of rock-embedded pyritized specimens from the Devonian in Germany suggest the presence of a tentacle apparatus at the conch aperture, but other soft parts remain unknown. Accordingly, the **taxonomy** of the group is based entirely on morphological structures in the conch. Among the genera represented in Ohio, *Viriatellina* Bouček and *Styliolina* Karpinsky are referred to the order Dacryoconarida, and *Tentaculites* von Schlotheim is included in the order Tentaculitida. Both these orders belong to the class Tentaculitoidea. Hence, the proper general designation for representatives of this class is tentaculitoids, whereas the term tentaculitids should be used only for forms of the order Tentaculitida, and the term tentaculites should be reserved for specimens of *Tentaculites*.

The mode of life of tentaculitoids remains a matter of speculation (see fig. 1-36). Species that have a fairly thick and heavy conch, such as *Tentaculites scalariformis*, are likely to have been **benthic** (bottom dwelling), but whether the conch was resting more or less horizontally or was oriented vertically is not known. The idea that these forms were benthic is supported by the fact that such species tend to have a limited geographic range. Species that have thin-walled and light conchs, such as representatives of *Styliolina*, have in many cases a wide geographic range and occur locally in black shales and other sediments deposited in environments in which bottom conditions were hostile to animal life. Such species are likely to have been **planktic** (floating) or **nektic** (swimming).

The zoological affinities of the tentaculitoids remain enigmatic because of the paucity of information about the appearance of the soft parts and the lack of informative morphological structures in the conch. It has been proposed that they might be mollusks and related to the cephalopods, but conclusive evidence for this is lacking, and the absence of a siphuncle casts doubt on this interpretation. It has also been suggested that they may be lophophorates and hence related to brachiopods and bryozoans, but there is no suggestion of such a relationship in the structures of the conch. Most recent specialists prefer not to group the class Tentaculitoidea with any higher unit in the zoological system.

Compared with that of most other fossil groups, the literature on North American tentaculitoids is quite limited, and little has been published on Ohio species during this century. The *Treatise on Invertebrate Paleontology* section on tentaculitoids (Fisher, 1962) gives an overview of these animals. The Devonian species of Ohio were dealt with in an unpublished M.S. thesis by Ghist (1976) that also provides much general information about the group. In a more recent monograph, Larsson (1979) gives an up-to-date summary of our knowledge about tentaculitoids along with detailed descriptions of Silurian species of the Baltic area. The list of references at the end of the book includes both classic (Meek and Worthen, 1868; S. A. Miller, 1874b; Hall, 1879, 1888) and recent (Bouček, 1964; Churkin and Carter, 1970; Hajlasz, 1974; Yoder and Erdtmann, 1975; Blind and Stürmer, 1977) studies that should make it possible for the reader to gain an insight into the literature of the group.

TENTACULITOIDS IN OHIO

The total known stratigraphic range of tentaculitoids is Lower Ordovician to Upper Devonian, but in Ohio they are recorded only from the Upper Ordovician to the Upper Devonian. They are typical marine fossils and occur together with brachiopods, trilobites, and bryozoans in many of the shallow-water deposits in the state. They can be collected in large numbers from the Devonian limestones and shales, but some occurrences also are known from the Upper Ordovician and the Lower Silurian. The group has been subjected to little recent study in North America, and the total number of species recorded from Ohio is less than 20. However, some of these are distinctive morphologically and easily identifiable.

ORDOVICIAN TENTACULITOIDS

The stratigraphically oldest tentaculitoids in Ohio are in Upper Ordovician rocks. Two species are relatively common in rocks of the Richmondian Stage.

The conch of *Tentaculites richmondensis* Miller (figs. 20-1.2 to 20-1.4) is straight or slightly curved, 25-30 mm long, and 2-3 mm wide at the aperture. The rings on the surface of the conch are quite distinct, essentially symmetrical, and have rather sharp crests. Adjacent rings are of rather uniform size, although there is a gradual increase in ring size from the proximal end to the distal end. There are 20-30 rings in an adult specimen and there are no **annulets**. Ornamentation on the conch surface includes about 40 longitudinal thin ribs (**lirae**), but these are clearly visible only in well-preserved specimens. The proximal portion of the conch has a few septa, but these can be seen only in thin sections. This species occurs in the Waynesville through Whitewater Formations. It is quite common locally, and dozens of specimens may be found together on a bedding plane (fig. 20-1.4).

The other widespread species in the Upper Ordovician of Ohio is *Tentaculites sterlingensis* Meek & Worthen (figs. 20-1.1, 20-1.5, 20-1.6). Its conch ornamentation is quite similar to that of *T. richmondensis* but is distinguished by being considerably smaller (10-15 mm long and 1-1.5 mm wide at the aperture) and having more densely spaced rings (about 20-25 rings in 10 mm).

SILURIAN TENTACULITOIDS

Tentaculitoids are poorly known and apparently uncommon in the Silurian rocks of Ohio. Several species of small conical fossils showing a general similarity to tentaculitoids have been recorded from Lower Silurian formations in southern and southwestern Ohio, but most, if not all, of these are probably the calcareous tubes of annelid worms and not tentaculitoids. However, relatively poorly preserved specimens of an unidentified tentaculitoid species occur in the Brassfield Formation in outcrops along Ohio Route 41 between West Union and the Ohio Brush Creek bridge in Adams County. Very small representatives of the group also are present in samples from the Estill Shale in a road cut along Ohio Route 41 south-southwest of Jacksonville in Adams County. These specimens were found in residues of carbonate samples dissolved in acetic acid by Mark A. Kleffner (The Ohio State University—Lima) during his studies of the Estill Shale conodonts. They are part of the micropaleontological collections at Ohio State.

DEVONIAN TENTACULITOIDS

Without any doubt, the most common and widespread tentaculitoid in Ohio is *Tentaculites scalariformis* Hall (figs. 20-1.7 to 20-1.11, 20-2.1). About 10 other species are recorded from the Devonian strata in the state, but among these only three are sufficiently common to merit description here.

Specimens of *Tentaculites scalariformis* are relatively robust and up to 45 mm long, although the average conch size is about 20 mm. Width at the aperture is 3-4.5 mm, and the apical angle (the rate of expansion of the conch in the proximal part) is 10°-15°. The surface of the conch has 25-40 regularly spaced, rounded, slightly asymmetrical transverse rings. There are 10-15 rings per 10 mm in the distal portion of the conch. Between the rings and on the rings themselves are annulets. There are 10-15 annulets between each pair of rings. The conch has no longitudinal ornamentation. The apical portion of the conch has five to six septa that are visible only in thin sections (fig. 20-1.9). This species is common in the Columbus and Delaware Limestones of central Ohio. Specimens also have been collected from the Silica Formation in Lucas County.

A closely related species, *Tentaculites bellulus* Hall (figs. 20-2.2 to 20-2.5), has very similar conch ornamentation but is distinguished by its smaller size (up to 25 mm; average size about 10 mm), smaller apical angle (about 6°), and somewhat more widely spaced annulets (about 13 in 10 mm). In Ohio, this species is best known from the Silica Formation in Lucas County, but it also has been recorded elsewhere in the state.

A morphologically different type of tentaculitoid is *Viriatellina gracilistriata* (Hall) (figs. 20-2.6 to 20-2.9). Its conch is straight, only up to 5 mm long, and about 0.75 mm wide at the aperture. The apical angle is between 4° and 14°. The conch surface has low, in many cases indistinct, transverse rings that number four to five per mm. Along the length of the conch up to its aperture there are 25-35 thin longitudinal ribs. This species is relatively common in the Silica Formation in Lucas County and also has been recorded from the Olentangy Shale.

Internal molds of another tentaculitoid are locally rather abundant in the Olentangy Shale of central Ohio. These specimens (fig. 20-2.10) are straight, about 3 mm long, 0.65 mm wide at the thick end, and lack surface ornamentation. In the absence of preserved shell, specific, and even generic, identification is impossible, but such forms have been referred to as *Styliolina*? sp. Specimens of this type occur near the contact between the lower and upper Olentangy Shale in outcrops along Camp Lazarus Run just south of Stratford in Delaware County.

FIGURE 20-1.—Ordovician and Devonian tentaculitoids. All specimens in lateral view. All scale bars equal 10 mm except that for figure 20-1.9, which equals 1 mm. Figure 20-1.2 is from S. A. Miller (1874b); figures 20-1.3 and 20-1.11 are from Hall (1888); figures 20-1.7 to 20-1.10 are from Ghist (1976).

1, 5, 6	*Tentaculites sterlingensis* Meek & Worthen. **1**, distally incomplete but otherwise well-preserved conch. Cincinnatian Series (Ordovician), southwestern Ohio; OSU 2976. **5**, bedding plane with several randomly oriented specimens (arrows). Upper Ordovician, probably Waynesville Formation (slab found loose), emergency spillway, Caesar Creek State Park, Warren County, Ohio; OSU 47998. **6**, large specimen with well-preserved conch ornamentation. Cincinnatian Series (Ordovician), southwestern Ohio; OSU 2976.
2-4	*Tentaculites richmondensis* Miller. **2**, original illustration of **type specimen**. Cincinnatian Series, Richmondian Stage (Ordovician), near Richmond, Indiana. **3**, well-preserved slightly curved conch. "Hudson River group" (= Cincinnatian Series) (Ordovician), Richmond, Indiana. **4**, typical occurrence of multiple conchs on a bedding plane. Whitewater Formation (Ordovician), Camden, Preble County, Ohio; OSU 14705.
7-11	*Tentaculites scalariformis* Hall. **7**, schematic drawing of an adult conch. **8**, well-preserved uncrushed conch. OSU 32470. **9**, thin section of proximal part of conch showing appearance of four septa. OSU 32472. **10**, large flattened specimen. OSU 32469. **11**, typical assemblage of many flattened conchs on bedding plane. All specimens from Delaware Limestone (Devonian), Delaware County, Ohio; **8** to **10** from quarry near Liberty Church, 5.6 km (3.5 miles) south of Stratford; **11** from city of Delaware.

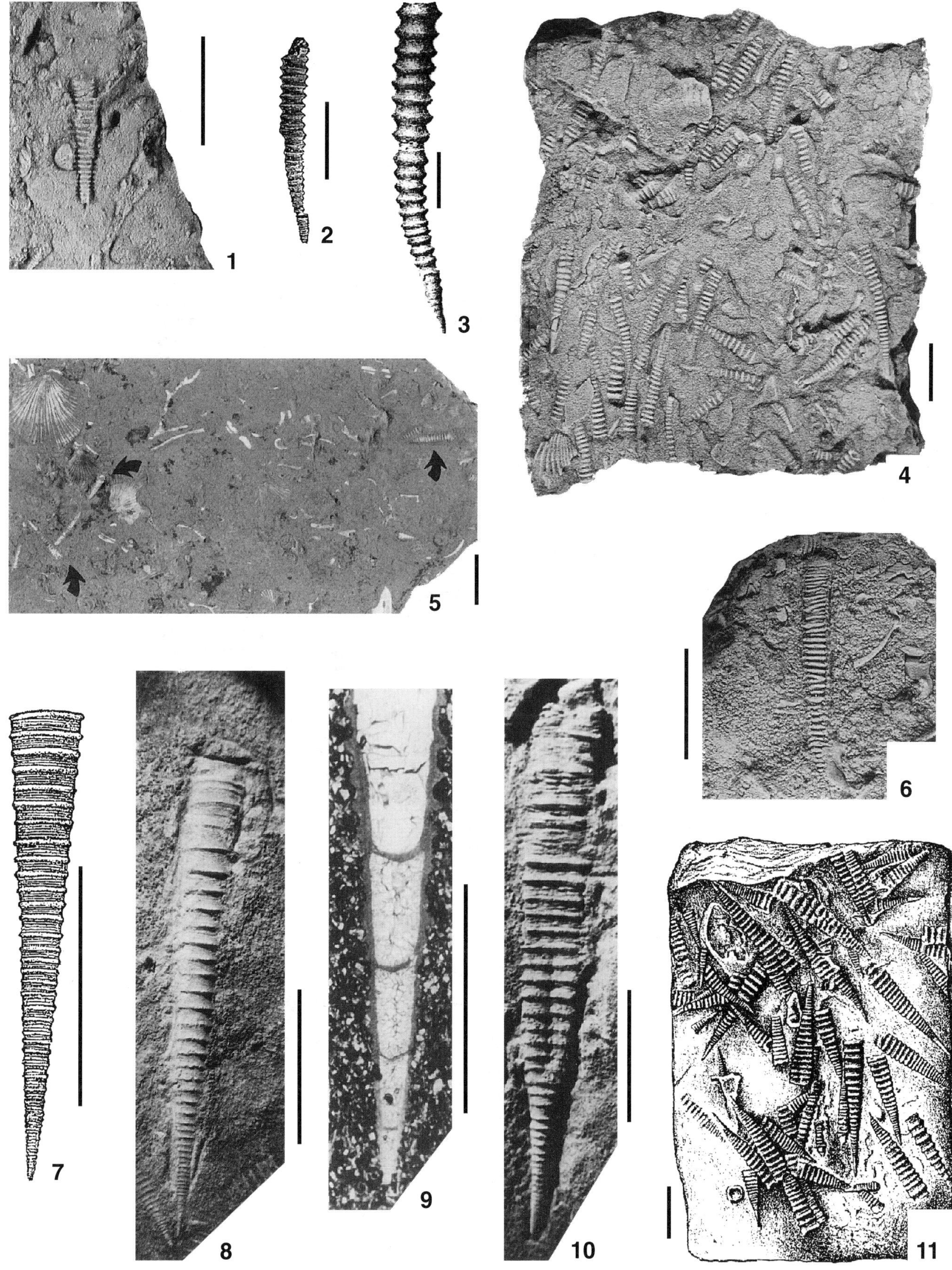
1
2
3
4
5
6
7
8
9
10
11

FIGURE 20-2.—Devonian tentaculitoids. All specimens are in lateral view. Scale bars for figures 20-2.1, 20-2.5 to 20-2.8, and 20-2.10 equal 1 mm; scale bars for figures 20-2.2 to 20-2.4 equal 10 mm; scale bar for figure 20-2.9 equals 0.1 mm. Figures 20-2.2 to 20-2.4, 20-2.6, 20-2.7, and 20-2.10 are from Ghist (1976).

1 *Tentaculites scalariformis* Hall. Enlarged view of ornamentation of conch surface. Delaware Limestone, quarry near Liberty Church, 5.6 km (3.5 miles) south of Stratford, Delaware County, Ohio; OSU 32479.

2-5 *Tentaculites bellulus* Hall. **2**, schematic drawing of adult specimen. **3**, adult conch, and **4**, one of Hall's (1879) type specimens. Hamilton beds, Bellona, New York; NYSM 558 (**3**) and NYSM 559 (**4**). **5**, large distally incomplete conch. Silica Formation, Medusa Portland Cement Company quarry, Silica, Lucas County, Ohio; OSU 32481.

6-9 *Viriatellina gracilistriata* (Hall). **6**, schematic drawing of adult specimen. **7**, moderately well-preserved conch partly embedded in shale. Genesee Slate, near Alden, New York; AMNH 5831/2. **8**, slightly flattened specimen, and **9**, enlarged view of ornamentation of conch surface. Same unit and location as **5**; OSU 32492.

10 *Styliolina*? sp. **Internal mold**. Lower Olentangy Shale, Camp Lazarus Run, just south of Stratford, Delaware County, Ohio; OSU 28705.

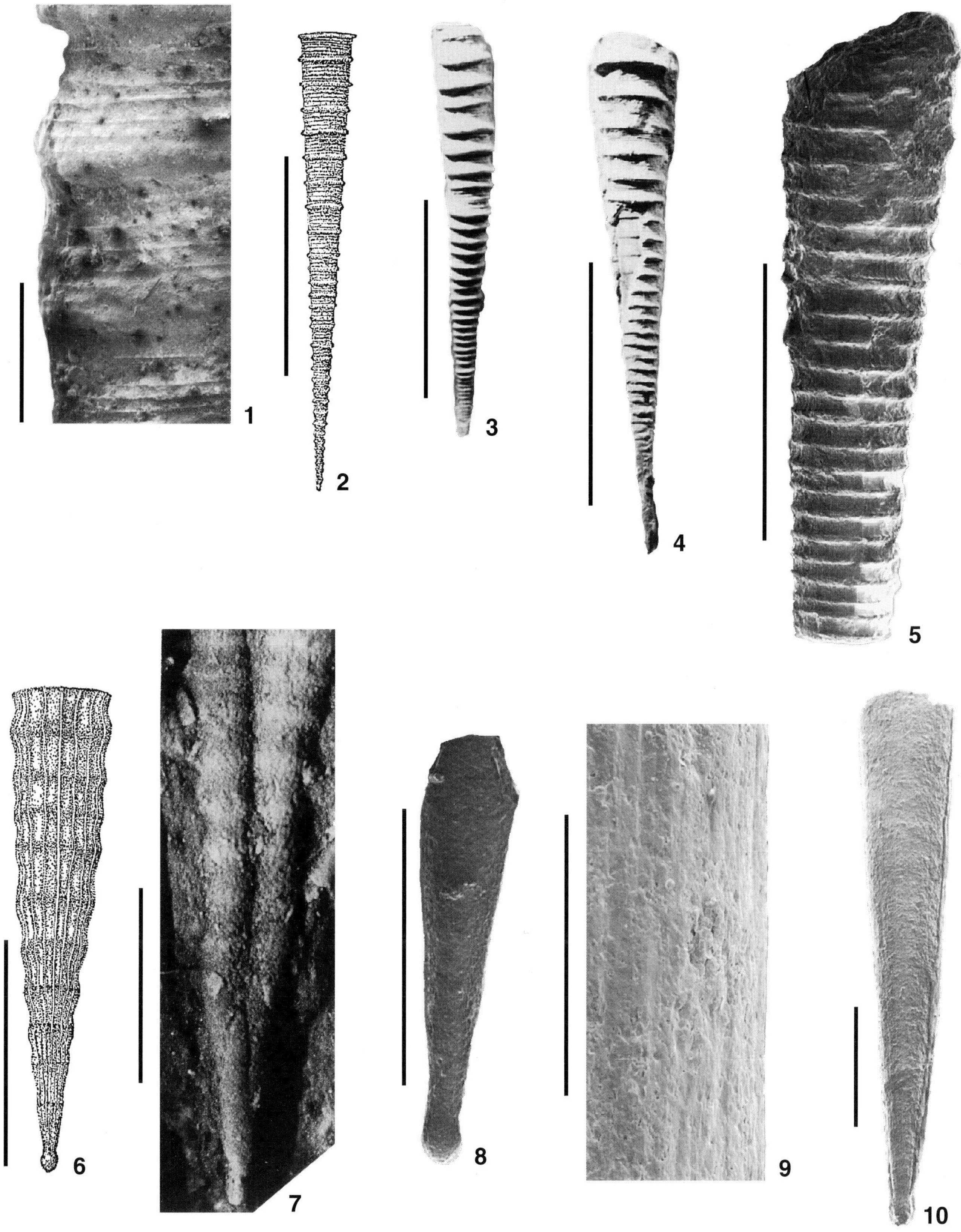
1
2
3
4
5
6
7
8
9
10

Chapter 21

PHYLUM CHORDATA—VERTEBRATE FOSSILS

by Michael C. Hansen

INTRODUCTION

Although most people are familiar with only a few invertebrate groups, almost everyone is aware that a vertebrate is an animal with a backbone and other internal skeletal elements. Many people are also familiar with the major subdivisions of the phylum Chordata, although differences between amphibians and reptiles, for example, are commonly indistinct to many individuals. Because of the complexity of vertebrate classification (table 21-1) and differences in higher **taxonomic** levels for the fishes (Long, 1995) and the **tetrapods** (Carroll, 1988), taxonomic ranks are not emphasized in this chapter.

Except for a few remarkable deposits, remains of fossil vertebrates are much less common than are those of invertebrates. Devonian fishes from the Cleveland area and Pennsylvanian tetrapods and fishes from Linton in eastern Ohio are known worldwide because of their diversity and abundance. Indeed, these two occurrences have furnished much of our perceptions of vertebrate life during these particular geologic periods.

Ohio's record of fossil vertebrates represents only a portion of the history of vertebrate life. The earliest known fish remains are from Upper Cambrian rocks, but it was not until the Middle Ordovician that these creatures become well known in the fossil record. Remains of Ordovician fishes have not as yet been found in the state. Vertebrate remains have been found in Ohio from Devonian, Mississippian, Pennsylvanian, and Permian rocks and in sediments from the Pleistocene Ice Age. Missing from Ohio is a rock record from the Mesozoic Era, the age of dinosaurs, and the Tertiary Period of the Cenozoic Era, the great age of mammals. Therefore, neither dinosaur nor Tertiary mammal remains have been found in Ohio, although these animals certainly must have lived here.

In many cases, fossil vertebrates are difficult to recognize and identify because their skeletons consist of many parts, which tend to become disarticulated soon after death. Thus, the collector is commonly faced with the dilemma of identifying an animal on the basis of a single bone or tooth rather than more complete material. Furthermore, such identifications commonly require the expertise of a specialized paleontologist.

Because vertebrate remains are so rare, each new discovery has the potential of providing valuable scientific information, especially if the discovery yields more skeletal elements than a single tooth, bone, or scale. Individuals who discover such remains should contact the nearest museum or university geology department or the Division of Geological Survey so that these fossils can be referred to an expert and properly identified and evaluated.

Skeletons of fossil vertebrates may require special techniques for collection and preservation. In some cases, the rock or sediment surrounding the specimen may yield important scientific information. For these reasons, it is best to seek the assistance of a professional paleontologist before disturbing vertebrate remains.

There is abundant literature on fossil vertebrates, including descriptions of specimens from Ohio. Carroll (1988) is a general reference on fossil vertebrates. Most of the vertebrates from Paleozoic rocks in Ohio were first described in the reports of the Second Geological Survey of Ohio under the direction of State Geologist John Strong Newberry (1873, 1875), who was one of the leading authorities on fossil fishes (see Dedication of this volume). He enlisted the expertise of Edward Drinker Cope of Philadelphia to describe the tetrapods from the famous Linton locality in Jefferson County. Numerous other references to fossil vertebrates from Ohio, not cited in this text, can be found in the *Bibliography of Ohio geology* (Smyth, 1979) and in the *Bibliography of vertebrate paleontology* (various authors, years, and publishers), available at many larger university libraries.

AGNATHA—JAWLESS FISHES

Although vertebrates probably began their expansion in late Precambrian or Cambrian time, it was not until the Early Ordovician that these early vertebrates (fishes) developed an extensive bony skeleton capable of fossilization. These early fishes were jawless (hence the name of the class: *a*, without, *gnathos*, jaw), relatively small, and four of the six subdivisions were protected by bony plates (Long, 1995). The anaspids, heterostracans, osteostracans, and thelodonts are known from North America. Modern lampreys and hagfishes are descendants of these early agnathans. Ecologically, they must have been "earthworms of the sea," as many species of these jawless fishes were detrital feeders that sucked up bottom sediment and digested the organic matter. Some may have been filter feeders or may have been capable of swallowing small bottom-dwelling or free-floating invertebrates (Long, 1995). The agnathans were the dominant fishes of the Ordovician and Silurian, but by the end of the Devonian they were extinct, except for the lampreys and hagfishes.

The fossil record of agnathans in Ohio is exceedingly meager. The best occurrence of these fishes was in the Holland Quarry Shale (Lower Devonian) in Lucas County, where J. Ernest Carman (1960) discovered a remarkable fossil-bearing deposit in a limestone quarry (Holland Quarry) about 16 km (10 miles) west of Toledo. On the west wall of this now long-abandoned and reclaimed quarry was exposed a small deposit of brownish-black shale, which has been interpreted as a channel that was filled in by sediments deposited in a brackish-water estuary. This tiny deposit, not more than about 15 meters across and only a meter or so thick in the exposure, yielded a remarkable number of agnathans, as well as eurypterids and other invertebrates. This outcrop was the only known occurrence of the Holland Quarry Shale and was the only known exposure of Lower Devonian rocks in Ohio. It is possible that similar Lower Devonian shales are present in northwestern Ohio; however, outcrops in this region are not common and are restricted to quarries and a few stream exposures.

The remains of Holland Quarry agnathan fishes consist of isolated plates that formed a protective armor. These well-preserved specimens were described by Denison (1960) as two new species of heterostracans: *Pteraspis carmani* Denison (figs. 21-1.1, 21-1.2) and *Allocryptaspis laticostatus* Denison.

The bone beds of the Columbus Limestone in the central part of the state have yielded microscopic **tubercles** that have a stellate (star-shaped) pattern. These microscopic fish remains may be referable to agnathans (Wells, 1944b) and appear as tiny black specks in the rock (fig. 21-1.3). These fossils can be extracted by acetic acid techniques such as those used for conodonts (see Chapters 2 and 18). Wells (1944b) named these tubercles *Ohioaspis* and ascribed them to a cephalaspid agnathan. Denison (1978), on the basis of the microscopic structure of these tubercles, referred them to the placoderm *Asterosteus stenocephalus* Newberry.

It may seem puzzling that the very fossiliferous Ordovician rocks and moderately fossiliferous Silurian rocks in Ohio have not yielded remains of agnathan fishes. In part, this lack could be the result of their remains escaping notice, but it is more likely that it is due to paleoecological factors. Early agnathans are found mostly in rocks deposited in nearshore marine waters. Ohio's Ordovician and Silurian rocks were deposited primarily in offshore marine waters.

PLACODERMI—ARMORED FISHES

Placoderms were some of the earliest jawed fishes and are characterized by a heavy armor of thick, bony plates that covered the head and **thorax**. These fishes lacked teeth, but the bony jaws were modified to form sharp spikes, shearing blades, or crushing plates that functioned like teeth. Some of these marine fishes were several meters in length and were obviously active predators, whereas others must have been slow-moving bottom feeders. This diverse group originated in the Silurian and became extinct by the end of the Devonian. Denison (1978) and Long (1995) have summarized the placoderms.

Ohio's fossil record of placoderm fishes is a remarkable one from which much of the knowledge of the group has been derived. Numerous placoderms were described in early Ohio Geological Survey reports (Newberry, 1873, 1875; Claypole, 1893; Wright, 1893) and in Newberry's monograph (1889) on Paleozoic fishes.

However, placoderms are rare fossils and many collecting trips may result in no specimens, even for experienced collectors. Numerous placoderm specimens were collected in the last century, before quarries became mechanized. A number of these specimens were probably found by quarry workers who used hand methods to process the limestone.

The earliest known placoderm remains from Ohio are isolated **cranial** and thoracic plates from the Lower Devonian Holland Quarry Shale of Lucas County (see section on Agnatha for more details on this unit). These specimens were referred by Denison (1960) to *Aethaspis ohioensis* Denison.

The Columbus and Delaware Limestones and the Silica Formation, all of Middle Devonian age, have produced remains of several placoderms, consisting mostly of isolated head or thoracic plates. Perhaps the best known and most spectacular of these remains are cranial shields of *Macropetalichthys rapheidolabis* Norwood & Owen (figs. 21-1.4, 21-1.5). These large (25 cm or more in maximum dimension) skulls are particularly striking because they exhibit large, circular **orbits** that give them an almost humanlike appearance. According to Denison (1978), the trunk shield of *Macropetalichthys* was originally described as a separate species, *Acanthaspis armata* Newberry (fig. 21-1.5), a fact that points out one of the difficulties facing paleontologists dealing with scattered skeletal remains.

The Columbus and Delaware Limestones also have yielded remains of other placoderms, including large dental plates of *Rhynchodus secans* Newberry (fig. 21-1.6), which are not uncommon in some of the bone beds, and rare remains of *Woodwardosteus spatulatus* (Newberry), originally described by Newberry (1873) under the generic name of *Liognathus* (Denison, 1978). Newberry (1875) also described plates of a poorly known placoderm, *Asterosteus stenocephalus* Newberry, from the Columbus Limestone. As noted above, isolated tubercles named *Ohioaspis* by Wells (1944b) are probably from *Asterosteus*. *Holonema* Newberry (Mitchell, 1971) and *Protitanichthys* Eastman (Larson, 1975) are two additional placoderms that are known from the Silica Formation in Lucas County. *Protitanichthys* also is known from the Delaware Limestone.

The most spectacular and abundant placoderm remains in Ohio have come from the Upper Devonian Ohio Shale, particularly from the uppermost member, the Cleveland Shale Member, in the vicinity of Cleveland, Cuyahoga County. The Cleveland Museum of Natural History has the world's largest collection of these fishes, which belong to the order Arthrodira. Many of these arthrodires are on display at the Cleveland Museum of Natural History. They have been described by Dunkle (1947), Dunkle and Bungart (1939, 1940, 1942a, 1942b, 1943, 1945a, 1945b, 1946), Hlavin and Boreske (1973), Hlavin (1976), and Carr (1991, 1994, 1996).

Isolated bones of arthrodires have been found in the Ohio Shale, but many specimens have come from the centers of large **calcareous** concretions that occur in zones within the Huron and Cleveland Members of the Ohio Shale (Clifton, 1957; Criss, Cooke, and Day, 1988; Hansen, 1994b). The Ohio Shale is interpreted as having been deposited in a comparatively deep sea in which the bottom waters were foul and stagnant. A diverse fauna of arthrodires, sharks, and bony fishes lived in the oxygenated upper waters of this sea. When these fishes died, their remains sank into the quiet bottom mud, where they were protected from destruction by currents and bottom scavengers.

The Huron Member of the Ohio Shale has yielded head and thoracic plates and jaws of a large arthrodire, *Dinichthys herzeri* Newberry (fig. 21-2.3), and plates of the arthrodires *Aspidichthys clavatus* Newberry and *Stenosteus glaber* Dean. *Aspidichthys* also has been reported from the Olentangy Shale (Sinclair and Walker, 1956).

At least 22 species of arthrodires, distributed among 18 genera, are known from the Cleveland Shale Member (Williams, 1990, 1992). Although some forms, particularly *Dunkleosteus* Lehman, are known from numerous specimens, other forms are known only from a few specimens. The large collection of these remains at the Cleveland Museum of Natural History and at other institutions may give the impression that arthrodire fossils are common and easily collected. This is certainly not the case. These specimens have been assembled over a long period of time by a small cadre of both professional scientists and amateur collectors. Significant additions were made to the Cleveland Museum collection in the mid-1960's when construction of Interstate 71 in Cuyahoga County cut through the Cleveland Shale Member. A dedicated effort by the Cleveland Museum of Natural History recovered numerous specimens.

Dunkleosteus terrelli (Newberry), featured on the cover of this book, is probably the best known of the Cleveland Shale Member arthrodires. These fishes (figs. 21-2.1, 21-2.2, 21-2.4) reached lengths of about 5 meters, weighed more than a ton (Williams, 1992), and had jaws that were well equipped for a predatory existence, although Long (1995) has suggested that some of these large arthrodires may have been carrion feeders. The lower jaws were armed with a spikelike process on their **anterior** margins. Behind this process was a sharp cutting blade that meshed with a corresponding blade in the upper jaw.

Another large arthrodire was *Titanichthys* Newberry, which may have been the largest vertebrate living during the Devonian Period, reaching a length of 7 meters. Two species are recognized, *Titanichthys agassizi* Newberry and *T. clarkii* Newberry. The latter species had a head that was 90 cm long. These arthrodires had long, slender jaws that lacked cusps or shearing edges. Their mode of life is poorly understood, but they may have been filter feeders similar to the modern whale shark. Other Cleveland Shale Member arthrodires include *Gymnotrachelus hydei* Dunkle & Bungart, *Gorgonichthys clarki* Claypole, *Heintzichthys gouldii* (Newberry), *Holdenius holdeni* Dunkle & Bungart, *Mylostoma variabile* Newberry, *Selenosteus brevis* (Claypole), and *Stenosteus angustopectus* Carr.

CHONDRICHTHYES—SHARKS

Sharks and sharklike fishes are characterized by their **cartilaginous** skeletons and a covering of scales, termed **dermal denticles**, on the surface of the skin of most species. Such denticles, which are absent or greatly reduced in some forms, are thought to have given rise to the teeth of sharks. Chondrichthyans are divided into two subclasses—the Elasmobranchii, which includes sharks, skates, and rays, and the Holocephali, which is composed of chimaeras or ratfish. Although this latter group is inconspicuous in modern seas, they were abundant in the seas of the Late Paleozoic.

Most sharks, both fossil and Recent, are inhabitants of marine waters; however, some fossil chondrichthyans lived in fresh or brackish waters, and some modern forms also occupy these environments. There are also modern sharks that have the ability to live in either marine or fresh waters and to move freely between the two environments.

Because of their cartilaginous skeletons, which decayed rapidily in oxygenated environments, most fossil sharks are known only from isolated teeth, dermal denticles, and fin spines. This circumstance has created numerous taxonomic problems because isolated teeth, dermal denticles, and median-fin spines have been named as separate genera and species. Most of these taxonomic problems have yet to be solved.

Rarely, whole sharks, including some soft parts such as muscles and internal organs, are preserved in **anaerobic** environments. Notable examples in North America include the Cleveland Member of the Ohio Shale (Upper Devonian) of northern Ohio, Pennsylvanian black shales of the Illinois and Midcontinent basins, and the Bear Gulch Limestone (Upper Mississippian) in Montana. These occurrences have provided a wealth of information about the anatomy of Paleozoic sharks. Zangerl (1981) has summarized information on Paleozoic elasmobranchs.

DEVONIAN SHARKS

Dermal denticles of sharks first appear in the fossil record in Ordovician rocks (none are known from Ohio as yet), but it was not until the middle to late part of the Devonian Period that sharks began a major expansion. The earliest known shark remains from Ohio consist of microscopic dermal denticles, assigned to *Cladolepis* Wells and *Ohiolepis* Wells, and teeth assigned to *Phoebodus* St. John & Worthen. These denticles and teeth occur with some abundance in bone beds in the Columbus and Delaware Limestones (Middle Devonian) (Wells, 1944b).

The Cleveland Shale Member of the Ohio Shale has produced a remarkable number of exquisitely preserved sharks that are among the earliest known fossil sharks in the world. Most of these specimens occur in large, ellipsoidal, calcareous concretions that are common in some zones within the Cleveland Member.

The most abundant Cleveland Member shark is *Cladoselache* Dean (fig. 21-3.1, 21-3.2), a fast-swimming predator that had sharp, spikelike teeth. Several species are known, including *C. fyleri* (Newberry), a small species averaging 0.75 meter or less; *C. clarki* (Claypole), which averaged about 1.2 meters in length; and *C. kepleri* (Newberry), which reached lengths of 1.5 meters or more (Williams, 1990). The preservation of these sharks is so remarkable that muscle fibers and other soft tissues can be studied in detail. A number of these specimens contained remains of prey in the gut region; 64 percent contained remains of a small palaeoniscoid fish, *Kentuckia hlavini* Dunkle (Williams, 1992) (see fig. 21-8). Dean (1909) described a number of Cleveland Shale Member specimens of *Cladoselache*. Other Cleveland Member sharks include *Diademodus hydei* Harris (Harris, 1951), *Stethacanthus altonensis* (St. John & Worthen) (Williams, 1985) (fig. 21-6.1), *Ctenacanthus compressus* Newberry, an undescribed ctenacanth (fig. 21-5.2), and crushing teeth of an early hybodont (a group of ctenacanths that became prominent in the Mesozoic) and three orodonts (Williams, 1990).

MISSISSIPPIAN SHARKS

Paleozoic sharks reached their greatest diversity during the Mississippian Period, as evidenced by the abundant teeth and other skeletal elements found in marine limestones of the Illinois and Midcontinent basins; however, the fossil record in Mississippian rocks of Ohio is poor. Most Mississippian rocks in the state consist of marine sandstones in which few fossils are well preserved. Newberry (1889) reported a median-fin spine, which he named *Ctenacanthus angustus*, from the Berea Sandstone at Berea, Cuyahoga County, and another species of this genus, *C. formosus* Newberry (Newberry, 1873), from the Cuyahoga Formation at Warren, Trumbull County. Little other information is known about the sharks that bore these large spines.

The black Sunbury Shale, of Early Mississippian age, has yielded scattered shark remains, some of which probably are referable to *Stethacanthus altonensis*, but they have not been studied in detail. The Maxville Formation, of Middle and Late Mississippian age, has yielded only a few fragmentary shark teeth.

PENNSYLVANIAN SHARKS

Pennsylvanian rocks in Ohio, both marine and nonmarine, yield a moderate number of teeth and dermal denticles and a few median-fin spines, isolated **calcified** cartilage fragments, and other elements of sharks. Most of these remains consist of isolated teeth in thin marine limestones and shales of eastern Ohio. Although **macroscopic** teeth and spines can be found in any of these marine units, the Ames limestone (Conemaugh Group) has yielded the largest number of specimens. Units such as the Brush Creek limestone and the Cambridge limestone (both in the Conemaugh Group) also have produced a considerable number of specimens. Most of these units contain a diverse and abundant fauna of microscopic teeth and scales (Hansen, 1986).

The most abundant shark teeth in Pennsylvanian marine rocks belong to the petalodontids, a group characterized by teeth that have an elongate, compressed crown that bears a more or less sharp and in some cases **denticulate** margin, and a long tooth base or root (Hansen, 1985a). These teeth appear to have had a nipping or shearing function. The most common shark tooth found in Pennsylvanian marine rocks in Ohio is *Petalodus ohioensis* Safford (figs. 21-3.3; 21-4.1 to 21-4.3), a species first named from a specimen collected near Cambridge, Guernsey County. Other common petalodontids are *Janassa* Munster (figs. 21-4.4, 21-4.5), *Cholodus inaequalis* St. John & Worthen (fig. 21-4.7, 21-4.8), and *Peripristis semicircularis* (Newberry & Worthen) (fig. 21-4.6).

Teeth that have a long, sharp central cusp and smaller lateral cusps are referred to in older literature as "*Cladodus*," a name that has served as a catchall for most Paleozoic shark teeth with this morphology and for which more than 50 nominal species have been named. The two most common species of macroscopic size are *Symmorium reniforme* Cope (fig. 21-5.1) and *Stethacanthus altonensis* (St. John & Worthen) (figs. 21-5.5 to 21-5.7). *Symmorium reniforme* was a large shark that must have been a top-level predator in Pennsylvanian seas (Williams, 1985). It is probable that most other fishes and even invertebrates such as cephalopods (Mapes and Hansen, 1984; Hansen and Mapes, 1990) served as prey for *Symmorium* (fig. 21-6.3).

Some Pennsylvanian chondrichthyans had teeth that were adapted to crushing the shells of invertebrates such as brachiopods, bivalves, and gastropods. Such teeth are thick, flattened plates or are massive and low ridged. These holocephalian sharks include cochliodontids such as *Cochliodus* Agassiz and *Deltodus angularis* Newberry & Worthen (figs. 21-4.9 to 21-4.11), orodontids such as *Orodus* Agassiz (fig. 21-4.12), and psammodontids such as *Lagarodus angustus* (Romanowsky) (figs. 21-4.13, 21-4.14).

Median-fin spines, some of which are several inches in length, are rare finds in Pennsylvanian rocks in Ohio. These spines are long, tapering structures that probably functioned as cutwaters in front of the dorsal fin(s) and as protective devices. The most common type has a series of grooves and ridges that are parallel to the long axis of the spine. The ridges may have a beaded appearance. These spines commonly are placed in the genus *Ctenacanthus* Agassiz. Wells (1944a) described a specimen as *C. lamborni* (fig. 21-5.9) from the Ames limestone of Guernsey County. Another species, described as *Ctenacanthus marshi* (fig. 21-5.11) by Newberry (1873), has been referred to the genus *Sphenacanthus* Agassiz by Maisey (1982, 1984). Slender median-fin spines that have longitudinal grooves and ridges may belong to the genus *Acondylacanthus* St. John & Worthen (fig. 21-5.8). An unusual spine, which was apparently curved forward on the shark and bears a series of tubercles, is *Physonemus acinaciformis* (St. John & Worthen) (fig. 21-5.10). Murphy (1971a) described a specimen of *P. acinaciformis* from the Lower Mercer limestone (Pottsville Group). It is not possible to determine which of these spines belonged to sharks known by teeth from the same rocks because these two skeletal elements have not been found in anatomic association.

Abundant teeth of xenacanths and rarer teeth of hybodonts occur in nonmarine shales and limestones in both Pennsylvanian and Permian rocks in eastern Ohio. Most of the xenacanth teeth found in these rocks are referable to *Orthacanthus compressus* (Newberry) (figs. 21-5.12 to 21-5.15) and are characterized by two long, sharp-pointed, compressed cusps on the lateral portion of the tooth and a small central cusp. These cusps bear tiny serrations along their margins.

Orthacanthus was a large shark that reached a meter or so in length and was characterized by highly mobile lateral fins (termed archipterygial fins, once thought to be the ancestral fin type), and a long, pointed tail (termed a diphycercal tail) (fig. 21-6.2). A long, sharp spine that had denticles on each side protruded from the back of the skull. Small, comblike structures with a long "handle" have been described as "kammplatten" or *Euctenius* Traquair (figs. 21-6.5, 21-6.6). Newberry (1873) illustrated an assemblage of these structures from the Linton deposit (Jefferson County) and interpreted them to be the tail of a crustacean. Further study of these elements has shown them to be the claspers (intromittent organs) of male *Orthacanthus compressus* (Hook and Hansen, 1985).

Coprolites—fossil excrement—have been found in nonmarine shales and limestones of both Pennsylvanian and Permian age, commonly in association with the remains of xenacanth sharks. Some coprolites also may have come from amphibians, such as those described from Permian rocks of Ohio by Stauffer and Schroyer (1920). There has been little study of coprolites from Ohio rocks. These tear-drop-shaped fossils (figs. 21-5.3, 21-5.4) exhibit a spiral twist at one end (heteropolar) or a spiral twist throughout the length of the specimen (amphipolar), reflecting their passage through the spiral-shaped valve of a shark's intestine. Some of these coprolites exhibit detailed impressions of the mucosal folds of the intestine and may represent actual fossilized intestines (Williams, 1972). Such structures are termed enterospirae. Coprolites commonly contain remains of prey such as scales of palaeoniscoid fishes.

Most xenacanth sharks lived in slow-moving nonmarine waters such as ponds and lakes associated with deltaic environments. It is probable that they preyed on the abundant bony fishes and amphibians that also inhabited these environments. Microscopic xenacanth teeth referable to *Xenacanthus tridentatus* (Harlton) are found in marine rocks of Early and Middle Pennsylvanian age (Hansen, 1986).

A Middle Pennsylvanian cannel coal at Five Points, near North Lima in Mahoning County, has yielded the remains of a ctenacanth shark, *Bandringa rayi* Zangerl (fig. 21-6.4), and tiny teeth of *Ageleodus pectinatus* (Agassiz) (figs. 21-4.15, 21-4.16), a shark of uncertain affinities and known only from isolated teeth (Hook and Baird, 1993). *Bandringa* was characterized by a long rostrum that may have been used to dislodge prey from bottom muds, similar to the technique employed by the modern spoonbill catfish.

PERMIAN SHARKS

Lower Permian rocks in Ohio are nonmarine or possibly brackish in a few cases. Remains of sharks are generally uncommon in these rocks but, like the underlying Pennsylvanian rocks, teeth and other elements can be locally abundant in some beds. Teeth of *Orthacanthus compressus* are the most common form.

ACANTHODII—EARLY JAWED FISHES

Acanthodian fishes first appeared in the Silurian, reached a peak in diversity in the Devonian, and survived through the middle Permian. Superficially, they resemble modern bony fishes. Acanthodians were among the earliest fishes with jaws and are characterized by pointed, recurved spines in front of each fin, except the caudal (tail) fin, and a covering of thick, rhomboid-shaped, nonoverlapping scales. Most of these fishes were small, but some reached a length of about 1.8 meters. Some groups possessed small, sharp teeth that indicate a predatory existence, whereas others lacked teeth and were probably filter feeders. Denison (1979) has summarized this group.

The fossil record of acanthodians in Ohio consists of fragmentary remains, primarily isolated scales and fin spines. The earliest known acanthodian remains from Ohio consist of small, isolated, fin spines from the Holland Quarry Shale (Lower Devonian). These specimens were referred to the genus *Onchus* Agassiz by Denison (1960). This Lucas County locality is discussed in more detail in the section on Agnatha.

The largest acanthodian fossils from Ohio are fin spines from the Columbus Limestone (Middle Devonian). These spines are known as *Machaeracanthus* Newberry (fig. 21-7.4) and may reach 30 cm in length (Newberry, 1873; Zidek, 1981). The bone beds of the Columbus Limestone also yield abundant microscopic scales of acanthodians (Wells, 1944b), most of which are probably referable to *Cheiracanthoides* Wells (figs. 21-7.5 to 21-7.7).

Mississippian rocks in Ohio have yielded only meager remains of acanthodians. Newberry (1873) reported large spines of *Gyracanthus* Agassiz (fig. 21-7.3) from the Meadville Shale Member of the Cuyahoga Formation in Medina County. *Gyracanthus* spines have been reported from Pennsylvanian rocks at Five Points, Mahoning County (Hook and Baird, 1993) (figs. 21-7.1, 21-7.2).

Microscopic scales of acanthodians are abundant in some marine limestones of Pennsylvanian age. The Dorr Run shale (Allegheny Group) near Nelsonville in Athens County has yielded well-preserved fin spines referable to *Acanthodes marshi* Eastman (Zidek, 1980). This shale appears to be of brackish origin. Similar spines have been found in the Washingtonville shale (Allegheny Group) in Carroll County and the Brush Creek and Portersville shales (Conemaugh Group) in Athens County, which are all marine units.

OSTEICHTHYES—BONY FISHES

Osteichthyans, or bony fishes, include most of the fishes living today. At least 23,000 species of living osteichthyan fishes are recognized (Long, 1995). They have an internal bony skeleton, teeth that are replaced in a regular pattern, and flattened, overlapping scales. There are three subdivisions: the Actinopterygii, or ray-finned fishes; the Crossopterygii, or lobe-finned fishes; and the Dipnoi, or lungfishes.

Actinopterygians are characterized by internal, parallel fin rays that support the paired and median fins. They first appeared in the Late Silurian. Most Paleozoic actinopterygians belong to the Order Palaeonisciformes (palaeoniscoids), which were small, fusiform (spindle-shaped) to deep-bodied fishes. The palaeoniscoids first appeared in the Silurian but did not become abundant until the Devonian. Complete specimens of palaeoniscoids are known from several localities in Ohio, but their most common fossils are distinctive, highly **ornamented**, rhomboidal scales or small, isolated, sharp-pointed, conical teeth that are capped by a clear substance. The earliest palaeoniscoids were marine, but they also inhabited brackish and freshwater environments after the Devonian. These small fishes were probably a primary food source for larger bony fishes, sharks, and aquatic amphibians during the Late Paleozoic.

Crossopterygians are characterized by unique paired fins that have a bony axis and internal musculature that allows the fin to be manipulated, perhaps as an aid to moving about on the substrate. This fin type is thought to be the precursor of paired limbs in terrestrial vertebrates. Crossopterygians are generally thought to include the ancestors of amphibians. The only surviving crossopterygian is the modern coelacanth, *Latimeria chalumnae* Smith.

Dipnoans are characterized by the possession of lungs as well as gills, giving them the ability to breath air. Surviving dipnoans are the lungfishes of Africa (*Protopterus*), South America (*Lepidosiren*), and Australia (*Neoceratodus*).

DEVONIAN OSTEICHTHYANS

The earliest known palaeoniscoid fossils from Ohio are found in the Cleveland Shale Member of the Ohio Shale (Upper Devonian). Isolated scales and teeth are common on bedding planes in this unit. Articulated specimens of *Kentuckia hlavini* Dunkle (fig. 21-8) have been found in the Cleveland Shale Member (Dunkle, 1964). Isolated jaws and crania also have been discovered. Both the scales and bones of this species have complexly ornamented outer surfaces. Other disarticulated skeletal elements and scales found in this unit may belong to the genus *Rhadinichthys* Traquair.

A rare palaeoniscoid of the Cleveland Shale Member is *Tegeolepis clarki* (Newberry) (fig. 21-9), a large predator that Newberry (1889) originally described as *Actinophorus clarki* (Dunkle and Shaeffer, 1973). Although this fish was large—up to 1.8 meters long—its scales were tiny, measuring only about 2 mm in length.

The Columbus and Delaware Limestones are noted for specimens of a large crossopterygian, *Onychodus sigmoides* Newberry (figs. 21-10.1 to 21-10.4), which may have reached a length of 2 meters. The most distinctive remains of these fishes are large, sharp-pointed, recurved teeth that formed two pairs of whorls where the lower jaws articulate (fig. 21-10.2). These teeth are found scattered in the limestone or concentrated in the bone-bed layers. *Onychodus* jaws may reach 30 cm in length and are studded with sharp, conical teeth (fig. 21-10.4). Scales and isolated skeletal elements of this fish (fig. 21-10.3) also have been reported (Newberry,

1873). On the basis of articulated specimens from the Devonian of Australia, Long (1991, 1995) has suggested that *Onychodus* captured prey by lurking among reefs, in a mode similar to the moray eel of present-day seas (fig. 21-10.1). There is evidence that the tooth whorls were retractable and were used to grasp and draw in prey.

The Chagrin Shale Member of the Ohio Shale has yielded a single but relatively well-preserved specimen of a coelacanth, *Chagrinia enodis* Shaeffer (1962). It is likely that a coelecanth that has been found in the Cleveland Shale Member is also this species. An undescribed crossoptergian also occurs in the Cleveland Shale Member.

A single specimen of a dipnoan lungfish, *Proceratodus* Romer & Smith, has been found in the Cleveland Shale Member and is in the collections of the Cleveland Museum of Natural History. It is probable that these remains were washed into the sea from a freshwater source.

MISSISSIPPIAN OSTEICHTHYANS

Mississippian rocks in Ohio have produced scattered remains of fishes, including only a few specimens of osteichthyians. Long-abandoned quarries in the upper part of the Berea Sandstone near Chagrin Falls, Cuyahoga County, produced numerous 30-cm-long specimens of a palaeoniscoid, *Gonatodus brainerdi* (Newberry) (fig. 21-10.5), described originally by Newberry (1873) as *Palaeoniscus brainerdi*. No additional specimens have been reported in this century. Newberry (1873) reported palaeoniscoid scales from the Cuyahoga Formation at Chagrin Falls.

PENNSYLVANIAN OSTEICHTHYANS

Although microscopic teeth and scales of palaeoniscoids are common in marine limestones of Pennsylvanian age in Ohio, no complete, articulated specimens have been found in these rocks. Nonmarine rocks, however, have yielded a diversity of articulated palaeoniscoids, and isolated scales and teeth are abundant. The most famous occurrence of these fishes is at the world-renowned Linton locality (fig. 21-13.1) near Wellsville, in Jefferson County. At this long-abandoned mine dump near the mouth of Yellow Creek, a bed of cannel coal (coal composed primarily of plant spores) at the base of the Upper Freeport coal (Allegheny Group) has produced numerous palaeoniscoids, including *"Elonichthys" peltigerus* Newberry, *Haplolepis corrugata* (Newberry), *Microhaplolepis ovoidea* (Newberry), *M. serrata* (Newberry), *Parahaplolepis tuberculata* (Newberry), and *Pyritocephalus lineatus* (Newberry) (fig. 21-11). These specimens are all small, most only a few centimeters in length.

Isolated teeth and scales of palaeoniscoid fishes also are common in some nonmarine shales associated with coal beds. A second cannel coal locality in the Allegheny Group discovered recently near Five Points, in Mahoning County, has yielded a diverse assemblage of bony fishes, including fragmentary remains of the palaeoniscoids *"Elonichthys," Haplolepis*, *Microhaplolepis*, and *Pyritocephalus*.

Fossils of sarcopterygians are not widespread in Pennsylvanian rocks of Ohio, but they can be extremely abundant at some localities. *Rhabdoderma elegans* (Newberry) (figs. 21-12.1, 21-12.2), a small coelacanth, is one of the most abundant fossils at Linton, as well as at Five Points. Although complete, articulated specimens have been collected, they more commonly are preserved as a hash of bones and scales (Lund and Lund, 1985). *Megalichthys* Agassiz & Hibbert, a large crossopterygian, and the smaller *Rhizodopsis* Young also are known from Five Points.

Two lungfishes are known from Linton and Five Points. The larger species is *Sagenodus serratus* (Newberry), which is recognized easily by its distinctive tooth plates that bear a series of radiating, coarsely tuberculate ridges, very similar (perhaps identical) to a Permian species, *Sagenodus* **cf.** *S. periprion* (Cope) (figs. 21-12.3, 21-12.4). *Conchopoma exanthematicum* (Cope) (fig. 21-12.5) is a smaller form that is unusual because it has teeth on the jaw margins as well as broad tooth plates.

PERMIAN OSTEICHTHYANS

Isolated teeth and scales of palaeoniscoid fishes are relatively common in some nonmarine limestones and shales of the Dunkard Group in southeastern Ohio. Stauffer and Schroyer (1920) mention palaeoniscoid scales and teeth in black shales associated with the Elm Grove limestone (Washington Formation). A crossopterygian, *Ectosteorhachis* Cope, has been reported from the Nineveh limestone (Greene Formation) at Clark Hill, Monroe County (Berman, 1978).

Teeth and skeletal elements of *Sagenodus serratus* have been reported from the Washington Formation at Belpre, Washington County (Hlavin, 1968; Olson, 1970), and from the Greene Formation in Monroe County near Cameron (Romer, 1952), and at Clark Hill (Berman, 1978). It is probable that remains of this lungfish are more common in Dunkard rocks than has been reported in the literature. Another lungfish, *Palaeophichthys* Eastman, formerly referred to the genus *Monongahela* Lund (Lund, 1970, 1973), has been reported from Pennsylvanian and Permian rocks in western Pennsylvania and probably occurs in these rocks in Ohio (Schultze, 1994).

PLEISTOCENE OSTEICHTHYANS

Bony fishes, including many species now living in Ohio, must have been common in postglacial lakes and streams; however, their tiny, delicate bones are easily overlooked if screening techniques are not employed when examining Pleistocene sediments. Consequently, only two systematicaly excavated sites have produced fish remains (see fig. 21-22.1). Eight species of fish were recovered from the Carter site in Darke County. One of these has been identified as a mudminnow, *Umbra limi* (Kirtland) (Todd, 1973). The Indian Trail Caverns site in Wyandot County has produced bones of a creek chub, *Semotilus atromacrulatus* (Mitchill), and four other as yet unidentified species of minnows; channel catfish, *Ictalurus punctatus* (Rafinesque), and blue catfish, *Ictalurus furcatus* (LeSueur); and sunfish, *Micropterus* sp. (K. M. Ford, personal commun., 1994). These sites are described in more detail in the section on Mammalia.

AMPHIBIA

Living amphibians, including frogs, toads, and salamanders, are familiar to almost everyone and, as the name of the group indicates, many species are capable of living in both water and on land, at least for a portion of their lives. They commonly lay large numbers of externally fertilized eggs in water, from which hatch gill-bearing larvae that, in most species, become air-breathing adults. Amphibians were derived from crossopterygian fishes prior to the Late Devonian and gave rise, eventually, to all other terrestrial vertebrates.

Paleozoic amphibians exhibited a wide range of morphologies and ecologic adaptations and are divided into two major groups: the labyrinthodonts and the lepospondyls. Labyrinthodonts had conical teeth that exhibit infolding of the dentine similar to that of their crossopterygian fish ancestors. Lepospondyls lack this infolding of the teeth, among other differentiating characteristics. Some labyrinthodonts were quite large, reaching more than 2 meters in length.

Devonian and Mississippian amphibians are rare worldwide and none have been reported from Ohio; this is not surprising considering that most rocks deposited in the state during these periods are of marine origin. However, an important fauna of Late Mississippian amphibians has been described from nearby Greer, West Virginia (Romer, 1969, 1970; Hotton, 1970).

PENNSYLVANIAN AMBHIBIANS

Pennsylvanian amphibian remains from Ohio are diverse and abundant at a few localities. The Linton locality in Jefferson County (fig. 21-13.1), has produced at least 22 species of amphibians, many of which are known from fewer than 10 specimens. Some of the common forms found at Linton, such as *Sauropleura pectinata* Cope, *Ptyonius marshii* (Cope) (fig. 21-13.2), and *Diceratosaurus brevirostris* (Cope) (fig. 21-16.1), were small aquatic lepospondyls that may have fed on small palaeoniscoid fishes. *Sauropleura*, the most abundant form, averaged approximately 25 cm in length and had a long, newtlike body and small limbs. Other lepospondyls, such as *Ophiderpeton amphiuminum* (Cope) and *Phlegethontia linearis* Cope, were small snakelike forms, whereas the aquatic labyrinthodont *Colosteus scutellatus* (Newberry) (figs. 21-14.1 to 21-14.3) reached 60 to 90 cm in length. *Brachydectes newberryi* (Cope) (figs. 21-19.1 to 21-19.5) was a snakelike form that reached lengths of about 12 cm (Wellstead, 1991).

Amphibamus lyelli (Wyman) (figs. 21-13.3, 21-13.4), a terrestrial amphibian found at Linton, has a remarkable resemblance to modern-day frogs. Further diversity of Pennsylvanian amphibians is demonstrated by the occurrence at Linton of rare, alligatorlike aquatic forms such as *Cochleosaurus* Fritsch, *Baphetes lineolatus* (Cope), *Megalocephalus enchodus* (Cope), and *Leptophractus obsoletus* Cope.

The Linton tetrapods were described by the famous Philadelphia paleontologist Edward Drinker Cope (1875) in a publication of the Second Geological Survey of Ohio; the specimens had been assembled by State Geologist John S. Newberry. Later works on Linton tetrapods and on the depositional environment of this deposit include those of Moodie (1916), Romer (1930), Steen (1931), Baird (1964), Carroll and Baird (1968), and, more recently, Hook (1983, 1986), Hansen (1984), Hook and Baird (1986, 1988), Hook and Ferm (1985, 1987), and Wellstead (1991).

A cannel coal associated with the Lower Kittanning coal (Allegheny Group) at two reclaimed strip mines near Five Points in Mahoning County has yielded 13 determinable species of amphibians (Hook and Baird, 1993). Nearly all of these **taxa** also are found at the slightly younger Linton deposit and include *Amphibamus*, *Colosteus*, *Diceratosaurus*, *Ophiderpeton*, *Sauropleura*, *Saurerpeton* (fig. 21-16.2), *Ctenerpeton* (figs. 21-16.3, 21-16.4), and *Tuditanus* (fig. 21-15). A large amount of this cannel coal was acquired and set aside by the Carnegie Museum of Natural History in Pittsburgh for future collecting.

Romer (1963) described a large partial skull of an anthracosaur labyrinthodont, *Neopteroplax conemaughensis* Romer (figs. 21-14.5, 21-14.6), from a shale above the Ames limestone (Conemaugh Group) in a railroad cut in Wayne Township, Jefferson County. Vaughn (1971) described a temnospondyl labyrinthodont, *Astreptorachis ohioensis*, from this locality.

Other than the Linton and Five Points localities, amphibian remains are rare in Pennsylvanian rocks in Ohio. In part, this circumstance is probably a function of a lack of intensive searching and recognition of such remains.

An interesting record of the presence and activities of tetrapods, presumably amphibians, is provided by footprints or trackways in Pennsylvanian rocks. Carman (1927) described these trace fossils from several localities. He gave the name *Anomoichnus ohioensis* (fig. 21-17) to tracks in strata above the Middle Kittanning coal (Allegheny Group) near New Straitsville in Perry County; he gave the name *Ancylopus ortoni* to tracks from a shale above the Upper Freeport coal (Allegheny Group) near Senecaville in Guernsey County; and tracks from strata beneath the Benwood limestone (Monongahela Group) in Center Township, Morgan County, he named *Megabaropus hainesi*. Mitchell (1931, 1933) described abundant tracks of *A. ortoni* and *M. hainesi* in a shale above the Upper Freeport coal in a coal mine near Senecaville, Guernsey County. Baird (1952) noted the presence of *Dimetropus* Romer & Price and *Dromopus* Marsh tracks (fig. 21-18) at the Morgan County locality, and Patterson (1971) redescribed the material from this site.

These tracks and trails provide important information on the size, mode of locomotion, and behavioral characteristics of amphibians and are probably more abundant than is indicated by the meager reports of them from Ohio. Such tracks most commonly are found as positive casts on the undersides of slabs of fine-grained sandstone that filled in the negative impression made by the foot of the animal.

PERMIAN AMPHIBIANS

The Permian record of amphibians from Ohio consists primarily of isolated bones at widely scattered sites. A few sites have produced relatively abundant but generally poorly preserved material. One of the most common amphibians was *Eryops* Cope (fig. 21-14.4; *Eryops* is the amphibian in the Pennsylvanian terrestrial reconstruction, p. xviii, and the Permian reconstruction, p. xix). This large labyrinthodont reached about a meter in length. Its remains have been found in rocks of the Dunkard Group near Cameron, Monroe County (Romer, 1952), and at Belpre, Washington County (Olson, 1970). Large tracks named *Limnopus waynesburgensis* (Tilton) (fig. 21-18) are thought to be those of *Eryops*.

Among the most bizarre yet common amphibians of the Dunkard rocks of southeastern Ohio was *Diploceraspis burkei* Romer (Romer, 1952). The head of this medium-sized, aquatic lepospondyl, reported from both the Cameron and Belpre localities, was about 15 cm wide (Beerbower, 1963). The most striking feature of *Diploceraspis* is that the head bears a large, projecting "horn" on each side that imparts a bananalike shape to the skull (fig. 21-20.1). The function of these unusual structures is uncertain.

Other Dunkard amphibians from Ohio include *Acheloma stonei* Olson (formerly called *Trematops stonei*) (Olson, 1970) from the Creston shale near Marietta, Washington County, and *Brachydectes* Cope, *Megamolgophis agostinii* Romer, and *Trimerorhachis* Cope (fig. 21-20.2), a large labyrinthodont, from the Belpre locality. *Trimerorhachis* also has been found at Clark Hill in Monroe County (Berman, 1978). *Broiliellus hektotopos* Berman & Berman was reported from the Cameron locality (Berman and Berman, 1975).

PLEISTOCENE AMPHIBIANS

Although frogs and salamanders may have been common in postglacial Pleistocene lakes, only Indian Trail Caverns in Wyandot County has produced such remains (fig. 21-22.1). As of 1994, ongoing excavations at this site have yielded remains of blue-spotted salamander, *Ambystoma lateralle* Hallowell; American toad, *Bufo americanus* Holbrook; Woodhouse's toad, *Bufo woodhouseii* Girard; chorus frog, *Pseudacris triseriata* (Wied-Neuwied); bullfrog, *Rana catesbeiana* Shaw; green frog, *Rana clamitans* Latreille; leopard frog, *Rana pipiens* Schreber; and wood frog, *Rana sylvatica* Le Conte (K. M. Ford, personal commun., 1994).

REPTILIA

Reptiles are a diverse group of vertebrates that are represented today by snakes, lizards, turtles, alligators, and crocodiles. In the fossil record, they are represented by these surviving groups, the well-known dinosaurs, and, particularly in the Paleozoic, by evolutionarily important groups such as mammal-like reptiles. Reptiles differ from their amphibian ancestors in a number of technical skeletal characteristics (see Carroll, 1988) and, significantly, in their ability to lay eggs on land. This reproductive capability permitted vertebrates to become fully terrestrial and independent of aquatic environments.

The earliest reptiles shared both reptilian and amphibian characteristics. The Linton locality in Jefferson County has produced some of the best-known early reptiles, one of which clearly demonstrates the difficulty in separating early reptiles from amphibians. A specimen that Cope (1875) named *Tuditanus punctulatus* (fig. 21-15) was proclaimed later by Williston (1910) to be the earliest known reptile and renamed *Eosauravus copei*. Restudy of this specimen (Carroll and Baird, 1968) has shown it to be a microsaur amphibian and it has now been reassigned its original name.

Although Ohio's fossil record of early reptiles is important, these remains are nowhere abundant in the state. The prolific Linton locality has produced only 10 specimens despite more than a century of collecting. Recent intensive collecting efforts at the Five Points locality in Mahoning County have yielded only one example. Nonetheless, two of the three major divisions of these early **amniotes** are represented—the lizardlike captorhinids and the morphologically diverse pelycosaurs.

Ohio has no preserved record of the great Age of Reptiles, the Mesozoic Era, when dinosaurs ruled the Earth. There is little doubt that dinosaurs lived in Ohio during the Mesozoic, but there are no existing rocks deposited during this era in the state and, therefore, no fossils from this period of time. Ohio was probably an elevated area in which erosion, rather than deposition, was the dominant geologic force. If any dinosaur-bearing sediments were deposited in Ohio during the Mesozoic, they were eroded away during the Tertiary Period, the Age of Mammals, another time for which Ohio has no fossil record.

PENNSYLVANIAN REPTILES

Reptile fossils are decidedly rare in Pennsylvanian rocks of Ohio. The Linton locality in Jefferson County has produced a total of 10 specimens assignable to the captorhinid genera *Anthracodromeus longipes* (Cope) (figs. 21-19.6, 21-19.7) and *Cephalerpeton ventriarmatum* Moodie (fig. 21-19.8) and a small pelycosaur, *Archaeothyris* Reisz (Reisz and Baird, 1983; Hook and Baird, 1986). The Five Points locality in Mahoning County has produced one indeterminate reptile (Hook and Baird, 1993).

Romer (1961) reported fragments of pelycosaurs, tentatively assigned to *Clepsydrops* Cope, from the Ewing and Summerfield limestones (Conemaugh Group) in Noble County and the Uniontown limestone (Monongahela Group) in Washington County. Romer (1961) also reported neural-spine fragments of another pelycosaur, *Edaphosaurus* Cope (see fig. 21-21.2), from Pennsylvanian rocks in Jefferson County.

Such reptile remains occur commonly as individual bones that are gray, black, or reddish in color and exhibit symmetry, cancellous (spongy) bone structure, and ornamentation on the surface. They can be found in a variety of lithologies, including nonmarine limestones, gray shales, or sandstones. These specimens are scientifically important and should be called to the attention of a specialist for identification.

PERMIAN REPTILES

Ohio's record of Permian reptiles is by no means prolific when compared to beds of similar age in Texas and elsewhere in the Southwest. However, a number of widely scattered localities in rocks of the Dunkard Group have produced an important record of reptilian life in the early Permian in Ohio and adjacent areas (Olson, 1975).

Perhaps the most typical reptiles of the Permian were two sail-backed pelycosaurs—*Dimetrodon* Cope (fig. 21-21.1; Permian reconstruction, p. xix) and *Edaphosaurus* (fig. 21-21.2; Pennsylvanian terrestrial reconstruction, p. xviii). These mammal-like reptiles were part of a lineage that gave rise to mammals in the succeeding Triassic Period. Both *Dimetrodon* and *Edaphosaurus* had large, skin-covered sails that were supported by bony elongations (neural spines) on the vertebrae. In *Dimetrodon*, a large carnivore that reached a length of nearly 3 meters, these spines were relatively smooth, whereas in *Edaphosaurus*, a smaller (1.5 meters) herbivore, the spines had transverse cross bars.

The function of the sail is conjectural, but many paleontologists think that it was used as a thermoregulatory device; that is, the sail could be exposed to the sun on cool days in order to warm the blood and, alternatively, the sail could be exposed to cool breezes on warm days in order to cool the blood and thus lower the body temperature. The sail was a fixed structure that could not be raised and lowered, a fact that leads to a question about how or if these large animals could have moved through thick vegetation.

A thin conglomerate, which represents the fill in an ancient stream channel, exposed in a large road cut near Belpre, Washington County, has been one of the most prolific sites for Permian reptile remains in Ohio. These remains consist mostly of isolated bones and teeth, most of which are broken and waterworn. Extensive collecting at this site by the Cleveland Museum of Natural History and by private collectors produced remains of several large reptiles (Hlavin, 1968; Olson, 1970, 1975), including the pelycosaurs *Edaphosaurus*, *Dimetrodon*, and *Ophiacodon* Marsh.

A site in the Washington Formation near Cameron, Monroe County (Moran, 1952; Romer, 1952), also has produced significant reptile remains. These fossils occur in nonmarine limestone and shale that probably were deposited in a small lake on a Permian delta plain. Reptiles represented at this site include *Protorothyris* Price, *Melanothyris morani* (Romer), *Edaphosaurus*, *Baldwinonus*? *dunkardensis* Romer, and indeterminate pelycosaurs.

Exposures of the Nineveh limestone (Greene Formation, Dunkard Group) at Clark Hill, Monroe County, has produced well-preserved reptile remains. Berman (1978) reported a new species of pelycosaur, *Ctenospondylus ninevehensis* Berman, from this locality.

Stauffer and Shroyer (1920) reported *Edaphosaurus* from the Creston shale (Washington Formation) near Marietta, Washington County. Stephens (1964) reported *Ophiacodon* from the Greene Formation in Monroe County.

PLEISTOCENE REPTILES

Pleistocene reptiles were very similar, if not identical, to living species. Although turtles, snakes, and lizards must have been abundant in Ohio, especially during warmer interglacial stages and in early postglacial time, they are not common fossils in Pleistocene sediments (fig. 21-22.1). This circumstance is probably a function of recognition of these commonly tiny bones.

Remains of turtles have been reported from the Johnstown mastodon site in Licking County, the Carter site in Darke County, from bog sediments in Erie County, and from a sinkhole at the Indian Trail Caverns site in Wyandot County. The turtles recovered at the Carter site are snapping turtle, *Chelydra serpentina* (Linnaeus), and painted turtle, *Chrysemys picta* Schneider (Holman, 1986); both species inhabit Ohio today and indicate that the climate was not boreal or tundra. The Indian Trail Caverns site has produced remains of *Chelydra serpentina* and *Chrysemys picta* as well as Blanding's turtle, *Emyoidea blandingii* (Holbrook). This site also has produced bones of seven species of snakes: racer, *Coluber constrictor* (Linnaeus); fox snake, *Elaphe vulpina* (Baird & Girard); milk snake, *Lampropeltis triangulum* (Lacepede); northern water snake, *Nerodia sipedon* (Linnaeus); green snake, *Opheodrys vernalis* (Harlan); queen snake, *Regina septemvittata* (Say); and eastern ribbon snake, *Thamnophis sirtalis* (Linnaeus) (K. M. Ford, personal commun., 1994).

AVES—BIRDS

Birds are familiar creatures to everyone, but few people realize that they are closely related to reptiles. Indeed, some paleontologists consider birds to be warm-blooded, flying reptiles. Birds evolved from reptiles in the Jurassic Period of the Mesozoic Era. The most famous and earliest known bird is *Archaeopteryx*, from rocks of Late Jurassic age at Solnhofen in southern Germany. The skeletal characteristics, including the presence of teeth and a long, bony tail, are so reptilian in character that *Archaeopteryx* would be classified as a reptile were it not for the presence of feathers.

Ohio's fossil record of birds is confined to sediments deposited during the latter part of the Pleistocene Epoch (fig. 21-22.1). The Carter site in Darke County and the Indian Trail Caverns site in Wyandot County have produced remains of birds, most of which have not been studied and identified. Turkey, *Meleagris gallopavo* Linnaeus, has been identified from Indian Trail Caverns. The claw of a hawk was found at the Orleton Farms mastodon site in Madison County (Thomas, 1952). Forsyth (1963) reported the remains of a Canada goose, which may be of Pleistocene age, from Castalia marsh in Erie County. Howard (1951) reported the occurrence of duck bones of the genus *Anas* Linneaus from Pleistocene (Wisconsinan) sediments in Hamilton County. A sparrow-sized bird, which has been identified as an English sparrow, has been found at Quillin bog in Medina County but may be a contaminant (Totten, 1988).

MAMMALIA

Mammals arose from mammal-like reptiles in the Triassic and coexisted with the dinosaurs throughout the Mesozoic. It was not until the Cenozoic Era, after extinction of the dinosaurs, that the mammals underwent an extensive expansion. The Tertiary Period of the Cenozoic was truly the Age of Mammals because they reached their greatest diversity and included many groups that are now extinct.

As with the dinosaurs of the Mesozoic, Ohio has no fossil record of this great Tertiary expansion of mammals because no sediments were deposited in the state during this time. Most certainly, the mature landscape of Ohio was roamed by great herds of beasts such as oreodonts, brontotheres, horses, camels, and a host of others, but their bones, like much of the rock blanketing the state, disintegrated into fine material that was washed to the sea by the streams that dissected the landscape during this 60-million-year period.

It was not until the Pleistocene Ice Age, and then only during the latter part of this epoch, that the fossil record of mammals began in Ohio. Our comparatively rich record of Pleistocene mammals is perhaps some small compensation for the long record that is missing from the state.

Although many people picture the Pleistocene Ice Age as a long-ago time characterized by bizarre, extinct animals, such was not really the case. The end of the Ice Age and its accompanying extinction of some mammals occurred only about 10,000 years ago—an instant, geologically speaking. Of the 40 species of mammals that are known from Ohio's Pleistocene deposits, 29 species—nearly three-fourths—still survive. Twenty-one of these surviving species still live in Ohio and the other eight—porcupine, grizzly bear, pine marten, fisher, bison, elk, caribou, and tundra muskox—still survive elsewhere in North America.

Most of the animals that did become extinct at the end of the Pleistocene were large herbivores such as mastodon, mammoth, giant beaver, ground sloth, and peccary or predators of these herbivores such as short-faced bear, sabertooth cat, and dire wolf. The reasons for this selective extinction are uncertain but it is probably related to changes in climate, vegetation, vegetational diversity, and to narrowly adapted vertebrate species that could not respond ecologically to these changes. Shane (1994) has summarized these vegetational and climatic changes in Ohio.

There is a comparatively voluminous literature on Pleistocene mammals in Ohio (see Smyth, 1979), although many occurrences of isolated teeth or bones of common forms such as mastodon or mammoth have not been recorded in the literature. These unpublished occurrences, many of which are noted on the accompanying distribution maps (figs. 21-22, 21-25, 21-30, 21-33), are in the files of the Division of

Geological Survey or other institutions. Hay (1923), Forsyth (1963), Hansen (1992a), and McDonald (1994) have published compilations of the occurrences of these mammals (and other Pleistocene vertebrates) in Ohio.

Remains of Pleistocene mammals are discovered in Ohio on a regular basis, although they are commonly found disarticulated or as individual elements such as teeth. Bones of large mammals such as mastodon and mammoth are reported more often than are those of smaller mammals. This circumstance is probably a factor of the ease of recognition of these large bones as those of something different than a recently deceased domestic animal. It is not always easy to differentiate bones of Pleistocene animals from those of animals that lived in postglacial or even historic times because Pleistocene bones retain their original composition and have not been signficantly **permineralized**. The dark color (patina) on bones of Pleistocene animals also may be present on bones of animals that died less than 100 years ago. For example, differentiating bones of a Pleistocene horse from those of a domestic horse requires the knowledge of a specialist.

Most discoveries of Pleistocene mammals in Ohio have been accidental, during surface excavations of boggy areas that were former glacial lakes. These lakes were widely distributed throughout the glaciated two-thirds of the state (see fig. 3-3), and most of them seem to have accumulated sediment, including Pleistocene mammal remains, in early postglacial time (about 15,000 years ago to about 10,000 years ago), as indicated by **radiocarbon dating**. Unfortunately, because bones generally must be removed quickly from these sites to minimize disruption of ongoing construction activities, much important information may be lost, including remains of small mammals and other vertebrates and paleoecological data. Detailed, systematic excavation of the Carter site (fig. 21-22.3) in Darke County by the Dayton Museum of Natural History in the early 1970's produced a diverse assemblage of Pleistocene mammals and vertebrates.

It is worth noting that the collection and ownership of remains of Pleistocene animals (or other fossils) is not governed by any existing Ohio law except by the laws of trespassing or collection from state or federal lands. There is a common misconception that the State of Ohio will shut down or delay construction or mining activities on private property if fossil animal bones are discovered and that such bones will be confiscated. In addition to the lack of such laws, the State does not have any agencies or individuals specifically assigned to such tasks. However, scientists from museums, universities, and the Division of Geological Survey commonly will visit such sites as volunteers and as a public service to assist in the salvage and recovery of bones and associated scientific information. Every effort is made to avoid any delay in construction schedules. Unfortunately for science, many important discoveries are probably never reported because of these unfounded fears of delay and confiscation.

Sand and gravel deposits that accumulated as outwash along major meltwater drainageways during melting of the Wisconsinan ice sheet also yield abundant remains of Pleistocene mammals. These remains generally consists of isolated, waterworn teeth and bones.

In many areas of the country, caverns and sinkholes developed in limestone terrains have yielded rich assemblages of Pleistocene mammals. Such sites appear to be rare in Ohio. The only known site is Indian Trail Caverns in Wyandot County, which has produced a rich assemblage of mammals and other vertebrates, some of which had not been previously recorded from the state (Hansen, 1992b).

SHREWS, BATS, RABBITS, AND RODENTS

Although small mammals such as shrews (*Blarina*, *Sorex*, and *Cryptotis*), bats (*Myotis*), rabbits (*Sylvilagus*), red squirrel (*Tamiasciurus*), tree squirrel (*Sciurus*), voles (*Microtus*, *Phenacomys*, and *Clethrionomys*), and field mice (*Peromyscus*) must have been common animals in the Pleistocene, as they are today, their remains are known primarily from sites that have been systematically excavated. The Carter site and Indian Trail Caverns have produced the majority of these remains (Hansen, 1992a, 1992b; McDonald, 1994). Quillin bog in Medina County has yielded remains of meadow vole, *Microtus pennsylvanicus* Ord (Totten, 1988).

Medium-sized rodents such as woodchuck, *Marmota monax* Linnaeus (fig. 21-23.4); porcupine, *Erethizon dorsatum* (Linnaeus) (fig. 21-23.7); beaver, *Castor canadensis* (Kuhl); and muskrat, *Ondatra zibethica* (Linnaeus) (fig. 21-23.5); similarly are known only from the Carter site and the Indian Trail Caverns site. An additional muskrat specimen was collected from Franklin County.

The largest rodent from Ohio's Pleistocene, and the only one now extinct, is the giant beaver, *Castoroides ohioensis* Foster (figs. 21-23.1, 21-23.2, 21-24). At least 15 specimens of this black-bear-sized rodent have been found in the state (fig. 21-22.2), including the type specimen from Muskingum County, near Nashport (fig. 21-24). J. W. Foster (1838) described and figured this specimen as part of the investigations of the First Geological Survey of Ohio. It has been suggested that, unlike modern beavers, *Castoroides* did not build dams or gnaw on trees, but probably subsisted on aquatic vegetation (McDonald, 1994).

EDENTATES

Edentates are mammals that are toothless or have weakly developed teeth. Ohio's Pleistocene sediments have yielded remains of a large edentate, the ground sloth, *Megalonyx jeffersonii* (Desmarest) (figs. 21-25.1, 21-26). These ox-sized herbivores originated in South America and migrated northward in the late Tertiary or during the Pleistocene. *Megalonyx* had large claws on the front feet. The Carter site in Darke County yielded a partial skeleton of *Megalonyx* (Mills, 1975), as did a site in Holmes County excavated in 1890 (Claypole, 1891; Hay, 1914). The Darke County specimen is at the Dayton Museum of Natural History, and the Holmes County specimen is displayed at Orton Geological Museum at The Ohio State University (fig. 21-26.8).

PERISSODACTYLS

Remains of perissodactyls, odd-toed ungulates (hoofed mammals), are not common in Ohio's Pleistocene sediments (fig. 21-25.1). Horses (*Equus*) became extinct in North America at the end of the Pleistocene but were reintroduced at the time of European exploration and settlement. Horse remains reported from Ohio consist primarily of isolated teeth (fig. 21-29.2) and jaws and have not been studied in detail. There is a distinct possibility that some reported occurrences of presumed Pleistocene horse remains represent modern horses interred into Pleistocene sediments during historic time.

A jaw of a tapir (*Tapirus* sp.) was discovered in Columbiana County, probably about 1850. The specimen is apparently now lost, but several paleontologists examined the specimen and confirmed the identification. Tapirs also were migrants from South America during the Pleistocene.

ARTIODACTYLS

The record of artiodactyls, even-toed ungulates, is diverse and widely distributed (fig. 21-25.2) in Ohio. These medium-sized to large herbivores are most abundantly represented by *Platygonus compressus* Le Conte (fig. 21-27), a Pleistocene peccary. Peccary remains are known from at least 16 sites in Ohio. Several sites had multiple specimens. Twelve complete skeletons of *Platygonus compressus* were discovered together in Columbus in 1873 (Klippart, 1875; Hay, 1914). Remains of at least four individuals were found in Sandusky County (Hoare and others, 1964). A mature female of this group was reconstructed and is displayed at Bowling Green State University (fig.21-29.1). Bones of at least 39 *P. compressus* individuals had been found at Indian Trail Caverns as of the end of the 1994 field season (K. M. Ford, personal commun., 1994; McDonald, 1994).

Cervalces scotti (Ledekker), the elk-moose or stag-moose (figs. 21-23.3, 21-28), was similar to the modern moose except it had a slimmer build and more elaborate antlers. These animals probably spent much of their time feeding on aquatic vegetation in glacial lakes. There were no records of *Cervalces* in Ohio until the early 1970's, when a single vertebra was found at the Carter site in Darke County. Since this first discovery, five additional specimens have been recovered, including, in 1987, a nearly complete specimen of a female from a bog near Hartville, Stark County (Hansen, 1988). This specimen, which was donated to the Ohio Historical Society, is one of the most complete skeletons known of *Cervalces*. McDonald (1989) has summarized the occurrences of *Cervalces* in Ohio.

Two types of muskox are known from Ohio. Seven specimens of the extinct woodland muskox, *Bootherium bombifrons* (Harlan), have been found, including a well-preserved skull from a road excavation in 1995 (fig. 21-29.5). Two specimens of the **extant** tundra muskox, *Ovibos moschatus* (Zimmerman) (figs. 21-29.3, 21-29.4), have been collected (McDonald, 1988; McDonald and Davis, 1989). All of these specimens consist of braincases, some of which have attached horn cores. Most of them were recovered from sand and gravel deposits. The braincase of the muskox consists of particularly dense bone and therefore is resistant to abrasion and destruction by stream currents. McDonald and Ray (1989) suggest that muskox specimens formerly referred to *Symbos cavifrons* Leidy represent male *Bootherium bombifrons*.

Modern bison, *Bison bison* Linnaeus, have been reported from a number of sites in Ohio, but it is possible that some of these specimens are post-Pleistocene in age. Horn cores attached to a partial skull of the extinct giant-horned bison, *Bison latifrons* (Harlan) (fig. 21-29.1), were discovered in Brown County in 1869 (Smith, 1887). This specimen, which measures at least 2 meters from tip to tip of the horns, is now at the American Museum of Natural History in New York. It may be the only Pleistocene mammal from Ohio that is Illinoian or Sangamonian in age, although this determination is speculative. Hay (1914) re-illustrated the specimen.

Elk or wapiti, *Cervus elaphus* Linnaeus, were common animals in Ohio from the end of the Pleistocene until historic times. It is uncertain if they were present in the state in the Late Pleistocene. Two nearly complete skeletons, one from Mercer County (Murphy and others, 1985) and one from Champaign County (Hansen, 1996), yielded radiocarbon dates of 9,370 and 9,020 years before present, respectively.

Caribou, *Rangifer tarandus* (Linnaeus), and white-tailed deer, *Odocoileus virginianus* (Zimmerman), have been reported from several sites in Ohio. Some of the specimens of *Odocoileus* may be of post-Pleistocene age.

PROBOSCIDEANS

Two types of elephantlike herbivores, the American mastodon, *Mammut americanum* (Kerr) (figs. 21-30.2, 21-31), and mammoths, *Mammuthus primigenius* (Blumenbach) (fig. 21-30.3) and *M. columbi* (Falconer), are the most commonly reported Pleistocene fossils from Ohio, a fact that reflects the easy recognition of enormous proboscidean bones. The term "mastodont" has replaced the traditional term "mastodon" in some recent technical literature (see Hayes, 1991). However, according to Daniel C. Fisher (University of Michigan, personal commun., 1996), the term "mastodon" is preferable both etymologically and historically in reference to the American mastodon, *Mammut americanum*.

Remains of nearly 250 proboscideans have been recorded in the state (fig. 21-30.1), mostly isolated teeth, bones, or tusks. Mastodon remains outnumber those of mammoths by about 3 to 1, a circumstance that is thought to reflect the lesser availability of grassland prairies preferred by mammoths. About 20 percent of these proboscidean remains, mostly tusk fragments, are indeterminate as to species.

Mammoths were taller than mastodons but more slimly built. Their teeth are particularly distinctive, being composed of alternating plates of enamel and dentine (fig. 21-30.3). The flat surface of these molars was an efficient shearing mechanism for grasses and other vegetation. No comprehensive study has been done on mammoth remains from Ohio. It is probable that many mammoth fossils from the state belong to *Mammuthus primigenius*, a common inhabitant of Pleistocene tundra and taiga environments. Some specimens may be referable to *M. columbi* (considered by some to be synonymous with *M. jeffersonii* Osborn), a larger, more southerly species that inhabitated prairie environments. *Mammuthus primigenius* is differentiated from *M. columbi* by the thinner enamel and higher frequency of tooth plates in *M. primigenius* (Graham, 1986).

Mastodons were sturdily built and had heavy, stout limbs, broad shoulders, and a low cranium. They reached a height of about 3 meters at the shoulder and weighed about 4 to 5 tons. Three teeth were present in each jaw **ramus**, in contrast to a single tooth in each jaw ramus of mammoths. These teeth have a series of cones (fig. 21-30.2), which were an aid in chewing twigs, branches, and aquatic vegetation. The postcranial bones of mastodons and mammoths are more difficult to differentiate, although those of mammoths tend to be more slender than those of mastodons. Olsen (1972) presents excellent comparative photographs of mastodon and mammoth bones.

More than a dozen complete or nearly complete proboscidean skeletons, particularly those of mastodons, have been found in Ohio in deposits that represent former glacial lakes. Several of these specimens received considerable notoriety at the time of their discovery.

Perhaps the most famous mastodon discovery in Ohio was the Johnstown mastodon in 1926 in Licking County (Mann and others, 1962; Hansen, 1990). This large, complete specimen, which is now displayed at the Cleveland Museum of Natural History (fig. 21-31.1), attracted national attention—more than 10,000 people reportedly visited the site to watch the excavation of the skeleton (fig. 21-32.1). Another well-known mastodon skeleton, referred to as the Conway mastodon, was discovered in Clark County in 1875 and is on display at the Ohio Historical Center in Columbus (fig. 21-31.2).

In 1989, a mastodon skeleton was found in Licking County, near Newark, that rivaled the Johnstown mastodon for widespread attention (Hansen, 1990). This specimen was discovered during the excavation of a bog for a pond at a golf course (fig. 21-32.2; also see the Pleistocene reconstruction, p. xix). The skeleton of a young male was complete except for the right rear leg. Marks on the bones were interpreted to represent butchering activities by Paleo-Indians (Fisher and others, 1991, 1994). Perhaps the most surprising aspect of this specimen, called the Burning Tree mastodon, was that material in the gut region of the specimen, which appeared to be intestinal contents, yielded plant materials consisting of low, herbaceous vegetation (see chapter 24) as well as bacteria (*Enterobacter cloacae*) that appear to be survivors or descendants of the mastodon's intestinal microflora (Lepper and others, 1991). The Burning Tree mastodon was purchased by a museum in Japan in 1993.

Further confirmation of the association of Paleo-Indians with mastodons in Ohio was revealed by the Martins Creek mastodon, excavated in Holmes County in 1993 (Hansen, 1994a). Several medium-sized flint flakes were found in association with this partial skeleton (fig. 21-32.3) and were tested for blood residue using the technique of immunological analysis. One of the flakes tested positive for elephant antiserum, indicating that it was used to butcher the mastodon.

CARNIVORES

Remains of carnivorous Pleistocene mammals are rare in Ohio (fig. 21-33.1). The Carter site has produced weasel, *Mustela erminea* Linnaeus; pine marten, *Martes americana* Turton; fisher, *Martes pennanti* Erxleben; and mink, *Mustela vison* Schreber. The Indian Trail Caverns site has produced short-faced bear, *Arctodus simus* (Cope) (figs. 21-23.6, 21-33.2); black bear, *Ursus americanus* Pallas; raccoon, *Procyon lotor* (Linnaeus); skunk, *Mephitis mephitis* (Schreber); red fox, *Vulpes vulpes* Linneaus; and river otter, *Lutra canadensis* Schreber; as well as mink, fisher, weasel, and pine marten (K. M. Ford, personal commun., 1994).

A skull of a grizzly bear, *Ursus arctos* Linnaeus, described by G. S. Miller (1899) as *Ursus procerus* Miller, was collected from Pleistocene outwash deposits near Overpeck, Butler County. This specimen is now in the collections of the National Museum of Natural History and its identification has been confirmed (Guilday, 1968). Additional grizzly bear specimens from Kentucky and West Virginia suggest that this western species had a much broader range in the late Pleistocene.

Remains of sabertooth cat, *Smilodon fatalis* (Leidy), and dire wolf, *Canis dirus* Allen, have not been found in Ohio, although they may have lived here because they have been found in nearby states. Such top-level predators have relatively small populations compared to herbivores and are found in the eastern United States as fossils preserved in caves and sinkholes.

COLLECTING LOCALITIES

The comparative rarity and sporadic occurrence of vertebrate remains in Ohio rocks and sediments makes it difficult to note specific, continually productive localities. Occurrences noted in the text serve more as a guide to stratigraphic units and geographic areas that may yield vertebrate remains rather than unique collecting sites. Always ask permission from the landowner before collecting on private property.

DEVONIAN

The Holland quarry, in Lucas County, has been closed for many years and is now reclaimed. However, there is always a possibility that channel fills of Lower Devonian rocks may exist elsewhere in northwestern Ohio and produce a rich fauna of agnathans, placoderms, and acanthodians similar to the Holland Quarry Shale.

The Columbus and Delaware Limestones (Middle Devonian) have yielded a rich fish fauna including possible agnathans, acanthodians, placoderms, chondrichthyans, and osteichthyans. Large bones and plates are discovered periodically on bedding planes. The bone beds (Wells, 1944b) yield a rich assemblage of most of the above fishes in the form of small elements and fragments. Quarries and natural outcrops of the Columbus Limestone from Pickaway County northward to the Marblehead Peninsula and Kelleys Island have produced fish remains, as have outcrops on the Bellefontaine Outlier in Logan County and in the small outcrop area in Paulding County in northwestern Ohio.

The Ohio Shale produces rare remains of placoderms, chondrichthyans, and osteichthyans throughout its area of outcrop. These specimens are found on bedding planes of fresh, unweathered shale or in the center of large carbonate concretions. Carbonate concretions in the lower part of the Huron Member of the Ohio Shale may be several feet in diameter and are very difficult to crack open. These concretions are abundant in high cliffs of Ohio Shale along such streams as Scioto Brush Creek in Adams County, Paint Creek in Ross County, Deer Creek in Pickaway County, the Olentangy River in Delaware and Franklin Counties, and the Huron River in Erie and Huron Counties. Excavations that cut through the Ohio Shale may produce concretions and fresh shale that might rarely produce fish remains.

The Cleveland Member of the Ohio Shale crops out along many of the drainage systems flowing into Lake Erie in Cuyahoga and neighboring counties. Many of the larger outcrops are within the Cleveland Metro Park system and are unavailable for collecting. Flattened, discoidal concretions occur in several vertical zones of the Cleveland Shale Member and are most common along Big Creek and its tributaries in the Cleveland area. Fossils of placoderms and other fishes are comparatively rare in the Cleveland Member and are generally fortuitious discoveries.

MISSISSIPPIAN

Fish remains are very rare in Mississippian rocks in Ohio. Isolated teeth and other skeletal elements of fishes have been found in the Sunbury Shale throughout its area of outcrop. The Berea Sandstone at Chagrin Falls, Cuyahoga County, produced specimens of a palaeoniscoid, *Gonatodus brainerdi*, in the last century. The Meadville Shale Member of the Cuyahoga Formation produces rare shark spines at the city park in Lodi, Medina County. Shark teeth are rare in the Maxville Formation in east-central Ohio.

PENNSYLVANIAN

Teeth and other skeletal elements of sharks can be found with some regularity in most of the beds of marine limestone and shale exposed in eastern Ohio. Marine beds of the Conemaugh Group, especially the Ames limestone, have the greatest abundance of these remains. Numerous localities that may potentially be productive are listed in Sturgeon and Hoare (1968), Hoare and others (1979), and Brezinski and others (1989).

Nonmarine dark-gray to black shales above coal beds may produce scales and teeth of palaeoniscoid fishes and teeth of a shark, *Orthacanthus compressus*. Some nonmarine limestones produce similar remains. Fin spines of an acanthodian, *Acanthodes marshi*, have been found in the Dorr Run shale (Allegheny Group) near Nelsonville, Athens County (Zidek, 1980). This shale appears to be of brackish-water origin.

The famous Linton locality, on the north bank of Yellow Creek near its confluence with the Ohio River in Jefferson County, has produced remains of *Orthacanthus compressus*, palaeoniscoids, coelacanths, lungfish, amphibians, and reptiles for nearly a century and a half. These specimens occur on bedding planes of a cannel coal associated with the Upper Freeport coal (Allegheny Group) at the long-abandoned mine dump of an underground coal mine. Although these specimens are important scientifically, they are heavily pyritized and generally unimpressive when exposed on bedding planes. Modern study of these specimens is done with the aid of latex peels.

Strip mines (now reclaimed) in the Lower Kittanning coal (Allegheny Group) near Five Points, Mahoning County, have produced a diverse fauna of nonmarine fishes and tetrapods rivaling those from Linton. These remains occur in a cannel coal at the base of the Lower Kittanning coal. Although this locality is no longer available for collecting, it demonstrates that similar deposits may be encountered from time to time in eastern Ohio.

Exposures of a shale in a channel fill about 3.5 meters above the Ames limestone (Conemaugh Group) between Seminary Road and the Penn Central Railroad, in SW¼SE¼ SE¼ sec. 24, Wayne Township, Jefferson County, have yielded remains of amphibians and lungfish (Vaughn, 1971).

PERMIAN

Nonmarine limestones and shales of the Dunkard Group in eastern Ohio have produced remains of *Orthacanthus compressus*; teeth and scales of palaeoniscoids; teeth, scales, and other skeletal elements of lungfish; and remains of amphibians and reptiles. Stauffer and Schroyer (1920) list several localities.

A channel conglomerate exposed approximately two-thirds of the way above the base of a large road cut on the west side of U.S. Route 50 near the junction of Ohio Route 7 near Belpre, Washington County, has produced fragmentary remains of fish, amphibians, and reptiles. This road cut, first exposed in the 1960's, is now heavily overgrown with vegetation.

The Cameron locality, in SW¼ sec. 18, Adams Township, Monroe County (Moran, 1952, p. 18-19), has produced numerous specimens of lungfish and tetrapods.

PLEISTOCENE

Almost all discoveries of Pleistocene fossils in Ohio are fortuitious. Particular attention should be given to excavations that expose peat or marl in boggy areas that represent infilled former glacial lakes. A large number of nearly complete, and scientifically important, specimens have been discovered in Ohio in this manner. Should such discoveries be made, particularly if multiple skeletal elements are present, a museum or university geology department should be contacted so that the specimen can be extracted properly and additional scientific data can be gathered.

Sand and gravel deposits along major meltwater drainageways consistently yield waterworn bones and teeth of Pleistocene mammals. These specimens generally are found in sand and gravel pits and in natural exposures along modern streams.

Caves and sinkholes are not common in Ohio, but some of them have the potential to yield important assemblages of Pleistocene mammals and lower vertebrates. The abundant remains of Pleistocene fossils recovered from the Indian Trail Caverns site in Wyandot County demonstrate this potential.

ACKNOWLEDGMENTS

A number of individuals have assisted with preparation of this chapter and, in some cases, the information presented here would be much less comprehensive without the intimate knowledge of various groups possessed by these researchers. Michael E. Williams (Cleveland Museum of Natural History) has provided information and illustrations of Cleveland Shale Member fishes and critically reviewed the section on fishes. William J. Hlavin (Bass Energy, Inc.) provided illustrations and information on Devonian fishes. Donald Baird (Carnegie Museum of Natural History) provided considerable information on Pennsylvanian vertebrates and generously furnished several illustrations. Robert W. Hook (Austin, Texas) critically reviewed the sections on tetrapods, provided a number of helpful suggestions on other portions of the manuscript, and provided several illustrations. H. Gregory McDonald (Hagerman Fossil Beds National Monument, formerly of the Cincinnati Museum of Natural History), critically reviewed the sections on Pleistocene vertebrates and provided illustrations and advice for this chapter. Kenneth M. Ford, III (Michigan State University) kindly provided unpublished faunal data from the Indian Trail Caverns site. Dale M. Gnidovec and Loren E. Babcock (The Ohio State University), were of great assistance in providing specimens from Orton Museum and photographic facilities. Additional photographs and illustrations have been provided by Joe H. Marak (Miami University), Richard Lund (Adelphi University), Christopher S. Duckworth and Robert Glotzhober (The Ohio Historical Society), and the Cincinnati Museum of Natural History.

TABLE 21-1.—CLASSIFICATION OF FOSSIL VERTEBRATES FROM OHIO

Fish classification is from Long (1995), with modification; not all taxonomic ranks are provided. Tetrapod classification is from Carroll (1988).

SUPERPHYLUM AGNATHA
Subphylum Craniata
CLASS PTERASPIDOMORPHI
Subclass Heterostraci
Suborder Cyathaspidiformes
Allocryptaspis laticostatus
Suborder Pteraspidiformes
Pteraspis carmani
Subphylum Gnathostomata
CLASS PLACODERMI
Order Ptyctodontida
Rhynchodus secans
Order Rhenanida
Asterosteus stenocephalus
Order Petalichthyida
Macropetalichthys rapheidolabis
Order Arthrodira
Infraorder Actinolepidi
Aethaspis ohioensis
Suborder Brachythoraci
Dinichthys herzeri
Dunkleosteus terrelli
Gorgonichthys clarki
Heintzichthys gouldii
Holdenius holdeni
Protitanichthys sp.
Woodwardosteus spatulatus
Suborder Phlyctaeniina
Holonema sp.
Suborder uncertain
Gymnotrachelus hydei
Mylostoma variabile
Selenosteus brevis
Stenosteus angustopectus
Stenosteus glaber
Titanichthys agassizi
Titanichthys clarkii
Uncertain arthrodire
Aspidichthys clavatus
CLASS CHONDRICHTHYES
Subclass Elasmobranchii
Order Cladoselachiformes
Cladoselache clarki
Cladoselache fyleri
Cladoselache kepleri
Order Corodontiformes
Diademodus hydei
Order Symmoriformes
Stethacanthus altonensis
Symmorium reniforme
Order Orodontiformes
Orodus sp.
Order Ctenacanthiformes
Acondylacanthus nuperus
Bandringa rayi
Ctenacanthus angustus
Ctenacanthus compressus
Ctenacanthus formosus
Ctenacanthus lamborni
Phoebodus sp.
Order Xenacanthiformes
Orthacanthus compressus
Xenacanthus tridentatus
Order Petalodontiformes
Cholodus inaequalis
Janassa sp.
Peripristis semicircularis
Petalodus ohioensis
Order uncertain
Ageleodus pectinatus
Cladolepis sp.
Ohiolepis sp.
Physonemus acinaciformis
Sphenacanthus marshi
(formerly *Ctenacanthus marshi*)
Subclass Holocephali
Order Psammodontiformes
Lagarodus angustus
Order Cochliodontiformes
Cochliodus sp.
Deltodus angularis
CLASS ACANTHODII
Order Acanthodiformes
Acanthodes marshi
Order Climatiiformes
Cheiracanthoides sp.
Gyracanthus sp.
Order uncertain
Machaeracanthus sp.
Onchus sp.
CLASS OSTEICHTHYES
Subclass Actinopterygii
Order Palaeonisciformes
"Elonichthys" peltigerus
Gonatodus brainerdi
Kentuckia hlavini
Rhadinichthys sp.
Tegeolepis clarki
Order Haplolepiformes
Haplolepis corrugata
Microhaplolepis ovoidea
Microhaplolepis serrata
Parahaplolepis tuberculata
Pyritocephalus lineatus
Order Siluriformes
Ictalurus spp.
Order Cypriniformes
Semotilus spp.
Umbra limi
Order Perciformes
Micropterus sp.
Subclass Dipnoi
Conchopoma exanthematicum
Palaeophichthys sp.
Proceratodus sp.
Sagenodus periprion
Sagenodus serratus

Subclass Crossopterygii
Order Onychodontiformes
Onychodus sigmoides
Order Actinistia (coelacanths)
Chagrinia enodis
Rhabdoderma elegans
Order Osteolepiformes
Ectosteorhachis sp.
Order Rhizodontiformes
Megalichthys sp.
Rhizodopsis sp.

DIVISION TETRAPODA
CLASS AMPHIBIA
Subclass Labyrinthodontia
Order Temnospondyli
Acheloma stonei
(formerly *Trematops stonei*)
Amphibamus lyelli
Astreptorachis ohioensis
Broiliellus hektotopos
Cochleosaurus sp.
Colosteus scutellatus
Eryops sp.
Saurerpeton obtusum
Trimerorhachis sp.
Order Anthracosauria
Leptophractus obsoletus
Neopteroplax conemaughensis
Order uncertain
Baphetes lineolatus
Megalocephalus enchodus
Subclass Lepospondyli
Order Aïstopoda
Ophiderpeton amphiuminum
Phlegethontia linearis
Order Nectridea
Ctenerpeton remex
Diceratosaurus brevirostris
Diploceraspis burkei
Ptyonius marshii
Sauropleura pectinata
Order Microsauria
Tuditanus punctulatus
Order Lysorophia
Brachydectes newberryi
Megamolgophis agostinii
Modern amphibian orders
Order Urodela
Ambystoma lateralle
Order Anura
Bufo americanus
Bufo woodhouseii
Pseudacris triseriata
Rana catesbeiana
Rana clamitans
Rana pipiens
Rana sylvatica

CLASS REPTILIA
Subclass Anapsida
Order Captorhinida
Anthracodromeus longipes
Cephalerpeton ventriarmatum
Melanothyris morani
Protorothyris sp.
Subclass Synapsida
Order Pelycosauria
Archaeothyris sp.
Baldwinonus? dunkardensis
Clepsydrops sp.
Ctenospondylus ninevehensis
Dimetrodon sp.
Edaphosaurus sp.
Ophiacodon sp.
Subclass Testudinata
Order Chelonia
Chelydra serpentina
Chrysemys picta
Emyoidea blandingii
Subclass Diapsida
Order Squamata
Coluber constrictor
Elaphe vulpina
Lampropeltis triangulum
Nerodia sipedon
Opheodrys vernalis
Regina septemvittata
Thamnophis sirtalis
CLASS AVES
Subclass Neornithes
Order Galliformes
Meleagris gallopavo
Order Anseriformes
Anas sp.
CLASS MAMMALIA
Subclass Theria
Order Insectivora
Blarina sp.
Cryptotis sp.
Sorex sp.
Order Chiroptera
Myotis sp.
Order Rodentia
Castor canadensis
Castoroides ohioensis
Clethrionomys sp.
Erethizon dorsatum
Marmota monax
Microtus pennsylvanicus
Ondatra zibethica
Peromyscus sp.
Phenacomys sp.
Sciurus sp.
Spermophilus tridecemlineatus
Synaptomys sp.
Tamias sp.
Tamiasciurus sp.

Order Lagomorphа
- *Sylvilagus* sp.

Order Xenarthra
- *Megalonyx jeffersonii*

Order Perissodactyla
- *Equus* sp.
- *Tapirus* sp.

Order Artiodactyla
- *Bison bison*
- *Bison latifrons*
- *Bootherium bombifrons*
- *Cervalces scotti*
- *Cervus elaphus*
- *Odocoileus virginianus*
- *Ovibos moschatus*
- *Platygonus compressus*
- *Rangifer tarandus*

Order Proboscidea
- *Mammut americanum*
- *Mammuthus columbi*
- *Mammuthus primigenius*

Order Carnivora
- *Arctodus simus*
- *Lutra canadensis*
- *Martes americanum*
- *Martes pennanti*
- *Mephitis mephitis*
- *Mustela erminea*
- *Mustela vison*
- *Procyon lotor*
- *Ursus americanus*
- *Ursus arctos*
- *Vulpes vulpes*

FIGURE 21-1.—Devonian agnathans and placoderms. Scale bars for figures 21-1.1 to 21-1.3, 21-1.5, and 21-1.6 equal 1 cm; scale bar for figure 21-1.4 equals 10 cm.

1, 2	*Pteraspis carmani* Denison, a heterostracan agnathan. **1**, dorsal disk. Holland Quarry Shale, Lucas County, Ohio, OSU 27564. **2**, restoration of the dorsal shield. From Denison (1960).
3	Hash of fish remains in a bone bed. Columbus Limestone, Franklin County, Ohio; OSU 3822.
4, 5	*Macropetalichthys rapheidolabis* Norwood & Owen, a placoderm. **4**, skull in dorsal view. Silica Formation, Lucas County, Ohio; MUGM T-100. Photo courtesy of Joe H. Marak (Miami University); **5**, spine from the trunk shield, originally named *Acanthaspis armata* Newberry. Columbus Limestone, Delaware County, Ohio; OSU 3797.
6	*Rhynchodus secans* Newberry, a placoderm. Upper tooth. Columbus Limestone, Delaware County, Ohio; OSU 3789.

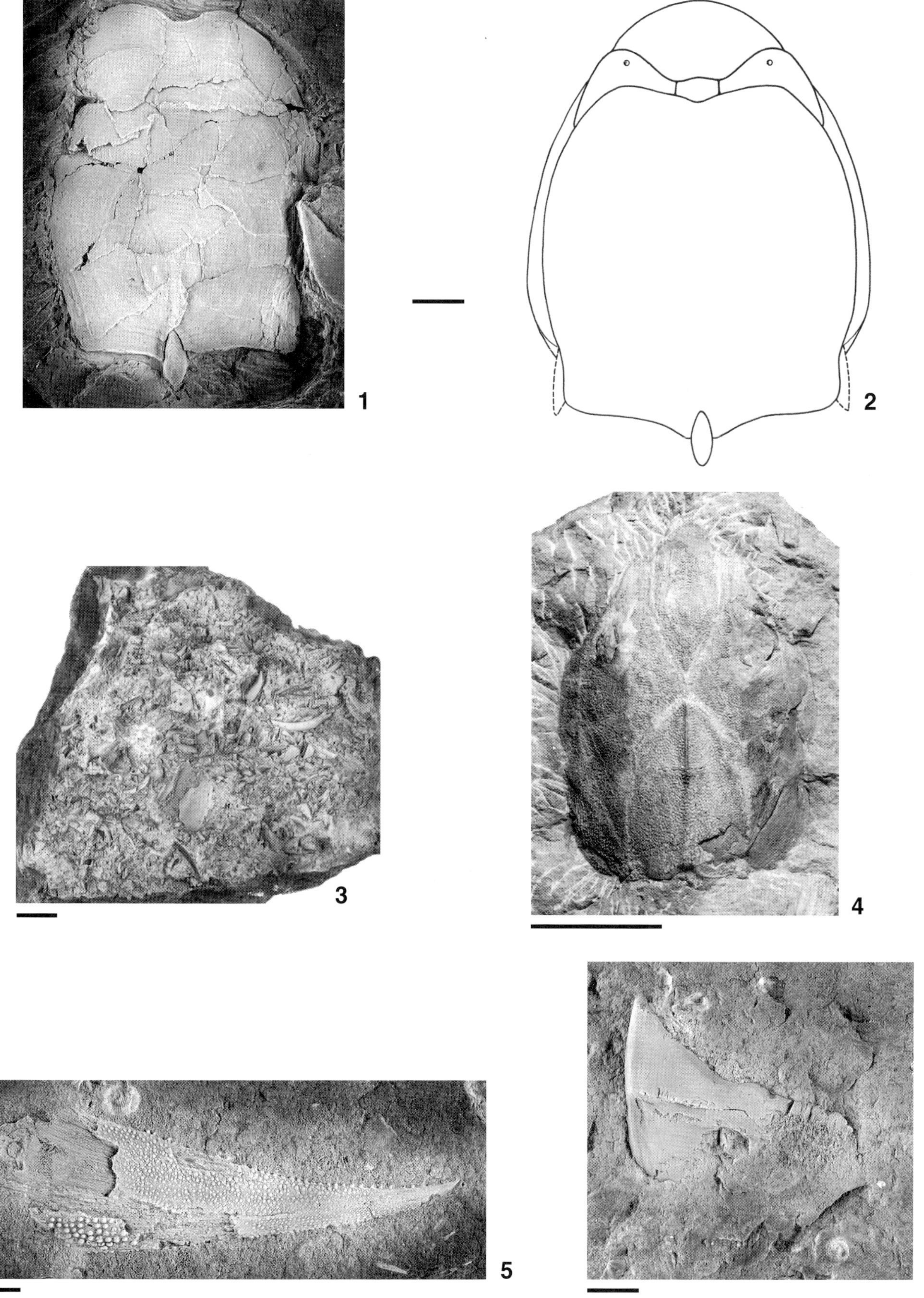
1
2
3
4
5
6

FIGURE 21-2.—Devonian arthrodires. Photo in figure 21-2.1 courtesy of the Cleveland Museum of Natural History. Scale bars for figures 21-2.2 and 21-2.3 equal 3 cm. Figures 21-2.2 and 21-2.3 are redrawn from Hlavin (1976). Figure 21-2.4 was drawn by William E. Scheele for the Cleveland Museum of Natural History.

1, 2	*Dunkleosteus terrelli* (Newberry). **1**, restored skull and thoracic shield. Cleveland Shale Member of the Ohio Shale (Upper Devonian), Cuyahoga County, Ohio. Specimen is nearly 1.4 meters long. **2**, left lower jaw (inferognathal element). Cleveland Shale Member of the Ohio Shale.
3	*Dinichthys herzeri* Newberry. Left lower jaw (inferognathal element). Huron Shale Member of the Ohio Shale.
4	Reconstruction of *Dunkleosteus terrelli* pursuing *Cladoselache*, a Devonian shark.

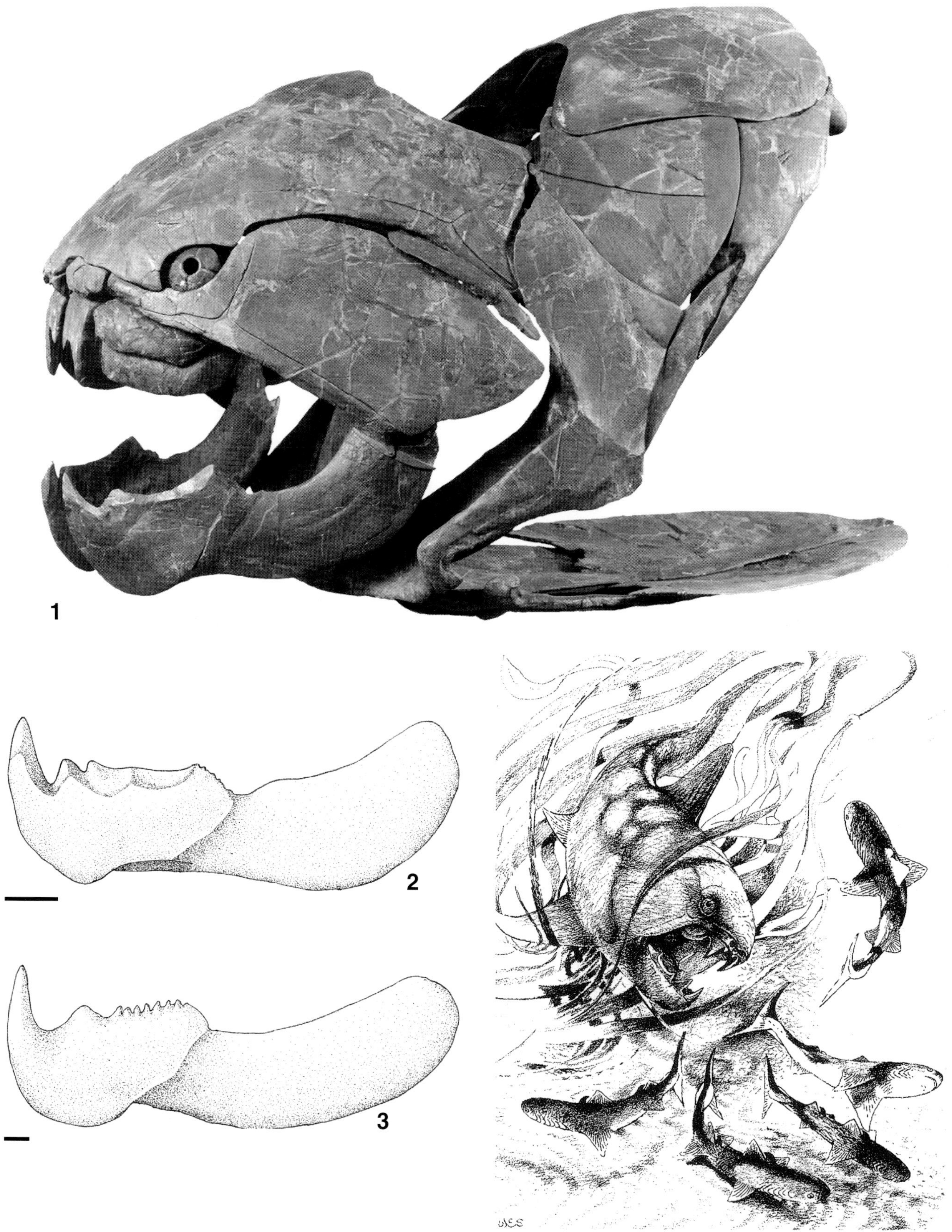
1
2
3
4

FIGURE 21-3.—Upper Devonian and Pennsylvanian sharks. Photo in figure 21-3.1 courtesy of the Cleveland Museum of Natural History. Scale bars for figures 21-3.1 and 21-3.2 equal 10 cm; scale bar for figure 21-3.3 equals 1 cm.

1, 2	*Cladoselache fyleri* (Newberry). **1**, nearly complete specimen preserved in a concretion. Cleveland Shale Member of the Ohio Shale, Cuyahoga County, Ohio; ClMNH 5408. **2**, reconstruction. From Schaeffer (1967).
3	*Petalodus ohioensis* Safford. Reconstruction of the dentition. Teeth of this genus of Pennsylvanian shark have never been found in anatomic association; however, the variability seen in large samples of isolated teeth suggests a multielement dentition that was used to slice or nip at prey. From Hansen (1986).

1

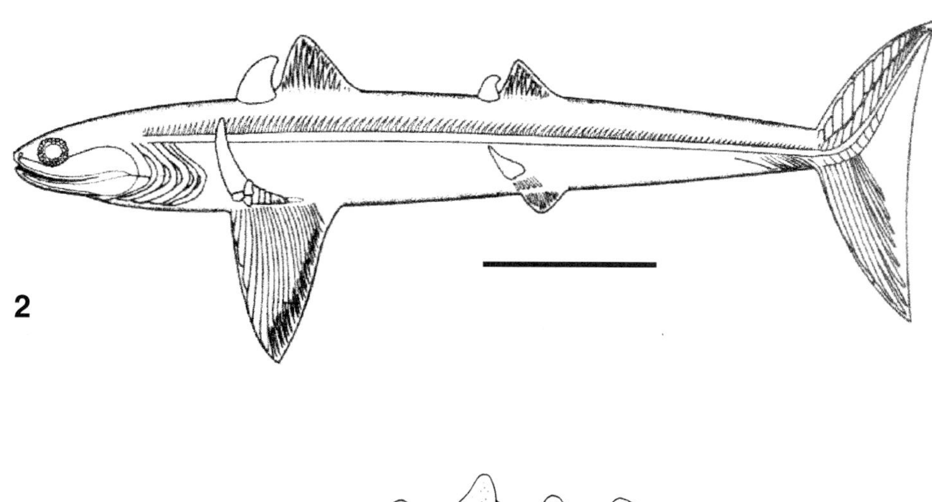
2

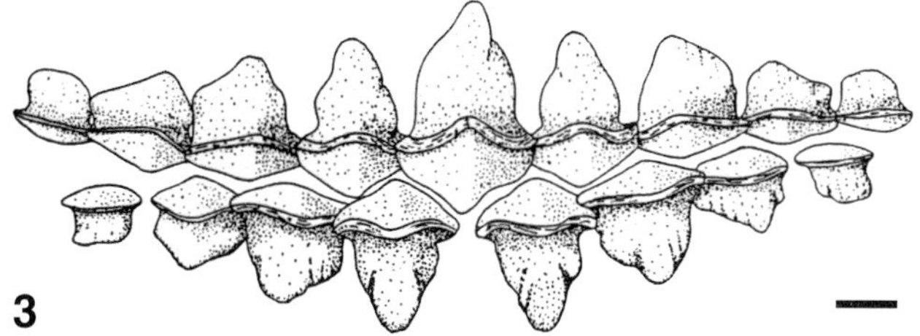
3

FIGURE 21-4.—Chondrichthyan teeth from Pennsylvanian rocks. Scale bars for figures 21-4.1 to 21-4.12 equal 1 cm; scale bar for figures 21-4.13 and 21-4.14 equals 1 mm; scale bar for figures 21-4.15 and 21-4.16 equals 2 mm.

1-3	*Petalodus ohioensis* Safford. Cambridge limestone (Conemaugh Group), Guernsey County, Ohio. **1**, **2**, **labial** and **lingual** views, respectively. USNM 244454. **3**, labial view. ClMNH 9184.
4, 5	*Janassa* sp. **4**, associated teeth, Brush Creek shale (Conemaugh Group), Columbiana County, Ohio; OSU 38669. **5**, lateral tooth. Ames limestone (Conemaugh Group), Harrison County, Ohio; OSU 33605b. Compare with teeth in the center of **4** (arrows).
6	*Peripristis semicircularis* (Newberry & Worthen). Labial view. Cambridge limestone (Conemaugh Group), Gallia County, Ohio; OSU 33565.
7, 8	*Cholodus inaequalis* St. John & Worthen. Profile (**7**) and lingual (**8**) and views. Ames limestone (Conemaugh Group), Carroll County, Ohio; ClMNH 9078.
9-11	*Deltodus angularis* Newberry & Worthen. Associated dentition. **9**, upper tooth, formerly referred to *Sandalodus carbonarius* Newberry & Worthen. **10**, articulated lower tooth plates. **11**, small tooth plate of uncertain position. Brush Creek shale (Conemaugh Group), Columbiana County, Ohio; OSU 38670.
12	*Orodus* sp. Lateral view. Cambridge limestone (Conemaugh Group), Guernsey County, Ohio; OSU 35068.
13, 14	*Lagarodus angustus* (Romanowsky). Lateral (**13**) and lingual (**14**) views. Putnam Hill limestone (Allegheny Group), Tuscarawas County, Ohio; OSU 35352.
15, 16	*Ageleodus pectinatus* (Agassiz). Labial views. Lower Kittanning coal (Allegheny Group), Mahoning County, Ohio; CM 29867 (**15**) and CM 34911 (**16**).

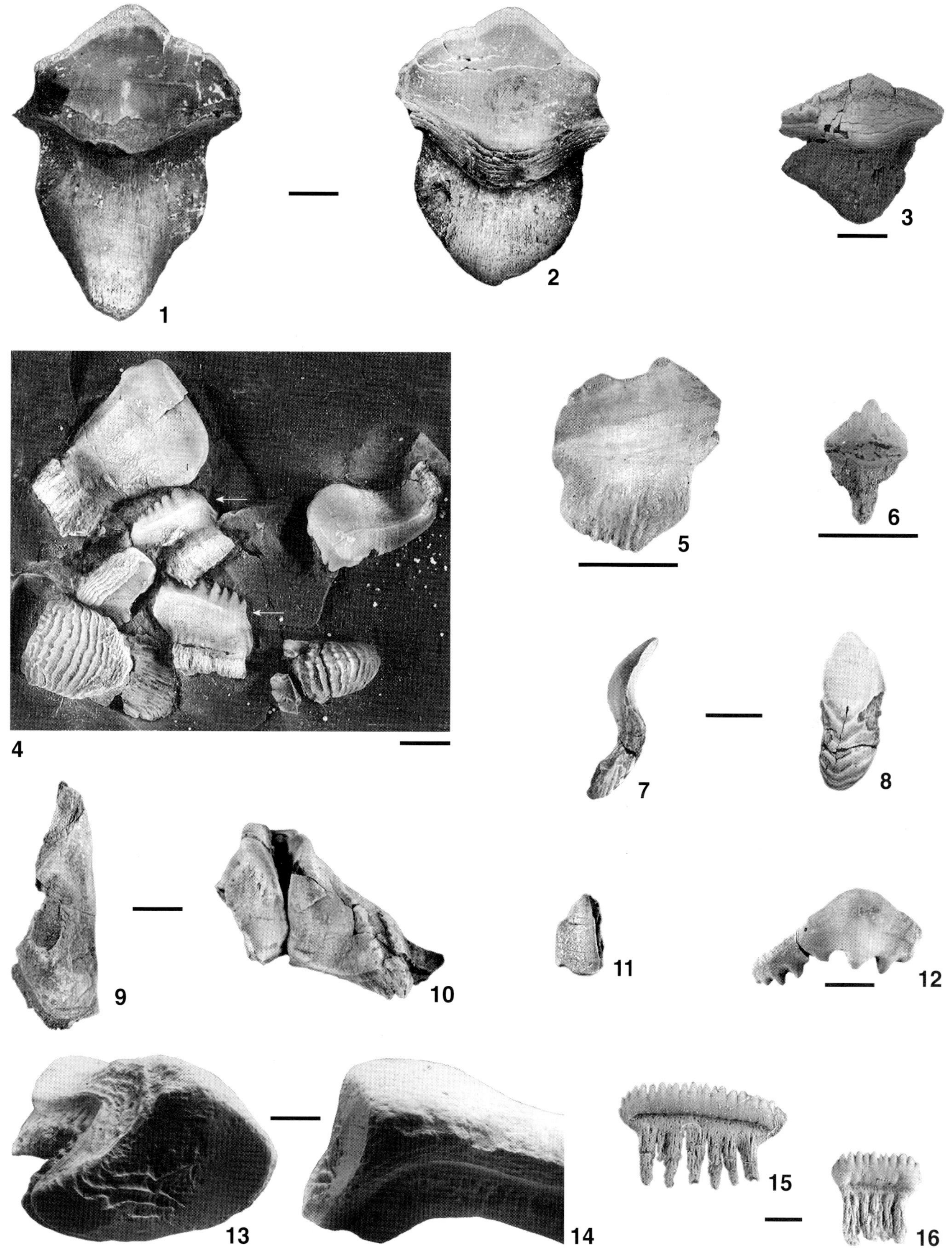
1
2
3
4
5
6
7
8
9
10
11
12
13
14
15
16

FIGURE 21-5.—Chondrichthyan remains from Devonian, Pennsylvanian and Permian rocks. Scale bars for figures 21-5.1, 21-5.2, 21-5.8 to 21-5.11, and 21-5.13 to 21-5.15 equal 1 cm; scale bars for figures 21-5.3 to 21-5.7 and 21-5.12 equal 0.5 cm.

1	*Symmorium reniforme* Cope. Tooth in labial view. Putnam Hill limestone (Allegheny Group, Pennsylvanian), Mahoning County, Ohio; OSU 35092.
2	Tooth file of undescribed “cladodont” shark. Cleveland Shale Member of Ohio Shale (Upper Devonian), Cuyahoga County, Ohio; ClMNH 8115.
3, 4	Spiral coprolites, probably from a xenacanth shark, *Orthacanthus compressus* (Newberry). Unnamed nonmarine shale in Conemaugh Group (Pennsylvanian), Athens County, Ohio; OSU 35166.
5-7	*Stethacanthus altonensis* (St. John & Worthen). Labial (**3**), oral (**4**), and lateral (**5**) views of tooth. Portersville shale (Conemaugh Group, Pennsylvanian), Athens County, Ohio; OSU 35143.
8	*Acondylacanthus nuperus* St. John & Worthen. Median-fin spine. Putnam Hill shale (Allegheny Group, Pennsylvanian), Tuscarawas County, Ohio; OSU 35114.
9	*Ctenacanthus lamborni* Wells. Median-fin spine. **Holotype**. Ames limestone (Conemaugh Group, Pennsylvanian), Guernsey County, Ohio; OSU 19501.
10	*Physonemus acinaciformis* (St. John & Worthen). Median-fin spine. Cambridge limestone (Conemaugh Group, Pennsylvanian), Lawrence County, Ohio; OSU 35107.
11	*Sphenacanthus marshi* (Newberry). Fragment of a tapered fin spine. Upper Brush Creek limestone (Conemaugh Group, Pennsylvanian), Athens County, Ohio; OSU 35108.
12-15	*Orthacanthus compressus* (Newberry). **12**, oral view of a tooth. Unnamed nonmarine shale in Conemaugh Group (Pennsylvanian), Athens County, Ohio; OSU 35095. Lateral (**13**), lingual (**14**), and oral (**15**) views of a tooth. Dunkard Group (Permian), Washington County, Ohio; ClMNH 11323.

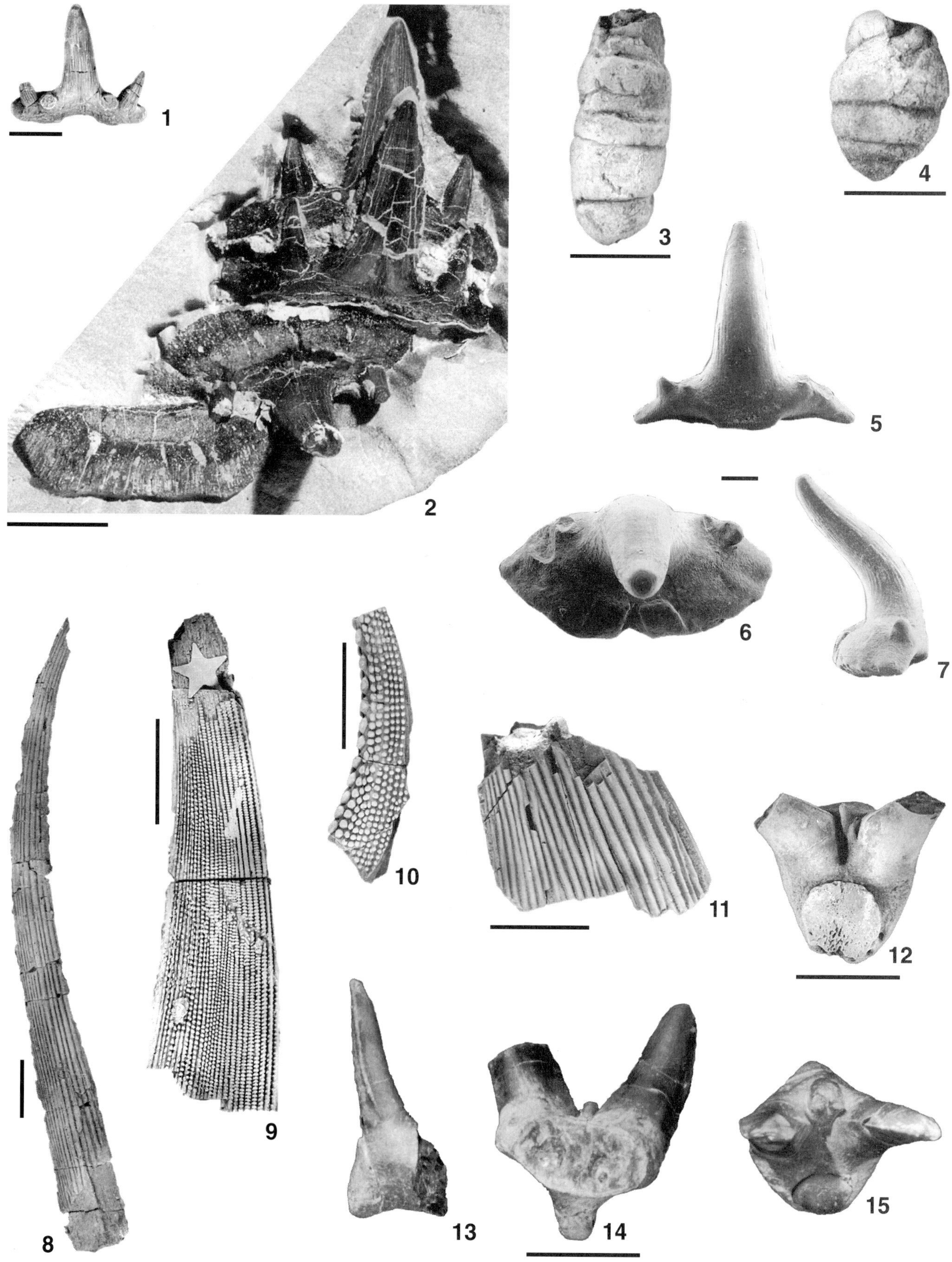
1
2
3
4
5
6
7
8
9
10
11
12
13
14
15

FIGURE 21-6.—Upper Devonian, Mississippian, and Pennsylvanian sharks.

1 Reconstruction of *Stethacanthus altonensis* Newberry, a symmoriid shark known from Upper Devonian, Mississippian, and Pennsylvanian rocks of Ohio. These small sharks reached 0.5 meter to about 1 meter in length. From Zangerl (1984).

2 Reconstruction of the general body form of xenacanth sharks. Scale bar equals 10 cm. A common species from Pennsylvanian rocks in Ohio is *Orthacanthus compressus* (Newberry), which reached lengths of 2 to 3 meters. From Moy-Thomas and Miles (1971).

3 Reconstruction of *Symmorium reniforme* Cope, a large Pennsylvanian shark, attacking a nautiloid cephalopod. A number of cephalopod shells with punctures from the spikelike teeth of this shark, which reached lengths of up to 3 meters, have been found in Pennsylvanian rocks of Ohio and adjacent areas (see Hansen and Mapes, 1990, and fig. 14-5.7 in Chapter 14 of this book). From Mapes and Hansen (1984).

4 Reconstruction of a nonmarine ctenacanth shark, *Bandringa rayi* Zangerl. It is speculated that this small (0.5 meter) Pennsylvanian shark used its long rostrum to stir up prey from bottom mud. From Baird (1978).

5, 6 Clasper element, part and counterpart, of *Orthacanthus compressus* (Newberry). Linton, Jefferson County, Ohio; AMNH 8507. Scale bar equals 5 mm. The terminal, comblike elements were called "kamplatten" or *Euctenius* and interpreted to be part of a crustacean tail. Drawing of the original specimen by Robert W. Hook.

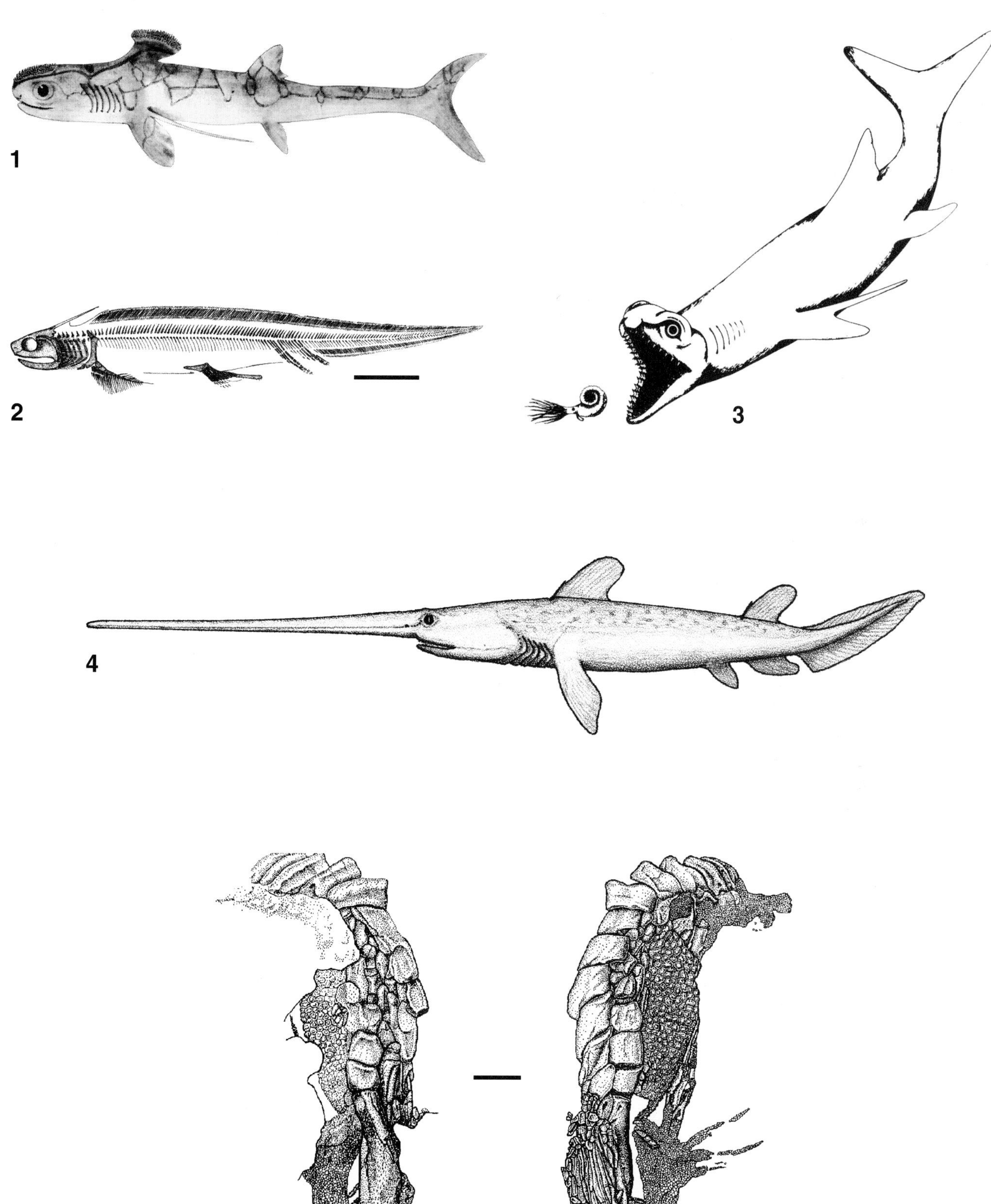
1
2
3
4
5
6

FIGURE 21-7.—Devonian, Mississippian, and Pennsylvanian acanthodians. Scale bars for figures 21-7.1 to 21-7.4 equal 1 cm; scale bars for figures 21-7.5 to 21-7.7 equal 1 mm.

1, 2 *Gyracanthus* Agassiz. **1**, prepectoral spine, CM 67137. **2**, pectoral spine, CM 67113. Lower Kittanning coal (Allegheny Group, Pennsylvanian), Mahoning County, Ohio. Photos of latex peels courtesy of Donald Baird and Robert W. Hook.

3 *Gyracanthus compressus* Newberry. Fin spine. Cuyahoga Formation (Mississippian), Medina County, Ohio; OSU 4328.

4 *Machaeracanthus peracutus* Newberry. Fin spine. Columbus Limestone (Middle Devonian), Erie County, Ohio: OSU 45578.

5-7 *Cheiracanthoides* Wells. Scales in lateral (**5**) and anterior (**6**, **7**) views. Bone beds in Columbus Limestone (Middle Devonian). From Wells (1944b).

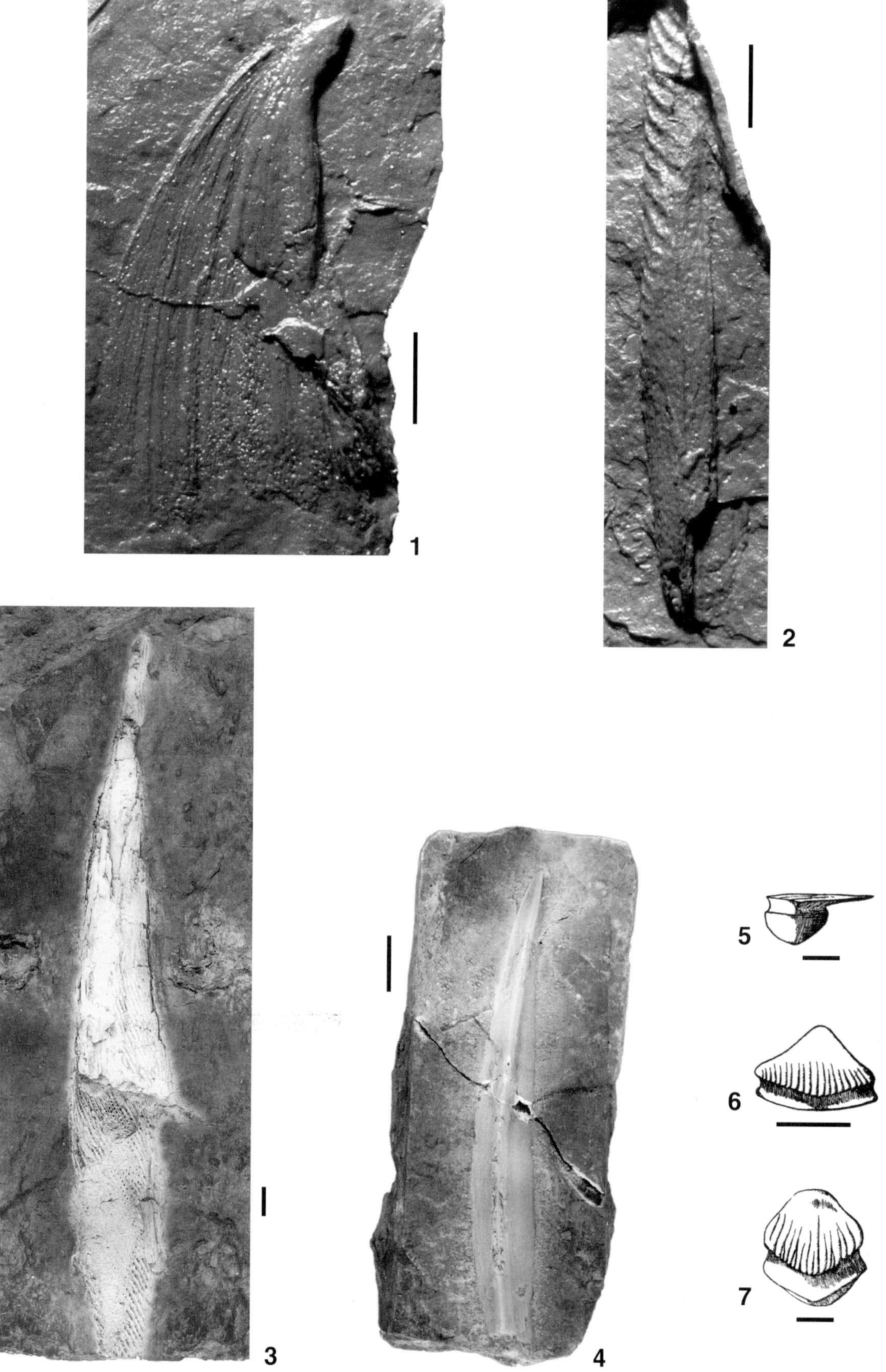
1
2
3
4
5
6
7

FIGURE 21-8.—*Kentuckia hlavini* Dunkle, an Upper Devonian palaeonsicoid from the Cleveland Shale Member of the Ohio Shale, Cuyahoga County, Ohio. Scale bars equal 1 cm. Photos courtesy of the Cleveland Museum of Natural History.

1 Holotype. ClMNH 8061.

2 Head and anterior portion of the body. Note the delicate ornamentation on the cranial bones. ClMNH 8060.

1

2

FIGURE 21-9.—*Tegeolepis clarki* (Newberry), a large (about 1.8 meters long) Upper Devonian palaeoniscoid. Scale bars equal 1 cm. Photos courtesy of the Cleveland Museum of Natural History.

1 Disarticulated head. Cleveland Shale Member of the Ohio Shale, Cuyahoga County, Ohio; ClMNH 8120.

2 Detail of right lower jaw showing sharp, conical teeth. Cleveland Shale Member, Cuyahoga County, Ohio; ClMNH 8124.

3 Reconstruction of the head. From Dunkle and Schaeffer (1973).

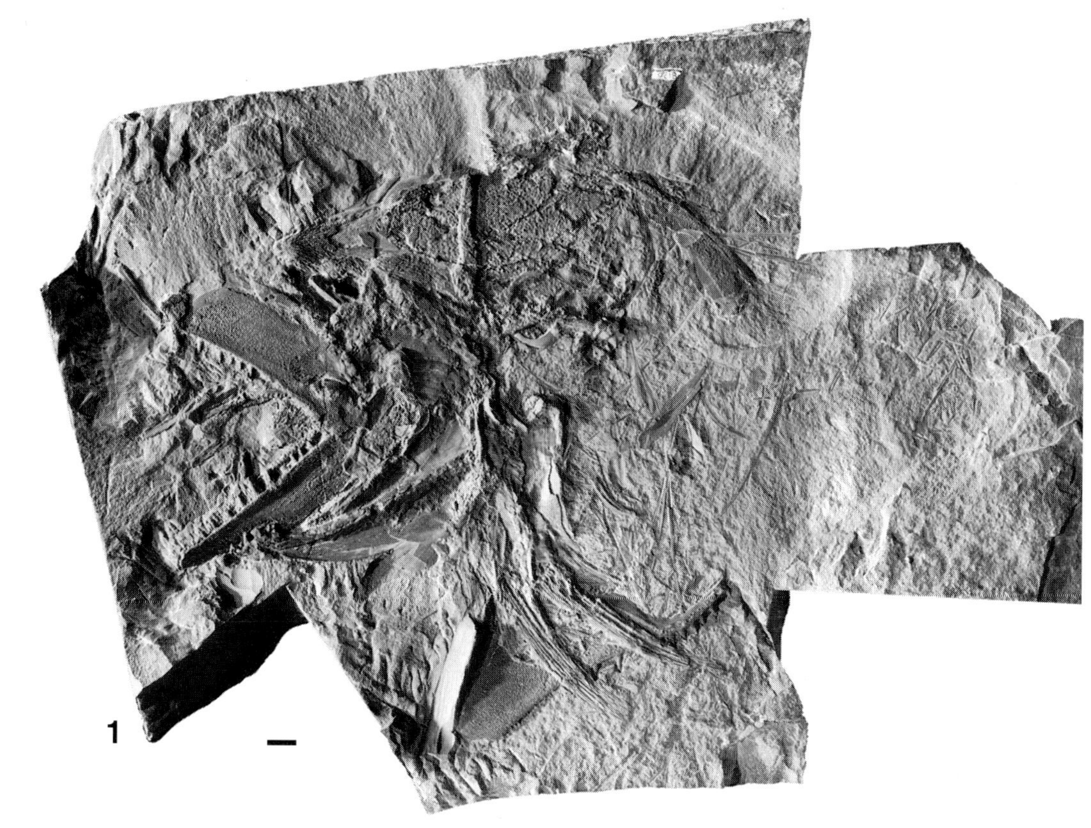
1

2

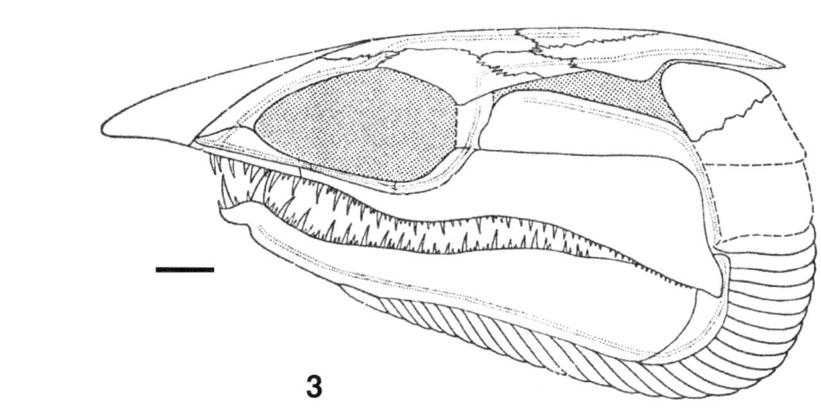
3

FIGURE 21-10.—Devonian and Mississippian osteichthyans. Scale bars equal 1 cm.

1-4	*Onychodus sigmoides* Newberry, a crossopterygian. **1**, Reconstruction of *Onychodus* attacking a placoderm. From Long (1991). **2**, tooth whorl. Columbus Limestone (Middle Devonian) Franklin County, Ohio; OSU 3812. **3**, clavicle ("shoulder" bone). Columbus Limestone, Delaware County, Ohio; OSU 38671. **4**, portion of lower jaw. Columbus Limestone, Paulding? County, Ohio; OSU 1832.
5	*Gonatodus brainerdi* (Newberry), a palaeoniscoid. Specimen illustrated by Newberry (1889). Berea Sandstone (Mississippian), Cuyahoga County, Ohio; ClMNH 9827.

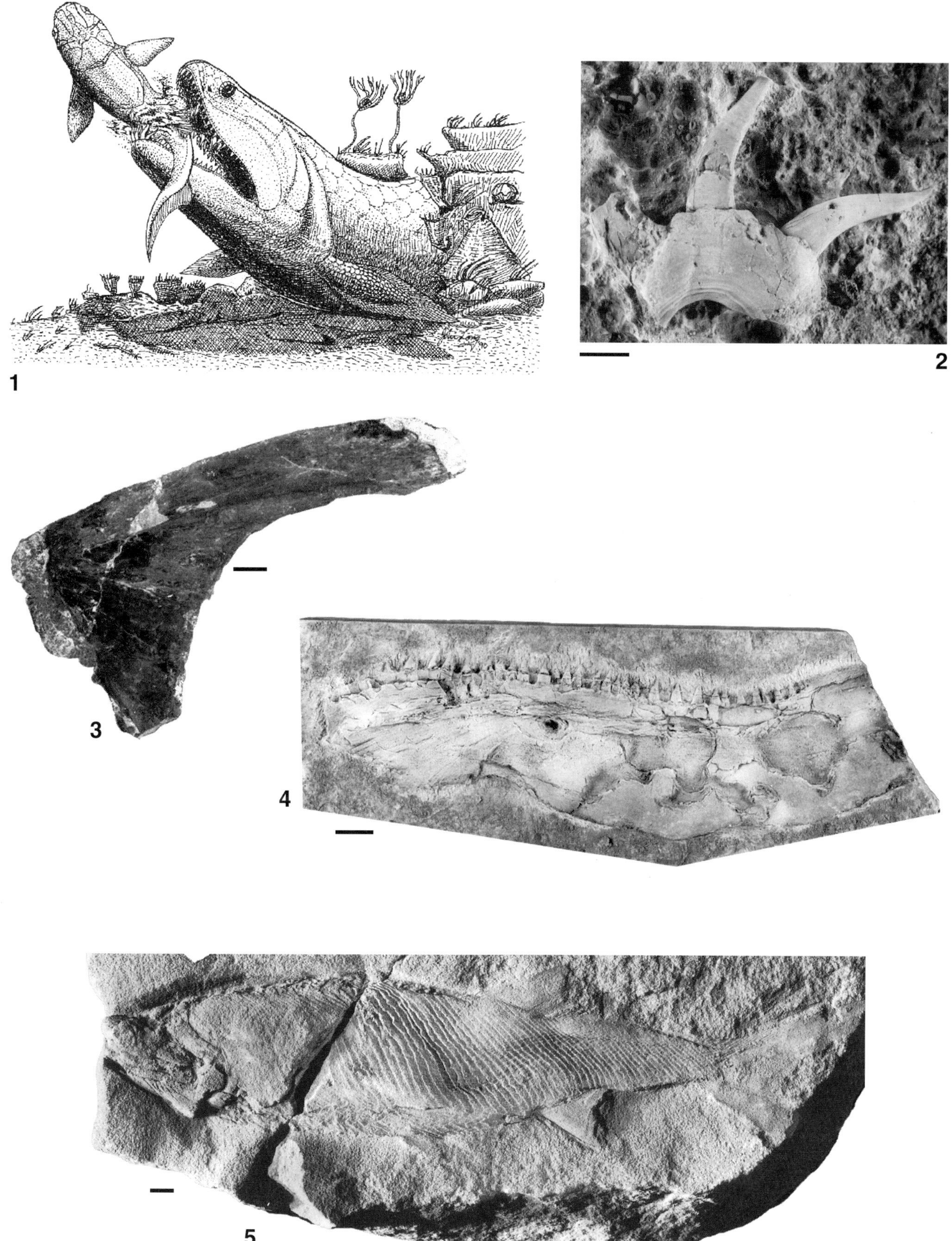
1
2
3
4
5

FIGURE 21-11.—Reconstructions of Pennsylvanian haplolepid palaeoniscoids from the Upper Freeport coal (Allegheny Group), Linton, Jefferson County. Scale bars for figures 21-11.1 to 21-11.3 equal 5 mm; scale bars for figures 21-11.4 and 21-11.5 equal 2 mm. From Lowney (1980).

1 *Pyritocephalus lineatus* (Newberry)

2 *Parahaplolepis tuberculata* (Newberry)

3 *Haplolepis corrugata* (Newberry)

4 *Microhaplolepis ovoidea* (Newberry)

5 *Microhaplolepis serrata* (Newberry)

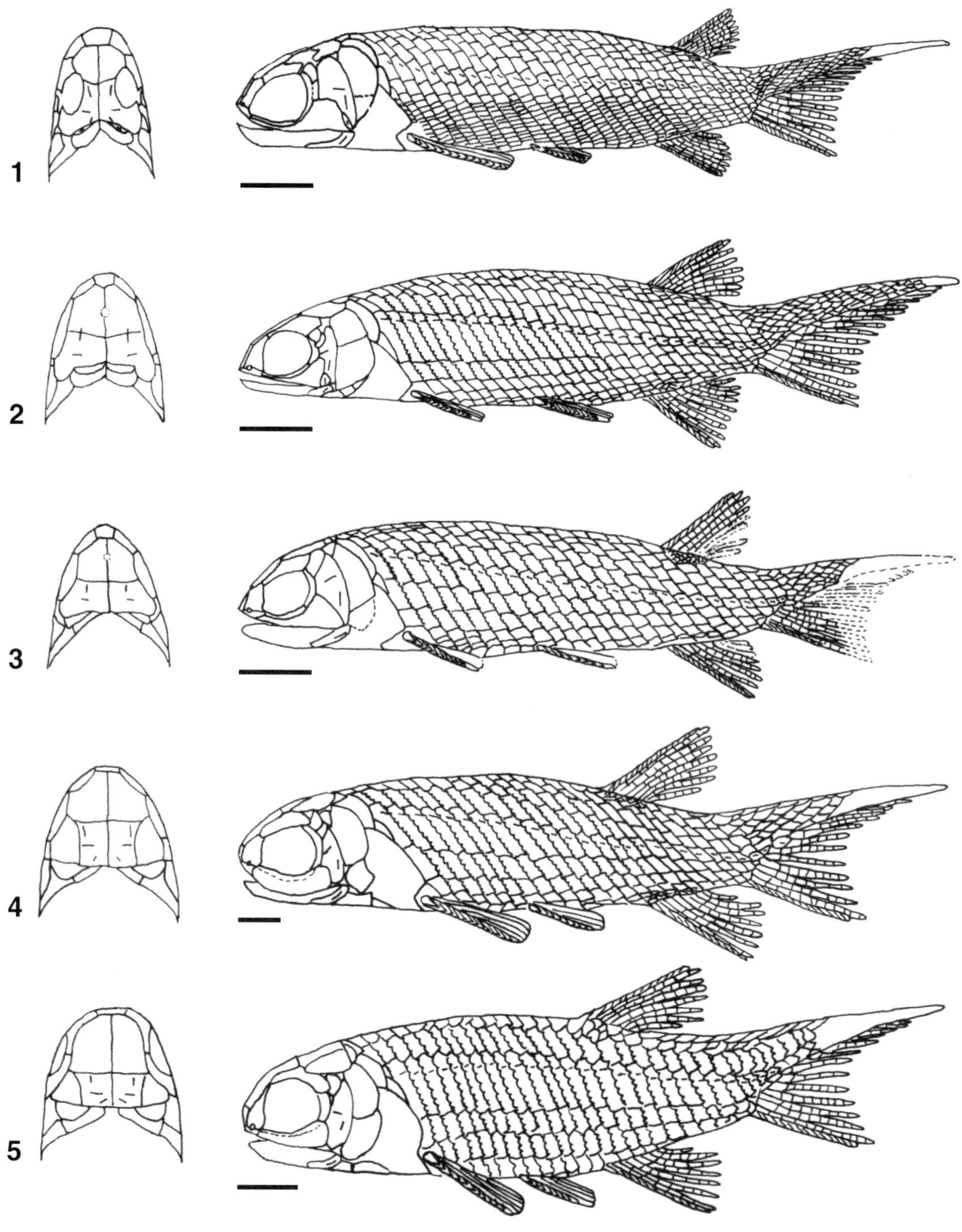
1
2
3
4
5

FIGURE 21-12.—Pennsylvanian and Permian osteichthyans. Scale bars equal 1 cm.

1, 2	*Rhabdoderma elegans* (Newberry), a coelacanth. **1**, complete specimen. Upper Freeport coal (Allegheny Group, Pennsylvanian), Linton, Jefferson County, Ohio; CM 23025b. Photo courtesy of Dr. Richard Lund. **2**, Reconstruction. From Hook and Baird (1986).
3, 4	*Sagenodus* cf. *S. periprion* (Cope), a lungfish. Mount Morris limestone (Washington Formation, Dunkard Group, Permian), Monroe County, Ohio. **3**, mandibular (lower jaw) tooth plate. CM 8502. **4**, pterygoid (upper jaw) tooth plate. CM 8501. Photos from Romer (1952), courtesy of Donald Baird.
5	*Conchopoma exanthematicum* (Cope), a Pennsylvanian lungfish. Reconstruction. From Hook and Baird (1986).

1

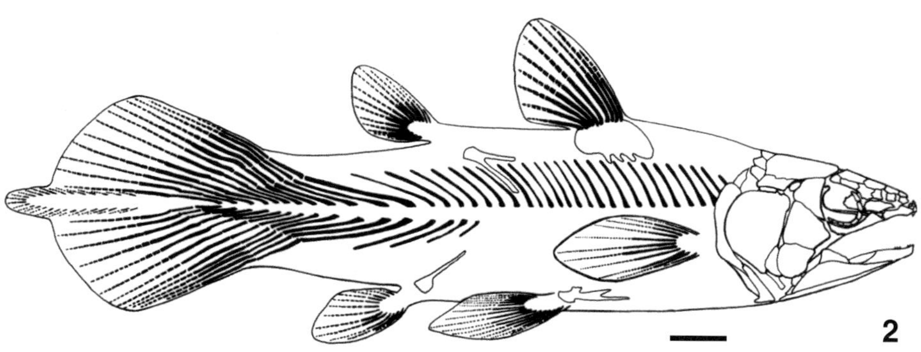
2

3
4

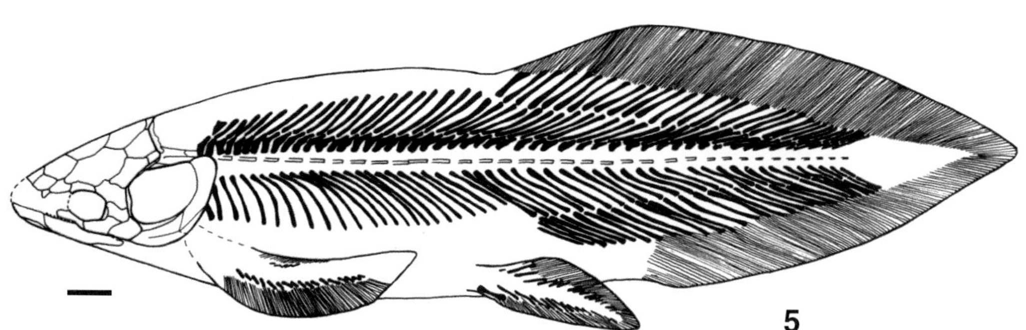
5

FIGURE 21-13.—View of the spoil pile and Pennsylvanian amphibians collected from the Upper Freeport coal (Allegheny Group, Pennsylvanian), Linton, Jefferson County, Ohio. Scale bars equal 1 cm.

1	Robert W. Hook is splitting the cannel coal on the spoil pile of the old Linton mine in search of specimens in 1983.
2	*Ptyonius marshii* (Cope), a snakelike amphibian. Latex peel. AMNH 6871.
3, 4	*Amphibamus lyelli* (Wyman), a froglike amphibian. **3**, AMNH 6841. From Moodie (1916). **4**, reconstruction, approximately life size. Model by Richard Rush Studios, Chicago. Photo courtesy of Robert W. Hook.

1

3

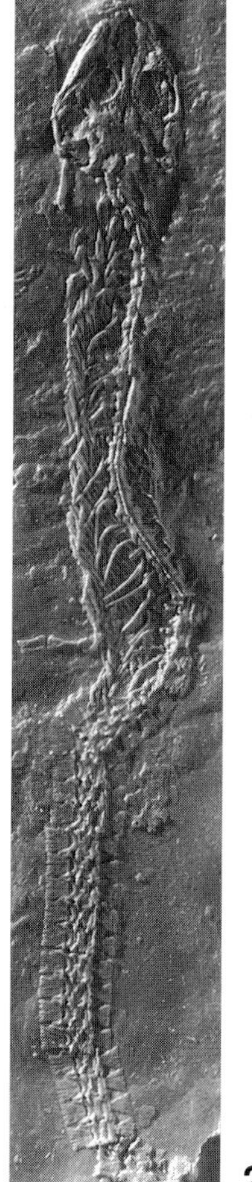
2

4

FIGURE 21-14.—Pennsylvanian labyrinthodont amphibians. Scale bar for figures 21-14.1 to 21-14.3 equals 1 cm; scale bar for figure 21-14.4 equals 2 cm; scale bar for figures 21-14.5 and 21-14.6 equals 10 cm.

1-3 *Colosteus scutellatus* (Newberry). Reconstruction of skull in dorsal (**1**), ventral (**2**), and lateral (**3**) views. Upper Freeport coal (Allegheny Group, Pennsylvanian), Linton, Jefferson County, Ohio. From Hook (1983).

4 *Eryops avinoffi* (Romer). Skull. Morgantown sandstone (Conemaugh Group), Braxton County, West Virginia; ClMNH 11025. From Murphy (1971b). Photo courtesy of Donald Baird.

5, 6 *Neopteroplax conemaughensis* Romer. Restored skull in dorsal (**5**) and lateral (**6**) views. Conemaugh Group, Jefferson County, Ohio; USNM 20636. From Romer (1963).

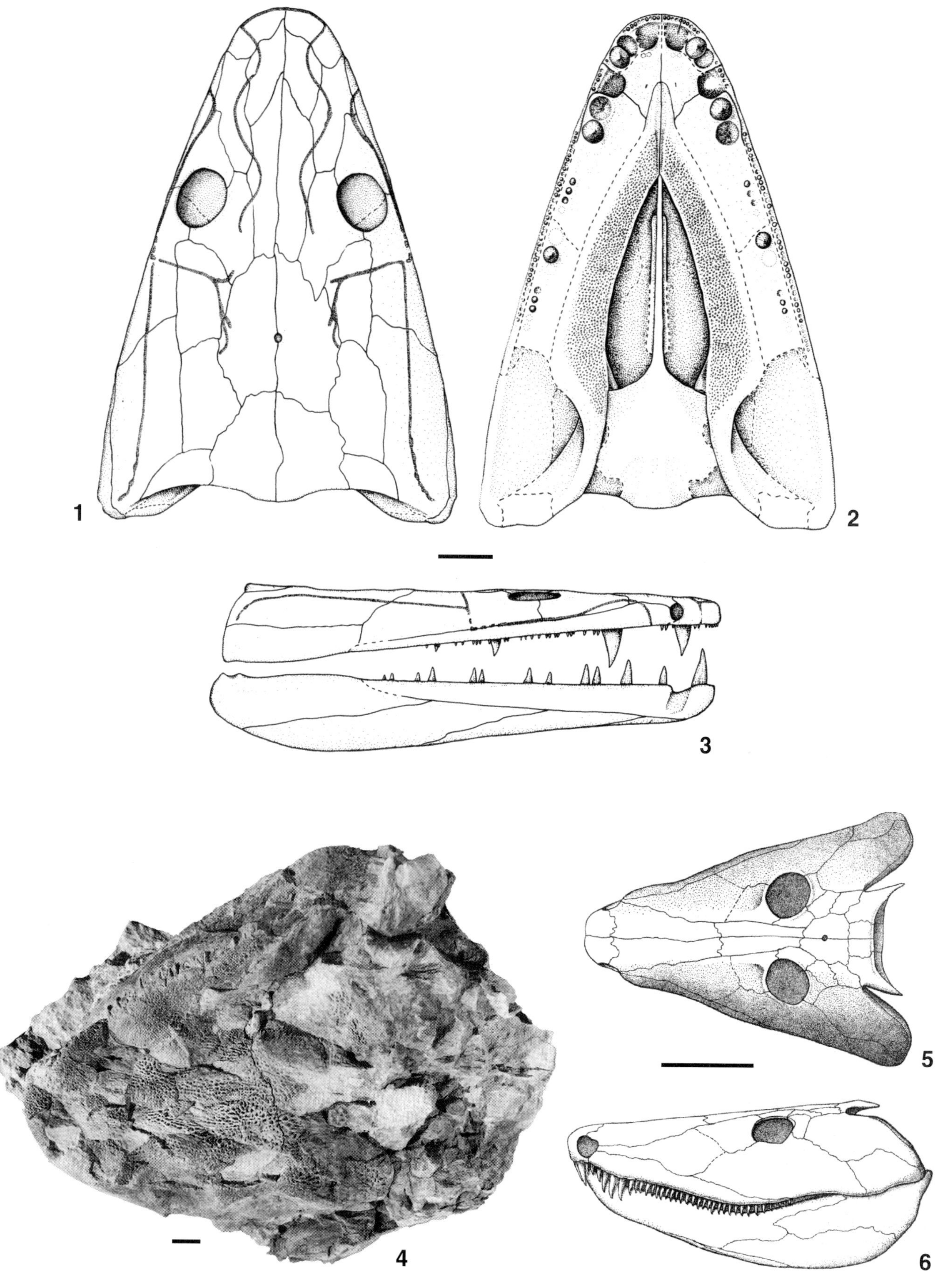
1
2
3
4
5
6

FIGURE 21-15.—*Tuditanus punctulatus* Cope, an amphibian from the Upper Freeport coal (Allegheny Group, Pennsylvanian) at Linton, Jefferson County, Ohio. Scale bars equal 1 cm. From Carroll and Baird (1968).

1	Posterior portion of skeleton. USNM 4457.
2	Line drawing of skeletal elements in **1**.
3	Reconstruction of skeleton.

1

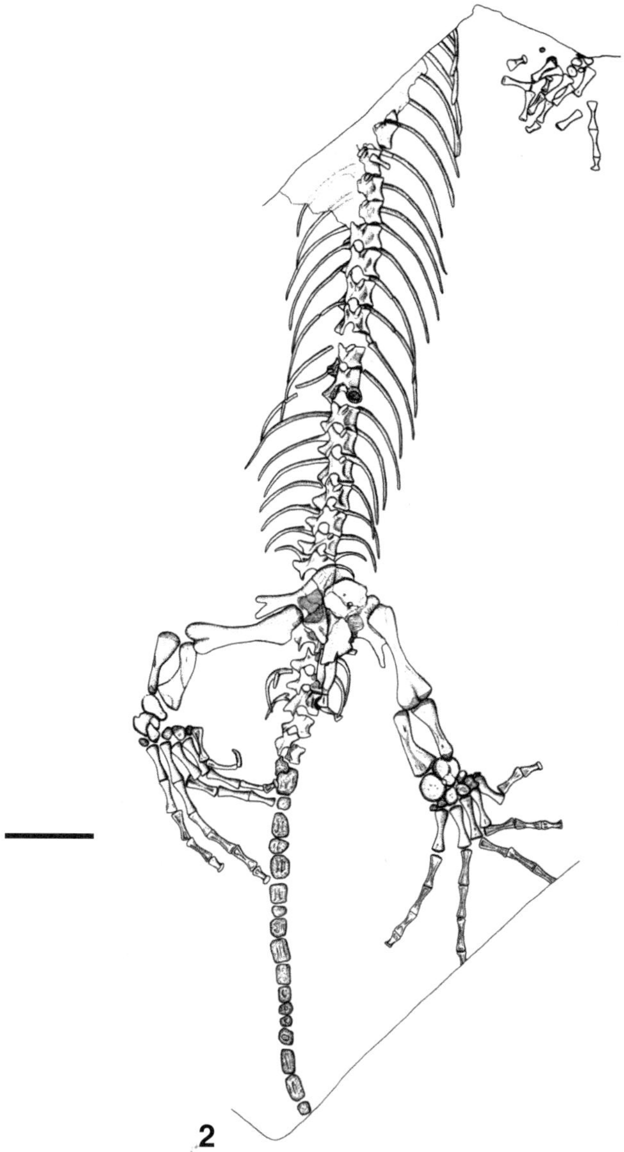

2

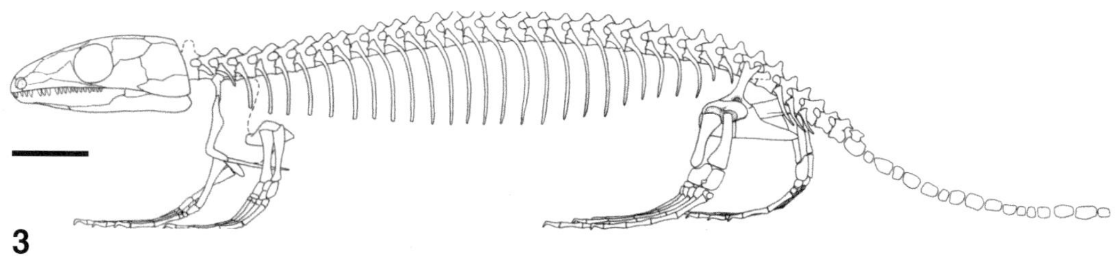

3

FIGURE 21-16.—Pennsylvanian amphibians from the Lower Kittanning coal (Allegheny Group) at Five Points, Mahoning County, Ohio. Scale bars equal 1 cm. Photos of latex peels courtesy of Donald Baird and Robert W. Hook.

1	*Diceratosaurus brevirostris* (Cope). Skull in dorsal view. CM 29603.
2	*Saurerpeton obtusum* (Cope). Partial skull in dorsal view. CM 29605.
3, 4	*Ctenerpeton remex* (Cope), part and counterpart of skull, dorsal (**3**) and ventral (**4**) views. CM 29884E.

1

2

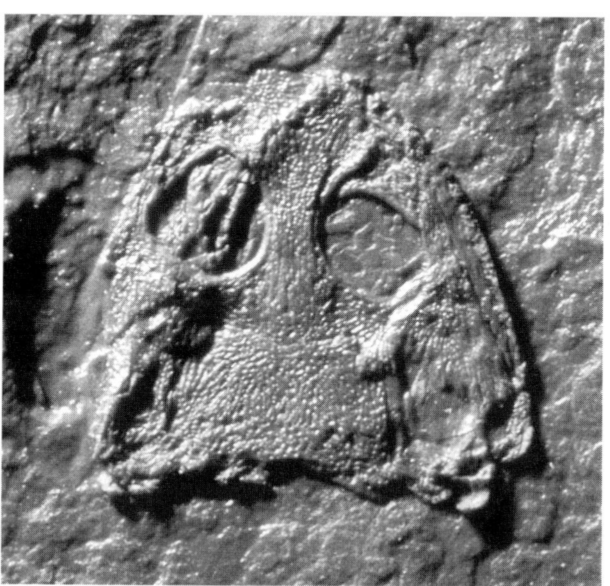

3

4

FIGURE 21-17.—Tetrapod trackway, *Anomoichnus ohioensis* Carman, from above the Middle Kittanning coal (Allegheny Group, Pennsylvanian), Perry County, Ohio. Scale bar equals 10 cm.

1 Trackway, preserved as casts. ClMNH 15329.

2 Carman's (1927) interpretation of the trackway.

1

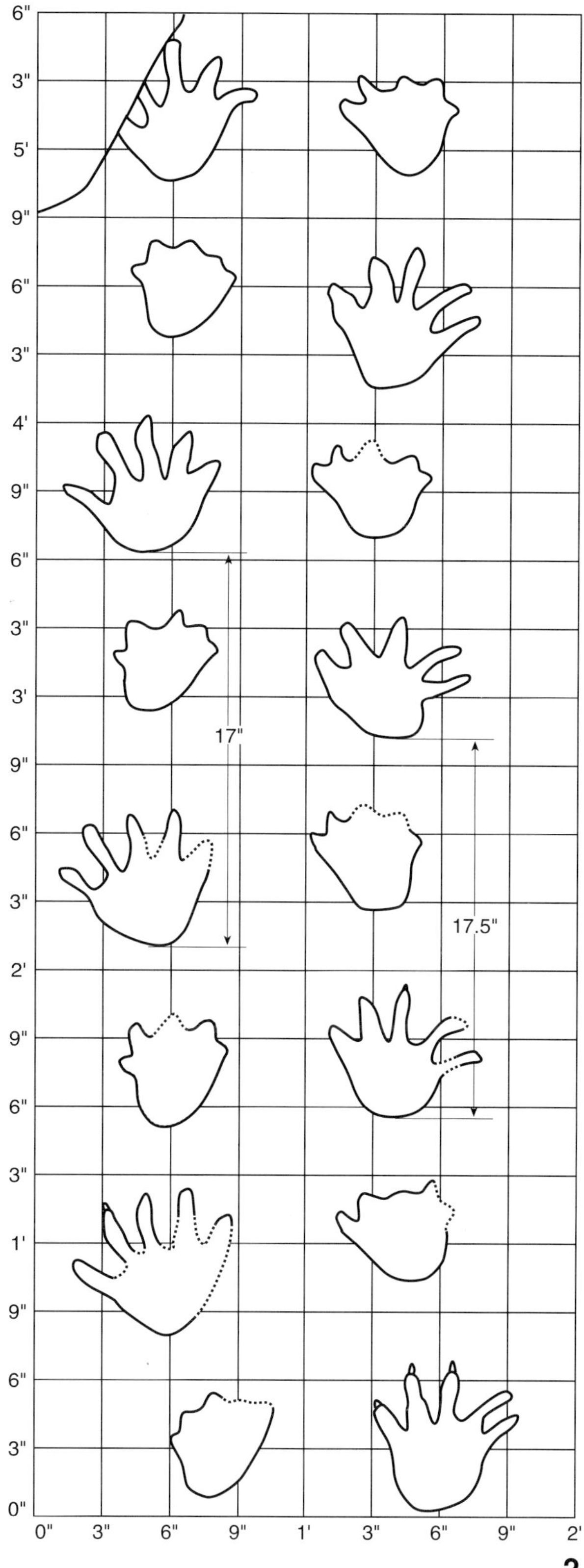

2

FIGURE 21-18.—Trackway preserving large tracks, named *Limnopus waynesburgensis* (Tilton) and attributed to the amphibian *Eryops* Cope, and small tracks, named *Dromopus* Marsh and attributed to a small reptile. Dunkard Group (Permian), Washington County, Ohio; Marietta College collection. Scale bar equals 10 cm. Photo by G. R. Case, courtesy of Donald Baird.

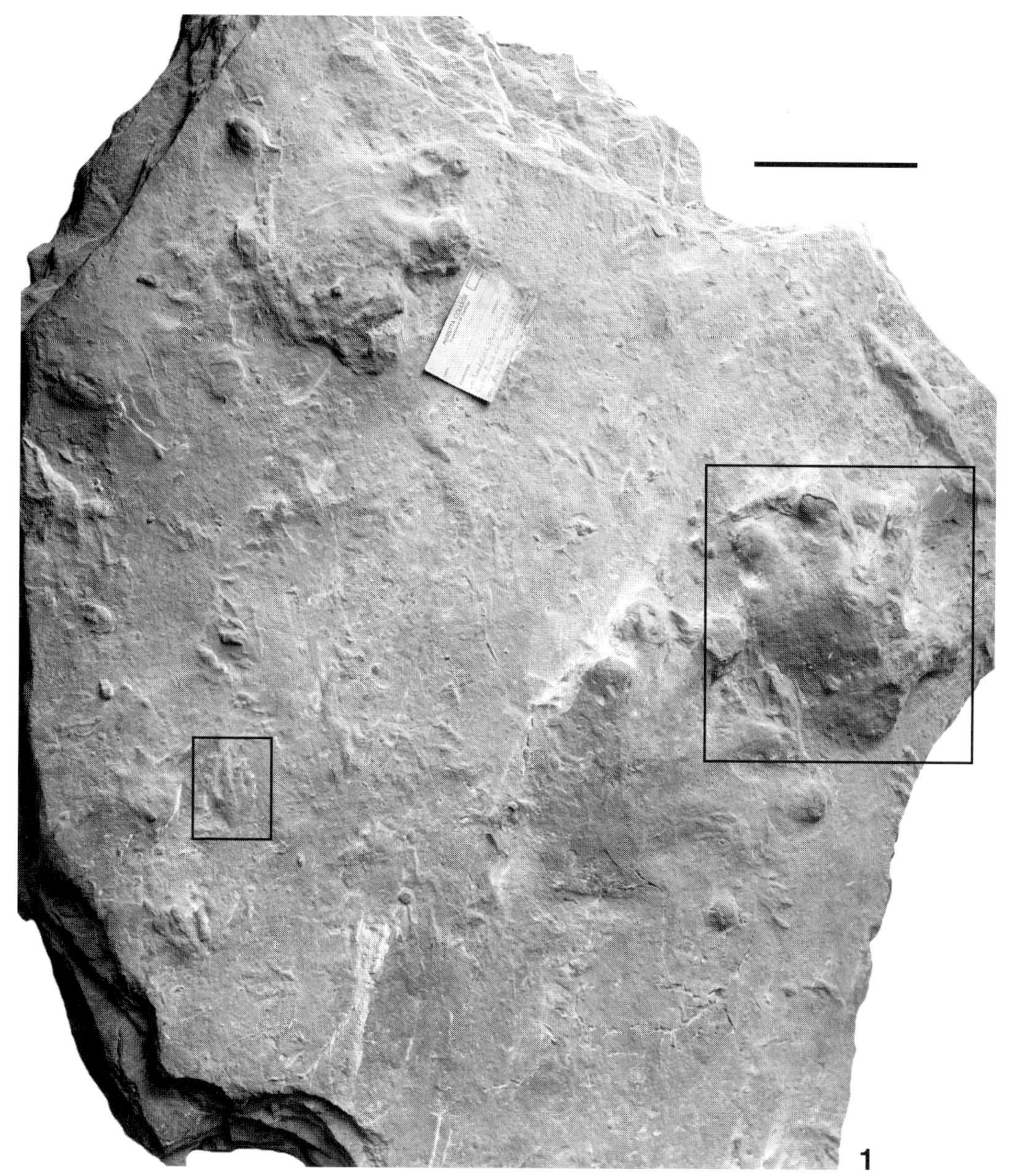

FIGURE 21-19.—Pennsylvanian tetrapods from the Upper Freeport coal (Allegheny Group), Linton, Jefferson County, Ohio. Scale bars for figures 21-19.1 to 21-19.3 and 21-19.6 to 21-19.8 equal 1 cm; scale bar for figures 21-19.4 and 21-19.5 equals 0.2 mm.

1-5	*Brachydectes newberryi* (Cope), a serpentine lepospondyl amphibian. **1**, reconstruction of skeleton. **2**, **3**, part and counterpart of holotype, AMNH 6941. **4**, **5**, reconstruction of skull in lateral (**4**) and dorsal (**5**) views. After Wellstead (1991).
6, 7	*Anthracodromeus longipes* (Cope), a captorhinid reptile. Partial skeleton (**6**) and reconstruction (**7**). From Hook (1986).
8	*Cephalerpeton ventriarmatum* Moodie, a captorhinid reptile. Lower jaw. BMNH R.2667. Photo by Donald Baird.

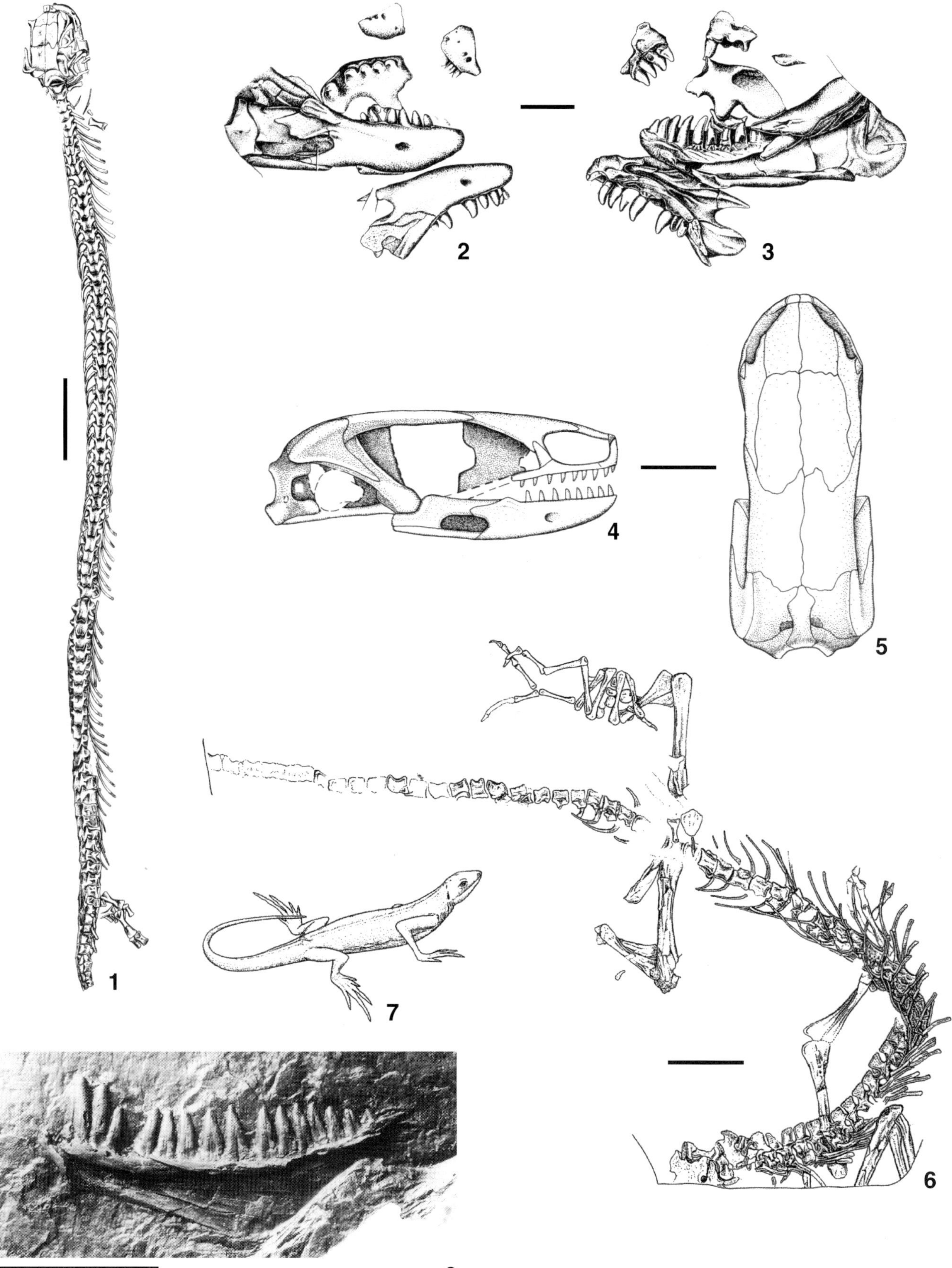
1
2
3
4
5
6
7
8

FIGURE 21-20.—Permian amphibians. Scale bars equal 1 cm (approximate for fig. 21-21.1).

1 *Diploceraspis* Romer. Reconstruction of skull. From Beerbower (1963). A smaller species, *D. conemaughensis* Romer, has been recognized from Pennsylvanian rocks; a larger species, *D. burkei* Romer (skull measures about 17 cm from horn tip to horn tip), has been recognized from Permian rocks in Ohio and adjacent parts of West Virginia.

2 *Trimerorhachis* Cope. Lower jaw. Washington Formation (Dunkard Group), Belpre, Washington County, Ohio; ClMNH 11322. Photo courtesy of the Cleveland Museum of Natural History.

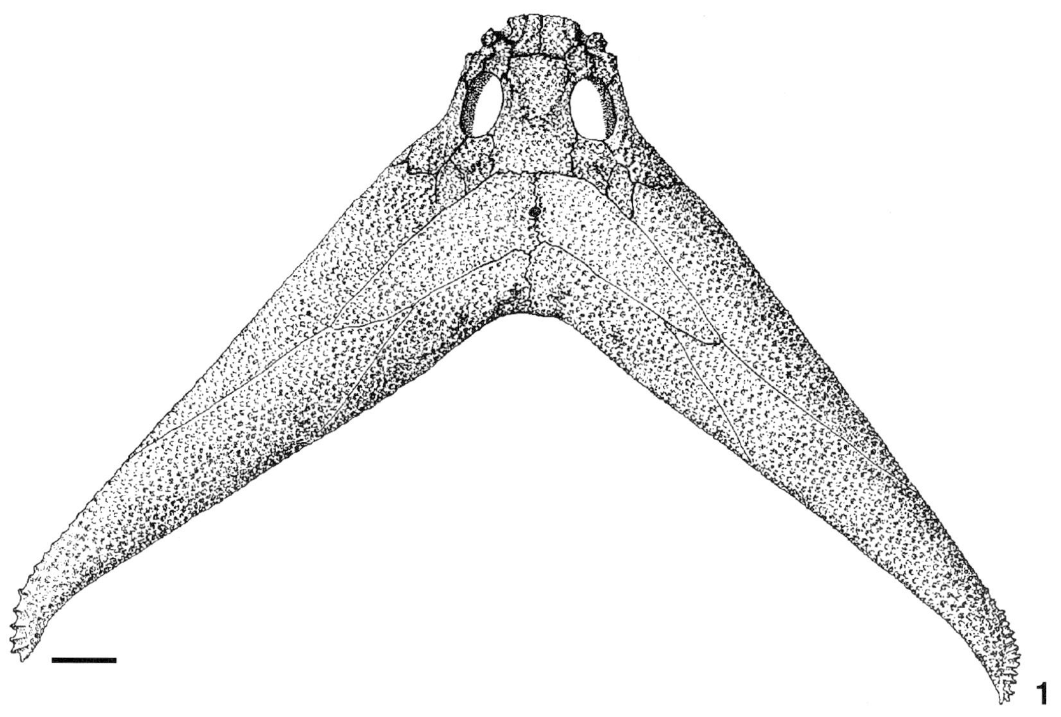
1

2

FIGURE 21-21.—Reconstructions of skeletons of Permian pelycosauran reptiles. Fragmentary remains of these animals are found in Permian rocks of southeastern Ohio. After Romer and Price (1940). Scale bars equal 0.5 meter.

1 *Dimetrodon* Cope.

2 *Edaphosaurus* Cope.

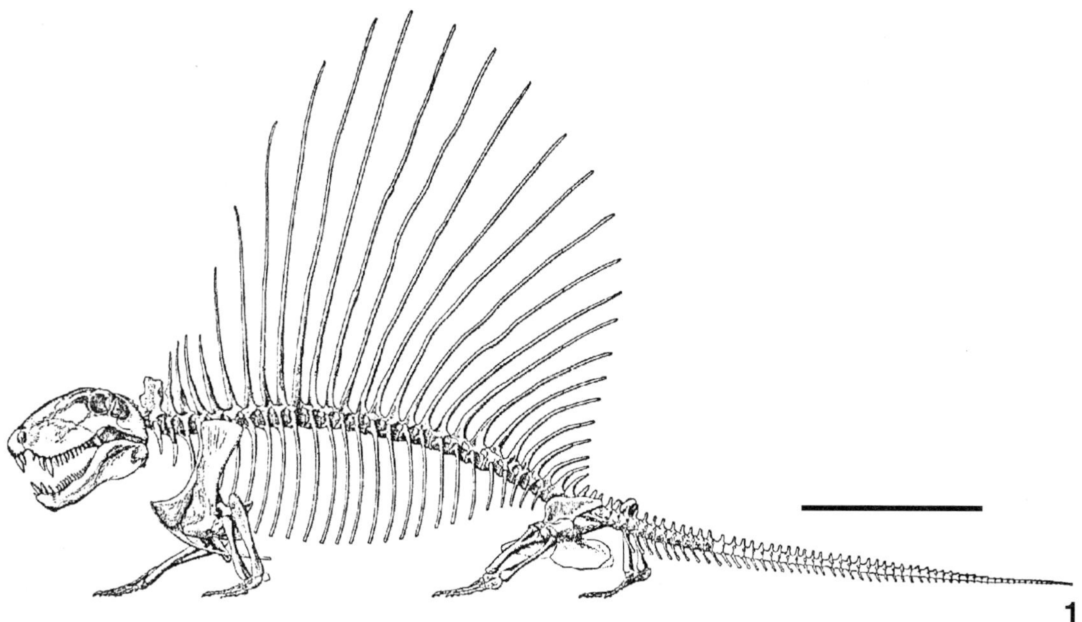
1

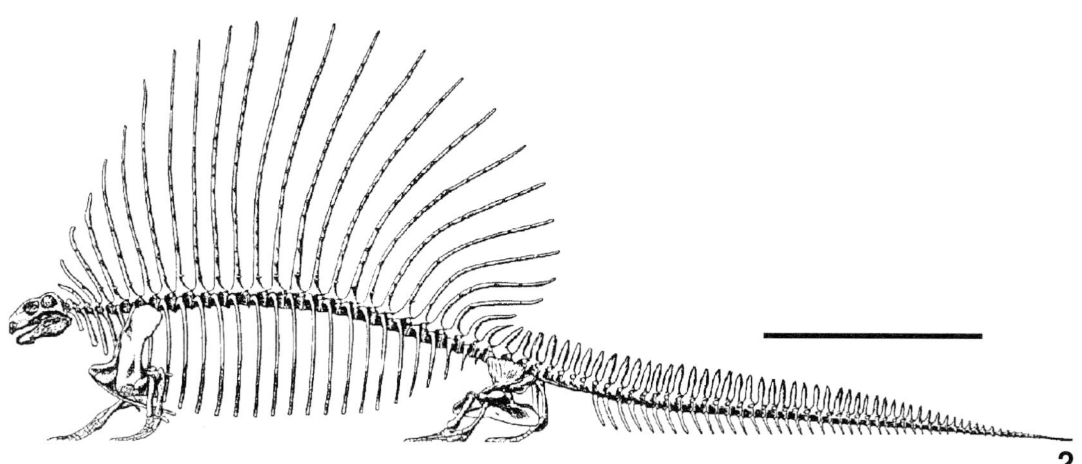
2

FIGURE 21-22.—Distribution of Pleistocene fishes, amphibians, reptiles, birds, shrews, bats, rabbits, and rodents and photo of the Carter site, Darke County, Ohio, *circa* 1971. The systematic excavation of this former early postglacial lake yielded one of the most diverse assemblages of Pleistocene vertebrates known from Ohio. Photo courtesy of Dayton Museum of Natural History.

1

○ Fishes
□ Amphibians
△ Reptiles
★ Birds
● Shrews
■ Bats
▲ Rabbits

2

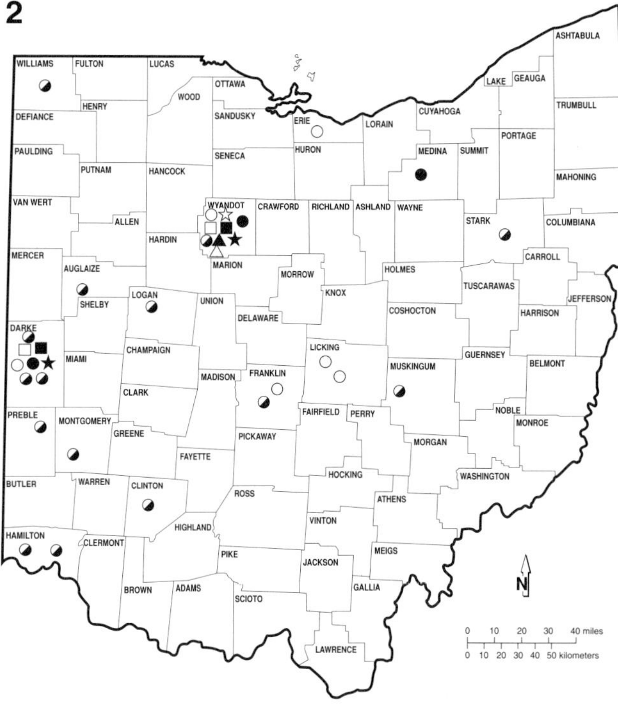

RODENTIA

○ Muskrat, *Ondatra zibethica*
● Voles and lemmings, *Microtus, Synaptomys, Clethrionomys, Phenacomys*
□ Field mouse, deermouse, *Peromyscus* spp.
■ Squirrels, *Sciurus* sp., *Tamiasciurus* sp., *Spermophilus tridecemlineatus*
△ Chipmunk, *Tamias* sp.
▲ Woodchuck, *Marmota monax*
☆ Porcupine, *Erethizon dorsatum*
★ Modern beaver, *Castor canadensis*
◐ *Giant beaver, *Castoroides ohioensis*

(* extinct)

3

FIGURE 21-23.—Pleistocene mammals from Indian Trail Caverns, Wyandot County, Ohio. All are Cincinnati Museum of Natural History (CiMNH) specimens. Photos by Chris Parrett, courtesy of Marie Huizing, Rocks & Minerals magazine. Scale bars equal 1 cm.

1, 2	*Castoroides ohioensis* Foster, giant beaver. **1**, incisor. **2**, partial scapula.
3	*Cervalces scotti* (Ledekker), elk-moose (stag-moose). Teeth of right upper jaw.
4	*Marmota monax* Linnaeus, woodchuck (groundhog). Skull.
5	*Ondatra zibethica* (Linnaeus), muskrat. Partial left lower jaw.
6	*Arctodus simus* (Cope), short-faced bear. Thoracic vertebra.
7	*Erethizon dorsatum* (Linnaeus), porcupine. Left lower jaw.

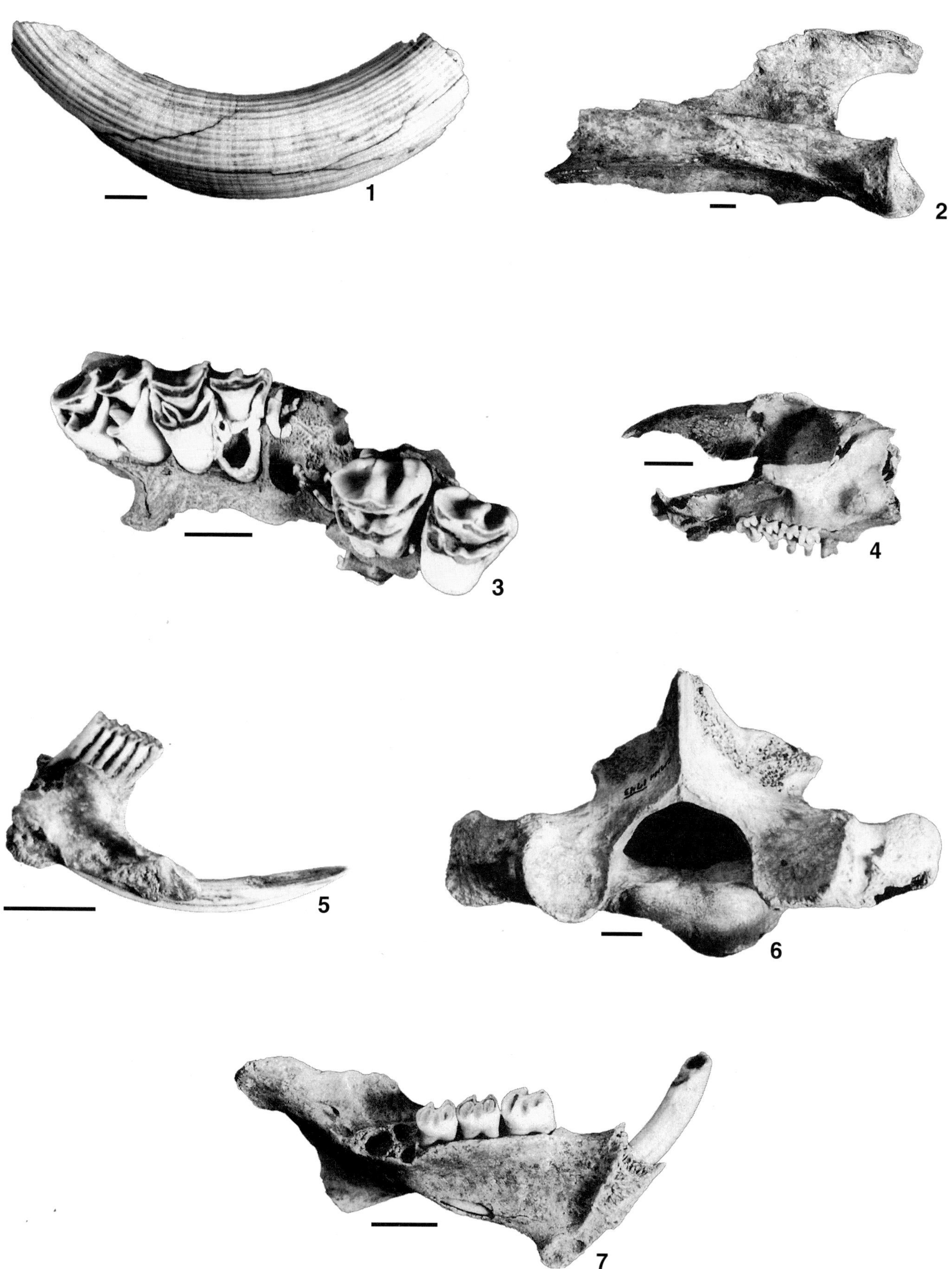
1
2
3
4
5
6
7

FIGURE 21-24.—*Castoroides ohioensis* Foster, giant beaver. Adults were about 2 meters long. Scale bar for figures 21-24.2 and 21-24.3 equals 2 cm; scale bar for figures 21-24.4 and 21-24.5 equals 1 cm.

1	Mounted skeleton. Photo courtesy of Field Museum of Natural History.
2-5	Lower jaw (**2**), upper incisor (**3**), and cheek teeth (**4, 5**) of **type specimen** (now lost). Nashport, Muskingum County, Ohio. From Foster (1838).

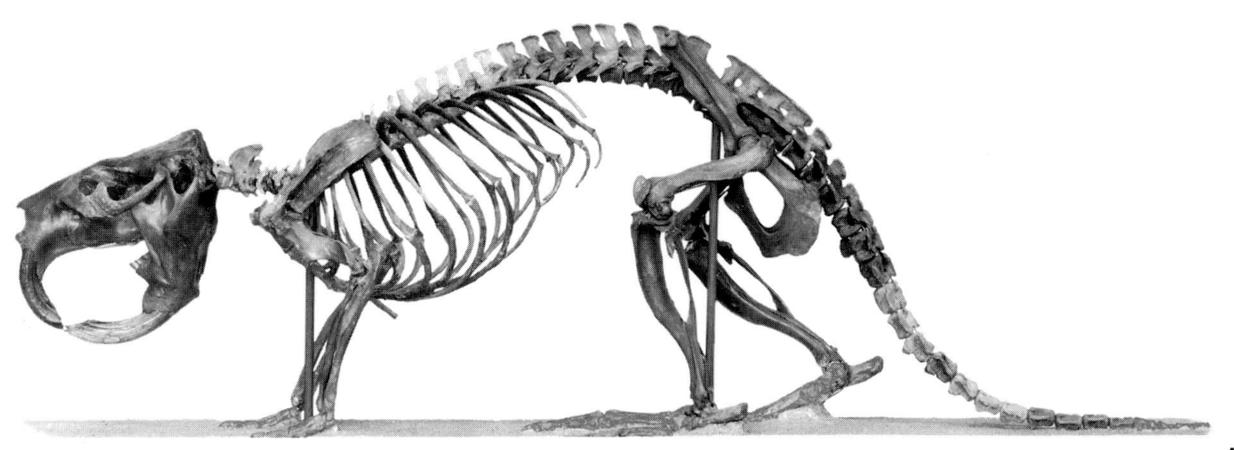
1

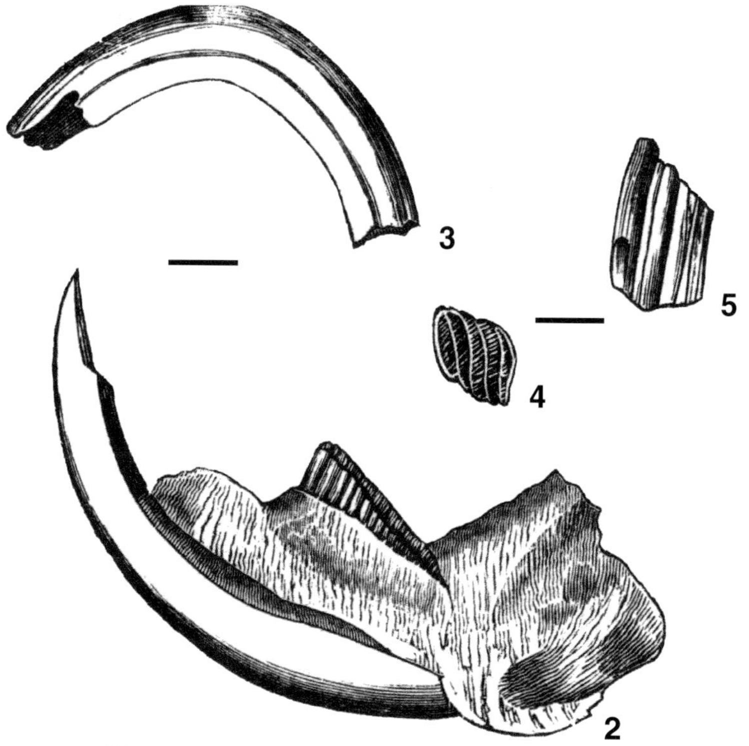
3
5
4
2

FIGURE 21-25.—Distribution of Pleistocene edentates, perissodactyls, and artiodactyls.

1

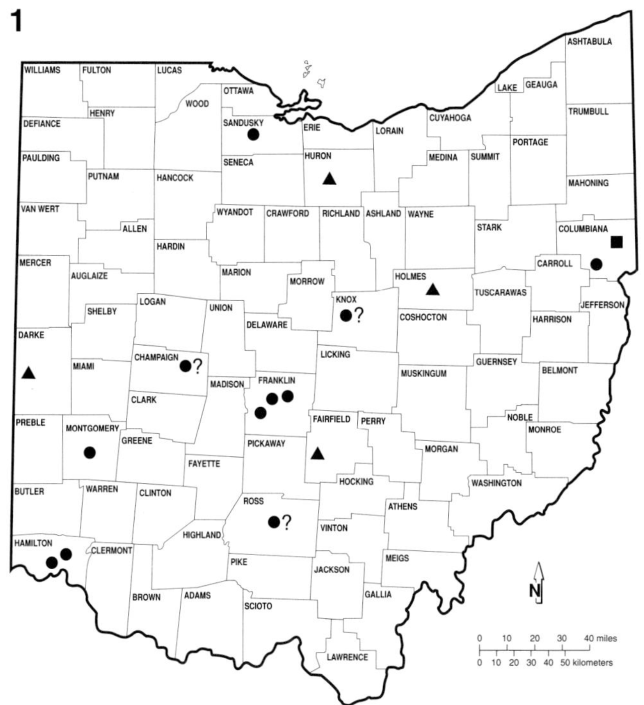

2

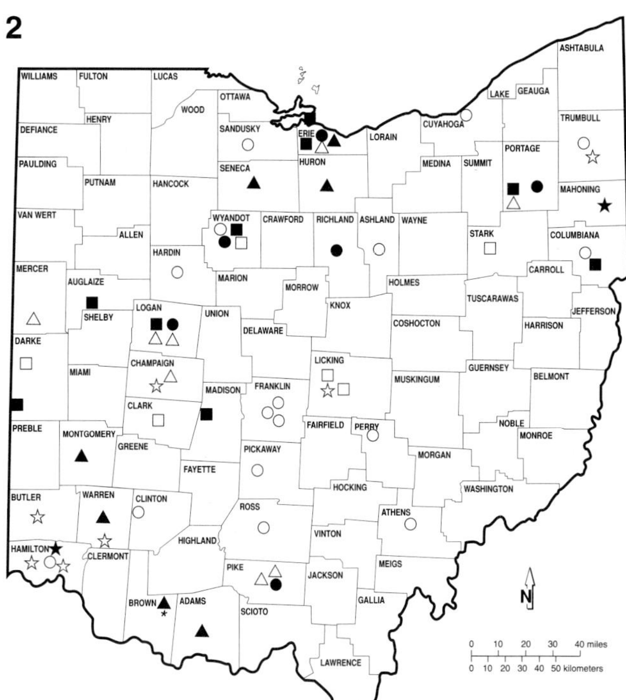

EDENTATA

▲ * Ground sloth, *Megalonyx jeffersonii*

PERISSODACTYLA

● * Horse, *Equus* sp. (?-possibly modern)
■ * Tapir, *Tapirus* sp.

(* extinct)

ARTIODACTYLA

○ * Flat-headed peccary, *Platygonus compressus*
□ * Elk-moose (stag-moose), *Cervalces scotti*
▲ Bison, *Bison bison*, * *Bison latifrons*
■ Deer, *Odocoileus virginianus*
● Caribou, *Rangifer tarandus*
△ Elk, *Cervus elaphus*
☆ * Woodland muskox, *Bootherium bombifrons*
★ Muskox, *Ovibos moschatus*

(* extinct)

FIGURE 21-26.—*Megalonyx jeffersonii* (Desmarest), ground sloth. Scale bar equals 10 cm and applies to figures 21-26.1 to 21-26.6, which are from Mills (1975). Figure 21-26.7 is from Guilday (1971).

1-6	Skeletal elements of a Dayton Museum of Natural History specimen from Darke County, Ohio. **1**, posterior view of lumbar (lower back) vertebra. **2**, lateral view of left side of skull. **3**, left-lateral view of lower jaw. **4**, posterior view of skull. **5**, occlusal (top) view of lower jaw. **6**, claw (index phalanx III).
7	Reconstruction of *M. jeffersonii* feeding on tree branches. These animals reached lengths of about 3 meters.
8	Mounted skeleton of specimen collected in 1890 from Holmes County, Ohio, and now on display at Orton Geological Museum, The Ohio State University.

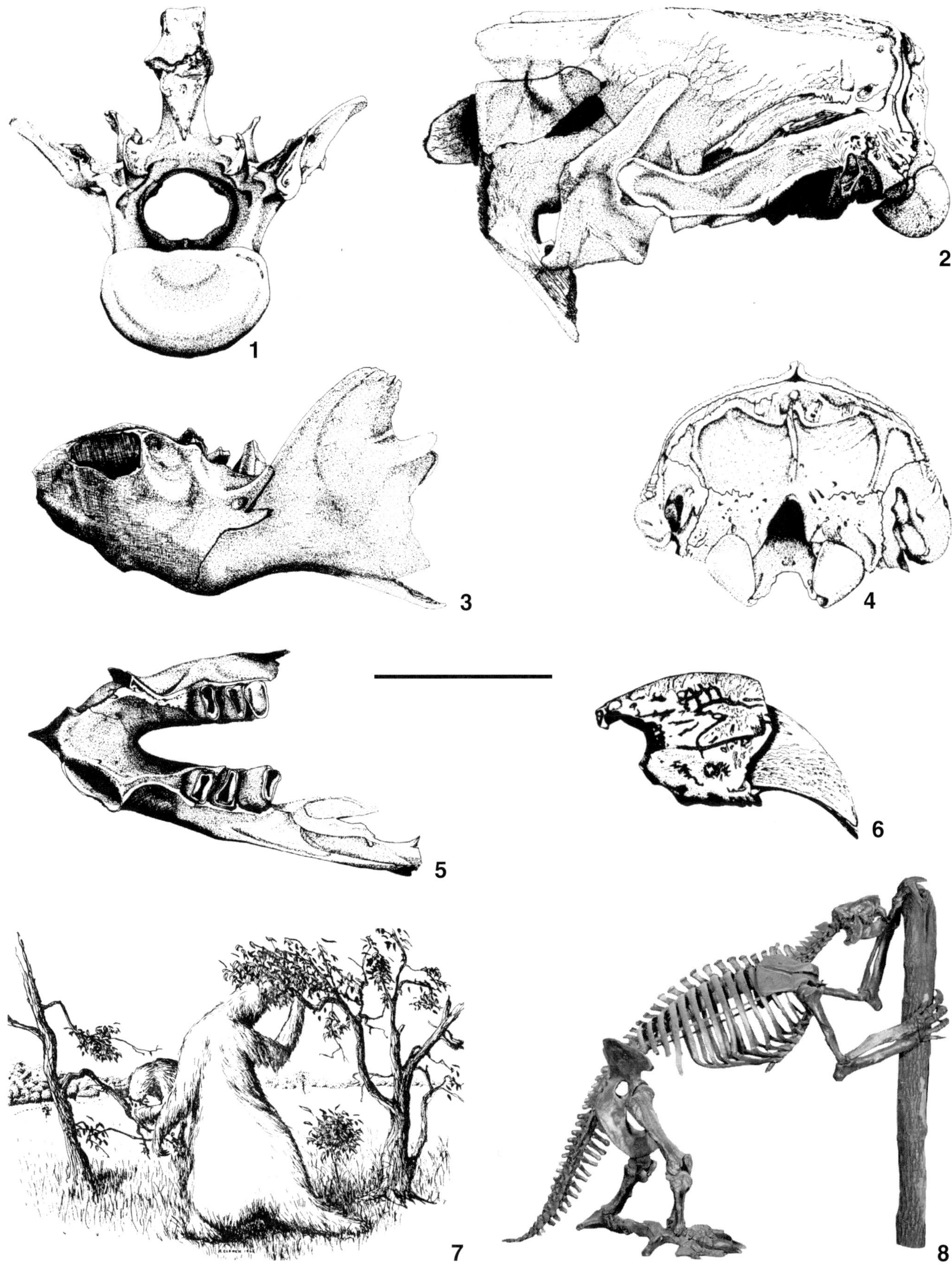
1
2
3
4
5
6
7
8

FIGURE 21-27.—*Platygonus compressus* Le Conte, a peccary.

1 Mounted skeleton of adult female from Sandusky County, Ohio; BGSU 2353. Specimen, which is about 1.2 meters long, is on display at the Department of Geology, Bowling Green State University. Photo courtesy of Richard D. Hoare.

2 Reconstruction. Courtesy of J. E. Guilday, Carnegie Museum of Natural History.

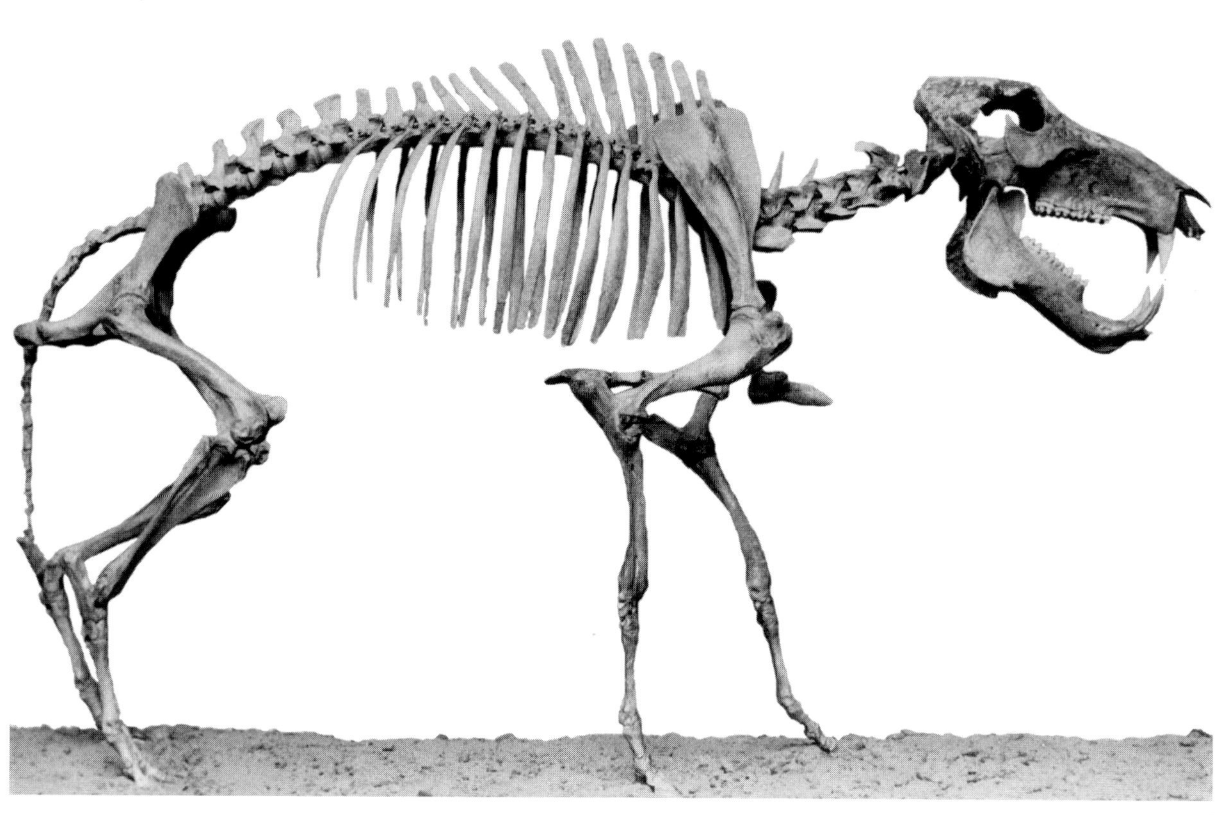

1

2

FIGURE 21-28.—*Cervalces scotti* (Ledekker), elk-moose (stag-moose).

1 Reconstruction by James L. Glover, Ohio Department of Natural Resources, Division of Parks and Recreation.

2 Posterior portion of right lower jaw. Licking County, Ohio; OSU 39145. Bar scale equals 10 cm.

1

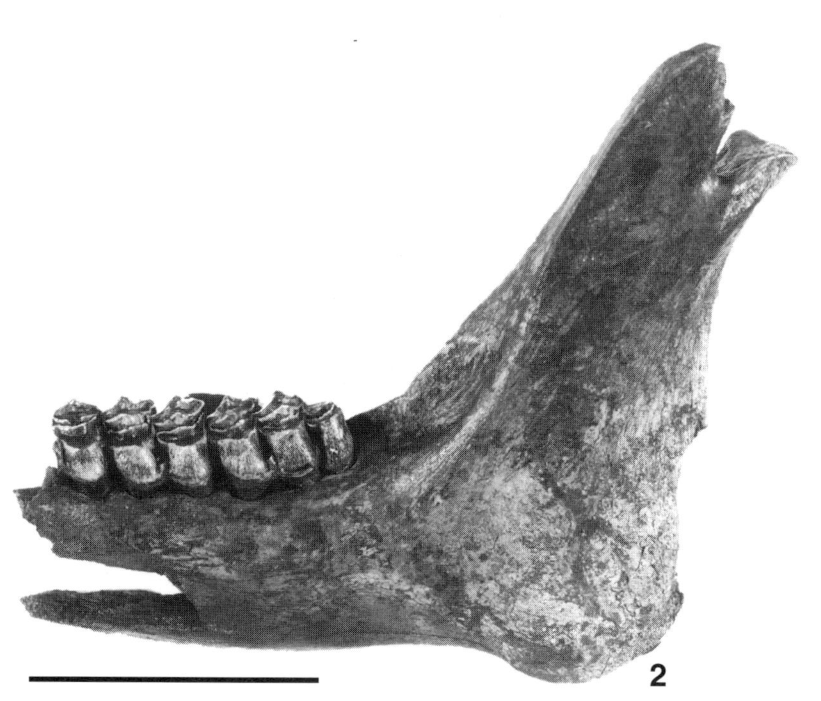

2

FIGURE 21-29.—Pleistocene herbivores. Scale bar for figure 21-29.1 equals 0.5 meter, scale bar for figure 21-29.2 equals 1 cm; scale bars for figures 21-29.3 to 21-29.5 equal 10 cm.

1	*Bison latifrons* Leidy. Horn cores and top of skull. Brown County, Ohio. Specimen in American Museum of Natural History. From Hay (1914).
2	*Equus* sp. Horse tooth. Champaign County, Ohio; OSU 17103.
3, 4	*Ovibos moschatus* (Zimmerman), muskox. **3**, dorsal view of cranium. Mahoning County, Ohio; OSU 11649. From McDonald and Davis (1989), courtesy of H. Gregory McDonald. **4**, sketch of skull in dorsal view. Courtesy of Cincinnati Museum of Natural History.
5	*Bootherium bombifrons* (Harlan), woodland muskox. Licking County, Ohio.

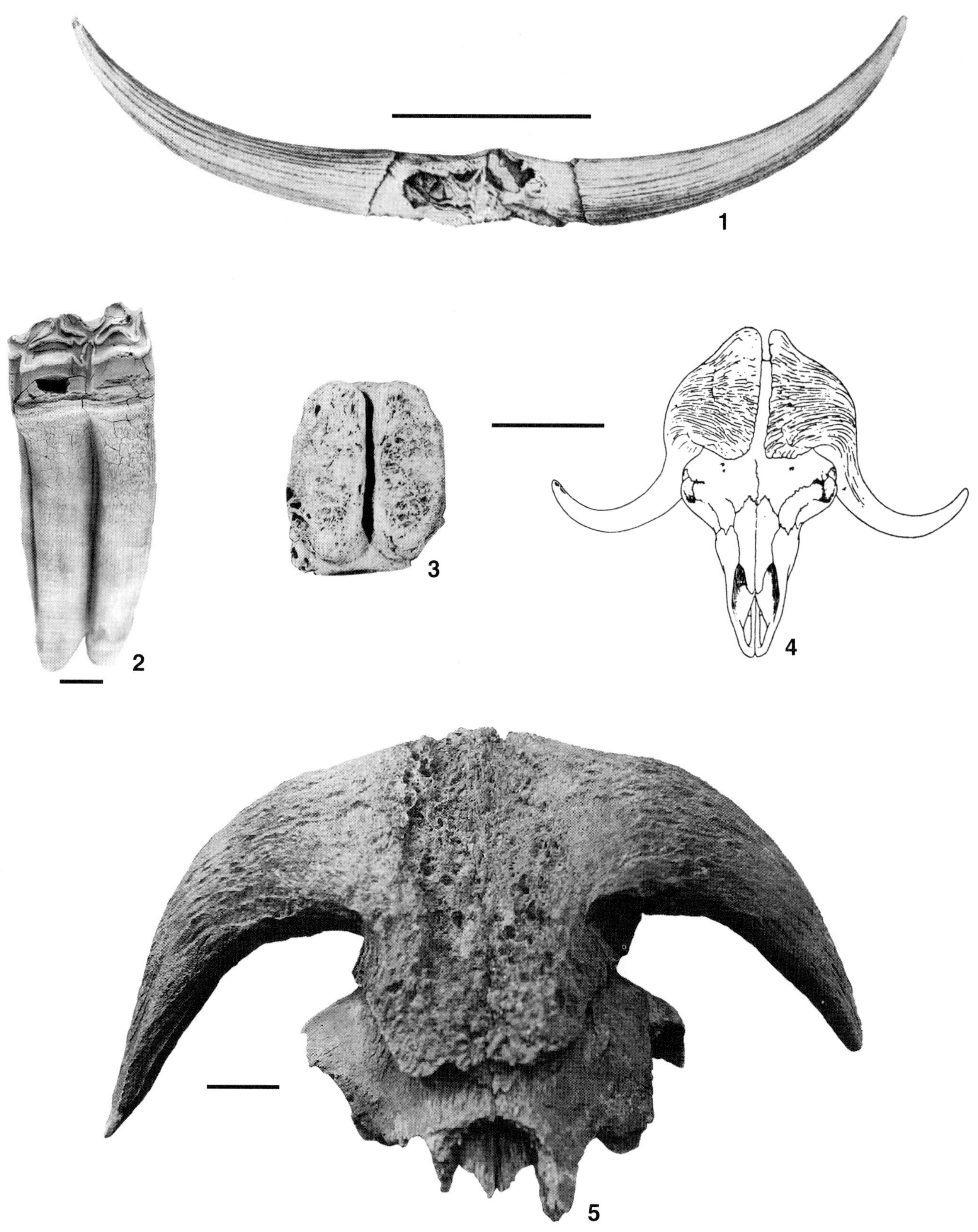
1
2
3
4
5

FIGURE 21-30.—Pleistocene proboscideans. Scale bars equal 5 cm.

1 Distribution of fossil finds in Ohio.

2 *Mammut americanum* (Kerr). Mastodon molar. Locality unknown; unnumbered OSU specimen.

3 *Mammuthus primigenius* (Blumenbach). Mammoth molar. Licking County, Ohio; OSU 12017.

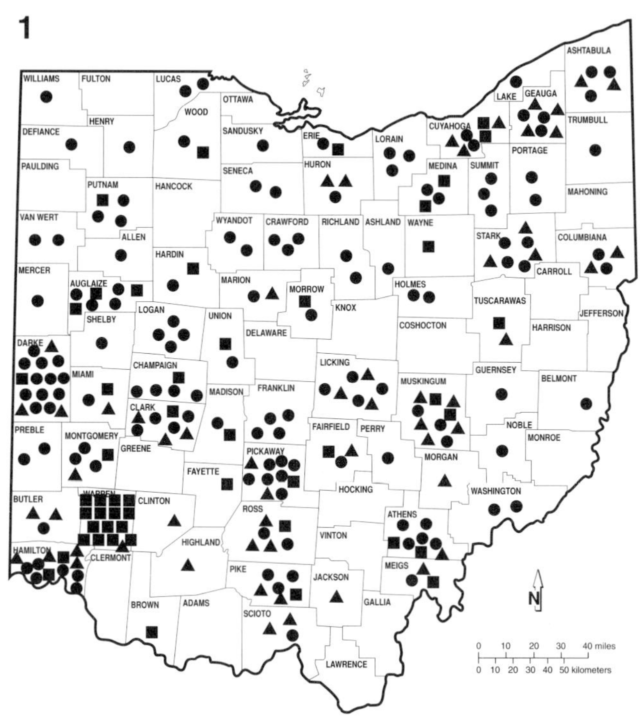

PROBOSCIDEA

● *American mastodon, *Mammut americanum*
▲ *Wooly mammoth, *Mammuthus primigenius*
■ Indeterminate proboscidean remains
(* extinct)

FIGURE 21-31. *Mammut americanum* (Kerr), mastodon. These animals attained shoulder heights of about 3 meters.

1 Mounted skeleton of Johnstown mastodon, discovered in 1926 in Licking County. Photo courtesy of the Cleveland Museum of Natural History, where the specimen is on display.

2 Mounted skeleton of Conway mastodon, discovered in 1875 in Clark County. This specimen is on display at the Ohio Historical Center in Columbus. Photo by Michael D. Williams, Ohio Department of Natural Resources, Office of Marketing Services.

1
2

FIGURE 21-32.—Excavations of Pleistocene mastodons.

1 Johnstown site, Licking County, 1926. Excavation of the skull of the Johnstown mastodon as a crowd watches. From photo postcard courtesy of Timothy Corriveau.

2 Burning Tree site, Licking County, Ohio, 1989. Portions of the skeleton are in the foreground. Photo courtesy of the Ohio Historical Society. (Also see Pleistocene reconstruction, p. xix.)

3 Martins Creek site, Holmes County, Ohio, 1993. Portions of the skeleton are visible. Flint flake (MM) at point of trowel tested positive for elephant antiserum, suggesting that the mastodon was butchered by Paleo-Indians.

WT-450 Lbs
REMOVING MASTODON HEAD
PHOTO By
BENEDICT
JOHNSTOWN OHIO
1

2

3

FIGURE 21-33.—Pleistocene carnivores.

1 Distribution of fossil finds in Ohio.

2 Reconstruction of *Arctodus simus* (Cope), short-faced bear, and its prey, *Platygonus compressus* Le Conte, a peccary, at a cave den site. Reconstruction by James L. Glover, Ohio Department of Natural Resources, Division of Parks and Recreation.

CARNIVORA

- ○ *Short-faced bear, *Arctodus simus*
- ● Black bear, *Ursus americanus*
- ★ Grizzly bear, *Ursus arctos*
- □ Raccoon, *Procyon lotor*
- ■ Weasel, *Mustela erminea*
- △ Martens, *Martes americana, Martes pennanti*
- ▲ Mink, *Mustela vison*
- ☆ Striped skunk, *Mephitis mephitis*
- ◐ Red fox, *Vulpes vulpes*
- ◩ River otter, *Lutra canadensis*

(* extinct)

2

Chapter 22

THE FOSSIL PLANTS OF OHIO: INTRODUCTION, OVERVIEW, AND NONVASCULAR PLANTS

by Aureal T. Cross, Ralph E. Taggart, and William H. Gillespie

INTRODUCTION

To most paleontologists, geologists, and amateur fossil collectors, mention of Ohio fossil plants brings to mind images of the remains commonly associated with the coal-bearing rocks of the Upper Paleozoic. As fascinating as these plants are, they represent only a small part of the rich plant-fossil heritage of the state. Ohio fossil plants range in age from the Ordovician, representing the oldest exposed rocks in the state, to remains that were incorporated into lakes and **bogs** when Native American tribes first encountered fur traders and settlers from the eastern seaboard. They occur in virtually all types of sedimentary deposits, ranging from ancient siliciclastic (shales, siltstones, and sandstones) and carbonate (limestones and dolomites) rocks to unconsolidated sediments of Pleistocene age.

The plants themselves are similarly diverse, ranging from microscopic single cells to petrified tree trunks over a meter in diameter and more than several meters long. At the single-cell end of this continuum, the fossils may represent virtually the entire organism, or they can be the dispersed stages in the life cycles of more complex plants, or fragments of larger organisms. At the large end of the size scale, a huge fossil log, as impressive as it may be, is only one part of a plant that produced many tissues and organs, any one of which may also be represented as a fossil in the form of leaves, twigs, reproductive structures, or fragments of dispersed tissue.

These plants represent many environments, from terrestrial forests, to coastal and **swamp** communities, to shallow-water marine and freshwater habitats, to floating/swimming communities of the open sea. Although the original growth site of specific plants may have been well defined, assemblages of fossils, representing the accumulation of plant debris, are typically far more diverse. Terrestrial plant remains can be carried far out to sea by currents, storms, or the destructive effect of tidal waves, to be deposited with plant and animal remains typical of marine communities. In contrast, a storm or tidal wave battering a coastline can produce floods that carry seaweeds, shells, and bones of marine vertebrates into coastal lowlands, to be deposited in what would otherwise be an assemblage dominated by the remains of terrestrial organisms.

Given the geological, botanical, and ecological scope of Ohio's fossil-plant record, it is impractical to provide even a cursory review in the context of a single chapter. This chapter begins with an overview of the fossil-plant history of the state. The overview is followed by a brief discussion of the nature of plant fossils and the practical problem of a fossil record dominated by dispersed parts rather than complete organisms. Finally, we review some of the major groups of plants and plantlike organisms that lack a **vascular system**; these groups are largely marine and form an important part of Ohio's fossil-plant record.

In Chapter 23 we examine the fossil record of Upper Paleozoic land plants. These fossils are the ones familiar to most collectors.

In Chapter 24 we examine the last million years of Ohio vegetation and climate, based to some extent on remains of wood, (see fig. 24-5.1), leaves, and **algae**, but primarily on fossil pollen and **spores** trapped in bog and lake sediments in the northern and central regions of the state. The plants of bogs, lakes, and other glacial deposits of the state tell a fascinating story of immense climatic changes. Given the fact that global climatic change is one of the major environmental issues of our time, we also review simple but effective techniques for the study of microscopic plant fossils in any science classroom to emphasize the range of climatic variation that Ohio has been subjected to since the retreat of the last major ice sheets (Wisconsinan) of the Pleistocene.

PALEOBOTANY AND THE HISTORY OF PLANTS IN OHIO

Paleobotany is the study of all aspects of the biology, geology, and ecology of ancient plants. Paleobotanists attempt to understand the evolutionary history of various groups, determine the form and function of the plants themselves, interpret the ecology of ancient plant associations (ranging from marine and freshwater habitats to marginal aquatic habitats to forests and other terrestrial habitats), and decipher the changing patterns of the Earth's geography and climate as reflected in changes in vegetation with time. The study and interpretation of plant fossils is widely used for resolving numerous geological problems.

The most obvious plant fossils are larger fragments of land plants, such as leaves, reproductive structures (for example, **sporangia**, cones, flowers, fruits, and seeds), twigs, bark, or wood. Even a modest forest produces several tons of such debris each year. Normally, such material accumulates as litter on the forest floor, where it generally decays within a few years as a result of the biological activity of a whole network of specialized organisms, including fungi and bacteria. This natural recycling of biological material is one of the fundamental processes that sustains natural communities, but there are specialized environments where the decay process is retarded or even arrested. Such environments include bogs, **fens**, swamps, **marshes**, and lakes.

Much plant litter and fragmented plant detritus may become buried and preserved in place by volcanic ash or by various types of sediments transported by wind or water. When plant parts fall or are blown into water, some of them become mixed with or buried by mud or other sediment. If the plant material is sealed off from sources of oxygen, decay is retarded. Should the layers of mud or other sediment be preserved and **lithified**, some of the plant parts may be preserved as fossils.

The areas most suitable for the burial and preservation of land-plant materials are lowland coastal regions, particularly in the complex environments associated with the deltas of major river systems. Mud and other sediment are deposited on these lowlands and deltas, burying standing plants, plant litter, or mixtures of floating and suspended plant material derived from the complex vegetation growing in the lowlands along the rivers, on the delta itself, or in coastal lowland environments.

Some inland swamps and many lowland environments, especially those behind coastal barriers (bars, spits, etc.), commonly are less affected by the influx of mud from rivers or delta distributaries. Today, in such places as portions of the Florida Everglades, or along lower courses and deltas of major rivers where natural levees have accumulated, or in lakes on glaciated landscapes, wet sites permit the accumulation of thick layers of **peat**. Peat is made up of a mixture of partially decayed plant debris, most of it from plants growing in or near the bog or swamp.

The relative isolation of swamps is transient and eventually natural levees fail, new channels form, or barrier beaches are breached during once-a-century storms or floods. Sediment-laden waters sweep through or over the old swamp, burying the peat mass with layers of mud or ripping channels through the peat beds. Peat deposits in some swamps may be buried more slowly, gradually accumulating successive layers of sediments deposited during less catastrophic annual or seasonal floods. Barring later uplift and erosion, the buried peat layers gradually become compressed or simply dewatered by the weight of the sediments above, losing 50 to 90 percent or more of their original volume. The physical compression of the peat, both vertically (mainly gravity) and laterally (tectonic), and heat from deeper layers of the Earth result in physical and chemical changes (**diagenesis**) that, with time, convert the organic layers to coal. The **coalification** process affects organic material ranging from dispersed fragments in the sedimentary matrix to massive deposits of economic importance.

The geologic record of ancient low coastlines, deltas, and alluvial plains is typically a complex layering and interfingering of coal deposits, shales, siltstones, sandstones, and limestones. The plant fossils in rocks associated with coal beds represent a broad sampling of plant parts. These are conspicuously dominated by leaves and wood, ranging from simple **impressions,** to **compression** specimens in which some of the original organic material is preserved. Where fallen logs, stumps, or even upright tree trunks were buried by mud or sand, the original structures may be represented by natural **casts** or **molds** (see figs. 23-7.2, 23-7.4, 23-11.2). If the wood becomes infiltrated by silica or calcium carbonate from mineral-rich water, the stump or log may become **permineralized** ("petrified"), preserving some of the fine cellular detail of the original wood (see figs. 23-1.5, 23-14.2 to 23-14.6).

Coal deposits themselves are rather amorphous records of the presence of ancient forests because of the extreme alteration of the original plant material. However, in some cases, small zones or masses of peat became permineralized, principally by calcium or magnesium carbonate, silica, or pyrite, preserving to varying degrees the structure of the plant parts making up the peat, even while the surrounding organic material was gradually transformed into layers of coal (see fig. 23-3). Such petrified peat masses, known as **coal balls**, are a problem to coal miners, but they are a bonanza for paleonbotanists because they preserve a record of plant parts, commonly in the most minute cellular detail (see fig. 23-2.3). Such characteristics are lacking or very difficult to observe or demonstrate in the coal beds themselves, or in other kinds of fossil plant material.

Most paleobotanists study the larger plant fragments preserved in a fossil deposit, but the coals and associated rocks also contain innumerable microscopic spores, pollen grains, and minute organic fragments resulting from natural shedding and decay or mechanical degradation of larger plant parts. Palynology is the specialized subdiscipline of paleobotany that deals with microscopic plant remains, encompassing materials as diverse as the **tests** and reproductive **cysts** of marine and freshwater **phytoplankton**, resistant fragments of larger algal **thalli** (body tissues), silica inclusions derived from higher plant cells and tissues, **cuticle** fragments, and, in the case of older rocks, microscopic cellular remains of unknown biological affinity. Palynology has become a very important part of paleobotanical research and a standard tool widely used in geological exploration. Because of their chemical composition and small size, pollen grains, spores, cells, cuticle fragments, and other organic-walled **microfossils** commonly are preserved in terrestrial and marine rocks, even where larger fossils are absent. Marine deposits typically contain a diverse array of microscopic remains derived from both marine and terrestrial sources. The ratio of marine to terrestrial material in a palynological assemblage can be used to reconstruct ancient land-sea relationships.

OVERVIEW OF THE FOSSIL-PLANT RECORD IN OHIO

The record of fossil plants in Ohio is a function of ancient land, sea, and climate relationships, intertwined with the evolutionary history of the plants themselves, and a variety of geological processes acting upon the plant matter and the associated sediments and rocks. Except for bacteria, algae, fungi, and possibly lichens growing on wet sites on land, there was virtually no terrestrial plant life during the Ordovician Period. The fossil evidence of ancient plants from the Ordovician is limited to sediment-trapping algal mats (division Cyanophyta, cyanobacteria or **blue-green algae**; see table 22-1) that form stromatolites (figs. 22-1.1 to 22-1.3); limestone-secreting red algae that formed the framework of the reef structures; relatively rare compression fossils of various seaweeds (figs. 22-3.10 to 22-3.14); dasyclads (figs. 22-1.4 to 22-1.9); and the microscopic remains of phytoplankton, such as acritarchs, that flourished in the coastal waters and open ocean.

The Silurian fossil-plant record for Ohio consists of rare marine algal remains that are not fundamentally different from those of the Ordovician. Elsewhere, however, during the Silurian a major evolutionary transition in plants was occurring. Clustered around bodies of fresh water, the first vascular land plants made their appearance in the late Silurian. Vascular plants contain internal cells modified and arranged to form tubes and other cellular systems for the internal transport of water and nutrients. The early vascular plants were mostly less than a meter in height and probably were derived from one or more lines of freshwater algae. They lacked later refinements such as leaves and roots. Small, fragile, branched stems bore structures adapted for the dispersal of airborne spores. Although the nearest shorelines were too far removed for these tiny plants themselves to appear in Ohio deposits, microscopic spores, blown or washed far out to sea, provide mute testimony to the earliest stages of the plant conquest of the land.

Lower and Middle Devonian rocks in Ohio contain a rich record of marine phytoplankton (figs. 22-4, 22-6.1 to 22-6.6); **calcareous** algae, including charophytes (figs. 22-2.4 to 22-2.15); and rare spores. Although they might have appeared similar from the surface, the Late Devonian seas had quite a different character than the placid, clear-water shell banks and coral reefs of earlier periods. Blocked off from oxygen-rich currents, the waters became foul and **anoxic** at some depth below the surface, restricting the variety of marine life and leading to the deposition of organic-rich black shales. Although such conditions were ideal for the preservation of plant remains, the ancient shorelines of the Devonian were still too distant to yield a significant terrestrial fossil-plant record in Ohio.

The Devonian was a time of unprecedented rates of evolution in early land plants. The vascular land plants of the Early Devonian are small and sparsely branched, but many plant lineages evolved swiftly, and innovations appeared at a steady pace. By Late Devonian time, the more advanced land plants had true leaves and roots and several types had attained the size of modern forest trees. Some Late Devonian plants bore the first seeds, the most ancient and primitive of which are found in nearby West Virginia (Rothwell and others, 1989).

Terrestrial fossil spores and pollenlike microfossils entombed in the sediments of the black-shale sea tell the story of this rapid period of evolutionary change, but larger plant fossils are rare. Fossil logs and wood fragments, which probably drifted from coastal woodlands on the great Catskill Delta of western New York, Pennsylvania, and Ontario or from an islandlike lowland in the Cincinnati region, are among the more common fossils. The Upper Devonian Ohio Shale (especially the Cleveland Member) yields sparse but tantalizing remains of still other plants. The cells and cysts of marine phytoplankton are abundant in the black shales. One thin widespread zone contains layers of *Protosalvinia* (figs. 22-3.1 to 22-3.9), a *Fucus*-like seaweed. Problematical fossils, including *Prototaxites* (fig. 22-5), a massive loglike fungus or alga, also are found sparingly in the black shales.

During the Mississippian, Pennsylvanian (the great Coal Age) and early Permian Periods, deposition of complex cycles of alternating marine and nonmarine rocks reflects the extreme depositional complexity of low coastlines, barrier-bar environments, and prograding delta systems. By this time in Earth history, land plants had reached a stage of evolutionary diversity in which the coastal lowlands and deltas were blanketed with the first true forests. Most of those plants are long extinct, and, were it possible to visit those forests, they would certainly have a bizarre, other-world quality (see Pennsylvanian terrestrial reconstruction, p. xviii, and Permian reconstruction, p. xix; also see Hook and Miller, 1996).

Great coastal swamps, undisturbed for millennia, accumulated beds of peat, commonly tens of meters thick. It is these peat deposits, cooked by heat flow from the Earth's interior, compressed by the weight of overlying rock, and chemically transformed through time, that formed the immense coal reserves of Ohio. With the passage of ages, the rivers and streams of eastern and southeastern Ohio cut deep valleys into the strata containing these fossil-rich deposits. Some of the earliest paleobotanical studies in North America (Hildreth, 1836; Morton, 1836; Foster, 1838; Andrews, 1875) were based on fossils from the valley of the Ohio River and its tributaries, the Muskingum, Hocking, and Mahoning Rivers, and the headwaters of the Cuyahoga and other smaller rivers flowing into Lake Erie.

In fact, Foster (1838, p. 101) noted "Few places in the world, perhaps, afford [plant fossils] in such abundance and perfection as the mines about Zanesville [Muskingum County]. Many of the plates in the splendid work, '*Histoire des Vegetaux Fossile*,' by M. Adolphe Brongniart, were figured from specimens furnished him by the late Ebenezer Granger, Esq., or from drawings sent by W. A. Adams, Esq.—all of which were procured near Zanesville."

During underground and open-pit coal mining in Ohio, Pennsylvania, West Virginia, and Kentucky, which sustained the growth of the Industrial Revolution, immense quantities of rock associated with the coals were excavated. These sandstones, siltstones, limestones, and shales have yielded a rich harvest of fossil material that is eagerly studied to this day. The Pennsylvanian plant fossils of Ohio are a scientific treasure trove, and most of the specimens illustrated in Chapter 23 come from this period in the geologic history of the state.

The end of the Permian marked one of the major periods of extinction in Earth history, in which many of the most conspicuous and characteristic plants and animals of the Coal Age disappeared. The collision of the major continental plates to form the supercontinent of Pangea (see Chapter 3) resulted in loss of coastline, draining of the great coastal swamps, and harsh, drier climatic conditions.

Only the faintest portent of these events is recorded in Ohio rocks, but the geography of Ohio was transformed. What had been low coastal plain became the foothills of a great range of mountains, the Appalachians, which, in their youth, rivaled today's Andes and Himalayas. Ohio was then no longer a place where sediments were being laid down. It became part of the continental interior, where rocks were eroded and transported to now-distant shorelines. With these changes in the ancient landscape, the record of consolidated rocks of Ohio ends. For the next 245 million years, Ohio was a land area subjected to the inexorable erosive action of wind, water, chemical solution, and frost.

The most recent chapter in the geologic history of Ohio includes the past few million years leading up to the present and is represented by the unconsolidated deposits of the Pleistocene Ice Age and the Recent. The great continental glaciers that moved southward across Ohio from Canada left behind innumerable lakes and ponds on the formerly glaciated landscape. They also left widespread, thick deposits of clay, silt, sand, gravel, and boulders in the form of till, moraines, eskers, and outwash. In some of these glacial deposits, logs and other plant debris have been found, generally as single specimens (see fig. 24-5.1), but in some cases in lenses or pockets.

Larger plant fossils found in bog peats and lake muds are largely restricted to logs, seeds, and wood fragments. Those same peat and clay sediments also contain a marvelously detailed record of fossil pollen grains and spores that document the recovery of vegetation as the front margins of the last of the glaciers melted back to the north. Initially, 11,000 to 12,000 years ago, conditions were cold and wet and the forests that developed along the retreating glacial front were dominated by spruce, fir, and pine. As recently (geologically speaking) as 8,000 years ago, conditions gradually became warmer and drier than the present, and the pollen grains reveal a history of encroaching prairie and stands of oak, hickory, and pine. The beech-maple and other woodlands that greeted the first settlers arriving from the east may have seemed eternal, but they were only the latest forests in a successional sequence manifesting the complex climatic cycles that once created, and may yet again trigger, the immense continental ice sheets of the geologically recent past.

NAMING THE DISPERSED PARTS OF FOSSIL PLANTS

One of the problems facing those who study fossil plants is the various, separately preserved parts of different plants that can be represented in a single deposit. The dimensions of the problem become clear if we examine just a single modern plant, such as a maple tree. At different times of the year, different plant parts are shed, augmented by pieces torn from the plant during storms. Leaves are the most obvious parts, but there are also flowers and microscopic pollen grains in the spring, seeds somewhat later in the year, and twigs, buds, fragments of bark, and even pieces of wood from branches. It is possible for any or all of these parts to be buried in place or dispersed varying distances to environments where they could be buried, and potentially fossilized, along with parts of other plants that grew in different habitats. There might be sites where all the parts were proportionally represented, but the different organs and pieces from a maple tree vary greatly in their size, weight, and aerodynamic and hydrodynamic characteristics, and thus in their potential for dispersal by wind, water, and insects or other animals. Certain parts may be completely missing from some deposits. It is unlikely that the numerical proportions of the various parts preserved in any one place will be similar to their occurrence on the tree itself.

Imagine now the dilemma of a paleobotanist, millions of years in the future, to whom the common maples of today might be completely unknown. He or she could encounter many of these parts while excavating fossils. Because each new item—a leaf, a flower, or pollen grains extracted from the rocks—are (or might be) new to science, each must be carefully described and given a name. Because our hypothetical scientist has no certainty that, of the several fossils found, all would have come from the same plant or even the same kind of plant, the names for the different parts will be as different as the parts themselves! As more fossils come to light, there may be as many as half a dozen different named fossils, all of which actually came from one lowly maple tree, or from several trees of the same species, or even from several closely related species.

If certain parts had a tendency to occur together in the same fossil deposits, one might be tempted to suggest that they were all part of the same plant, but what about the possibility that they are parts from unrelated plants that commonly grew together in the same habitat? If we found a leaf, preserved attached to a twig with characteristic buds, or were successful in isolating pollen grains from a fossil flower, we might reach the point where we were quite certain about the common identity of many of the isolated parts. Even in that case, however, a conservative paleobotanist would still use different names for individual parts, because we can never be sure that all the parts grouped together under a given name were invariably produced by just one kind of plant.

This complex situation, involving multiple named parts that may have come from a single species of ancient plant, is the rule in fossil-plant studies. We may name the hypothetical whole plant on the basis of the most common or prominent part preserved in the fossil record but still use the names that apply to other fragments. For example, *Psaronius* (see fig. 23-14) was a magnificent tree fern that grew in the Coal Age swamps of Ohio about 300 million years ago. The name *Psaronius* is actually the name first applied to the unique petrified stumps of the plant (see figs. 23-14.4, 23-14.5). Pieces of the stem that have prominent scars where leaves had been shed are called by several names (*Caulopteris*, fig. 23-14.3; *Megaphyton; Stipitopteris;* etc.), depending on which species of *Psaronius* they belonged to. Leaves of these ferns are grouped under still other names. Some which have attached spore-bearing structures are called *Scolecopteris* or *Asterotheca*. Just to confuse things further, if the leaves lack spore-bearing structures, they are called, among other things, *Pecopteris*! The spores of the plant have been found isolated in the rocks and given still other names.

Another good example is *Lepidodendron* (see reconstruction illustrated in fig. 23-4.1). Different names have been applied to each of the organs of the **vegetative** body, reproductive structures, and distinctive surface features of the wood or bark, which in turn vary considerably, depending on the precise layer of the trunk or branch that was preserved or is now exposed as a fossil.

All of these names seem quite confusing. However, their continued use reflects the need to keep careful track of the occurrence of different plant parts. Eventually we may accumulate enough information about some of the long-extinct ancient plants that we can piece together a reconstruction of the entire plant, even though no single fossil specimen would be adequate for the task. Over a century of paleobotanical research has given us a whole-plant perspective for many long-extinct species, but hundreds of named and described parts serve as tantalizing reminders of all that we have yet to learn.

In the sections that follow, known patterns of association of fossils will be noted, but there is still much work to be done, and many parts, large and small, may never be adequately linked to a single ancient species of plant.

NONVASCULAR FOSSIL PLANTS

The plants that dominate terrestrial habitats today all have one thing in common—a complex of tissues, the vascular system, that functions to transport water and nutrients throughout the body of the plant, as well as specialized surface tissues and products (epidermis, cuticle, bark, etc.). The evolution of vascular systems was a critical adaptation, if plants were to colonize terrestrial habitats. For most of the history of life, organisms were confined to marine and freshwater environments. In aquatic habitats, plants and plantlike organisms, ranging in complexity from single cells to very large, multicellular seaweeds, function quite effectively without the complexity of a vascular system. These nonvascular plantlike organisms include aquatic algae, fungi, and bacteria (which may all occur in terrestrial habitats if there is sufficient moisture) and the bryophytes (mosses, liverworts, and hornworts), which are characteristic of moist terrestrial sites. Most of these organisms are relatively inconspicuous, but many have a significant presence in the fossil record of Ohio. The most significant nonvascular plants and enigmatic plantlike organisms of Paleozoic age from Ohio are described below.

ALGAE

The term "algae" is no longer used in a formal sense in plant classification, but it is still useful when referring to simple, typically single-celled, nonvascular plants characteristic of marine and freshwater habitats. This definition encompasses plants in three different biological kingdoms: the Monera, the Protista, and the Plantae (table 22-1). The algae are placed in divisions on the basis of their photosynthetic pigments: blue-green algae or cyanobacteria (division Cyanophyta), green algae (division Chlorophyta), yellow-green algae (division Chrysophyta), red algae (division Rhodophyta), and brown algae (division Phaeophyta).

Phytoplankton, the microscopic, single-celled algae that swim or drift in the water, form the base of most aquatic food chains. The shallow tropical seas that covered Ohio during most of the Paleozoic Era supported diverse phytoplankton populations, and a variety of these organisms are preserved in rocks as microscopic cells and reproductive cysts. The ecological dominants of these phytoplankton assemblages, the acritarchs (fig. 22-4), are a nearly extinct group. Morphologically and ecologically, fossil acritarchs were probably quite similar to dinoflagellates, which are among the dominant phytoplankton in today's oceans. The dinoflagellates may have evolved from one or more groups of acritarchs, and the Lower Paleozoic rocks of Ohio record part of their initial evolutionary diversification. Acritarchs are preserved in a wide range of Paleozoic rocks, commonly where other fossils are rare or absent, and are used to zone or date the strata with great precision. They are also useful in reconstructing the ecology of ancient marine environments, including determination of water depth, salinity, and the relative proximity of ancient shorelines.

Most large, multicellular algae (**macrophytes**) are marine. Modern kelps and seaweeds tend to decay rather quickly and their fossil record is generally poor. A major exception in the Paleozoic marine record of Ohio are groups of red algae (Division Rhodophyta) that secrete calcium carbonate as part of their normal metabolism. Such algae create the basic framework of so-called coral reefs and are common fossils associated with the reefs that characterized the shallow Paleozoic seas. Corals have a far more recognizable structure, but anyone collecting fossil corals will also certainly collect calcareous red algae, even if they are unaware of it.

The largest and most obvious marine macrophytes in today's oceans are kelps and seaweeds (brown algae, division Phaeophyta). Impression fossils, known as "fucoids" (the name is derived from that of the common seaweed, *Fucus*), are regularly encountered in Paleozoic marine deposits. Some fucoids are now known to be tracks, trails, or burrows of animals (see Chapter 25), but others are considered to be of algal origin. Even though these specimens bear a superficial resemblance to modern seaweeds, the material is too poorly preserved (with a few exceptions) to permit definitive description and identification. Some taxa have been described in detail, for example, *Tasmanites*, an algal cyst; *Protosalvinia* (*Foerstia*), an alga of uncertain affinity; and the receptaculitids; all of these are described later in this chapter. These organisms, while generally presumed to represent algae, have no analogs in the modern flora and are thus impossible to classify with precision. Ancestral forms of dasyclads and charophytes (stoneworts), both in the green algae (division Chlorophyta), are widely distributed in Silurian and Devonian limestones and calcareous shales in Ohio.

Stromatolites

The most primitive and most ancient of the algae, the Cyanophyta (cyanobacteria or blue-green algae), are grouped with the bacteria in the kingdom Monera. These organisms are very small, single cells, 1 to 20 micrometers (0.001-0.020 mm) in diameter, and commonly form filaments, loose chains, or balls. The actual organisms are rarely seen as fossils in the rocks, but they form distinctive laminated mats or columns called stromatolites. Great thicknesses or masses of stromatolitic rock have accumulated as a result of the metabolic activity of these primitive unicellular organisms. Some such masses are called "oncolites" or, mistakenly, "stromatoporoids" (see Chapter 5).

Stromatolites are layered structures (figs. 22-1.1 to 22-1.3) in limestones, calcareous shales, or dolomites. They consist of **laminae** that are more or less laterally continuous over several centimeters. The laminae may be stacked in domes or pillars from 5 cm to more than a meter thick. The domes or pillars may be a few centimeters to over a meter in diameter and commonly are separated by similar distances from each other. A bed of pillars may extend laterally for hundreds of meters. Oncolites are formed in a somewhat similar way except that most oncolites have been moved back and forth or rolled around by currents on the bottom of the lake or sea. In such cases, the successive layers accumulated as concentric laminae (like onions) around a center (an animal shell, a rock, etc.) rather than forming a laterally continuous bed.

Although no actual cells or filaments are present in most stromatolites, the layers consist of grains or minute particles of clastic or precipitated carbonate sediments that were trapped in the mucilaginous (jellylike) sheath that surrounded the individual cells and which coated the cellular mats. Some of the limy particles were precipitated from the sea water as a result of photosynthesis by the algal cells. Fine silt layers spread over the surface of the mats and became incorporated in the mats.

In some cases, salt crystals, precipitated from hypersaline (salt content greater than normal seawater) waters in arid climates along shallow coastal seas, accumulated intermittently on the algal surfaces. In the Cleveland area, underground salt mines in Silurian rocks contain banded, conical stromatolites in salt-impregnated dolomite (fig. 22-1.1). It is postulated that blue-green algae were growing in dense mats concurrently with rapid evaporation of hypersaline tidal pools in hot or arid coastal margins.

Algal bands (fig. 22-1.2) are found sporadically in the more ledgelike layers of the Pennsylvanian-age Benwood limestone (Monongahela Group) exposed at several places along the Ohio River in southeastern Belmont County and eastern Monroe and Washington Counties. Stromatolites also have been found in the Upper Sewickley shale directly below the lowermost limestone beds of the Benwood limestone along strip-mine highwalls and around an artificial lake near the common corner of Noble, Morgan, and Muskingum Counties (fig. 22-1.3). The stromatolites there occur in discontinuous balls (oncolites) or in continuous layers elsewhere in an area of several square kilometers.

Bacteria are unlikely to be recognized on an ordinary fossil-collecting foray, but the product of bacterial activity in various environments has made significant contribution to rock accumulations, both by the degradation of other organisms and organic detritus and by their metabolic precipitation of iron and sulfur (chemosynthesis). A diverse assemblage of iron-forming sheath bacteria of two families have been described (Schopf and others, 1965) from a pyrite nodule found on the dump of a former mine in the Middle Kittanning coal (Allegheny Group, Pennsylvanian) in Vinton County. The bacteria were associated in a biocoenosis (natural environmental assemblage) very similar to that of modern stagnant pools and swamps. Such bacteria are probably widespread but unstudied in the Ohio coal measures.

Dasyclads

The Dasycladales is an order of fossil calcareous algae in the division Chlorophyta (green algae). It includes two families, the Receptaculitaceae (now extinct) and the Dasycladaceae (both fossil and recent). Fossils of this order are only rarely recognized by collectors. The two most important types of dasyclad fossils in Ohio are the cyclocrinitids (tribe Cyclocriniteae) and receptaculitids (tribe Receptaculiteae), both in the family Receptaculitaceae. For many years some dasyclads (for example, *Ischadites*) were variously considered to be sponges, corals, bryozoans, cystoid echinoderms, or other unrelated groups (Kesling and Graham, 1962). Their limited or sporadic occurrence among much more common brachiopods, bryozoans, corals, and other fossils in calcareous or manganese-rich marine rocks makes them especially prized specimens.

Fossil dasyclads are globose to cylindrical or club shaped in outline. They grew on the sea floor to several centimeters in height. Internally, a central, noncalcareous structure, the stem or **stipe**, was surrounded by whorled branches or protuberances (rays) (fig. 22-2.1). The central stipe and lateral branches of the fossils typically are preserved only as molds or casts. They are generally visible only in cracked or broken specimens. The primary branches or rays of some dasyclads are rounded at the tip; some have bristlelike or spinelike appendages; others have cuplike or prismlike tips that may be fused as an outer covering of small polygons (figs. 22-1.5, 22-1.7, 22-1.8, 22-2.2).

In cyclocrinitids, the end of each branch is expanded or branched to form a terminal rhomboidal plate. Each plate is one facet in a fused network of terminal plates of other lateral branches so that the surface of the whole body appears as a **reticulate** shell of calcareous prisms (fig. 22-1.7).

The cyclocrinitids range from Middle Ordovician to late Middle Silurian in various limestones and dolomites of the region. Three genera are found in southwestern Ohio and adjacent areas of Kentucky and Indiana. *Anomaloides* (fig. 22-1.9) and *Lepidolites* (fig. 22-1.4) are rare in Upper Ordovician strata of this region, but *Cyclocrinites* (figs. 22-1.5 to 22-1.8) occurs more widely in Middle Ordovician to Middle Silurian rocks.

Cyclocrinites is generally a somewhat flattened sphere that has an indentation where the stem (pedicel) was attached. The main central axis was short; lateral branches were very slender, almost rodlike, and arranged in whorls around the central axis. The **distal** ends of the branches were swollen, and adjacent swollen branch tips coalesced to form the heads, which were polygonal (generally six sided) in outline at the surface of the spherical body. These polygonal facets were **calcified**. Several early discoveries of *Cyclocrinites darwinii* (Miller) in southwestern Ohio and across the Ohio River in Kentucky were published originally under the generic name *Pasceolus* (S. A. Miller, 1874a) and many species were described. Nitecki (1970a) justified transferring this genus and several species to *Cyclocrinites darwinii* (Miller) (fig. 22-1.7). Another species, *Pasceolus camdenensis* Foerste, found near Camden, Ohio, was transferred by Nitecki (1970a) to *Cyclocrinites*? sp. (fig. 22-1.5) as an uncertain species because the type specimen had been misplaced.

The **holotype** of *Anomaloides reticulatus* Ulrich (fig. 22-1.9) was collected from Cincinnatian (Maysvillian) rocks in Covington, Kentucky, 275 feet above the nineteenth-century low-water mark of the Ohio River. Its main stem is not calcified and is greatly enlarged upward. The upper end is club shaped, somewhat like an upside-down bowling pin. Much more slender, primary, lateral, club-shaped branches are given off in a cycle or whorls (25-70 in a whorl), increasing in number upward, coincident with increased dimension of the axis. Calcification of each lateral branch forms hollow, tubelike struts from axis to margin. The rounded tip of each primary branch gives off three spinelike branches, and each of these terminal, bristlelike branches divides once again. The six tips of the spines fuse with tips of spines from adjacent primary branches to form a reticulate, external network of polygonal facets. These algae ranged up to several centimeters in height.

The genus *Lepidolites* is of less certain affinity than the other Cyclocrinitidae. The holotype of *Lepidolites dickhautii* Ulrich (fig. 22-1.4) was found in the Upper Ordovician Kope Formation on the lower bluffs of the Ohio River in Covington, Kentucky. Specimens generally are flattened, but were subcylindrical to subspherical (length-to-width ratio about 3.5) in original outline, and about 2 cm tall. A basal attachment commonly is present.

Another genus of importance, *Ischadites* (figs. 22-2.1, 22-2.2), is representative of the tribe Receptaculiteae. A specimen found in the Middle Silurian Niagaran Series near Yellow Springs, Ohio, was originally illustrated and named *Receptaculites ohioensis* by Hall and Whitfield (1875). This specimen was restudied by Nitecki (1971), who assigned it to the family Receptaculitaceae and named it *Ischadites abbottae*.

An excellent specimen that was originally named *Receptaculites hemisphericus* (Hall) was recovered from the Silurian Cedarville Dolomite at Wilmington, Clinton County. When restudied by Nitecki (1972), this specimen (fig. 22-2.2) and similar forms were renamed *Ischadites hemisphericus* on the basis of distinctive reproductive bodies (**gametangia**) occupying a central position of each prism on the surface of the body (thallus). Other specimens have been found near the top of Niagaran reefs in Illinois and Wisconsin.

Ischadites is present in abundance at some localities representing high-energy sedimentary environments. The extensive calcification (fig. 22-2.1) and a robust form may have served to adapt to such environments.

Tasmanites

A very common algal reproductive body (cyst) in Devonian rocks in Ohio is *Tasmanites* (fig. 22-2.3). It is abundant principally in the Devonian and Mississippian black shales; it is less common in other Devonian and Mississippian shales, siltstones, and limestones. *Tasmanites* specimens also weather free from the Paleozoic rocks and are recycled into younger sediments. Large numbers may be found in shoreline deposits of silt and sand along Lake Erie, in glacial deposits of fine sands and silts where the underlying bedrock is of Late Devonian and Early Mississippian age, and particularly in sediments of streams and tributaries flowing across Devonian and Lower Mississippian black shales.

Tasmanites belongs to one of the classes of green algae, the Prasinophyceae. The Prasinophyceae are represented in the marine realm today by both **planktic** and **benthic** forms (Wall, 1962). *Tasmanites* specimens from the Upper Devonian-Mississippian strata in Ohio are spherical, amber- to black-walled cells 0.1 to 0.8 mm in diameter. Where present, they may be very numerous. They appear as golden amber, tan, or black spots, which can be noted even on very small chips of shale. Under a strong hand lens, the walls of these spherical bodies appear smooth, but under a microscope, minute perforations (openings to minute canals) dot the surface of the thick wall (Schopf and others, 1944).

The most common species is *Tasmanites huronensis* (Dawson), which is found widely in the Olentangy Shale (Middle-Upper Devonian), the Ohio Shale (Upper Devonian) below the *Foerstia* zone (probably throughout the Huron Member), and reworked in Pleistocene till. Winslow (1962) described several other species from Ohio. *Tasmanites sinuosus* Winslow was found in subsurface drill-hole samples of the Columbus and Delaware Limestones (Middle Devonian) in central Ohio. It also has been found in samples from Erie County. This species is present in the Olentangy and Ohio Shales, particularly the lower part of the Ohio Shale below the *Foerstia* zone and in the upper part of the Ohio Shale (Chagrin Member), in the Bedford Shale (Devonian-Mississippian), and in the lower part of the Cuyahoga Formation (Mississippian). *Tasmanites sommeri* Winslow has been described from drill-hole samples of the Olentangy Shale and the lower part of the Ohio Shale below the *Foerstia* zone in eastern and south-central Ohio.

Charophytes (stoneworts)

The charophytes are in the class Charophyceae in the division Chlorophyta (green algae). Modern charophytes, commonly known as stoneworts, inhabit lakes and ponds and, less commonly, **brackish** waters of lagoons, estuaries, and bays. Charophytes range in age from Late Silurian to the present. Calcified female reproductive structures (gyrogonites) are common in the Columbus Limestone (Middle Devonian) in quarries, road cuts, and outcrops in west-central Ohio (fig. 22-2.15). The presence of these fossils in this marine limestone may be the result of transport by currents from brackish, nearshore habitats or by stream transport from terrestrial sites. The primitive Devonian-age charophytes are grouped in the family Trocholiscaceae and are called trocholisks.

Charophytes generally grow submerged, upright, from a few centimeters to over 1 meter in height, and attached to the bottom or other substrate. The slender stalk is constructed of greatly elongated cells wrapped tightly in a high spiral around a much larger, single, tubelike central cell, which appears as a cavity in cross section. The spiral cells surrounding the central cell are calcified in some species. The stem is jointed, superficially similar to the modern *Equisetum* (scouring rush or horsetail). Slender "branches," which are generally greatly elongated single cells, arise in a whorl at the joints (**nodes**). These branches simulate the whorls of leaves of the unrelated vascular-plant fossil *Sphenophyllum* (see fig. 23-10). The male reproductive structure is a seedlike, globose body, 0.3 to 0.8 mm in diameter, that emerges from the stem at the base of one or more branches of one to several nodes. These structures are extremely complex and are rarely preserved as fossils.

The female reproductive body (**oogonium**) is a slightly larger (generally 0.5-1.2 mm diameter), ovoid or somewhat spindle-shaped body attached to the stem at a node on the upper side of the base of a branch. The oogonium is a large egg cell surrounded by five or more tubular cells rising in a spiral around the egg cell (figs. 22-2.7, 22-2.9, 22-2.11). These wall cells enclose the egg cell except for a small pore at the top. The tips of the cells form a crown or coronula in some species (figs. 22-2.7, 22-2.12, 22-2.14). The oogonium wall may become calcified by secretion from the wall cells. These calcified reproductive bodies, collectively called gyrogonites, are the most common charophyte fossils. The stems also become calcified in some species by external deposition on the outer cell walls but are less commonly preserved. They generally disintegrate to form a calcite mud where the plants have grown in abundance. Gyrogonites in the Columbus Limestone (Middle Devonian) are 0.5 mm to 1.0 mm in diameter. They appear as round bodies on the broken surface of a rock sample, but on a cut, polished surface, such as the block in figure 22-2.15, they appear as thick-walled circles or smaller, dark, filled circles.

The Devonian gyrogonites of Ohio were first described as *Calcisphaera* by Williamson, in 1880, from the Columbus Limestone of Kelleys Island. In 1883, Dawson described the same kinds of gyrogonites from Kelleys Island as *Saccamina*. In 1886, Ulrich described the same type of fossils from the Falls of the Ohio in Indiana as *Moellerina greenei*. This name is the correct one, according to the **taxonomic** code, as explained by Peck and Morales (1966, p. 314).

Moellerina greenei Ulrich (figs. 22-2.8 to 22-2.10) has nine wall cells spiraling dextrally (to the right) for one-half revolution of the gyrogonite from base to top. They join, only loosely, at the top, leaving a porelike opening (fig. 22-2.10). There is no coronula.

Another Devonian gyrogonite from the Columbus Limestone is *Karpinskya bilineata* (Peck) (figs. 22-2.4 to 22-2.7). This form was originally named *Trocholiscus bilineatus*, but *Trocholiscus* was later divided (Peck and Morales, 1966) on the basis of the presence or absence of a coronula. The upper ends of the seven to 10 wall cells of *Karpinskya bilineata* join to form a strong coronula. These wall cells spiral dextrally upward in a one-quarter revolution around the gyrogonite.

A third type of charophyte, *Stomochara moreyi* Grambast (figs. 22-2.11 to 22-2.14) has been described from Ohio (as *Catillochara moreyi* in Peck and Eyer, 1963; see Peck and Eyer, 1964). *Stomochara* is found in the Arnoldsburg limestone (Monongahela Group, Pennsylvanian) at several localities in Belmont and Monroe Counties. *Stomochara* also was reported from Monroe County in the freshwater Nineveh limestone (Greene Formation, Dunkard Group), of Early Permian age.

Stomochara has the more modern features of charophyte gyrogonites. There are a reduced number of spiral cells (five) twining sinistrally (to the left) around the central cell. The spiral wall cells end in a small beak (fig. 22-2.12) or are flattened around a summit opening. Species of this genus have a basal pore that is pentagonal in outline (fig. 22-2.13).

Protosalvinia (*Foerstia*)

Fossils of *Protosalvinia* (*Foerstia*) (figs. 22-3.1 to 22-3.9), an alga of uncertain affinity, are concentrated on the bedding planes of the widespread *Foerstia* zone in the upper part of the Ohio Shale (Upper Devonian). They occur as carbonaceous compressions, which may appear very shiny black, on the dull surface of the black shale. Under a hand lens the surface of the *Protosalvinia* fossil appears netlike or reticulate. This network conforms to the outlines of the surface cells (fig. 22-3.6) of these discoid, lobed, or branched fossils. Nearly all specimens, whether circular or branched, show a ragged remnant or portion of a broken-off stalk (figs. 22-3.3, 22-3.4), which may have been the means of attachment to the sea floor or other surface, or it may be the remnant of a decayed branch from the parent plant. Schopf and Schwietering (1970, p. 2) suggested this condition resulted when new growth of the plant occurred and the new part broke off from older portions of the thallus or the old parts died back.

The fossils appear to represent several stages in the life cycle. They range from minute (1 mm), circular (figs. 22-3.1, 22-3.2) or slightly elongate black disks, generally very short stalked (fig. 22-3.3), to bilobed (fig 22-3.5) to branched (fig. 22-3.6) to, rarely, multiple-branched, staghorn-shaped forms several centimeters long. Both sides of the thallus types show the surface cells (figs.22-3.1, 22-3.2, 22-3.4, 22-3.6). The upper side of the thallus of discoid and bilobed types show the **conceptacles**, or rimmed fields of conceptacles (figs. 22-3.5, 22-3.7, 22-3.9). Each conceptacle contains one to several **tetrads** of spores (fig. 22-3.8).

Protosalvinia (*Foerstia*) has long been regarded as a fossil of uncertain relationships, but is probably most closely compared in its form and distribution to the modern *Fucus*, a common seaweed of the brown algae (division Phaeophyta, order Fucales). Schopf and Schwietering (1970, p. 4-7) suggested that this plant may have been comparable to *Sargassum* and its distribution in the Sargasso Sea. The Late Devonian sea in the eastern and central United States was widespread, relatively shallow, and anoxic at the bottom. They suggested that this plant may have reproduced in shallow pools or among the rocks of irregular coastlines in the Appalachian region. As the plants matured, they spread widely as plankton or, when mature, floated in the currents as **nekton** in the **littoral** zone or in surface waters of this inland sea.

Protosalvinia has been found principally in one zone of the Huron Member of the Ohio Shale in Ohio and eastward into Pennsylvania and western New York State in the Chagrin Shale Member (Murphy, 1973). It is widespread in a very limited stratigraphic zone, generally less than 2 meters thick, mostly in black shales of comparable age in Kentucky, Tennessee, Virginia, Oklahoma, and Ontario. It is found in outcrops and has been recovered from both cores and rock cuttings from wells. Associated fauna (radiolaria, conodonts, and fish dermal plates) are entirely marine.

Several thousand specimens of *Protosalvinia* were collected from the Huron Member just west of the intersection of I-270 and U.S. Route 23 in Worthington, Franklin County, Ohio, when this unit was exposed at several places during construction of the interstate highway. More than 1,500 specimens were examined by Niklas and Phillips (1976).

Larger algae—seaweeds

Many seaweedlike compressions have been collected from Ordovician, Silurian, and Devonian rocks in western Ohio and more widely from the western Great Lakes area eastward to New York and south to southern Indiana and Tennessee. Study of some of this fucoid compression and impression material suggests a wide range of sources, from animal **body fossils** and **ichnofossils** (burrows, tracks, and trails) to sedimentary features of nonbiological origin. However, many of the compression fossils, including some in early collections, have been demonstrated later to represent fossils of ancient seaweeds. Three seaweeds from central North America are illustrated here: *Buthotrephis newlinii* White (fig. 22-3.10), *Buthotrephis speciosa* (White) (figs. 22-3.11, 22-3.12), and *Thalassocystis striata* Taggart & Parker (figs. 22-3.13, 22-3.14). The nature of branching of these attached or floating marine plants is one of the first characteristics used to differentiate the **frondose**, *Fucus*-like, macrophytic algal fossils. A more valuable characteristic is the cellular pattern, which can be seen in two of the specimens illustrated here (figs. 22-3.10, 22-3.13). In other specimens, the carbonaceous film appears to be without any cellular detail. A third important characteristic is the presence of some type of reproductive structure, generally located near the tips of the distal (last) set of branches.

The branching on some of the frondose types, such as *Buthotrephis speciosa* (figs. 22-3.11, 22-3.12), is very closely spaced and the two to four branches are more or less equally divided and of equal length. Some specimens, such as *Buthotrephis newlinii* (fig. 22-3.10), have paired elongation of only one branch of some **dichotomies**, resulting in a staghorn system of branches. Because the fossils commonly have a broken or decayed base (**proximal** portion), it is believed that some broke off or rotted and fell away from a more extensive thallus. It is entirely possible they are remnants of broken multibranched thalli that were dispersed widely by drifting in the currents after they were torn loose from the bottom, but before they broke up and then sank to the bottom as single fronds. However, some probably were small plants attached to the bottom in shallow seas. The base of the *Thalassocystis* specimen illustrated in figure 22-3.14 may have been a bottom attachment structure (**holdfast**) or just the decayed remnant of a multibranched thallus.

The cellular detail or a network of stronger and weaker fibers characterizes the bladder of some of these algae. Parallel longitudinal strands are prominent in *Thalassocystis* (fig. 22-3.13), especially on the inflated floats. Irregular, longitudinally oriented fibers interconnected by random, high-angle fibers form a network in *Buthotrephis newlinii* (see inset diagram, fig. 22-3.10). A coarse network is present in *B. speciosa* (fig. 22-3.11).

Reproductive structures (spore-bearing cavities or conceptacles) are present near the terminal ends of some of these frondose algae. They are clearly visible as small, lighter colored ovals near the tips of the lobes of *B. speciosa*. The swollen ends of *B. newlinii* may be conceptacles, but they also may be floats. Inflated bladders appear on most of the branches of *Thalassocystis*, but no conceptacles have been identified.

A Devonian fossil from New York State, *Hungerfordia* Fry & Banks (Fry and Banks, 1955), appears to be similar in general size and growth habit to *Buthotrephis*. Another species, *Manitobia patula* (Whiteaves) (Fry, 1983), is perhaps even more similar in growth habit but seems to lack the terminal conceptacles. It is abundant in the Red River Formation (Upper Ordovician) near Lake Winnipeg, Manitoba.

These algae have been compared with modern green, red, and brown algae, but without more details and chemical analyses they are difficult to assign. Taggart and Parker (1976) compare *Thalassocystis* with brown algae; Fry (1983) compares *Manitobia* with some red algae.

Single compression specimens of branching, macrophytic algae that have a definitive carbonaceous film, derived from the in-place coalification of the original thalloid body, may be found in marine limestones, limy shales, siltstones, and fine-grained sandstones in southwestern and west-central Ohio. We have found such fossils in quarries in the vicinity of Maumee, in Lucas County. The few specimens found in Ordovician rocks of the Cincinnati region are so poorly preserved or nondescript that they generally are ignored and not collected. In Silurian and Devonian limestones, and less commonly in the Ohio Shale, compression specimens that have a carbonized film may be uncovered but go unrecognized. Some fossil algae also have been collected in Mississippian strata near Granville, in Licking County.

Acritarchs

The acritarchs are a very important artificial group of microscopic, algal-like, planktonic, organic-walled organisms. Some are of uncertain biological affinity (Evitt, 1963). Some are very similar in morphology and ecology to **extant** dinoflagellates (division Pyrrophyta)—unicellular, planktonic algae that have a durable resting-cyst stage. Others are known to be allied with plant divisions other than the Pyrrophyta, such as the division Chlorophyta, class Prasinophyceae (table 22-1).

Dinoflagellate resting cysts are represented widely as fossils in marine and brackish-water and a few freshwater sedimentary rocks around the world from the Mesozoic to the present. A few specimens have been tentatively described from as early as the Silurian. Dinoflagellates are best known from their widespread blooms (bursts of abundance) that result in so-called red tides. All the characteristics just stated for the dinoflagellates, except age, seem to apply to the acritarchs as well.

Acritarchs are known from the Precambrian to Recent, but their greatest importance is in Lower and Middle Paleozoic strata. Their several basic forms suggest that they may represent a number of distinct groups of organisms. They generally evolved very rapidly, and new forms appear to have spread around the world's oceans in a very short time. The distinctive, durable resting cysts are excellent **guide fossils** for interpreting age and environments or habitats and for close correlation of marine rocks worldwide.

Acritarchs are abundant and diverse in the Ordovician and Silurian limestones and shales in Ohio. They decline gradually through the Devonian and are less abundant from early Mississippian on (Wicander and Wood, 1981). The diversity of fossil acritarchs makes it impractical to survey the group as a whole. Only a select group of acritarchs from a well-studied Middle Devonian section in a quarry near Sylvania, Ohio, are illustrated here (fig. 22-4). The acritarchs in the limestones and shales can be used to distinguish between several environments, from nearshore, high-energy, clear-water limestones to deeper shelf, quiet-water, limy shales and siltstones. The species illustrated here are from a study by Wicander and Wood (1981); see that publication for detailed stratigraphic and faunal information.

Dictyotidium cohora Wicander & Wood (fig. 22-4.6) and *Pterospermella reticulata* Loeblich & Wicander (fig. 22-4.5) are both algal cysts of the class Prasinophyceae (division Chlorophyta). The thick wall of *Dictyotidium cohora* is reinforced with a very strong network or reticulum of ridges that form 20 to 23 five- to seven-sided polygonal, smooth-surfaced fields (areas between ridges) per hemisphere. The specimens measured range from 66 to 79 micrometers in diameter. *Dictyotidium cohora* generally is present in very low numbers (fewer than 10) in the midportion of the section, mainly from rocks interpreted to represent deeper shelf environments. *Dictyotidium cohora* was first named from the Silica quarry, but has since been found in other upper Middle Devonian (Givetian Stage) localities in Ohio and Ontario. Another species, *D. variatum* Playford, also has been identified from the Lower to Middle Devonian of Ontario.

The central vesicle of *Pterospermella* is 41 to 48 micrometers in diameter and is surrounded by a thin equatorial flange. The warty appearance of the vesicle surface may be due to framboids (microscopic aggregates of pyrite grains) crystallized inside the vesicle. *Pterospermella reticulata* is most abundant near the base of the Silica Formation, but a few specimens have been identified in overlying layers of calcareous shale and limestone. *Pterospermella reticulata* also has been identified in the Lower Devonian of Oklahoma. Another species, *P. hermosita* (Cramer), ranging from lowermost Devonian to Middle Devonian, has been found in the Sylvania quarries and also is known from France, Spain, and Algeria.

The vesicle of *Diexallophasis simplex* Wicander & Wood (fig. 22-4.10) is somewhat quadrangular to oval in outline, 25 to 45 micrometers in diameter, and has a very weakly scabrate (rough or scaly) surface. The hollow, flexible processes range from 35 to 45 micrometers in length and are characterized by short (1-2 micrometers) spines. Some of the tips of the processes are tapered to a point; others are blunt or, rarely, forked. The specimens designated as *Diexallophasis simplex* by Wicander and Wood (1981) were previously included in *D. remota* (Deunff). *Diexallophasis simplex* appears to be limited to upper Middle Devonian rocks of Ohio and Ontario, although it previously was given a range of upper Lower Devonian through Middle Devonian of eastern Canada and western Europe.

Estiastra rhytidoa Wicander & Wood (fig. 22-4.12) appears to be triangular but is actually stellate (star shaped). The enlarged proximal portions of the four processes come together to form the central vesicle in such a way that the flattened microfossil appears to be triangular in outline. The dimension between the points of two processes is about 75 to 80 micrometers. The base of each process is about 30 to 35 micrometers wide and tapers to a point at the **apical** end. The surface of the processes is pebbly, warty, or scabrate, as is the body surface, but these small bumps become aligned into striationlike ridges and appear as wrinkles or in a shrunken condition in the terminal 20 to 25 micrometers of each process. *Estiastra rhytidoa* is found in small numbers in most samples of the Silica Formation except in rocks representing low-energy environments. It is limited to the upper Middle Devonian of Ohio and Ontario.

The vesicle of *Exochoderma arca* Wicander & Wood (fig. 22-4.2) is nearly square and about 40 micrometers in diameter. One very wide process extends about 40 micrometers from each corner, and two or three similar hollow processes extend perpendicular to the four corner processes from either side of the vesicle. Processes are tapered very slightly to a simple or once-forked distal tip. *Exochoderma arca* was first described from the quarry at Silica and is present in great abundance in most of the open-water, deeper shelf sediments of the section. It has since been found at other sites in North America, but only in upper Middle Devonian strata. Several previously discovered acritarchs, misassigned to other taxa, are now grouped with *E. arca*. If these forms are included, the range would extend from upper Lower Devonian to upper Upper Devonian.

Exochoderma triangulata Wicander & Wood (fig. 22-4.8) has a very slender triangular form in which one side is much shorter than the other two. The longer sides are 45 to 50 micrometers long. Three processes appear as long, attenuated, tapering extensions of the corners of the body. The processes are nearly as long as the shortest side. A fourth process, perpendicular to the others, may arise from one side of the vesicle about midway between the other three. Some of the processes may be **granulose** or have tiny spines near the tip. *Exochoderma triangulata* has been found only in the upper Middle Devonian Silica Formation in Ohio and is present in small numbers throughout most of the samples from the unit.

Hapsidopalla chela Wicander & Wood (fig. 22-4.3) is characterized by a thick-walled central vesicle 30 to 35 micrometers in diameter that has a pebbly surface. Protruding from the surface are flexible, thin-walled, hollow processes, 8 to 20 micrometers long, that taper slightly to their terminal, branched tips. Three to four spinelike branches extend nearly at right angles at the tip of each process. The cyst wall opens by a split, which is generally not visible, along the equator. This acritarch is found in very small numbers mainly in samples representing deeper shelf sediments. It is known only from the upper Middle Devonian of Ohio and Ontario. Another species, *H. exornata* (Deunff), ranges through the Middle and Upper Devonian of Ontario.

Hapsidopalla invenusta Wicander & Wood (fig. 22-4.7) is characterized by multiple spines. The thick-walled vesicle is spherical to ovoid, 30 to 40 micrometers in diameter, and has small rosettelike bumps on the surface. Numerous hollow processes extend out 15 to 20 micrometers from the vesicle and taper terminally to a short point. This acritarch is present in small numbers in most of the shaly or calcareous siltstones of deeper shelf waters. It has been recorded only from the Sylvania quarries of Ohio, thus its range is limited to the upper Middle Devonian.

The most striking characteristic of *Multiplicisphaeridium ramusculosum* (Deflandre) (fig. 22-4.11) is the presence of several multiply branched processes. The vesicle is only 20 to 25 micrometers in diameter and the processes are about the same length. There are commonly three orders of forking, and a fourth terminal dichotomy may be present. The surfaces of the vesicle and processes range from smooth to granulose. This species is especially abundant in the upper part of the Silica Formation. It is the one of the most cosmopolitan species of the assemblage; it is widespread in Africa, the Americas, Europe, and the eastern Eurasian region. *Multiplicisphaeridium ramusculosum* ranges from Upper Ordovician to Upper Devonian.

The clearly defined vesicle of *Palacanthus ledanoisii* (Deunff) (fig. 22-4.9) is about 40 to 45 micrometers in diameter and has five or six hollow processes. These processes generally are shorter than the diameter of the body, although in figure 22-4.9 they appear to be about the same length as the diameter of the vesicle body measured between adjacent spine bases. The vesicle surface is granulose, and the same **ornamentation** extends along the lower part of each process. Near the vesicle margin and at the base of some processes there are also some very small spinose projections. The processes taper to a small point. *Palacanthus ledanoisii* is found in small numbers throughout the entire section at the Silica quarry. It is known throughout the Devonian from sites in Africa, South America, and Canada.

Tunisphaeridium tentaculaferum (Martin) (fig. 22-4.1) is somewhat similar to *Hapsidopalla chela*. The central vesicle is slightly larger, 40 to 55 micrometers in diameter, and the hollow processes are longer, 25 to 35 micrometers in length. The processes have branched tips and are very slender, irregularly crooked, and densely arranged over the surface. This species is distributed throughout the Silica Formation in all environments but always in very low numbers. *Tunisphaeridium tentaculaferum* is known from Europe, Africa, and North and South America. It ranges from Upper Ordovician to Devonian and reached its zenith in the Silurian.

Tyligmasoma alargadum (Cramer) (fig. 22-4.4) also is found in very low numbers in the Silica Formation but is widely distributed in Silurian and Lower and Middle Devonian rocks in Europe, Africa, and the Americas. The vesicle is triangular, 41 to 55 micrometers along a side, and has rounded corners and three wide, tapering processes extending 15 to 25 micrometers from the corners. The vesicle wall is essentially without ornamentation except for small wartlike processes along the margin.

Prototaxites

Specimens of *Prototaxites* Dawson (fig. 22-5) have the appearance of woody fossils. When first described from Lower Devonian rocks of the Gaspé Peninsula, Québec, they were thought to be logs of a *Taxus*-like coniferous tree. Later studies have shown *Prototaxites* to be more nearly similar to the stipe (axis) of a giant, kelplike alga or possibly a woody fungus. However, *Prototaxites* is still of uncertain affinity. Specimens typically are **silicified**, black or brownish, and have no clearly defined surface markings except indistinct striations. Larger specimens of *Prototaxites* generally resemble permineralized prostrate logs. Smaller pieces have the appearance of dense wood from branches or roots of higher plants (fig. 22-5.4).

Under low magnification, the tissue appears to consist of packed, intertwined tubes, generally of two sizes. The larger tubes have very thick walls and range from 12 to 70 micrometers in diameter in various species. The smaller tubes or filaments are thin walled and range from 1 to 8 micrometers diameter. The tubes are arranged longitudinally into a more or less spongy tissue. In some species (for example, *Prototaxites clevelandensis* Chitaley, figs. 22-5.1, 22-5.2), the large tubes constitute most of the tissue. In other species (for example, *P. southworthii* Arnold, fig. 22-5.3), the small tubes predominate and the whole tissue appears very spongy to loosely organized. The larger tubes were originally misinterpreted as **tracheids** (water-conducting cells) of a higher plant. The tubes may be branched or forked and may have very thin cross-walls and a pit opening through the center (Schmid, 1976). The large tubes are surrounded by a sheath made up of a single layer of cells. In longitudinal section, the small tubes appear tangled or intertwined in some zones, but in other parts of a section they are arranged more nearly parallel with the long axis of the stem.

A silicified block of *Prototaxites*, over 50 cm long and 25 cm in diameter, found by Edward Orton in the Huron shale of central Ohio, was originally described as *Nematophyton ortoni* by Penhallow (1896). Slides of this material are still available at the Peter Redpath Museum at McGill University in Montreal. The original specimen and locality data are not available. The specimen appears to be well preserved (figs. 22-5.5, 22-5.6). Large tubes, nearly 70 micrometers in diameter, are mostly longitudinal with respect to the long axis of the specimen, but many are at other angles, appearing interwoven in some areas. The orientation of the smaller cells (5-10 micrometers in diameter) is less well defined, except in the tight clusters of small cells (center of fig. 22-5.5). These clusters are similar to the "medullary spots" of

Arnold's (1952) specimens of *P. southworthii*. *Prototaxites ortonii* (Penhallow) is similar in many respects to Arnold's **taxon**, but the large tubes are more numerous and have a somewhat greater diameter.

Specimens of *Prototaxites* have been found around the world in Upper Silurian and Devonian rocks. *Prototaxites ortonii* (figs. 22-5.5, 22-5.6) and *P. clevelandensis* (figs. 22-5.1, 22-5.2) have been found in Ohio in the Huron and Cleveland Shale Members, respectively, of the Ohio Shale. *Prototaxites southworthii* (figs. 22-5.3, 22-5.4) has been found in the Kettle Point Shale in Ontario (equivalent to the Ohio Shale) and in glacial drift in northwestern Ohio and near Dayton, Montgomery County. Small fragments also have been identified from lag deposits at Skinners Run in western Cuyahoga County and from other localities of similar age.

CHITINOZOA

Chitinozoans (fig. 22-6.1 to 22-6.6) are sack-, flask-, or bottle-shaped organisms of uncertain biological affinities. They are black to dark brown and generally opaque, although better preserved forms may be translucent. In life, many were probably a component of the marine plankton; others may have been bottom dwellers (benthic). Chitinozoans are widely dispersed in shales, siltstones, dolomites, limestones, and cherts of Ordovician to Devonian age in Ohio. They may have had a few ancestral forms in late Precambrian, and, though they almost die out by Late Devonian, the last few kinds disappeared by the end of the Paleozoic. Chitinozoans are classified here (table 22-1) in the kingdom Protista but are of uncertain affinity. The wall of the test is pseudochitin, not **chitin**, as originally assumed, much like the walls of graptolites, to which group some workers suggest a relationship based on some common similarities, such as pseudochitinous wall, marine habitat, functional morphology, and co-occurrence. The ecological conditions of ocean waters controlled the distribution of chitinozoans. They show maximum diversity in carbonate facies deposited under normal marine conditions and are greatly reduced in diversity (or absent) from dolomite facies of shelf flats or embayments (Wright, 1978).

The body chamber (vesicle) ranges in size from 40 micrometers to a little over a millimeter in length. Chitinozoans generally are solitary, but some are found in chains. The basal (aboral) end is generally closed, except for a small pore in some species. The basal end is wider than the upper (oral) end, which is open. The oral end in many species is drawn out into a small, commonly very slender neck. In some groups, the opening (**aperture**) of the neck is closed by a platelike lid (operculum), an important diagnostic feature. The base commonly is enlarged, and the other parts of the outer wall of the test may be ornamented with various simple or complex spines. The base may be flared into a netlike skirt or **carina**. A good introduction to this group may be found in Jansonius and Jenkins (1978).

Chitinozoa are widespread in Ohio and are especially abundant in the Columbus and Delaware Limestones (Wright, 1976) and the Silica Formation (Wood, 1974), all of Middle Devonian age. A few species of chitinozoans from the Silica Formation are illustrated in figure 22-6 as examples of this interesting group of fossils.

TROCHOPHYLLUM

Trochophyllum is a plant of uncertain affinity that has been found at two or three localities in Ohio. Our principal information comes from early reports of E. B. Andrews (1875) and Leo Lesquereux (1879-1884). Five specimens described by Lesquereux were found by Carl Rominger in a quarry in the "Waverly Sandstone" (Cuyahoga Formation) near Granville, Licking County. E. B. Andrews found additional specimens, which are now in the collections at Marietta College; two of these specimens are illustrated in figures 22-6.7 and 22-6.8. Fragmentary specimens have been found in outcrops of the Cuyahoga and Logan Formations, but they are generally overlooked or misinterpreted as roots of higher plants. *Trochophyllum* fossils may be found singly, but more typically there are several on a small slab. In a few cases, specimens are superimposed, lying tangled in several layers.

These delicate fossils have been variously interpreted as algae, sphenopsids, and lycopods. The uncertain taxonomic position of the genus makes it difficult to properly describe and name the various parts of the fossil. The plants had a stemlike axis and leaflike processes, but "stem" and "leaf" are terms applicable only to vascular plants. We will use the terms "axis" and "blade" for these structures. The very slender axis and long narrow blades of *Trochophyllum lineare* Lesquereux (fig. 22-6.7) resembles some charophytes. However the regular arrangement of the scars on the axis is more typical of a lycopod, if the scars encircle the stem in a low spiral, or a horsetail, if the scars are in whorls. The type specimen of *T. lineare* (fig. 22-6.7) clearly shows minute scars or punctae very closely spaced across the axis, apparently in whorls. The blades are very long and narrow for such a slender axis. The specimen illustrated in figure 22-6.8 has shorter, wider blades that are spaced very closely.

Two other fossils that have gross similarity in appearance to *Trochophyllum* but quite different morphology should be noted, as they might be expected to occur in Ohio strata. *Winnipegia cuneata* (Whiteaves) was established from abundant excellent carbonaceous compressions in Upper Ordovician marine dolomites from the Lake Winnipeg region of Manitoba (Fry, 1983). Superficial similarities with the much younger (Mississippian) *Trochophyllum* are dispelled by major morphological dissimilarities. In *Winnipegia* there is only one branch or blade at each node, there is no continuous central axis but rather a zigzag axis made up of one branch of the dichotomous branching at each node continuing on as the main axis (**sympodial** branching), and there is no orderly arrangement of blade or branch scars evident along the main axis.

Another superficially similar plant is *Lennea schmidtii*, reported by Krausel and Weyland (1934) from Devonian marine shales in Germany. It is a much larger plant than *Trochophyllum* and has a very strong, wide, central axis, also formed by sympodial branching. The blade-bearing branches may fork and some appear to be hollow. The scars appear to be much larger, oval, and quite irregular in arrangement.

BRYOPHYTES

Bryophytes are simple, nonvascular land plants that include mosses, liverworts, and hornworts. Traditionally, they have been viewed as evolutionary intermediates between aquatic green algae and the earliest vascular land plants. Bryophytes are certainly an ancient group, but today they are generally thought to represent one or more independent lineages that have made a marginal adaptation to life on land, without being directly involved in the evolution of more complex land plants. Because they lack a vascular conducting system, they tend to be small in stature, ranging from the low-sprawling liverworts to mosses a few centimeters high. They are generally confined to moist habitats.

The Upper Paleozoic rocks of Ohio contain spores that are certainly derived from bryophytes. Larger fossils of Paleozoic bryophytes are rare worldwide, and only a few possible types are present in Ohio (for example, *Muscites*). Pleistocene bog deposits in Ohio contain peat, much of which is derived from several species of *Sphagnum*. Remnants of other mosses are relatively common in some layers of peat. Both the peat and Pleistocene lake-mud deposits contain bryophyte spores.

COLLECTING LOCALITIES

Most of the localities listed below are on private property. Permission must be obtained before entering to collect. Please remember that many road cuts are dangerous, and stopping along interstate highways is forbidden.

Stromatolites have been found in Belmont and northeastern Monroe Counties in the bluffs of the Ohio River and exposures in tributary valleys, especially in the lower ledges of tan to white Benwood limestone (Monongahela Group, Upper Pennsylvanian). They also have been collected from the Upper Sewickley shale, just below the Benwood limestone ledges, in coal strip pits in northwestern Noble County and northeastern Monroe County.

Dasyclads have been collected from uppermost Middle Ordovician (Point Pleasant Formation) and Upper Ordovician (Cincinnatian Series) rocks in the Ohio River bluffs, tributary ravines, and highway cuts in the Cincinnati area (Hamilton County), the Covington-Newport area across the Ohio River in Kentucky, and the New Richmond-Point Pleasant area (Clermont County). Upper Ordovician dasyclads also are present in outcrops and quarries in the Camden area (Preble County). Middle Silurian dasyclads have been collected from the Yellow Springs area (Greene County) and the Wilmington area (Clinton County).

Tasmanites has been found in the Columbus Limestone (Middle Devonian) in road cuts east of the Erie-Sandusky County line and in the Ohio Shale (Upper Devonian) along Skinners Run in southwestern Cuyahoga County and in stream cuts in central and southeastern Delaware County. *Prototaxites* also has been found at the Skinners Run locality.

Charophytes have been collected from the Columbus Limestone (Middle Devonian) on Kelleys Island in Lake Erie; from quarries, outcrops, and road cuts in the vicinity of Marblehead, in Ottawa County, north of Sandusky Bay; and from excavations in the vicinity of Sandusky, Erie County. Permian-age charophytes are present in the Nineveh limestone (Greene Formation, Dunkard Group) at Clark Hill in eastern Monroe County, 300 meters south of the Opossum Creek bridge on Ohio Route 7, and near the top of the hill on the river bluffs above the Ohio River along Monroe County Road 43, uphill from Ohio Route 7.

Protosalvinia (*Foerstia*) localities in the Ohio Shale (Upper Devonian) are listed in Schopf and Schwietering (1970). They include: Frink Run south of Monroeville, Huron County; Bristol Ridge, 3.5 km (2.25 miles) east of Zanesfield, Logan County; stream cuts in Glen Echo Park 3.1 km (2 miles) south of Worthington and Flint Park 3.1 km (2 miles) north of Worthington, the Narrows of the Olentangy River 1.6-4.9 km (1-3 miles) north of Worthington, and a deep road cut on I-270 just west of the U.S. Route 23 interchange, all in Franklin County; the Ohio River bluffs near Vanceburg, Lewis County, Kentucky, about 40 km (25 miles) southwest of Portsmouth, Scioto County, Ohio, and other outcrops southwest of Portsmouth. Murphy (1973) reported *Protosalvinia* along Conneaut Creek in Ashtabula County.

Upper Silurian acritarchs and chitinozoans have been collected in Sandusky County east of Fremont and vicinity from road cuts, Ohio Turnpike cuts, and quarry sites. Middle Devonian acritarchs and chitinozoans have been collected from the Columbus and Delaware Limestones in the Hamilton Bros. quarry on the east side of Ohio Route 4, 6.5 km (4 miles) north of Marion (Marion County) and low road cuts along the Ohio Turnpike (I-80) east of the Erie-Sandusky County line. They have been well studied from the Silica Formation in the quarries at Silica, west of Sylvania, in Lucas County.

ACKNOWLEDGMENTS

We extend gratitude and thanks to Gordon D. Wood (Amoco Oil Company) and E. Reed Wicander (Central Michigan University) for loan of photographs and assistance with the section on acritarchs; Dr. Wood for the photos and guidance during preparation of the section on chitinozoans; Shya Chitaley (The Cleveland Museum of Natural History) for photos of *Prototaxites clevelandensis*. We owe Aleen Cross deep appreciation for typing and correcting the manuscript through several extensive revisions. We also extend our sincere thanks to the following colleagues at Michigan State University: Diane K. Baclawski, Geology Librarian, and Huang Wei, former Ph.D. candidate, for help in locating and retrieving literature and specimens, and Catherine D. Caswell, Administrative Assistant, for generous assistance in many ways. Lisa Van Doren (Ohio Division of Geological Survey) enhanced many of the photographs in scanning them for publication.

TABLE 22-1.—A BASIC CLASSIFICATION OF THE FOSSIL PLANTS IN CHAPTERS 22 TO 24

The precise phylogenetic placement of some fossils is poorly understood or subject to controversy, particularly in the case of fragmentary and microscopic material from Ordovician, Silurian, and Devonian rocks. Such uncertainties are noted in this table as "rank uncertain" at the general equivalent level of classification. The genera of flowering plants are not listed. The botanical rank of division is generally equivalent to the zoological rank of phylum. A tribe is a botanical rank between subfamily and genus.

KINGDOM MONERA (prokaryotes, Chapter 22)
DIVISION EUBACTERIA (bacteria)
iron/sulfur bacteria
DIVISION CYANOPHYTA (cyanobacteria or blue-green algae)
stromatolites, oncolites

KINGDOM PROTISTA (predominantly unicellular eukaryotes, Chapter 22)
DIVISION PYRROPHYTA (dinoflagellates)
Rank uncertain—Acritarcha
Diexallophasis
Estiastra
Exochoderma
Hapsidopalla
Multiplicisphaeridium
Palacanthus
Tunisphaeridium
Tyligmasoma
Rank uncertain—Chitinozoa
Ancyrochitina
Angochitina
Conochitina
Desmochitina
Eisenackitina

KINGDOM PLANTAE (multicellular, autotrophic eukaryotes)
DIVISION RHODOPHYTA (red algae, Chapter 22)
"reef-forming" carbonate forms
Manitobia
DIVISION PHAEOPHYTA (brown algae, Chapter 22)
Class Phaeophyceae
Order Fucales
Buthotrephis
Hungerfordia
Thalassocystis
Rank uncertain
Protosalvinia (*Foerstia*)
Prototaxites (*Nematophyton*)
DIVISION CHLOROPHYTA (green algae, Chapter 22)
Class Ulvophyceae
Order Dasycladales
Family Receptaculitaceae
Tribe Cyclocriniteae
Anomaloides
Cyclocrinites
Lepidolites
Tribe Receptaculiteae
Ischadites
Receptaculites
Class Prasinophyceae
Dictyotidium (acritarch)
Pterospermella (acritarch)
Tasmanites
Class Charophyceae
Family Trochiliscaceae
Karpinskya
Moellerina
Stomochara
Rank uncertain
Lennea
Trochophyllum
Winnipegia
DIVISION BRYOPHYTA (mosses, liverworts, hornworts)
Drepanocladus (Chapter 24)
Muscites (Chapter 22)
Sphagnum (Chapter 24)
DIVISION LYCOPHYTA (lycopods, quillworts, Chapter 23)
Order Isoetales
Isoetes (extant)
Order Lycopodiales (herbaceous lycopods)
Lycopodites (Chapter 23)
Lycopodium (extant)
Selaginella (extant)
Order Lepidodendrales (arborescent lycopods)
Asolanus
Aspidaria
Bergeria
Bothrodendron
Cyperites
Knorria
Lepidocarpon
Lepidodendron
Lepidophloios
Lepidophylloides
Lepidostrobophyllum
Lepidostrobus
Sigillaria
Sigillariophyllum
Sigillariostrobus
Stigmaria
Syringodendron
Ulodendron
DIVISION SPHENOPHYTA (horsetails, Chapter 23)
Order Sphenophyllales (vinelike horsetails)
Bowmanites
Sphenophyllostachys
Sphenophyllum
Order Calamitales (arborescent horsetails)
Annularia
Asterophyllites
Astromyelon
Calamites
Calamostachys
Macrostachya
Palaeostachya
Pinnularia

Order Equisetales
Equisetum (extant)
DIVISION PTERIDOPHYTA (ferns, Chapter 23)
Order Marattiales
Acitheca
Asterotheca
Caulopteris
Lobatopteris
Megaphyton
Pecopteris
Psaronius
Ptychocarpus
Scolecopteris
Order Botryopteridales
Botryopteris
Order Zygopteridales
Alloiopteris
Corynepteris
Danaeides
Nemejcopteris
Rank uncertain
Oligocarpia
Renaultia
Sphenopteris
DIVISION PROGYMNOSPERMOPHYTA (progymnosperms, Chapter 23)
Order Aneurophytales
Archaeopteris
Callixylon
Order Noeggerathiales
Discinites
Plagiozamites
Russellites
DIVISION PTERIDOSPERMOPHYTA (seed ferns, Chapter 23)
Order Medullosales
Alethopteris
Aphlebia
Aulacotheca
Bernaultia
Callipteridium
Carpolithes
Cyclopteris
Dicksonites
Dolerotheca
Holcospermum
Laveineopteris
Lescuropteris
Linopteris
Macroneuropteris
Mariopteris
Medullosa
Neurocallipteris
Neuropteris
Odontopteris
Pachytesta
Paripteris
Protoblechnum
Pseudomariopteris
Reticulopteris
Rhabdocarpus
Trigonocarpus
Whittleseya
Order Lyginopteridales
Calymmathotheca
Crossotheca?
Eremopteris
Lagenostoma
Lyginopteris
Palmatopteris
Rhacopteris
Sphenopteris
Order Megalopteridales
Megalopteris
Orthogoniopteris
Samaropsis
Order Peltaspermales
Autunia
Callipteris
Rhachiphyllum
DIVISION CYCADOPHYTA (cycads, Chapter 23)
Order Cycadales?
Taeniopteris
DIVISION CONIFEROPHYTA
Order Cordaitales (cordaites, Chapter 23)
Artisia
Cardiocarpus
Cordaicladus
Cordaitanthus
Cordaites
Cordaixylon
Mesoxylon
Mitrospermum
Order Voltziales (extinct conifers, Chapter 23)
Emporia
Gomphostrobus
Lebachia
Utrechtia
Walchia
Walchiostrobus
Order Coniferales (extant conifers, Chapter 24)
Abies
Juniperus
Larix
Picea
Pinus
Thuja
Tsuga
DIVISION ANTHOPHYTA (flowering plants, Chapter 24)

FIGURE 22-1.—Stromatolites and dasyclads. Scale bars for figures 22-1.1, 22-1.2, 22-1.5, 22-1.8, and 22-1.9 equal 1 cm; scale bars for figures 22-1.4, 22-1.6, and 22-1.7 equal 5 mm. Figures 22-1.4, 22-1.7, and 22-1.9 are reproduced from Nitecki (1970a, figs. 14, 33, 48), with permission.

1	Portion of a domed dolomitic stromatolite in an Upper Silurian salt bed showing deformation caused by movement of crystalline salt. Individual growth layers of algae are coupled together in packets or bands of several layers; bands show microdoming. Some stromatolites in this deposit are spherical (isolated) rather than in continuous or domed beds. "A" salt, lower Salina Group (Upper Silurian), International Salt Company Cleveland Mine, under Lake Erie offshore from Cuyahoga County, Ohio; MSU FPH 5-10-74 I-2-1.
2	Close-up view of tabular stromatolite from ledge of freshwater Benwood limestone (Monongahela Group, Pennsylvanian), lower bluffs of Ohio River along Ohio Route 7, northeastern Monroe County, Ohio. MSU FPH unnumbered specimen.
3	Discontinuous layer of stromatolites (arrows) near the top of the Upper Sewickley shale, about 15 cm below the base of the Benwood limestone (Monongahela Group, Pennsylvanian). Exposure in highwall of coal mine near Beaver Run Park, northeastern Morgan County, Ohio.
4	*Lepidolites dickhautii* Ulrich. Holotype of *L. elongatus* Ulrich, transferred to *L. dickhautii* by Ulrich (1879). Kope Formation (Upper Ordovician), Covington, Kentucky; USNM 46533.
5	*Cyclocrinites*? sp. (see Nitecki, 1970a, p. 138). Cincinnatian Series (Upper Ordovician), near Camden, Preble County, Ohio; AMNH specimen (misplaced). Reproduced from Foerste (1910, pl. II, fig. 6 as *Pasceolus camdenensis* Foerste).
6, 7, 8	*Cyclocrinites darwinii* (Miller). **6, syntype**. Note five- or six-rayed stellate mark on each plate. Bellevue Member of Grant Lake Limestone (Cincinnatian Series, Upper Ordovician), hills above Cincinnati, Hamilton County, Ohio (about 123 meters above nineteenth-century low-water mark; see James, 1881); FMNH, James Collection No. 1222. Reproduced from Foerste (1916, pl. III, fig. 1). **7**, apical view of holotype. Cincinnatian Series (Upper Ordovician), Maysville, Kentucky; FMNH. **8**, six-rayed stellate plates (facets) visible at upper left. Specimen originally assigned to *Pasceolus globosus* Billings. Point Pleasant Formation (upper Middle Ordovician), southeast of New Richmond, Clermont County, Ohio. Reproduced from Foerste (1914, pl. IV, fig. 4).
9	*Anomaloides reticulatus* Ulrich. Holotype. Kope? Formation (Upper Ordovician), Covington, Kentucky; FMNH UC 8820.

1
2
3
4
5
6
7
8
9

FIGURE 22-2.—Dasyclads, *Tasmanites*, and charophytes. Scale bars for figures 22-2.1, 22-2.3, and 22-2.15 equal 1 cm; scale bar for figure 22-2.2 equals 5 mm; scale bar A equals 0.5 mm and applies to figures 22-2.4 to 22-2.10; scale bar B equals 0.225 mm and applies to figures 22-2.11 to 22-2.14. Figure 22-2.1 is reproduced from Nitecki (1971, fig. 12); figure 22-2.2 is reproduced from Nitecki (1972, fig. 1); figures 22-2.4 to 22-2.10 are reproduced from Peck and Morales (1966, pls. 3 and 4); figures 22-2.11 to 22-2.14 are reproduced from Peck and Eyer (1963, pl. 100); all with permission.

1	*Ischadites abbottae* Nitecki. Each of the two specimens has about 50 lateral branches in a whorl (spiral?) radiating from the hollow center that marks the stipe. Niagaran Series (Middle Silurian), near Yellow Springs, Greene County, Ohio; AMNH 1975/1.
2	*Ischadites hemisphericus* (Hall). Reproductive bodies are visible in many of the prisms (facets) of the body. Cedarville Dolomite (Middle Silurian), Moody (or Moodie) Quarry, Wilmington, Clinton County, Ohio; FMNH UC 23753.
3	*Tasmanites* cysts scattered over split surface of block of Grassy Creek Shale (Upper Devonian), Mississippi River bluffs a short distance above Champ Clark Bridge, Pike County, Missouri; MSU FPH 10-63 BS.
4-7	*Karpinskya bilineata* (Peck). **4**, basal view, and **5**, thin section showing basal and apical openings, the thickness of the lime shell, and calcified coronula cells. UM 31029-4. **6**, apical view. UM 31029-3. **7**, side view. UM 31029-5. Snyder Creek Shale (Middle Devonian), Missouri.
8-10	*Moellerina greenei* Ulrich. **8**, basal view, **9**, side view, and **10**, top view of **neotype**. Jefferson (Onondaga) Limestone (lower Middle Devonian), Falls of the Ohio, Indiana; USNM 42079.
11-14	*Stomochara moreyi* Grambast (*Catillochara moreyi* in Peck and Eyer, 1963). **11**, thin section showing wall structure, basal plate, and distal and lateral walls of pedicel (stem) cell. UM 31028-6. **12**, side view, **13**, basal view, **14**, top view. UM 31027-10. Cherokee Group (Pennsylvanian), Boone County, Missouri.
15	Abundant charophytes, mainly specimens of *Moellerina greenei* Ulrich, on cut surface of block of Columbus Limestone (Middle Devonian) from quarry at Marblehead, Ottawa County, Ohio; MSU FPH 3-25-75 I-1. Median sections through these charophytes range from about 0.6 to 0.9 mm in diameter.

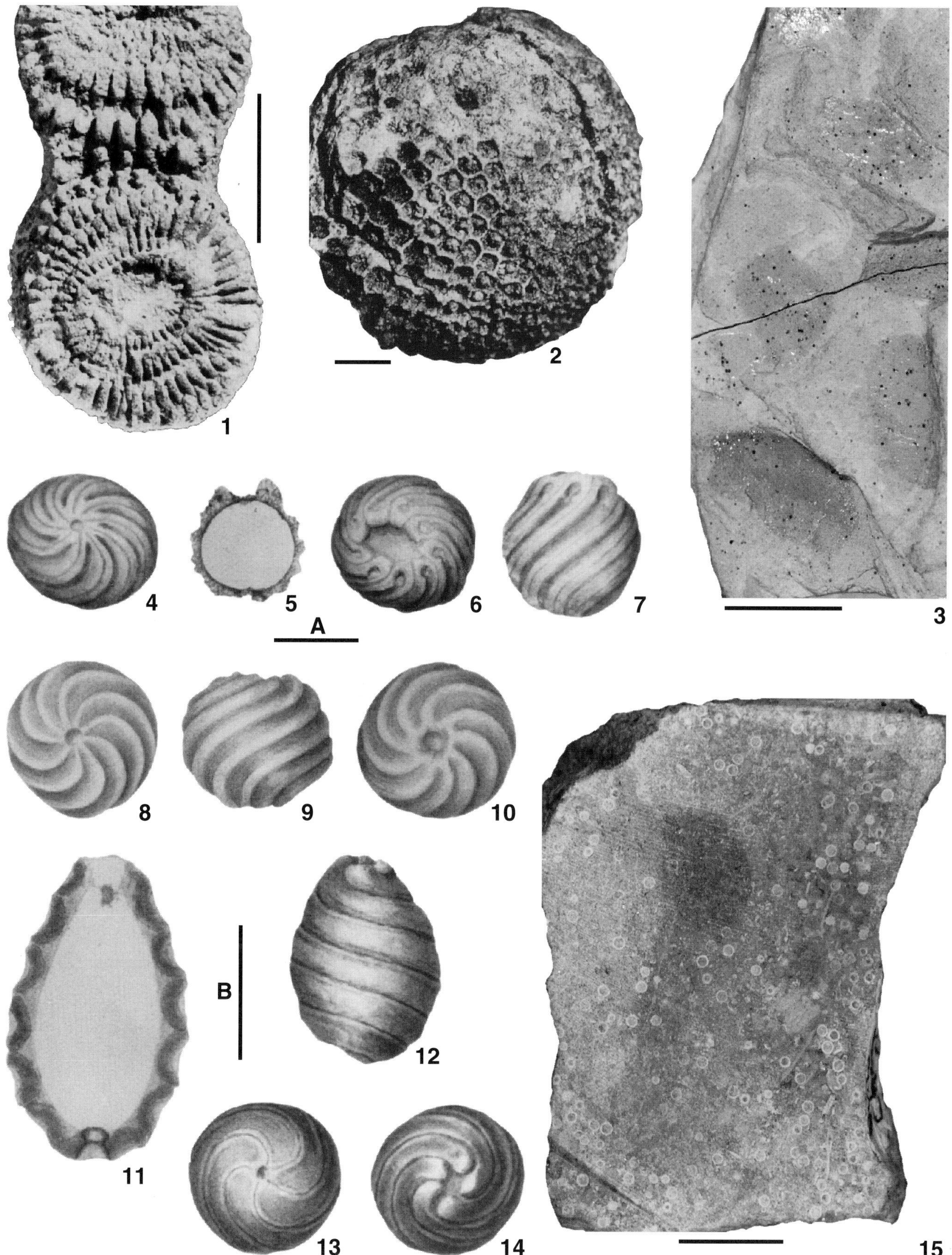
1
2
3
4
5
6
7
A
8
9
10
11
B
12
13
14
15

FIGURE 22-3.—*Protosalvinia* (*Foerstia*) and macrophytic algae. Scale bars for figures 22-3.1 and 22-3.2, 22-3.4 to 22-3.7, 22-3.9, and 22-3.10 equal 1 mm. Scale bars for figures 22-3.11 to 22-3.14 equal 2 cm. Scale bars for figures 22-3.3 and 22-3.8 are noted in descriptions. Figures 22-3.1 to 22-3.4 are reproduced from Schopf and Schwietering (1970, pl. 1, all forms identified as *Foerstia ohioensis*). Figures 22-4.5 to 22-4.9 are reproduced from Niklas and Phillips (1976, figs. 5, 8, 11, 31, and 4, respectively). Figures 22-3.10 to 22-3.12 are reproduced from White (1901, pls. XVII and XVI). Figures 22-3.13 and 22-3.14 are reproduced from Taggart and Parker (1975). All reproduced with permission.

1, 2, 4	*Protosalvinia ravenna* White & Stadnichenko. **1**, upper surface, and **2**, lower surface of a discoid form. Thallus is complete, very small (2.3 mm diameter), flattened, and has acute apical lobes. **4**, bilobed form. Ohio Shale (Upper Devonian), Bristol Ridge, Jefferson Township, Logan County, Ohio.
3, 5	*P. arnoldii* Bharadwaj & Venkatachala (= *Foerstia ohioensis* White). **3**, lower surface. Same unit and location as **1**, **2**, **4**. Scale bar equals 2 mm. **5**, bilobed form. Side view showing apical folds (ridges) surrounding fields of several tetrads. Huron Member of the Ohio Shale (Upper Devonian) just west of the intersection of Interstate 270 and U.S. Route 23, Worthington, Franklin County, Ohio.
6	*P. furcata* (Dawson). Branched form. Apical groove at arrow. Intersecting curved lines accent cellular pattern. Same unit and location as **1**, **2**, **4**.
7	Portion of large thallus with *P. ravenna* (large discoid body) in center and tips of *P. arnoldii* lobes at two arrows. Same unit and location as **3**, **5**.
8	Tetrad of spores from one conceptacle of *P. arnoldii*. Each spore is about 200 micrometers in diameter. Scale bar equals 5 micrometers. Same unit and location as **1**, **2**, **4**.
9	Upper (dorsal) side of thallus of *P. ravenna* with cluster of conceptacles. Each tetrad site is surrounded by a low rim. Same unit and location as **3**, **5**.
10	*Buthotrephis newlinii* White. Holotype. Photo tracing inset (2.6 times natural size) shows irregular **venation**. The swollen ends may be reproductive structures or floats. Eurypterid beds (Upper Silurian), Kokomo, Indiana; USNM 8175.
11, 12	*Buthotrephis speciosa* (White). Two magnifications. Small, lighter colored ovals near the tips of the lobes may be reproductive structures. Same locality and unit as **10**. In 1901 this specimen was in the collection of C. E. Newlin of Irvington, Indiana (White, 1901).
13, 14	*Thalassocystis striata* Taggart & Parker. Inflated tips are float bladders. **13**, holotype. MSU 9-10-72-I-3a. **14, paratype**. MSU 9-10-72-I-6a. Manistique Group (Middle Silurian), 3.2 km (2 miles) east of Manistique, Schoolcraft County, Michigan.

1
2
3
4
5
6
7
8
9
10
11
12
13
14

FIGURE 22-4.—Acritarchs from the Silica Formation (Middle Devonian) in the North Quarry of the Medusa Portland Cement Company (quarry owned by France Stone Company in 1996), 2.4 km (1.5 miles) north of Silica, Lucas County, Ohio. Scale bars on all figures equal 10 micrometers. All figures are reproduced from duplicate prints made by E. Reed Wicander and Gordon D. Wood (see Wicander and Wood, 1981). The depository of all samples, fossil slides, and scanning electron microscope (SEM) stubs is the Central Michigan University Museum of Paleontology, Mount Pleasant, Michigan (CMUMP and MNRW). Location coordinates of individual specimens on slides are given following the slide number.

1	*Tunisphaeridium tentaculaferum* (Martin). Slide 71-22-A-2; 38.0 x 100.2.
2	*Exochoderma arca* Wicander & Wood. Slide 71-10-A-3.
3	*Hapsidopalla chela* Wicander & Wood. Slide 71-32-A-3; 26.0 x 94.0.
4	*Tyligmasoma alargadum* (Cramer). Slide 71-10-A-3; 31.2 x 96.5.
5	*Pterospermella reticulata* Loeblich & Wicander. Slide 71-6-A-3; 34.0 x 100.2.
6	*Dictyotidium cohora* Wicander & Wood. Slide MNRW#6, +20,2; 15.2 x 101.0.
7	*Hapsidopalla invenusta* Wicander & Wood. Sample 71-24; SEM stub S-4.
8	*Exochoderma triangulata* Wicander & Wood. Slide 71-10-A-2; 26.3 x 103.0.
9	*Palacanthus ledanoisii* (Deunff). Sample 71-30; SEM stub S-6.
10	*Diexallophasis simplex* Wicander & Wood. Sample 71-23; SEM stub S-3.
11	*Multiplicisphaeridium ramusculosum* (Deflandre). Sample 71-32; SEM stub S-7.
12	*Estiastra rhytidoa* Wicander & Wood. Sample 71-13; SEM stub S-2.

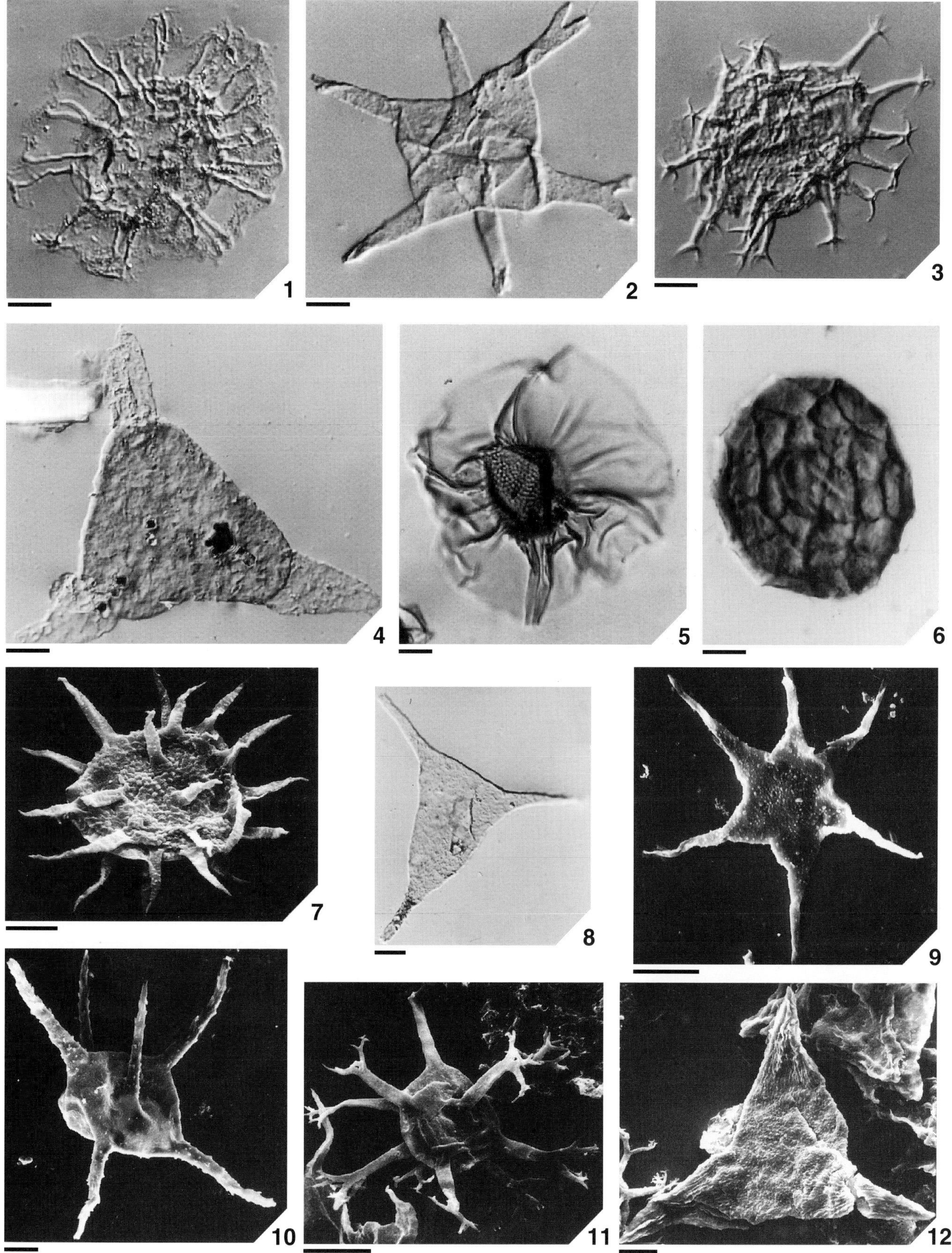
1
2
3
4
5
6
7
8
9
10
11
12

FIGURE 22-5.—*Prototaxites* Dawson, an Upper Devonian plant of uncertain affinity. Scale bars for figures 22-6.1 to 22-6.3 equal 100 micrometers; scale bar for figure 22-6.4 equals 10 mm; scale bar for figures 22-6.5 and 22-6.6 equals 60 micrometers. Figures 22-6.1 and 22-6.2 reproduced from original photographs provided by Shya Chitaley (Cleveland Museum of Natural History) and are a portion of a photograph published in Chitaley (1992, fig. 3).

1, 2 — *Prototaxites clevelandensis* Chitaley. Holotype. **1**, longitudinal section. **2**, transverse section. From a concretion in the lower part of the Cleveland Shale Member of the Ohio Shale (Upper Devonian), intersection of West 130th Street and I-71, southwestern Cleveland, Cuyahoga County, Ohio; ClMNH P-4743.

3, 4 — *Prototaxites southworthii* Arnold. **3**, transverse section of holotype showing abundant small tubes (filaments) and a paucity of large tubes. Kettle Point Shale (Upper Devonian), Kettle Point, Lambton County, Ontario; UMMP 31615. **4**, sample block (MSU collection) from holotype.

5, 6 — *Prototaxites ortonii* (Penhallow). Reproduction of illustrations from original description by D. D. Penhallow (1896). Specimen found by Orton in the Huron ("Erian") shale, probably in central Ohio near Columbus. Original specimen and locality data lost. Prepared slides are in Peter Redpath Museum at McGill University, Montreal, Québec.

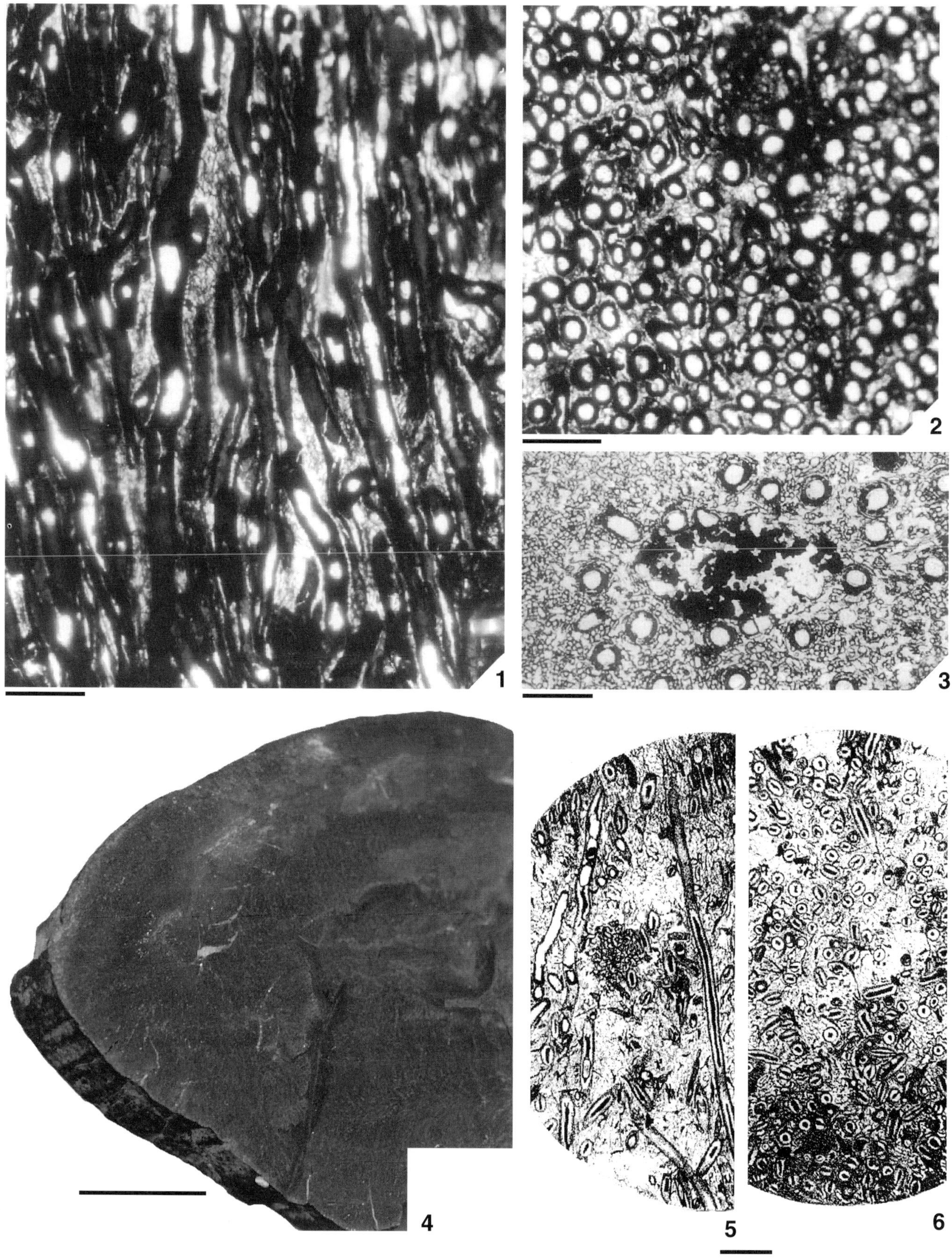
1
2
3
4
5
6

FIGURE 22-6.—Chitinozoa and *Trochophyllum*. Scale bars for figures 22-6.1 to 22-6.6 equal 20 micrometers. Scale bars for figures 22-6.7 and 22-6.8 equal 1 cm. The chitinozoa in figures 22-6.1 to 22-6.6 are from the Silica Formation (Middle Devonian) in the North Quarry of the Medusa Portland Cement Company (quarry owned by France Stone Company in 1996), 2.4 km (1.5 miles) north of Silica, Lucas County, Ohio; all SEM photos from original negatives courtesy of Gordon D. Wood and reproduced from G. D. Wood (1974) with permission. The *Trochophyllum* specimens in figures 22-6.7 and 22-6.8 are from the Cuyahoga Formation ("Waverly Sandstone") (Lower Mississippian) near Granville, Licking County, Ohio; photos by William H. Gillespie.

1 *Eisenackitina sylvaniensis* Wood. UMMP 57281-57286.

2 *Desmochitina spinosa* Wood. Holotype. UMMP 57275, slide S-18B2; SEM stub X. From Wood (1974, pl. 10, fig. 1a).

3 *Angochitina gilbertsoni* Wood. Holotype. UMMP 57266 or 57267, slide S-3, SEM stub J. From Wood (1974, pl. 1, fig. 1a).

4 *Ancyrochitina kutasii* Wood. Holotype. UMMP 57271, slide S-11, SEM stub H. From Wood (1974, pl. 5, fig. 1).

5 *Conochitina turgifunda* (Wood). UMMP 57260-57265. From Wood (1974, pl. 15, fig. 2 as *C. inflata*).

6 *Ancyrochitina doylei* Wood. Holotype. UMMP 57249. From Wood (1974, pl. 3, fig. 2a).

7 *Trochophyllum lineare* Lesquereux. Holotype. Blades rounded at point of attachment and spaced 1 mm apart up the axis. MCGM C-Pl-278. Published in Lesquereux (1880, pl. III).

8 *Trochophyllum* sp. Blades obovate to pointed, two to three times as long as wide, undivided, paired (opposite); central axis is of uniform size throughout most of length. MCGM C-Pl-277.

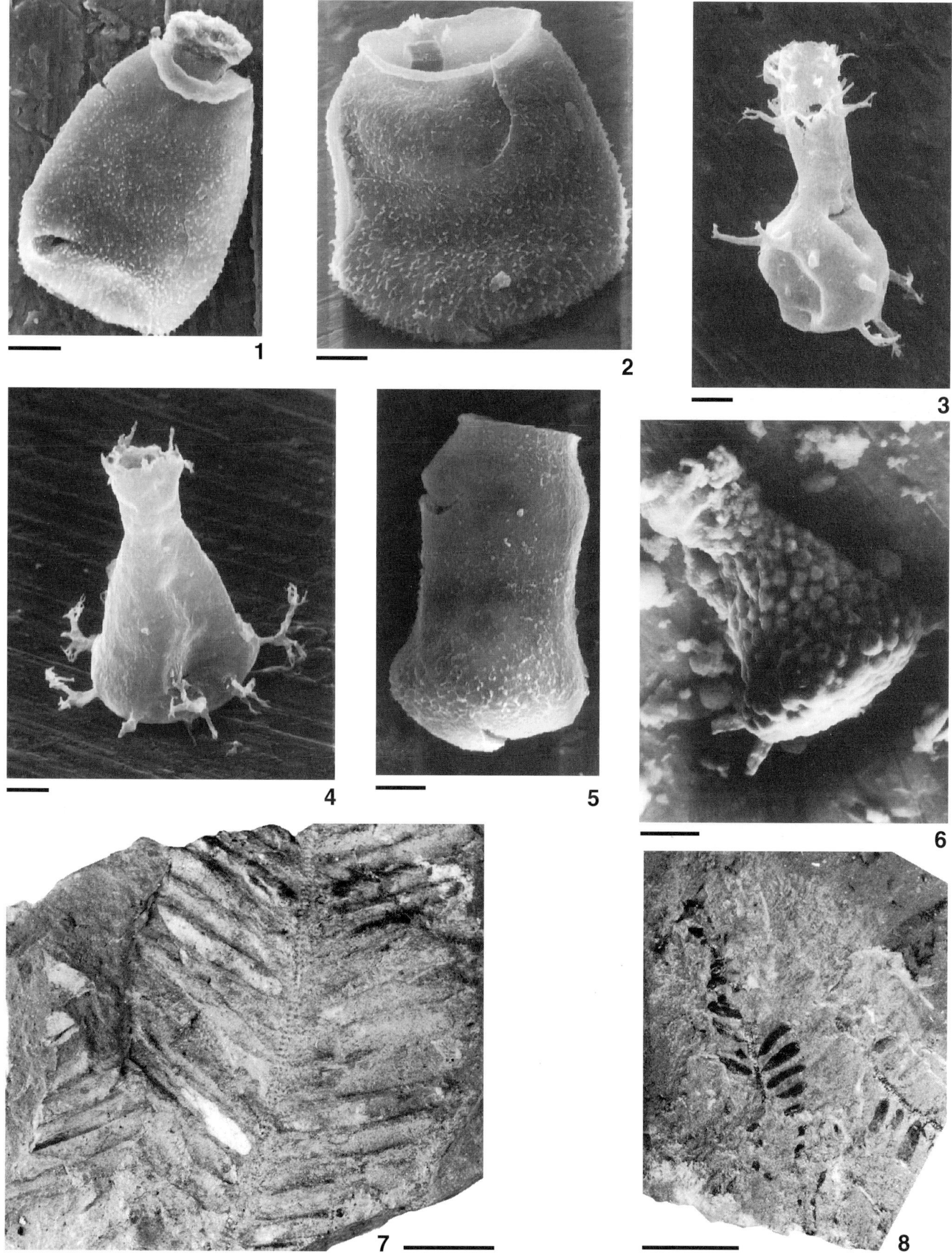
1
2
3
4
5
6
7
8

Chapter 23

UPPER PALEOZOIC VASCULAR PLANTS

by Aureal T. Cross, William H. Gillespie, and Ralph E. Taggart

INTRODUCTION

During the Pennsylvanian Coal Age (approximately equivalent to the Upper Carboniferous of Europe), the geography of Ohio was dominated by a complex mosaic of nearshore, fluvial-deltaic, and other coastal-margin environments. This setting was ideal for the burial and preservation of debris from the terrestrial lowland plant communities. So much fossil plant material has been discovered as a result of coal-mining operations in Ohio and adjacent states that, to many persons, paleobotanical research from the Appalachians to the Upper Mississippi Valley region is virtually synonymous with the study of fossil remains associated with the Pennsylvanian Coal Measures (see Lyons and others, 1995).

Most of this chapter is devoted to Ohio's Coal Age flora, but we begin with a review of fossil remains of the progymnosperms, which first appear in Upper Devonian rocks. The progymnosperms are plants thought to be ancestral to the seed ferns and conifers (**gymnosperms**).

PROGYMNOSPERMOPHYTA

Callixylon Zalessky is the name applied to fossil wood that has been found as drift logs throughout the Huron Shale Member of the Ohio Shale (Upper Devonian) and as pieces of wood in the Cleveland and Chagrin Shale Members of the Ohio Shale. Rarely, blocks of *Callixylon* wood have been found in glacial drift as far south as Dayton. *Callixylon* logs and smaller fragments also have been found in rocks of comparable age in all surrounding states and in Illinois, Arkansas, Oklahoma, New York, and Ontario.

Fossil wood identified as *Callixylon* has been demonstrated to be from the roots, woody trunk, and branches of a large, tree-size plant (fig. 23-1.1) called *Archaeopteris* Dawson (Beck, 1964), after the name applied to the leaves (fig. 23-1.2). The leaves have long been known from many localities in rocks deposited as sediments along coastal margins of Late Devonian landmasses and only rarely in sediments deposited farther offshore.

Five species of *Archaeopteris* leaves are known from the eastern United States but none have been identified from rocks in Ohio. The plants were probably growing widely on deltas or in coastal lowlands far from Ohio. Some of the dead, fallen logs were carried out to sea by marine currents, some for great distances, but the leaves probably sank to the bottom or disintegrated much nearer shore. The whole plant has been an enigma because it was so long before the relationship between *Callixylon* and *Archaeopteris* was finally demonstrated by Beck (1960, 1962).

The leafy structures of *Archaeopteris* are fernlike and bear **sporangia** and **spores** (fig. 23-1.2), and some of the internal tissues are like those of ferns. However, the **secondary xylem**, the main part of the logs, is similar to that of gymnosperms, consisting of **tracheids** (vertical conducting cells) that have clusters of circular, **bordered pits** on the radial walls. Because this group of plants is intermediate between true ferns and gymnosperms, Beck named a new group of plants, the Progymnospermopsida. Following current trends in plant classification, this group is now recognized as a division, the Progymnospermophyta (see table 22-1). One other major group of plants now generally included in the progymnosperms is the order Noeggerathiales.

A block of *Callixylon* wood found in the black Cleveland Shale Member in Cuyahoga County was described as a new species, *Callixylon clevelandensis*, by Chitaley (1988). Abundant small pieces and slivers of *Callixylon* wood are found in coarse, current-winnowed (lag) deposits at several exposures in the Cleveland vicinity. An excellent locality of this type is at the mouth of Skinners Run, where *Callixylon* wood as well as spores and vertebrate fossils recycled from the Cleveland Shale Member are found in a pyrite bed at the base of the Bedford Shale. Pieces of wood also have been found in the center of some concretions, as at Beaver Pond in Adams County (Hoskins and Blickle, 1940). Some very large logs from Ohio have been described by Arnold (1931) and by Wells (1939) (fig. 23-1.3). The longest single trunk segment of *Callixylon* known to date is 8.5 meters long and was found in Texas (Beck, 1962). The specimen of largest diameter is 1.5 meters across and is reconstructed on a campus at Ada, Oklahoma (Wilson, 1958).

Shrinkage cracks generally are present on larger branches and logs (figs. 23-1.4, 23-1.5). They are aligned both across the logs and parallel to the long axes. These cracks were caused by drying of the very homogeneous wood, much the same as the blocky shrinkage of some modern logs burned to charcoal, or like some very dry driftwood. Smaller specimens of logs and branches that have shrinkage cracks have been misinterpreted as *Calamites* (see fig. 23-11). Remains of *Callixylon* wood are most commonly in a partially flattened, **permineralized** state (fig. 23-1.5) or a nearly completely flattened, coalified condition (fig. 23-1.4). Shrinkage cracks generally are filled with silt, sand, or crystalline quartz, or in some cases with dense, granular pyrite. The filled cracks may form low ridges on **silicified** specimens (fig. 23-1.5), indicating early cementation or infilling of the cracks with less compactable sand, silt, or mud as the log lay on the sea floor and as the water-soaked log was gradually compressed. The quartz cement or infilling mud or sand in the cracks compacted less than the wood, resulting in ridges.

The specimen in figure 23-1.3 was found as 13 pieces that fit together to form a log 3.5 meters long, 18 by 53 cm in partially flattened cross section at the large end, and 13 by 36 cm at the small end. It is mainly silicified but contains considerable pyrite and has well-preserved cell structure (only secondary xylem identified). A thin, jet-black, coaly outside rind of glassy texture was originally present when the specimen was discovered. The condition of this log is fairly typical of the numerous logs found in the Upper Devonian black shales in the eastern U.S., Arkansas, Oklahoma, and Ontario.

Crinoid stems appressed against and impressed into the surface of the wood of this specimen were tentatively identified as *Melocrinus* (Wells, 1939). Two pieces of a *Callixylon* log from Adams County also had associated portions of several crinoid heads, numerous **columnals**, and **holdfasts** ("root disks") (Wells, 1941). The holdfasts were attached to the underside, indicating that the log had floated for some time before it settled into the bottom mud. Crinoid stems have been found on at least three other logs in Indiana and Ohio. These unique fossils commonly are overlooked by collectors.

Although the earliest progymnosperms are **index fossils** for the Late Devonian, several groups of progymnosperms persisted into the Pennsylvanian and Permian, but their phylogenetic relationships are poorly understood. One such group is the noeggerathians, an artificial group of plants, allied, by most workers, with the progymnosperms on the basis of the organization of their reproductive structures and the widespread occurrence of **heterospory**. One foliage genus in this group, *Plagiozamites* Zeiller (fig. 23-2.1), is the one most likely to be encountered in Upper Pennsylvanian strata in Ohio.

When Zeiller first described *Plagiozamites* in 1894, he considered it to be related to cycads (hence the reference in the name to the **extant** cycad *Zamia*). No definitive reproductive material is known, but some suggestion of possible relationships can be inferred based on the fact that *Plagiozamites*-like foliage (*Russellites* Mamay) has been found in Permian-age strata in association with a distinctive **bisporangiate** cone, *Discinites* Feistmantel. The closest analog to these cones are those of some heterosporous sphenopsids (horsetails). If the plant which produced *Plagiozamites* **fronds** bore cones of this general type, a tenuous phylogenetic link with the horsetails is indicated.

Fossils of *Plagiozamites* are found in Upper Pennsylvanian and Lower Permian strata in Ohio, West Virginia, and Pennsylvania. *Plagiozamites planchardi* (Renault) Zeiller (fig. 23-2.1) is characteristic of the genus. The fronds are **pinnate** or bipinnate, and the **pinnules** range from 4 to 7 cm long and 8 to 15 mm wide. Variation is common. The base is weakly clasping. The parallel **venation** rarely forks and averages about 25 veins per centimeter of width. The bluntly rounded tip may have weak serrations along the lateral margins.

PENNSYLVANIAN COAL-SWAMP COMMUNITIES

During Pennsylvanian time, much of eastern Ohio consisted of nearly flat terrain along ancient coastal margins. These ancient shorelines were located within a few degrees of the Equator, and the humid climate and extensive freshwater and brackish-water swamps encouraged the proliferation of lush vegetation. These swamps, commonly undisturbed for hundreds or even thousands of years, accumulated thick layers of plant debris. The material shed or washed into the swamps consisted of a wide range of plant parts, including microscopic spores, leaves, assorted reproductive structures, slabs of barklike material, limbs and branches, and even whole tree trunks. Through chemical and biological degradation, the buried debris was transformed into **peat**.

When nearby rivers flooded or the sea inundated the coastal **marshes** and **swamps**, the peat was covered with layers of mud and sand transported by the rivers, coastal currents, or storm surges. When the waters retreated, plants became re-established on the new, barren surfaces, and swamps would develop again. These irregular cycles of peat, mud, marl, and sand deposition commonly were repeated many times at a specific site. Later, through a variety of physical processes, including compaction and heat, and chemical and biological changes (**diagenesis**), the buried peat was gradually transformed into coal. The coal beds are separated by intervening limestones, mudstones, shales, and sandstones.

Although the fossil remains of Pennsylvanian plants may be found in most lithologies, they are typically better preserved and most abundant in the **roof rock** of the coal beds or as masses of permineralized peat (**coal balls**) in the coal itself. The roof rocks are typically gray shales resulting from the consolidation of muds and silts deposited with each episode of flooding or marine inundation. The influx of mud and sand commonly was so rapid that whole trees were buried in place. The **casts** or **molds** of some of these tree trunks may extend several feet upward into the roof rocks overlying the coal (see figs. 23-7.2, 23-7.4).

The terrestrial plants that formed the Pennsylvanian coal-swamp communities and associations on surrounding lowlands during Pennsylvanian time are mainly representative of three divisions of spore-bearing vascular plants: the lycopods (Lycophyta), the horsetails (Sphenophyta), and the true ferns (Pteridophyta), and two divisions of seed-bearing plants: the seed ferns (Pteridospermophyta), and conifers (Coniferophyta). Pennsylvanian coniferophytes include two major orders: the Cordaitales and the Voltziales, the earliest of the true conifers. Together, these six plant groups constitute virtually all of the swamp and coastal vegetation of the Pennsylvanian Period.

The discussion of Upper Paleozoic vascular plants in this chapter is based on these major groups. Both episodic and continuous evolution can be recognized within most of these groups from the Late Mississippian through the Early Permian. Plants that can be recognized at the species level may be used for biostratigraphic zonation. The rocks of this interval have a cumulative thickness of at least 1,000 meters in eastern Ohio. Extensive coal mining in Ohio and the greater Appalachian region has provided particular insight into the plants of the swamp (peat/coal-forming) communities. These plants evolved rather slowly, as they are rather specialized and occupied habitats that were stable over extended periods of time. To facilitate the identification of the major leaf and stem **taxa** of the coal-swamp flora, two keys are included following the discussion of coal balls.

In contrast to the well-documented flora of the coastal swamps, the plants of more inland and upland areas are poorly known. It is generally accepted that the peat-forming swamps were conservative environments, buffered from minor climatic oscillations, where evolution occurred at a slow pace. In contrast, drier and ecologically more stressful environments higher on the ancient coastal plain may have been the sites for adaptive radiation of new plant groups, such as the earliest true conifers (Voltziales). According to this view, such advanced plants appear in the fossil record of swamp environments somewhat later than their actual time of evolutionary origin. The relatively poor fossil record of presumed inland/upland taxa makes this a difficult hypothesis to test.

COAL BALLS

Coal balls are masses of permineralized peat that formed after the peat was buried by sediments that later formed the sandstone, shale, or limestone overlying a coal bed. Certain zones or local spots in the peat became infiltrated with minerals from ground water, perhaps by downward circulation from waters which drowned the peat swamp (during rising sea level) or from springs below the peat bed. The minerals that preserve the balls or masses of peat are generally calcite, dolomite, or pyrite. The plant matter preserved in the balls is an intermingled, generally somewhat layered arrangement, and is very little flattened, indicating very early permineralization. The state of decay of plant material in individual coal balls is highly variable and may be correlated with the position in the coal seam. Decay may be extensive, as if the plant matter had been in later stages of peat accumulation when permineralized or had become oxidized as a consequence of exposure and drying due to a lowering of the water table. In other instances, the plant tissues and organs are very little modified. Cells, cell contents, and very delicate structures commonly are found. Some of the tissues are better preserved than others, but in many coal balls the tissue arrangement and structure are essentially unmodified.

Some of the plants are so well preserved that careful study of serial (successive) sections may reveal organ attachment as well. From these studies we can generally relate some of the detached permineralized organs to **compression** or **impression** fossils. Because the original peat deposit was formed from the various parts of plants actually in place where they grew, the study of coal balls can provide insight into the composition of local coal-swamp communities. The relative proportion of the peat mass comprising organs from major plant groups provides the principal means to estimate the quantitative or ecological importance of each group in the swamp community and their contribution to the origin and constitution of coal.

Plant organs, especially stems, roots, and various **fructifications**, may be identified on broken surfaces of coal balls. These plant structures generally are better observed by cutting serial sections through the permineralized plant mass with a rock saw and analyzing the cut and polished surfaces (see fig. 23-14.2), or by preparing **thin sections** or **acetate peels** (see figs. 23-2.2, 23-2.3, and 23-14.6), as described in Chapter 2. Figure 23-2.2, from a coal ball at a road cut west of Steubenville, represents a broken surface that exposed a pair of pinnules of the seed fern *Alethopteris* Sternberg. These two pinnules were first exposed by splitting the coal ball along the bedding plane (equivalent to an old peat surface), then making an acetate peel. Venation, hairs, and other anatomical features are clearly visible. Figure 23-2.3 illustrates cross-sectional views of numerous pinnules as well as a small seed.

Some coal balls consist largely of permineralized wood. Figure 23-2.4 is a reconstruction of a small portion of the trunk of the tree fern *Psaronius* Cotta. These trunks are principally a mantle of aerial **adventitious roots** surrounding the true stem. The roots originate just below the crown of leaves and grow down the trunk to the ground. As new roots develop and grow down over and among the earlier roots, the trunk is enlarged by the continuous accumulation of roots, forming a mantle of roots or false trunk. Other fern species may become established in this mantle, growing as **epiphytes**, their roots penetrating between and intermingling with the adventitious roots of *Psaronius*.

The reconstruction in figure 23-2.4 also illustrates the importance of coal-ball studies in demonstrating organic connections of plant organs. Two large, multiply **dissected** fronds of the small epiphytic fern *Botryopteris forensis* Renault have developed on the *Psaronius* trunk. Globose fructifications replace pinnules in places on these fronds. Two plants in enrolled stage (croziers) are just emerging from the root mantle of *Psaronius*. The stem (**rachis**) of the *Botryopteris* frond extends out through the new layers of aerial roots. Rothwell (1991) worked out the anatomy of these plants by studying acetate peels of serial sections, which enabled him to trace each of the stems of the epiphytic *Botryopteris* from their rootlike beginnings to the base of the fronds at the surface of the mantle of aerial roots of the host *Psaronius* trunk.

Coal balls have been found at several locations in eastern Ohio. The most widely studied is the Steubenville locality in Wayne Township, Jefferson County (fig. 23-3; locality described on p. 419). Coal-ball masses near the top of the exposure (fig. 23-3.1) at the position of the Duquesne coal (fig. 23-3.2) continue to weather away, and many coal balls (figs. 23-3.3, 23-3.4) break loose and roll down the slope, where they can be safely collected near the bottom and in the ditch. A slightly older layer of coal balls is found in the "Ames coal" (possibly the Harlem coal) below the Ames limestone at this locality. These coal balls are not as abundant as the Duquesne coal balls and the plant remains are less well preserved.

The Steubenville coal-ball flora is one of the most well-studied peat-forming floristic communities of Pennsylvanian plants. Five major groups of plants—lycopods, horsetails, true ferns, seed ferns, and cordaites—are known from this mid-Conemaugh-age (Late Pennsylvanian) locality. At least 25 natural species, derived from the more than 55 **macrofossil** taxa of leaves, stems, fructifications, etc., are now known mainly from the Duquesne coal (Rothwell, 1988a) and from the thinner coal below the Ames limestone.

Another important coal-ball locality in Jefferson County is near the mouth of Yellow Creek in Saline Township. Here the coal balls are exposed in several masses at or near road level in the Upper Freeport (No. 7) coal (Allegheny Group).

A coal-ball locality in the Anderson coal (Conemaugh Group) in an abandoned strip mine near Bloomfield, Muskingum County, is no longer open, but some material may still be found by excavating in old coal-mine dumps. Pigg and Rothwell (1983) described a new lycopod genus, *Chaloneria*, from specimens found at this locality.

KEY TO SOME PENNSYLVANIAN FOSSIL-LEAF COMPRESSIONS FROM OHIO

1A. Leaves in **whorls** 2
1B. Leaves not in whorls 4

2A. Leaves narrowly to broadly wedge shaped; veins fork .... *Sphenophyllum* (figs. 23-10.1 to 23-10.8)
2B. Leaves linear; each has one central, unforked vein 3

3A. Leaves in spokelike whorls that are typically flat .... *Annularia* (fig. 23-12)
3B. Leaves cup upward around stem, always attached .... *Asterophyllites* (figs. 23-13.2 to 23-13.4)

4A. Leaflike structure irregularly lobed or split into complicated tufts .... *Aphlebia* (fig. 23-22.2)
4B. Leaf or pinnule clearly defined 5

5A. Leaves or leaf fragments thin and grasslike or broad and straplike 6
5B. Leaves or leaf fragments not grasslike or straplike but resemble fern pinnules 10

6A. Leaves or leaf fragments thin and grasslike, generally broken .... *Cyperites* (fig. 23-6.1)
6B. Leaves broader and straplike 7

7A. Leaves **simple** 8
7B. Leaves **compound** 9

8A. Midvein indistinct, veins longitudinally aligned .... *Cordaites* (figs. 23-25.7, 23-29.1 to 23-29.3)
8B. Midvein distinct, veins perpendicular to margin .... *Taeniopteris* (figs. 23-27.3, 23-27.4)

9A. Leaves **palmately** compound, leaflets generally deeply **bifurcated** .... *Megalopteris* (figs. 23-24.3 to 23-24.6)
9B. Leaves pinnately compound, leaflets not bifurcated .... *Protoblechnum* (figs. 23-26.4, 23-26.5)

10A. Pinnule margins not distinctly lobed or **toothed** 11
10B. Pinnules distinctly lobed or toothed 22

11A. Pinnules attached at a single point, base may be **cordate** 12
11B. Pinnules broadly attached, base never cordate 15

12A. Pinnules subcircular to circular, generally 0.5-4 cm long, but may be up to 10 cm long .... *Cyclopteris* (figs. 23-21.6, 23-23.1, 23-23.2)
12B. Pinnules not subcircular to circular 13

13A. Veins coalesced into a mesh .... *Linopteris* (figs. 23-18.3, 23-23.8)
13B. Veins fork repeatedly but do not touch or coalesce into a mesh 14

14A. **Pinnae** have a double terminal pinnule, pinnules scythe shaped .... *Paripteris* (fig. 23-25.7)
14B. Pinnae have a single terminal pinnule, pinnules not scythe shaped .... *Neuropteris* (figs. 23-20.1, 23-25.1, 23-25.2, 23-25.6, 23-25.7) or closely allied genera, distinguished by **cuticular** differences

15A. More than one vein enters pinnule base of fully developed pinnules 16
15B. Single vein enters pinnule base of fully developed pinnules 21

16A. **Intercalated** pinnules or short pinnae present on main rachis between secondary rachises 17
16B. No intercalated pinnules 20

17A. Pinnules scythe shaped; intercalated pinnules half rounded; some veins may touch .... *Lescuropteris* (figs. 23-23.6, 23-23.7)

17B. Pinnules not scythe shaped; intercalated pinnules resemble regular pinnules; veins never touch 18

18A. Fronds have multiple tips; midvein strong, sunken; lateral veins thick, straight, single or forked only once .... *Autunia* (fig. 23-22.1)

18B. Fronds have single tip (**monopodial** apex); midvein not sunken; lateral veins thin, at least some fork more than once 19

19A. Lateral veins fork two to five times (usually two to three); pinnules commonly markedly **decurrent**; intercalated pinnules commonly prolonged and lobed .... *Rhachiphyllum* (fig. 23-22.4)

19B. Lateral veins generally fork once, or in some cases twice; pinnules generally not markedly decurrent; intercalated pinnules rarely lobed .... *Callipteridium* (fig. 23-22.3)

20A. Midvein absent; veins or forks run length of pinnule .... *Odontopteris* (figs. 23-26.1, 23-26.3)

20B. Midvein present; lateral veins more or less perpendicular to midvein .... *Alethopteris* (fig. 23-21)

21A. Base of pinnules generally somewhat constricted (**fertile** pinnules, if present, resemble sow bugs) .... *Danaeides* (figs. 23-16.1, 23-16.3)

21B. Base of pinnules not constricted 22

22A. Pinnules have essentially parallel sides, not decurrent .... *Pecopteris* (figs. 23-15.2, 23-16.4, 23-17.4 to 23-17.6, 23-18.3 to 23-18.5, 23-18.7)

22B. Pinnules somewhat triangular, leathery; basal pinnule on lower side of pinnae generally larger and bilobed .... *Mariopteris* (figs. 23-24.1, 23-24.2) and related genera distinguished by frond organization

23A. Pinnules split into narrow, linear segments consisting of a central vein bordered by a very narrow strip of leaf blade .... *Palmatopteris* (fig.23-26.6)

23B. Pinnules not split into narrow segments 24

24A. Pinnules small, commonly basally fused; three or more prominent teeth at tip, a veinlet fork goes to each tooth .... *Alloiopteris* (figs. 23-15.3, 23-15.4, 23-15.6 to 23-15.8)

24B. Pinnules not toothed as above 25

25A. Midvein absent, veins fork **dichotomously**; pinnules irregularly toothed or lobed .... *Eremopteris* (fig. 23-23.4)

25B. Midvein discernible for at least half of pinnule length, pinnules variously lobed, base constricted or stalked..... *Sphenopteris* (figs. 23-19, 23-20.1, 23-20.2)

KEY TO SOME PENNSYLVANIAN FOSSIL STEMS FROM OHIO

1A. Stem has evident **nodes** (joints); area between nodes (**internodes**) vertically grooved 2

1B. Stem without evident nodes 3

2A. Stems thin (1 mm-1 cm), nodes swollen .... *Sphenophyllum* (figs. 23-10.1 to 23-10.6)

2B. Stems wider (2-30 cm), nodes not swollen .... *Calamites* (figs. 23-11.2 to 23-11.7)

3A. Stem generally less than 5 cm wide and has closely spaced transverse (encircling) lines .... *Artisia* (fig. 23-29.4)

3B. Stem without closely spaced transverse lines 4

4A. Stem has sharp, triangular projections resembling spines .... *Neuropteris* (fig. 23-25.5)

4B. Stem without such projections 5

5A. Stem without clearly defined leaf and/or branch scars 6

5B. Stem has well-defined leaf and/or branch scars 7

6A. Stem generally less than 4 cm wide, smooth, may be irregularly **striated** .... pteridosperm or fern axis (not assignable to genus or species) (figs. 23-20.5, 23-25.5)
6B. Stem generally larger; surface irregularly fluted or has rounded ridges .... *Knorria* (**decorticated** *Lepidodendron*) (fig. 23-5.2)

7A. Stem 6-25 cm wide, has circular, depressed scars; ribbonlike "rootlets" may be attached at some or all scars .... *Stigmaria* (figs. 23-9.1, 23-9.4, 23-9.5)
7B. Stem has flat or raised scars 8

8A. Scars are or appear to be in vertical rows 9
8B. Scars in ascending spirals 10

9A. Scars angular to ellipsoidal, commonly on vertical ridges .... *Sigillaria* (figs. 23-7.2 to 23-7.4, 23-8.1)
9B. Scars oval to oval-elongate, in pairs; not on vertical ridges .... *Syringodendron* (figs. 23-8.2, 23-8.3)

10A. Scars small, oval to ellipsoidal, not closely adjacent or touching 11
10B. Scars rhomboidal, angled, closely adjacent, generally touching 12

11A. Thin, wavy, horizontal or vertical lines present on surface between scars but do not form a definite pattern .. *Bothrodendron* (fig. 23-5.3)
11B. Lines on surface between scars form herringbone pattern .... *Asolanus* (fig. 23-7.1)

12A. Scars higher than wide .... *Lepidodendron* (figs. 23-4.5, 23-5.1)
12B. Scars wider than high .... *Lepidophloios* (figs. 23-4.3, 23-4.4)

LYCOPHYTA—THE LYCOPODS

Lycopods (Division Lycophyta) are spore-bearing vascular land plants that have scalelike to grasslike, spirally arranged leaves (fig. 23-4.1). Spores (see section on plant reproduction on p. 410) typically are produced in terminal **strobili** or cones, derived from modified branchlets and leaves. Lycopods are dichotomously branched (each branch point results in a pair of equal-sized branches), a branching mode characteristic of several of the earliest land plants but uncommon among today's vascular plants. Modern lycopods are typically small, inconspicuous plants classified in three genera, *Lycopodium*, *Selaginella*, and *Isoetes*.

Lycopods were the first modern group to have evolved from the early land plants. Although the earliest lycopods of the Devonian were **herbaceous**, much like *Lycopodium* or *Selaginella*, which are still found in Ohio woodlands, one lineage evolved rapidly in size, reaching treelike proportions by Late Devonian time. These **arborescent** lycopods dominated the Coal Age swamp forests of Ohio, reaching heights of 12 to 30 meters or more. Some Pennsylvanian lycopods were unbranched, others demonstrated several orders of simple dichotomous branching (fig. 23-4.1). The largest lycopod recorded to date is a specimen of *Lepidodendron aculeatum* Sternberg recovered from the roof shales of a mine in the British Isles. The main trunk is 34.7 meters long and had dichotomous, leaf-bearing branches extending for another 6 meters. *Lepidodendron aculeatum* (fig. 23-4.5) is commonly found in Ohio. Lycopod trunks having diameters over 1 meter are not rare, and specimens up to 1.2 meters in diameter have been collected in Ohio and West Virginia (figs. 23-7.2, 23-7.4, 23-8.3). Repeated branching at short intervals resulted in densely clustered crowns of short branches (one-fourth to one-fifth of the total height of the plant). The leaves of modern lycopods are small and scalelike, but the arborescent lycopods of ancient Ohio were clothed in a dense mantle of spirally arranged, grasslike leaves. In most species the leaves were from one to a few centimeters in length (figs. 23-4.6, 23-5.5), but in some forms the leaves were up to 1 meter long.

Some of these plants grew to treelike stature in a way that was quite different from that of modern trees. Instead of a dense woody trunk, these plants had a central **vascular cylinder**, 1 to 10 cm in diameter, that contained the only wood and a tiny central **pith**. The outer zone of the trunk consisted of a multiple-layered, tough, barklike rind called **periderm** (fig. 23-4.1). Between these two zones was a thick zone of thin-walled, water-filled **cortex**. The trunk, with its periderm casing and inner, water-filled cortex and vascular cylinder, may have grown quite rapidly. These swamp plants certainly depended on abundant water to retain the rigidity required to support the tree-sized stems. The peat that accumulated in the swamp forests contained large quantities of lycopod periderm. Some coal beds, known as paper coals, are composed almost entirely of periderm material.

The decay-resistant sheets of periderm are covered with rhomboidal (diamond-shaped) or circular leaf cushions or bolsters on the outer surface that were probably masses of corky tissue remaining when the leaves became detached. The inner surface of the periderm may show scars of a similar nature, but some are more precise and others are less precise. Leaf cushions provide one basis for the differentiation of the three major groups of arborescent lycopods known from the Coal Age rocks of Ohio: *Lepidodendron* (figs. 23-4.5, 23-5.1, 23-5.2), *Lepidophloios* (figs. 23-4.3, 23-4.4), and *Sigillaria* (figs. 23-7.3, 23-8.1 to 23-8.3). The lycopods also are represented by common fossils such as detached leaves (fig. 23-6.1) and twigs with leaves still attached (fig. 23-4.6), spore-bearing cones (figs. 23-6.1, 23-6.3, 23-9.3), cone scales (fig. 23-9.2), and the dispersed spores (figs. 23-6.5 to 23-6.7) produced in the cones.

The "roots" of the various arborescent lycopods are all quite similar and are assigned to the genus *Stigmaria* (figs. 23-4.1, 23-9.1, 23-9.4, 23-9.5). *Stigmaria* is one of the most common Coal Age plant fossils in Ohio and elsewhere, especially in the clays that are present below most coal seams. Stigmarian axes are dichotomously branched, like the aerial stems, and must have spread out on or just below the surface of the swamp peat and mud flats. The stigmarian casts are covered by spirally arranged, small, circular scars (fig. 23-9.4), the points of former attachment of the tubelike or ribbonlike "rootlets" (fig. 23-9.5), which extended into the surrounding peat or clay like bristles on a bottle brush. The terms "root" and "rootlet" are in quotation marks because, in the case of the arborescent lycopods, such structures are not roots at all! Rather, the "roots" are modified stems, and the "rootlets" are modified, tubelike leaves adapted to absorb water and dissolved minerals from the soil. In a very real sense, the more we know about these plants, the more odd they appear in comparison with more familiar types. These odd features may be explained, in part, by theories that the lycopods represent a lineage that originated completely independently of the common origin of other vascular plants. If they do, in fact, have a completely unique evolutionary origin, their peculiarities with respect to other plants are less surprising than they might otherwise be.

Although the arborescent lycopods dominated the swamp forests for much of the Coal Age, their dependence on copious supplies of water may have been their undoing. There was an abrupt decline in the importance of these plants in the latest Pennsylvanian. This decline has been linked to a slight drying of the global climate at that time. During the Permian, the group was subjected to large-scale extinction, and it has long been thought that the last of the arborescent lycopods became extinct during the Mesozoic. It turns out, however, that they may not be completely extinct after all. Some botanists have proposed that the quillwort (*Isoetes*), a small, inconspicuous, and rare swamp plant today, is actually a survivor of this group, despite its diminutive size. Studies (Rothwell, 1984; Rothwell and Erwin, 1985) of stigmarian root development by Ohio University researchers serve to support this theory.

UPPER DEVONIAN LYCOPOD CONES

Outcrops of the Upper Devonian Cleveland Shale Member of the Ohio Shale have yielded only a small number of larger plant fossils, but these include lycopod cones (strobili). Some very good specimens were collected at a few sites during the construction of Interstate Route 71 southwest of Cleveland in 1971. Excavation at the intersection of West 130th Street and I-71 yielded several lycopod stems and cones (fig. 23-4.2), which Chitaley noted in a preliminary report (1982).

ARBORESCENT LYCOPOD STEMS

Lepidodendron Sternberg (fig. 23-4.1) is the name given to trunk and limb casts or molds of large and small arborescent and shrubby lycopods that exhibit leaf bases in vertically ascending spirals. On smaller limbs and twigs, these leaf bases or cushions are somewhat reminiscent of scales, a feature that has led some miners to mistakenly identify them as snakes. The common name "scale tree" probably reflects a similar misunderstanding.

The leaf cushion is in part the expanded leaf base, left behind after leaf detachment (abscission). Leaves did not continue to grow on the mature trunk, and lateral trunk growth generally obliterated or greatly distorted the existing cushions. Consequently, leaf cushions are generally absent or not evident in basal portions of the tree. The cross-sectional anatomy of *Lepidodendron* trunks, described from specimens found in coal balls, shows that most of the trunk was cortex and barklike material (periderm) instead of wood. It is probable that such trees could have been felled with just a few well-placed cuts from a machete were they still living in the swamps today.

The crown of *Lepidodendron* consisted of branching limbs and twigs bearing leaves (figs. 23-4.6, 23-5.5), which ranged from about 1 cm to more than 100 cm in length. The branching was always more or less equal (dichotomous) and once branching started, at 10 to 40 meters, it continued until the growing tip became too small for effective division. This growth is conjectured to have required only a short period of time.

Cones bearing spores were borne at the tips of the smaller branches. Underground rootlike organs that had smooth tubelike "rootlets" anchored the plant and absorbed the water and minerals necessary for plant growth. *Lepidodendron* occupied the wetter areas in the swamp.

Lepidodendron aculeatum Sternberg (fig. 23-4.5), a common fossil in the lower two-thirds of the Pennsylvanian, is characterized by spindle-shaped leaf bases that are three to four times higher than wide and have the greatest diameter at or just above the middle. The upper and lower ends commonly are drawn out and curved, giving the cushion an S-shaped appearance. The leaf scar is located near but slightly above the center of the cushion and is somewhat circular. The vascular scar may be visible; **parichnos** (aerating tissue) scars (fig. 23-4.1) are rarely visible.

Lepidodendron obovatum Sternberg (fig. 23-5.1), is similar to *L. aculeatum* but the leaf bases are more or less rhomboidal and only slightly higher than wide, the tips curve only slightly if at all, and the leaf scar is located approximately three-fourths of the way up the cushion.

Several names have been used for decorticated *Lepidodendron* stems. Deeply decorticated stems that have an irregularly fluted surface have been named *Knorria* Sternberg (fig. 23-5.2). This name has been retained for general descriptive purposes. The name *Aspidaria* Presl has been applied to specimens that have less extensive decortication. Specimens in which only the epidermis has been lost have been called *Bergeria* Presl.

Lepidophloios Sternberg (figs. 23-4.3, 23-4.4) is another genus of arborescent lycopods that has grasslike leaves, leaf cushions in vertical spirals, and *Stigmaria* as the underground system. The leaf bases are wider than high, the leaf scar appears to be near the bottom, and each cushion slightly overlaps the next lower one. The cones were borne on specialized, leafless axes located some distance behind the branch tip. Neither the leaves nor the rootlike axes, when found detached, can be distinguished from those of *Lepidodendron* unless diagnostic cellular detail is preserved. *Lepidophloios laricinus* Sternberg has leaf cushions that are up to two times as wide as high. *Lepidophloios* is not nearly as common as *Lepidodendron* in Ohio strata, but appears to have had similar ecological requirements.

Bothrodendron Lindley & Hutton (fig. 23-5.3) is an arborescent lycopod that grew up to 10 meters or more in height. It had a stout stem, a crown of branches, small **lanceolate** leaves, and may have looked somewhat like *Lepidophloios*. It differed, however, in having circular leaf scars borne almost flush on the surface of the stem, in contrast to being borne on raised cushions, and having wavy vertical or horizontal lines between scars. This genus had grasslike leaves, reproduced by spores borne in cones, and had a *Stigmaria*-type base.

Ulodendron Lindley & Hutton (fig. 23-5.4) is a form genus for arborescent lycopod stems bearing **oppositely** arranged, circular to elliptical scars that may range up to 14 cm or more in diameter. The origin of these scars is unclear. Although they may represent **vegetative** branch scars, it is more probable that they are the scars of cone-bearing branches. Similar scars have been documented on specimens of *Lepidodendron*, *Lepidophloios*, and *Bothrodendron*. *Ulodendron* may represent a unique group of lycopods, or the fossils could be derived from other known genera.

Sigillaria Brongniart (figs. 23-7.2 to 23-7.4, 23-8.1 to 23-8.3) is the generic name of a group of arborescent lycopods that have columnar trunks that were unbranched or had only a few branches. Several subgenera have been recognized on the basis of the pattern of ribbing on the periderm surface. The somewhat hexagonal leaf scars occur in vertically aligned rows, separated by linear grooves. The apparent vertical alignment of the scars is an illusion created by the vertical periderm ridges, as the leaf scars, like those of all arborescent lycopods, are spirally arranged.

The linear leaves of *Sigillaria* could exceed a meter in length. Neither the dispersed leaves nor the "root" axes can be distinguished from those of other arborescent lycopods unless diagnostic cellular detail is preserved. The cones were borne on short axes interspersed among the lower leaves. *Sigillaria* is believed to have grown on somewhat drier sites not far from the wetter swamps that supported stands of other arborescent lycopods.

The specimen identified as *Sigillaria brardii* Brongniart in figure 23-7.3 has elliptical-appearing, closely packed leaf bases on unribbed stems. The specimen may be *S. ichthyolepis* Brongniart. *Sigillaria brardii* is found in Upper Pennsylvanian strata and is the most commonly found arborescent lycopod in the Pennsylvanian-Permian Dunkard Group.

Sigillaria schlotheimiana Brongniart (fig. 23-8.1) is characterized by scars that are more or less six sided and have sharp to slightly rounded lateral angles. The scars are in vertical ranks and somewhat distinct from one another. A distinctive tuftlike plume may occur above each scar, although this structure is not visible on every scar.

Asolanus Wood (fig. 23-7.1), another stem genus of arborescent lycopods, was seldom branched. The leaf scars are rhomboidal, have sharp lateral angles, and contain, when well-preserved, a large circular to oval vascular scar. *Asolanus* appears to be closely related to *Sigillaria*. The trunk surface around each scar has a pattern of parallel lines between diagonally adjacent cushions resembling a herringbone pattern. Grasslike, linear leaves and a stigmarian "root" system also are characteristic of this genus. *Asolanus camptotaenia* Wood is not common but has been found in Allegheny and Conemaugh strata.

The outermost surface of sigillarian trunks commonly is eroded or otherwise lost before the plant is preserved as a fossil. *Syringodendron* Sternberg (figs. 23-8.2, 23-8.3) is a form genus generally representing partially decorticated lower portions of the trunk. In this condition, the ends of the parichnos strands are exposed (see fig. 23-4.1). They follow a vertical path in the outer part of the stem and turn 90° to pass through the leaf cushion. This tangential view of the scars shows part of the vertical path and the scars therefore appear as vertical rows of large, double elliptical scars.

ARBORESCENT LYCOPOD LEAVES

Cyperites Lindley & Hutton (fig. 23-6.1) is the name given to detached, grasslike, parallel-sided leaves of arborescent lycopods that can't be identified as belonging to a particular genus. When the identity of the source plant is known the names *Lepidophyllum* Brongniart, *Lepidophylloides* Snigirevskaya, *Sigillariophyllum* Grand 'Eury, and others are used. Although the name *Lepidophyllum* was widely used in the paleobotanical literature, it had previously been used for an extant genus of Compositae prior to Brongniart's (1828-1838) description and, according to the Code of Botanical Nomenclature, it should not be applied to fossil lycopod leaves. *Lepidophylloides* (Snigirevskaya, 1958) has priority for valid application to detached or dispersed *Lepidodendron* leaves. These leaves varied in size; the longest ones generally were borne on stems that had not yet forked and the smallest ones were on the last-formed twigs in the crown of the mature plant. The leaves on undivided stems are up to 1.3 meters in length and 6 mm wide at the base to less than 5 mm long by 1 mm wide on the terminal branches.

Cyperites has a prominent, central, unbranched vein. In addition, there are two rows of **stomata** on the lower surface, one on either side of the vein, which may or may not be visible, depending on the preservation and the angle from which the fossil is viewed. Consequently, *Cyperites* fossils may exhibit one, two or three prominent longitudinally aligned lines.

ARBORESCENT LYCOPOD CONES

Lepidostrobus Brongniart (figs. 23-4.2, 23-6.1, 23-6.3) is the name used for cones (strobili) borne at the tips of the branches of *Lepidodendron*. There are several species, ranging from less than 2 cm to at least 36 cm in length; a length of 3 to 20 cm is more typical. Each cone has a central axis on which cone leaves (**sporophylls**) are arranged in an ascending spiral; the base of each cone leaf is overlapped by one or more from below. The upper surface of each sporophyll bore a sporangium near the base, and commonly the outside part of the sporophyll near the upward bend was extended downward as a heel. Some cones were heterosporous, having male and female spores in different sporangia. Some species produced bisexual cones (both types of sporangia borne on the same cone); others were unisexual, containing **megaspores** or **microspores** (figs. 23-6.5 to 23-6.7). The specimen of *Lepidostrobus* in figure 23-6.3 has widely flared broad sporophylls. The specimen in figure 23-6.1 has tightly appressed sporophylls.

Lepidostrobophyllum (Hirmer) Allen is a name applied to individual detached (dispersed) cone scales (fig. 23-6.2) or sporophylls of *Lepidostrobus*. The specimen of *Lepidostrobophyllum* in figure 23-5.6 is a **sporangiophore**, but because of its leaflike appearance it could be confused as a leaf of *Lepidodendron* (*Cyperites*). *Lepidostrobophyllum majus* (Brongniart) Hirmer has been described as being 60 mm or more long and about 10 mm wide, and widest near the base. The specimen in figure 23-6.2 is 72 mm long and 11 mm wide.

Lepidocarpon Scott (fig. 23-6.4) is a **megasporangiate** cone scale borne on *Lepidophloios* strobili. Each megasporangium contained a single **tetrad** of spores. Three of the megaspores of a tetrad apparently aborted and the fourth developed to fill the entire megasporangial cavity. The edges of the sporophyll grew upward around the megasporangium, and the entire seedlike structure was shed as a unit. In essence, each such dispersed *Lepidocarpon* was functionally equivalent to a seed and thus represented a significant evolutionary advance over the simpler, spore-bearing cones of most arborescent lycopods.

Sigillariostrobus (Schimper) Feistmantel (figs. 23-9.2, 23-9.3) is the cone of *Sigillaria*. It was borne on a fertile axis interspersed among the leaf bases. Different species range in length from about 1 cm to 30 cm. The cone scales, which commonly are missing, have finely toothed margins and are arranged in a low spiral. In the specimen of *Sigillariostrobus* in figure 23-9.3, the lower scales overlap the base of the next scales above. The sporophyll **lamina** or cone scale in figure 23-9.2 is very short, thick, and sharp pointed and may have been directed nearly perpendicular to the cone axis.

ROOTLIKE ORGANS OF ARBORESCENT LYCOPODS

Stigmaria Brongniart (figs. 23-9.1, 23-9.4, 23-9.5), the form genus for underground rootlike organs of arborescent lycopods, originated from the lower trunk as four large axes that forked equally three or four times as they spread as much as several meters horizontally less than half a meter below the surface. The tubelike "rootlets" had a featureless surface and must have served for water and nutrient absorption. These appendages were arranged in a longitudinal spiral along the axis (fig. 23-9.4); some became detached in a fashion reminiscent of leaves, leaving only a circular depression or scar on the axis. *Stigmaria* is the only fossil regularly found in the underclays beneath coal beds. An underclay (also called a seat earth) represents the soil in which the plants grew.

Stigmaria ficoides (Sternberg) Brongniart (figs. 23-9.4, 23-9.5) is an axis having circular scars arranged in a longitudinal spiral. Some specimens have the "rootlets" attached. Arborescent lycopods of *Lepidodendron*, *Lepidophloios*, *Bothrodendron*, and *Sigillaria*, as well as others, all possessed basal branch systems of the *Stigmaria* type. In evolutionary terms, stigmarian axes are quite conservative, having little structural diversity and no clear evolutionary trends. Isolated *Stigmaria* specimens thus cannot be related to specific stem genera.

HERBACEOUS LYCOPODS

Lycopodites Brongniart (figs. 23-8.4, 23-30.2), the form genus used for herbaceous lycopods, includes stems that have an ascending spiral of needlelike leaves that greatly resemble the leaf-bearing twigs of the extinct arborescent forms (fig. 23-4.6) and the extant *Lycopodium*. It is also readily confused with leafy twigs of the conifer *Walchia* (fig. 23-30.1).

SPHENOPHYTA—THE HORSETAILS

The horsetails (Division Sphenophyta) are another group of living plants that, like the lycopods, are far less diverse and significant today than they were in the Late Paleozoic. Changing climates at the close of the Coal Age had the same catastrophic effect on Pennsylvanian horsetails as it did on the lycopods, to the point that only a single genus, the very distantly related *Equisetum* (which has approximately 25 species), has survived to the present. As you view a modern clump of scouring rushes (horsetails), you would have to imagine yourself reduced to the height of a house cat to truly appreciate the appearance of the calamitean plants of the Coal Age forests of Ohio.

The horsetails are spore-bearing vascular plants that have two characteristics that allow them to be easily recognized. First, the stems have the appearance of being jointed (figs. 23-11.4 to 23-11.7). The prominent joints, or nodes, at intervals along the length of the stem have led to the common use of the term "articulates" for the group. The second characteristic is the similarly jointed branches that have very small, scalelike leaves. The small leaves are arranged in whorls at each node (figs. 23-10.1 to 23-10.7, 23-12, 23-13.4). Spores (see section on plant reproduction on p. 410) are borne in terminal cones (figs. 23-13.5, 23-13.6) derived from modified leaves and, not surprisingly, the cone "scales" are also in whorls at nodes (fig. 23-11.1), much like the vegetative leaves and branches.

Modern horsetails range in size from several centimeters in height to a meter or more. They are common on disturbed ground and around lakes and ponds throughout the temperate zone. The cells of leaves and stems of many species accumulate angular particles of silica as metabolic byproducts, making them quite abrasive. Early settlers in Ohio found horsetails to be very useful for cleaning pots and pans; hence, the derivation of the term "scouring rush" as a common name for the group.

The earliest horsetails appear in rocks of Late Devonian age. The group is differentiated into three orders: Sphenophyllales, Calamitales, and Equisetales. The first two groups reached their maximum development during the Pennsylvanian and are common in the Coal Age rocks of Ohio. The Sphenophyllales, represented by *Sphenophyllum* Brongniart, had a vinelike growth form; the plants depended on neighboring plants for support. An exceptional specimen of *Sphenophyllum*, found near Pittsburgh, Pennsylvania, was nearly 6 meters long. The Calamitales, referred to as the arborescent sphenopsids or articulates, is exemplified by the genus *Calamites* Suckow, which grew to heights of 15 to 20 meters.

SPHENOPHYLLALES

The vinelike *Sphenophyllum* plants probably grew intertwined in the undergrowth of a Pennsylvanian swamp forest and climbed, in a limited way, on other plants. A typical fossil specimen in Ohio consists of a short length of thin (1 mm-1 cm), jointed stem with one to several nodal whorls of wedge-shaped leaves (figs. 23-10.3, 23-10.4). The nodes are typically somewhat swollen, and the leaf whorls are relatively symmetrical (figs. 23-10.1, 23-10.4, 23-10.6). *Sphenophyllum* produced very complex spore-bearing cones (strobili); the *Bowmanites* (*Sphenophyllostachys*) type (figs. 23-10.9, 23-11.1) is the most common.

Sphenophyllum Brongniart is characterized by wedge-shaped (elongate-triangular) leaves borne in whorls on narrow, jointed, longitudinally ribbed stems that have swollen nodes and terminally borne cones. Leaf form may be very variable on large specimens of some species. Each leaf whorl generally had six to nine leaves, although some had 12 or more. One or two veins enter the base of each leaf and divide repeatedly along their course toward the leaf margin.

Sphenophyllum angustifolium (Germar) Goeppert (fig. 23-10.5) has four to six small, narrow, wedge-shaped leaves, each about 2 mm wide, in each whorl. The tip of each leaf splits and each of the resulting halves generally has two or three prominent, sharp teeth. A single vein enters the base and forks one to three times.

Sphenophyllum cornutum Lesquereux (fig. 23-10.6) has six broadly wedge-shaped leaves to a whorl. Each leaf is 1 to 2 cm wide and generally split from one-fourth to one-third of its length. This species name is used for detached leaves, although it is now recognized that it represents a more deeply dissected leaf form from the older portions of *S. cuneifolium* axes and perhaps other species, as well as variable leaves from the main axis of *S. emarginatum* (see fig. 23-10.4).

Sphenophyllum cuneifolium (Sternberg) Zeiller (fig. 23-10.3) generally has six leaves to a whorl, but may have up to 18. The leaves are 6 to 9 mm long and 2 to 6 mm wide and may be deeply lacerated (split). One vein enters the base; the tip bears sharp teeth. This species is common in Lower Pennsylvanian rocks.

Sphenophyllum emarginatum (Brongniart) Brongniart (fig. 23-10.4), the **type species**, has six to nine leaves to a whorl; leaves are 4 to 9 mm long and 3 to 8 mm wide. The leaf tip bears rounded teeth. Two veins enter the base, and each vein forks several times during passage to the margin.

The specimen in figure 23-10.1 identified as *Sphenophyllum fasciculatum* (Lesquereux) White has 6 to 12 narrow, sharp-pointed leaves to a whorl. Each leaf is cleft from half to two-thirds of its length. The leaves of this specimen range from 5 to 11 mm in length and are the longest known for this species, which more typically has leaves up to 8 mm in length (White, 1899; Abbott, 1958).

Sphenophyllum **cf.** *S. majus* (Bronn) Bronn (fig. 23-10.7) has six to eight leaves to a whorl. Each leaf is 5 to 12 mm wide, exceeds 15 mm in length, and is deeply split or divided into two or more lobes. Two veins enter the base, and the tip of each segment bears large, blunt serrations or teeth. This species has been collected from Lower Conemaugh strata in Columbiana County.

Sphenophyllum oblongifolium (Germar & Kaulfuss) Unger (figs. 23-10.2, 23-10.9) leaves occur six to a whorl; two are oriented downward (deflexed) at about 90°. The main (undeflexed) leaves average about 1 cm in length; the deflexed leaves generally are only about half as long. The deflexed leaves may represent a differential developmental response to the contact with a supporting plant. This species is an index fossil for Upper Pennsylvanian rocks.

The specimen in figure 23-10.8 identified as *Sphenophyllum* cf. *S. myriophyllum* Crepin was identified by Abbott (1958) as *S. tenerrimum* Ettingshausen, but it does not correspond with either the description (9-12 leaves to a whorl; leaves split into two or four shallow, blunt-tipped segments; internodes only 1-3 mm wide) or the geologic range (Upper Mississippian) for that plant. It does compare somewhat favorably with *S. myriophyllum* Crepin, which has long, thin, forked leaves and is found in Pottsville-age rocks; however, the "leaves" in our specimen could be adventitious roots. *Sphenophyllum myriophyllum* has four to eight leaves in a whorl and the leaves are deeply cleft (commonly nearly to the base) into thin, sharp segments. The internodes are 6 to 12 mm wide.

Bowmanites Binney (figs. 23-10.9, 23-11.1) is a variable genus of strobili of *Sphenophyllum* that includes at least 18 species. The unifying characteristic is the fusion of a portion of the lateral edges of the **bracts** in each whorl to form a basal disk to which sporangiophores bearing terminal sporangia are attached. The name *Sphenophyllostachys* Seward also has been applied to the cones of *Sphenophyllum*.

CALAMITALES

The Calamitales takes its name from *Calamites* Schlotheim, a common fossil plant stem. The individual erect stems originated from a sprawling, branching **rhizome** that grew along or just under the surface of the peat or mud of the swamp forest floor. Branches arose in whorls at the nodes of the rhizome, twisting to form erect clumps of closely spaced stems (fig. 23-11.2). In growth form, *Calamites* must have been much like the larger extant bamboos (to which they are completely unrelated), forming dense thickets in which adjacent stems provided a measure of mutual support. Typical *Calamites* specimens have prominent nodes (figs. 23-11.5, 23-11.7), and the internodal areas are marked by pronounced longitudinal striations (figs. 23-11.6, 23-11.7). Stem specimens typically have a whorl of round scars at some nodes (figs. 23-11.4, 23-11.6) marking the points of former attachment of lateral branches. Well-preserved specimens also may have much smaller circular or oval scars (**infranodal canals**) just below each node at the upper end of each longitudinal ridge; these scars represent specialized conducting tissue.

In a sense, the typical *Calamites* specimen is a bit deceptive, for although such a fossil looks like a simple segment of stem, the specimens actually represent the inside of the stem. *Calamites* stems had secondary growth, resulting in concentric rings of wood, as in most modern trees. The center of the stem was occupied by a large pith cavity. When a branch or main stem became buried, either in place (a common occurrence, see fig. 23-11.2) or as a result of falling into the swamp, the thin-walled pith cells decayed rapidly and the hollow interior generally became filled with fine sand or mud. Later, the buried specimen, if lying horizontally, was compressed and the outer wood decayed. At many sites, standing plants were buried by mud or sand, either a little at a time or by one or two major floods. Mud or other sediment displaced the decayed or broken-down tissue in the pith cavities of these specimens as well. In either case, the resulting fossil is a **pith cast** in which little or no surrounding tissue is preserved. The longitudinal striations that are so prominent in the internodal segments of the stem actually represent the impressions of small ridges of wood that formed the wall of tissue surrounding the pith cavity (fig. 23-11.3). In life, the external surface of the internodes of typical *Calamites* branches were probably quite smooth, much like bamboo.

Branches of *Calamites* were whorled and the leaves were born in nodal whorls along the length of the smallest branches. The whorls are typically asymmetrical, and the individual leaves range from linear with needlelike tips (*Asterophyllites*, fig. 23-13.4) to **spatulate** or wedge shaped with rounded tips (*Annularia*, figs. 23-12.1, 23-12.3). Spore-bearing cones were born terminally on fertile branches (figs. 23-13.5, 23-13.6) and have the same whorled/nodal organization as the rest of the plant. A number of calamitean cone types have been recognized, but *Calamostachys* (fig. 23-13.6) is one of the more common ones.

Calamitean roots that have structure preserved are classified as *Astromyelon* Williamson. Compressions or impressions are identified as *Pinnularia* Lindley & Hutton. They are typically adventitious from the rhizomes or arise from the nodes of subterranean portions of the stem. The underground axis resembled the above-ground stems in overall appearance except for absence of nodes.

The arborescent *Calamites* was subdominant to the arborescent lycopods and tree ferns in the coal swamps and probably did not exceed 10 to 12 meters in height. It generally grew in thick stands on mud flats and sandy areas along rivers. Several subgenera have been described on the basis of the regularity of branching, as shown by the arrangement of branch scars (figs. 23-11.4, 23-11.6). The genus name *Calamites* was originally used only for pith casts, but some authors now use the name for the entire plant.

Small wedges of **primary xylem** that jutted into the pith cavity (fig. 23-11.3) created the longitudinally oriented internodal furrows on the cast, and embayments between wedges, marking the position of a vascular ray, created the ribs. The small oval to round scar at the top of the node, representing the position of an infranodal canal, is a useful guide in orienting specimens. A coalified rind derived from the thin ring of vascular tissue that surrounded the pith may be preserved. Any soft pith tissue remaining in a fallen stem commonly was displaced by a filling of fine sand or silt. The tissues that were more resistant to decay persisted long enough to become coalified.

Long, tapered *Calamites* stems (fig. 23-11.5) that have been found in growth position are branched from horizontal rhizomes or from nodes in lower positions of erect stems of plants buried by flood muds. Other organs, such as leaves, cones, and roots, also may be buried individually or in masses. It is not unusual to find cross sections of stems and roots on bedding planes (fig. 23-11.3).

Calamites carinatus Sternberg (fig. 23-11.4) is characterized by elongated internodes, which are finely striated on the periphery by narrow ribs and grooves. The ribs converge toward the branch scars—the larger the branch the larger the scar and the greater the convergence distortion. The branch scars on the specimen in figure 23-11.4 are small and numerous.

Calamites cistii Brongniart (fig. 23-11.7) internodes are higher than wide and the infranodal canals are never as wide as the ribs. The upper ends of the ribs taper to a sharp point. The infranodal canals are elongated-oval, and the furrows have a U-shaped profile showing a double line.

Calamites suckowii Brongniart (fig. 23-11.5) has strong, bluntly rounded ribs, nearly circular infranodal scars almost as wide as the ribs, parallel-sided internodes that are wider than high, and nonconstricted nodes. The furrows have a V-shaped profile showing a single line.

Calamites undulatus Sternberg (fig. 23-11.6) has nearly flat ribs that may be finely cross hatched and broadly pointed at the upper end, internodes that are broader than high, nearly circular infranodal canals, and undulating margins along the lengths of the internodal ribs. The shortest internodes generally occur just above the branch-bearing nodes and the longest are just below.

Annularia Sternberg is probably the most common foliage type of arborescent *Calamites*. The linear, single-nerved leaves are fused into a rosettelike disk at the point of attachment. The number of leaves per whorl ranges from 5 to 40 according to species.

Annularia asteris Bell (fig. 23-12.2) has sharply pointed leaves in whorls of 7 to 12. The leaves at each whorl are roughly equal in length, typically 1.5 to 2.5 mm (maximum of 5 mm); length-to-width ratio is approximately 6:1.

Annularia radiata (Brongniart) Sternberg (fig. 23-12.4) has 8 to 20 (generally 10 to 14) sharp-pointed leaves per whorl. The leaves are roughly equal in length and average about 1 cm; in robust specimens, they may exceed 1.5 cm. The leaves are widest in the middle, and the length-to-width ratio is approximately 6:1 or more.

Annularia sphenophylloides (Zenker) Gutbier (fig. 23-12.3) has 12 to 20 crowded, straight-sided leaves per whorl that commonly vary in length from 3 to 12 mm in different whorls. The leaves are typically 1 to 3 mm wide, and the length-to-width ratio is approximate 4:1. Variability within a whorl is slight. The leaves are somewhat spatulate, broadening toward their rounded tips, which have a terminal point or bristle.

Annularia stellata (Schlotheim) Wood (figs. 23-12.1, 23-12.5) has a variable number of leaves per whorl, but generally between 16 and 32, although some authors report as many as 40. The whorls vary in overall size, according to their position on the branch, and individual leaves commonly vary in length. The leaves are widest just above the middle and have blunt tips. The leaves average about 2.5 cm in length, although some may approach 7 cm. The length-to-width ratio is at least 5:1.

Annularia cf. *A. galioides* (Lindley & Hutton) Kidston (fig. 23-12.6) has 8 to 12 leaves per whorl. The leaves have blunt tips, are widest at the midpoint, from 1.5 to 4 mm long, and have a length-to-width ratio of 3:1.

Asterophyllites Brongniart is a second foliage type borne by *Calamites*. The thin, single-nerved leaves differ from those of *Annularia* in that they are not fused at the base, they arc upward, and the tips touch or overlap the base of the next leaf whorl.

Asterophyllites charaeformis (Sternberg) Goeppert (figs. 23-13.2, 23-13.3) has four to five stout, strongly incurved leaves per whorl, ranging in length from 1 to 3 mm. The twigs commonly fork into numerous tiny branchlets.

Asterophyllites equisetiformis (Schlotheim) Brongniart (fig. 23-13.4) is characterized by 12 to 20 narrow, grasslike, sharp-pointed, straight or curved leaves in each whorl. The leaves average about 1 mm wide and 1 to 2 cm long and are widest near the center. This species is an exceedingly common fossil plant in Ohio.

Calamostachys Schimper (fig. 23-13.6) is one of several genera of cones of *Calamites* that vary considerably in size (1-12 cm long) and complexity. All have whorls of sterile leaves, fused at their lower or **distal** end, forming cuplike structures at alternate nodes. Intermediate nodes between the sterile, cuplike leaf whorls have highly modified fertile leaves (sporangiophores). The sporangia are borne on T-shaped (peltate) sporangiophores that project perpendicularly from the axis at nodes between the whorls of sterile bracts. Some calamitean species produced bisporangiate *Calamostachys* cones, containing both **microsporangia** (typically borne toward the **apex**) and megasporangia (typically produced near the base of the cone). The specimen of *Calamostachys* illustrated in figure 23-13.6 has a ribbed axis and whorls of upturned sporophylls (bracts) at each node. One cone has dense whorls of sporangia between each whorl of bracts.

Palaeostachya Weiss (fig. 23-13.5) differs from *Calamostachys* in that the sporangiophores are borne at the junction of the cone bract and the central cone axis, projecting at an angle of approximately 45° with respect to the cone axis. This characteristic, easily observed in coal-ball material, is difficult or impossible to demonstrate in many compression specimens. *Palaeostachya* cf. *P. elongata* (Presl) Weiss (fig. 23-13.5) is a small, lax (flexible or weak) type of cone. It generally has many cones on a branching stem. The cones are slender, on very slender stems. There are only five to nine sporangia above the five to nine bracts at each node. The sporangiophore is attached at the junction of the sterile bracts with the cone axis, extending upward at a 30° to 60° angle.

Macrostachya Schimper (fig. 23-13.1) is a larger cone, at least 20 mm in diameter; the axis is at least 5 mm in diameter. The bracts are united into a collar around the cone axis, a feature that tends to obscure the sporangiophores in most specimens.

PTERIDOPHYTA—THE TRUE FERNS

The record of fossil ferns in Ohio is both prolific and frustrating. When early and mid-nineteenth century paleobotanists began the study of fossil plants recovered from coal-bearing rocks in Europe and eastern North America, a seemingly endless array of fern leaves came to light. Fern leaves were so abundant in the shales associated with coals that the Carboniferous soon became known as the "Age of Ferns." As is so often the case, nature is far more subtle than a superficial view might suggest, and the case of the "ferns" of the Coal Age reinforces this lesson. In a magnificent piece of botanical detective work, two British paleobotanists, F. W. Oliver and D. H. Scott, demonstrated that some isolated seeds and pollen-bearing structures known from Coal Age rocks were produced by plants that bore fernlike leaves! The true ferns of the Carboniferous, like those in modern woodlands and gardens, reproduced by means of dispersed spores (see section on plant reproduction, p. 410). These new plants described by Oliver and Scott (1904) may have produced leaves that looked like those of ferns, but their seeds and pollen grains meant they were a different kind of plant entirely. These plants came to be known as seed ferns or pteridosperms, and will be discussed after the true ferns. The problem lies in how to properly classify fernlike leaf fossils that have no diagnostic reproductive structures similar to sori and sporangia of true ferns.

Definitive identification of true fern foliage (as opposed to seed ferns) depends on the presence of reproductive structures. Foliage that bears attached spore-producing structures can confidently be assigned to a specific fern group, depending upon the nature of the reproductive structures. Sterile foliage that lacks any trace of reproductive structures is a continuing problem. Similarities between various types of sterile foliage and known fern and seed-fern foliage can provide some clues, but many examples of fernlike foliage, although named as a result of scientific study, are still unknown in terms of their botanical affinities. In some cases, pseudofossils such as dendrites (fig. 23-15.1) may have the general appearance of a fern frond or pinna. Dendrites result from mineral growth on bedding planes and are fairly common in the sandstones and siltstones associated with coal beds. Some dendrites may also resemble mosses or even conifer branches.

Although the compression and impression remains of Coal Age fernlike foliage are commonly the most conspicuous fossils in a deposit, permineralized material, known primarily from coal balls, is actually the most useful in critical identification and the reconstruction of the evolutionary history of the group. The internal vascular anatomy of ferns is extremely complex (figs. 23-14.2, 23-14.6) and, together with the detailed anatomy of reproductive (spore-bearing) structures, the permineralized stems, leaves, spore-bearing structures, rhizomes, and roots provide the key to reconstructing patterns of relationship. Most of these anatomical features will not be considered here. The fossils most commonly collected, including impressions, compressions, casts, and molds, either have not retained such features or require special, highly technical preparation techniques. Valid comparisons require the reconstruction of the plants using serial sections and detailed anatomical study and thus are beyond the scope of this chapter.

Ferns first appear in the fossil record of the Upper Devonian. Although the early ferns generally lacked true leaves, their internal anatomy clearly allies them with the more typical ferns of the Late Paleozoic and Mesozoic. In Ohio, the Devonian-Mississippian record of this phase in fern evolution is quite sparse. However, the fossil record from the Pennsylvanian shows a clear pattern of extensive diversification into several major groups. Although the ferns of today bear a superficial resemblance to those from Coal Age rocks, the ancient lineages generally became extinct in the Permian, and most modern forms are derived from secondary episodes of fern diversification in the Late Permian and the Mesozoic.

There is one fascinating exception to this generality. Modern tropical rain forests are the habitat for seven genera of ferns, comprising nearly 100 species, that are grouped together into the order Marattiales. The Pennsylvanian-age swamp forests of Ohio served as the habitat for an earlier fern in this order, *Psaronius* Cotta (fig. 23-14.1), which was at least as grand in aspect as any fern in the modern tropics.

PSARONIUS

The whole plant is known as *Psaronius*, but the name also is applied to the permineralized trunks. These trunks are typically about 50 cm in diameter at the base, but can range to twice that size. One specimen found in upper Monongahela Group strata (Uniontown coal zone) near Powhatan Point in Belmont County had a diameter of 102 cm. The apex of a *Psaronius* stem, as high as 8 meters above the swamp forest floor, supported an immense crown of giant fronds.

There are several sites in Athens, Monroe, and Belmont Counties in southeastern Ohio where numerous silified *Psaronius* stumps or logs have been found in Upper Pennsylvanian rocks (see Carlson, 1991). Some of the finest collection sites are along the tributaries of Middle Branch Shade River in Athens County. Excavation of these stumps has shown that some were preserved in growth position (figs. 23-14.4, 23-14.5).

Silicifed trunks of this type are typically tapered toward the upper (and in some cases the lower) end of the specimen (fig. 23-14.4). Incomplete preservation at the upper end of the axis generally concides with the depth to which the standing stump was buried by mud. The trunk was either broken off or completely disintegrated above the level of burial and partially decayed at the mud surface. The tapering at the lower end of the trunk is generally the consequence of incomplete preservation of the adventitious roots that mantled the periphery of the stump at its base.

At maturity, *Psaronius* tree ferns may have reached a height of 10 meters. The trunk tapered from the base upward. The term trunk is best qualified, however, for its internal organization was quite different from that of modern woody plants. Much of the cross-sectional area, particularly in the basal portion of the axis, consisted of a dense mantle of tough, fibrous adventitious roots, which reached a considerable thickness at the base of the axis. The true stem, containing the vascular tissue, was quite small when the plant was young (at the base of the axis) and did not increase in diameter at that level as the plant continued to grow. The cross-sectional area of vascular tissue did increase at the apex as the plant matured, and new adventitious roots were continually produced from slightly below the growing tip, adding to the diameter of the trunk below. Thus, although the trunk increased in diameter toward the base, owing to the accumulated thickness of the root mantle, the true stem tapered from a small diameter at the base to the entire diameter of the trunk axis at the top of the plant.

Figure 23-14.6 is a cross section of part of a trunk, shown in figure 23-14.4, that had been slightly flattened prior to becoming permineralized. The true stem (upper center of fig. 23-14.6) has a relatively small diameter and is surrounded by a thick root mass. Farther up the axis of the specimen in figure 23-14.4, the true stem had increased in diameter to 10 cm, concurrent with a reduction in the thickness of the root mantle. At the growing tip, where the true stem took up the entire cross-sectional area of the trunk, adventitious roots were absent.

The crown of large, arching fronds, bearing *Pecopteris*-type pinnules, is borne at the apex (fig. 23-14.1). The apical region of the trunk had large, spirally arranged, circular or crescentic scars (fig. 23-14.3) marking the points of attachment of the compound fronds. Isolated specimens of *Psaronius* stem tips are variously named, depending on the arrangement of the frond attachment scars. Specimens of *Psaronius* trunks showing four ranks of spirally arranged frond scars are assigned to the genus *Caulopteris* Lindley & Hutton (fig. 23-14.3). Specimens in which the scars alternate, first on one side then the other, in a two-ranked spiral are assigned to the form genus *Megaphyton* Corsin. At all stages in the life of the plant, adventitious root formation occurred below the point of attachment of the topmost crop of fronds.

The bases of in-place erect stump fossils generally are emplaced in a coal seam or coaly shale (fig. 23-14.5). This position suggests that the plants were preferentially rooted in the peat base of the swamps. As noted earlier, peat swamps were subject to seasonal flooding, which covered the peat with incremental layers of mud. The layers of mud restricted the oxygen available to deeply buried roots and probably killed most plants. *Psaronius* was uniquely adapted to withstand the consequences of such flooding because the bulk of the lower part of the trunk was made up of adventitious roots, which constantly grew downward from the leaf-bearing crown of the plant. If the tree fern was partially buried by successive layers of mud, new roots grew down as far as the new soil surface and then diverged outward, providing a steady supply of water and nutrients to the large canopy of compound fronds. The layering of mud (now represented by bedded layers of clay shale or silty mudstone) at the base of many stems, the number of lateral root layers, and the layers of fronds and other plant litter suggest that the tree ferns continued to grow for many years after the initial flooding.

As the plants continued to grow during this period, old fronds were shed, falling to the soil surface at the base of the plant. Each episode of flooding resulted in the burial of the previous accumulation of fronds and other litter in new layers of mud. Mute testimony to this ancient cycle of annual growth and episodic flooding is the well-preserved fronds of *Pecopteris* (fig. 23-15.2) that are uncovered as the base of each erect stem is excavated, almost 300 million years after the individual *Psaronius* tree fern finally succumbed to the relentless tide of mud that had permanently altered the swamp in which the plant had initially become established.

Psaronius tree ferns are considered to have replaced the arborescent lycopods as dominants in the Late Pennsylvanian peat swamps. Toward the end of the Pennsylvanian, global climatic conditions may have become somewhat drier, resulting in an abrupt decline in the abundance of the large lycopods and allowing the tree ferns to become the major arborescent plants of the later Pennsylvanian peat-forming swamps. This slight adaptive advantage was not sufficient, however, in the face of even greater environmental change in the middle and late Permian, an interval of time not recorded in Ohio rocks, when most *Psaronius* species became extinct.

FERN LEAVES

Alloiopteris Potonié is a leaf/frond genus of herbaceous ferns that have small, **alternately** attached, generally decurrent, basally fused pinnules. A single vein enters the broadly attached base and divides; the veinlets pass to the margin, where they terminate in prominent teeth. An **aphlebia** occurs at the base of each major leaf segment, but this characteristic is unlikely to be evident unless relatively complete fronds are preserved on large slabs. The frond is at least tripinnate. The fertile form of this genus is called *Corynepteris* Baily.

Alloiopteris coralloides (Gutbier) Potonié (fig. 23-15.4) pinnules are small (up to 1 mm wide) and subopposite. The lobes appear symmetrical and square cut, although each is generally indistinctly bilobed or trilobed. The frond is large and tripinnate. A single vein enters the base of each pinnule and forks once or twice; the veinlets terminate in the lobes.

Alloiopteris erosa (Gutbier) Potonié (fig. 23-15.3) pinnules are small (up to 3 mm wide) and have one main rounded to angular lobe and one small, laterally placed, pointed lobe. The main lobe bears three small teeth. A single vein enters the base of each pinnule and forks; one veinlet extends to the subsidiary lobe and the other branches twice more and terminates in the teeth of the primary lobe.

Alloiopteris essinghii (Andrae) Potonié (fig. 23-15.6) pinnules are variable in size, ranging from 1.5 to 5 mm in length, and are distinctly asymmetrical. A single vein enters the base of each pinnule and parallels the more or less unlobed side; two veinlets depart, fork, and terminate in the small, rounded lobes.

Alloiopteris sternbergii (Ettingshausen) Potonié (figs. 23-15.7, 23-15.8) pinnules are tiny, as small as 1 mm by 1 mm. They are crowded and attached to adjoining pinnules along the base. The pinnae appear thin and ribbonlike. The upper margin of each pinnule has two to three small teeth and there is at least one lateral tooth on each side. A single vein enters the base of each pinnule and splits, one veinlet going to each lateral and terminal tooth.

Danaeides (Goeppert) Schimper is a leaf/frond genus of probable tree ferns. The fronds were quadripinnate and some exceeded a meter in length. The pinnules, which may be basally constricted, are oblong, blunt tipped, have straight to convex sides, and are attached by the entire base. The pinnules vary in size according to their position on the pinnae. The smaller, more terminal ones may be basally fused to other pinnules. The venation commonly is obscured, but lateral veins arise from a well-developed midvein and arch to the margin, in some cases singly, but generally forking once just after departing. Accessory or rachial veins may enter directly from the rachis. Fertile pinnules, which superficially resemble sow bugs, have rows of linear, laterally fused sporangia arranged along lateral veins on the lower surface. Fertile pinnules may occur singly on an otherwise sterile pinna, pinnae bearing only fertile pinnules may be intercalated among sterile pinnae, or all pinnules on a frond can be fertile (fig. 23-16.1). It is rare, however, when an entire frond is fertile, but they do occur. Many sterile pinnae have been mistaken for various species of *Pecopteris*. *Danaeides emersonii* Lesquereux (figs. 23-16.1, 23-16.3) occurs in great numbers from above the level of the Pittsburgh (No. 8) coal (basal Monongahela Group, Pennsylvanian) through the lower Dunkard Group (Pennsylvanian-Permian).

Lobatopteris Wagner was separated from the pecopterid complex on the basis of characteristic lateral vein bundles in the pinnule lobes. The midvein is strong. Lateral veins are widely spaced (20-25 per centimeter of margin), perpendicular to the midvein and pinnule margin, forked at least once, and gradually evolving as the pinnules become lobed into three- and four-pronged bundles. Lobing occurs beyond the four-pronged stage, the so-called lobatopterid pattern.

Lobatopteris lamuriana (Heer) Wagner (figs. 23-17.1 to 23-17.3) has large quadripinnate fronds. The smaller pinnule of the ultimate divisions are 2 to 4 mm long and 1 to 2 mm wide, but the average for the larger blunt-tipped pinnules is about 3 mm by 15 mm. The midvein is strong to the apex, and the lateral veins depart at a 45° angle, forking about one-fourth of the way to the margin. The upper veinlet divides again. This group of three veinlets supplies a single rounded lobe of the larger pinnules. The fertile equivalent of this species, *Asterotheca (Pecopteris) lamuriana*, has five sporangia per synangium. This plant may be mistaken for *Lobatopteris (Pecopteris) miltonii*.

Lobatopteris (Pecopteris) miltonii (Artis) Cleal & Shute (figs. 23-18.1, 23-18.2) has large quadripinnate fronds. The pinnules are subopposite to alternate. In well-preserved specimens, the upper epidermis is covered with fine hair that obscures the venation. The pinnules are variable in size and appearance, ranging from 2 to 9 mm in length and about 2 to 4 mm in width. Pinnae have abruptly rounded apices, and the terminal pinnule is about the same size as the adjacent lateral lobes. The sinuous midvein gives off lateral veinlets at an acute angle. These veinlets divide a short distance from the midvein, and the upper fork divides again to provide the characteristic three-veinlet cluster, although a few veins may divide only once and others may divide twice. Fertile pinnules of this species, called *Lobatopteris (Asterotheca) miltonii*, have three to five ovoid sporangia per synangium.

Nemejcopteris Schlotheim, for years classified as *Pecopteris*, was transferred to *Nemejcopteris* in 1968 by Barthel, who determined it was a zygopterid fern. Each frond is subtended by a pair of aphlebiae. The pinnules are recognized by the strongly toothed margin and the thick, rigid-appearing, lateral veinlets that depart the thick midvein at an acute angle and terminate in a tooth or a point on the serrated margin. Most ferns have two rows of pinnules, forming a planar frond structure. In *Nemejcopteris*, pinnules were born in four ranks at right angles to one another, forming a three-dimensional frond system. *Nemejcopteris feminaeformis*, (Schlotheim) Barthel (fig. 23-16.2) is found from the Kittanning coals (lower Allegheny Group) up into the Dunkard strata. The perpendicularly inserted, serrate pinnules that have acute tips and steeply inclined, straight, rigid, single veins are exclusively characteristic.

Pecopteris Brongniart is a form genus for fronds borne primarily on the marratialian tree fern *Psaronius*, although the name has been applied to several herbaceous ferns and at least one seed fern (pteridosperm). The pinnules are attached by their entire base, have nearly parallel margins, a prominent midvein, and lateral veins that extend straight or arched, simple or undivided, to the margin. Some species have hair or scales on the lamina or the rachis. The immature frond is tightly coiled in a structure called a crozier (fig. 23-15.5), from which it unrolls and expands. The terms "fiddlehead" and "shepherd's crook" are applied to this structure in living ferns. Many of the fertile forms of *Pecopteris* compressions and even impressions are classified as *Asterotheca* Presl (figs. 23-16.5, 23-16.6, 23-18.1). Many fertile species initially assigned to *Asterotheca* were later transferred to *Scolecopteris* Zenker, *Acitheca* Brongniart, *Ptychocarpus* Weiss, or other genera when permineralized or particularly well-preserved compression material was found that permitted the reproductive structures to be described with greater precision.

Pecopteris arborescens (Schlotheim) Kidston has large tripinnate fronds. The pinnules are small, alternate to somewhat subopposite, 2 to 6 mm in length, and only about 1.5 mm wide, although all pinnules on an individual pinna are approximately the same length. The sides of the pinnules are essentially parallel, giving a rectangular appearance, and the pinnules have a rounded tip. The straight midvein extends to the pinnule apex, and the lateral veins are simple, coursing at a slight upward angle to the margin. In a recent redescription of *Pecopteris arborescens*, the fertile form was shown to be *Scolecopteris elegans* Zenker (figs. 23-16.5, 23-16.6), which was originally described from permineralized material. The **synangia** have three to five, generally four, oval sporangia in a single row on each side of the midvein.

Pecopteris candolleana (Brongniart) Kidston (figs. 23-17.4 to 23-17.6) has large tripinnate fronds. The pinnules are alternate, up to 10 mm long, and appear widely spaced. The midvein is prominent. Lateral veins arise at a wide angle and fork once about one-fourth of the way to the margin. The resulting veinlets curve and meet the margin at nearly 90°.

Pecopteris cyathea (Schlotheim) Stur (fig. 23-16.4) has large tripinnate fronds. The pinnules are somewhat similar in overall appearance to those of *P. arborescens*, but are slightly larger, ranging from 5 to 10 mm in length and 1.5 to

2 mm in width; the pinnules on an individual pinna vary in length. The lateral veins are both simple and once divided, and the patterns commonly alternate, although divided veinlets are most common.

Pecopteris hemitelioides (Brongniart) Stur (fig. 23-18.4) has large tripinnate fronds. The secondary rachis bears scales. The pinnules are 5-7 mm long and about 2 mm wide, subopposite, blunt tipped, nearly perpendicular to the rachis, and vary in length along any individual pinna. The thick epidermis, when **carbonized**, commonly obscures the veins, but a thick midvein gives off simple, straight veinlets that follow a somewhat oblique course to the margin. There may be a slight constriction at the base of the pinnule. The fertile equivalent of this species, *Asterotheca (Pecopteris) hemitelioides*, has synangia consisting of four or five sporangia.

Pecopteris polymorpha (Brongniart) Schimper (fig. 23-18.3) has large, more or less parallel-sided pinnules that taper gradually in the upper third to a blunt point. The prominent midvein has regularly twice bifurcate lateral veins perpendicular to the pinnule margin.

Pecopteris squamosa Lesquereux (fig. 23-18.7) has more or less alternate pinnules; straight, generally unbranched lateral venation; and hairs on the rachis.

Pecopteris unita (Brongniart) Weiss (figs. 23-18.5, 23-18.6) has subopposite to alternately placed pinnules that are united laterally to adjacent pinnules. The midvein enters the base at an angle, turns, and follows a straight course to the tip, giving off several opposite, nondividing lateral veinlets that curve strongly upward, more or less paralleling the course of the midvein. The fertile form of *P. unita*, long described as *Ptychocarpus unita* (Brongniart) Weiss, has been reassigned to *Scolecopteris unita* (Brongniart) Jennings & Millay (fig. 23-18.6). The fertile pinnules have two irregular rows of clustered sporangia arranged along each side of the midvein on the lower surface of each pinnule. Each circular cluster or synangium has five to seven sporangia that are attached laterally and are free at the tips.

Sphenopteris Brongniart is a form genus for small lobed or dissected pinnules that are oval to oblong in overall appearance and have a constricted (stalked) base. The venation is generally well defined, consisting of a straight or sinuous primary vein, from which lateral veins arise at an acute angle, dichotomizing two or more times before terminating in the lobes. Species that have elongate lobes have a single veinlet running through the lobe. The fronds are several times pinnate. Dozens of species of *Sphenopteris* have been named. The systematics of the group is currently undergoing extensive revision, a task complicated by the fact that the name *Sphenopteris* has been applied to both fern (pteridophyte) and seed fern (pteridosperm) fossils and so is not a natural genus. If the fronds are attached to, or even associated with, reproductive structures (sporangia in the case of the true ferns, or pollen and seed-bearing structures in the case of the pteridosperms), the proper **taxonomic** placement of the material is assured. Otherwise, unless other diagnostic features such as fine venation or **cuticle** are preserved, assignment to *Sphenopteris* usually is based entirely on the general appearance of the sterile fronds.

Sphenopteris schatzlarensis Stur (fig. 23-19.1) has alternate ultimate pinnae that arise at an acute angle from a somewhat flexuous rachis, each (generally) having five or seven narrow, bilobed or trilobed, subopposite or alternate pinnules. A sinuous primary vein forks as needed to provide a veinlet that terminates in each lobe. The frond is at least tripinnate. The fertile form, classified as *Renaultia* Zeiller, is characterized by several single, ovoid sporangia in ones and twos near the tips of the lobes on the underside of the fertile pinnules.

Other fertile types of *Sphenopteris* foliage are named *Oligocarpia* Goeppert. When new fossil material is discovered that bears diagnostic reproductive structures or other definitive features, specimens previously assigned to *Sphenopteris* are transferred to other, more nearly natural genera or even to other families.

Sphenopteris (Oligocarpia) mixta (Schimper) Abbott (fig. 23-19.2) has 6 to 10 alternately arranged, lobed, pinnules and a terminal pinnule. In order to identify compression fossils of *S. mixta* it is generally necessary to find specimens that expose the underside of fertile pinnules such as those in the lower part of figure 23-19.2, which have distinct, but very small, oval bumps near the margin of the lobes of the ultimate lobed pinnules (see especially pinnules at arrows). These bumps are synangia composed of several sporangia in an oval to circular cluster; they are about equal in thickness and length but slightly narrower in width. The scattered distribution of the synangia near the margins of some lobes on some pinnules is an important characteristic.

The specimen of *Sphenopteris (Oligocarpia)* cf. *S. (O.) gracilis* Brongniart in figure 23-20.2 also shows the underside of part of a frond that has similar synangial clusters. The central vein of each pinnule is **pseudomonopodial** (zigzag); one branch of each dichotomy becomes the main vein and the other branch simply extends into the next lobe, may divide once, and terminates at the margin. The synangium, composed of several sporangia, is very small (<0.5 mm). Synangia are irregularly scattered near the margins and tip of several lobes on some pinnules.

Both sterile and fertile foliage of several other species of *Sphenopteris* have been collected and identified from Ohio. These include *S. coemansii* Andrae (fig. 23-20.1), *Sphenopteris (Oligocarpia)* cf. *S. (O.) capitata* White (fig. 23-19.4), and *Sphenopteris (Oligocarpia)* sp. (fig. 23-19.3).

VASCULAR SEED-PLANT REPRODUCTION

All of the land plants discussed to this point are defined by botanists as free-sporing plants, meaning that reproduction is accomplished by means of spores disseminated by gravity, wind, or water. The conquest of the land by plants, which, according to current evidence, began in the late Silurian, was far from complete by the Pennsylvanian. Free-sporing plants have one major ecological limitation. The spores themselves are quite resistant to drying, but they need abundant water to germinate once they fall upon soil or other growth medium. The spores germinate to produce an inconspicuous, free-living stage (**gametophyte**) in the life cycle that actually bears the sex organs. The gametophyte has no roots, leaves or other proper adaptations to life on land. In most extant ferns, the gametophyte is typically only a few millimeters in diameter. Abundant moisture is necessary for growth, and actual droplets of water must be present for the fusion of egg and sperm. The range of terrestrial environments that provide such conditions is very limited, and most of today's lycopods, horsetails, and ferns are confined to moist habitats near wetlands or margins of bodies of water or to the interior of forests where other plants serve to buffer or moderate the microclimate of the forest floor or canopy.

Most extant and ancient free-sporing plants produce a

single type of air-borne spore (**homospore**) that develops into a bisexual gametophyte having both male and female sex organs. In contrast to such homosporous life cycles, by the Late Devonian some plants, including *Archaeopteris*, had evolved more complex free-sporing life cycles. These plants had heterosporous life cycles, producing two distinctly different types of spores, microspores and megaspores. A microspore (figs. 23-6.6, 23-6.7) is comparable in size to spores of homosporous plants, but produces a gametophyte bearing only male or sperm-producing sex organs. A megaspore (fig. 23-6.5) is quite large in comparison to the microspores. Dispersed megaspores produce large female or egg-bearing gametophytes. Free-sporing heterosporous life cycles are not common in extant plants, but were common in many different lineages in the plants of the Coal Age, including lycopods and sphenopsids.

Because homospores and microspores are similar in both morphology and size range, differentiating the two spore types requires detailed characterization of spores prior to dispersal from their respective sporangia. Because we cannot relate most dispersed fossil spores to specific sporangia, it is not possible, in most cases, to determine if a specific small spore is a microspore produced by a heterosporous plant or simply a dispersed homospore. The term **miospore** commonly is used for dispersed spores smaller than 200 micrometers that cannot be definitively characterized in terms of the original plant life cycle. Although the number of free-sporing heterosporous plants that have survived to the present is limited, such life cycles are an evolutionary link to more advanced terrestrial life cycles involving the production of seeds.

During the rapid plant diversification of the Late Devonian, a new complex of plants that produced seeds instead of spores made their appearance. The seed habit represents a far more complex reproductive cycle than that of free-sporing plants. All seed plants are heterosporous, but they are not free sporing, because the megaspores and microspores are not shed from their respective sporangia. Instead, the spores are retained in the sporangia and develop into their respective gametophyte stages, protected and supplied with nutrients by the parent plant. Megaspores develop into characteristic female reproductive structures, called **ovules**, consisting of the female gametophyte surrounded by an **integument** derived from the megasporangium. Microspores develop into small, simple male gametophytes that are shed from the microsporangium as **prepollen** or pollen grains, depending on their state of development when shed.

In a modern seed-plant life cycle, pollen (or prepollen) grains are transferred, generally by air but also by insects and other vectors, to the ovules, where fertilization occurs. The end result of this process is the creation of the seed. Each seed is essentially a complete, dormant embryonic plant, embedded in nutrient-rich tissues (the female gametophyte) and surrounded by a protective seed coat derived from the ovular integument. The nutrient-rich tissue provides energy and nutrients for the developing embryo during germination and initial establishment.

Seed-plant life cycles eliminate the need for free water in fertilization, a requirement for free-sporing plants, and the seed itself greatly extends the environmental range for the establishment of young plants. The major adaptive advantage of seed production is in water-stressed environments. Several significant groups of seed plants made their appearance in the Late Devonian and Coal Age floras, but none of them assumed a dominant role in the swamp forests for which we have the best fossil record. The Late Paleozoic fossil record of Ohio is typical in that it documents low-lying, wet, coastal environments, where the complexities of seed production confer no particular advantage, relative to simpler, free-sporing life cycles. This factor alone is probably sufficient to explain the dominant role of arborescent lycopods and tree ferns in the swamps and associated environments.

With the change to a drier climate in the continental interior of Pangea in the Upper Pennsylvanian and Permian, free-sporing plants may have been particularly vulnerable and many types became extinct at that time. Some seed plants, particularly those adapted to swamp environments, also suffered extinctions, but others survived that harsh interval to evolve a wide range of new lineages which would come to dominate the world of the Mesozoic. Ohio's fossil record is largely limited to the Pennsylvanian and the Pennsylvanian-Permian boundary, where three groups of seed plants, the seed ferns (pteridosperms), the cordaites, and the first conifers (the Voltziales), played roles of varying importance in the ancient forests of this region.

SEED PLANTS

PTERIDOSPERMOPHYTA—THE SEED FERNS

As previously noted, Oliver and Scott (1904) demonstrated that some of the Coal Age plants that bore fernlike leaves were actually seed plants. The close association of large, conspicuous seeds, pollen-producing organs, and fernlike leaves had led some paleobotanists to speculate that there was a group of Upper Paleozoic plants that combined both seed-plant and fernlike features. The name Cycadofilicales had actually been proposed for this hypothetical group of plants. The work of Oliver and Scott demonstrated the fact that such plants were indeed present in the Coal Age swamp forests and it is their name for the group, the Pteridospermae or seed ferns, that is the basis for the current division name Pteridospermophyta.

The internal anatomy of the stem of the seed fern *Medullosa* Cotta (fig. 23-20.4) is a complex of two to four vascular segments that divided and rejoined at various levels to form a longitudinal network of woody tissues. Cortical-type tissues were interspersed and surrounded them. A band of secondary xylem surrounded each vascular segment. A periderm developed around the whole stem, whatever the number of segments. The periderm and adjacent cortical tissues included greatly elongated cells containing secretory products (resins and gums). The numerous very large leaf bases (**petioles** or rachises) (fig. 23-20.5) remained on the stem, considerably increasing external dimensions. Near the base of the tree or vine, adventitious roots supplemented the main roots, which are generally unknown. Figure 23-20.3 illustrates a cast of a strong root system that may have belonged to a seed fern; it was found by John C. Ferm in the same strata in which the stigmarian stump in figure 23-9.1 was later found. The several main roots of this unique specimen may indicate the base of a very strong small tree or large vine. The direct downward penetration to more than 25 cm is unusual in comparison with other known root systems, such as stigmarian lycopods or the large number of strandlike adventitious roots of the tree ferns, both of which spread laterally for several meters within a few centimeters of the surface. None penetrated more than a few tens of centimeters, although some may have been later buried more deeply by episodic sedimentation during floods.

Although they were not dominant in the Coal Age swamp forests, the seed ferns were a significant group, ranging in growth form from shrubs and vinelike plants to small understory trees (fig. 23-20.4). Of the several groups of seed ferns, two groups, the lyginopterid and the medullosan complexes, were the most significant in the Ohio flora. Each complex has numerous named structures now known to be associated in individual plants:

organ	lyginopterid genera	medullosan genera
stems	*Lyginopteris*	*Medullosa*
leaves	*Sphenopteris*	*Neuropteris*
		Alethopteris
pollen organs	*Crossotheca?*	*Aulacotheca*
		Bernaultia
		Dolerotheca
		Whittleseya
seeds	*Lagenostoma*	*Pachytesta*
		Trigonocarpus
cupules	*Calymmathotheca*	

Medullosan seed ferns are particularly abundant in Ohio strata and show a remarkable diversity in terms of leaf, seed, and pollen-organ genera and species. Only the most common genera are listed above, and the list is somewhat arbitrary. In some cases, stems, large rachises, and even the subdivisions of fronds can be identified.

To compound the difficulty in determining true biological diversity in this group, organs such as leaves typically tend to be highly variable in form (**polymorphic**). In rare instances, fossils identified as fern pinnules may not even be the leaves of plants. At least one type of insect (*Phylomylacris*, a cockroach) produced wings that appear to mimic the frond pinnules of *Odontopteris* (Scott and Taylor, 1983), probably achieving a measure of protection as it foraged in the dense undergrowth of the ancient forest.

The leaves of many of the medullosan seed ferns were quite tough and thick, which may help to explain why they are so well represented and commonly so well preserved as compression fossils. Leaves and reproductive structures also are well represented in coal-ball assemblages. The most prominent Coal Age types all disappeared by the end of the Permian. A few forms persisted into the Mesozoic, but the seed ferns, as a group, are now extinct.

Although reproduction by means of seeds is inherently more advanced than a free-sporing life cycle, the seed ferns bore their seeds in a more-or-less unprotected fashion attached in various positions to their leaves or in specialized organs called cupules. Depending upon the plant in question, seeds might be produced at the leaf apex, along the margins, in **sinuses** between marginal lobes, or in positions normally occupied by leaflets in the case of compound fronds. The relatively exposed position of the unprotected seeds may have been a factor that made the seed ferns vulnerable to the progressively drier environment of the late Pennsylvanian and Permian.

Pteridosperm leaves

The pinnules of *Alethopteris* Sternberg are thick and leathery and were organized into complex compound frond systems. They are attached by their entire base, which is decurrent and nearly always laterally fused with neighboring pinnules. The midvein is thick and lies at the bottom of a groove on the upper surface of the pinnule, forming a ridgelike projection from the lower surface. Numerous lateral veins arise perpendicularly from the midvein and course in a straight line, with or without forking, to the margin, which is smooth (**entire**). Rachial or accessory veins also pass directly from the leaf axis into the base of the pinnule. The pollen organs are specialized structures and the seeds vary greatly in size and place of origin on the leaf.

Alethopteris bohemica Franke (fig. 23-21.1) has a small oval-triangular terminal pinnule; lateral pinnules are 12 to 18 mm long. The pinnules are rather rigid and closely arranged, and the lateral margins touch but do not overlap. The upper surface is very smooth and has a strong furrow above the midvein that disappears about 2 to 3 mm from the tip. The midvein of the pinna is very wide and straight. The pinnules are similar to *Callipteridium* in appearance, especially if found in red or greenish shales, but can easily be differentiated if venation is evident.

Alethopteris decurrens (Artis) Zeiller (fig. 23-21.2) has long, narrow pinnules 8 to 35 mm long and 2 to 3 mm wide; terminal pinnules may be as much as 4 cm long. Shorter pinnules have an elongated-triangular appearance. All pinnules are somewhat pointed, have an evident decurrent base (hence the name of the plant), and are arranged alternately to subalternately. The midvein runs to the pinnule apex. Moderately thick lateral veins arise nearly perpendicularly to the midvein and extend directly to the margin, either singly or forking once about one-third of the distance to the margin. The sinus between pinnules is V shaped.

The pinnules of *Alethopteris serlii* (Brongniart) Goeppert (fig. 23-21.3) vary greatly in size, from 10 to 40 mm long and 3 to 10 mm wide, but average about three times longer than wide. They are opposite to slightly subopposite and crowded. The convex margins may be recurved or enrolled (see fig. 23-2.3). The terminal pinnule ranges from 15 to 30 mm in length. The numerous fine lateral veins are nearly at right angles to the midvein. Some remain simple, some fork once, and a very few fork a second time. The density of vein endings along the margin ranges from 30 to 35 per cm.

Alethopteris virginiana Fontaine & White (figs. 23-21.4, 23-21.5) pinnules are long and slender, 12 mm long and 3 mm wide, and have parallel margins, although those near the tips of pinnae are shorter and subtriangular to triangular. Some pinnules are twisted or have somewhat irregular margins. The lamina is thick and vaulted. The rather coarse lateral veins depart the prominent midvein at a 90° angle and pass straight to the margin, forking once shortly after departing; a very few divide a second time. The venation is crowded; there are approximately 44 vein endings per centimeter of pinnule border. This plant was originally found and named from the strata above the Waynesburg coal (Washington Formation, lower Dunkard Group) near Cassville, Monongalia County, West Virginia (Fontaine and White, 1880). Wagner (1959) independently named it *A. leonensis* in Europe, where it is widespread and used as an index species for uppermost Carboniferous (Stephanian Stage) strata. The name *A. virginiana* is now accepted as the correct one.

Alethopteris zeillerii (Ragot) Wagner (fig. 23-21.6) is also an index fossil for uppermost Carboniferous (Stephanian Stage) strata in Europe. It is very similar to *A. serlii*, but differs in having a short terminal pinnule, in contrast to the elongated terminal pinnule of *A. serlii*. The necessity of having the complete tip of a pinna and in most cases the entire base of both the pinna and the pinnules reinforces the importance of having a complete specimen for identification of fossil leaves.

Rhachiphyllum Kerp pinnules resemble those of *Alethopteris*. *Rhachiphyllum* was formerly referred to *Callipteris* Brongniart but, after an extensive study of the fundamental characteristics of various collections of *Callipteris*, Kerp (1988a, 1988b) concluded that *Callipteris* foliage should be classified under several different genera. Fertile *Callipteris* foliage was placed in the genus *Autunia* Kessler.

The form genus *Rhachiphyllum* is characterized by a frond that has monopodial apex and intercalated and in many cases prolonged and lobed pinnules on the rachis between the pinnae. The lateral veins are generally thin and bifurcate two to five, but usually two to three times. Accessory or rachial veins are present. The pinnules may vary considerably in length-width ratio (may be two to five times longer than wide) and are roundly tapered to a short tip in the last third of the length. The lower edge of the blade of most pinnules extends downward along the midvein to the next pinnule below. *Rhachiphyllum schenkii* (Heyer) Kerp (fig. 23-22.4) has been found only above the Upper Washington limestone (upper Dunkard Group, Permian) in Ohio.

The natural genus *Autunia* has a dichotomous apex. The pinnules have a strong, usually sunken midvein and lateral veins that are thick, straight, and single or once bifurcated. The intercalated pinnules are seldom if ever lobed. Specimens of *Autunia* (*Callipteris*) *conferta* (Sternberg) Kerp (fig. 23-22.1) were found in Monongalia County, West Virginia, in a freshwater (or possibly slightly brackish) limestone in the upper Dunkard Group just above the top of the Washington coal. This unit is a close stratigraphic equivalent of the horizon in which the only verifiable *Autunia* has been found in Ohio. Fragmentary specimens tentatively identified as *Autunia* (*Callipteris*) have been found in Ohio in a brackish-water zone in and above the Washington coal and at the top of the Lower Washington limestone at several localities in Belmont County and northeastern Monroe County.

The name *Aphlebia* Presl is applied to vascularized foliar organs that are attached to a main rachis near the point of attachment of secondary pinnae. They are generally irregularly lobed or highly dissected leaflike or feathery thalluslike structures. They have irregular tufts, pleats, or folds and indistinct veins. They range in size from a few centimeters to over 30 cm and have been interpreted as anomalous pinnules and/or protective structures. *Aphlebia* sp. (fig. 23-22.2) commonly is associated with dispersed pecopterid and neuropterid foliage.

Callipteridium Weiss is a genus of seed-fern foliage that somewhat resembles *Alethopteris*, but generally has a *Pecopteris*-like aspect. Subsidiary pinnules occur on the rachis between the pinnules of the last orders of branching. Pinnules are attached by their entire base at a low angle or nearly perpendicular to the rachis. The midvein extends nearly to the tip, and rather fine, twice-forked lateral veins reach the margin at an acute angle. The pinnules are crowded and commonly touch on both sides. Accessory veins enter the base on both sides of the midvein. *Callipteridium* sp. (fig. 23-22.3) is a fairly common type of fragmented pinna in many red and green clay shales of the Conemaugh, Monongahela, and lower Dunkard strata.

Cyclopteris Brongniart is a genus of somewhat circular to ovoid pinnules that have neuropteroid venation. Veins radiate from the point of pinnule attachment, dividing dichotomously from one to several times before reaching the pinnule margins. There is no midvein. Most authors place these pinnules under the *Neuropteris* species on which some have been demonstrated to have been borne, but, as they are commonly found detached from *Neuropteris* frond material, they are treated here as a distinct form genus.

Cyclopteris fimbriata Lesquereux (fig. 23-23.1) is consistently associated with *Neuropteris ovata*, although only a few specimens have been found attached. They are borne on the main rachis, range in size from about 2 to 5 cm, and are broadly to deeply fringed (laciniate) along the distal margin, typically beginning in the middle. The fine veins radiate from the generally cordate base and divide from two to several times.

Cyclopteris orbicularis Brongniart (fig. 23-23.2) is a large cyclopterid pinnule borne on the rachis of *Neuropteris*. These pinnules range from about 3 to 12 cm in diameter and are common on *Laveineopteris* (*Neuropteris*) *rarinervis* (Brongniart) Cleal & Shute and *L.* (*N.*) *loshii* (Brongniart) Cleal & Shute axes (species not described or illustrated here). They are more or less circular to broadly oval, cordate or notched at the point of attachment, and have moderately coarse, radiating, widely spaced veins that dichotomize two to several times before reaching the margin.

Cyclopteris trichomanoides Sternberg (fig. 23-21.6) includes the numerous small (1-2.5 cm), detached, circular, orbicular, or somewhat reniform pinnules of the neuropterid group. Thin, crowded veins radiate from the point of attachment and divide three or more times on their way to the margin. Many of these pinnules represent one of the paired pinnules attached at the base of each tongue-shaped leaf of *Macroneuropteris* (*Neuropteris*) *scheuchzeri* (Hoffman) Cleal, Shute & Zodrow.

Dicksonites Sterzel is a genus of pecopteridlike foliage characterized by blunt-tipped pinnules that are at a slight angle to the rachis. The base may be slightly constricted and the margins lobate or sinuous. The midvein is sinuous. Lateral veins fork up to three times, forming characteristic veinlet bundles. *Dicksonites* (*Pecopteris*) *pluckeneti* (Schlotheim) Sterzel (fig. 23-23.5) has fronds that are somewhat rounded in overall appearance. Individual pinnae are stalked. Pinnules are rounded in outline and some are moderately lobed. The margins are not toothed, and the most basal pinnule is normally larger and more developed than the others. The strong veins generally divide three times in their course toward the margin.

Eremopteris Schimper is a genus of fernlike foliage that almost certainly belongs to the pteridophytes. It resembles *Sphenopteris* in overall appearance and is included in that genus by some paleobotanists. The pinnules, however, are generally larger, decurrent, and lack a definite main vein.

In *Eremopteris gracilis* White (fig. 23-23.4), the apical part of the primary pinna has a dense arrangement of sinuous pinnules. The lower margin of each lateral pinnule extends down the rachis as a narrow wing and joins the upper margin of the next pinnule below, near the rachis. Each pinnule is slightly and irregularly lobed or toothed at the terminal end. The main vein enters the axial wing extension at an angle of 80° to 85°, well below the lower edge of the pinnule. The main vein divides immediately, and both veins then divide again where they begin to turn laterally into the main body of the pinnule. Each of the four veins dichotomizes twice more, after which most of the veins continue to the pinnule margin. Pinnules toward the base of the pinnae are typically alternate. The lower lobes on the basal pinnules are alternate to subopposite and generally have three to five unequal lobes. The lower lobes tend to be more deeply notched or dissected than those above. The axial wings on these basal pinnules are inconspicuous or absent.

Lescuropteris Lesquereux has tripinnate fronds that exceed 1.5 meters in length. The pinnules are broadly attached, scythe shaped (falcate), have an acute tip, and measure 12 to 14 mm wide and 25 to 30 mm long. In addition, semicircular pinnules, measuring about 25 mm wide and 10 to 12 mm high, are intercalated on the axis between each two pinnule-bearing axes. The venation in the scythe-shaped pinnules is coarse and widely spaced. A midvein enters at about a 45° angle, turns upward near the center of the pinnule, divides, each vein divides again, and most, although not all, of the resulting veinlets divide yet again. The lateral veinlets may appear to **anastomose**, but a regular network is not formed. A pair of rachial veins generally enters on each side of the midvein; the outer ones divide once and the inner ones divide twice. *Lescuropteris moorii* (Lesquereux) Schimper (figs. 23-23.6, 23-23.7) is the type species. A specimen of *L. moorii* from Pennsylvania bears seeds on the pinnules, similar to another genus, *Emplectopteris*, from China.

Linopteris Presl has strap-shaped pinnules that are attached at a single point, similar to *Neuropteris*, except that the lateral veins anastomose to form a polygonal mesh. The pinnules vary greatly in size according to species, and the fronds are at least tripinnate. *Linopteris neuropteroides* (Gutbier) Zeiller (figs. 23-18.3, 23-23.8) has pinnules similar in outline to those of *Paripteris* (*Neuropteris*) *gigantea* (see fig. 23-25.7). They are about three times as long as broad, slightly cordate at the base, have a clearly defined point of attachment, and the upper third curves laterally while tapering to a rounded tip. As with *P.* (*N*). *gigantea*, the tip of each ultimate axis of *L. neuropteroides* bears double terminal pinnules. The pinnules average about 1 cm by 3 cm. The midvein is not strongly evident. Thin lateral veins depart at a narrow angle, ascend along the midvein briefly, then arch to the margin, anastomosing to form rather perfect, narrow, sharply pointed meshes or networks on the way. The number of meshes between the midvein and the margin average about eight.

Mariopteris Zeiller is characterized by a naked primary axis that bifurcates, then both branches immediately bifurcate again. These axes generally exhibit transverse bars. The pinnules are opposite, subopposite, or alternate and have pinnate or bipinnate ultimate divisions, varying with the species and the position on the frond. The pinnules are broadly attached and commonly decurrent or stalked; margins are entire or lobate. The basal pinnule commonly is larger and bilobed. The ultimate axis is prolonged into a spinelike tip. Pinnule veins are prominent; a midvein that may be basally decurrent extends about two-thirds of the length of the pinnule and has alternate lateral veins at an acute angle. These lateral veins may be further divided. The pinnule lamina appears to have been thick and possibly leathery (coriaceous).

Mariopteris muricata (Schlotheim) Zeiller (fig. 23-24.1) has elongated, triangular pinnules that are four to five times as long as wide. The margins tend to be asymmetrically wavy to weakly lobed.

Mariopteris nervosa (Brongniart) Zeiller (fig. 23-24.2), the type species, exhibits considerable variability in pinnule form, although specific patterns are more or less constant for individual parts. The primary characteristic is strong, widely spaced venation in a pinnule that is thick, leathery, more-or-less triangular (length-to-width ratio equals 1:1.5), and has entire margins. This species is thought to have evolved from *M. muricata*.

Pseudomariopteris Danzé-Corsin resembles *Mariopteris* in pinnule venation, presence of some spinelike prolongations of the ultimate rachises, and excessively developed basal pinnules, but differs in not having transverse bars on the rachises. *Pseudomariopteris* occurs only in Upper Pennsylvanian strata. The pinnules of *Pseudomariopteris* cf. *P. busqueti* (Zeiller) Danzé-Corsin (fig. 23-23.3) are divided into three major lobes. The basal lobes are unbalanced ovate; the largest lobes generally are incised into two, three, or more elongated lobes, each drawn into short, sharp tips. The pinna rachis is straight and rigid, and some parts are ridged or grooved.

Megalopteris (Dawson) Andrews fronds range from about 10 to 30 cm in length. The terminal end of the simply compound pinna is deeply split, more or less palmately, into straplike lobes or pinnules that have sharp or rounded tips. The lower pinnules are at low angles to the main axis; the upper ones are at higher angles. The main rachis below the pinnules is winged in some species. Pinnule bases are strongly decurrent and commonly asymmetrical. The midvein is very wide and slightly recessed on the upper side but forms a thick ridge on the underside. Lateral veins depart from the main veins at a 15° to 60° angle, curve slightly, and divide at least once immediately after departing the main axis. Some veins divide one to three more times before reaching the margin. Rachial veins generally are present in the lower part of the pinnule. Complete fronds, or even pinnae, are rarely found.

Megalopteris ovata Andrews (figs. 23-24.5, 23-24.6) is the name E. B. Andrews (1875) applied to large detached, in some cases bifurcated pinnules, 3 to 6 cm and more wide and 24 cm or more long. They are comparable in size and shape to *M. dawsonii* (Hartt) Andrews (see fig. 23-24.4), but the venation is slightly different. The veins divide twice soon after leaving the midvein, but pass to the margin at a lower angle than those in *M. dawsonii*. Most veins do not fork again, but pass almost straight to the margin. This species is one of several important plants that Andrews described from the Rushville flora in Perry County (see section on localities on p. 418).

Megalopteris minima Andrews (fig. 23-24.3) has lateral veins that emerge from the conspicuous midvein at an acute angle, divide twice or in a few cases three times, bending somewhat abruptly toward the margin at the first division and then continuing in a broad curve. The **paratype** in figure 23-24.3, also from the Rushville flora, shows a tip of a pinna, or it may represent a different growth stage than the much larger **holotype**, in which the pinnules measure about 6 to 7 mm wide and 35 to 50 mm long.

Megalopteris cf. *M. dawsonii* (Hartt) Andrews (fig. 23-24.4) has pinnately dissected leaves in which the lobes depart at an angle of 40° to 50°, prominent decurrent pinnules, and rachial veins in the wings on the main rachis or on the midvein of the pinna, all typical characteristics of *M. dawsonii* (the type species). The veins emanating from the midvein of each lobe on the specimen in figure 23-24.4 are coarser and have a lower angle as they approach the margin than in more typical *M. dawsonii* specimens. An unusual feature on some specimens, especially *M. dawsonii* from the Rushville locality as well as a few specimens from

Indiana and Michigan, is the dots, which in figure 23-24.4 appear as holes or spaces lined up between the veins as they arch toward the margin. As many as 10 dots occur between some veins. The origin of these dots is not clear, but they may represent secretions or deposits of gum or resin, as the dots in acetate peels of some specimens have an amber, brown, or gold color.

Seeds in definitive attachment to fronds or pinnae of *Megalopteris* have not been reported. However, abundant seeds assigned to the genus *Samaropsis* Goeppert (see fig. 23-28.1) have been found in association with *Megalopteris* pinnules and broken or incomplete fronds at some localities.

The form genus *Neuropteris* was established by Brongniart in 1822 for compound fronds, found mostly in the Carboniferous, whose broad pinnules have a constricted base and venation that does not anastomose (see Cleal and Shute, 1995). These fronds are typically about 2 meters long but may be up to 7 meters long and are classified in the Medullosales. *Neuropteris* impressions and compressions are common and easily recognized leaf fossils in the coal-bearing rocks of Ohio. Their pinnules are usually blunt tipped and attached at a single point instead of the entire base. Oval to round pinnules (see *Cyclopteris*, fig. 23-23.2) occur at the base of the larger pinnae on some species and at various places on the frond axis on others.

As originally described, *Neuropteris* was a large and obviously quite artificial genus, but pinnule morphology and venation patterns were not enough to separate this form genus into more natural genera. Pinnules that have a similar form but whose veins are united into a **reticulate** network are classified as *Linopteris* Presl or *Reticulopteris* Gothan. Several authors attempted to sort out more natural genera, but, overall, *Neuropteris* remained essentially unchanged. A breakthrough occurred when Cleal and Zodrow (1989) and later Cleal, Shute, and Zodrow (1990), on the basis of cuticular studies, were able to recognize discrete groups that also had distinctive gross morphology. At the current time, most paleobotanists recognize nine genera in the *Neuropteris* complex: *Neuropteris, Neurocallipteris, Macroneuropteris, Paripteris, Laveineopteris, Margaritopteris, Neuralethopteris, Neurodontopteris*, and *Sphenoneuropteris*. These taxonomic refinements of the original neuropterid complex are proving helpful in the biostratigraphic zonation of Carboniferous strata.

Neuropteris heterophylla (Brongniart) Sternberg (figs. 23-25.1, 23-25.2, 23-25.7) is the type species. The pinnules are 4 to 8 mm wide, 10 to 20 mm long, and ovate. The average length is about 1.5 times the width. The terminal pinnule is significantly longer. The midvein is not apparent in the upper third of the pinnule. Lateral veins are thin, originate at an acute angle, and divide about one-third of the way on their gradually curving course to the margin. In the basal two-thirds of the pinnule, each resulting veinlet typically divides again. Pinnae that have pinnules with enlarged (3-4 cm), fringed (laciniate) margins are present on the primary and secondary rachises.

Neuropteris ovata Hoffman (fig. 23-25.6) has straight-sided, round-tipped pinnules characterized by a nearly straight base. The upper corner is rounded and the lower corner is prolonged into an **auricle** or ear. The midvein is indefinite. Lateral veins arch gradually toward the margin, dividing two and in some cases three times. The large terminal pinnule is asymmetrical. Large *Cyclopteris*-like pinnules (fig. 23-23.1) on pinnae borne on the primary axis have fringed upper margins.

Neurocallipteris (Neuropteris) neuropteroides (Goeppert) Cleal, Shute & Zodrow, which is not illustrated here, is very similar to *Neuropteris ovata*, and probably is a descendant of that plant, as it appears immediately following it in the geologic record. Without cuticular studies, it may be impossible to separate many specimens of *N. (N.) neuropteroides* from *N. ovata*. Generally, however, the pinnules of *N. (N.) neuropteroides* are much shorter, the tip is more rounded, the terminal pinnule has a bulge on one side, and the midvein may be visible in the lower part of the pinnule.

Macroneuropteris (Neuropteris) scheuchzeri (Hoffman) Cleal, Shute & Zodrow (figs. 23-25.3, 23-25.4) fronds are 5 meters or more in length, 2 meters or more in width, and composed of hundreds of pinnules. The pinnules range from about 4 to 10 cm in length and 8 to 25 mm in width. The pinnule base is broadly cordate and the pinnule narrows distally to a usually blunt tip. Numerous 1.5- to 3-mm-long hairs are prominent on the lower surface and are present on the upper surface, especially along the midvein. Two oval cyclopterid pinnules (fig. 23-21.6) are attached near the base of many of the larger pinnules, and large cyclopterid pinnules are present on the main and secondary rachises. When the pinnules break off the axis of a main rachis, downward-directed stubs or pointed projections resembling spines remain (fig. 23-25.5).

Macroneuropteris (Neuropteris) macrophylla (Brongniart) Cleal, Shute & Zodrow, which is not illustrated here, is like *M. (N). scheuchzeri*, but lacks hairs on the upper and lower surfaces of the pinnules. It is the type species. The large cyclopterid pinnules on the main rachis may be as much as 12 cm in length.

Paripteris (Neuropteris) gigantea (Sternberg) Gothan (fig. 23-25.7) is the type species for this genus of neuropterid-type pinnae having two terminal pinnules. The pinnules typically are curved at the tip, giving them a sickle shape (falcate). They range from 4 to 10 mm wide and 10 to 35 mm long. The midvein is noticeable for about two-thirds of the length of the pinnule, but may be hard to see in small pinnules. The lateral veins each fork several times and intersect the margin at an acute angle.

Odontopteris Brongniart has pinnules that are attached by the entire base. Several veins enter the base and divide one or more times before reaching the margin. *Odontopteris* becomes more abundant in Upper Pennsylvanian and Lower Permian strata in Ohio and adjacent states.

Odontopteris brardii (Brongniart) Sternberg (fig. 23-26.1) is characterized by sickle-shaped pinnules up to 1.5 cm long and 7 mm wide. Several thin veins enter the base and divide one to several times before reaching the margin. It is a common form in Dunkard Group rocks in Monroe, Washington, and Belmont Counties.

Odontopteris osmundaeformis (Schlotheim) Zeiller (fig. 23-26.3) has parallel-sided, round-tipped pinnules of varying size (4-12 mm) that are nearly as wide as long. The several veins are moderately coarse and fork only once or twice as they pass to the margin. Fossils of this species typically are found as impressions in the green-gray to purplish-red clay shales of the upper Monongahela, Conemaugh, and Dunkard Groups in southeastern Ohio.

Orthogoniopteris Andrews is the name applied to simply pinnate fronds very similar to those of *Megalopteris dawsonii*, except for the unusual vein patterns. The fronds are also similar to those of *Taeniopteris* (figs. 23-27.3, 23-27.4), except that *Orthogoniopteris* produces pinnately compound fronds (fig. 23-26.2). It is also virtually identical to fronds known as *Megalopteris kelleyi*, commonly found at Grand Ledge sites in the Michigan Basin. The frond axis of *Orthogoniopteris* is about 3 mm wide. The pinnules are alternate, linear, entire, attached by their entire base, and decurrent, at least toward the terminal end of the frond. Pinnules are attached to the rachial axis at an angle ranging from 35° to 45° and taper to a sharp point. A portion of the basal edge of each pinnule typically overlaps the upper edge of the pinnule below. The midvein is prominent and visible to the tip. Lateral veins are fine, very crowded, and depart from the midvein at an acute angle, then immediately turn almost horizontally, following a straight path to the pinnule margin, which they intersect at an angle of 90°. In essence, *Orthogoniopteris* represents a pinnate form of the basic taeniopterid leaf.

Orthogoniopteris clara Andrews (fig. 23-26.2) is the type species. The holotype frond, from the Rushville flora locality in Perry County, is 37 cm long. Pinnules are 9 to 11 cm long and 1.8 to 2 cm wide. Lateral veins number approximately 35/cm along the pinnule margin. The only other species of the genus, *O. gilbertii* Andrews, not illustrated here, was collected as small, broken pieces from the Rushville locality. *Orthogoniopteris gilbertii* is quite similar to *O. clara* but has a relatively thicker axis (5 mm in the only known specimen) and the pinnules are about 6 cm long and 1.5 cm wide. The venation pattern of the two taxa is similar, but the lateral veins of *O. gilbertii* have a higher density at the margin (approximately 45/cm).

Palmatopteris Potonié is characterized by pinnules of sphenopterid aspect. The pinnules typically are subdivided again into slender segments, following the bifurcation of the veins. The distinguishing characteristic is the widely divergent, regular dichotomous branching of the flexible axis; the first pinnule turns downward or back in the direction of the axis.

Palmatopteris furcata (Brongniart) Potonié (fig. 23-26.6) is several times pinnate. Pinnules dichotomize into three to four acute-tipped, linear segments; the ultimate segments are about 1 mm wide and 7 to 8 mm long. Although highly dissected, the pinnules are somewhat circular in outline. The single vein is generally clearly visible in each segment. The rachises of the secondary branches, and even of the pinnae, are as wide (thick) as the primary segments of the pinnae.

Protoblechnum Lesquereux has a simply pinnate leaf or frond 30 to 60 cm long. It is more or less **oblanceolate** in overall appearance. The longest pinnules are above the middle of the whole leaf (or frond). The central axis (rachis of the compound leaf) is thick (1 cm) and scaly at the base. The pinnules are 4 to 8 cm long and 1.5 to 2 cm wide. They are subalternate near the base of the frond to subopposite near the tip. The prominent midvein of the pinnule extends to the apex. The pinnules are decurrent, have an auricle, and taper from the base to the long, pointed tip. Lateral veins curve and divide once just after exiting the midvein and again about one-third of the way to the margin, which they intersect at an acute angle. *Protoblechnum holdenii* (Andrews) Lesquereux (figs. 23-26.4, 23-26.5) is typical of the genus. The illustrated specimen was collected in 1952 at the original Rushville flora site where, 80 years earlier, E. B. Andrews had collected the holotype, which he named *Alethopteris holdenii* (Andrews, 1875).

Some characteristics of *Rhacopteris* Schimper are similar to those of *Sphenopteris*. Both pinnae and pinnules are stalked. The multiple branching of the main vein of a pinnule is sphenopterid but the veins are straighter and moderately strong.

Rhacopteris cf. *R. elegans* (Ettingshausen) Schimper (figs. 23-27.1, 23-27.2) is a beautiful fernlike frond from the Rushville flora site. It was originally described by Andrews (1875, p. 418) as *Archaeopteris stricta*. The first-order pinnae diverge from the main rachis (midrib of frond) suboppositely or alternately at angles of 45° to 75°; some are nearly at right angles. Each pinna bears simple, stalked, alternate to subopposite pinnules at angles of 50° to 75°. Each pinnule has up to 16 veins, derived from two to four dichotomies. The straight, strong veins extend directly to the margins like a straight-ribbed fan. No reproductive structures are known.

Sphenopteris Brongniart is described in the section on true ferns, although, when dealing with sterile material (lacking sporangia, ovules, pollen organs, or seeds), it is not possible to distinguish remains derived from true ferns from those produced by most Paleozoic seed ferns.

Taeniopteris Brongniart is now classified as a cycadlike plant (see table 22-1), but is included here with the seed ferns. The leaves of *Taeniopteris* are simple, linear, and have a wide midvein and a leathery appearance. The thick midvein forms a ridge on the underside (**abaxial** surface) (fig. 23-27.3). The midvein on the upper (**adaxial**) surface (fig. 23-27.4) is marked by a deep groove that extends the length of the leaf. The lateral veins arise perpendicularly and pass straight to the margin or arise at a steep angle and turn almost immediately, then pass to the margin on a straight line that intersects the margin at about 90°. Lateral veins are undivided or divide one to three times. Leaves range in size from 1 to 6 cm in width and 10 to 30 cm in length. *Taeniopteris jejunata* Grand 'Eury is the only species found to date in Ohio.

Pteridosperm reproductive structures

Bilaterally symmetrical seeds that have a broad winglike appendage (wall extension) surrounding the greater circumference (primary plane) of the ovule are assigned to the form genus *Samaropsis* Goeppert (fig. 23-28.1). The seeds are found in fossil beds in association with *Walchia* (an early conifer, see p. 418), *Megalopteris*, and *Cordaites* leaves but have not been found attached. Compressed specimens look much like overly large *Cardiocarpus* seeds (cordaitaleans), but have a broader marginal wing. This wing or flange is a flattened marginal zone of the ovular integument, which may consist of two or more definable tissue layers. They have been found in Ohio at the Rushville flora locality, at two sites in Indiana, and in Michigan at Grand Ledge, in fossil beds dominated by *Megalopteris* species. No *Walchia* specimens have been found at these localities. The outline of *Samaropsis* ranges from heart shaped to harp shaped; there is an apical notch or saddle in the area of the **micropyle**, surmounted by peripheral lobes of the winglike wall. A central ovule with an attenuated micropyle can be clearly seen on the specimen on the left in figure 23-28.1.

Trigonocarpus Brongniart (fig. 23-28.4) is a seed characterized by three prominent longitudinal ribs, extending from base to apex, that divide the seed into three equal valves. A minor rib may be noted between each of the three major ribs, extending from the base partway to the tip. The seeds are somewhat common as sandstone casts and range from 1 to 8 cm in length and 0.3 to 4 cm in diameter. The seeds were borne on medullosan axes bearing neuropterid and alethopterid foliage. Permineralized seed remains of the same general type that preserve internal structure and cellular detail are placed in the genus *Pachytesta* Brongniart. Specimens that have more ridges are placed in other genera such as *Rhabdocarpus* Goeppert & Berger (fig. 23-28.2) or *Holcospermum* Nathorst (fig. 23-28.5). When compressed, seeds may appear to have more than three ribs and may be assigned to still other form genera.

A variety of conspicuous seeds of less certain affinity are commonly found in Pennsylvanian collections. One example is *Carpolithes* Schlotheim (fig. 23-28.3). These specimens lack diagnostic features that would permit placement in a specific group or genus.

The several different pollen organs of medullosan seed ferns are rather large. All are composed of multiple sporangia united into synangia of considerable diversity. Three taxa of pollen organs are considered to be associated with medullosan seed ferns. One type collected from Ohio is *Aulacotheca campbellii* (White) Halle (fig. 23-28.10), an elongate, capsulelike structure, 1.5 cm long, consisting of a row of linear sporangia fused in a circle around a hollow center. Another is *Whittleseya elegans* Newberry (fig. 23-28.9), first discovered in the roof shales of the Sharon (No. 1) coal in Ohio. It also consists of elongate, tubular sporangia. This organ is a bell-shaped (campanulate) synangium, in which the tubular sporangia form the wall of the bell. However, as seen in figure 23-28.9, when compressed, it resembles a small, longitudinally ribbed leaf. A third type of pollen organ is *Dolerotheca* Halle (figs. 23-28.6, 23-28.7), a relatively large, complex, campanulate structure that has the tubular sporangia embedded in a ground tissue. When the internal anatomy can be reconstructed, as in permineralized material from coal balls, some *Dolerotheca* specimens are referred to the genus *Bernaultia* Rothwell & Eggert.

Remains of pollen organs of lyginopterid seed ferns are relatively rare, or possibly not yet known, in Ohio. The most common organ genus that has been assigned to the lyginopterids in the U.S. is *Crossotheca* Zeiller (fig. 23-28.8). This genus is a short, many-branched pinna structure having a loose arrangement of arrowhead-shaped pinnules, each bearing marginal pendulous synangia. However, some paleobotanists have assigned *Crossotheca* to the true ferns.

CORDAITALES—THE CORDAITES

The cordaites, represented primarily by the genus *Cordaites* Unger, are an extinct order of distinctive Upper Paleozoic seed plants that are well-represented in the Pennsylvanian rocks of Ohio. Stem and leaf compressions can be noted at most fossil-plant localities in Ohio. The growth habit of these plants ranged from shrubs to small trees. It has been proposed that some species may have had an ecological role similar to modern mangroves, in that a shrubby form was tolerant of brackish water and formed dense stands along distributary channels, well within the range of tidal influence. Other species, including the larger arborescent forms, were distributed in depressions along upper distributaries and in lowlands behind river levees.

The most distinctive feature of the cordaites is their relatively narrow, parallel-sided, straplike leaves (figs.23-25.7, 23-29.1, 23-29.2), which were up to a meter long. Although the name *Cordaites* has been applied to the plant as a whole, the name is most properly applied to compression leaf remains. The leaves of *Cordaites* are easily recognized, even in fragmentary condition, by the numerous distinctive veins that are parallel to the long axis of the leaf. These leaves were spirally arranged on stems that are called *Cordaixylon*, if anatomical features are preserved, or *Cordaicladus*, if compressed and carbonized. Cordaitean wood is a common constituent of coal balls; *Mesoxylon* is one of the more common types identified by anatomical features of the wood (Rothwell, 1988b).

Cordaites principalis Germar (figs. 23-29.1 to 23-29.3) is characterized by narrow, lanceolate leaves up to 50 cm long and 6 cm wide. The leaves have a short taper at the tip. From one to six, but generally two to three, false veins occur between each pair of large veins. The large veins range from 15 to 30 per centimeter of width. Split leaf tips are common.

The arborescent cordaitean stems had a prominent pith cavity, interrupted at closely spaced intervals by distinctive septa. When cordaitean branches and trunks were inundated or fell into the swamp, the cells of the central pith cavity commonly decayed, leaving a void that, when filled with sediment, hardened to form a pith cast. These pith casts, which are not uncommon as fossils, are named *Artisia* Sternberg (fig. 23-29.4). They are cylindrical, 1.5 to 9 cm in diameter, and have numerous irregular, transverse ridges that are anastomosed in many specimens. These ridges mark the slightly thickened remnant margins of the septa.

Seeds and pollen of the Cordaitales were produced on small, loosely organized, **microphyllous** branch systems called *Cordaitanthus* Feistmantel (figs. 23-29.5, 23-29.6), borne in the **axils** of the much larger vegetative leaves. These *Cordaites* fructifications range from 10 to 25 cm in length. The axis has two rows of dwarf shoots or "cones" from which monosaccate pollen (pollen grain surrounded by a single bladder or membranous sac) and heart-shaped ovules were produced. Most of the microsporophylls of these lateral branchlets were sterile, but some, near the apex of the branch system, produced fingerlike pollen sacs (fig. 23-29.6). Other branchlets consisted primarily of sterile scales but, near the apex of the branch system, produced ovules at the ends of thin stalks at the terminal end of the modified leaves. When fertilized, the ovules developed into small, distinctive heart-shaped seeds known as *Mitrospermum* Arber (fig. 23-29.7) and *Cardiocarpus* Brongniart (fig. 23-29.8). Dispersal of the seeds was apparently quite effective, for the seeds commonly are found at localities where other cordaitean remains are rare or absent.

In addition to their possibly unique ecological role in the plant communities of the Carboniferous, the cordaites are significant in that some paleobotanists believe they were the ancestors of the conifers. Although at first glance cordaites seem to have little in common with today's conifers such as spruce, fir, and pine, evolutionary trends within the cordaites point very convincingly toward the origin of the prominent woody cones that characterize the female reproductive apparatus of most ancient and modern conifers. Most, if not all, cordaites appear to have become extinct by the end of the Permian. Their exposed ovules/seeds may have made them vulnerable to the climatic change that became progressively more severe during the Permian. In contrast, the conifers, which may have evolved from ancestral cordaites, were much better adapted to dry conditions and prospered and diversified in the Mesozoic.

VOLTZIALES—UPPER PALEOZOIC CONIFERS

Conifers (Coniferales) are seed plants, mostly trees (there are a few shrublike growth forms), that have needlelike leaves and produce cones as part of their sexual life cycle.

Most modern conifers, such as spruce, fir, and pine, are evergreen, that is, some leaves are always present as a result of a controlled, continuous rate of shedding. But some species, such as the bald cypress of the southeastern United States and the tamarack or larch of northern **bogs**, are deciduous, that is, the leaves are shed seasonally. Conifers as a group first appeared in the Late Pennsylvanian.

Conifers are not common in the Coal Age deposits of Ohio. They have been found in Conemaugh Group shales, such as at the 7-11 site in Columbiana County, and in scattered Dunkard localities. Conifers made their first appearance, in an evolutionary sense, very near to the time that the richest period in Ohio's fossil-plant history was drawing to a close. The earliest conifers are easily recognized, when well preserved, on the basis of their distinctive foliage and include plants such as *Utrechtia*, *Lebachia*, and *Emporia*. When poorly preserved, these plants are assigned to the form genus *Walchia* Sternberg (figs. 23-30.1, 23-30.3).The spiral arrangement of the small needles and formal branching pattern of these plants is almost identical to that of a modern conifer, the Norfolk Island pine (*Araucaria excelsis*), a common decorative indoor plant for homes and offices.

Isolated ovulate "coniferous" cones that cannot be specifically correlated with foliage genera are assigned to the form genus *Walchiostrobus* Florin (fig. 23-30.4). These cones are somewhat variable in size, ranging from 1 by 4 cm to 3 by 10 cm. When the bifurcated bracts of these cones are found singly in rocks, they are assigned to *Gomphostrobus* Marion. The cones of the early conifers were much more loosely organized than those of some extant types, such as pine, spruce, or fir. Cone morphology is used as evidence for the derivation of the conifers from the cordaites by botanists favoring that lineage.

All of the seed plants discussed so far, including the conifers, belong to a group of seed plants informally known as gymnosperms—a term meaning "naked seed." The exposed ovules/seeds of the seed ferns, cordaites, and conifers are clear examples of seeds produced generally without elaborate protective structures, such as the ovary/fruit of the more advanced flowering plants, the **angiosperms**. The exposed nature of the ovules of the seed ferns and cordaites may well have been a factor in the decline and extinction of these groups by the end of the Permian Period. Although conifers are also gymnosperms, because the ovules and the resulting seeds are borne on the surface of the female cone scales, the structure of the conifer cone provides a high measure of protection. The spirally arranged cone scales of extant conifers are densely packed and, as a result, when the cone is closed, there is a degree of protection equivalent to the ovary of flowering plants.

This protection, together with the small, needlelike leaves, meant that conifers could more readily adapt to the ever drier conditions of the late Permian and early Triassic. Although the most archaic conifers became extinct during this interval, more advanced conifers rapidly evolved to fill numerous ecological niches vacated by the diminution or extinction of free-sporing plants and less advanced seed plants. The conifers were perhaps the most abundant plant group during most of the Mesozoic, although several other gymnosperms, including the cycads, and bennettites were very conspicuous.

The precise time of cessation of Paleozoic sediment deposition and rock formation in Ohio is unknown. The strata of the Dunkard Group of late Pennsylvanian to early Permian age are the youngest rocks present in southeastern Ohio, western West Virginia, and southwestern Pennsylvania and are terminated by an erosional surface. Thus, an unknown amount (thickness) of younger sedimentary rocks is believed to have been removed by erosion. As a consequence, most of the history of conifers and more advanced seed plants, including the angiosperms, is unrecorded in Ohio fossil deposits. The historical record of fossil plants in Ohio was resumed about a million years ago during the Pleistocene Epoch of the Quaternary Period. The Quaternary record is discussed in Chapter 24.

SIGNIFICANT COLLECTING LOCALITIES

Numerous localities in Ohio have provided excellent plant fossils. Some of the more significant localities are listed below. Localities in strip mines in many cases are no longer accessible because they have been reclaimed. Also, as stated many times in this volume, all localities belong to someone, and the landowner's permission must be obtained before entering a site to collect. Furthermore, strip mines and road cuts are dangerous places, and extreme caution should be exercised at these sites.

At Beaver Pond east of Peebles, in Adams County, in the headwaters of Scioto Creek, concretions in the lower Ohio Shale (Upper Devonian) contain *Callixylon*. Irregular small, broken blocks of *Callixylon* also weather out.

Blocks and slivers of *Callixylon* and, rarely, parts of logs have been found in stream cuts in the Ohio Shale along Ohio Route 37 and southward in central and southeastern Delaware County.

An excellent fossil compression flora is present along a road paralleling an east headwater branch of Wyatt Creek, 3.3 km (2 miles) west of Broadwell, 2.2 km (1.4 miles) south-southwest of Utley, and 4 km (2.5 miles) north of Kilvert, near the southwest corner of Berne Township (SE¼SW¼ sec. 25), Athens County. The plants are in the Cassville shale, between two benches of the Waynesburg (No. 11) coal (Monongahela-Dunkard transition zone, Pennsylvanian-Permian).

The J. H. Hoskins Collection at the Cleveland Museum of Natural History contains plant fossils collected from many localities in Ohio. An especially large collection came from the roof shale of the Upper Freeport (No. 7) coal (Allegheny-Conemaugh transition zone, Pennsylvanian) in strip mines, now reclaimed, in the vicinity of Kimberly, about 3.2 to 5 km (2-3 miles) southeast of Nelsonville, near the center of York Township (secs. 16, 17, 28, 29), Athens County.

Fossil plants have been collected from the roof shale of the Upper Freeport (No. 7) coal (Allegheny-Conemaugh transition zone) in strip mines (some reclaimed) and old drift mines near Buchtel and Doanville, about 3.2 km (2 miles) east of Nelsonville in York Township (secs. 5 and 6), Athens County.

A prolific flora (as well as insects and other animals; see Cross, 1988; McComas, 1988; McComas and Mapes, 1988) was collected in a strip mine, called the 7-11 mine by paleontologists, 1.3 km (0.8 mile) northwest of the junction of Ohio Route 7 and Ohio Route 11/U.S. Route 30, in Madison Township (N½ sec. 13, T10N, R2W), Columbiana County. A channel-fill sequence of Conemaugh age cut into the roof shales down to the top of the Upper Freeport (No. 7) coal is overlain by the Mahoning coal and above that the marine Brush Creek limestone, which is about 18 to 30 meters above the Upper Freeport coal, depending on the presence and thickness of shale or sandstone above the Mahoning coal. This strip mine was operated by several different coal companies and is now reclaimed.

Excellent specimens of fossil plants have been collected in and above the marine shale below the Middle Kittanning (No. 6) coal (middle Allegheny Group) in abandoned strip mines on the northwest edge of Nelsonville, north of U.S. Route 33 at first main ravine north and east from Dorr Run, in Ward Township (SW¼SE¼ sec. 25), Hocking County. A few compression fossils also are associated with the shales above and below the Lower Kittanning (No. 5) coal at this locality.

Old strip mines and road cuts in the vicinity of Coalton and Wellston, in Milton Township, Jackson County, produced fossil plants, probably from the Quakertown (No. 2) coal (also called the Wellston or Jackson Hill coal) (Pottsville Group, Pennsylvanian).

Plant fossils have been collected from stream beds, road cuts, former mine dumps, and small strip-mining operations south and west of Jackson, in Jackson, Liberty, and Scioto Townships, Jackson County. The productive units were the roof shales of the Sharon (No. 1) coal (Pottsville Group) above the Sharon conglomerate.

Old strip mines and road cuts in the vicinity of the Walton mine, now reclaimed, in Milton Township (sec. 33?), Jackson County, produced plant fossils from the roof shale of the Brookville (No. 4) or Clarion (No. 4A) coal (lower Allegheny Group); these coals are separated by 4 to 5 meters of clay and shale.

Stigmarian roots and stumps were collected in underclays below and above the Middle Kittanning (No. 6) coal (middle Allegheny Group) along the bluffs of Yellow Creek along Ohio Route 213, 0.6 km (0.3 mile) southwest of its junction with Ohio Route 7, 3.5 km (2.2 miles) south of Wellsville, in Saline Township (NE¼NW¼ sec. 7, T4N, R2W), Jefferson County.

Coal balls have been collected at the roadside outcrop in the Ohio River bluffs at the mouth of Yellow Creek above Ohio Route 7, about 300 meters south of the bridge over the railroad, in north-central Saline Township (sec. 7, T4N, R2W), Jefferson County. The beds are in association with the Lower Freeport (No. 6A) and the Upper Freeport (No. 7) coals (upper Allegheny Group) just below the massive Mahoning sandstone. Fossil wood also has been found about 200 meters south of the bridge in a ditch and in a sandstone lens in shale below the Upper Freeport coal.

The Steubenville coal-ball locality (Cross, 1988; Rothwell, 1988a) is along U.S. Route 22, 150 to 350 meters west of the Cross Creek bridge, 14.5 km (9 miles) west of its junction with Ohio Route 7 in Steubenville, in Wayne Township (SE¼SE¼ sec. 6, T9N, R3W), Jefferson County. The coal balls are mainly in local masses in the Duquesne coal (Conemaugh Group) on the south side of the highway (see fig. 23-3). They weather out and roll down the slope as far as the road ditch, where they are easily collected. Some coal balls also are found in the "Ames" (Harlem?) coal.

Another of the few known sites for coal balls in Ohio was in a strip mine in the Anderson coal (Conemaugh Group) operated by the Horizon Coal Corp. 1.8 km (1.1 miles) northwest of Bloomfield, in Highland Township (NW¼NE¼ sec. 10), Muskingum County. The flora has been described by Pigg and Rothwell (1983).

The clay pits of the Rush Creek Clay Co. in Perry County once had excellent exposures of the Middle Kittanning (No. 6) coal and associated clays that contained abundant well-preserved compression floras. These pits, which are now abandoned and overgrown or are building sites, were on the north side of Ohio Route 37, 400 meters (0.25 mile) east of its junction with Ohio Route 668 at Junction City.

The classic Rushville flora locality was discovered in the 1860's by E. B. Andrews, who described (Andrews, 1875) several new plants from this site. It is located 3.2 km (2 miles) east of Rushville near the intersection of Avalon Road and Old Stage Coach Road in Reading Township (sec. 26), Perry County. The collection site is very restricted—a 2- or 3-meter space along the road ditch in a thin (5-7 cm thick), hard, carbonaceous or bituminous shale at the Quakertown (No. 2) or Bear Run coal horizon (Pottsville Group), 7 to 10 meters above the Mississippian-age Maxville Limestone.

The Blickle-Lambert collection at Ohio University came from the roof shale of the Sharon (No. 1) coal (Pottsville Group) along roads and in an old local mine entry mainly west of Ohio Route 335 about 6.4 km (4 miles) southwest of Beaver in Marion Township (secs. 17, 19, 20, 28, 29), Pike County.

Plant fossils were collected from the roof shale of the Clarion (No. 4A)? coal (lower Allegheny Group) in a road cut on U.S. Route 50 and in stream-bed exposures 2.4 km (1.5 miles) east of Hooper Park, north of Elk Run, in Elk Township (secs. 26, 27), Vinton County. Strip mines and old exposures along stream beds and roads in secs. 14, 15, 23, and 24 of Elk Township produced similar floras.

Rocks and plant fossils are not restricted by political boundaries, and some of the best collecting localities for Pennsylvanian-age floras similar to the Ohio fossil flora are in West Virginia (see Gillespie and others, 1978), Pennsylvania, Indiana, and Illinois. Another notable site is at Grand Ledge, Michigan. The locations of some of these collecting sites are given in the figure captions of specimens from these sites.

ACKNOWLEDGMENTS

We extend our thanks to the curators and other officials at the following institutions for permission to examine several thousand specimens in their collections and to photograph several hundred: The Cleveland Museum of Natural History, J. H. Hoskins Paleobotanical Collections; Ohio University, Fossil Plant Herbarium; West Virginia University; West Virginia Geological and Economic Survey; University of Michigan Museum of Paleontology; Michigan State University, Fossil Plant Herbarium. We thank the staff members at these institutions for their cordial encouragement and help in locating, examining, and identifying specimens, especially Shya D. Chitaley and several volunteer assistants (The Cleveland Museum of Natural History); Gar W. Rothwell, Arthur H. Blickle (retired), Gene K. Mapes, and Rudolph Serbet (Ohio University); Bascome M. (Mitch) Blake (West Virginia Geological and Economic Survey); Robyn J. Burnham (University of Michigan Museum of Paleontology); and former graduate students Richard Carroll, Patrick Fields, and Huang Wei (Michigan State University). We also thank Geology Librarian Diane K. Baclawski (Michigan State University) for considerable assistance; Aleen Cross for patient typing of many editions of this manuscript; Lisa Van Doren (Ohio Division of Geological Survey) for digital enhancement of some of the illustrations; Dr. Chitaley for loan of photographs; and John C. Ferm (University of Kentucky) for loan of the specimen in figure 23-20.3.

FIGURE 23-1.—*Archaeopteris*, an Upper Devonian progymnosperm. The woody parts are called *Callixylon*. Figures 23-1.1 and 23-1.2 are reproduced from Beck (1964), and figure 23-1.3 is reproduced from Wells (1939), all with permission.

1 Reconstruction of the *Archaeopteris* Dawson tree. Scale bar equals 2 meters.

2 Branch and parts of three fronds of *Archaeopteris*. Some leaves are replaced by sporangia. Scale bar equals 2 cm.

3 Conceptual reconstruction of a log of *Callixylon newberryi* (Dawson) Elkins & Wieland adrift in the Late Devonian sea. Specimens of the crinoid *Melocrinites* (*Melocrinus*) *bainbridgensis* (Hall & Whitfield) are attached to the log. Actual specimen was found in the Ohio Shale in Delaware County, Ohio. OSU collection, unnumbered. Scale bar equals 1 meter.

4 Flattened, coalified (vitrinized), branching specimen on shale. Note one longitudinal and three transverse shrinkage cracks. Ohio Shale, Delaware County, Ohio; MSU FPH (Fossil Plant Herbarium) collection, unnumbered. Scale bar equals 1 cm.

5 Permineralized log section. New Albany Shale, near Vienna, Scott County, Indiana; ClMNH B-2422. Scale bar equals 15 cm.

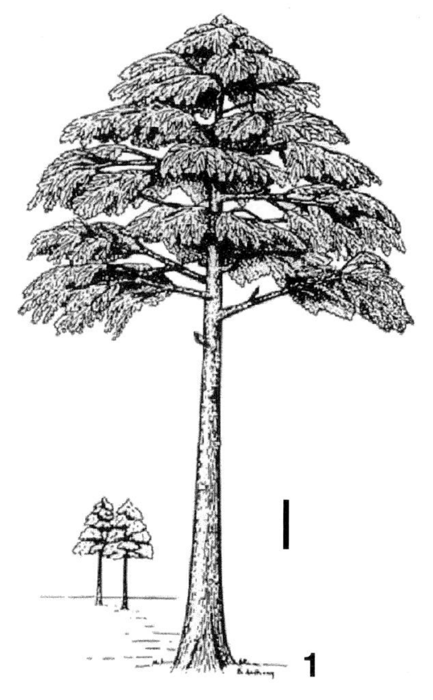
1

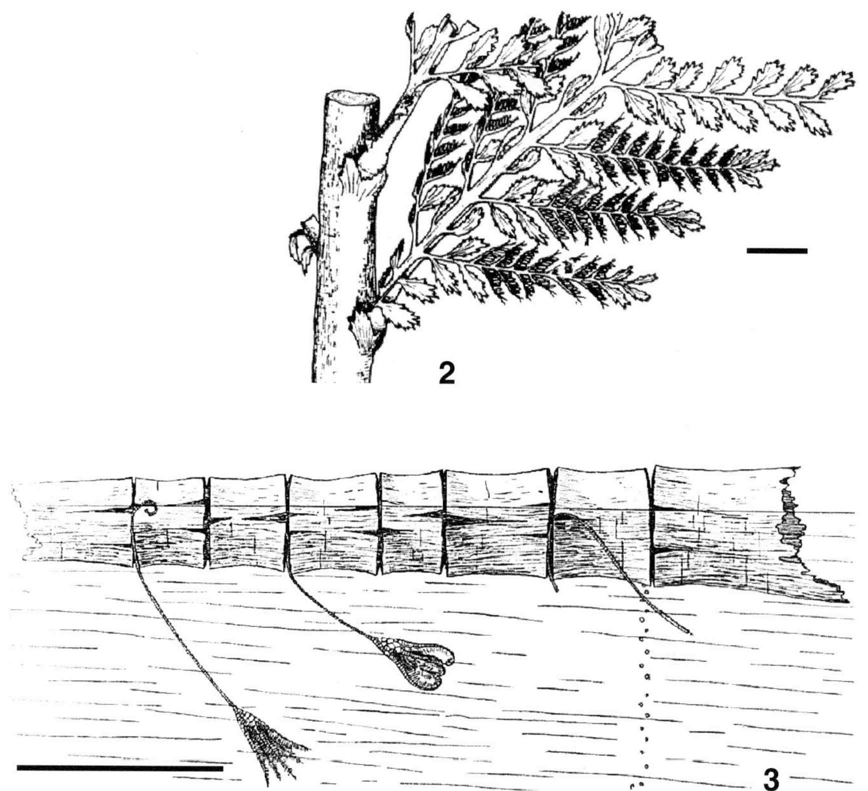
2
3

4

5

FIGURE 23-2.—*Plagiozamites* and plants from Upper Pennsylvanian coal balls. Photos for figures 23-2.2 to 23-2.4 were provided by Gar W. Rothwell (Ohio University). Figure 23-2.2 was published in Mickle and Rothwell (1982), and figure 23-2.3 was published in Rothwell (1991), both reproduced with permission.

1 *Plagiozamites planchardi* (Renault) Zeiller. Unusual specimen showing four distinctive pinnules on a very rigid rachis; of uncertain affinity. Shale between Upper Freeport (No. 7) coal and Mahoning (No. 7A) coal (Conemaugh Group), 7-11 mine, Madison Township, Columbiana County, Ohio; OU PH 7-11-39. Scale bar equals 1 cm.

2, 3 *Alethopteris* Sternberg. Steubenville coal-ball locality, Duquesne coal (Casselman Formation, Conemaugh Group), along south side of U.S. Route 22 west of bridge over Cross Creek, Wayne Township, Jefferson County, Ohio. **2**, acetate peel of two pinnules attached to pinna rachis. OU CB 1617 A#15. Scale bar equals 5 mm. **3**, acetate-peel cross section of pinnules, seed (lower left), and other tissues. Across the middle of figure is one complete pinnule and the right and left edges of two other pinnules on the same bedding plane. Center pinnule shows enrolled edges, central **vascular bundle**, and other anatomical features. The darker cells toward the upper surface are part of the main photosynthetic tissue (palisades parenchyma). The conducting cells of the midvein are clustered near the center. Cross sections of other leaves and stem tissues all show good cellular arrangement and anatomy. OU CB 126C top #5. Scale bar equals 2 mm.

4 Reconstruction of epiphytic fern *Botryopteris forensis* Renault growing through outer portion of root mantle of *Psaronius* Cotta, a tree fern. The two globose structures attached to frond rachises of *Botryopteris* each replaces a primary pinnule of one frond. These structures are unusual, densely packed sporangial masses, each ±5 cm in diameter. Same unit and location as **2, 3**. OU PH 9518-9527 (slab and peels). Scale bar equals 10 cm.

1

2

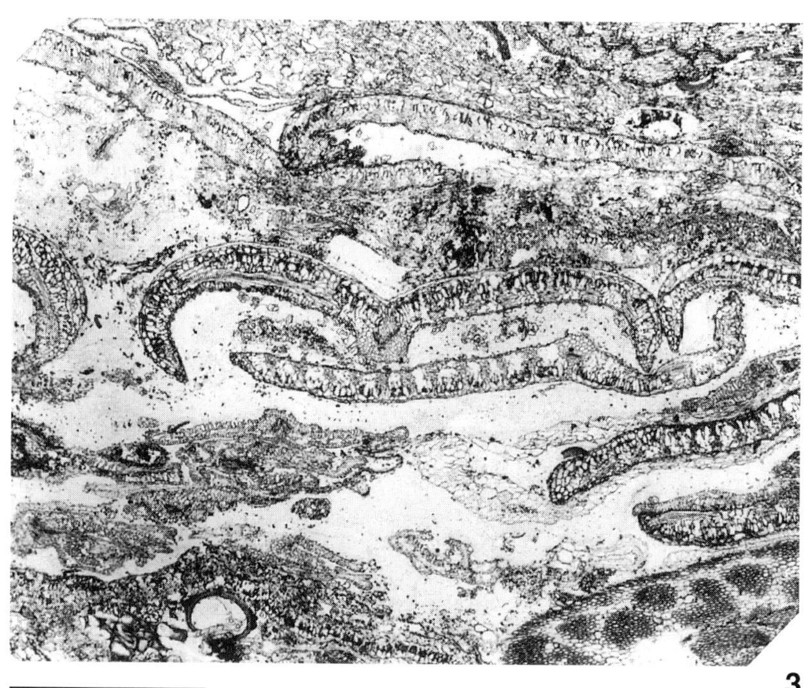

3

4

FIGURE 23-3.—Steubenville coal-ball locality in Conemaugh Group rocks on south side of U.S. Route 22 west of Steubenville, Wayne Township, Jefferson County, Ohio. Anatomically identifiable plants of at least 25 natural species have been described from the original peat-swamp community at this site.

1	View of coal-ball outcrop; a diagrammatic sketch of the outcrop is included. Arrows indicate coal-ball masses. The Ames limestone zone is near the level of the rectangular rock in the lower left of the photo.
2	Diagrammatic stratigraphic section of Conemaugh Group rocks exposed on south side of U.S. Route 22 at west end of bridge over Cross Creek. Revised from Rothwell (1976). Unit thicknesses are in meters.
3	Coal-ball mass occupying entire thickness of Duquesne coal. This mass is indicated by the left arrow in **1**. More than 70 coal balls were exposed on this broken surface in 1988. Scale bar equals 50 cm.
4	Enlarged view of two coal-ball masses shown in **1**. Early permineralization of some of the peat prevented later compaction and loss of volume, as evidenced by the thinner coal seam between the two masses. Scale bar equals 1 meter.

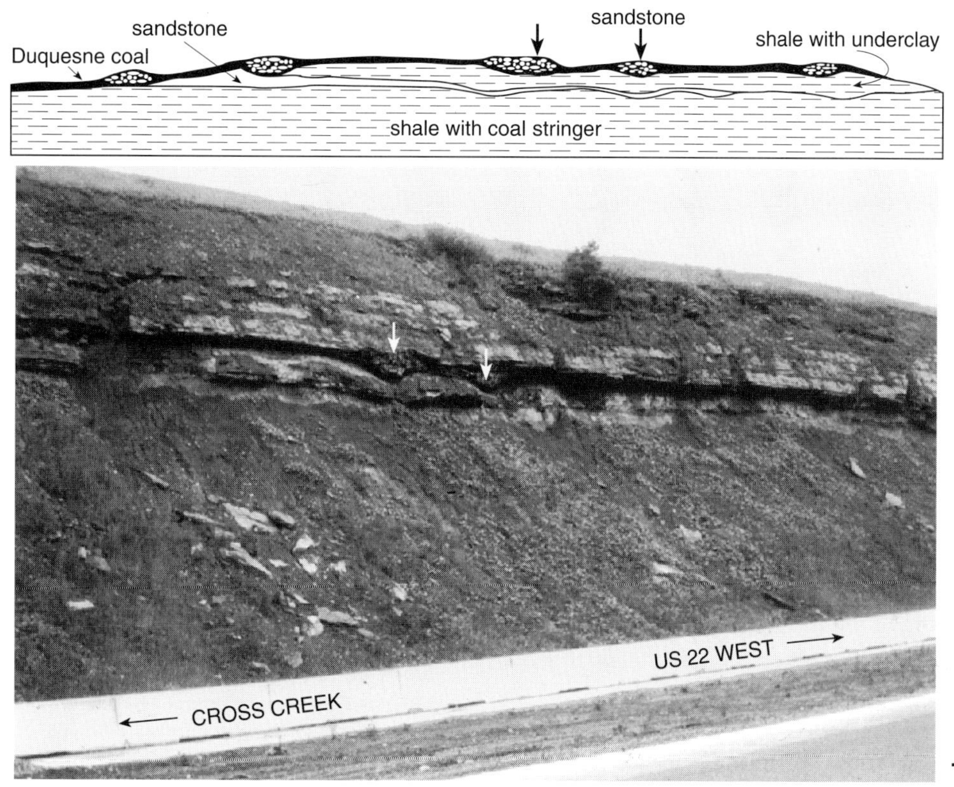
sandstone
sandstone
Duquesne coal
shale with underclay
shale with coal stringer
US 22 WEST
CROSS CREEK
1

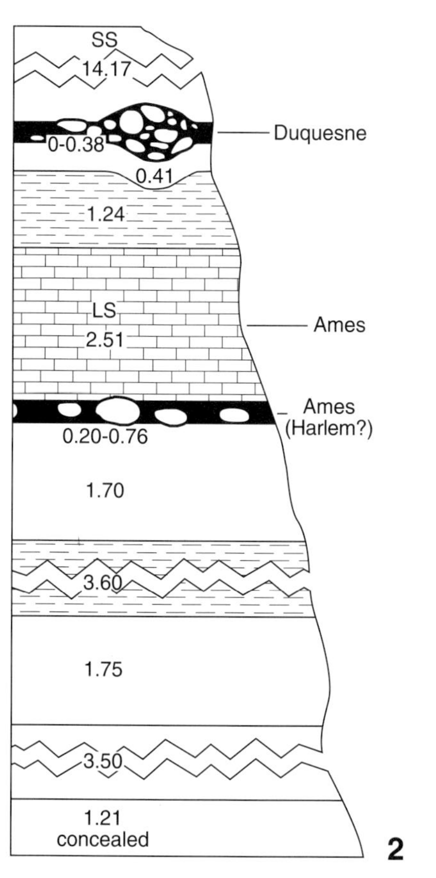
SS
14.17
Duquesne
0-0.38
0.41
1.24
LS
2.51
Ames
Ames
(Harlem?)
0.20-0.76
1.70
3.60
1.75
3.50
1.21
concealed
2

3

4

FIGURE 23-4.—Devonian and Pennsylvanian lycopods.

1 Composite diagram of *Lepidodendron* Sternberg illustrating organs and anatomical terminology, including *Stigmaria* Brongniart rhizomes.

2 Large (>25 cm long) lycopod cone of *Lepidostrobus* type. Cleveland Shale Member of Ohio Shale (Devonian), intersection of I-71 and West 130th St., southwestern Cleveland, Cuyahoga County, Ohio; ClMNH 4207 (8970). Scale bar equals 5 cm. Photo courtesy of Shya D. Chitaley (Cleveland Museum of Natural History).

3 *Lepidophloios laricinus* Sternberg. Small (immature) branch illustrating diagnostic characteristics.Upper left part is partially decorticated. Leaf cushion at upper end consists of a thick coaly film. Upper Pottsville Group (Pennsylvanian), White Cottage, Muskingum County, Newton Township, Ohio; ClMNH collection, unnumbered. Scale bar equals 5 cm.

4 *Lepidophloios* cf. *L. laricinus* Sternberg. Mature specimen. Upper Pennsylvanian, unit and locality unknown; ClMNH P-1356 (B-8826). Scale bar equals 1 cm.

5 *Lepidodendron aculeatum* Sternberg. Allegheny? Group (Pennsylvanian), no locality data available; ClMNH P-5516. Scale bar equals 1 cm.

6 *Lepidodendron* cf. *L. ophiuroides* Arnold (Arnold, 1949). Forked lycopod twig. Leaves densely arranged in low spiral. Middle Kittanning clay (Allegheny Group, Pennsylvanian), Rush Creek Clay Co. pit, east of junction of Ohio Routes 37 and 68 at Junction City, Perry County, Ohio; ClMNH P-9195 (B-2888). Scale bar equals 1 cm.

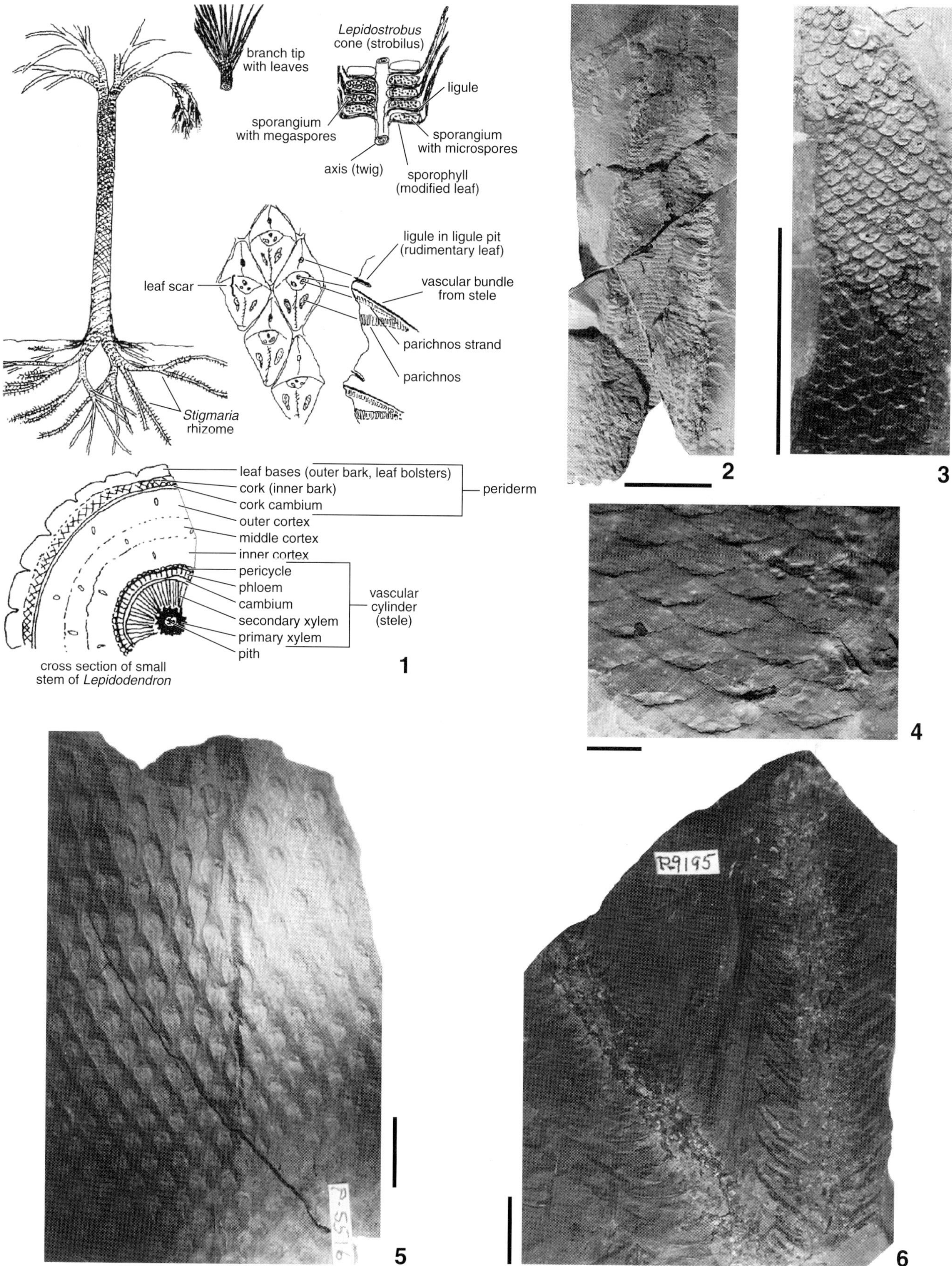
branch tip
with leaves
Lepidostrobus
cone (strobilus)
ligule
sporangium
with megaspores
sporangium
with microspores
axis (twig)
sporophyll
(modified leaf)
ligule in ligule pit
(rudimentary leaf)
leaf scar
vascular bundle
from stele
parichnos strand
parichnos
Stigmaria
rhizome
leaf bases (outer bark, leaf bolsters)
cork (inner bark)
cork cambium
periderm
outer cortex
middle cortex
inner cortex
pericycle
phloem
cambium
secondary xylem
primary xylem
pith
vascular
cylinder
(stele)
cross section of small
stem of Lepidodendron
1
2
3
4
P.5516
5
R9195
6

FIGURE 23-5.—Pennsylvanian lycopod stems, leaves, and reproductive structures.

1 *Lepidodendron obovatum* Sternberg. Arrangement of leaf cushions at upper part of photo indicates beginning of division into two branches. Quakertown (No. 2) or Bear Run coal zone (Pottsville Group), Rushville flora locality, east of Rushville, Reading Township, Perry County, Ohio; MSU FPH CH-5527-7-52 II. Scale bar equals 1 cm.

2 *Lepidodendron aculeatum* Sternberg, decorticated stages. **2A** shows inside of the bark or periderm and represents the *Bergeria* Stur stage of decortication, or possibly the *Aspidaria* Stur stage. **2B** is the outer layer of the same specimen in which only the center part of the secondary woody zone shows and represents the *Knorria* Stur stage of decortication; outward protuberances mark the position of the leaf cushions. The surface in **2A** fits over the surface in **2B**. Saginaw Formation (equivalent to Pottsville Group), south pit of Grand Ledge Clay Products Co., Oneida Township, Eaton County, Michigan; MSU FPH collection, unnumbered. Scale bar equals 4 cm.

3 *Bothrodendron* cf. *B. punctatum* Lindley & Hutton showing two nondescript twig or leaf scars. Lower Conemaugh Group, on Booths Run, near Uffington, Monongalia County, West Virginia. MSU FPH Uff.-56. Scale bar equals 1 cm.

4 *Ulodendron* Lindley & Hutton branch scar (below) and a broken branch scar (above) on a *Bothrodendron* stem. Eaton Sandstone (equivalent to Pottsville Group), Lincoln Brick Factory Park, northwest edge of Grand Ledge, Oneida Township, Eaton County, Michigan; MSU FPH collection, unnumbered. Scale bar equals 1 cm.

5 *Lepidodendron* leaves. Terminal spray. Same unit and locality as **1**; MSU FPH CH-5520-10c. Scale bar equals 25 mm.

6 *Lepidostrobophyllum* (Hirmer) Allen. Leaf or sporangiophore, 63 mm long. Possibly immature sporangium at base. Conemaugh Group, 7-11 mine, Madison Township, Columbiana County, Ohio; OU PH 7-11-3. Scale bar equals 1 cm.

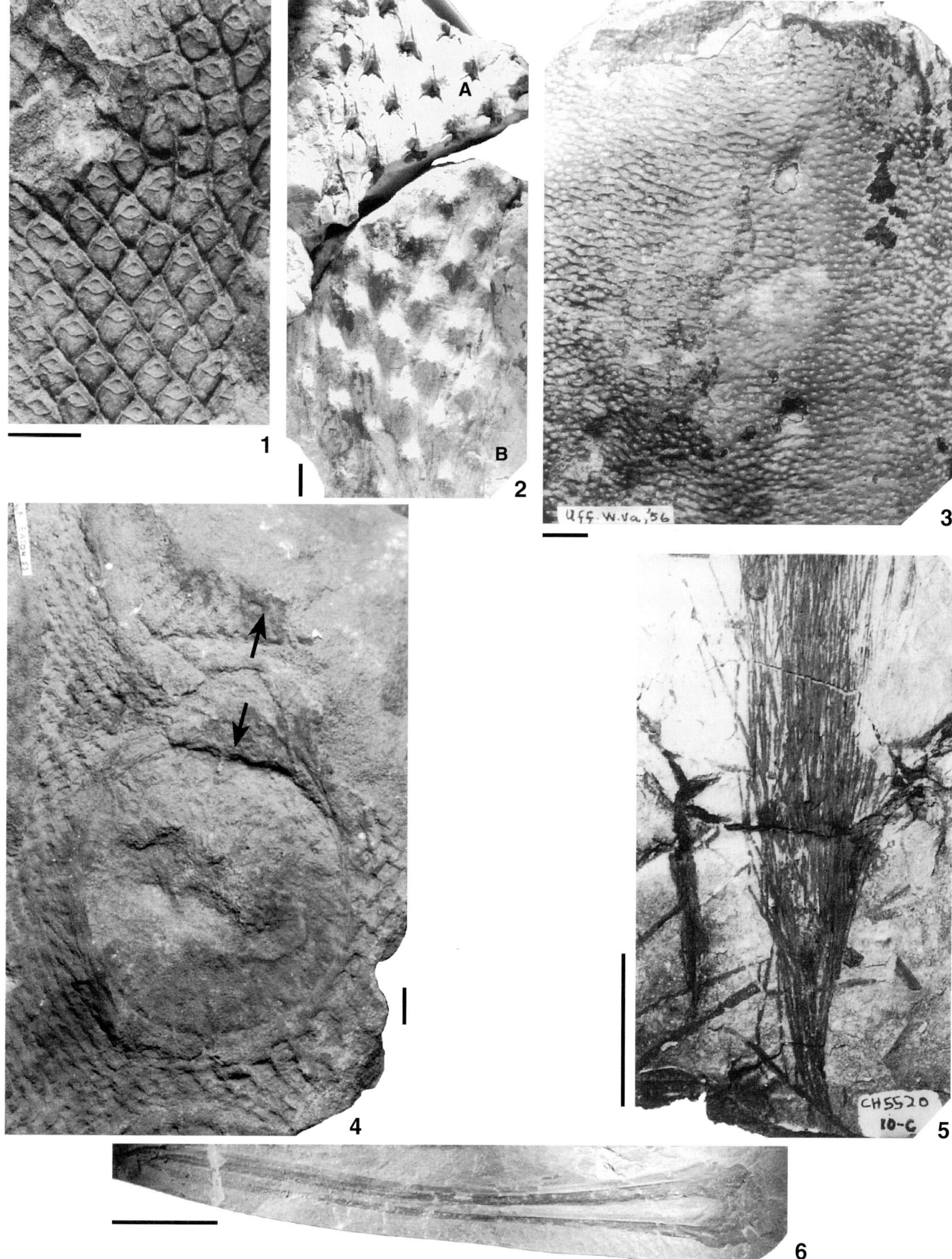
A
B
1
2
3
4
5
6
CH5520
10-C

FIGURE 23-6.—Pennsylvanian lycopod reproductive structures.

1 Terminal end of a strobilis of *Lepidostrobus* Brongniart and several detached leaves of *Lepidodendron* Sternberg, called *Cyperites* Lindley & Hutton (or *Lepidophylloides* Snigirevskaya). Unit and locality unknown; ClMNH P-16762 (B-8810). Scale bar equals 1 cm.

2 *Lepidostrobophyllum majus* Brongniart. Middle Kittanning clay (Allegheny Group), Rush Creek Clay Co. pit, east of junction of Ohio Routes 37 and 68 at Junction City, Perry County, Ohio; ClMNH P-1341 (B-2888). Scale bar equals 2 cm.

3 Base of a specimen of *Lepidostrobus* showing central axis of strobilis. Conemaugh Group, 7-11 mine, Madison Township, Columbiana County, Ohio; OU PH 7-11-1. Scale bar equals 1 cm.

4 *Lepidocarpon* Scott. A seedlike megaspore in its sporangium and its attached sporophyll. Quakertown (No. 2) or Bear Run coal zone (Pottsville Group), Rushville flora locality, east of Rushville, Reading Township, Perry County, Ohio; MSU FPH CH-5520-7b. Scale bar equals 1 cm.

5 *Triletes reinschi* (Ibrahim) Schopf. Large megaspore of an arborescent lycopod. Note smooth, unornamented surface and **trilete** aperture with very short rays (arms). A number of small (less than 100 micrometers in diameter) microspores are appressed to the surface. The two spores at the arrows are magnified in **6** and **7**. Scale bar equals 0.5 mm.

6 *Lycospora granulata* Kosanke. SEM photograph of one of the lycopod microspores in **5**. Spores of this type are considered to have been produced by *Lepidodendron oldhamius* Williamson. Scale bar equals 10 micrometers.

7 *Lophotriletes rarispinosus* Peppers. SEM photograph of one of the lycopod microspores in **5**. Scale bar equals 10 micrometers.

1
2
4
6
7
5
3
6
7

FIGURE 23-7.—Pennsylvanian lycopods *Asolanus* and *Sigillaria*.

1 *Asolanus camptotaenia* Wood. Two small, circular parichnos scars, an indentation of the surface, and an interruption of the vertical continuity of the somewhat sinuous ridges mark the position of each of the spirally arranged leaf-attachment sites. The nearly vertical alignment of the "leaf scars" indicates a sigillarian affinity, possibly representing a decorticated *Sigillaria brardii*. Conemaugh Group, 7-11 mine, Madison Township, Columbiana County, Ohio; OU PH 7-11-6. Scale bar equals 1 cm.

2, 4 Decorticated *Sigillaria* trunks. **2**, two trunks rooted in the roof shale of the Upper Freeport (No. 7) coal (Allegheny Group) and entombed in overlying Mahoning sandstone (Conemaugh Group). Scale bar equals 1 meter (hammer is 33 cm long). **4**, enlarged view of the trunk on the right in **2**; arrows indicate two of the main roots (*Stigmaria*) exposed in place in the roof shale. Scale bar equals 0.5 meter. Highwall in strip mine of East Fairfield Coal Co., Mahoning County, Ohio. Photos courtesy of Tim Miller (East Fairfield Coal Co.).

3 *Sigillaria brardii* Brongniart (or possibly *S. ichthyolepis* Brongniart). Pyritized specimen preserved in horizontal position. Internal structure is preserved. Meigs Creek (No. 9) coal (Monongahela Group), Baker and Noon Coal Co. mine, southeast of Macksburg, Aurelius Township, Washington County, Ohio; MSU FPH 7-30-77 III 1. Scale bar equals 1 cm.

7-11 ⑥
1
2
3
4

FIGURE 23-8.—Pennsylvanian and Permian lycopods *Sigillaria*, *Syringodendron*, and *Lycopodites*. All scale bars equal 1 cm; rod in figure 23-8.3 equals 30 cm.

1 *Sigillaria schlotheimiana* Brongniart. Note the intercalation of additional rows of leaf cushions upward. Upper Pottsville Group (Pennsylvanian), White Cottage, Newton Township, Muskingum County, Ohio; ClMNH collection, unnumbered.

2 *Syringodendron* Sternberg. A decorticated *Sigillaria*, possibly *Sigillaria elongata* Brongniart. Allegheny Group? (Pennsylvanian), locality uncertain, possibly Junction City, Perry County, Ohio; ClMNH P-1328.

3 *Syringodendron*. Base of a large, decorticated, vertical sigillarioid trunk; the four angles in the outline of the stem indicate this section was near the base of the trunk. Rows of double scars are paired parichnos scars marking positions of vertically oriented rows of leaf bases. Base of tree extended from the top of the Cassville shale up into the Waynesburg sandstone (lower Dunkard Group, Pennsylvanian-Permian), east of Sardis, on Havely Run, Monroe County, Ohio; University of Cincinnati specimen.

4 *Lycopodites* Brongniart twigs. Roof shale above Sharon (No. 1) coal (Pottsville Group, Pennsylvanian), small mine south of Jackson, Jackson County, Ohio; OU PH J-250-5.

1

2

3

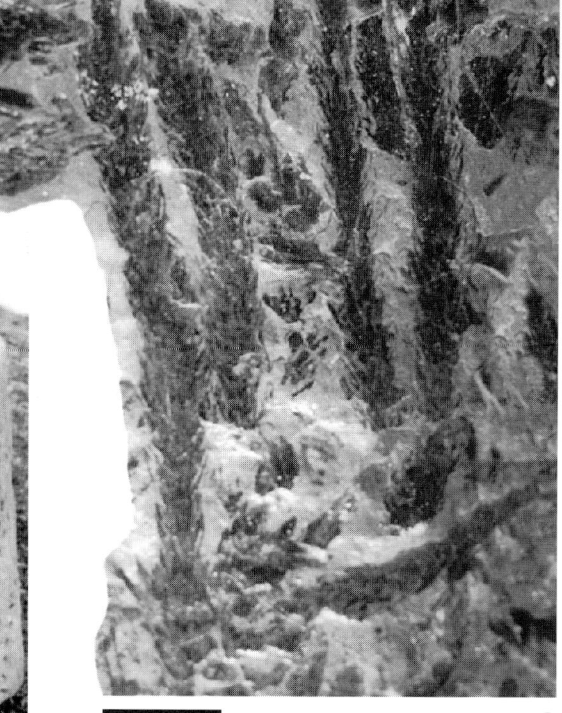

4

FIGURE 23-9.—Pennsylvanian lycopods *Stigmaria* and *Sigillariostrobus*.

1, 4, 5	*Stigmaria ficoides* (Sternberg) Brongniart. **1**, base of plant penetrating gray shale (**SH**) underlying a sandstone (**SS**) below the Middle Kittanning (No. 6) coal (**MK**) (Allegheny Group). Exposed ends or oblique sections of roots (main axes) noted by arrows. Near mouth of Yellow Creek along Ohio Route 213 south of Wellston, Jefferson County, Ohio. Mattock handle is 90 cm long. **4**, spiral pattern of scars shows where rootlets have been stripped away. Strip mine of East Fairfield Coal Co., Mahoning County, Ohio; ClMNH P-11539. Scale bar equals 10 cm. **5**, rootlets in place. Same unit and location as **4**; ClMNH P-11541. Scale bar equals 10 cm.
2, 3	*Sigillariostrobus* (Schimper) Feistmantel. **2**, single sporophyll (cone scale) of a cone. Conemaugh Group, 7-11 mine, Madison Township, Columbiana County, Ohio; OU PH 7-11-4. Scale bar equals 5 mm. **3**, strobilus with upturned sporophyll scales similar to the scale in **2**. Strobilus is 19 cm long and 24 mm in diameter. Roof shale of Coalburg-Stockton coal (Upper Kanawha Group) (equivalent to upper Pottsville Group), strip mine on West Virginia Route 43 at Werth, north of Summersville, Nicholas County, West Virginia; William H. Gillespie collection, PSS-82. Scale bar equals 1 cm.

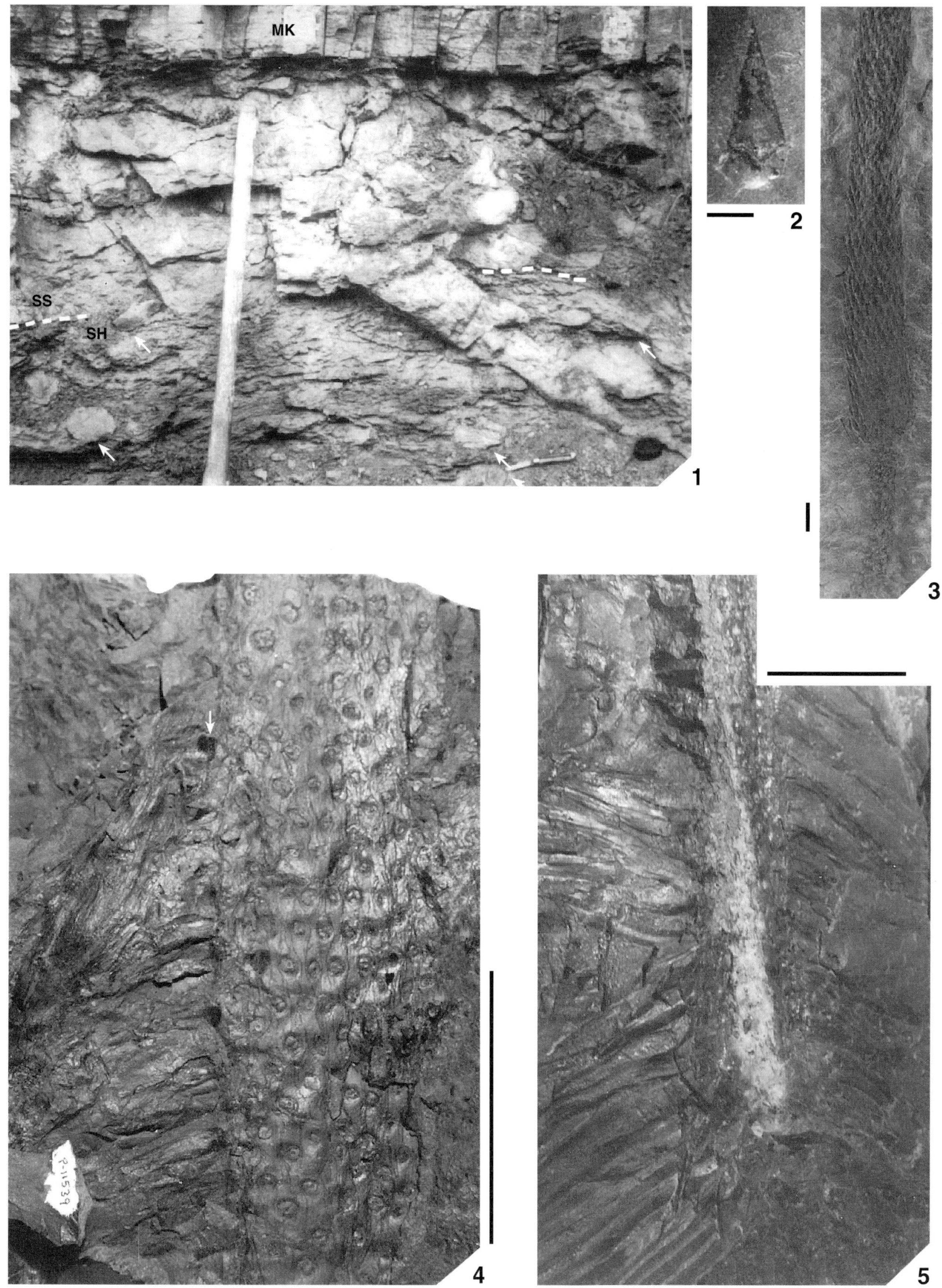
MK
SS
SH
1
2
3
P-11539
4
5

FIGURE 23-10.—Pennsylvanian sphenopsids *Sphenophyllum* and *Bowmanites.* All scale bars equals 1 cm except that for figure 23-10.8, which equals 12 mm.

1 *Sphenophyllum fasciculatum* (Lesquereux) White. Pittsburgh (No. 8) coal (Monongahela Group) in strip mines adjacent to Fairfax Stone State Park, east of Davis, Tucker County, West Virginia; MSU FPH CH-5575 FS-CG-27.

2 *Sphenophyllum oblongifolium* (Germar & Kaulfuss) Unger. Note three pairs of leaves at each node, the shortest pair arranged along one side of the stem and deflexed. Same unit and location as **1**; MSU FPH CH-5575 FS-CG-75.

3 *Sphenophyllum cuneifolium* (Sternberg) Zeiller. Underclay above No. 2 Gas coal (Kanawha Group) (equivalent to upper Pottsville Group), off U.S. Route 60 at Ansted, Fayette County, West Virginia; William H. Gillespie collection, PSS-40, Unit 31, No. 42.

4 *Sphenophyllum emarginatum* Brongniart (Brongniart). Note dissected bracts (leaves) of *S. cornutum* on main stem and on lower whorl of one branch. Allegheny-Conemaugh transition zone in old strip mines near Kimberly, York Township, Athens County, Ohio; ClMNH P-16766 (B-5620). Previously illustrated in Abbott (1958, pl. 44, fig. 66).

5 *Sphenophyllum angustifolium* (Germar) Goeppert. Three whorls of bifid leaves. Same unit and locality as **1**; MSU FPH CH-5575 FS-CG-109.

6 *Sphenophyllum cornutum* Lesquereux. Single whorl of dissected leaves at one node. Note ribs on stem typical of *Sphenophyllum.* Same unit and locality as **1**; MSU FPH FS-CG unnumbered.

7 *Sphenophyllum* cf. *S. majus* (Bronn) Bronn. Two whorls of leaves. Roof shale of Coalburg coal (Kanawha Group) (equivalent to upper Pottsville Group), same location as **3**; William H. Gillespie collection PSS-40, Unit 157, 8-26-74.

8 *Sphenophyllum* cf. *S. myriophyllum* Crepin. This specimen may be an underwater root. Quakertown (No. 2) or Bear Run coal zone (Pottsville Group), Rushville flora locality, east of Rushville, Reading Township, Perry County, Ohio; MSU FPH CH-5520A.

9 *Bowmanites* Binney. Strobilus and associated *Sphenophyllum oblongifolium* leaves. Same unit and locality as **4**; ClMNH P-1277.

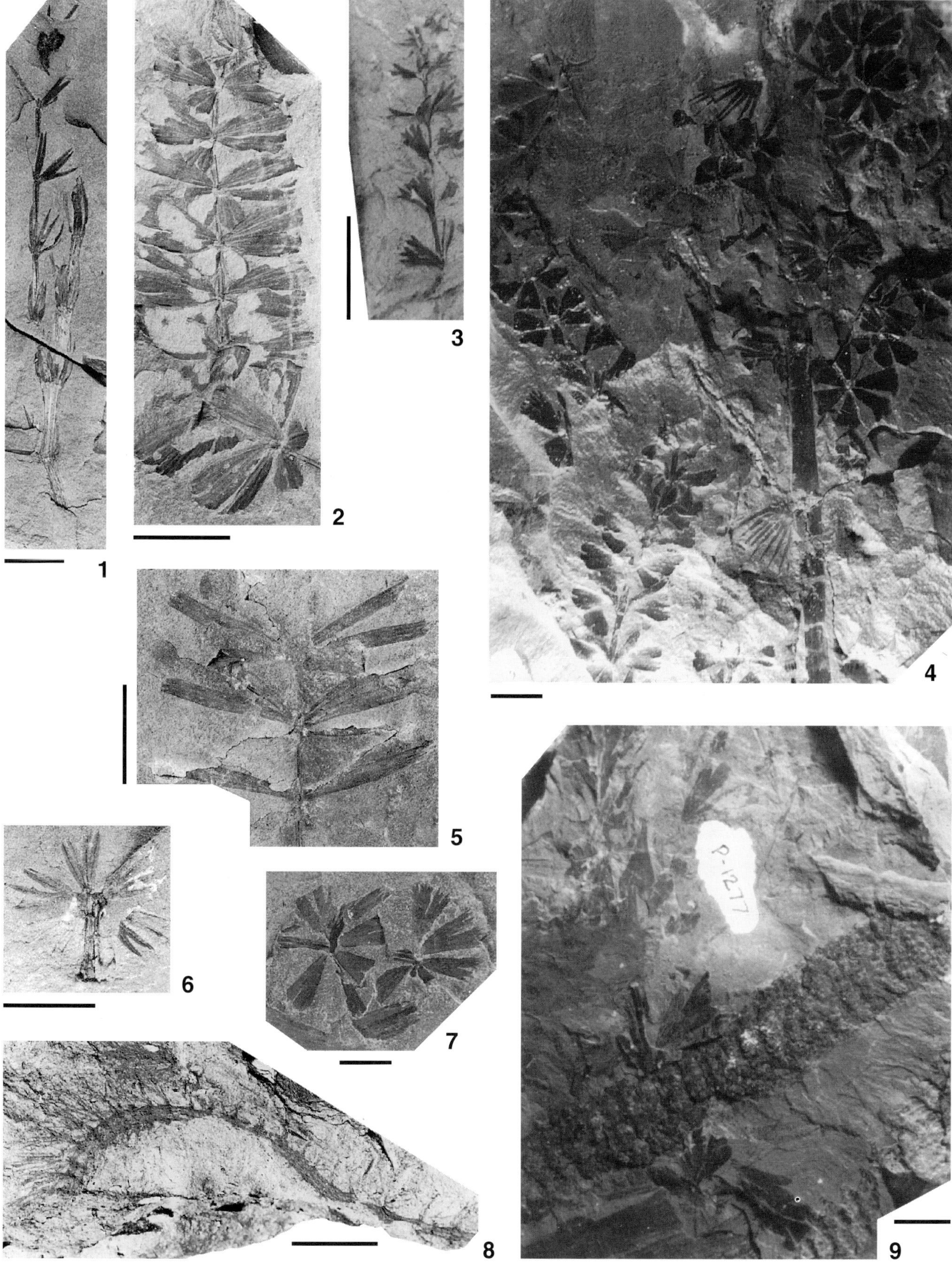
1
2
3
4
5
6
7
8
9
P-1277

FIGURE 23-11.—Pennsylvanian and Permian sphenopsids *Bowmanites* and *Calamites*.

1 *Bowmanites* Binney. Eleven whorls of sporangiophores bear double rows of sporangia. Arrow points to cross section of a small *Calamites* stem or root. Allegheny-Conemaugh transition zone (Pennsylvanian) in old strip mines near Kimberly, York Township, Athens County, Ohio; ClMNH P-1329 (B-8504). Scale bar equals 1 cm.

2 *Calamites* Schlotheim. Three internal pith casts standing where the plants grew. They were later entombed in fluvial sandstone. Campbell Creek zone (Kanawha Group, equivalent to upper Pottsville Group, Pennsylvanian), on ridge between Buffalo Fork and Tony Fork, Raleigh County, West Virginia; William H. Gillespie collection, PSS-22, 9-20-74. Hammer is 23 cm long.

3 *Calamites* sp. Cross sections of two stems (or roots?). **PC**, pith cast filling; **W**, woody cylinder. Conemaugh Group (Pennsylvanian), 7-11 mine, Madison Township, Columbiana County, Ohio; OU PH 7-11-14, Hor. E., 1984. Scale bar equals 1 cm.

4 *Calamites carinatus* Sternberg. Arrow points to a branch scar, indicated by distortion of ends of ribs both above and below node. Dunkard Group (Permian), Monroe County Ohio; MSU FPH Dunkard 136. Scale bar equals 3 cm.

5 *Calamites suckowii* Brongniart. Cast of upward expanding pith of lower part of stem branched from horizontal rhizomes. Upper Pennsylvanian, West Virginia; MSU FPH collection, unnumbered. Scale bar equals 5 cm.

6 *Calamites undulatus* Sternberg. Arrow points to one of five small branch scars at one node. Roof shale above Lower Kittanning (No. 5) coal (Allegheny Group, Pennsylvanian), Bablin, Lewis County, West Virginia; MSU FPH C&A 532. Scale bar equals 2 cm.

7 *Calamites cistii* Brongniart. Partially pyritized cast. Kittanning coal (Allegheny Group, Pennsylvanian), near Hubbard, Trumbull County, Ohio; ClMNH P-5223 (B-4762), Miller collection. Scale bar equals 1 cm.

1

2

3

4

5

6

7

FIGURE 23-12.—*Annularia*, Pennsylvanian sphenopsid. All scale bars equal 1 cm.

1, 5	*Annularia stellata* (Schlotheim) Wood. Note very narrow leaves on specimen in **5**. Allegheny-Conemaugh transition zone in old strip mines near Kimberly, York Township, Athens County, Ohio; ClMNH P-1261 (B-5607-8) (**1**) and ClMNH 12-1304 (B-5609-1) (**5**).
2	*Annularia asteris* Bell. Roof shale above Sharon (No. 1) coal (Pottsville Group), mine near Jackson, Jackson County, Ohio; OU collection, unnumbered.
3	*Annularia sphenophylloides* (Zenker) Gutbier. Whorls of leaves flattened on bedding plane. Conemaugh Group, 7-11 mine, Madison Township, Columbiana County, Ohio; OU PH 7-11-56.
4	*Annularia radiata* (Brongniart) Sternberg. Brazil Formation (Middle Pennsylvanian), Roaring Creek mine, Parke County, Indiana; MSU FPH 10-2-82 I4.
6	*Annularia* cf. *A. galioides* (Lindley & Hutton) Kidston. Same unit and locality as **2**; OU PH J-365-12.

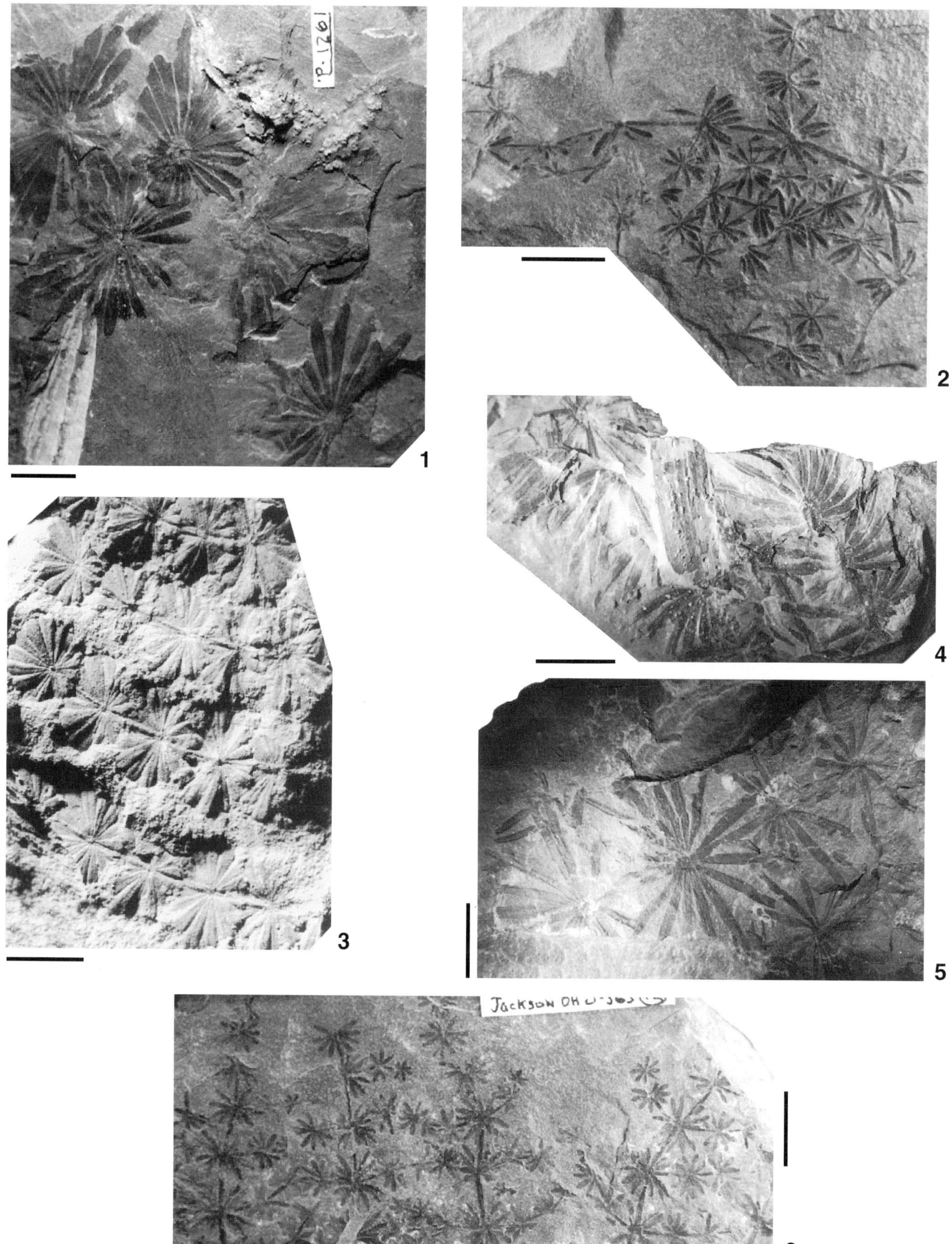
P.1261
1
2
3
4
5
6

FIGURE 23-13.—Pennsylvanian sphenopsid *Asterophyllites* and calamitean strobili. All scale bars equal 1 cm except that for figure 23-13.3, which equals 0.5 mm.

1	*Macrostachya* cf. *M. thompsonii* Darrah. Large strobilus with greatly reduced sporophylls and dense whorls of sporangia. Arrow points toward apex. Pittsburgh (No. 8) coal (Monongahela Group) in strip mines adjacent to Fairfax Stone State Park, east of Davis, Tucker County, West Virginia; ClMNH P-1299.
2, 3	*Asterophyllites charaeformis* (Sternberg) Goeppert. **2**, Brookville shale and coal zone (Allegheny Group), strip mine near Strasburg, Tuscarawas County, Ohio; ClMNH collection, unnumbered. **3**, roof shale above Little Fire Creek coal (New River Group) (equivalent to lower Pottsville Group), on West Virginia Route 10 northwest of Wyoming-Mercer Co. line, West Virginia; William H. Gillespie collection PSS-12.
4	*Asterophyllites equisetiformis* (Schlotheim) Brongniart. Right edge of a *Pecopteris* pinnule is at left margin. Allegheny-Conemaugh transition zone in old strip mines near Kimberly, York Township, Athens County, Ohio; ClMNH P-1287 (B-5606-13).
5	*Palaeostachya* cf. *P. elongata* (Presl) Weiss. Several loosely organized strobili on branches of *Calamites*. Same unit and location as **4**; ClMNH P-1276 (B-8690).
6	*Calamostachys* Schimper. Three strobili of *Calamites*. Arrows point toward apex of each cone. Cone in lower right has dense whorls of sporangia between each whorl of bracts. Same unit and locality **1**; MSU FPH CH-5575-88 FS-CG-88.

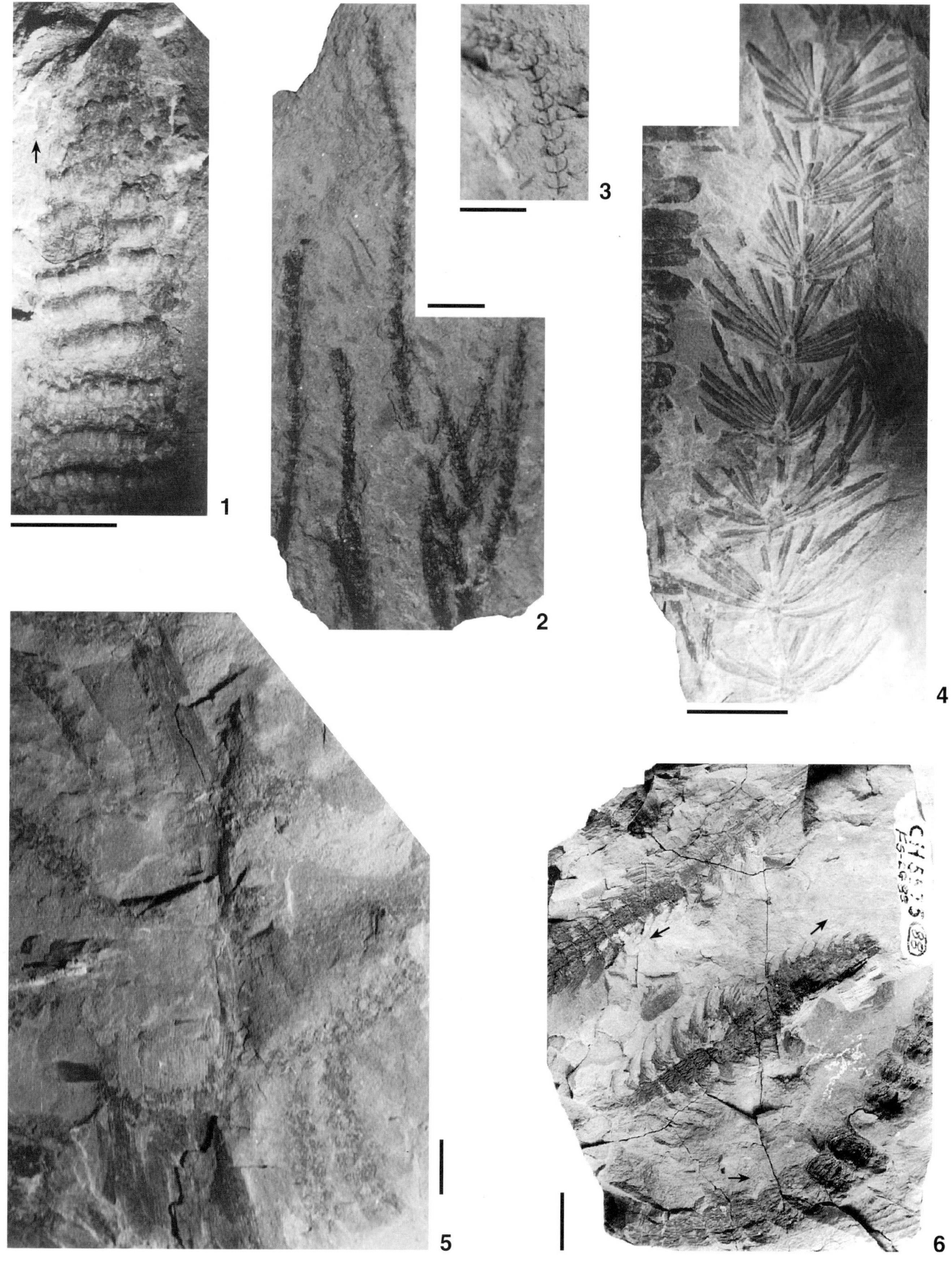

FIGURE 23-14.—Pennsylvanian tree fern *Psaronius*. Specimens in figures 23-14.2 to 23-14.6 were collected from roof shales above the Pittsburgh (No. 8) coal (Monongahela Group) along Middle Branch Shade River and its tributaries, Athens County, Ohio. Figure 23-14.1 is from Morgan (1959), and figures 23-14.2 and 23-14.3 are from Rothwell and Blickle (1982); all reproduced with permission. Photo in figure 23-14.2 courtesy of Gar W. Rothwell (Ohio University).

1	Artist's reconstruction of a mature *Psaronius* Cotta. Scale bar equals 1 meter.
2, 3	*Psaronius magnificus* (Herzer) Rothwell & Blickle. **2**, cut and polished cross section of middle upper part of trunk. Central area surrounded by dark zone is the stem; remainder is the root mantle (mass of adventitious roots), divided into an inner zone of bound roots radiating in orderly rows and a less organized peripheral zone of free roots. OU PH P-032. Scale bar equals 1 cm. **3**, portion of a permineralized specimen very near the apex of a stem. These leaf-scar-bearing stems are called *Caulopteris* Lindley & Hutton. The large, elongated, oval scars are arranged in a low spiral and have horseshoe-shaped vascular tissue marking the inside of the rim. No adventitious roots surround the stem at this level. OU PH P-001. Scale bar equals 10 cm.
4, 5, 6	*Psaronius schopfii* Mickle. **4**, reassembled base of specimen in **5**. Larger arrows indicate position of cross section in **6**; smaller arrows denote natural fractures, probably due to frost action, as stump was gradually exposed by downcutting of stream. Stump axis has total length of 105 cm. Scale bar equals 15 cm. **5**, partially excavated specimen. Hammer marks the upper end of the stump axis and is 28 cm long. **6**, acetate-peel cross section from level indicated by two larger arrows near base of specimen in **4**. Small stem at this level consists of five cycles of vascular strands near top center of peel; these are distorted and laterally compressed. MSU FPH collection. Scale bar equals 2 cm.

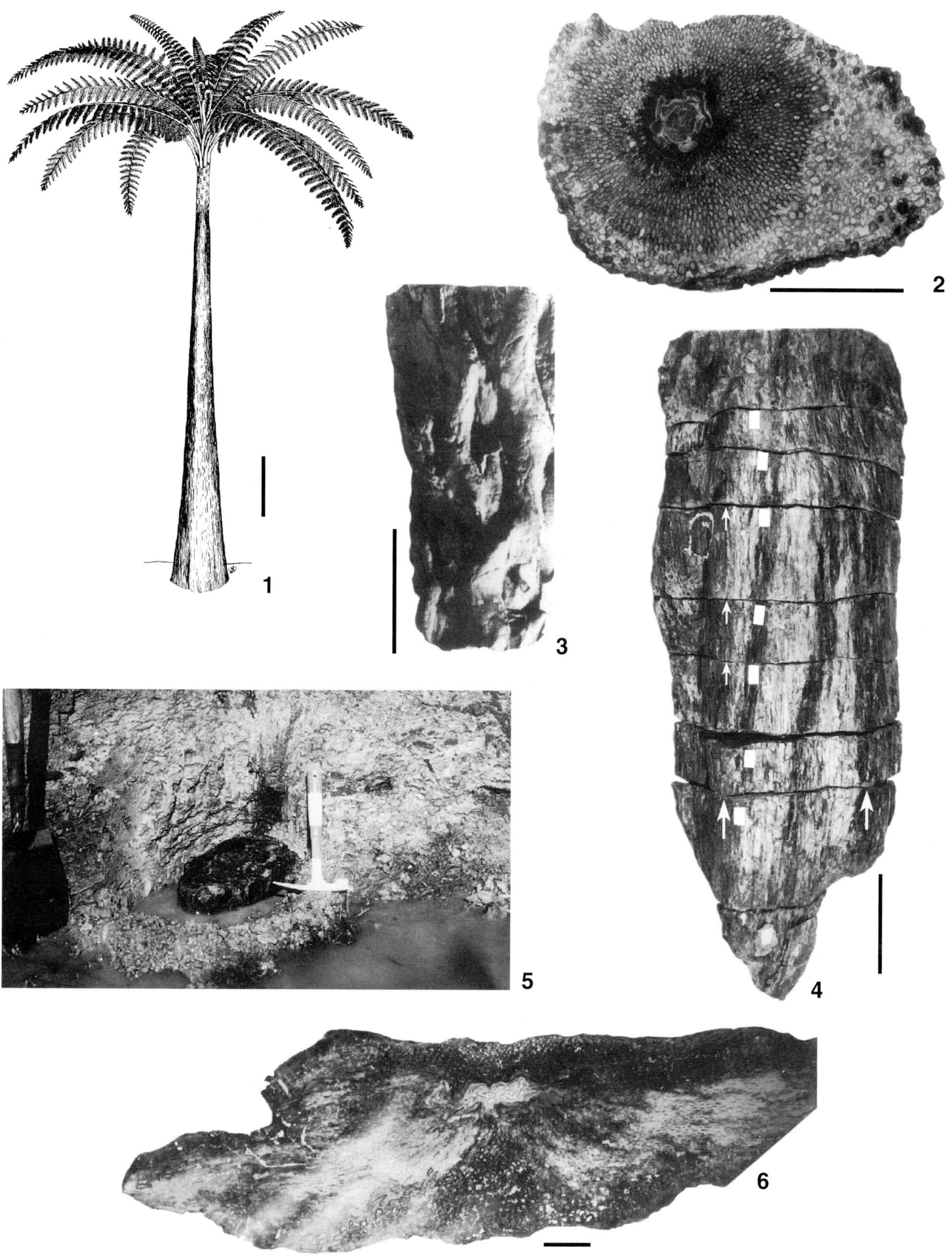
1
2
3
4
5
6

FIGURE 23-15.—Dendrites and Pennsylvanian ferns. All scale bars equal 1 cm except that for figure 23-15.2, which equals 5 cm.

1 Dendrites. Crystallization of manganese oxide on bedding surfaces produces pseudofossil patterns that resemble fern fossils.

2 *Pecopteris* frond fragments in blocks of shale (overbank flood mud) removed in successive layers during excavation around base of *Psaronius schopfii* stump in figure 23-14.5. In life, these fronds probably were borne on plants represented by that stump and neighboring trunks. Monongahela Group, along tributary of Middle Branch Shade River, Athens County, Ohio.

3 *Alloiopteris erosa* (Gutbier) Potonié. Lower and Middle Kittanning (No. 5 Block and No. 6 Block) coals (Allegheny Group), on east side of U.S. Route 19 north of Braxton-Nicholas County line, West Virginia; William H. Gillespie collection 11-12-78.

4 *Alloiopteris coralloides* (Gutbier) Potonié. Sharon (No. 1) coal (Pottsville Group), near Jackson, Jackson County, Ohio; OU PH J-4.

5 Fern crozier uncoiling (fiddlehead stage), showing two 360° coils. Main axis is on left. Details of rudimentary pinnules at lower right outside coil indicate this may be a *Pecopteris* tip. Conemaugh Group, 7-11 mine, Madison Township, Columbiana County, Ohio; OU PH 7-11 unnumbered.

6 *Alloiopteris essinghii* (Andrae) Potonié. Main rachis of one branch of frond with four pinnae on left side. Pinnae on right are small as a result of proximity to another small rachis branching off in the fork between the dichotomous division of the main axis of the frond (lower right corner). Same unit and location as **5**; OU PH 7-11-55.

7, 8 *Alloiopteris sternbergii* (Ettingshausen) Potonié. **7**, lower (abaxial) surface. **8**, upper (adaxial) surface. Pinnules appear to have enrolled edges. Same unit and locality as **5**; OU PH 7-11-34.

1
2
3
4
5
6
7
8

FIGURE 23-16.—Pennsylvanian and Permian ferns. All scale bars equal 1 cm.

1, 3	*Danaeides emersonii* Lesquereux. **1**, fertile tip with 10 pinnae. Conemaugh Group (Pennsylvanian), 7-11 mine, Madison Township, Columbiana County, Ohio. OU PH 7-11-30. **3**, sterile pinna; includes main rachis of frond. Roof shale above Pittsburgh (No. 8) coal (Monongahela Group, Pennsylvanian) in strip mines adjacent to Fairfax Stone State Park, east of Davis, Tucker County, West Virginia; MSU FPH CH-5575 FS-CG-98.
2	*Nemejcopteris feminaeformis* (Schlotheim) Barthel. Same unit and location as **1**; OU PH 7-11 unnumbered.
4	*Pecopteris cyathea* (Schlotheim) Stur. Lower surface of pinna. Same unit and location as **1**; OU PH 7-11-27.
5, 6	*Scolecopteris elegans* Zenker. **5**, several individual fertile pinnae on broken chips; pinnules crowded. Red and greenish claystones of Washington Formation (Dunkard Group, Pennsylvanian-Permian), Bares Run, eastern Monroe County, Ohio; MSU FPH C&A 400. **6**, two main branches of a large compound frond, in place as exposed. The plant probably had several other branches of equivalent size, and the entire frond was probably 1.5 to 2 meters long. Cassville shale zone (Dunkard Group, Pennsylvanian-Permian) below Waynesburg sandstone and above Waynesburg (No. 11) coal zone, north of Cutler, Fairfield Township, Washington County, Ohio; MSU FPH 10-3-70.

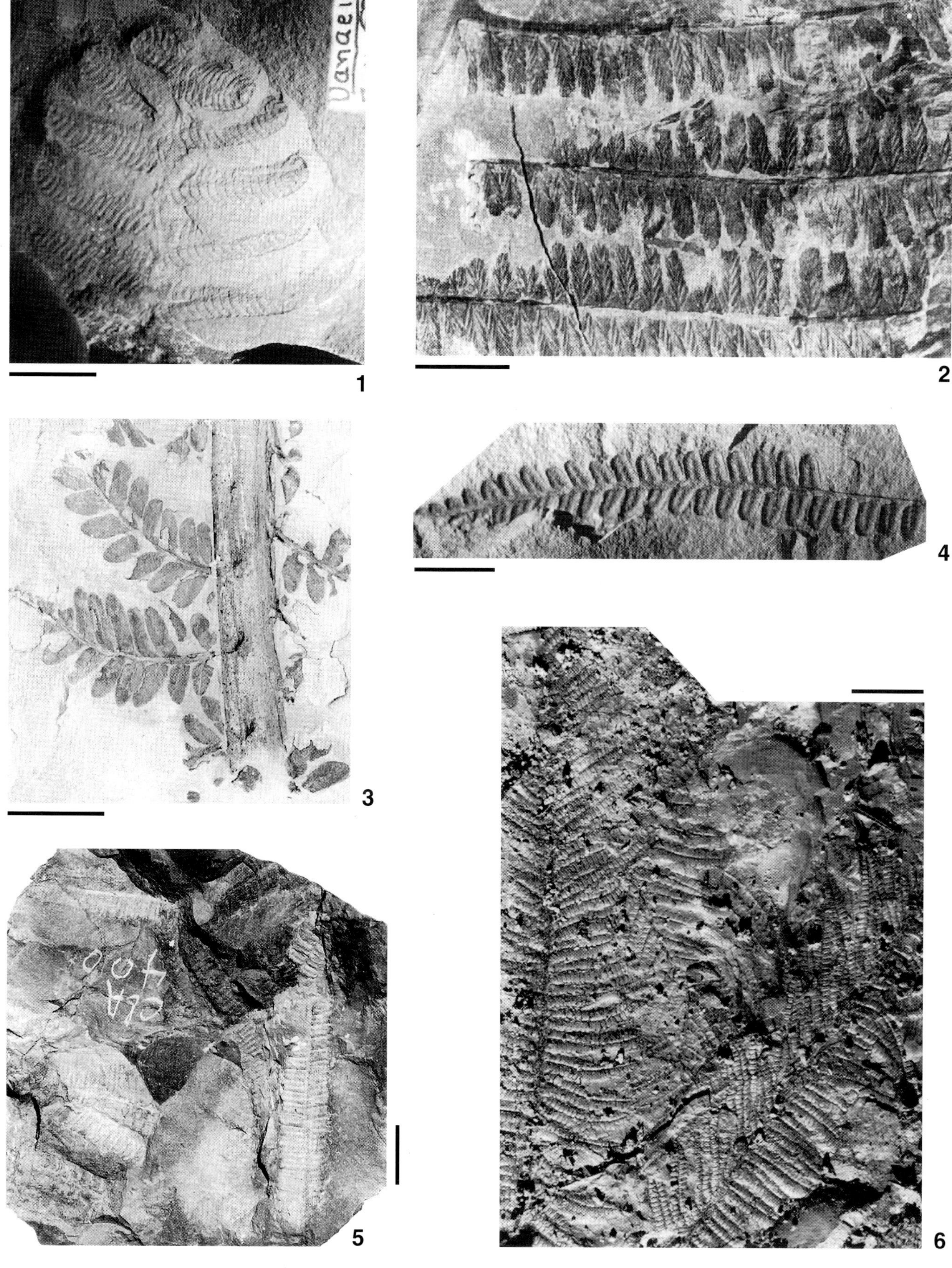

FIGURE 23-17.—Two species of ferns showing range of variation. All scale bars equal 1 cm.

1-3 *Lobatopteris lamuriana* (Heer) Corsin, a quadripinnate species. **1**, secondary pinna with 18 tertiary pinnae alternately arranged on midvein. The 18 pinnae have 10 to 14 fourth-order pinnules alternately arranged, some of which are lobed. Conemaugh Group (Pennsylvanian), 7-11 mine, Madison Township, Columbiana County, Ohio; OU PH 7-11 unnumbered. **2**, only some of the lowermost pinnules have fourth-order subdivisions. Same unit and location as **1**; OU PH-7-11 unnumbered. **3**, an extreme example of an attenuated pinna with scarcely lobed long pinnules. Allegheny Group? (Pennsylvanian), near New Springfield, southeastern Mahoning County, Ohio; ClMNH collection, unnumbered.

4-6 *Pecopteris candolleana* (Brongniart) Kidston, a tripinnate species. **4**, probably from a loosely ranked lower portion of a frond. Cassville shale (Monongahela-Dunkard transition, Pennsylvanian-Permian), SSW of Utley, Berne Township, Athens County, Ohio; MSU FPH B-5001 10-1-56. **5**, considerably smaller pinnule from a terminal portion of a frond and a rachis that had closely arranged pinnae. Roof shale above Brookville (No. 4) or Clarion (No. 4A) coal (Allegheny Group, Pennsylvanian), Wellston area, Milton Township, Jackson County, Ohio; MSU FPH B-5001 10-1-56 I-2. **6**, large pinnules loosely arranged along the main rachis of the pinna. Same unit and location as **1**; OU PH 7-11 unnumbered.

1
2
3
4
5
6

FIGURE 23-18. Pennsylvanian and Permian ferns. All scale bars equal 1 cm.

1 *Lobatopteris (Asterotheca) miltonii* (Artis) Cleal & Shute. Fertile specimen. Brookville shale (Allegheny Group, Pennsylvanian), strip mine near Strasburg, Tuscarawas County, Ohio; ClMNH collection, unnumbered.

2 *Lobatopteris (Pecopteris) miltonii* (Artis) Cleal & Shute. Lower surface of sterile pinna. Conemaugh Group (Pennsylvanian), 7-11 mine, Madison Township, Columbiana County, Ohio; OU PH 7-11-35.

3 *Pecopteris polymorpha* (Brongniart) Schimper. Detached pinna has 28 lateral pinnules and one terminal pinnule. A single pinnule of *Linopteris neuropteroides* (Gutbier) Zeiller is at upper left. Same unit and location as **2**; OU collection, unnumbered.

4 *Pecopteris hemitelioides* (Brongniart) Stur. Same unit and location as **2**; OU PH 7-11 unnumbered.

5 *Pecopteris unita* (Brongniart) Weiss. Sterile pinna. Same unit and location as **2**; William H. Gillespie collection, unnumbered.

6 *Scolecopteris (Pecopteris) unita* (Brongniart) Jennings & Millay. Lower (abaxial) surface of single fertile pinna. There are two rows of sporangial masses along midvein of each pinnule. Roof shale above Pittsburgh (No. 8) coal (Monongahela Group, Pennsylvanian) in strip mines adjacent to Fairfax Stone State Park, east of Davis, Tucker County, West Virginia; MSU FPH CH-5575 FS-MS-19.

7 *Pecopteris squamosa* Lesquereux. Small chip at lower left is counterpart of split from right side of larger specimen. Venation of pinnules shows well on counterpart. Cassville shale zone above Waynesburg (No. 11) coal (Monongahela-Dunkard transition, Pennsylvanian-Permian), SSW of Utley, Berne Township, Athens County, Ohio; MSU FPH B-5001 10-1-56 I-9.

FIGURE 23-19.—*Sphenopteris*, a Pennsylvanian fern. All scale bars equal 1 cm except that for figure 23-19.1, which is in millimeter/centimeter increments.

1 *Sphenopteris* cf. *S. schatzlarensis* Stur. Part of a large frond on a large slab of roof shale from above the Sharon (No. 1) coal, mine near Jackson, Jackson County, Ohio; OU PH J-6-9.

2 *Sphenopteris* (*Oligocarpia*) *mixta* (Schimper) Abbott. Sterile (upper right) and fertile (lower half) foliage. Arrows point to sporangia (discernible with hand lens). Roof shale above Upper Freeport (No. 7) coal (Allegheny-Conemaugh transition zone) in old strip mines near Kimberly, York Township, Athens County, Ohio; ClMNH P-1319 (B-5601-24).

3 *Sphenopteris* (*Oligocarpia*) sp. Tip of a branch of a fertile frond with sparsely scattered synangia (some indicated by arrows). Same unit and location as **2**; ClMNH P-1325 (B-5602-43).

4 *Sphenopteris* (*Oligocarpia*) cf. *S.* (*O.*) *capitata* White. Single pinna with several deeply lobed pinnules illustrating the zigzag (pseudomonopodial) character of the main vein due to alternate development of one branch from each successive dichotomy which continues on as the main axis to the next dichotomy. Same unit and location as **2**; ClMNH P-1314 (B-5602-42).

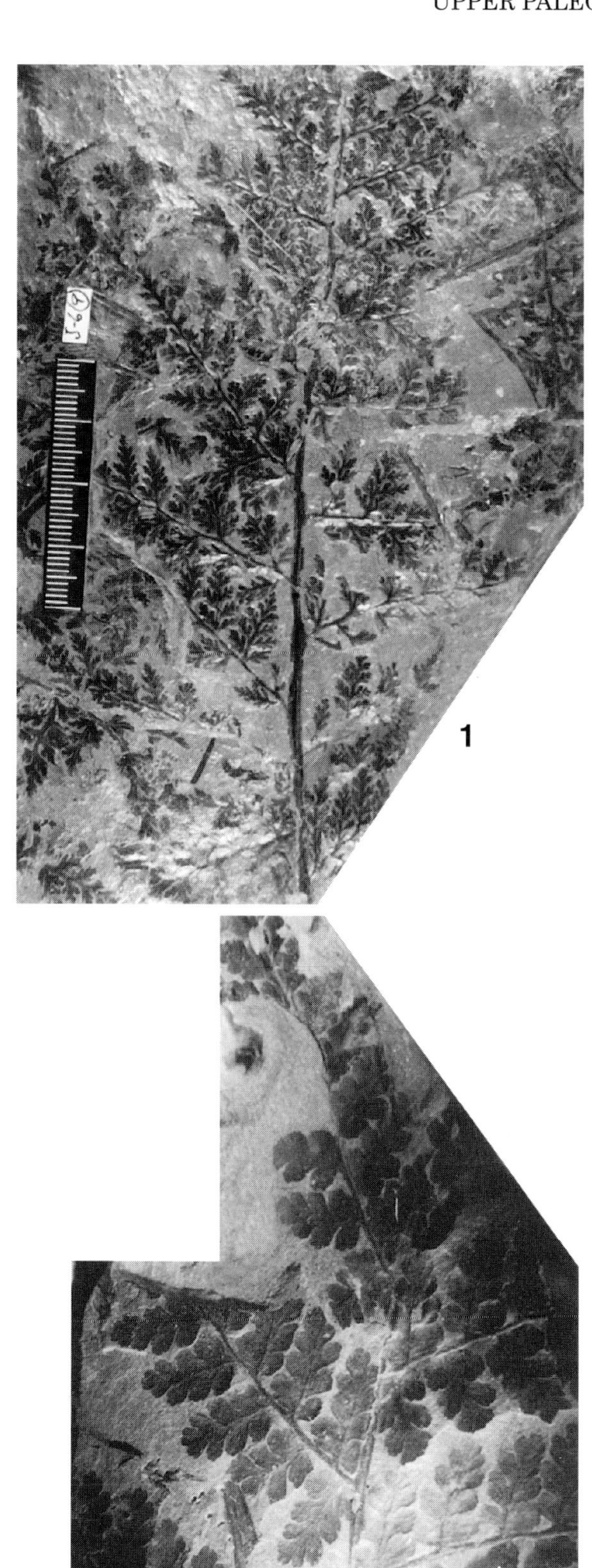
1
3

2

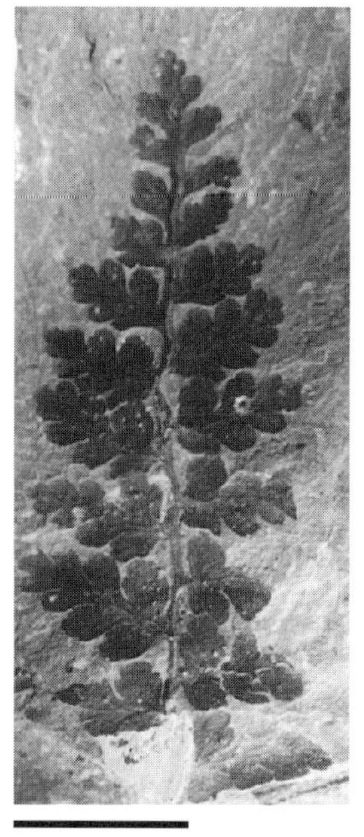
4

FIGURE 23-20.—Pennsylvanian and Pennsylvanian-Permian ferns and seed ferns. Scale bar for figure 23-20.3 equals 5 cm; scale bar for figure 23-20.4 equals approximately 1 meter. Scale bars for other figures equal 1 cm. Figure 23-20.4 reproduced from Stewart and Delevoryas (1956), with permission.

1 *Sphenopteris coemansii* Andrae. Excellent, robust specimen of *Neuropteris heterophylla* at upper left. Shale of split of Coalburg? coal (equivalent to upper Pottsville Group, Pennsylvanian), right fork of Naugatuck Creek, 6 km (3.75 miles) east of Millett, Lincoln District, Wayne County, West Virginia; MSU FPH 8-13-52 C&A 695.

2 *Sphenopteris* (*Oligocarpia*) cf. *S.* (*O.*) *gracilis* Brongniart. Arrows indicate scattered synangia (sporangial clusters). Conemaugh Group (Pennsylvanian), 7-11 mine, Madison Township, Columbiana County, Ohio; OU PH 7-11-24A.

3 Cast of **proximal** portion of a pteridosperm? root system; roots penetrate downward instead of horizontally. Strata below Middle Kittanning (No. 6) coal (Allegheny Group, Pennsylvanian), along Ohio Route 213 south of junction with Ohio Route 7 at mouth of Yellow Creek, south of Wellston, Jefferson County, Ohio; temporary **repository** MSU.

4 *Medullosa noei* Cotta. Classic reconstruction showing crown of giant fronds on very thick, strong petioles and bases of fronds that have been shed, forming a significant mantle surrounding the stem.

5 Pteridosperm branch. Pustulose or warty surface of large rachis or petiole base of *Medullosa*. Cassville shale zone above Waynesburg (No. 11) coal (Monongahela-Dunkard transition, Pennsylvanian-Permian), SSW of Utley, Berne Township, Athens County, Ohio; MSU FPH B-5001 10-1-56 I-8.

1
2
3
4
5

FIGURE 23-21.—Pennsylvanian and Permian seed ferns. All scale bars equal 1 cm.

1 *Alethopteris bohemica* Franke. Red shales of Washington Formation (Dunkard Group, Permian) near Sardis, Monroe County, Ohio; OU PH S-342-1.

2 *Alethopteris decurrens* (Artis) Zeiller. Terminal portion of a pinna, lateral pinnules strongly decurrent. Roof shale of Sharon (No. 1) coal (Pottsville Group, Pennsylvanian), mine near Jackson, Jackson County, Ohio; OU PH J-3-10.

3 *Alethopteris serlii* (Brongniart) Goeppert. Pinna showing single terminal pinnule and classic form of this species. Roof shale above Middle Kittanning (No. 6) coal (Allegheny Group, Pennsylvanian), outcrop on Gladesville Road southeast of U.S. Route 119, Monongalia County, West Virginia; William H. Gillespie collection 56-9-62.

4, 5 *Alethopteris virginiana* Fontaine & White. **4**, underside (abaxial surface). Accessory veins from midvein of pinna to decurrent wing of pinnule are well displayed (arrow at base near midvein). Washington Formation (Dunkard Group, Permian), Turkey Run of Fishing Creek, Wetzel County, West Virginia; MSU FPH C&A 443 I-1. **5, topotype**. Cassville shale (lower Washington Formation, Pennsylvanian-Permian) in old mine opening along west side of West Virginia Route 7, at curve near head of Scotts Run, Monongalia County, West Virginia; William H. Gillespie collection 29-11-59 (unnumbered).

6 *Alethopteris zeillerii* (Ragot) Wagner on right and *Cyclopteris trichomanoides* Sternberg on left. *Cyclopteris* specimen is a stipular pinnule generally associated with *Macroneuropteris* (*Neuropteris*) *scheuchzeri*. Roof shale above Pittsburgh (No. 8) coal (Monongahela Group, Pennsylvanian) in strip mines adjacent to Fairfax Stone State Park, east of Davis, Tucker County, West Virginia; William H. Gillespie collection CH-5575.

1
2
3
5
4
6

FIGURE 23-22.—Pennsylvanian and Permian seed ferns. All scale bars equal 1 cm except that for figure 23-22.3, which is in millimeter/centimeter increments.

1 *Autunia (Callipteris) conferta* (Sternberg) Kerp. Main rachis of branch of frond (arrow indicates intercalary pinnule). Lower Washington limestone and adjacent beds (Washington Formation, Dunkard Group, Permian), Browns Mill, Monongalia County, West Virginia; MSU FPH BM-1977.

2 *Aphlebia* sp. Laminar growth with fountainlike tufts on a main rachis of a frond at or below the point of attachment of a secondary rachis. Roof shale of Upper Freeport (No. 7) coal (Allegheny Group, Pennsylvanian) near Buchtel, York Township, Athens County, Ohio; OU PH Bu-53-1.

3 *Callipteridium* sp. Typical incomplete specimen. Red shales of Washington Formation (Dunkard Group, Permian) near Sardis, Monroe County, Ohio; OU PH S-342-1.

4 *Rhachiphyllum schenkii* (Heyer) Kerp. Enlarged view showing decurrent pinnules on pinnae and intercalary pinnules on rachis between points of pinnae attachments above and below. Shales above Lower Washington limestone (Washington Formation) north of Waynesburg, Greene County, Pennsylvania; William H. Gillespie collection 1967, unnumbered.

1

2

3

4

FIGURE 23-23.—Pennsylvanian seed ferns. All scale bars equal 1 cm.

1 *Cyclopteris fimbriata* Lesquereux. Note fringed (laciniate or fimbriate) margin. More than 150 veins reach the margin in this specimen. Roof shale above Middle Kittanning (No. 6) coal (Allegheny Group), outcrop on Gladesville Road southeast of U.S. Route 119, Monongalia County, West Virginia; William H. Gillespie collection 10-1962-WG 56.

2 *Cyclopteris orbicularis* Brongniart. Robust circular-ovate stipular pinnule. Two basal lobes extend nearly half the diameter below the point of attachment at the base of a pinna (or at the base of a branch of the frond). A few trichomes (hairs), 1 to 3 mm long, are seen near attachment point nearly paralleling the veins. This specimen may be the stipular pinnule of *Macroneuropteris* (*Neuropteris*) *scheuchzeri*, based on the presence of a few trichomes (plant hairs) and many trichome bases. Roof shale above Pittsburgh (No. 8) coal (Monongahela Group) in strip mines adjacent to Fairfax Stone State Park, east of Davis, Tucker County, West Virginia; William H. Gillespie collection FS-CG, unnumbered.

3 *Pseudomariopteris* cf. *P. busqueti* (Zeiller) Danzé-Corsin. Eighteen alternately arranged pinnules and a terminal pinnule on a single pinna. Same unit and location as **2**; William H. Gillespie collection CH-5575 FS-CG-4.

4 *Eremopteris gracilis* White. Fernlike terminal pinna. Basal Conemaugh Group, 7-11 mine, Madison Township, Columbiana County, Ohio; OU PH 7-11-48.

5 *Dicksonites* (*Pecopteris*) *pluckeneti* (Schlotheim) Sterzel. Note strong venation pattern on pinnules. Marine shale and fluvial interbeds between Lower Kittanning (No. 5) and Middle Kittanning (No. 6) coals (Allegheny Group), abandoned strip mine 2 km (1.3 miles) northwest of Nelsonville, Ward Township, Hocking County, Ohio; MSU FPH 8-25-77 I-1.

6, 7 *Lescuropteris moorii* (Lesquereux) Schimper. **6**, parts of frond with several pinnae. **7**, enlarged view showing venation, which on some pinnules is pseudoreticulate (arrows). Shale between Upper Freeport (No. 7) and Mahoning (No. 7A) coals (Conemaugh Group), same location as **4**; OU PH 7-11-41 (**6**) and OU PH 7-11-47 (**7**).

8 *Linopteris neuropteroides* (Gutbier) Zeiller. Single typical pinnule with conspicuous net (reticulate) venation. Shale above Upper Freeport (No. 7) coal (Conemaugh Group), same location as **4**; OU PH 7-11-21

5

8

FIGURE 23-24.—Pennsylvanian seed ferns *Mariopteris* and *Megalopteris*. All scale bars equal 1 cm.

1 *Mariopteris muricata* (Schlotheim) Zeiller. Robust form preserved as coalified (vitrinized) compression. When freshly exposed on rock surface this specimen would have made a good acetate peel. Brookville shale (Allegheny Group), near Strasburg, Tuscarawas County, Ohio; ClMNH collection, unnumbered.

2 *Mariopteris nervosa* (Brongniart) Zeiller. Photo of acetate peel of several pinnae of a frond. Light is transmitted through the preserved leaf tissue, mainly the cuticles of the upper and lower surface; veins are nearly opaque. Allegheny-Conemaugh transition zone in old strip mines near Kimberly, York Township, Athens County, Ohio. MSU FPH unnumbered.

3 *Megalopteris minima* Andrews. Paratype illustrating tip of a pinna. Quakertown (No. 2) or Bear Run coal zone (Pottsville Group), Rushville flora locality, east of Rushville, Reading Township, Perry County, Ohio; MC C-P1-79-13. Specimen illustrated by Andrews (1875, pl. 48, fig. 3).

4 *Megalopteris* cf. *M. dawsonii* (Hartt) Andrews. Pinnules near terminal end of a branch or frond. Light dots in ranks between the veins may be sites of resin or gum globules. Same unit and location as **3**; MSU FPH CH-5520-1952.

5, 6 *Megalopteris ovata* Andrews. Parts of holotype. **5**, apical portion of frond. **6**, portion of frond near basal end. Same unit and location as **3**; MC C-P1-77.

1
2
3
4
5
6

FIGURE 23-25.—Pennsylvanian seed ferns and *Cordaites*. All scale bars equal 1 cm.

1, 2 *Neuropteris heterophylla* (Brongniart) Sternberg. **1**, roof shale of Sharon (No. 1) coal (Pottsville Group), mine near Jackson, Jackson County, Ohio; OU PH J-3-10. **2**, siderite zone above Upper Freeport (No. 7) coal (Conemaugh Group), 7-11 mine, Madison Township, Columbiana County, Ohio; OU PH 7-11-28-2.

3, 4 *Macroneuropteris (Neuropteris) scheuchzeri* (Hoffman) Cleal, Shute & Zodrow. **3**, pinnules illustrating two critical characteristics of this species: the basal lobes below the point of pinnule attachment to the rachis, and the long hairs (trichomes) that extend at angles of about 0° to 30° away from the midvein on either side. The hairs cross the arching veins at increasingly oblique angles as the veins approach the pinnule margins. Brookville (No. 4) or Clarion (No. 4A) coal (Allegheny Group), Walton mine, Wellston area, Milton Township, Jackson County, Ohio; OU PH W-1. **4**, typical pinnule in center has unusually conspicuous hairs. Roof shale above Pittsburgh (No. 8) coal (Monongahela Group), Hanna Coal Co. Georgetown mine, Harrison County, Ohio; William H. Gillespie Cadiz collection, unnumbered.

5 Pteridosperm frond rachis with spinelike protuberances (broken off bases of subordinate rachises or pinnules). This rachis probably bore *Macroneuropteris (Neuropteris) scheuchzeri* fronds or pinnae. Same unit and location as **4**; William H. Gillespie collection, unnumbered.

6 *Neuropteris ovata* Hoffman. Large terminal pinnule consisting of terminal lobe (broken off) and three pairs of large lobes, opposite to subopposite, not dissected to midvein. Lowermost lobe on right may be a fully separate lateral pinnule. Strata above Upper Freeport (No. 7) coal (Conemaugh Group), same location as **1**, **2**; OU PH 7-11-33.

7 *Paripteris (Neuropteris) gigantea* (Sternberg) Gothan (upper left center), *N. heterophylla* (lower left), and *Cordaites* Unger (right). This specimen of *Cordaites* represents a splitting up of an old leaf into fanlike segments. Roof shale above Sharon (No. 1) coal (Pottsville Group), Jackson, Jackson County, Ohio; OU PH J-54-11.

1
2
3
4
5
6
7

FIGURE 23-26.—Pennsylvanian and Permian seed ferns. Scale bars for figures 23-26.1 to 23-26.6 equal 1 cm; scale bar for figure 23-26.4 equals 30 mm; scale bar for figure 23-26.5 equals 90 mm.

1 *Odontopteris brardii* (Brongniart) Sternberg. Pinnules vary from very stubby and wide to more similar to neuropterid type. Lower left pinnule shows typical appearance of venation. Pustules on veins, due to crystallization of iron pyrite from the iron carbonate of the concretions in the shale, distort the vein patterns and form the bumpy or warty surface. Some veins pass into the base of the pinnule from the rachis. Lower Conemaugh Group (Pennsylvanian), 7-11 mine, Madison Township, Columbiana County, Ohio; OU PH 7-11-47.

2 *Orthogoniopteris clara* Andrews. Apical poriton of holotype. Quakertown (No. 2) or Bear Run coal zone (Pottsville Group, Pennsylvanian), Rushville flora locality, east of Rushville, Reading Township, Perry County, Ohio; MC C-P1-78.

3 *Odontopteris osmundaeformis* (Schlotheim) Zeiller. Note small, blocky pinnules. Clay shales of Dunkard Group (Permian), Monroe County, Ohio; MSU FPH B-4996.

4, 5 *Protoblechnum holdenii* (Andrews) Lesquereux. Remarkable topotype specimen, 31.5 cm tall. **4** is an enlarged view of tip of specimen in **5**. Same unit and location as **2**; MSU FPH CH-5520-59-3.

6 *Palmatopteris furcata* (Brongniart) Potonié. Excellent specimen illustrating repeated bifurcations of pinnules. Shale above Pocahontas No. 6 coal (equivalent to Pottsville Group, Pennsylvanian), on top of Mt. Bellwood, on West Virginia Route 20 south of Rainelle, near Fayette-Greenbrier County line, West Virginia; William H. Gillespie collection 6-18-85.

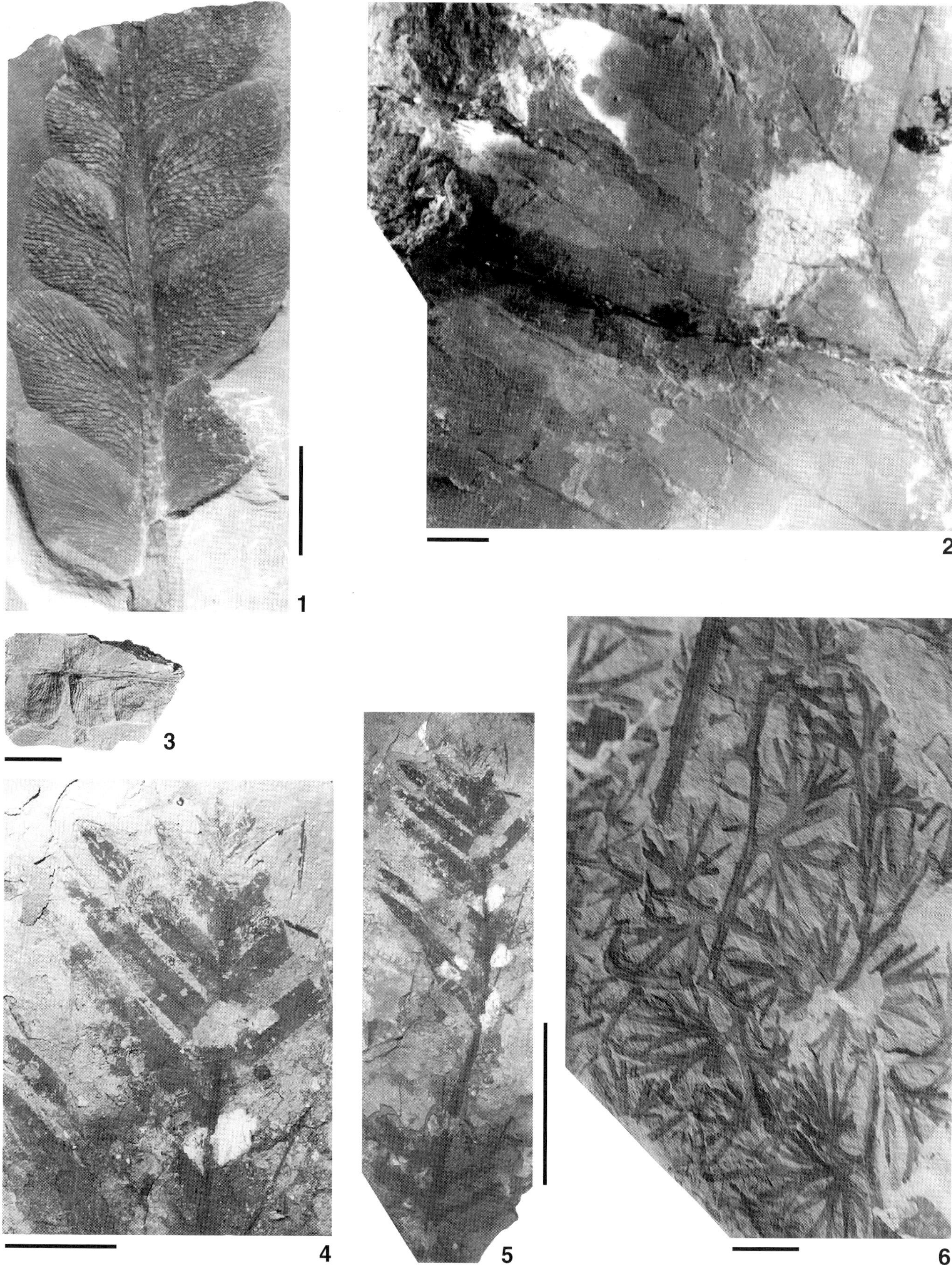
1
2
3
4
5
6

FIGURE 23-27.—Pennsylvanian seed fern *Rhacopteris* and the cycadlike *Taeniopteris*. All scale bars equal 1 cm.

1, 2 — *Rhacopteris* cf. *R. elegans* (Ettingshausen) Schimper. Two views of an elegant specimen. Quakertown (No. 2) or Bear Run coal zone (Pottsville Group), Rushville flora locality, east of Rushville, Reading Township, Perry County, Ohio; MSU FPH CH-5520-1952.

3, 4 — *Taeniopteris jejunata* Grand 'Eury. Underside (**3**) and upper surface (**4**) of thick, leathery leaf (or pinnule). Shale between Upper Freeport (No. 7) and Mahoning (No. 7A) coals (Conemaugh Group), 7-11 mine, Madison Township, Columbiana County, Ohio; OU PH 7-11-50 (**3**) and OU PH 7-11-52 (**4**).

1

2

3

4

FIGURE 23-28.—Pennsylvanian seed-fern reproductive structures. All scale bars equal 1 cm.

1 *Samaropsis* Goeppert. Broad-winged, bilaterally symmetrical seeds. Shale between Upper Freeport (No. 7) and Mahoning (No. 7A) coals (Conemaugh Group), 7-11 mine, Madison Township, Columbiana County, Ohio; OU PH 7-11-44 (left) and 7-11-45 (right).

2 *Rhabdocarpus* Goeppert & Berger. Cast (left) and mold (right) of base of one type of seed that has about 24 ribs. Allegheny Group, Youngstown area, Mahoning County, Ohio; ClMNH, Otto Kuntze collection, un numbered.

3 *Carpolithes* Schlotheim. Seed. Sewell coal zone (New River Group), New River gorge just west of bridge below U.S. Highway 19, Fayette County, West Virginia; William H. Gillespie collection, 1974.

4 *Trigonocarpus* Brongniart. Sandstone casts of two seeds. Upper seed, in basal view, shows point of attachment and three main ribs at 60°, 180°, and 300° as oriented here. Lower seed, in side view, shows one main rib extending from top (micropylar end) on right to base on left as oriented here; a second main rib is at lower margin and a partial ridge is intermediate between. Allegheny Group, Jackson Gulch, Youngstown, Mahoning County, Ohio; ClMNH P-8060 (B-4916) (upper seed) and ClMNH P-8067 (B-4814) (lower seed).

5 *Holcospermum maizeretense* Stockmans & Willière. Four seeds. Each has 10 to 12 well-defined ribs extending from base (arrow) to micropylar end. Outcrop of shale in basal Pocahontas Group along Virginia Route 659 within city limits of Pocahontas, Tazewell County, Virginia; William H. Gillespie collection PSS-34-3.

6, 7 *Dolerotheca* Halle. Top (**6**) and bottom (**7**) of a complex, bell-shaped pollen-bearing structure of a medullosan seed fern. Pinnules of *Alethopteris zeillerii* at lower left in **7**. Roof shale above Pittsburgh (No. 8) coal (Monongahela Group) in strip mines adjacent to Fairfax Stone State Park, east of Davis, Tucker County, West Virginia; William H. Gillespie collection WHG FS-141 (**6**) and MSU FPH CH-5570 FS-CG-39 (**7**).

8 *Crossotheca? sagittata* (Lesquereux) Lesquereux. Branched pollen-bearing organ of a lyginopterid seed fern. Shale above Middle Kittanning (No. 6) coal (Kanawha Group) (equivalent to upper Pottsville Group), Cannelton strip mine, Kanawha County, West Virginia; William H. Gillespie collection, Aug. 1976.

9 *Whittleseya elegans* Newberry. Campanulate (bell-shaped) pollen-bearing structure. Middle Kittanning (No. 6) coal (Allegheny Group), East Fairfield Coal Co. pit near North Lima, Mahoning County, Ohio; Gregory McComas collection, L-1.

10 *Aulacotheca campbellii* (White) Halle. Synangium of five or six elongated, tubelike pollen sacs borne on a long stalk (upper left) attached to a rachis. Same unit and location as **5**; William H. Gillespie collection PSS-34.

1
2
3
4
5
6
7
8
9
10

FIGURE 23-29.—Pennsylvanian cordaitean leaves, stems, and reproductive structures. All scale bars equal 1 cm.

1, 2 *Cordaites* cf. *C. principalis* (Germar) Geinitz. **1**, leaf base. Note longitudinal veins, one to four minor veins between major veins, intercalation of new veins distally, and splitting of blade of leaf distally. Quakertown (No. 2) or Bear Run coal zone (Pottsville Group), Rushville flora locality, east of Rushville, Reading Township, Perry County, Ohio; MSU FPH CH-5570-41a-1952 ATC-JHH. **2**, enlargement of the base of a similar leaf from the same locality to show the straight basal attachment and the venation in detail.

3 *Cordaites* Unger. This unusual leaf may be a stipule at the base of a branch or one of a terminal cluster of short leaves; there are 77 to 92 veins at midpoint. Shale between Upper Freeport (No. 7) and Mahoning (No. 7A) coals (Conemaugh Group), 7-11 mine, Madison Township, Columbiana County, Ohio; OU PH 7-11-28.

4 *Artisia transversa* (Artis) Sternberg. Cast represents sediment that has replaced broken-down pith tissue inside the vascular cylinder of a *Cordaites* stem. The transverse lines that form disklike segments resulted from septa of stronger tissue that extended into or across the pith cavity. Roof shale above Pittsburgh (No. 8) coal (Monongahela Group), Hanna Coal Co. Georgetown mine, Harrison County, Ohio; William H. Gillespie collection, unnumbered.

5, 6 *Cordaitanthus* Feistmantel. *Cordaites* fertile shoot. **5**, probably an immature seed-bearing shoot, though bracts generally subtend each seed group. **6**, fertile shoot with conspicuous pollen-bearing structures (pollen sacs at arrows). Same unit and location as **3**; OU PH 7-11-8 (**5**) and OU PH 7-11-23 (**6**).

7 *Mitrospermum* Arber. Incomplete cordaitean seed, flattened in growth in a wide primary plane and narrow secondary plane. The extended wall (integument) in the primary plane gives the appearance of a wing. Same unit and location as **3**; OU PH 7-11-42.

8 *Cardiocarpus* Brongniart. Partially exfoliated seed exposing the central ovule and edges of the surrounding seed coat. Oriented with micropyle end up, though in life such seeds probably hung with micropyle end down. Same unit and location as **3**; OU PH 7-11-42.

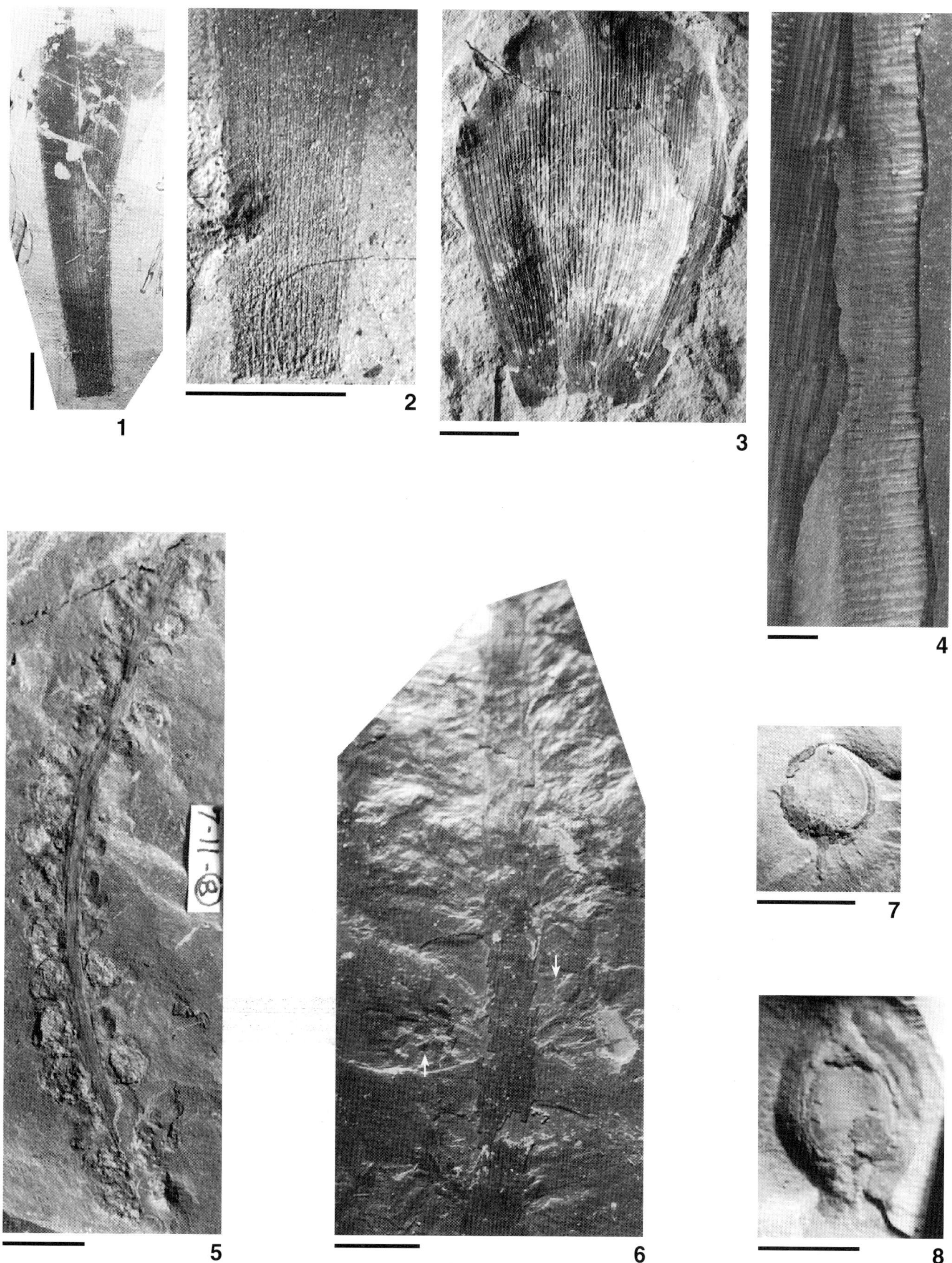
1
2
3
4
5
6
7
8

FIGURE 23-30.—Pennsylvanian Voltziales and *Lycopodites*. All scale bars equal 1 cm.

1, 3 — *Walchia* Sternberg. **1**, branch tip with stiff, bristlelike, sharp-pointed, spirally arranged leaves. Shale between Upper Freeport (No. 7) and Mahoning (No. 7A) coals (Conemaugh Group), 7-11 mine, Madison Township, Columbiana County, Ohio; OU PH 7-11-10. **3**, several branch tips with leaves densely arranged. Conemaugh Group, locality not available; ClMNH collection, unnumbered.

2 — *Lycopodites* Lindley & Hutton. A leafy branch of a lycopod for comparison with *Walchia* twigs in **1** and **3**. The lycopod twigs are distinguished from *Walchia* twigs by the sporangia, the small oval or dome-shaped protuberances scattered along the stem at the base of the leaves. Strata above Eagle coal (Kanawha Group) (equivalent to upper Pottsville Group), Armstrong Mountain, above West Virginia Route 61, Fayette County, West Virginia; William H. Gillespie collection PSS 50-45.

4 — *Walchiostrobus* Florin. Walchian cone. Several of the spirally arranged bracts, which bear the ovuliferous scales, are missing, exposing the axis. Same unit and location as **1**; OU PH 7-11-20.

1

2

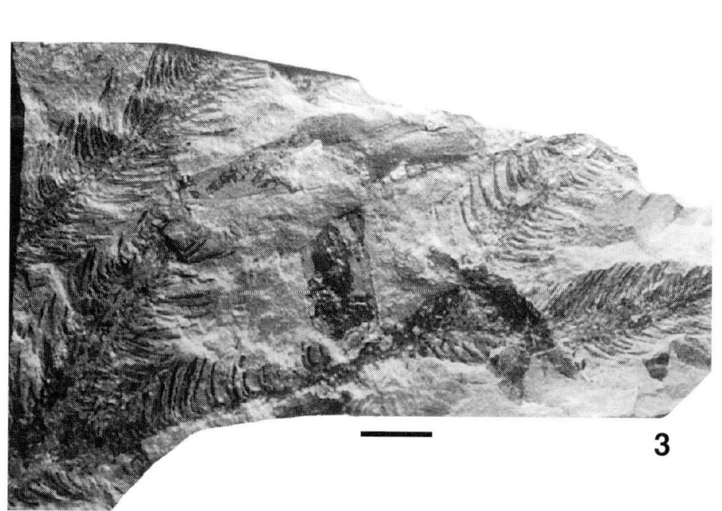

3

4

Chapter 24

OHIO VEGETATION—THE LAST MILLION YEARS

by Ralph E. Taggart, Aureal T. Cross, and William H. Gillespie

INTRODUCTION

For most of the Mesozoic and Cenozoic Eras, Ohio, now located in the continental interior, was primarily a site for erosion of older rocks. If any fossil-bearing deposits were laid down during this interval, they have either been eroded by subsequent geological activity or have yet to be discovered. For much of the Mesozoic Era, the vegetation of Ohio probably was dominated by advanced **gymnosperms** such as conifers, cycads and cycadlike plants, and a few surviving pteridosperms and ferns. Ohio also may have been home to dinosaurs and exotic reptiles. Unfortunately, no known rocks in Ohio record this rich tapestry of life. One must look westward to the sediments of the western interior or to the deposits laid down along the southeastern coastal plain to document this fascinating period in Earth history.

About 150 million years ago, in the early Cretaceous (the last of the three periods of the Mesozoic), flowering plants (**angiosperms**) made their first appearance in the fossil record. Today, such plants range from large woody trees to annual weeds. They are so ubiquitous in the modern flora, dominating all terrestrial **biomes** with the exception of northern (boreal) or high-altitude (montane) conifer forests, that it is difficult to imagine a world without them.

The angiosperms began a pattern of rapid diversification in the late Early Cretaceous. A few tenuous angiosperm fossils are known from the Early Cretaceous, but by Late Cretaceous time, flowering plants, mostly woody trees and shrubs, had largely displaced conifers and other gymnosperms in tropical, subtropical, and temperate habitats. Some of this rapid success can be attributed to the fact that angiosperms were able to colonize a wide range of arid and semi-arid environments, which may have been essentially barren in terms of plant cover. But the greatest impetus to the expansion of the angiosperms may well reflect the most unusual but effective adaptation of the flowering plants: the use of a wide range of animals, primarily insects, as agents of pollination.

In terms of the history of plants, the Mesozoic and Cenozoic Eras were marked by a steady modernization of the Earth's flora. In the strictest sense, it is incorrect to suggest that biomes and ecosystems have evolved, but they certainly have changed over time as a result of the evolution of new taxa, the impact of global climatic change, and possible influence of catastrophic events in Earth history. As the Cenozoic progressed, biomes certainly assumed a more modern aspect, both in their composition and in the specifics of the relationship of vegetation types to prevailing climate. The final stage in this process began, perhaps 30 million years ago, with the rapid evolution of **herbaceous** flowering-plant taxa. This group includes the grasses, familiar weedy and garden-type herbs and shrubs such as the sunflower family (Compositae), and other plants capable of establishment and growth on disturbed or low-moisture sites (for example, plants of the families Chenopodiaceae, Amaranthaceae, and Malvaceae). This diversification in the greening of the land began in the later Silurian and led to the present, where all but the driest landscapes are characterized by permanent or ephemeral (seasonal) vegetation.

The fossil-plant record of the late Mesozoic indicates a mild climatic regime and poorly defined latitudinal zonation of vegetation. During the Late Cretaceous and Early Cenozoic, temperate vegetation developed as far north as the high arctic islands such as Axel Heiberg and Spitzbergen, and polar ice caps were absent. In general, the later Cenozoic is characterized by greater climatic variability and a progressive decline in global temperatures. These trends reached their peak in the Pleistocene Epoch of the Quaternary Period, which began approximately 2 million years years before present (**B.P.**), when northern North America was buried under several hundred to several thousand feet of glacial ice.

In North America, the Pleistocene Epoch includes at least four major episodes of continental glaciation, traditionally named the Nebraskan, the Kansan, the Illinoian, and the Wisconsinan, from oldest to youngest (table 24-1). During

TABLE 24-1.—GLACIAL STAGES OF THE QUATERNARY PERIOD (MODIFIED FROM WHITE, 1982, TABLE 1)

Epoch	Glacial and interglacial stages	Deposits in Ohio
Holocene (Recent)		stream deposits (alluvium); swamp deposits (peat, muck); beach and other deposits along Lake Erie
Pleistocene	Wisconsinan	drift (including till)
	Sangamonian	period of weathering and erosion; rare buried soils (paleosols)
	Illinoian	eroded till in widely separated areas
	Yarmouthian	long period of weathering and erosion; some very rare paleosols
	Kansan	till in widely separated areas
	Aftonian	period of weathering and erosion
	Nebraskan	none definitely known from Ohio

the intervening interglacial stages the climate was actually warmer than that of today (Imbrie and Imbrie, 1979). With the onset of the Kansan glaciation, major westward- or northward-flowing streams such as the Ohio, Monongahela, and New Rivers were dammed, creating lakes in eastern Ohio, northern West Virginia, and western Pennsylvania. Sediments containing abundant plant remains accumulated in these lakes. These sediments are found today at higher elevations along the upper Ohio and Monongahela Rivers. The remarkable flora of Lake Monongahela is discussed briefly later in this chapter.

The most recent glacial interval, the Wisconsinan, reached its peak between 25,000 and 16,000 years B.P. Post-Wisconsinan time, between 16,000 years B.P. and the present, has a rich fossil record and is within the range of precision **radiocarbon dating**. As a result, the post-Wisconsinan time interval has been extensively studied in Ohio and elsewhere. Data from such studies represent most of the information available on vegetation development during the North American Pleistocene.

In contrast to the post-Wisconsinan, the peak Wisconsinan glacial interval and all earlier glacial and interglacial stages have a far less extensive record. Although the retreat phase of each of the earlier glacial stages left a rich fossil record, many of their surficial deposits typically were overridden and partially to extensively destroyed or were buried by later glacial activity. The glacial sediments (drift) may be stratified outwash, kames, eskers, or fluvial, lacustrine, or **bog** deposits or unstratified till in ground-moraine or end-moraine deposits (see fig. 3-3).

Plant materials commonly were incorporated in the glacial deposits in the form of isolated logs, stumps, and, more rarely, leaves and seeds. In Pleistocene silts, clays, organic mucks, and other stratified deposits of fluvial or lacustrine origin (lake muds, bogs, **swamps**, etc.), diverse twigs, wood splinters, leaves, seeds, abundant pollen and **spores**, diatoms (one-celled plants that have a siliceous **test**), charophytes, and other **algal** types are generally plentiful.

These deposits range from a few thousand years old to estimated ages of over 100,000 years B.P. Fossils of wood and other megascopic plant matter are found in greater abundance in the younger deposits, particularly those of Late Wisconsinan and Recent age. Hundreds of logs, stumps, blocks of wood, and thousands of splinters of wood and twigs have been exposed in caving stream banks, road and railroad cuts, ditches, water wells, irrigation trenches, building foundations, farm ponds, and cultivated fields.

PLEISTOCENE MEGAFLORA

WOOD

Fossil wood is widely distributed in tills (fig. 24.5-1), in forest beds overridden by advancing glaciers, in or at the margins of glacial lakes, and in **peat** bogs or swamps. The common occurrence of fossil (or **subfossil**) wood has been noted by numerous researchers.

In letters to the fledgling American Journal of Science in 1833, Gazlay noted that there were many logs and forest litter masses being found widely in Ohio, primarily in hand-dug water wells. He recounted reports, locations, and numbers of such fossils in a wide region in southwestern Ohio centered in the Springfield area (Clark County) and the Miami, Little Miami, and Ohio River corridors. According to Gazlay and his sources, depth to the forest bed generally ranged from 5 to 12 meters, thickness ranged from a few centimeters to several meters, and the size of the logs and stumps ranged from 15 to 45 cm in diameter and up to 6 meters in length.

Orton (1870) reviewed the distribution of other forest beds and peat deposits and described in some detail deposits in the vicinity of Germantown, in Montgomery County: "The uppermost layers of the peat contain undecomposed sphagnous mosses, grasses, and sedges"; "there is a great accumulation of wood, in trunks, roots, branches, and twigs, much of which has been flattened by the pressure of 80 feet of clay and gravel that overlie it"; "trunks of cedar nearly two feet in diameter have been taken"; "there is a large amount of wood buried beneath the drift throughout this region generally"; "there is scarcely a square mile in the thickly settled portions . . . in which instances of this kind cannot be found." In 1958, Goldthwait wrote, "well drillers today turn in reports of buried wood at the rate of nearly one a month."

Dachnowski (1912) listed 206 peatlands in 45 of the 65 Ohio counties that have primary glacial deposits or that had glacial activity. His original estimate of the area of the wetlands was over 2 million hectares. Because of building of cities and highways and draining of wetlands for agriculture, industry, commerce, and residential areas, wetlands have been reduced to about 200,000 hectares (Andreas and Knoop, 1992).

Even the unglaciated areas of Ohio have terraces and other valley deposits in which Pleistocene to Recent fossil material can be found (for example, fig. 24-2, locality 42). So in every corner of the state there is potential for unearthing some of this rich heritage from our past.

Logs and stumps may be found singly or in numbers in exposures of tills and outwash-plain deposits. Such subfossils commonly are in such bent, folded, or other distorted conditions that they appear to have been derived from live, standing trees that were overridden by slowly advancing ice. Fossil or subfossil woods look very much like modern woods in texture, annual rings, rays, etc., but they are all partially altered physically and chemically. Generally the wood is tan or brown, but it may be black or red, similar in color to the wood of red cedar (*Juniperus virginiana*). Identification of these woods requires making transverse, radial, and tangential **thin sections** and the use of a compound microscope (100X to 500X magnification), although some woods may, with experience, be identified at the generic level using a 10X hand lens.

Fossil wood commonly is the preferred material for radiocarbon dating. Bone, shell, collagen, and even peat can be dated, but, for a variety of technical reasons, woods generally yield more consistent results. Abundance of material generally decreases with increasing age. On the map in figure 24-2, only five samples exceed 32,000 years B.P., but there are numerous samples from the Late Wisconsinan (24,000 to 14,000 years B.P.). Radiocarbon-dated woods have proved useful in ascertaining the age of the many mastodon occurrences in Ohio.

The logs, stumps, leaves, seeds, pollen, spores, and peat beds found in till or other unconsolidated deposits at many places in Ohio represent several stages of the Wisconsinan. Most Pleistocene plant material, if sufficiently well preserved, can be assigned to **extant** species. Because ecological-tolerance ranges for most taxa have probably not changed significantly in the last 100,000 years, identifiable plant remains can be used to reconstruct prevailing climatic conditions at or near the time of deposition of the material.

Although patterns of species associations in fossil deposits generally mirror those found in extant communities, some patterns of fossil species association have no modern analogs. There are several possible reasons for such anomalous associations. First, the closest modern analogs commonly are northern hardwood and boreal associations that have existed for only the last few thousand years. In such cases, modern patterns of association may not fully reflect ecological potentials that may require longer time periods for development. It is also possible that the glacial and interglacial intervals may have been characterized by habitats and environments that have no modern equivalents. Finally, species ranges respond individually to environmental change and, where such change is rapid, it is possible that ephemeral associations of species occurred that did not reflect our current understanding of the relationship between extant plant associations and climate.

An interesting condition has been noted in the wood of some fossil logs found in pre-Late Wisconsinan tills. The annual rings in trees that were pushed down by the advancing ice front show a gradual reduction in width to the last (outermost) ring present. White spruce (*Picea glauca*) trees in normal forests have an average life span of about 250 years. A gradual reduction in ring width was measured on a number of white spruce trees at several sites in Ohio. The reduction began about 70 to 100 years before the death or the destruction of the tree, presumably by overriding ice. Burns (1958) illustrated this decline in ring thickness in several trees at three sites in Butler County (fig. 24-2, localities 3-5) and at two sites in Ross County (fig. 24-2, localities 40 and 41). Trees growing near ice fronts or in cold climates bordering alpine tree limits or tundra zones generally show very slow growth and very narrow rings. Burns indicated that growth rate was affected by proximity to the ice front beginning about 70 years before the ice overrode the forests.

Exposures of earlier glacial sediments are widely scattered in western and southwestern Ohio (fig. 24-2), beyond the margin of maximum advance of the Wisconsinan ice and, in places, beneath Wisconsinan-age tills and lake deposits. Layered deposits of various quality, thickness, and age attest to the multiple periods of glaciation or the advance of separate glacial lobes at different stages of a major glacial period. Thus, different plant fossils or plant assemblages, representing different climatic regimes and ecologic communities, may be found in stratigraphic superposition at a single locality (for example, fig. 24-2, locality 16).

SEEDS AND LEAVES

Seeds can be locally abundant in bog peats and, when present, are easily recovered by washing the peat through screens. Considering their abundance and ease of collection, they have generally been understudied. Seeds played a critical role in the analysis of an 11,500-year-B.P. mastodon (see fig. 21-32.2) recovered from a pond excavation at the Burning Tree golf course in Licking County (fig. 24-2, locality 32B; see Lepper and others, 1991). Mastodon finds are not rare in Ohio (see Chapter 21), but this well-preserved skeleton was unique in that an elongate organic mass was recovered that proved to be a sample of the material contained in the animal's gut cavity. The difference between the seed content of the peat and that of the gut mass (table 24-2) was a major element in identifying the nature of the mass and provided evidence that mastodon feeding behavior involved

TABLE 24-2.—COMPARISON OF SEED CONTENT OF PEAT MATRIX AND GUT MASS OF BURNING TREE MASTODON (FROM LEPPER AND OTHERS, 1991)

Seed type	No. of species	
	Peat matrix	Gut mass
Najas (naiad)[1]	1	2
Potamogeton (pondweed)	3	1
Nymphaea (water lily)	1	1
Carex (sedge)[2]	3	3
Amaranthus (pigweed)	-	1
Cladium (sawgrass)	-	1
Trifolium (clover)	-	1
Cyperus (flat sedge)	1	-
Eleocharis (spike-rush)	1	-
Hypericum (St.-John's-wort)	1	-
Juncus (rush)	1	-
Sparganium (bur-reed)	1	-

[1]Many thousands of naiad seeds were noted in the peat matrix but were relatively uncommon in the gut mass.

[2]Although the number of sedge species is similar, the recognizable species are distinct in terms of peat vs. gut occurrence.

both browsing and grazing and that the animals made little use of the dominant coniferous vegetation as a food source. The known time of flowering and seed setting for the various species encountered in the gut samples suggests that the animal died in early autumn. Figures 24-3 (herbaceous species) and 24-4 (woody trees and shrubs) document modern examples of seeds known from Ohio deposits.

Thalli of mosses and liverworts also can be recovered from both peats and detrital sediments. Remains of a moss (*Drepanocladus fluitans*) were recovered from the Castalia Prairie in northwestern Erie County (fig. 24-2, locality 21). Bryophyte material is probably more common than generally recognized, but the plants are inconspicuous and quickly degrade if not recognized when excavated. For example, Farrand and others (1969) described a 1-cm-thick bryophyte deposit from northern Lower Michigan that contained remains of eight species of mosses. The material was uncovered during excavation of a farm pond, and the observant landowner alerted botanists from the University of Michigan. Many mosses and liverworts have well-defined ecological requirements and are thus useful environmental indicators. A greater awareness of the nature of such fossils would undoubtedly result in the recognition of more occurrences in Ohio.

Leaves of trees and shrubs are certainly more common in unconsolidated glacial sediments than is generally recognized or reported (figs. 24-4.27 to 24-4.30, 24-5.2, 24-5.3). If leaf **impressions** or **compressions** are discovered in clays, the specimens should be carefully wrapped in several layers of newspaper and set aside for six months or more to allow the specimens to dry very slowly. Drying them in the open or attempts to hasten the drying process will almost certainly result in the degradation or destruction of the specimen. Once the sediment has dried, the specimens may be stored and studied with reasonable care.

Entire leaves as well as leaf fragments commonly are found buried in clays and silts, particularly in the thicker sediments deposited in proglacial lakes—lakes that form in front of glaciers when rivers are dammed by glacial ice. Lake

Monongahela (Gillespie and Clendening, 1968), which once covered parts of what is now West Virginia, Ohio, and Pennsylvania and whose drainage led to the formation of the present Ohio River, is an example of such a proglacial lake. Where leaves appear to be present, it is best if one or more blocks of sediment can be excavated, wrapped while wet, and returned to the laboratory for study. Gentle soaking and washing of the blocks will free any leaves which may be present. Figure 24-4.27 shows a leaf fragment recovered from the silts of the Beale mastodon site in Athens County (fig. 24-2, locality 42). Such leaves are typically extremely fragile and deteriorate very quickly if allowed to dry out. With care, specimens can be run through a standard histological dehydration sequence (see Sass, 1958), after which they can be mounted between glass plates using a standard permanent slide-mounting medium.

POLLEN ANALYSIS

Each major glacial advance was followed by a period of retreat, during which the ice sheets wasted away and exposed the barren surface of the recently glaciated terrain. The advancing ice sheets generally scoured and smoothed the landscape, but the topography along the retreating ice front was more variable. Depressions, called kettles, were formed by the melting of buried ice blocks, and a variety of ridgelike features, such as end moraines, kames, and eskers, were formed. Tremendous volumes of cold meltwater drained from the retreating ice front, resulting in the formation of innumerable bodies of water ranging from small ponds to the incomparable Great Lakes.

The sedimentary record of most of the smaller ponds and lakes began with layers of mud and marl, but most of these sites eventually developed floating bog mats and began to accumulate peat. The accumulation of peat, which has continued to the present day in many bogs, incorporated a wide range of plant debris, including pollen grains and spores derived from the bog vegetation as well as material blown in from plants growing in the immediate region. Postglacial lake muds and bog peats thus contain a record, in the form of entombed pollen grains and spores, of the sequence of vegetation development in and around the bog from the time of its formation until the cessation of active peat accumulation.

Pollen analysis, the systematic quantitative study of the stratigraphic distribution of pollen grains in bog sediments, began in Europe about 1916 and rapidly developed into the primary means for the reconstruction of patterns of postglacial vegetation change (Faegri and Iversen, 1975). Pollen grains and spores in peat and associated glacial and postglacial sediments provide an excellent record of plants. The types of plants identified and numerical changes in their representation can be used to interpret general composition of the various plant associations. The reconstruction of the changing plant communities serves as an indicator of the nature of environments and the changes in climate that occurred following deglaciation. One limitation of pollen analysis is that the dominant pollen types in peat and other sediments are derived from plants that are pollinated by wind. Insect-pollinated plants tend to be significantly underrepresented. Fortunately, in temperate climates, vegetation tends to be dominated by wind-pollinated trees and shrubs. Pollen analysis is much more limited in its ability to document tropical and subtropical vegetation, where plants pollinated by insects and other animals tend to be dominant.

One of the earliest examples of the application of pollen analysis in North America (Sears, 1930) dealt with Ohio deposits. While of historical interest, most pollen analytical work prior to 1950 suffered from several deficiencies (judged by current standards), including: consideration of fluctuations in arboreal pollen (**AP**) types (woody trees and selected shrubs) while ignoring nonarboreal pollen types (**NAP**) and spores of ferns and bryophytes; relatively small pollen sample sizes (commonly as low as 100 grains per sample); a general lack of application of statistical techniques in data analysis; and lack of stratigraphic control through the use of radiocarbon dating. Most of these issues are addressed in modern studies, which also include analysis of pollen from sediments other than peats.

PRE-WISCONSINAN VEGETATION

The sedimentary record in the ponds and lakes that formed in great numbers on formerly glaciated sites generally can be assumed to span the post-Wisconsinan. In contrast, pre-Wisconsinan sedimentary environments are far less common beyond the maximum extent of former glaciations and, where sedimentary records are present, they may encompass a melange of glacial and interglacial intervals. Definitive age assessment of these older deposits is difficult, as many exceed the age limit (about 40,000 years B.P.) for conventional radiocarbon dating. In glaciated areas, sediments between or buried by tills or other deposits dated by other means may be encountered, but, in most cases, dating is highly inferential. Marine and terrestrial sections may be dated by reference to the magnetostratigraphic time scale (Shackleton and Opdyke, 1976) or by reference to volcanic ash layers, but definitive records are rare. Few studies of pre-Wisconsinan or early Wisconsinan pollen sites have been published for Ohio, although Holloway and Bryant (1985) discussed four pre-Wisconsinan and 11 early-middle Wisconsinan sites from the Great Lakes region.

LATE WISCONSINAN FULL-GLACIAL VEGETATION IN OHIO

Considering the great antiquity of most of Ohio's fossil-plant history, it might seem a simple matter to reconstruct the nature of vegetation in the unglaciated regions of the state at the Late Wisconsinan glacial maximum (20,000 to 18,000 years B.P.), when glacial ice covered much of the state (figs. 3-3, 24-2). The distribution of glacial ice did not conform to simple latitudinal boundaries. The dynamics of each major interval of ice advance were extremely complex and were influenced by the dynamics of glacial source areas, pre-Pleistocene and pre-Wisconsinan physiography, and meteorological patterns. In the central and eastern parts of the state, the Scioto lobe extended as far south as Lancaster; to the west, the Miami lobe extended south of Dayton. The ice-covered regions of the state must have resembled the great ice fields of Greenland, and vegetation of any sort was absent. The unglaciated area of the state, primarily southeastern Ohio, was certainly vegetated, but the nature of plant cover is both conjectural and controversial. Because of the lack of definitive studies of pollen from sediments from unglaciated regions of the state, suppositions about the nature of **periglacial** vegetation have been derived from the successional dynamics of glaciated areas and inference based on present-day vegetation zonation.

The 18,000-year-B.P. vegetation map of Delcourt and Delcourt (1985) indicates that periglacial tundra characterized significant areas of southern Ohio, Indiana, and Illinois. No definitive evidence of tundra at these southern sites during the Late Wisconsinan full-glacial coverage has yet been documented. The fossil-wood records discussed previously all suggest that advancing ice sheets buried spruce-dominated forests of boreal aspect. These trees were alive as the ice sheets advanced over them, although tree-ring studies (Burns, 1958) suggest that their growth became progressively retarded as the glacial front approached to within a few miles of the growth sites. It seems highly probable that periglacial vegetation during full-glacial time consisted primarily of spruce-dominated communities.

How far south of the glacial margin such boreal forests extended and how they related to other community types is an open question. The Beale mastodon site (fig. 24-2, locality 42) in Athens County is the only locality providing information on vegetation in the unglaciated region of the state. The mastodon bones were found in silt deposits emplaced in the headwaters of a small tributary of the Hocking River. This deposit, and others like it in neighboring tributary valleys, may have been formed as a result of the flooding of the Hocking River, due to a temporary ice dam where the river flows through a narrows a short distance downstream from the valleys in question. The mastodon site has been radiocarbon dated at 13,200 years B.P. The silty mud deposits contained hemlock twigs (*Tsuga*); leaves of bishop's cap (*Mitella*), a common herb of northern hardwood forests; beetle remains characteristic of northern hardwood forests; and a pollen spectrum dominated by broad-leaved forest trees including beech (*Fagus*), maple (*Acer*), oak (*Quercus*) and hickory (*Carya*). All of these lines of evidence indicate a broad-leaved-dominated forest vegetation only slightly cooler in aspect than that which occupies the region today and do not support the presence of forests of boreal aspect.

LATE PLEISTOCENE AND HOLOCENE VEGETATION TRENDS

Compared to the paucity of data from earlier intervals, there appears to be ample data for the Late Wisconsinan and Holocene. Holloway and Bryant (1985) cite 26 studies of Ohio bog and lake deposits. However, all but four of these studies were conducted prior to 1950 and, although they provide relative frequency data for AP types, they lack radiocarbon dates and typically ignore the role of NAP types.

POSTGLACIAL POLLEN ZONATION

Workers generally subdivide the time interval represented by a pollen diagram on the basis of major vegetation changes inferred from pollen data. This technique is known as pollen zonation, and, prior to the expanded use of radiocarbon dating, it provided the primary means of correlating pollen diagrams across wide geographic areas. Sears (1942) defined three primary pollen/vegetation zones characteristic of complete pollen diagrams from the Great Lakes region:

Position/ zone	Dominant pollen	Inferred vegetation	Inferred climate
Top			
III	oak (*Quercus*)	mixed deciduous	warmer, moist
II	pine (*Pinus*)	pine/hardwoods	warmer, drier
I	spruce (*Picea*)	boreal forest	cold/cool, wet
Base			

Although there is some evidence for tundralike vegetation in basal levels from pollen diagrams in New England (Deevey, 1949), there is no clear evidence for such vegetation in the southern Great Lakes region.

In many cases, these major zones can be further subdivided on the basis of smaller changes in pollen composition. An example of one such subzone is the Hypsithermal interval, which commonly can be differentiated in the lower half of Zone III. The Hypsithermal corresponds to a warmer, drier interval between about 8,500 and 4,000 years B.P. It is marked, particularly in the western Great Lakes region, by an eastward spread of tall-grass prairie vegetation, characterized by a relative decrease in AP types and an increase in grasses and other NAP types.

Some zones may be missing or distorted in specific pollen profiles for a variety of reasons. Failure to core in the deepest part of a bog may result in some or all of Zone I being missed. Zone III can present several problems. Drier conditions during the Hypsithermal may have reduced or even stopped peat accumulation early in the interval, and plowing, drainage, or other types of site disturbance can distort the representation of later phases (see Shane, 1975). Well-developed pollen zonations from complete profiles can assist in the relative dating of individual pollen samples from mastodon and archaeological sites.

SILVER LAKE—A CASE STUDY

Ogden (1966) reported on the results of the pollen analysis of an 8.9-meter core from Silver Lake in Logan County (fig. 24-2, locality 17). Silver Lake is a classic kettle lake developed in an area of lime-rich soils derived from the weathering of Lower Paleozoic limestones. Figure 24-1 is a simplified pollen diagram for Silver Lake. Major pollen types represented in this diagram, as well as others commonly noted in Ohio pollen samples, are illustrated in figures 24-6 through 24-9.

One of the notable features of the Silver Lake study is the extensive age control provided by 19 radiocarbon dates. Most studies are supported by significantly fewer dates because of the cost of commercial determinations. In the case of the Silver Lake study, the Radiocarbon Laboratory, then at Ohio Wesleyan University under Ogden's direction, conducted extensive dating as part of a larger study of variation in radiocarbon dates and rates of sedimentation in hard- and soft-water lakes (Ogden and Hay, 1964, 1965, 1967; Ogden, 1967b).

Zone 1, boreal forest

Zone 1 is strongly dominated by the pollen of spruce (*Picea*) (relative pollen frequencies in excess of 50 percent), fir (*Abies*), and pine (*Pinus*). NAP levels, including grass pollen (Gramineae), are relatively high. Ogden did not suggest that tundra elements were present but did note that tree cover appeared to increase through the interval. The end of Zone 1 is marked by a precipitous decline in spruce pollen (but not fir). Extrapolating from the oldest date in the core, this event began approximately 11,700 years B.P.

Zone 2, pine-oak forest

The beginning of Zone 2 is marked by an abrupt increase in NAP types (including the grasses) and an initial rise in oak (*Quercus*) pollen. Both increases are consistent with warmer and drier conditions. Relatively warm and dry sum-

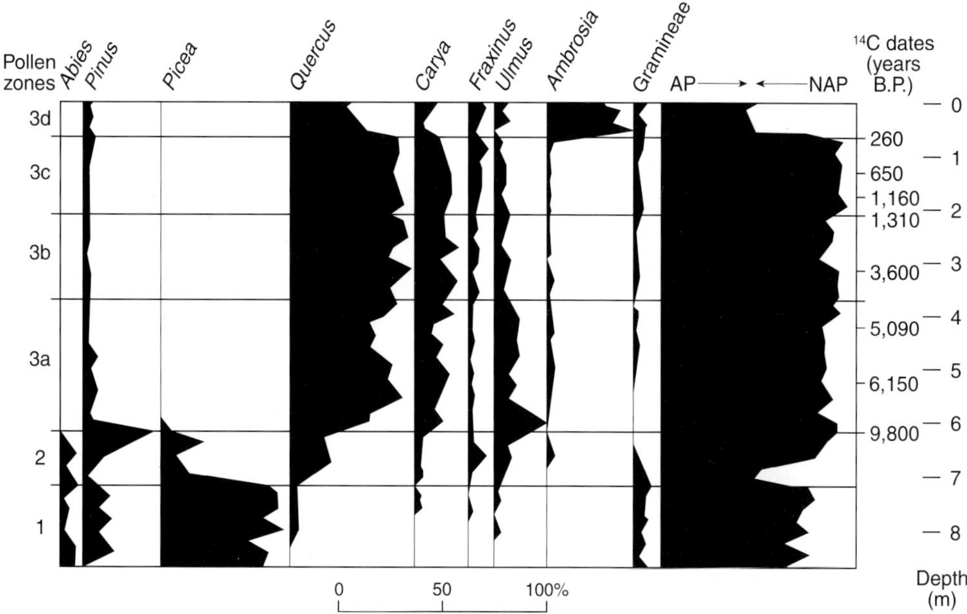

FIGURE 24-1.—A simplified version of the Silver Lake pollen diagram of Ogden (1966), modified from Holloway and Bryant (1985, fig. 3). Reproduced with permission. The baseline (0) for the radiocarbon (^{14}C) dates is 1966.

mer conditions would inhibit the establishment of spruce seedlings and may mark a climatic event that successfully disrupted the large-scale spruce-dominated forests that had persisted on the formerly glaciated landscape for over 4,000 years following the initial ice retreat.

The second half of Zone 2 is marked by a decline in oak and NAP taxa, a minor increase in spruce pollen, and a major peak in pine pollen. The end of Zone 2 is marked by an abrupt decline in spruce and pine pollen and a rapid rise in oak pollen. This transition occurs at approximately 9,800 years B.P. at Silver Lake. Ogden (1967a) proposed that this change occured essentially synchronously at about 10,000 years B.P. throughout eastern North America and that it marks a rapid climatic change throughout the region. At Silver Lake, this transition was completed in approximately 1,200 years. Spruce and fir apparently were excluded from the lower Great Lakes region after this transition and pine became relatively insignificant. The disappearance of spruce in Ohio pollen profiles is a convenient marker for the end of the Pleistocene and the beginning of the Holocene, a boundary generally placed at about 10,000 years B.P.

Zone 3, deciduous forest

By 9,000 years B.P., deciduous forests had become reestablished in the formerly glaciated landscape of Ohio. The shift from conifer-dominated to broad-leaved-dominated forests also coincides approximately with the disappearance of mastodons from the Ohio fossil record. It is a matter of some debate as to the extent to which the disappearance of mastodons was the result of climatic change (with concomitant changes in forest composition) or the result of Paleo-Indian hunting activity (see Dreimanis, 1968).

The composition of the deciduous forest mosaic was sensitive to changes in climate. Ogden (1966) defined four subzones (3a-3d) that reflect changing associates of oak, the arboreal pollen dominant throughout Zone 3. Zone 3a was apparently relatively warm and moist, as indicated by the presence of beech (*Fagus*) and walnut (*Juglans*) in association with oak in the Silver Lake area. Hemlock (*Tsuga*) became locally abundant in this interval.

Beech reached a maximum in Zone 3b about 4,500 years B.P., and peaks of hickory (*Carya*) pollen suggest drier conditions. The period between 8,000 and 4,000 years B.P. is the Hypsithermal discussed previously. Ohio forests were generally unaffected during this time, and, to the extent that it can be recognized, the Hypsithermal is primarily noted by subtle changes in deciduous-forest species composition. Hemlock, locally abundant in Zone 3a, was excluded from most sites late in the Hypsithermal. On protected sites or specialized soil types, some samples of this ancient vegetation remain as living testimony to the patterns of vegetation change in Ohio pollen diagrams. For example, relict hemlock stands persist in protected coves, such as Old Man's Cave in Hocking County, and represent remnants of the far more extensive distribution of hemlock in Zone 3a. Prairie patches or forest openings can be noted in Adams, Clermont, and Hamilton Counties. Such prairies relicts may date from the Hypsithermal or from the pre-Wisconsinan Sangamonian Interglacial Stage.

The transition from Zone 3c to Zone 3d about 300 years ago is marked by an abrupt rise in ragweed (*Ambrosia*) pollen to levels generally in excess of 50 percent of the pollen sum. This rise in ragweed pollen is matched by the appearance of pollen of European weeds and marks the clearing of forests and the agricultural activities of settlers from the east.

At this point the fossil record of Ohio effectively comes to an end. Land-survey records and the accounts of early settlers replace the interpretation of fossils as the primary tool for understanding the composition of the forests that greeted the first settlers who penetrated the Ohio wilderness.

CLASSROOM EXPLORATION OF THE LAST 10,000 YEARS OF OHIO HISTORY

The concept of global climatic change is an important topic in introductory college and secondary school courses in life, earth, and general science. Demonstrating the reality of major environmental change commonly is difficult. Students tend to view the world around them as static and unchanging in terms of environment, although they are naturally accepting of social and technological change. Simple exercises involving elementary pollen analysis of organic deposits from local wetlands can demonstrate the reality of environmental change and provide hands-on experience with the scientific method and techniques of environmental analysis.

The scale and design of such an exercise can be quite variable, depending on local resources and the time available. At one end of the scale, the teacher, either working locally or participating in a summer science workshop, could collect samples and prepare a set of reference slides that could then be examined by students as part of a classroom laboratory exercise. At the other end of the scale, students, either in the normal classroom setting, the activity of science clubs, or individual science fair projects, can participate in field collection, preparation, and analysis of samples. Potential collecting sites in bogs and wetlands are widespread in Ohio. All aspects of such a project are well within the abilities of ordinary students, particularly if they are motivated with a sense of adventure in terms of reconstructing unknown worlds of the past.

Exploring the glacial and postglacial forests of Ohio as a classroom exercise rather naturally breaks down into four phases—sample collection, sample preparation, pollen analysis, and evaluation or interpretation of the results. These basic aspects are described below. Those who are interested in pursuing the subject in greater depth can consult standard texts such as Traverse (1988) or government circulars such as Doher (1980) for a detailed description of equipment needs and analytical techniques.

SAMPLE COLLECTION

The kinds of samples that are collected determine what kind of sample processing is required. Extraction of pollen from marls, lake muds, and fossil soils is a more demanding exercise than processing peats. Processing such samples requires more steps and involves chemicals that require special handling. Thus, we recommend that classroom projects concentrate on the analysis of peat samples. In a sense, we will be retracing the steps of the European and American pioneers in pollen analysis, but with the advantage of a much wider perspective than was available at the time of those early studies.

If you are located in the glaciated part of the state (see figs. 3-3 and 24-2), there is probably a small bog or peat-forming wetland relatively close by. If you are not already aware of a possible site, your county Soil Conservation Service office may be able to provide assistance, particularly if you explain your objectives. You must obtain permission from the landowner prior to making any collections.

There are two basic approaches to obtaining samples—trench sampling and coring. Unfortunately, many wetlands are being systematically drained to expand agriculture or enhance land values for development. Local county offices can usually indicate where such activities are occurring. The trenching excavations that accompany drainage projects commonly expose sections of peat up to a meter in thickness. In many cases, such trenching may cut completely through a relatively thin peat down to underlying marl, lake mud, or sand. Assuming the trench or other excavation is relatively recent, the exposed peat face can be cleaned and samples obtained at different levels with a small trowel or spoon. Samples from different levels can be stored in glass jars, small plastic freezer containers, or even plastic freezer bags. Each sample container should be labeled with the locality and the position of each sample with respect to the top of the exposure. Sampling tools should be thoroughly washed between samples to avoid contamination.

Field collection is the most troublesome aspect of such a project. Because a sample requires only a few grams of peat for processing, it is quite feasible to collect enough samples in one outing to meet classroom needs for several years if the samples are frozen after collection.

Although professional palynologists generally obtain their samples from cores using specialized sampling equipment, a perfectly suitable core can be obtained by driving a length of electrical conduit tubing down into the peat, if the deposit to be sampled is no more than a meter or two thick. The tube containing the peat sequence is then pulled out of the ground. The peat core inside the tube can be extruded onto a length of aluminum foil using a wooden dowel as a piston. The core can then be cut up into 10-cm increments and wrapped in foil. Each segment should be permanently labeled on the foil wrapper with the locality, location of the segment in relation to the total core, and the top and bottom end of each segment. If the core segments are frozen, they can actually serve as a resource for several years, as each class can study a few subsamples each term, gradually expanding the database for the entire core. Such an activity can emphasize the stepwise nature of scientific study, as the contribution of each group adds to the total understanding of the system.

A 1- to 2-cm-long segment from each 10-cm core segment is entirely suitable as a sample for processing, as long as careful records are kept of the position of each unit removed from the frozen core segments. Inserting small segments of dowel or styrofoam to replace the sample removed from the core will assist in record keeping and provide visual feedback to the students as to how the long-term project is proceeding.

SAMPLE PROCESSING

Depending upon the size of the group or class involved in the project, it is typically most convenient to have a small group of students process a single sample. In the case of a professional palynology laboratory, the air would be filtered to eliminate the possibility of sample contamination by airborne pollen, and distilled water would be used for the various processing steps for a similar reason. Such care is probably not required for this sort of an exercise, but it may be worthwhile to encourage student discussion as to why one would want to avoid sample contamination and how unwanted pollen could enter a sample.

Sample preparation requires some simple equipment and modest quantities of chemical reagents and supplies:

1. a table-top (clinical) centrifuge
2. 15-ml conical Pyrex centrifuge tubes
3. several glass rods and dissecting needles and several eyedroppers or pipettes equipped with rubber bulbs
4. small sample vials with screw caps
5. glass microscope slides and cover slips
6. 5% solution of potassium hydroxide (KOH)
7. 5% solution of hydrochloric acid (HCl)

8. Safranin O stain solution (available from most scientific supply companies)
9. commercial glycerin jelly (available from scientific supply companies)
10. a bottle of clear nail polish

A simple yet effective approach to extracting pollen from a peat sample is to place a few grams of peat in a small beaker with approximately 10 ml of 5% potassium hydroxide (KOH). Heat the sample gently to boiling under a fume hood while stirring with a glass rod. The KOH solution typically turns brown, owing to the extraction of humic acids, and the peat breaks apart (deflocculates), helping to free much of the pollen trapped in the sample. Filter the KOH solution through a fine metal or nylon screen to remove the coarse fragments of plant debris. If desired, this coarse material can be washed several times with water to remove all traces of the KOH solution and examined in a water-filled petri dish under a dissecting microscope. Fragments of mosses and other bryophytes, primarily *Sphagnum*, will be noted, but other pieces of plant debris, including fragments of leaves, twigs, and seeds, may be recognizable.

The pollen and spores in the sample will be in the KOH solution that passes through the fine screen. The use of a desk-top (clinical) centrifuge (most models accept 15-ml conical glass tubes) is the most convenient approach to concentrating the pollen and spores; suitable models are listed in the catalogs of most scientific supply companies, or a local hospital might be willing to donate a used centrifuge. If a centrifuge cannot be obtained, suitable samples can be prepared by allowing the sample to settle out in a standard test tube for 6 to 12 hours for each of the steps listed below for the centrifuge procedure. However, extreme care is required in decanting (pouring off) the liquid after each settling because the pollen and other residue will not be compacted at the bottom of the tube, as they would be in a centrifuge.

When using the centrifuge, each sample tube should be of essentially equal weight to prevent excessive vibration. Bringing all sample tubes up to the same volume by adding water generally is adequate. Each tube should be balanced by the presence of another tube opposite it in the centrifuge. If there are odd numbers of samples, a tube filled with water can be used to balance the odd sample tube. Running the centrifuge for 5 minutes at maximum speed should be adequate at each step. The centrifuge cover should be closed when the unit is in operation and the rotating head should come to a complete stop before opening the cover and removing sample tubes. The liquid can then be decanted and properly disposed of, depending on the nature of the material. All utensils should be thoroughly rinsed in water between samples to prevent transfer of pollen and spores from one sample to another.

1. Add the pollen-bearing KOH sample to a 15-ml conical centrifuge tube, centrifuge, and decant the KOH solution.
2. Add water, suspend the sample residue (stir the compacted residue in the bottom of the tube using a dissecting needle or glass rod to mix it with the liquid), centrifuge, and decant and discard the water solution. Repeat this step three times.
3. Acidify the solution with a few drops of dilute (5%) HCl and add a few drops of Safranin O. Suspend the sample and allow it to stand for approximately 5 minutes.
4. Wash the sample as in step 2 several times until the liquid shows no trace of the stain.
5. Heat a small quantity of glycerin jelly in a beaker in a water bath until it liquifies. Add 2 to 3 ml of glycerin jelly to each sample tube, suspend the sample, and transfer as much as possible of the material to labeled sample vials.

Slides are prepared by gently heating the sample vials in a water bath until the glycerin jelly liquefies. Gently shake the vial to suspend the stained residue in the jelly and transfer a drop of the suspension to the center of a warm, clean microscope slide. Gently add a cover slip; the weight of the cover slip should cause the jelly drop to thin and spread to the edges of the slip. A slight pressure on the cover slip can be used to facilitate spreading, but the sample should not be pressed out beyond the edge of the cover slip. Allow the slide to cool and the glycerin jelly will solidify. Seal the edges of the cover slip with a bead of clear nail polish and allow the slide to dry for several hours.

SAMPLE ANALYSIS

One of the biggest hurdles to analysis of peat samples is the limited capability of the microscopes that are available to students in secondary schools and introductory-level college classes. Even professional palynologists using the best research microscopes available can have problems in recognizing subtle differences between pollen types. Despite their limitations, however, typical school microscopes are sufficient for careful students to recognize some of the major pollen types that define the pollen zones previously discussed. Using the illustrations in figures 24-6 through 24-9 as a guide, the students should be able to differentiate some of the major plant groups. The simplest approach to analysis is to simply prepare lists of recognizable pollen and spore types observed in different samples. While this is useful in guiding students in the early stages of identification, the true significance of the pollen/spore samples can only be appreciated when the importance of the various types can be expressed in meaningful quantitative terms.

A first-stage approach to assigning importance in a sample might be to group the various pollen/spore types into broad categories such as abundant, common, rare, etc. Quite apart from the practical difficulties of assigning real definitions to such terms, there are other problems as well. Pollen of conifers such as pine, spruce, hemlock, and fir tend to be quite large and easy to recognize. In contrast, the pollen of common broad-leaved forest trees such as beech, maple, and oak tend to be much smaller, harder to recognize, and more easily overlooked. The result is a natural tendency to overemphasize the role of conifer pollen at the expense of pollen of broad-leaved types.

The most precise approach would be to assign teams of students to examine specific samples, counting the first 100 pollen grains they encounter when the samples are examined at the highest practical magnification. Although many pollen grains and spores might not be identifiable (they can be tallied as unknowns), the result will be the ability to express each identifiable pollen type in terms of its percentage contribution to the pollen of the entire sample. Such an exercise presents ample opportunities to discuss the merits and problems associated with qualitative vs. quantitative data and the complexities of gathering such data in real-world situations as opposed to the simplistic world of textbooks.

Preparing a quantitative tabulation for each sample is just an exercise. The only reason for doing the work is to assemble information that is useful in answering real questions—such as the age of a specific sample and what it means in terms of ancient vegetation and environment.

On the basis of the importance of various pollen types in each sample, it should be possible to assign samples to the various pollen zones and even subzones as outlined above. Using the dated Silver Lake profile as a guide, it should be possible to make rough approximations as to the age of the various samples. Do these dates make sense in terms of the relative stratigraphic position of the samples? Ideally, they will, but if there is a problem, discussion can logically turn to the problems of identification, counting, labeling, record keeping, and contamination.

Ecological and environmental reconstruction presents the greatest challenge, as many students, especially those in urban schools, may have no familiarity with the trees and other plants that are recognized on the basis of pollen grains and spores. The color photographs and range maps in tree and shrub guides can be a help. Photographs of forest vegetation from different parts of North America keyed to maps and the plant ranges in the field guides can all help to bring the plants to life in the minds of the students. Ideally, the final stage in such a project is the reconstruction of the nature of vegetation and climate at different points in the past, on the basis of the samples.

Paleontology is, in effect, a detective story in which the investigators use as many clues as possible to reconstruct past worlds that we can never visit or actually see. In a modest but nontrivial way, students can reconstruct the history of their own area. Given the reality of major environmental change over the past 10,000 years, the groundwork is laid for a discussion of the complexities involved in predicting future environmental changes, be it the result of natural or human-induced factors.

ACKNOWLEDGMENTS

We thank Peter H. Carrington (Michigan State University) for the design of figure 24-2. We extend our appreciation to Myron T. Sturgeon (Ohio University) and Michael C. Hansen (Ohio Division of Geological Survey) for information on mastodon sites and for assistance in field work at the Beale mastodon site, and to Diane K. Baclawski and Huang Wei (Michigan State University) for literature assistance. We also thank Dr. Hansen, Jane L. Forsyth (Bowling Green State University), Martha A. Case (Michigan State University), and Rodney M. Feldmann (Kent State University) for their advice. We gratefully acknowledge Jo Ann Harris (Charleston, West Virginia) and Aleen Cross (East Lansing, Michigan) for typing the many drafts of this chapter. Lisa Van Doren (Ohio Division of Geological Survey) enhanced many of the photographs in scanning them for publication.

FIGURE 24-2.—Distribution and description of selected Quaternary sites, including mastodon sites, from which wood and other plant materials have been collected and, in most cases, radiocarbon dated. Sites are listed by nearest town and county, followed by radiocarbon-date sample number (example, W-415) and age (example, >37,000 years B.P.) in parentheses. Some sites have more than one date. Genus names for plants are listed only at first use.

1. Cincinnati, Hamilton County (OWU-140B, 24,790±780 years B.P.), Ross Well no. 3, on property of National Lead Co. (U.S. Atomic Energy Corp. reservation). Spruce (*Picea*) wood came from thick deposit in glacial outwash buried beneath part of Wisconsinan-age Hartwell terminal moraine.

2. Sharonville, Hamilton County (averaged date of 19,760±68 years B.P.), along east side of Mill Creek valley, northwest of Sharonville Rd. This site is at the southern limits of the Late Wisconsinan Miami lobe. Three beds of till containing wood overlie a pre-Late Wisconsinan-age dense lacustrine clay. Beneath the clay is an organic silt marking the initial advance of ice over a forested valley bottom. The date came from a cluster of rooted stumps and stem sections. The overlying Late Wisconsinan tills are thin and greatly deformed by ice movements. The first till above the lake clay contains wood fragments without bark. The next overlying till contains abundant logs that are circular in cross section (indicating they have not been compressed), up to 2 meters long, and still have bark intact. The third till contains bent, broken, and frayed logs, some with bark attached.

3. Westchester, Butler County (W-304, 20,500±800 years B.P.), Skinner Sand and Gravel Co. pit along East Fork Mill Creek, NE¼SW¼ sec. 22, Union Twp. Gray till in creek bank at base of 15.3-meter-thick exposure contained many logs up to 30 cm in diameter; 18 logs were identified as spruce (Burns, 1958). A sample also contained needles of white spruce (*Picea glauca*), although Burns believed that some or most of the logs were probably black spruce (*Picea mariana*).

4. Darrtown, Butler County (Y-450, 16,560±230 years B.P.), stream cut on Fourmile Creek, SE¼SE¼ sec. 31, Milford Twp. Wood near base of 3.0-8.6 meters of till above a 0-7.5-cm-thick woody peat included 20 specimens of spruce wood and larch/tamarack (*Larix*) twigs.

5. Oxford, Butler County (W-92, 19,980±500 years B.P.), on Bull Run, 0.8 km (0.5 mile) west of U.S. Route 27, NE¼SW¼ sec. 26, Oxford Twp. This forest litter layer produced 24 specimens of spruce; also larch wood, twigs, leaves, and insect wings. A nearby location on Collins Run, in sec. 26, Oxford Twp., produced willow (*Salix*) leaves (see figs. 24-4.28 to 24-4.30) and spruce and larch twigs (see Berry, 1934; Goldthwait, 1958).

6. Germantown, Montgomery County (W-96, >34,000 years B.P.), on Twin Creek, SE¼ sec. 18, German Twp. The flora includes oak (*Quercus*) wood; other wood tentatively identified as ash (*Fraxinus*), hickory (*Carya*), and sycamore (*Platanus*); also beech (*Fagus*) and grape (*Vitis*) leaves. This flora indicates warmer climate, possibly a very early interglacial age (Orton, 1870; Goldthwait, 1958). The abundant compressed logs are in a saucer-shaped lens 70 meters long and 0-6 meters thick overlying 0.6 meter of black soil and overlain by 12-25 meters of blue-gray till and 12-25 meters of mixed yellow and gray till.

7. Southern Hills, Montgomery County (W-37, 20,700±600 years B.P.), bed of Holes Creek. Logs in lower 60 cm of 1.5-meter-thick sticky, blue-gray till.

8. Lebanon, Warren County (OWU-102 bis., 20,275±620 years B.P.), on Turtle Creek near intersection of I-71 and Ohio Route 123, NW$^1/_4$ sec. 22 or NW$^1/_4$ sec. 16, T5N, R3W, Turtle Creek Twp. Spruce wood 3 meters deep in till, 100 meters north of Wisconsinan boundary.

9. Clarksville, Clinton County (Y-473-1, >37,000 years B.P.), on Todd Fork, in Vernon Twp., 4.8 km (3 miles) downstream from locality 10B. Fossil wood from Illinoian (?) till beneath gravel.

10A. Cuba, Clinton County (Y-448, 18,500±420 years B.P.), farm-pond excavation at Faris Rd., 1.8 km (1.1 miles) southeast of Cuba, Washington Twp. Date is based on one spruce log in a 60-cm-thick gray till containing logs overlain by 2.2 meters of buff till and a 1.2-meter-thick leached soil zone. Small branches in the gray till indicate a second wave of Late Wisconsinan ice overriding the Cuba Moraine to the northwest at Sligo.

10B. Sligo, Clinton County (two dates: OWU-159, 21,140±1,435 years B.P.; OWU-160, 22,255±1,650 years B.P.), on Todd Fork just north of Wisconsinan terminal moraine near Sligo, Adams Twp. Both dates are on spruce wood from a forest bed buried by the first wave of advancing Wisconsinan ice. The forest bed is just north of (somewhat behind) the Wisconsinan terminal moraine front.

11. Yellow Springs, Greene County. A large mound of limonitic (iron oxide) travertine, a **calcareous** precipitate, of postglacial to Recent? age, has built up over a length of several hundred meters in the valley of Yellow Springs Creek. Leaves (see figs. 24-5.2, 24-5.3) and some twigs are preserved in the travertine, which has enveloped plant material that has fallen onto the surface or into the spring. The mound has built up in an incised valley since the last ice sheet retreated from the region. The springs were once thought to be fed by fissures emanating from the Silurian bedrock beneath the Wisconsinan moraines. More recent studies suggest that the springs are seeps from water-bearing layers in the glacial drift.

12. North Hampton, Clark County (W-152, >40,000 years B.P.), on East Branch Honey Creek near junction of Marquart Rd. and St. Paris Rd. Five layers of leaves and twigs in 75 cm of sands and silts. Only angiosperms have been identified, including oak, ash (two species), beech, and tentatively black locust (*Robinia*) or osage orange (*Maclura*) (Burns, 1958). These plants indicate a warmer climate. Fossil-bearing beds overlie a few centimeters of sand above limestone bedrock and are overlain by about 12 meters of laminated sand/silt and a silty clay till.

13. West Jefferson, Madison County (University of Michigan, 8,420±400 years B.P.), Orleton Farms mastodon site (see Goldthwait, 1952), 152 meters northeast of Ohio Route 29, 2.4 km (1.5 miles) northwest of West Jefferson, northeastern Somerford Twp. Mastodon was extensively disarticulated; deer bones and a bird claw also were found. The wood used for dating came from beneath the skeleton and was too poorly preserved for identification. The pollen analysis (Sears and Clisby, 1952) was limited because of shallow burial and surface disturbance by agricultural practice and heavy machinery. However, the spruce and fir (*Abies*) forests of early postglacial time had been succeeded by spruce and pine (*Pinus*) forests and increasing numbers of deciduous trees (oak, hickory) at the time the mastodon was buried, indicating approach of the Hypsithermal.

14. Cedar Bog, Champaign County, on east side of Mad River 9.7 km (6 miles) south of Urbana, secs. 31 and 32, T5N, R11W, Mad River and Urbana Twps. There were extensive presettlement groves of arbor vitae/white cedar (*Thuja occidentalis*) in the surrounding poorly drained river valley (see Dachnowski, 1910).

15. Sidney, Shelby County (W-188, 23,000±800 years B.P.), B & O Railroad cut 1.2 km (0.75 mile) west of U.S. Route 25, 1.6 km (1 mile) south of railroad bridge over the Great Miami River, SW¼SE¼ sec. 14, Orange Twp. Spruce log (see fig. 24-5.1) at base of till 4.6 meters from top of cut (see Goldthwait, 1959, fig. 1; also see Forsyth, 1965).

16. Kirkwood, Shelby County (two dates: W-415, >37,000 years B.P.; W-414, 22,000±1,000 years B.P.), 3.6 km (2.25 miles) northeast of confluence of Loramie Creek with the Great Miami River, 0.8 km (0.5 mile) east of U.S. Route 25, NW¼NW¼ sec. 6, Orange Twp. Older date (W-415) is on twigs at base of thin peat overlying leached and reduced gravel soil and overlain by thick till with logs; younger date (W-414) is on logs near base of till. Only spruce wood has been found (Burns, 1958).

17. Silver Lake, Logan County (19 dates ranging from 9,800±210 years B.P. to 260±108 years B.P.), 11.2 km (7 miles) south of Bellefontaine, secs. 10 and 16, T3N, R14W, Harrison Twp. Detailed pollen analysis. See discussion on p. 484-485 and Ogden (1966).

18. Cranberry Prairie, Mercer County (9,370±70 years B.P.), near the edge of St. Johns Moraine, SE¼SE¼ sec. 26, Granville Twp. Peat 1 meter below surface beneath black, peaty loam and overlying more than 3.5 meters of tan to brown marl. Plant material includes larch/tamarack wood, lotus (*Nelumbo*) and pondweed (*Potamogeton*) seeds, willow leaves, and stonewort (*Chara*) **oogonia**. A nearly complete skeleton of an elk (*Cervus*) was the primary interest at this locality (see Murphy and others, 1985).

19. Edon, Williams County (W-198, 14,300±450 years B.P.), near west gate of Ohio Turnpike and Ohio Route 49, NW¼NW¼ sec. 3, Northwest Twp. Wood fragments in thin silt zone in middle of lacustrine silt-sand facies below 1-meter-thick soil zone and overlying 2.5-4.6 meters of clay-rich gray till. Silts suggest small lake in an ice-block hole or on top of a readvance of the Wabash Moraine (Goldthwait, 1958).

20. Bellevue, Sandusky County (Y-240, 12,800±250 years B.P.), water well, NW¼ sec. 10, York Twp. Driftwood in sand of a beach ridge of a higher level (226 meters/735 feet) Pleistocene precursor of Lake Erie.

21. Castalia, Erie County (C-526, 8,513±500 years B.P.), Medusa Cement Co. marl pit along Ohio Route 269, SW¼SE¼ quarter-township 3, Margaretta Twp. This area is part of the extensive Castalia **marshes**. A forest bed 7.6-30 cm thick covers an area of several hundred hectares and contains rooted stumps up to 62 cm in diameter. The forest bed overlies a 30-107-cm-thick sand bed that overlies plastic lacustrine clay more than 15 meters thick (Goldthwait, 1958). A 30-76-cm-thick travertine bed overlying the forest bed contains logs and mollusks. A second, much earlier date of 14,790±420 years B.P. (OWU-168B) taken on a moss (*Drepanocladus fluitans*) from this location is puzzling because this area was not ice free at that time according to other dates and moraine evidence. The date may be faulty because of uptake of fossil carbon from limestones of the region. However, wood from a depression in the Wabash Moraine to the west was dated at 14,300±450 years B.P. (W-198), and a date from the Cleveland area was 13,360±500 years B.P. (W-33). The forest beds and early stages of wood and peat accumulations in the Erie Basin need much more study.

22. Parkertown, Erie County (W-430, 12,920±400 years B.P.), junction of Ohio Route 4 and Ohio Turnpike, NW¼SE¼ quarter-township 2, Groton Twp. A forest litter or flotsam of a lakeshore contains wood, needles, and cones at base of 31-cm-thick plastic clay overlying 31 cm of sandy brown humus. These units are about 90 cm below the base of the 1.5-meter-thick surface deposit of shingled beach gravel from Lake Whittlesey, one of a series of Pleistocene precursors of Lake Erie (Goldthwait, 1958).

23. Bucyrus bog, Crawford County, on North Robinson Rd., 3.2 km (2 miles) east of Bucyrus. This area is 27 km (17 miles) southwest of the southernmost of the retreating ice-front lakes of the New Haven Marsh in southwestern Huron County. Pollen analysis (see Sears, 1930) of four cores at 15- to 30-cm intervals of the more than 4.5-meter-deep bog indicates a cold to cool humid climate at the base and that most (3.5± meters) of the accumulation of the peat took place before the appearance of significant numbers of deciduous trees (especially oak and hickory).

24. Cleveland, Cuyahoga County (W-33, 13,600±500 years B.P.), Canal Sand and Gravel Co. pit, near Cuyahoga River. Sample was from till. Trees were drowned by the rise of water at the end of Lake Arkona, one of a series of Pleistocene precursors of Lake Erie.

25. Garfield Heights, Cuyahoga County (three dates: K-361-3, 28,195±535 years B.P.; W-71, 24,600±800 years B.P.; K-361-4, 23,313±391 years B.P.), Schmidt Brothers Sand and Gravel Co. pit east and west of McCracken Blvd. in the Mill Creek valley. See White (1968) for an excellent account of the stratigraphy. Illinoian-age gravel is overlain by a thick Sangamonian-age fossil soil (paleosol), which is overlain by two thin loess (wind-blown dust and silt) beds. The K-361-3 date was on a piece of carbonized wood near the top of the upper loess. Above this loess is a varved (layered) lacustrine silt and clay containing marl, carbonaceous streaks, beetle remains, fragments of moss, broken leaf remains (willow?), and wood fragments. The K-361-4 and W-71 dates were on these wood fragments. Logs were up to 3 meters long, 15 cm in diameter, and were intermixed with abundant twigs and macerated leaves.

26. Battaglia bog, Portage County. A date of 16,500 years B.P. for the base of a 3.8-meter core was extrapolated from sedimentation rates determined from dated pollen zones within the core sequence.

27. Alliance, Stark County (two dates: OWU-224A, 5,490±235 years B.P.; OWU-224B, 5,560±245 years B.P.), Whitaker mammoth site. Dates are from peat overlying gray clay and are not in agreement with dates based on pollen analysis of the clay and tooth scrapings. The clay and tooth pollen samples indicate a spruce-dominated forest, in contrast to the oak-hickory-beech assemblage indicated by pollen analysis of the radiocarbon-dated peat. The animal remains are almost certainly older than the published dates. Although this location is designated as a mammoth site and Ogden and Hay (1967) refer to mammoth remains, they also refer to them as *Mammut* sp., the genus name for mastodon (the genus name for mammoth is *Mammuthus*).

28. Chambersburg (formerly New Chambersburg), Columbiana County (OWU-194, 9,460±305 years B.P.), Cole mastodon site. Spruce wood in blue clay associated with mastodon. Pollen analysis of clay had high spruce dominance and minor amounts of fir, birch (*Betula*), and pine (Ogden and Hay, 1967).

29. Brown's Lake bog, Wayne County (many dates ranging from OWU-304, 10,595±370 years B.P. to OWU-289, 565±105 years B.P.), west of Shreve, sec. 21, Clinton Twp. A 14-meter core was taken in this kettle lake near the margin of a peatland, a few hundred meters south of hills draped with till and surrounded by kames (see White, 1967; also see Sanger and Crowl, 1979).

30. Mud Lake bog, Holmes-Ashland County line, between Wooster and Loudenville, near intersection of Ohio Routes 3 and 179. Vegetation was described by Dachnowski (1912). Pollen analysis reported by Sears (1931) indicates an expanded section of the post-cool dry climate. The upper 7.4 meters indicates continuous peat accumulation during the last 8,000 years.

31. Johnstown, Licking County (OWU-141, 19,180±160 years B.P.), Johnstown mastodon site. Restored skeleton, collected in 1926, is on display at Cleveland Museum of Natural History (see figs. 21-31.1, 21-32.1). Date is on spruce wood. Pollen analysis on blue clay adhering to spruce wood indicated predominantly spruce and pine, minor amounts of grass and sedge, and less than 3 percent deciduous-tree pollen (oak, elm, and birch).

32A. Torren's bog, Licking County (many dates, ranging from OWU-92, 14,160±160 years B.P., to OWU-207, 420±200 years B.P.) Most dates are on woody peat, but some are on muck and clay. This site was a kettle hole that began to fill shortly after ice retreated from this area. The transition from spruce-dominated forests to the rise of oak was about 11,000 years B.P.

32B. Heath, Licking County (11,500 years B.P.), Burning Tree mastodon site. This remarkably preserved skeleton (see fig. 21-32.2) included an intact sack or pouch that appears to be part of the intestine and contained twigs, leaves, and seeds of several plants plus a gut bacterium. See discussion on p. 482 and in Chapter 21.

33. Newark, Licking County (W-88, 21,400±600 years B.P.), 0.4 km (0.25 mile) west of Ohio Route 79 at NYC railroad crossing at Ramp Creek. A very thick (>62 meters) accumulation of till in the incised valley of the Pleistocene-age Newark River is overlain by 18.5 meters of sticky dark-gray till containing logs and twigs in the lower 4.6 meters.

34. Buckeye Lake and Cranberry Bog, at the common corner of Licking, Fairfield, and Perry Counties. Extensive floristic studies (Dachnowski, 1911) and pollen analyses have been carried out. Peat is 9-10 meters thick at south edge of Cranberry Island and about 3-4 meters thick on the north side.

35. Gahanna, Franklin County (W-263, >37,000 years B.P.), on Rocky Fork Creek, SE¼SW¼ sec. 2, Jefferson Twp. Sample was taken 14-20 meters above bedrock (Bedford Shale); a spruce wood layer is interbedded near the top of 3.6-6.2 meters of stratified sand and gravel and cross-bedded outwash, which are overlain by 7.6-12.2 meters of till.

36. Columbus, Franklin County (four dates: OWU-197, 13,200±480 years B.P., OWU-177A, 13,125±475 years B.P.; OWU-177B, 12,695±240 years B.P.; OWU-196, 12,600±265 years B.P.), beaver site on Refugee Rd. near its intersection with Ohio Route 317 (Hamilton Rd.) (see Garrison, 1967). The OWU-196 and OWU-197 dates are on peat, the latter from peat associated with wood samples. Spruce wood constituted 80 percent of the wood recovered, willow or poplar 15 percent, and juniper 5 percent. Pollen analysis showed predominance of spruce, fir, pine, sedge, and grass and less than 10 percent deciduous hardwood pollen.

37. Columbus, Franklin County (Y-449, 23,000±250 years B.P.), 4th and Long Sts., two blocks northwest of State House. Wood at base of 4.6 meters of gray till above 15 meters of bedded gravel.

38. Harrisburg, Pickaway County (W-127, 21,600±100 years B.P.), road cut along U.S. Route 62, 0.4 km (0.25 mile) south of Harrisburg, Darby Twp. Wood at base of 6.2 meters of till and soil overlying 1.5 meters of gravel.

39. Hallsville, Ross County (OWU-220, 13,180±520 years B.P.), Pontius Farm mastodon site. Spruce wood from marl deposits, which also contain mollusks, ostrocodes, and stonewort oogonia. Pollen analysis of the marl showed 64 percent spruce, 16 percent pine, 8 percent fir, 4 percent larch, and 2 percent oak.

40. Chillicothe, Ross County (W-91, 18,050±400 years B.P.), cut bank on Biers Run, 0.8 km (0.5 mile) northwest of U.S. Route 35, Union Twp. Over 200 limonite-encrusted logs observed; 67 were identified by Burns (1958) as spruce and one as larch; some were piled in masses against twisted black pods of forest litter in compact gray till containing numerous sand lenses underlying a till 9.2 to 12.2 meters thick.

41. Northern Twin Twp., Ross County (W-331, 17,980±400 years B.P.), meander-cut banks along Anderson Run, 2.4 km (1.5 miles) south of U.S. Route 35. A 0-60-cm-thick lens within a bed of sand and gravel lies 1.4-4.6 meters above Devonian-age bedrock (Ohio Shale) in the creek bed; the lens is a veritable tangle of forest logs, twigs, and silt from which Burns (1958) identified 43 logs as spruce, two as larch/tamarack, and one as white cedar/arbor vitae. Above this lens is a greatly contorted, moundlike till 3-9 meters thick containing another intermixed mass of logs, up to 30 cm in diameter, and pods of conifer needles identified as white spruce.

42. Athens, Athens County (13,320±155 years B.P.), Beale mastodon site, on north branch of Willow Creek, 7 km (4.25 miles) ESE of Athens, sec. 21, Canaan Twp. Twigs, leaves (see fig. 24-4.27), and beetle fragments in lake clays accumulated in a drowned tributary in Hocking River drainage basin. Date is on hemlock (*Tsuga*) twigs.

FIGURE 24-3.—Modern seeds of common herbs, grasses, and sedges representative of seeds found in peat and muck deposits of Ohio. The plant family is listed in parentheses. Insets indicate approximate natural size. Bar in each inset is 3 mm. Photos reproduced from Martin and Barkley (1961) with permission.

1 Cattail, *Typha domingensis* (Typhaceae). Scale bar = 2 mm.

2 Bur-reed, *Sparganium chlorocarpon* (Sparganiaceae). Scale bar = 2 mm.

3 Pondweed, *Potamogeton pectinatus* (Potamogetonaceae). Scale bar = 1 mm.

4 Pondweed, *Potamogeton spirillus* (Potamogetonaceae). Scale bar = 1 mm.

5 Naiad, *Najas flexilis* (Najadaceae). Scale bar = 1 mm.

6 Arrowhead, *Sagittaria latifolia* (Alismataceae). Scale bar = 2 mm.

7 Marsh grass, *Spartina alternifolia* (Gramineae). Scale bar = 1 mm.

8 Panic grass, *Panicum agrostoides* (Gramineae). Scale bar = 0.5 mm.

9 Flat sedge, *Cyperus strigosus* (Cyperaceae). Scale bar = 0.5 mm.

10 Spike-rush, *Eleocharis palustris* (Cyperaceae). Scale bar = 0.5 mm.

11 Sedge, *Carex aequatilis* (Cyperaceae). Scale bar = 1 mm.

12 Sedge, *Carex comosa* (Cyperaceae). Scale bar = 1 mm.

13 Rush, *Juncus effusus* (Juncaceae). Scale bar = 2 mm.

14 Smartweed, *Polygonum punctatum* (Polygonaceae). Scale bar = 1 mm.

15 Water hemp, *Amaranthus cannabinus* (Amaranthaceae). Scale bar = 1 mm.

16 Yellow water lily (?), *Nuphar luteum* (Nymphaeaceae). Scale bar = 2 mm.

17 Water lily, *Nymphaea tuberosa* (Nymphaeaceae). Scale bar = 2 mm.

18 Clover, *Trifolium tridentatum* (Leguminosae, Papilionoideae). Scale bar = 0.5 mm.

19 St.-John's-wort, *Hypericum perforatum* (Guttiferae, Hypericaceae). Scale bar = 0.3 mm.

20 American lotus, *Nelumbo lutea* (Nymphaeaceae). Scale bar = 5 mm.

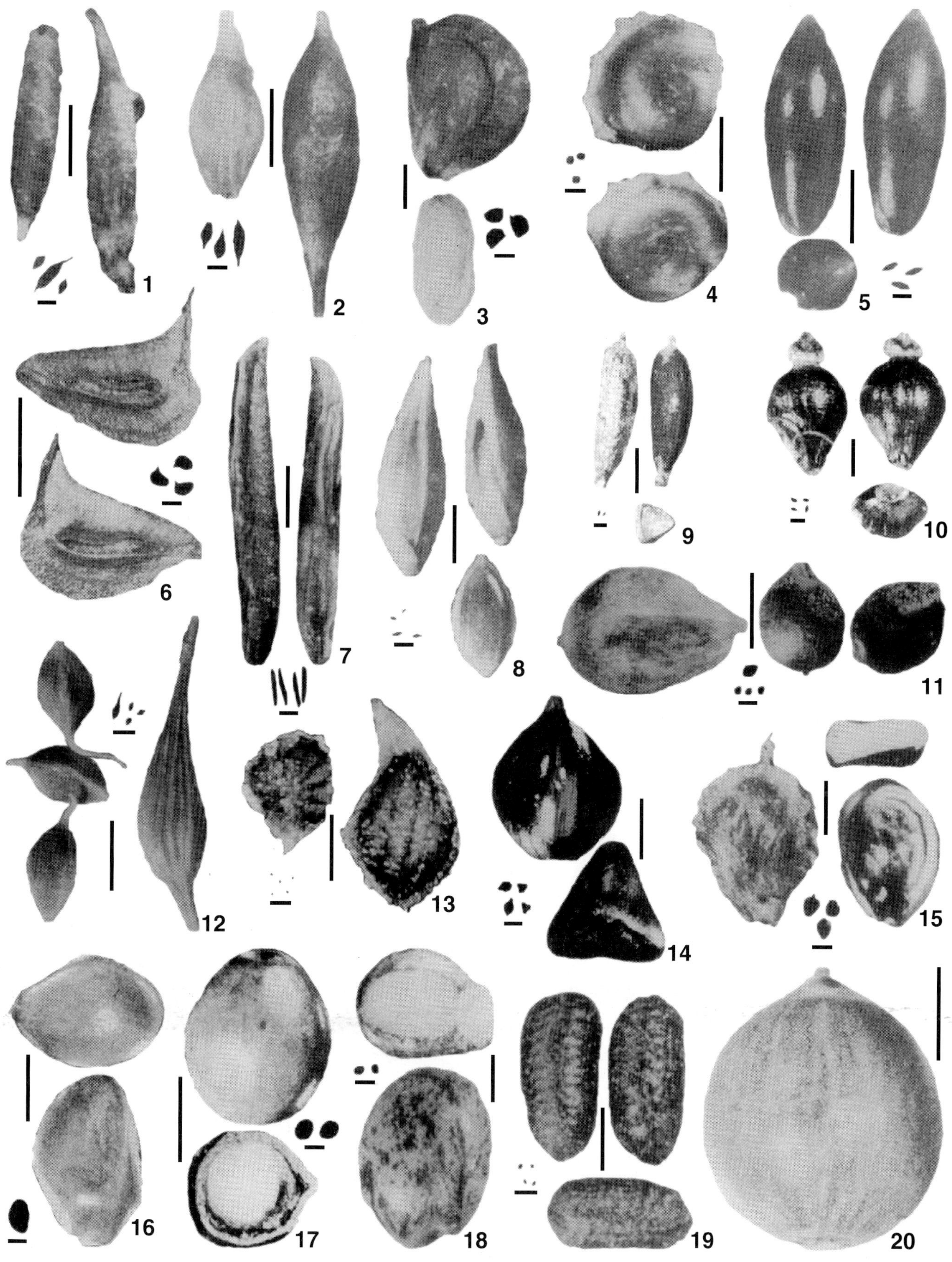
1
2
3
4
5
6
7
8
9
10
11
12
13
14
15
16
17
18
19
20

FIGURE 24-4.—Modern seeds and leaves of common trees, shrubs, and vines representative of those that occur in late-glacial and Recent peat and muck deposits in the Great Lakes region. The plant family is listed in parentheses. Figures 24-4.1 to 24-4.23 are from the *Woody-plant seed manual* prepared by the U.S. Forest Service (1948). Many of the seeds and leaves reproduced here are the same species as Pleistocene plants; a few illustrations are of similar species of the same genus or family.

1 Balsam fir, *Abies balsamea* (Pinaceae). **A**, side view, and **B**, face view with wing broken off. Scale bar = 1 mm.

2 Western mountain hemlock, *Tsuga mertensiana* (Pinaceae). Exterior view with base of wing adhering (top). *T. canadensis* would be more commonly found in swamps. Scale bar = 1 mm.

3 Western hemlock, *Tsuga heterophylla*. Scale bar = 1 mm.

4 White spruce, *Picea glauca* (Pinaceae). Four seeds with bases of wings attached at top of two upper seeds. Scale bar = 2 mm.

5 Black or bog spruce, *Picea mariana*. Four seeds with bases of wings attached at top of two upper seeds. Scale bar = 2 mm.

6 Black larch/tamarack, *Larix laricina* (Pinaceae). **A**, side view, and **B**, face view with lower part of wing attached. Scale bar = 1 mm.

7 Jack or scrub pine, *Pinus banksiana* (Pinaceae). Eight seeds with wings removed. Scale bar = 5 mm.

8 Eastern white pine, *Pinus strobus*. Five seeds with wings removed except for base of wing on seed at lower right. Scale bar = 5 mm.

9 Arbor vitae or northern white cedar, *Thuja occidentalis* (Pinaceae, Cupressineae). Exterior view with two wings attached. Scale bar = 1 mm.

10 Cedar, *Thuja plicata*. Three seeds with wings. Scale bar = 5 mm.

11 Box elder, *Acer negundo* (Aceraceae). A single winged seed. Scale bar = 20 mm.

12 Red or swamp maple, *Acer rubrum*. Three winged seeds. Scale bar = 20 mm.

13 Paper, canoe, or white birch, *Betula papyrifera* (Betulaceae). Winged seed. Swamp forms may be hybrids; *B. pumila* and other dwarf varieties commonly are found in bogs and swamps, as is *B. michauxii*. Scale bar = 2 mm.

14 Yellow birch, *Betula lutea*. Winged seed. Scale bar = 2 mm.

15 River or red birch, *Betula nigra*. Winged seed. Scale bar = 2 mm.

16 Alder, *Alnus rubra* (Betulaceae). Exterior of winged seed. Scale bar = 2 mm.

17 Green or mountain alder, *Alnus crispa*. Four seeds with narrow wings. *Alnus rugosa* and *A. serrulata* and their varieties are much more commonly associated with bogs and swamps in Ohio. Scale bar = 5 mm.

18 Alder-leaved viburnum, *Viburnum alnifolium* (Caprifoliaceae). Seed has one or two ventral grooves. Scale bar = 5 mm.

19 Wild raisin viburnum, *Viburnum cassinoides*. Flattish seed with weak grooves. Widespread in swamps and bogs along with swamp haw, *V. nudum*, which has similar seed. Scale bar = 5 mm.

20 Hackberry, *Celtis occidentalis* (Ulmaceae). *Celtis pumila* is found in moist thickets and swamp margins. Berrylike fruit (a drupe) has a large seed and thin pulp that shrinks into conspicuous wrinkles upon drying. Scale bar = 5 mm.

21 Sugarberry, *Celtis laevigata*. Five dried fruits showing wrinkled skin around hard seed. This tree inhabits moist bottomlands. Scale bar = 5 mm.

22 Sycamore or buttonwood, *Platanus racemosa* (Platanaceae). Two elongate, pendulous seeds. Scale bar = 5 mm.

23 American sycamore, *Platanus occidentalis*. Scale bar = 5 mm.

24 Buttonbush, *Cephalanthus occidentalis* (Rubiaceae). Capsule splits longitudinally from base upward to release two to four nut-like seeds. Scale bar = 3 mm.

25 Basswood or linden, *Tilia cordata* (Tiliaceae). Four seeds, two in dried husks. Scale bar = 5 mm.

26 Tupelo or sour gum, *Nyssa sylvatica* (Nyssaceae). Fruits 1-2 cm long, ribbed. *Nyssa sylvatica biflora* inhabits inundated swamps and has larger fruits; *N. aquatica* also is found mostly in seasonally inundated swamps. Scale bar = 5 mm.

27 Portion of leaf of herbaceous plant (**cf.** bishop's cap, *Mitella*) that washed out of the matrix of sandy gray clay (gumbo till) of the Beale mastodon site in Athens County, Ohio (locality 42, fig. 24-2). Age is about 13,320 years B.P. Scale bar = 1 cm.

28, 29 **28**, lower portion of willow leaf identified as bearberry, *Salix uva-ursi* Pursh (Salicaceae). Leaves are very small, less than 1 cm wide and 2.5 cm in length, attached to prostrate, mat-forming, woody branches; presence generally indicates cold, barren exposed surfaces, such as tundra. **29**, sketch of **venation** pattern of leaf in **28** and estimated original outline of the leaf. Collins Run, sec. 26, Oxford Twp., Butler County, Ohio, near locality 5 on figure 24-2. Late Wisconsinan age. Reproduced from Berry (1934), with permission. Scale bar = 5 mm.

30 Poorly preserved portion of leaf from same locality as **28**, **29**, and possibly the same species. Reproduced from Berry (1934), with permission. Scale bar = 5 mm.

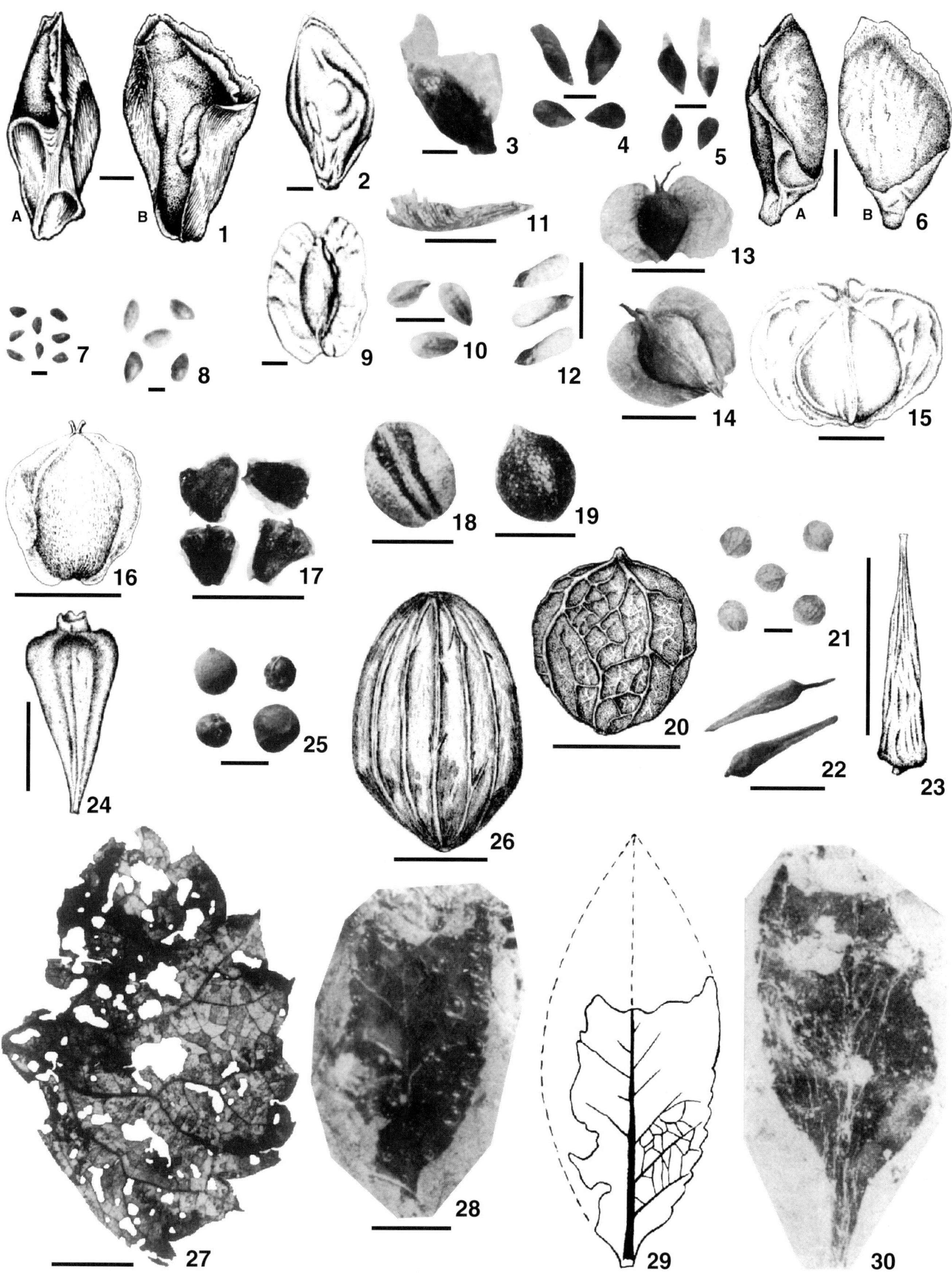
A
B
1
2
3
4
5
A
B
6
7
8
9
10
11
12
13
14
15
16
17
18
19
20
21
22
23
24
25
26
27
28
29
30

FIGURE 24-5.—A log and leaves from Wisconsinan-age or Recent deposits in Ohio. Scale bar for figures 24-5.2 and 24-5.3 equals 1 cm.

1 Cedar (*Thuja*) log in till in a railroad cut near Sidney, Shelby County, Ohio (locality 15, fig. 24-2). Photograph courtesy of Jane L. Forsyth (Bowling Green State University).

2 Several leaves from poorly cemented, iron-stained travertine deposits in moundlike accumulations near Yellow Springs, Greene County, Ohio (locality 11, fig. 24-2). The center leaf is dogwood (*Cornus*) and the specimen on the left may be as well. The leaf on the right is too poorly preserved for definitive identification but may be cherry (*Prunus*). Age is uncertain and could range from early postglacial to Recent. ClMNH P-15934, Hoskins-Cross collection B-5461.

3 Partial impression of a sycamore (*Platanus*) leaf from the same deposit as **2**. ClMNH P-15946, Hoskins-Cross collection B-5461.

1

2

3

FIGURE 24-6.—Pollen of conifers and willow. Scale bars for all figures equal 10 micrometers.

1 Eastern white pine (*Pinus strobus*). The body of a pine pollen grain is characterized by two prominent bladders, a trait (termed **vesiculate**) shared by spruce (**3**) and fir (**5**). In contrast to these latter genera, pine pollen grains generally are somewhat smaller, although this is not an infallible guide. The dorsal surface of the body may be ornamented in various ways, and the bladders typically demonstrate a prominent internal **reticulum**. Common eastern North American pines show two distinct morphologies with respect to the attachment of the bladders to the body of the grain. In haploxylon pines the dorsal contact between the bladders and the body of the grain is a relatively smooth arc, as in this specimen. White pine is the only native species that has this morphology. Diploxylon pines have bladders that resemble spheres appended to the body of the grain, resulting in a distinctly angular contact between the bladder and the body. The diploxylon pine species most likely to be encountered in Ohio deposits is jack pine (**2**).

2 Jack pine (*Pinus banksiana*). Jack pine pollen can be distinguished from that of white pine by the notably smaller size of the pollen grains and the angular junction between the bladders and the dorsal region of the body of the grain.

3 White spruce (*Picea glauca*). The vesiculate pollen grains of spruce generally are larger than those of pine and the bladders join the body in a smooth arc. The bladders may be strongly inflated (as in this specimen) or commonly are wrapped beneath the body of the grain, as if clasping the body.

4 Canadian hemlock (*Tsuga canadensis*). Of the common conifers in Ohio bog deposits, hemlock pollen is easily recognized, as it looks like the detached bladders of vesiculate pollen grains, except that the grains do not have a reticulate appearance.

5 Balsam fir (*Abies balsamea*). The bladders of fir pollen grains are distinctly spherical and the grains tend to look like those of pine. They are typically distinctly larger, however, and the size of the body is larger relative to the size of the bladders.

6 Willow (*Salix* sp.). Willow pollen grains are relatively small, distinctly **tricolporate** (having three prominent longitudinal furrows, each with a single pore in the center), and have prominent reticulate sculpturing of the pollen-grain wall.

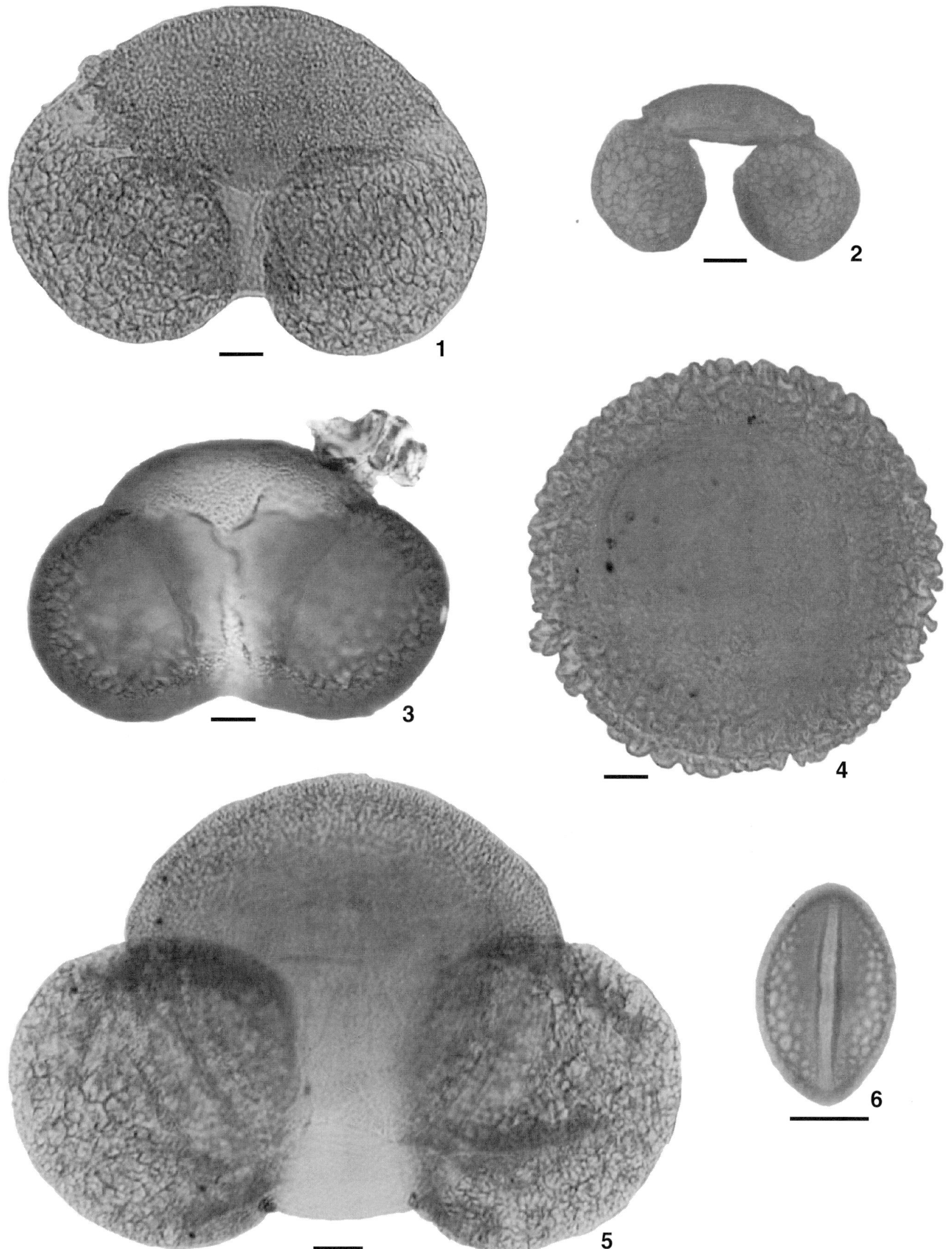
1
2
3
4
5
6

FIGURE 24-7.—Pollen of broad-leaved trees. Scale bars for all figures equal 10 micrometers.

1 Butternut (*Juglans cinerea*). Pollen grains of butternuts and walnuts are thin walled and have multiple pores (**polyporate**). Most of the pores are located around the equator of the grain, but a small number (arrows) are located away from the equator and have a tendency to favor one hemisphere. The pores have a very slightly thickened rim or annulus, but this feature may be difficult to observe without a high-quality microscope. The various walnut species are difficult to differentiate on the basis of their pollen.

2 Shagbark hickory (*Carya ovata*). A number of hickories are native to Ohio. The individual species are difficult to differentiate on the basis of pollen features, although the genus is readily recognized. The grains, which are typically oriented in polar view (as in this specimen), tend to be fairly large and have a rounded to subtriangular outline. Three (typically) prominent pores (arrows) are present, offset slightly from the equator.

3 Beech (*Fagus grandifolia*). Beech pollen grains are relatively large (compared with most common broad-leaved pollen types), indistinctly sculptured, relatively thin walled, and have three prominent, generally gaping furrows (**tricolpate**). Their appearance in Ohio pollen diagrams marks the return of relatively mild and moist climatic conditions.

4 Elm (*Ulmus* sp.). Elm pollen grains typically have three to five equatorial pores. Their most diagnostic feature is the sculpturing on the walls that gives the grains the appearance of a cauliflower.

5 Swamp white oak (*Quercus bicolor*). Oak pollen grains appear to be somewhat nondescript but are none-the-less easily recognized. The grains have a fairly thick wall (for their size) that appears to lack obvious sculpturing. The wall is tricolporate, but the pores are rarely visible in fossil material. The various species of oak cannot be differentiated readily with a light microscope.

6 Sweetgum (*Liquidambar styraciflua*). Sweetgum pollen is polyporate, and the pores are rather evenly distributed on the surface of the grain. It is most likely to be confused with pollen of the Chenopodiaceae and Amaranthaceae (see fig. 24-9.5), but sweetgum pollen tends to be larger, individual pores are larger and fewer in number, the pores are somewhat less distinct, and each pore has a membrane with small but distinct surface sculpturing.

7 Red maple (*Acer rubrum*). Although it is difficult to differentiate the various species of maple on the basis of pollen, they all share a characteristic that makes them easy to recognize—a complex sculpturing of longitudinal striations (as in this specimen). Maple pollen is tricolporate; the three longitudinal furrows are easily seen, but the pores rarely are.

8 Basswood (*Tilia americana*). Basswood pollen grains are typically seen in polar view, where their three uniquely thickened and prominent pores make them easy to recognize.

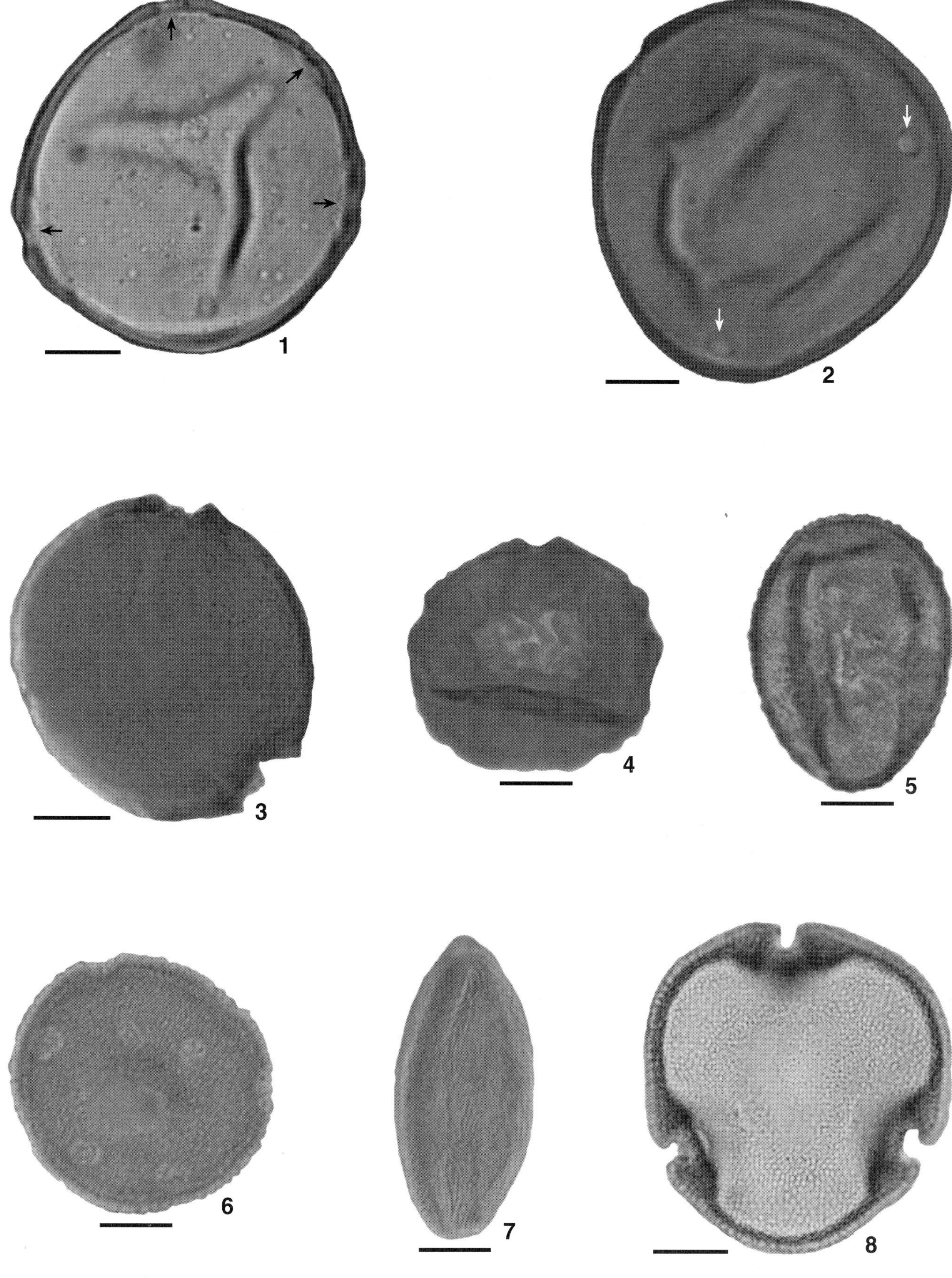
1
2
3
4
5
6
7
8

FIGURE 24-8.—Pollen of broad-leaved trees and shrubs. Scale bars for all figures equal 10 micrometers.

1 Sycamore (*Platanus occidentalis*). Although sycamores are common on Ohio floodplains, the pollen is rare in bog deposits, possibly because the grains decay more readily that those of other pollen types.

2 Ohio buckeye (*Aesculus glabra*). This species and *A. octandra* (yellow buckeye) are both native to Ohio and are difficult to distinguish on the basis of pollen. Grains are typically observed in polar or near-polar view (as in this specimen) and are easily recognized by the presence of five to eight (typically six or seven) prominent furrows. Even where the trees are present locally, the pollen tends to be rare in deposits as the trees are insect pollinated.

3 American chestnut (*Castanea dentata*). Chestnut pollen is among the smallest grains one is likely to encounter and is easily overlooked at low power. The tricolporate grains have prominent furrows and pores. There is a short, transverse furrow at each pore, making the grains quite distinctive.

4 Ash (*Fraxinus* sp.). Ash pollen bears a superficial resemblance to willow pollen (fig. 24-6.6) in that both genera produce somewhat elongate, tricolporate grains that have a distinct reticulate sculpturing of the pollen wall. The furrows of ash pollen grains are distinctly thickened in the equatorial region, giving the outer furrow margin a distinctly angular appearance, in contrast to willow grains, in which the margins of the furrow appear almost straight with very little thickening in the equatorial region.

5 Mountain laurel (*Kalmia latifolia*). Pollen of the heath family (Ericaceae) is characterized by three-dimensional **tetrads** that have a prominent slit or furrow on the exposed face of each individual pollen grain. In addition to laurel and rhododendrons, this family includes huckleberries, blueberries, and a number of other small shrubs that commonly are locally important in bogs and peaty wetlands. Distinctions between genera are difficult.

6 Flowering dogwood (*Cornus florida*). The flowers of this common understory tree are insect pollinated, so the pollen tends to be underrepresented in bog deposits dominated by wind-pollinated taxa. The pollen of this species cannot readily be distinguished from the pollen of several shrubby species (many having inconspicuous flowers) that commonly occur on the margins of ponds, wetlands, and other moderately wet sites.

7 Holly (*Ilex* sp.). Pollen of this shrub is easily recognized as the grains have a distinct, dense, club-shaped sculpturing of the outer wall. Holly is not common in Ohio bog deposits and, when encountered, the most likely species is *I. verticillata* (winterberry), although other species are possible, particularly in the southern part of the state.

8 Common elder (*Sambucus canadensis*). Shrub.

9 Yellow birch (*Betula lutea*). Birch pollen is quite distinctive—the thin-walled, somewhat inflated pollen grains have three (typically) protruding pores. The walls show no obvious sculpturing. Individual birch species are difficult to differentiate on the basis of pollen morphology.

10 Alder (*Alnus* sp.). Alder pollen grains are somewhat like those of birch (**9**), but pore numbers can range from three to as many as six, and alder grains have a thickening of the wall that gives the appearance of distinct arcs connecting the pores.

11 American hornbeam (*Carpinus caroliniana*). Shrub.

12 American hazel (*Corylus americana*). Shrub.

13 Choke cherry (*Prunus serotina*). Wild cherries belong to the rose family (Rosaceae), a large and diverse family whose individual genera can be very difficult to differentiate on the basis of pollen. Many common genera such as *Prunus* (cherry), *Amelanchier* (juneberry), *Crataegus* (hawthorn), *Rosa* (rose), and *Rubus* (raspberry) are characterized by distinctly tricolporate pollen, and pollen identification typically depends on the analysis of wall sculpturing, which can be difficult to evaluate without a research-quality microscope. The flowers in this family are insect pollinated, so the genera typically are underrepresented in bog deposits dominated by wind-pollinated taxa.

14 Bayberry (*Myrica pennsylvanica*). Shrub.

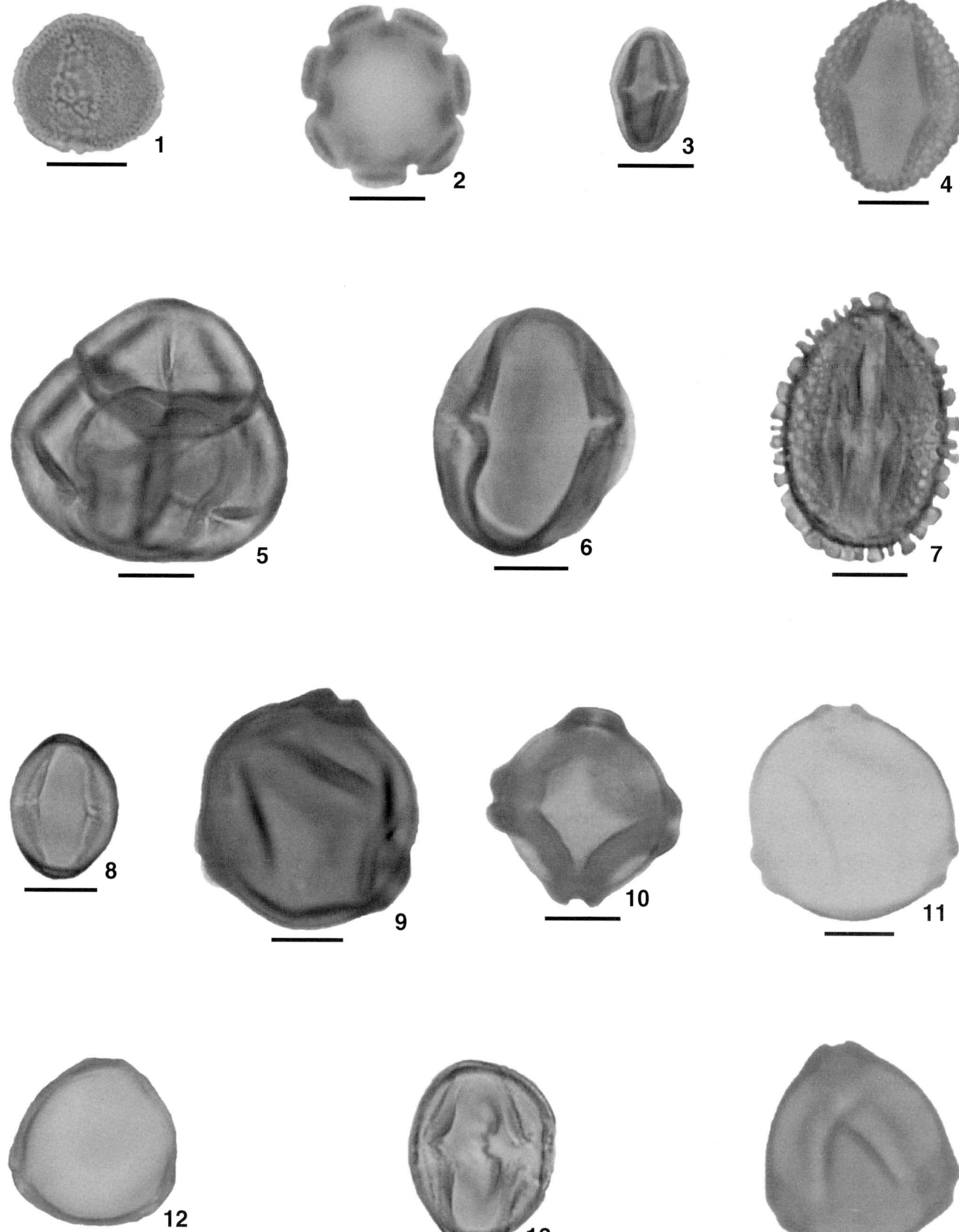
1
2
3
4
5
6
7
8
9
10
11
12
13
14

FIGURE 24-9.—Spores of ferns and club moss and pollen of barley, sedge, and other herbaceous species. Scale bars for all figures equal 10 micrometers.

1 Regal fern (*Osmunda regalis*). Fern spores are generally of two morphological types—**trilete**, as in the regal fern, or **monolete**, as in the polypody fern (**3**). The Osmundaceae characteristically have trilete spores, in which one face of the spore has a distinctive three-armed (triradiate) thickening or scar. The spore walls may be variously sculptured.

2 Barley (*Hordeum* sp.). Pollen in the grass family (Gramineae) is remarkably uniform, making identification of individual genera almost impossible. The pollen grains have a thin, almost featureless wall that, because of the size of the grain, commonly is collapsed or folded. The grains have a single pore (**monoporate**) and a slightly thickened marginal annulus. The thin wall makes the pore relatively inconspicuous in most cases and it may be obscured by folds in the pollen wall. Although the pollen of typical wild grasses and cultivated grains (such as this barley) cannot be distinguished, the pollen grains of cultivated corn (*Zea mays*) are much larger (100 micrometers or more in diameter) than those of typical grasses and thus can be distinguished from other grass pollen. The appearance of small quantities of *Zea* pollen in the upper part of a pollen profile generally marks the onset of Native American cultivation. A major increase, when accompanied by pollen of the Chenopodiaceae (**5**) and Amaranthaceae families and others such as ragweed (**7**), typically marks the onset of extensive forest clearing and agriculture by European settlers from the east.

3 Polypody fern (*Polypodium* sp.). These monolete spores are kidney bean shaped and have a single longitudinal scar on the concave surface. The walls may be sculptured (as in this specimen) or may be smooth and virtually featureless except for the monolete scar.

4 Club moss (*Lycopodium* sp.). Trilete spores that have a well-developed reticulum of high ridges can confidently be assigned to *Lycopodium*, one of the two surviving genera of herbaceous lycopods (see Chapter 23). The rays of the trilete scar extend only about halfway to the periphery of the spore. Aside from the large and conspicuous pollen of the common conifers, club moss spores are among the most recognizable taxa in pollen diagrams, although typically they are not abundant.

5 Pigweed, goosefoot (*Chenopodium* sp.). Pollen grains that have a large number of very distinct pores evenly distributed on the surface of the grains are characteristic of the families Chenopodiaceae and Amaranthaceae. An increase in the numbers of pollen of these weedy plants near the top of a pollen profile is one of the markers of European settlement. Generic distinctions on the basis of pollen are difficult.

6 Cattail (*Typha latifolia*). Pollen grains of cattail commonly are shed as a tetrad in which the four grains are in a single plane. A single indistinct pore may be visible on each individual grain.

7 Ragweed (*Ambrosia artimisiifolia*). Pollen of ragweed and other members of the aster/sunflower family (Compositae) is tricolporate but the pores (as in this specimen) may be quite indistinct. The three longitudinal furrows commonly appear as constrictions in an otherwise somewhat globose body, and the grains are always spinose to some degree. Two major morphological subtypes can be recognized within the Compositae. One type, represented by ragweed, has inconspicuous spines; these types are referred to as low-spined composites. The other type has conspicuous spines; these are referred to as high-spined composites. Composites generally are difficult to differentiate at the generic level, although the pollen of ragweed typically can be recognized. An abrupt increase in ragweed pollen in a pollen profile, typically accompanied by pollen of the Chenopodiaceae, Amaranthaceae, and corn (*Zea mays*), is a reliable marker for the onset of European settlement. Ragweed pollen is highly allergenic and the onset of flowering in late summer marks the start of hay fever season for the many people sensitive to this pollen.

8 Yellow water lily (*Nuphar* sp.). Pollen of this common member of the water lily family (Nymphaeaceae) is large and has conspicuous spines. The spines are constricted above their point of attachment to the wall of the pollen grain. The genus is easily differentiated from other pollen types.

9 Sedge (*Carex* sp.). Sedges are extremely diverse and occur on the margins of ponds and wetlands. Their pollen bears a superficial resemblance to that of grasses (see **2**). The thin-walled grains have a distinct tendency to collapse or fold. They typically bear a single pore, which, when visible, is the most reliable diagnostic feature. In sedges, the pore lacks any annular thickening and has an irregularly defined margin, in contrast to grasses, in which the pore is more clearly defined and surrounded by a thickened margin or annulus.

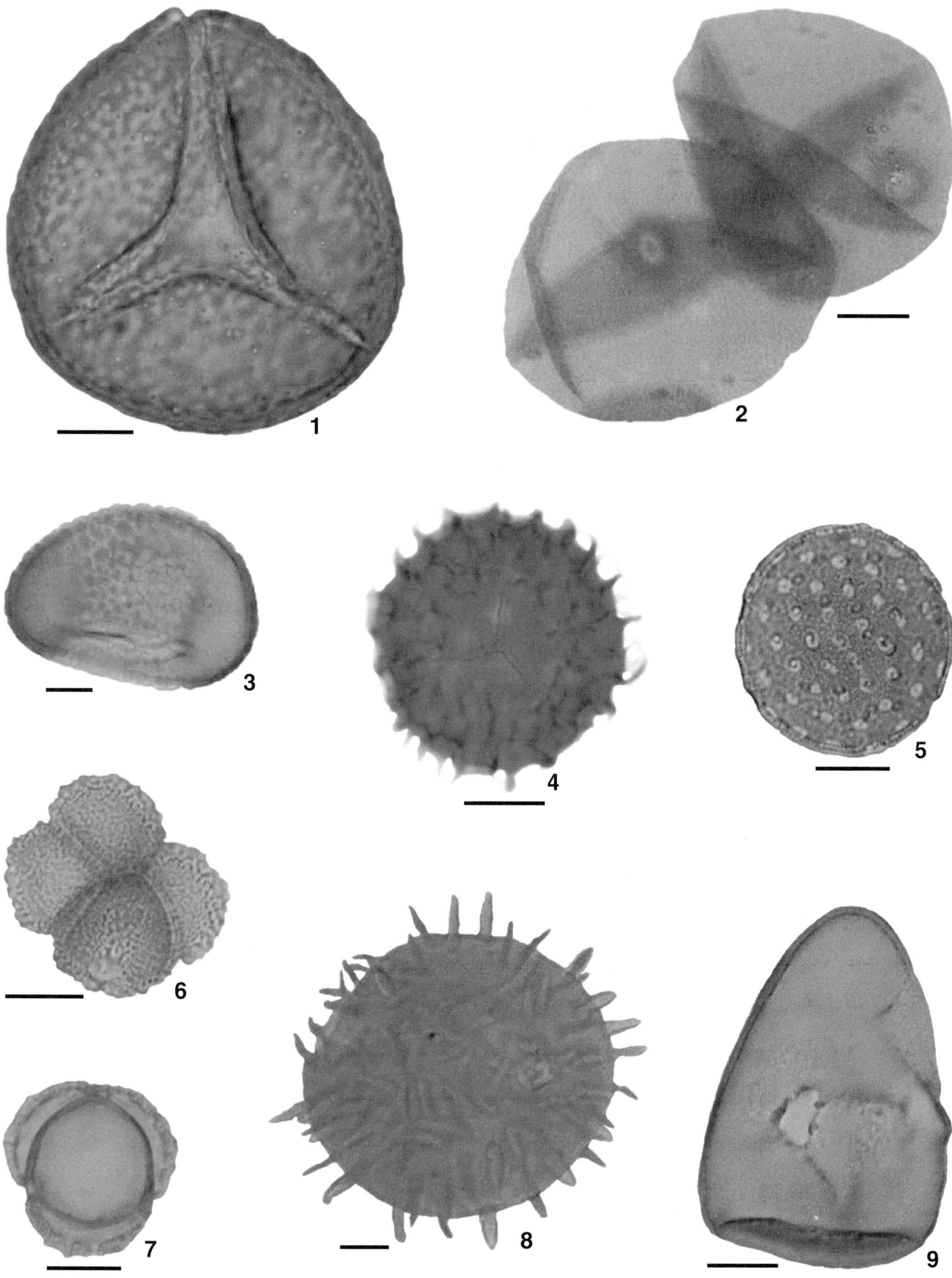
1
2
3
4
5
6
7
8
9

Chapter 25

ICHNOFOSSILS

by Joseph T. Hannibal

INTRODUCTION

Ichnofossils include tracks, trails, burrows, borings, and other indirect evidence of organisms. These types of fossils are also called trace fossils, as distiguished from **body fossils**, which are fossil remains that give morphological details of the organisms themselves. Ichnofossils are important, for they can provide information on the behavior of animals in the past, and also may be the only indication of past life in beds in which body fossils are absent. Ichnofossils also may provide information on the environments of deposition of a rock unit, especially if body fossils are lacking.

Ichnofossils are classified at two levels, the **ichnospecies** and the **ichnogenus**. Generally speaking, ichnogenera are erected based on major behavioral traits, whereas ichnospecies are based on distinctive yet less important features (Bromley, 1990, p. 156). There may or may not be any relationship between ichnogenera and genera and between ichnospecies and species. Some animals produce very distinctive trackways, but some other types of trackways may be made by more than one type of organism. Also, some animals make more than one type of trackway. Complicating the picture is the fact that ichnogenera may grade into one another. The ichnogenera *Rusophycus* and *Cruziana*, for instance, grade into one another: they are distinguished from one another by their relative lengths (see fig. 25-7).

Many types of ichnofossils can be found in Ohio; selected examples of some of the more common and distinctive forms are discussed in this chapter. Ichnofossils have been found in the rocks of all the geologic systems exposed in Ohio. In some of Ohio's rock units they are very abundant—as common, or even more so, than body fossils. The abundant ichnofossils of the Ohio Valley region drew the attention of nineteenth-century paleontologists; as a result, much early work on ichnofossils was done on Ohio specimens (James, 1884-1885, 1892).

Many of these ichnofossils originally were thought to be "seaweeds" and were described as plants ("fucoids" or marine algae) in early geological reports. This idea accounts for ichnogeneric names reminiscent of plants. The name of the common ichnogenus *Palaeophycus*, for instance, is derived from the Greek for "ancient seaweed." Despite this confusion, some ichnofossils were recognized as early as the nineteenth century as the work of animals (James, 1892); others have been redescribed as trace fossils made by animals only in recent decades.

Today, ichnofossils are less commonly confused with plant fossils. They are, however, commonly referred to as "worm tracks." Indeed, many forms are thought to have been formed by the activities of marine worms. Various other organisms, including marine arthropods and terrestrial vertebrates, also are represented by trails and tracks. The type of animal thought to have made a particular trace is noted in the descriptions in this chapter if there is general agreement over the identity of the maker.

Since the initial work on Ohio ichnofossils in the nineteenth century, several important works, notably the late Richard Osgood's monograph (1970) on ichnofossils of the Cincinnati area, have appeared, but published work on Ohio ichnofossils is rather meager, especially considering their abundance.

PRESERVATION AND OCCURRENCE OF ICHNOFOSSILS IN OHIO

Ichnofossils are preserved in various ways. They may have distinct tops and bottoms, and even internal structures may be preserved. In many cases the remains of tracks, for instance impressions originally made in sea-bottom muds, are preserved as infillings of material such as silt. These silts covered the muddy bottom and filled in the trackways. Resultant tracks are then found as positive features on the bottom of siltstone beds. More information on preservation can be found in Osgood (1987) and Bromley (1990).

Ichnofossils can be found in many of Ohio's carbonate and siliciclastic rocks, but are most common in limestones, siltstones, and fine-grained sandstones. Ichnofossils can be found on the tops, insides, and bottoms of beds of these types of rock.

Shales and mudstones in Ohio commonly contain ichnofossils, but these are generally difficult to collect, especially in the softer shales. With a few exceptions, ichnofossils are uncommon in Ohio's coarse-grained sandstones and conglomerates.

Marine ichnofossils are particularly noteworthy in the Ordovician rocks of Ohio. They are especially common on the undersides of, and in many cases within, limestone beds. Borings also are common, especially in **hardgrounds** and corals. Ichnofossils are found in Ohio's Silurian carbonate rocks, particularly the limestones.

Marine ichnofossils occur in the Middle Devonian limestones of Ohio and are common in the siltstones of the Upper Devonian Ohio Shale. In some of these rocks, including much of the Chagrin Shale Member of the Ohio Shale in northeastern Ohio, ichnofossils are more abundant and much more prominent than body fossils.

Marine ichnofossils also are found in siltstones and calcareous rocks of Mississippian age in Ohio. Various types of ichnofossils made by invertebrates are found in Pennsylvanian rocks of southeastern Ohio, especially in marine limestones and sandstones. Some of Ohio's Pennsylvanian-age rocks contain the fossil footprints of **tetrapods** (see Chapter 21 and figs. 21-17 and 21-18). Ichnofossils do occur in Ohio's Permian rocks, but these have been little studied.

Various Ohio rocks used as building stone provide excellent examples of ichnofossils. Ichnofossils found in weathered stone used in older buildings are particularly interesting. Examples are burrows in the Columbus Limestone used in the State Capitol in Columbus (Melvin and McKenzie, 1992), in monuments made of limestone from the Dayton Formation in Woodland Cemetery in Dayton (Sandy, 1992), and in the Buena Vista sandstone used for the abutments of Cincinnati's Roebling Suspension Bridge (Hannibal and Davis, 1992).

IDENTIFYING ICHNOFOSSILS

Care must be taken in identifying an object as an ichnofossil. Inorganic sedimentary structures as well as body fossils of various plants and animals can be confused with ichnofossils. If there is a question about a possible inorganic origin for a particular object, one should refer to a work such as Pettijohn and Potter's *Atlas and glossary of primary sedimentary structures* (1964), which illustrates numerous sedimentary structures as well as some ichnofossils, and D. W. Boyd's chapter, "False or misleading traces," in Frey (1975).

Long known as "fucoids," or algae, ichnofossils are still confused with plants by some people, especially by those who have had no previous introduction to ichnofossils. This confusion is understandable as some forms do resemble plants. Some forms also resemble body fossils of invertebrates. Unlike plant body fossils, however, ichnofossils are seldom if ever **carbonized**, and their component parts are not as regular as the veins, leaf scars, and other features of plants or the body parts of invertebrates. In cases where there is doubt whether a specimen is an ichnofossil or a body fossil, reference should be made to other chapters in this book.

In this chapter, ichnofossils are arranged alphabetically by ichnogenus under geologic systems. The primary description of each form is listed under the earliest geologic system in which it is abundant. Forms found in several geologic systems are briefly noted, and in some cases also illustrated, under other systems as well.

The following key was designed as an aid to the identification of ichnofossils discussed in this chapter. Trackways of tetrapods are not included in the key, as they are only briefly described in this chapter. Users should remember, however, that only selected common and distinctive ichnofossils are discussed in this chapter and that many additional forms can be found. For further information one should turn to additional works on the topic, such as the references cited above and Häntzchel's 1975 volume on trace fossils in the *Treatise on Invertebrate Paleontology*.

KEY TO SOME ICHNOGENERA FROM OHIO

1A. Orientation (in relation to bedding) primarily vertical, or a dumbbell-shaped horizontal trace, or a boring of any orientation 2
1B. Orientation primarily horizontal unless dumbbell shaped 8

2A. Boring (may be bored into a shell, other animal hard parts, or rock) 3
2B. Not a boring 5

3A. Shape cylindrical 4
3B. Shape elongate and edges rounded .... *Petroxestes* (fig. 25-3.4)

4A. Straight or gently curved (commonly a circular hole in top view) .... *Trypanites* (figs. 25-3.1 to 25-3.4)
4B. Undulating .... *"Clionolithes"* (fig. 25-8.5)

5A. A U-shaped tube and/or a dumbbell-shaped horizontal trace 6
5B. Not a U-shaped tube 7

6A. U-shaped tube having **spreiten** (curved arcs of sediment) between the arms of the U, or a dumbbell-shaped form retaining some evidence of a U-tube and spreiten (both forms may be present) .... *Diplocraterion* (figs. 25-1, 25-2.2, 25-2.3)
6B. U-shaped tube without spreiten between the arms of the U, or a dumbbell-shaped form having a knob in middle of dumbbell ends (depending on preservation, there may be a depression instead of a knob) (both forms may be present) .... *Bifungites* (fig. 25-8.1)

7A. A simple vertical tube, commonly filled with sediment .... *Skolithos* (figs. 25-6.4, 25-6.5)
7B. Tube slitlike in top view, tonguelike or spadelike in side view .... *Lingulichnus* (figs. 25-5.5, 25-5.6)

8A. Entirely or partly bilobate, longer than wide, or consisting of two parallel series of short ridges or grooves 9
8B. Not bilobate 13

9A. Long (more than about four times longer than wide) 10
9B. Short (no more than about four times longer than wide) 12

10A. Trackway consists of two parallel sets of ridges or grooves .... *Diplichnites* (figs. 25-9.1, 25-9.2)
10B. Trackway elongate, bilobed 11

11A. When preserved in positive relief, trace has a ridge running down the center .... *Psammichnites* (fig. 25-8.7)
11B. When preserved in positive relief, trace has a depression running down the center .... *Cruziana* (fig. 25-7.4)

12A. Entirely or mostly bilobed .... *Rusophycus* (figs. 25-4.1, 25-4.3, 25-7.1, 25-7.2)
12B. Bilobed on one end, commonly has a raised medial area on the other end .... *Chagrinichnites* (figs. 25-5.1, 25-5.2)

13A. With spreiten 14
13B. Without spreiten 15

14A. Spreiten link arms of a U tube .... *Rhizocorallium* (fig. 25-7.5)
14B. Spreiten arranged in a spiraling coil (may resemble a pinwheel or a rooster's tail) .... *Zoophycos* (figs. 25-7.3, 25-8.6)

15A. Burrow system composed of branching cylindrical or subcylindrical burrows 16
15B. Elongate, cylindrical or subcylindrical burrow that does not branch or has very few branches 17

16A. Small-diameter (typically less than 1 cm) burrows .... *Chondrites* (figs. 25-2.1, 25-4.2, 25-5.7)
16B. Large-diameter (more than 1 cm) burrows that have swellings and Y-shaped bifurcations .... *Thalassinoides*-like burrows (fig. 25-6.7)

17A. Meandering, bending, or looping 18
17B. Straight or curved 21

18A. Bending or looping, typically resembling a knot .... *Gordia* (fig. 25-5.4)
18B. Undulatory or loosely meandering 19

19A. Scaly .... *Scalarituba* (figs. 25-8.3, 25-8.4)
19B. Smooth 20

20A. Regularly meandering .... *Cochlichnus* (fig. 25-5.3)
20B. More randomly meandering .... *Helminthopsis* (fig. 25-8.2)

21A. With a lining .... *Palaeophycus* (figs. 25-6.1, 25-6.3)
21B. Unlined .... *Planolites* (figs. 25-4.2, 25-6.1, 25-6.2, 25-6.6)

ORDOVICIAN ICHNOFOSSILS

Ichnofossils are plentiful in Ordovician rocks of Ohio—more than 30 ichnospecies can be found in these rocks. Because of their abundance and their occurrence in an area that has received a great deal of paleontological attention by professionals and amateurs since the second half of the nineteenth century, Ordovician ichnofossils have received more attention than ichnofossils found in younger rocks of Ohio. Many of the same ichnogenera found in Ohio's Ordovician rocks, however, also can be found in the younger rocks of the state.

Chondrites von Sternberg (fig. 25-2.1) is composed of a system of branching tunnels. Most of the tunnels are horizontal or nearly horizontal, commonly paralleling bedding. Individual tunnels typically range in width from 1 to 7 mm. Size is generally consistent in the same system of tunnels. Osgood (1970, p. 328) noted that *Chondrites* is one of the most common of the "fucoids." In Ohio, *Chondrites* is common in Ordovician rocks of the Cincinnatian Series and also can be found in younger rocks, including Silurian rocks of western Ohio (fig. 25-4.2), the Devonian Ohio Shale (fig. 25-5.7) in northeastern Ohio and in a north-south band through the middle of the state, and the Mississippian Logan Formation east of the Ohio Shale. *Chondrites* probably represents the work of sediment-feeding worms. Osgood (1970) distinguished several types of *Chondrites* by letter (such as type C).

Diplocraterion Torell (figs. 25-1, 25-2.2, 25-2.3) consists of a vertical, U-shaped tube; in some specimens, small extensions emanate from each side of the base of the tube. Curved spreiten extend between the two arms of the U. Some specimens are found with all of these elements present. However, partial specimens, such as impressions of the bottom of the tube, also are common (see fig. 25-2.3). *Diplocraterion* is similar in shape to *Rhizocorallium* (see fig. 25-7.5); however, *Rhizocorallium* is oriented horizontal to the rock bedding. *Diplocraterion* is common in the Cincinnatian Series. It can also be found in other Ohio rocks, including the Mississippian Logan Formation. It was probably formed by filter-feeding worms.

Petroxestes Wilson & Palmer (fig. 25-3.4) is an elongate boring that has rounded edges. It generally has a length-to-width ratio of about 5 to 1 and ranges up to 30 mm in length. *Petroxestes* can be shallow or deep, ranging from a little less than 2 mm to 20 mm in depth. The name *Petroxestes* is derived from the Greek for "rock boring" and is especially descriptive. This ichnofossil is common throughout the Cincinnatian Series of southwestern Ohio (Wilson and Palmer, 1988). *Petroxestes* was formed by boring clams.

Rusophycus Hall (figs. 25-4.1, 25-4.3) is a relatively short, bilobed trace. Each lobe commonly has subhorizontal markings (**striae**). This ichnofossil is typically found as a convex form on the bottom of beds. *Rusophycus* is a very distinctive trace, but could be confused with the longer bilobed trace known as *Cruziana* (see fig. 25-7.4). *Rusophycus*, however, is generally only up to about three times or so as long as wide; *Cruziana* typically is longer. *Rusophycus* also could be confused with short segments of *Psammichnites*, but *Psammichnites* has a distinctive medial ridge (see fig. 25-8.7). There is evidence that some ichnospecies of *Rusophycus* were made by trilobites. Commonly, in Ordovician rocks, specimens of trilobites or parts of trilobites are found associated with *Rusophycus*. In the Cincinnati area, thin slabs of rock have been found that have *Rusophycus* on one side and the trilobite that produced the *Rusophycus* on the other. Groupings of *Rusophycus* have long been known as "trilobite nests," implying that they represent egg-laying activity, but this origin has not been demonstrated. *Rusophycus* probably represents a site related to feeding. In addition to Ordovician rocks, *Rusophycus* and *Rusophycus*-like ichnofossils are found in younger rocks in Ohio, including the Devonian Ohio Shale (figs. 25-7.1, 25-7.2).

Trypanites Mägdefrau (figs. 25-3.1 to 25-3.4) is a cylindrical boring ranging in width from about 1 to 2 mm; it is longer than wide. This boring is typically found in a vertical position in hardgrounds, but may be bored perpendicular or parallel to the surface of corals and other thick-shelled organisms. *Trypanites* is probably the most common boring in Paleozoic rocks. It is very common in Ordovician rocks of Ohio, where it can be found as borings in fossil brachiopods, bryozoans, and corals, as well as in hardgrounds. It is particularly common in rugose corals, such as the common Ordovician coral *Grewingkia* (figs. 25-3.1, 25-3.2). *Trypanites* also is found in Middle Devonian marine organisms. *Trypanites* was probably made by filter-feeding polychaete annelid worms. Additional examples of *Trypanites* are illustrated in Elias (1982, 1986).

Another boring found in the Ordovician of Ohio and also in the Devonian is made by the bryozoan *Ropalonaria* Ulrich. See Chapter 15 and figure 15-1.1 for discussion and illustration of this boring.

Other common ichnofossils found in the Ordovician rocks of Ohio include *Planolites*, which is described in the section on Silurian ichnofossils; *Palaeophycus*, *Skolithos*, and *Zoophycos*, which are described in the section on Devonian ichnofossils; and *Diplichnites*, which is described in the section on Mississippian and Pennsylvanian ichnofossils. Additional forms are beautifully illustrated in Osgood (1970), although the names of many of these forms have been subsequently updated.

SILURIAN ICHNOFOSSILS

Ichnofossils are common in some of the rock units of Silurian age in Ohio. However, they have not received the attention of those in Ordovician rocks.

Chondrites (fig. 25-4.2) is found in the Osgood Shale of western Ohio. It is described in the section on Ordovician ichnofossils.

Planolites Nicholson (fig. 25-4.2) is a more or less horizontal, straight to curved burrow that does not have any apparent lining. This form can easily be confused with *Palaeophycus* (see figs. 25-6.1, 25-6.3), another horizontal to subhorizontal burrow, which does have a distinct lining. Also, *Palaeophycus* can be branched, but *Planolites* is rarely branched. Pemberton and Frey (1982) discuss the differences in greater detail. In theory, differentiating the two genera is straightforward, but in practice, distinguishing them may require detailed study of the composition of the specimen and its surrounding matrix. To confuse matters, the two forms may occur on or in the same rock slab. It may be necessary to cut and polish the edge of a rock slab to distinguish the two forms. Even then, it may be difficult to determine if a specimen has a lining. If this determination can't be made, it is generally best to assign specimens to the ichnogenus *Planolites* (Christopher G. Maples, personal commun., 1992). Additional information on *Palaeophycus* is given in the section on Devonian ichnofossils. *Planolites* is common in Silurian rocks of western Ohio. It is also one of the most common Ohio ichnofossils overall and can be found in many of the Ordovician, Devonian (figs. 25-6.1, 25-6.2, 25-6.6), Mississippian, and Pennsylvanian rocks of Ohio. This ichnofossil was formed by predaceous or filter-feeding worms.

Other ichnofossils found in the Silurian rocks of Ohio include *Diplocraterion* and *Rusophycus*, which are described in the section on Ordovician ichnofossils, and *Palaeophycus* and *Skolithos*, which are described in the section on Devonian ichnofossils.

DEVONIAN ICHNOFOSSILS

Ichnofossils are common in both the carbonate and clastic (shale and siltstone) sequences of the Devonian of Ohio. In some rock units (for instance, the Chagrin Shale Member of the Ohio Shale) they are more common than body fossils.

Chagrinichnites Feldmann, Osgood, Szmuc & Meinke (figs. 25-5.1, 25-5.2) is a **bilaterally symmetrical** trackway that is somewhat longer than wide. It is commonly found as a positive feature on both the tops and the bottoms of thin (about 1 to 3 cm thick) beds of siltstone. This ichnofossil typically bears repetitive, subhorizontal, transverse markings. One end of the ichnofossil, as seen on the bottom of slabs of rock, typically bears a raised medial area flanked by paired depressed areas. The other end may be bilobed, resembling *Rusophycus* in part. The form of *Chagrinichnites* varies quite a bit; compare figures 25-5.1 and 25-5.2. Cross sections of rock slabs containing well-preserved specimens may show deflection of the sediment layers, indicating that the maker of this ichnofossil passed through the sediment while it was still soft. This ichnofossil could be confused with *Rusophycus*. However, *Chagrinichnites* is more complex than *Rusophycus*, which consists simply of a bilobed form (see Hannibal and Feldmann, 1983, and references therein for additional information). In Ohio, *Chagrinichnites* has been reported only from the Chagrin Shale Member of the Ohio Shale, in which it can be very abundant. *Chagrinichnites* was formed by crustaceans, including the phyllocarid *Echinocaris* (see Chapter 10).

Chondrites (fig. 25-5.7) is found in siltstones and shales of the Ohio Shale. It is described in the section on Ordovician ichnofossils.

Cochlichnus Hitchcock (fig. 25-5.3) is a smooth, regularly undulating trackway. It is found in the Chagrin Shale Member of the Ohio Shale.

Cruziana d'Orbigny (fig. 25-7.4) is an elongate trace that has two lobes. A depression runs down the center of the ichnofossil between the two lobes. Ridges cross each of the lobes. This trace could be confused with *Rusophycus*, but that form is shorter. If a specimen is at least about four times as long as wide, it can be safely assigned to the ichnogenus *Cruziana*. *Cruziana* could also be confused with *Psammichnites*, but *Psammichnites* has a distinctive medial ridge (see fig. 25-8.7) when preserved in positive relief. *Cruziana* probably represents the moving or grazing sites of arthropods. Most *Cruziana* ichnofossils probably were formed by trilobites, but the specimen illustrated in figure 25-7.4 is from the Chagrin Shale Member, a rock unit without known trilobites.

Gordia Emmons (fig. 25-5.4) is a smooth, long, thin trail that commonly is looping. This ichnofossil is not regularly meandering as is *Cochlichnus* (fig. 25-5.3). *Gordia* is common in the Chagrin Shale Member of the Ohio Shale. This ichnofossil was probably made by a wormlike animal.

Lingulichnus Hakes (figs. 25-5.5, 25-5.6) is a vertical, very narrowly conical form. In top view it appears as a narrow, ovoid slit. In side view it can be tonguelike or may resemble a spade with its handle extending downward. This ichnofossil is common in some exposures of the Chagrin Shale Member of the Ohio Shale in northeastern Ohio (Szmuc, and others, 1976). These vertical traces were made by a linguloid brachiopod.

Palaeophycus Hall (figs. 25-6.1, 25-6.3) is a straight to somewhat curved, unbranched or branched, horizontal to subhorizontal, lined, cylindrical burrow. The material filling the burrows is typically of the same type as the rock containing the burrows. The lining may show up as a thickening of burrow edges (fig. 25-6.3). This form is easily confused with *Planolites*, an ichnogenus discussed below and in the section on Silurian ichnofossils; *Palaeophycus* commonly is found on or in the same slabs containing *Planolites* (fig. 25-6.1). *Palaeophycus* is one of the most common Devonian ichnofossils. It can be found in various Devonian rock units, including the Ohio Shale. It is also one of the most common Ohio ichnofossils overall, and can be found in many of the Ordovician, Devonian, Silurian, Mississippian, and Pennsylvanian rocks of Ohio. This ichnofossil was formed by predaceous or filter-feeding worms.

Planolites is common in the Devonian rocks of Ohio, including the Middle Devonian Silica Formation in northwestern Ohio (fig. 25-6.6) and the Upper Devonian Chagrin Shale Member of the Ohio Shale in northeastern Ohio (figs. 25-6.1, 25-6.2). *Planolites* is described in the section on Silurian ichnofossils.

Rhizocorallium Zenker (fig. 25-7.5) is a more or less horizontal, U-shaped tube. The area between the two arms of the U-tube is filled with spreiten. Typically the tube is very elongate. This trace is similar in shape to *Diplocraterion* (see fig. 25-2.2), but *Diplocraterion* is oriented perpendicular to the rock bedding. *Rhizocorallium* is found in the Chagrin Shale Member of the Ohio Shale in northeastern Ohio.

Rusophycus, an ichnogenus described in the section on Ordovician ichnofossils, also is found in Devonian rocks in Ohio. It is fairly abundant in Upper Devonian rocks of the state. Most of the Ordovician forms of this ichnofossil appear to be the work of trilobites, but that is not true for Late Devonian forms, such as those found in the Chagrin Shale Member of the Ohio Shale of northeastern Ohio (figs. 25-7.1, 25-7.2). There is no evidence of trilobites in these Upper Devonian rocks, so it is likely that the *Rusophycus* and *Rusophycus*-like ichnofossils were made by arthropods other than trilobites.

Skolithos Haldeman (figs. 25-6.4, 25-6.5) is a vertical, unbranched tube, generally ranging from 1 to 15 mm in width. In side view it is cylindrical; in top or bottom view it is typically subcircular. *Skolithos* typically occurs in closely spaced groups. *Skolithos* is commonly confused with *Trypanites* (see fig. 25-3), but *Skolithos* formed as burrows in soft sediment, and *Trypanites* represents a boring into a hard substrate. *Skolithos* is found in the Chagrin Shale Member of the Ohio Shale. *Skolithos* or *Skolithos*-like ichnofossils also have been reported from the Ordovician rocks of the Cincinnati area and the Mississippian Logan Formation.

Large, three-dimensional burrow systems that have Y-shaped burrow junctions can be found in the Chagrin Shale Member of the Ohio Shale (fig. 25-6.7). These burrows may be the ichnofossil *Thalassinoides* Ehrenberg, which is a system of branching horizontal burrows. The burrows of this ichnofossil range in width from about 1 cm to 20 cm. *Thalassinoides* commonly has swellings along the burrows. *Thalassinoides* or *Thalassinoides*-like traces also can be found in Devonian and Mississippian rocks of Ohio, and may occur in older rocks as well. Most *Thalassinoides* ichnofossils were probably made by crustaceans.

Zoophycos Massalongo (fig. 25-7.3) is composed of a large (more than 2 cm in diameter, commonly 10 cm or more), spiraling coil of spreiten surrounded by a tube. The tube is seldom as well preserved as the tubes of forms such as *Rhizocorallium* (fig. 25-7.5). *Zoophycos* commonly resembles the tail of a rooster. In some occurrences, entire bedding planes in the Chagrin Shale Member of the Ohio Shale are covered with this trace. *Zoophycos* also can be found in Ordovician, Mississippian (fig. 25-8.6), and Pennsylvanian rocks of Ohio. *Zoophycos* was probably made by a soft-bodied, wormlike, sediment-feeding animal.

A similar but less common ichnofossil, *Spirophyton* Hall, lacks a marginal tube and is commonly smaller (10 cm in maximum width, but typically less) than *Zoophycos*. However, most specimens referred to as *Spirophyton* in older references to Ohio geology are probably specimens that would now be classified in the genus *Zoophycos*.

The boring *Trypanites*, which is described in the section on Ordovician ichnofossils, also is found in Middle Devonian rocks. *Bifungites* and *Scalarituba*, which are described in the section on Mississippian and Pennsylvanian ichnofossils, also are found in Devonian rocks.

MISSISSIPPIAN AND PENNSYLVANIAN ICHNOFOSSILS

Many of the ichnofossils found in older rocks in Ohio also can be found in the Mississippian and Pennsylvanian rocks of Ohio. In addition, forms not found in older rocks, such as *Psammichnites* and the footprints of tetrapods, can be found in these upper Paleozoic rocks.

Bifungites Desio (fig. 25-8.1) is a dumbbell-shaped to double-arrow-shaped ichnofossil that is commonly found in positive relief on the base of a bed. Well-preserved specimens show it to be a U-shaped burrow without spreiten between its vertical arms. *Bifungites* can be confused with *Diplocraterion* (figs. 25-2.2, 25-2.3) and another similar ichnofossil, *Arthraria* Billings (not illustrated). All three can appear dumbbell-like. True *Bifungites* specimens, however, have portions of the arms of the U present and there are no spreiten between them. *Bifungites* also may be recognized by the presence of a knob or boss on the lobe or arrowlike terminal portions of the bottom of the ichnofossil. Gutschick and Lamborn (1975) and Fillion and Pickerill (1984) discuss these differences in more detail. *Bifungites* is found in Pennsylvanian rocks. It also is found in Devonian rocks in Ohio.

"*Clionolithes*" (fig. 25-8.5) consists of undulatory, branched or unbranched tubular borings in shells. They are generally about 1 mm or less in diameter and typically have rounded terminal ends. This ichnofossil may be short or long, and slender to thick. Specimens may be sparsely distributed or may occcur thickly intertwined. They are found in brachiopods, snails, and clams. Such borings are very common in certain taxa, for instance the snail *Platyceras*, found in Mississippian rocks of Ohio (see Hyde, 1953). The specimens described as *Clionolithes* Clarke from Ohio (Hyde, 1953) are similar to specimens definitely belonging to that genus, but are smaller. Therefore, the genus is used in quotation marks here.

Diplichnites Dawson (fig. 25-9) is a trackway, typically 1 to 2 cm wide, consisting of two parallel series of ridges or grooves that commonly occur in pairs. This trackway is found in Mississippian rock units such as the Bedford Shale. It is also found in the Ordovician of Ohio (see Osgood, 1970, where it is illustrated under the name *Petalichnus*). *Diplichnites* is the trackway of an arthropod. Most forms are the work of trilobites.

Helminthopsis Heer (fig. 25-8.2) is very simple, small (½ to 1 mm wide and commonly less than 2 cm long), and consists of sinuous to meandering burrows. The color of the sediment infilling of this ichnofossil commonly contrasts with the color of the rock matrix. Weathering may accentuate this difference. These trackways have been known informally as "curly worm tubes." This ichnogenus is abundant in the Mississippian Logan Formation, especially at outcrops in the Hocking County region.

Psammichnites Torell (fig. 25-8.7), formerly known as *Olivellites*, is a distinctive Pennsylvanian ichnofossil. It consists of a convex, curving, commonly sinuous trackway that has a prominent, raised medial (longitudinal) ridge flanked by transverse ridges. *Psammichnites* is generally about 12 to 25 mm wide. Its medial ridge is about 1 to 3 mm wide. *Psammichnites* is found in the rocks of the Pottsville Group in Ohio.

Scalarituba Weller (figs. 25-8.3, 25-8.4), as its name implies, consists of a burrow that has scalelike, irregularly transverse ridges. It is generally curved or sinuous, and its width commonly ranges from 1 to 5 mm. It is much longer than wide. The ridges are irregularly but closely spaced. *Scalarituba* is typically horizontal to subhorizontal in relation to the bedding plane. As with the ichnofossil *Helminthopsis*, with which *Scalarituba* is commonly associated, the color of the sediment filling of *Scalarituba* generally contrasts with the color of the matrix. Weathering may accentuate this difference. *Scalarituba* is abundant in the Mississippian Logan Formation, including various members that outcrop in Hocking County. *Scalarituba* also is found in Upper Devonian rocks. The trace maker was a sediment-ingesting organism, probably a worm.

Zoophycos (fig. 25-8.6), which is described in the section on Devonian ichnofossils, is common in rocks of Mississippian age in Ohio. It is especially abundant in the Meadville, Sharpsville, and Buena Vista Members of the Cuyahoga Formation; it may cover entire bedding planes. *Zoophycos* also may be found in Pennsylvanian rocks.

Other ichnofossils found in the Mississippian and Pennsylvanian of Ohio include *Chondrites* and *Diplocraterion*, which are described under Ordovician ichnofossils; *Planolites*, which is described in the section on Silurian ichnofossils; and *Palaeophycus*, *Rhizocorallium*, *Skolithos*, and *Thalassinoides*, which are described in the section on Devonian ichnofossils.

VERTEBRATE FOOTPRINTS

Footprints of tetrapods are found in rocks of the Allegheny, Conemaugh, and Monongahela Groups, all of Pennsylvanian age, in Morgan, Noble, and Perry Counties in southeastern Ohio. Several genera of such trackways have been described (see, for example, Carman, 1927), but these trackways are more common than one would expect from reading the scientific literature (Donald Baird, personal commun., 1992). Vertebrate trackways are covered in greater detail in Chapter 21 (see figs. 21-17, 21-18).

COLLECTING LOCALITIES

Ordovician ichnofossils are especially common in the Cincinnatian Series and may be found in numerous outcrops of these rocks in southwestern Ohio. A well-known, accessible locality is the emergency spillway in Caesar Creek State Park in Warren County (Shrake, 1992). A permit must be obtained from the U.S. Army Corps of Engineers to collect at this site; permits are available at the Visitor Center. Ordovician traces also may be collected in Hueston Woods State Park in Preble County.

Silurian ichnofossils can be found in exposures of the Osgood Shale, the Brassfield Formation, and the Dayton Formation in south-central Ohio. However, landowner permission must be obtained before collecting.

Ichnofossils are common in portions of the Middle Devonian carbonates and in the Upper Devonian Ohio Shale, particularly in siltstone beds. Ichnofossils can be examined along the many outcrops of the Chagrin Shale Member of the Ohio Shale in various metropolitan parks in northeastern Ohio. However, collecting is not permitted in these parks. Permission must be obtained from landowners before collecting fossils from exposures of the Chagrin Shale Member on private property.

Ichnofossils can be found in many rock units of Mississippian age in Ohio, which crop out in a broad arc from just north of the Youngstown area, passing through the Akron, Newark, and Hocking County areas, and extending southward to the Portsmouth area. The trace fossils *Helminthopsis* and *Scalarituba* may be observed in outcrops of the Logan Formation along the Dining Lodge Road in Hocking Hills State Park. However, collecting is prohibited in this park. Several types of ichnofossils can be found at exposures of the Cuyahoga Formation at Lodi City Park, a well-known fossil locality in the center of Lodi, Medina County. Fossil collecting is not prohibited at Lodi City Park.

The Pennsylvanian rocks of eastern Ohio contain ichnofossils made by both invertebrates and vertebrates. Old, unreclaimed strip mines are generally excellent localities, but, again, permission must be obtained from the property owner before entering these areas.

ACKNOWLEDGMENTS

Information in this chapter was drawn from a number of sources, including unpublished theses by Donald Stukel II (Kent State University, 1987), Eugene J. Murray (Western Michigan University, 1975), and A. Allen Middleman (Ohio University, 1976). A number of specimens used in this study were loaned or donated by Richard Arnold Davis (while at the Cincinnati Museum of Natural History), Mark A. Wilson (College of Wooster), Michael R. Sandy (University of Dayton), and Dale M. Gnidovec (Orton Geological Museum, The Ohio State University). Information on the distribution and other aspects of various ichnofossils was provided by a number of colleagues, including Mark Wilson, Michael Sandy, Roger J. Bain (University of Akron), Donald Baird (Carnegie Museum of Natural History), Robert J. Elias (University of Manitoba), Thomas W. Bjerstedt (U.S. Department of Energy), Christopher G. Maples (Kansas Geological Survey), and Douglas L. Shrake and Gregory A. Schumacher (Ohio Division of Geological Survey). Thanks also are due to Mark Wilson for his review comments. Field assistants in the summer of 1991 were supported in part by the Kirtlandia Society of The Cleveland Museum of Natural History and the Cleveland Education Fund. Most of the photographs used in this chapter were taken by Bruce Frumker and Dan Flocke (The Cleveland Museum of Natural History). Additional photographs were provided by Mark Wilson and Roger Bain.

FIGURE 25-1.—Reconstruction of *Diplocraterion biclavatum* (Miller) showing the U-shaped tube and the spreiten between the arms (from Osgood, 1977). In the upper, cross-sectional view of this two-part diagram, the sparsely stippled area indicates shaly or clayey material, and the densely stippled area indicates siltstone or dense limestone. When the trace fossil penetrates both shaly material and denser material, only the part of the ichnofossil penetrating the denser material (siltstone or dense limestone) would be preserved (bottom view; see also fig. 25-2.3). When the entire trace is in siltstone or a dense carbonate, however, most of the U-tube and the spreiten are preserved (see also fig. 25-2.2).

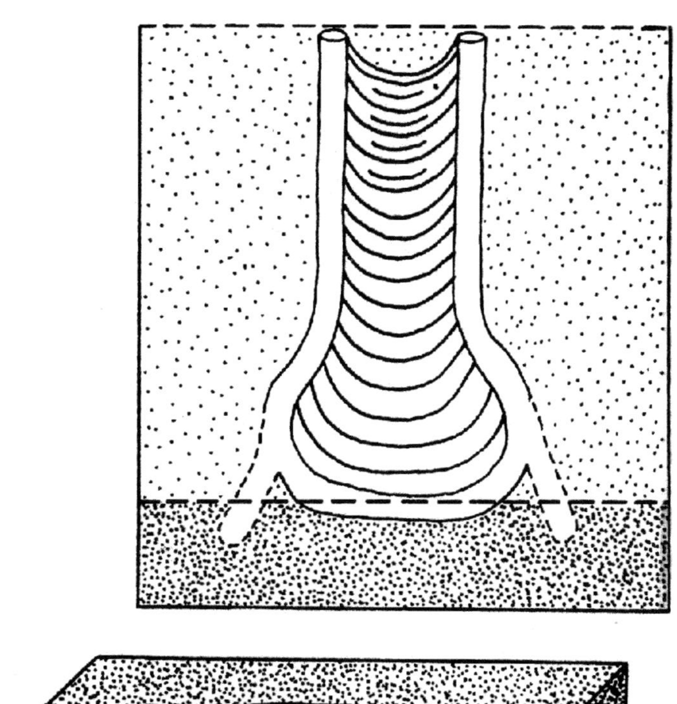

FIGURE 25-2.—Ordovician ichnofossils. Scale bars equal 1 cm.

1	*Chondrites*. A variety that Osgood (1970) designated as Type C. Liberty Formation, emergency spillway, Caesar Creek State Park, Warren County, Ohio; ClMNH 8841.
2, 3	*Diplocraterion biclavatum* Miller. **2**, side view. Kope Formation, Backbone Creek, Clermont County, Ohio; ClMNH 5755. **3**, top view. Upper surface of a limestone bed from the Liberty Formation, emergency spillway, Caesar Creek State Park, Warren County, Ohio; ClMNH 8842. The circumstances leading to the mode of preservation of these specimens are similar to those illustrated in figure 25-1.

1

2

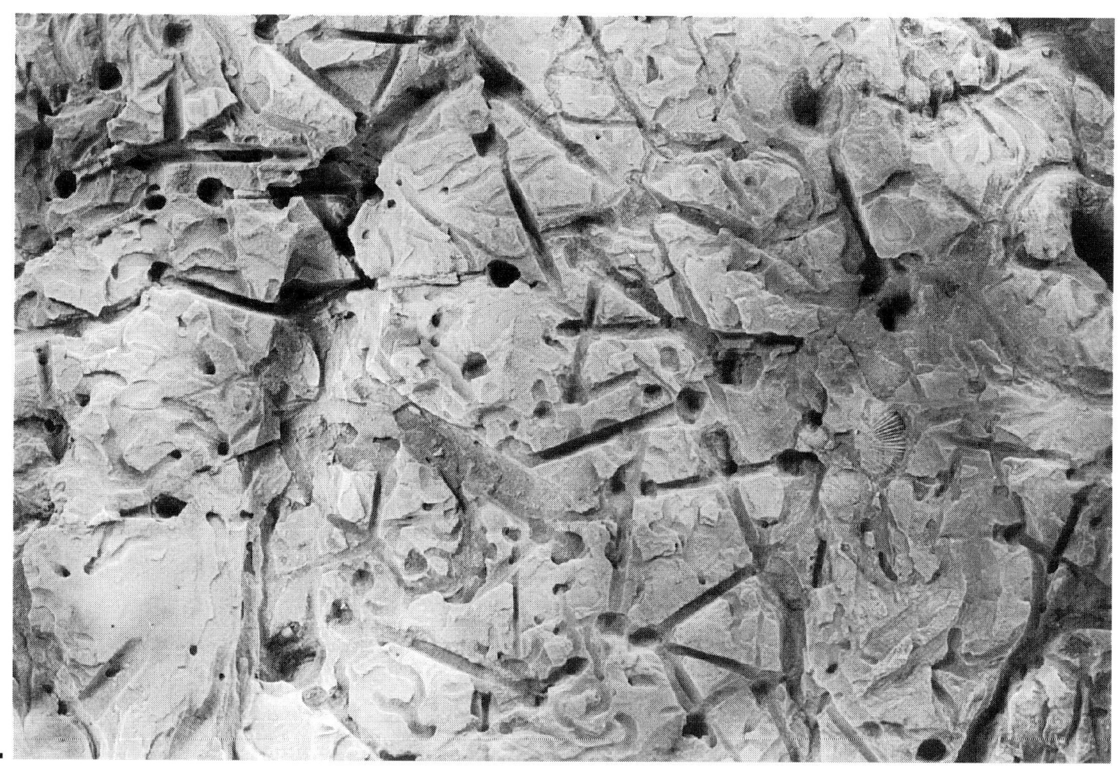
3

FIGURE 25-3.—Ordovician borings. Scale bars for figures 25-3.1 to 25-3.3 equal 1 cm; scale in figure 25-3.4 is in centimeters.

1-3 *Trypanites weisei* (Mägdefrau). Circular or elongate borings. **1**, **2**, in the coral *Grewingkia*. The circular *Trypanites* are bored directly into the coral; the elongate *Trypanites* are preserved as grooves along the wall of the coral. These borings can occur in great numbers (**2**). Liberty or Whitewater Formation, emergency spillway, Caesar Creek State Park, Warren County, Ohio; ClMNH 8843 (**1**) and ClMNH 8844 (**2**). **3**, in a hardground. Note that some of these borings pass through a brachiopod as well as the carbonate hardground. Liberty Formation, Oliver Township, Adams County, Ohio; CW 43.

4 *Petroxestes pera* Wilson & Palmer (elongate borings) and *Trypanites* (circular borings). Bull Fork Formation (equivalent to Arnheim through Whitewater Formations), near Manchester, Adams County, Ohio; CW 17. Photograph courtesy of Mark A. Wilson, reproduced from Wilson and Palmer (1988) with permission.

CENTIMETER

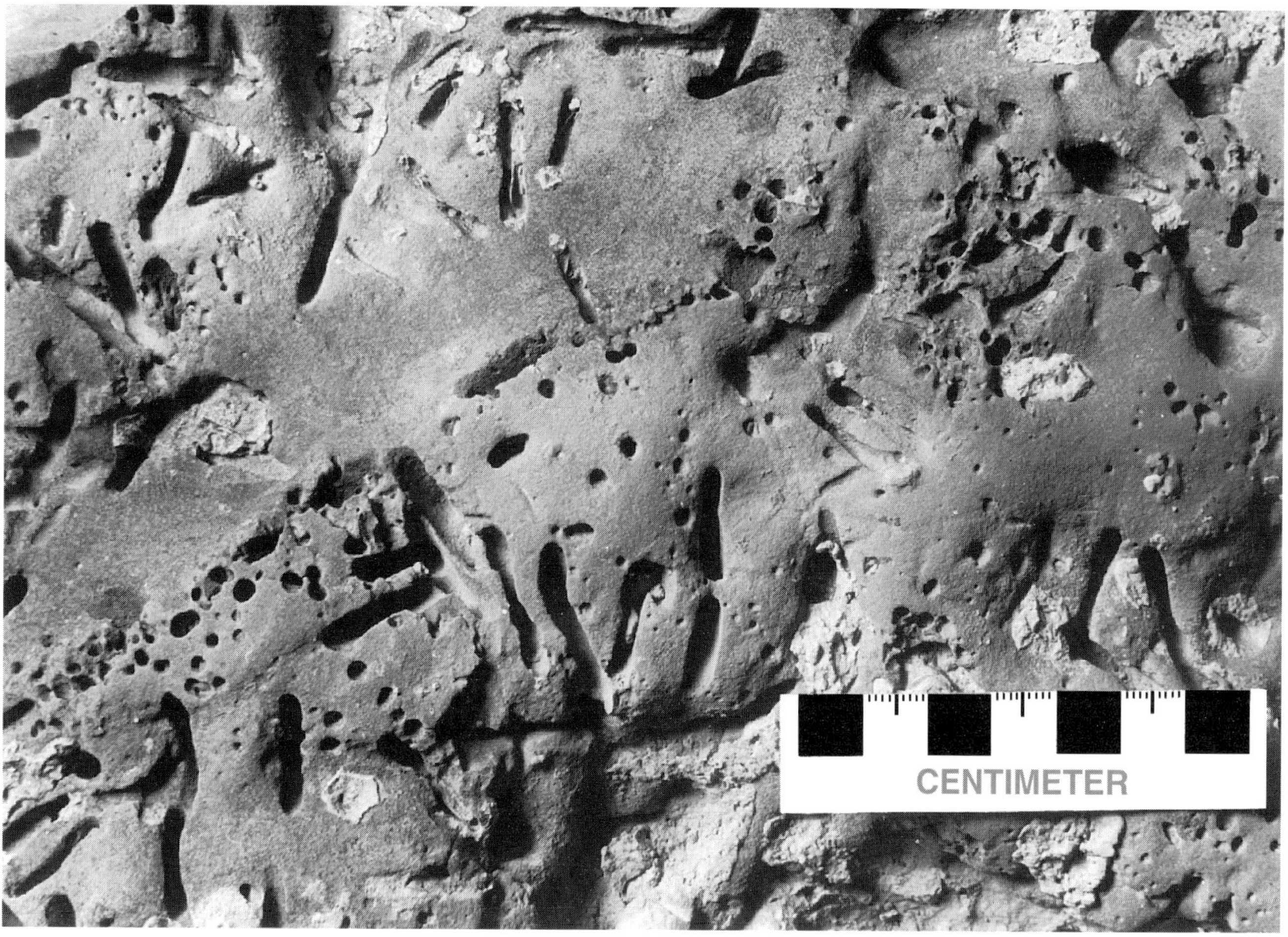

4

FIGURE 25-4.—Ordovician and Silurian ichnofossils. Scale bars equal 1 cm.

1, 3 *Rusophycus pudicum* Hall. **1**, close-up view of one specimen among a group of *R. pudicum* on the base of a limestone slab, illustrated in **3**. This specimen is toward the bottom right of the slab. An impression made by a genal spine of a flexicalymenid trilobite is present along the upper left margin of this specimen. These *Rusophycus* may be considered evidence for an Ordovician equivalent of a smorgasbord (Loren Babcock, personal commun., 1992). This slab contains other traces, including thin, slightly curved scratch marks that may have been made by trilobites. Cincinnatian Series (Ordovician), Hamilton County, Ohio; CiMNH P24.

2 *Planolites* ichnosp. (larger, straighter burrows) and *Chondrites* ichnosp. (much smaller burrows between the larger burrows). The *Planolites* burrows average about 1/2 cm in width. Osgood Shale (Silurian), Warren County, Ohio; ClMNH 8845.

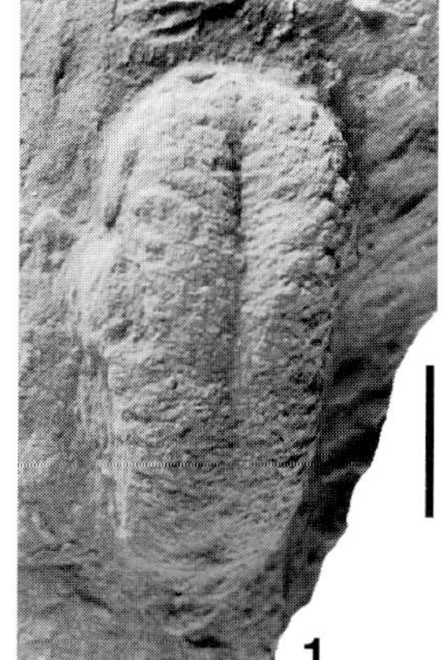

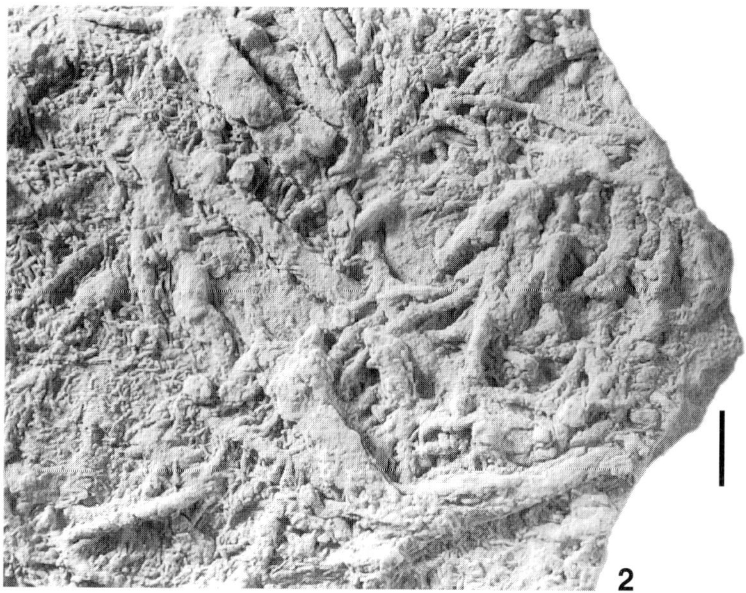

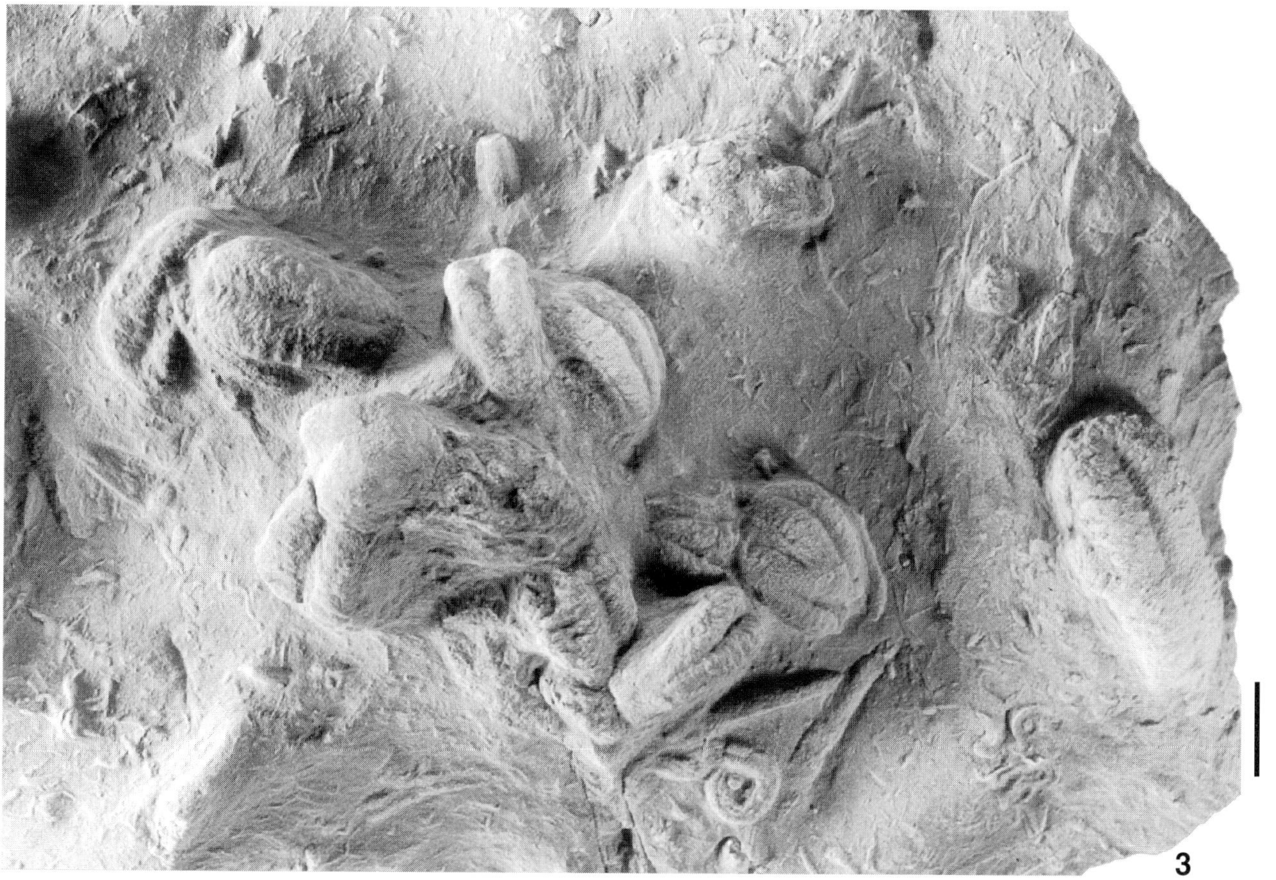

FIGURE 25-5.—Devonian ichnofossils. Scale bars equal 1 cm.

1, 2 — *Chagrinichnites osgoodi* Hannibal & Feldmann. This species was named (Hannibal and Feldmann, 1983) in honor of the late Richard Osgood, Ohio's best known ichnofossil worker. Note the variability of this ichnospecies. **1**, on bottom of a siltstone slab from the Chagrin Shale Member of the Ohio Shale, Cleveland, Ohio; ClMNH (BW 3-241). **2**, Chagrin Shale Member, northeastern Ohio; ClMNH 1347.

3 — *Cochlichnus* ichnosp. On base of a siltstone slab from the Chagrin Shale Member, western Ashtabula County, Ohio; ClMNH 1314.

4 — *Gordia* ichnosp. Chagrin Shale Member, western Lake County, Ohio; ClMNH 8846.

5, 6 — *Lingulichnus verticalis* Hakes. **5**, cross-sectional view. Bottom of a siltstone slab from the Chagrin Shale Member, western Ashtabula County, Ohio; KSU 3090. **6**, top view. Siltstone of the Chagrin Shale Member, north-central Ashtabula County, Ohio; ClMNH 8606.

7 — *Chondrites* ichnosp. View of top and side of a tilted slab of siltstone from the Chagrin Shale Member, Lake County, Ohio; ClMNH 8632. Density of the burrows increases upward.

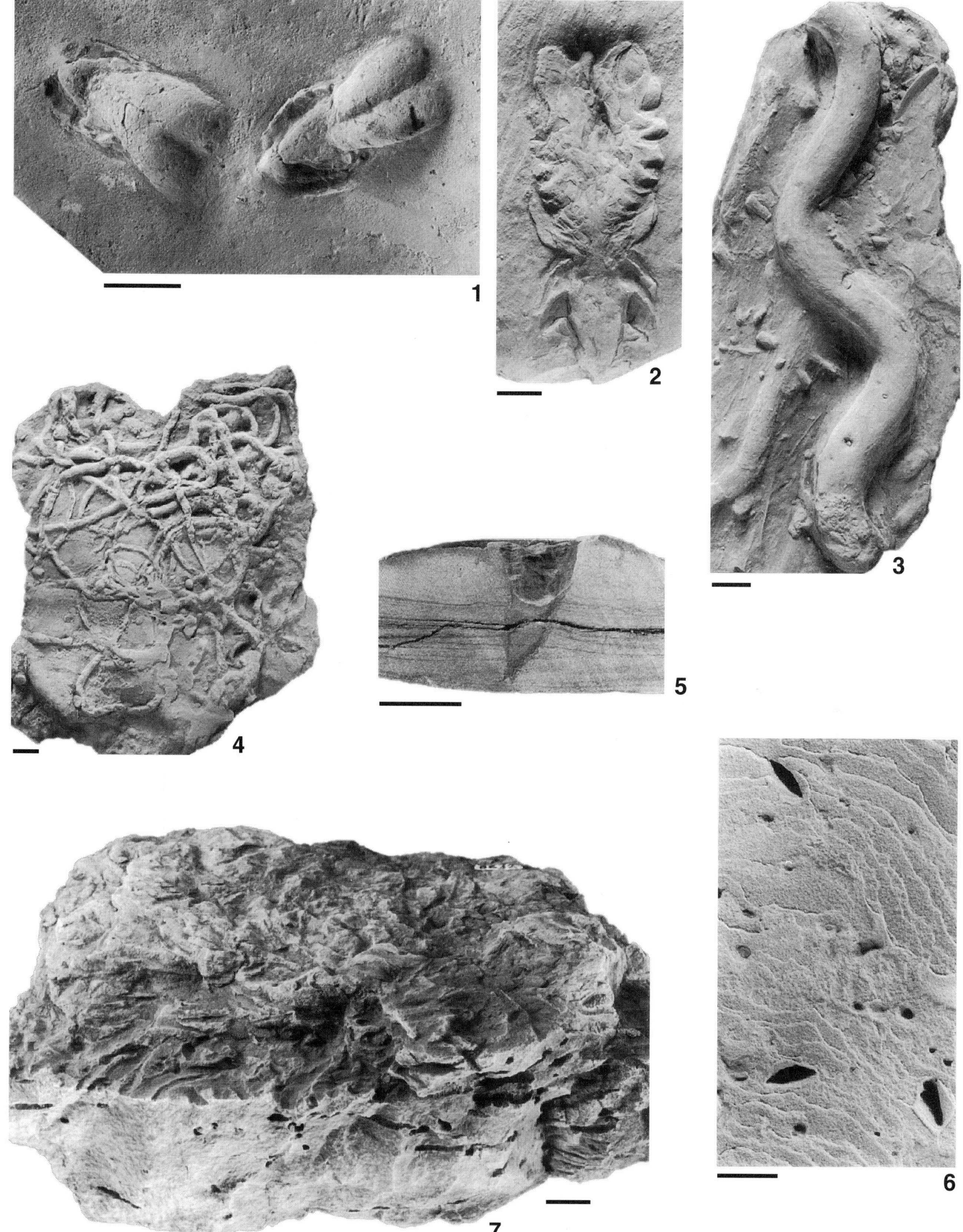
1
2
3
4
5
6
7

FIGURE 25-6.—Tubular and more or less cylindrical Devonian ichnofossils. Scale bars equal 1 cm.

1	*Planolites* and *Palaeophycus*. Most specimens shown are *Planolites*. Chagrin Shale Member of the Ohio Shale, Lake County, Ohio; ClMNH 1315.
2	*Planolites* ichnosp. On base of a siltstone slab from the Chagrin Shale Member, Lake County, Ohio; ClMNH 8158. This ichnofossil closely resembles *Palaeophycus striatus* Hall (not illustrated), but lacks a lining.
3	*Palaeophycus tubularis* Hall. Close-up view of slab in **1**. Note the thickened walls, indicating a burrow lining.
4, 5	*Skolithos linearis* Haldeman. Chagrin Shale Member, Cuyahoga County, Ohio. **4**, cross-sectional view of vertical burrow. Note that this particular specimen passes through siltstone layers with different bedding thicknesses. ClMNH 8848. **5**, three specimens in top view, from a slab of rock adjacent to that shown in **4**. The slab is from the lower layers seen in that figure. ClMNH 8849.
6	*Planolites beverleyensis* (Billings). Especially large (4 cm wide) specimens. These unlined burrows are found as convex forms on the base of limestone beds in the Silica Formation at Silica, Lucas County, Ohio; ClMNH 8847.
7	Complex, *Thalassinoides*-like burrows. Note swelling of midsection of central branch. Chagrin Shale Member, Ashtabula County, Ohio; ClMNH 1307.

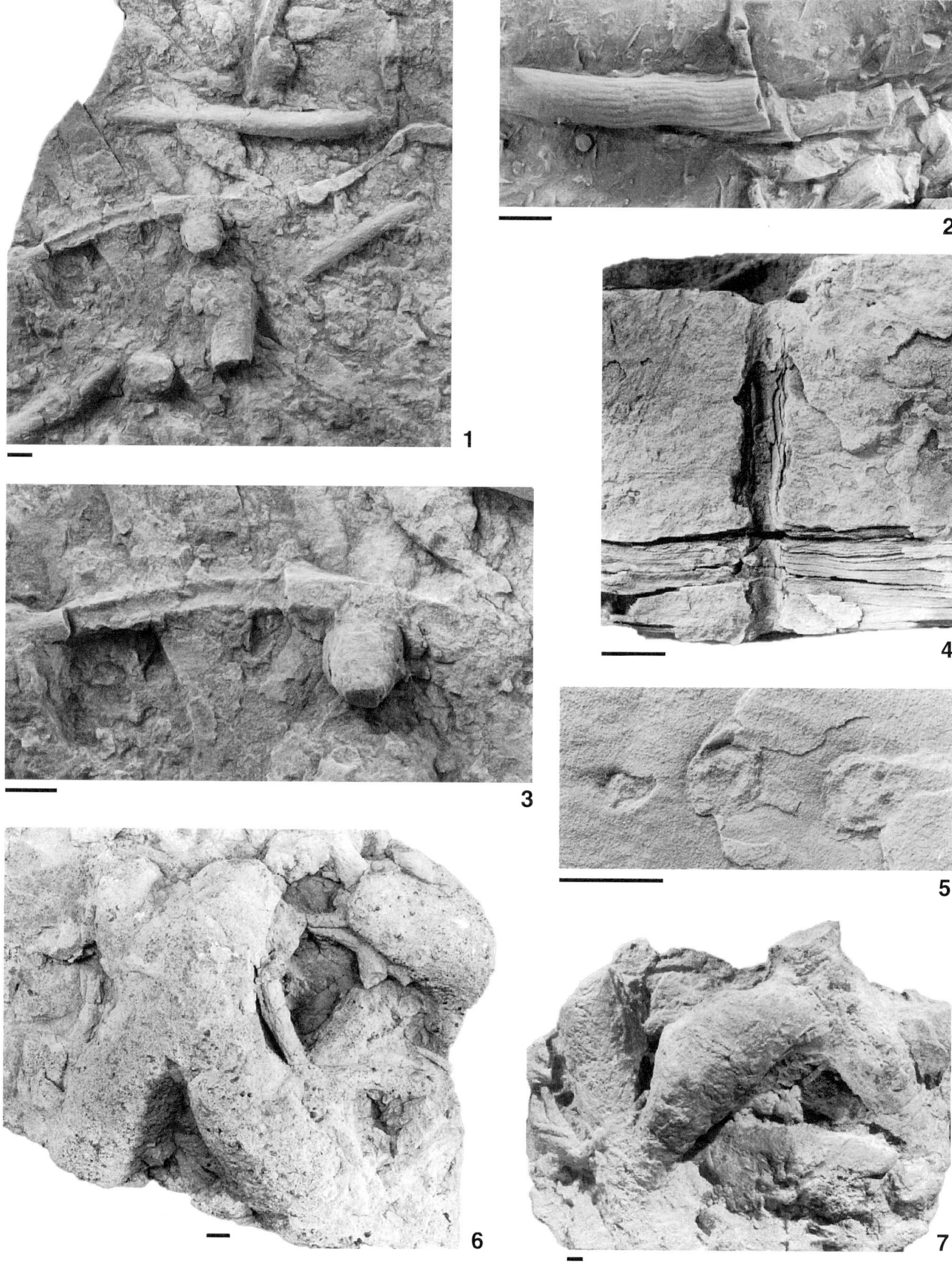
1
2
3
4
5
6
7

FIGURE 25-7.—Devonian ichnofossils. Scale bars equal 1 cm.

1 *Rusophycus* ichnosp. On slab of siltstone from the Chagrin Shale Member of the Ohio Shale, Lake County, Ohio; ClMNH 1390.

2 Trace similar to *Rusophycus*. Note the larger size and less bilobate nature of this form compared to that in **1**. Chagrin Shale Member, north-central Ashtabula County, Ohio; ClMNH 8607.

3 *Zoophycos* ichnosp. Typical group occurrence. Chagrin Shale Member, western Lake County, Ohio; ClMNH 8850.

4 *Cruziana* ichnosp. Note the greater length-to-width ratio of this specimen compared to *Rusophycus*. Chagrin Shale Member, Lake County, Ohio; ClMNH 1740.

5 *Rhizocorallium jenese* Zenker. Slab of siltstone from the Chagrin Shale Member near the Lake-Ashtabula County line; ClMNH 1353.

1

2

3

4

FIGURE 25-8.—Mississippian and Pennsylvanian ichnofossils. Scale bars equal 1 cm.

1	*Bifungites* ichnosp. On base of a slab of Pennsylvanian siltstone, near Girard, Liberty Township, Trumbull County, Ohio; OSU 29710. Note bosses (knobs) in center of each of the arrow-shaped portions of the trace.
2	*Helminthopsis* ichnosp. Byer Member of the Logan Formation (Mississippian), Dining Lodge Road, Hocking Hills State Park, Hocking County, Ohio; ClMNH 8851.
3, 4	*Scalarituba missouriensis* Weller. Large, tube-shaped traces. Same unit and locality as **2**. ClMNH 8852 (**3**) and ClMNH 8853 (**4**).
5	"*Clionolithes*" *implicatus* Hyde, **holotype**. The "*Clionolithes*" were bored into a specimen of the snail *Platyceras*. The shell material, however, has been lost; only the borings and a mold of the outer surface of the shell remain. Byer Sandstone Member of the Logan Formation (Mississippian), Sciotoville, Scioto County, Ohio; OSU 12598 (H-710).
6	*Zoophycos* ichnosp. Cuyahoga Formation (Mississippian), southwestern Cuyahoga County, Ohio; ClMNH 7850.
7	*Psammichnites plummeri* (Fenton & Fenton). Two trackways. Uppermost specimen crosses the entire photograph; a shorter specimen is at lower right. Homewood sandstone (Pottsville Group) or an adjacent Pennsylvanian unit, northern Tuscarawas County, Ohio. Photograph by Roger J. Bain, University of Akron.

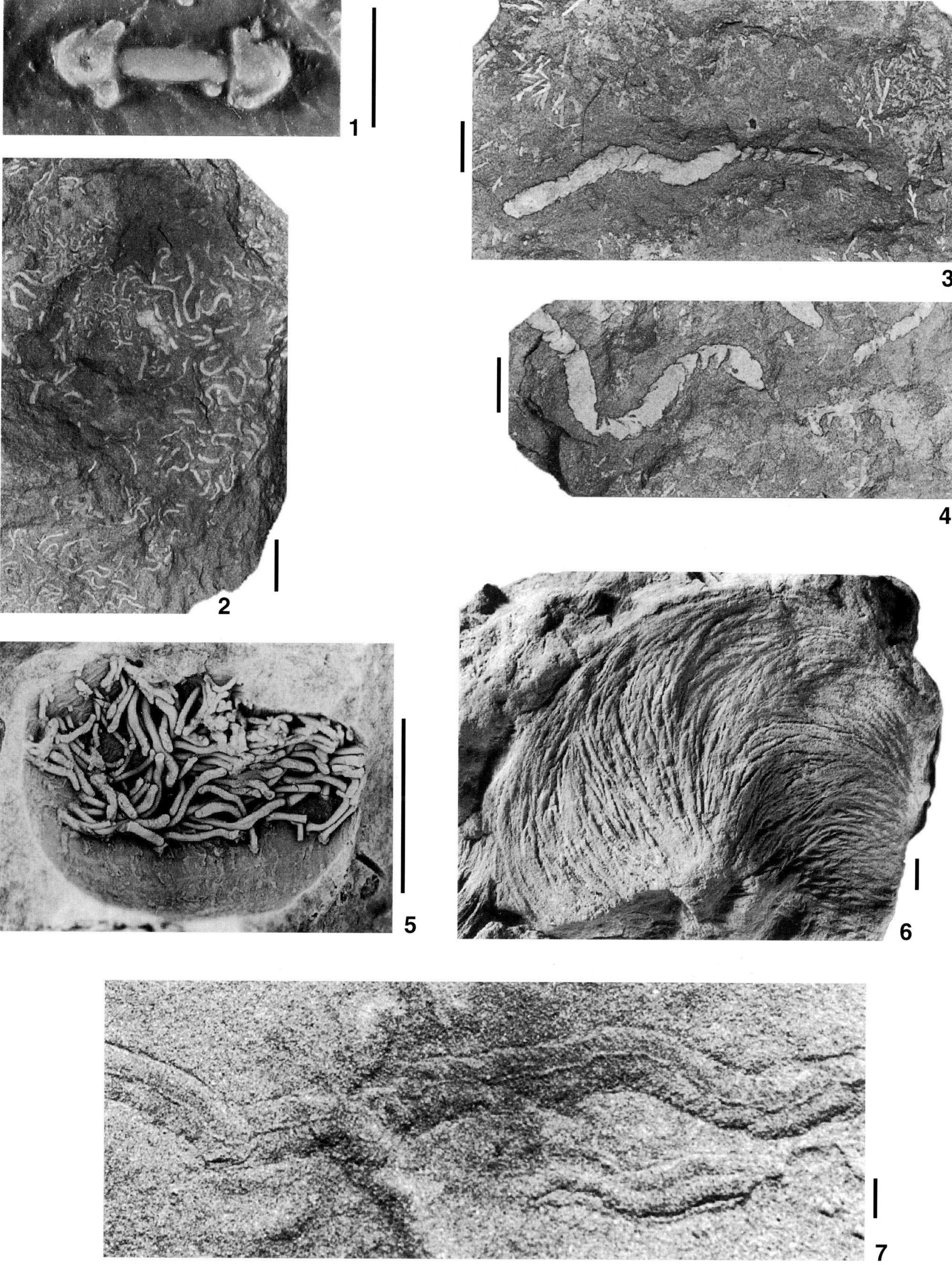
1
2
3
4
5
6
7

FIGURE 25-9.—*Diplichnites*, a Mississippian ichnofossil. Scale bars equal 1 cm.

1 Two sets of trackways, crossing at an angle. This specimen is presumed to be from Mississippian-age rocks of Ohio. ClMNH 8930.

2 Close-up view of trackways in **1**.

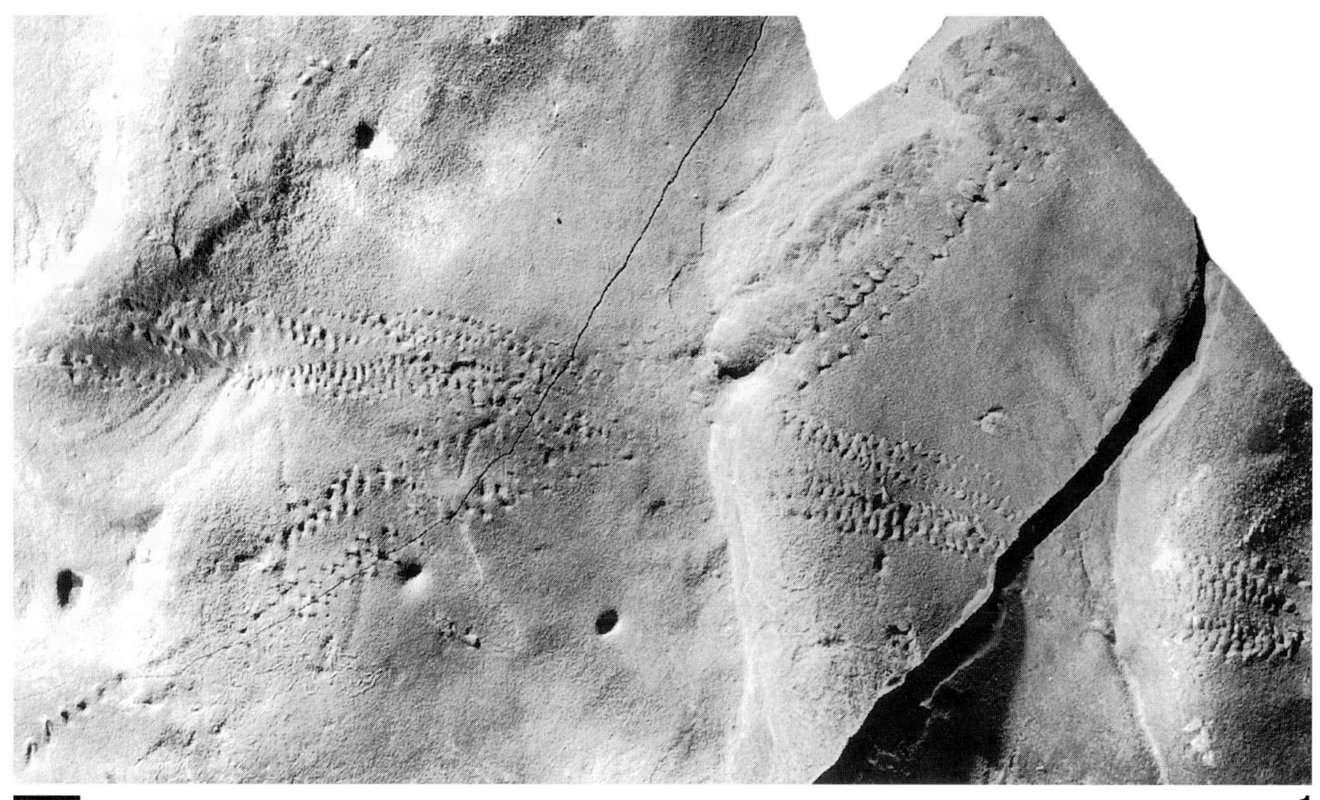

1

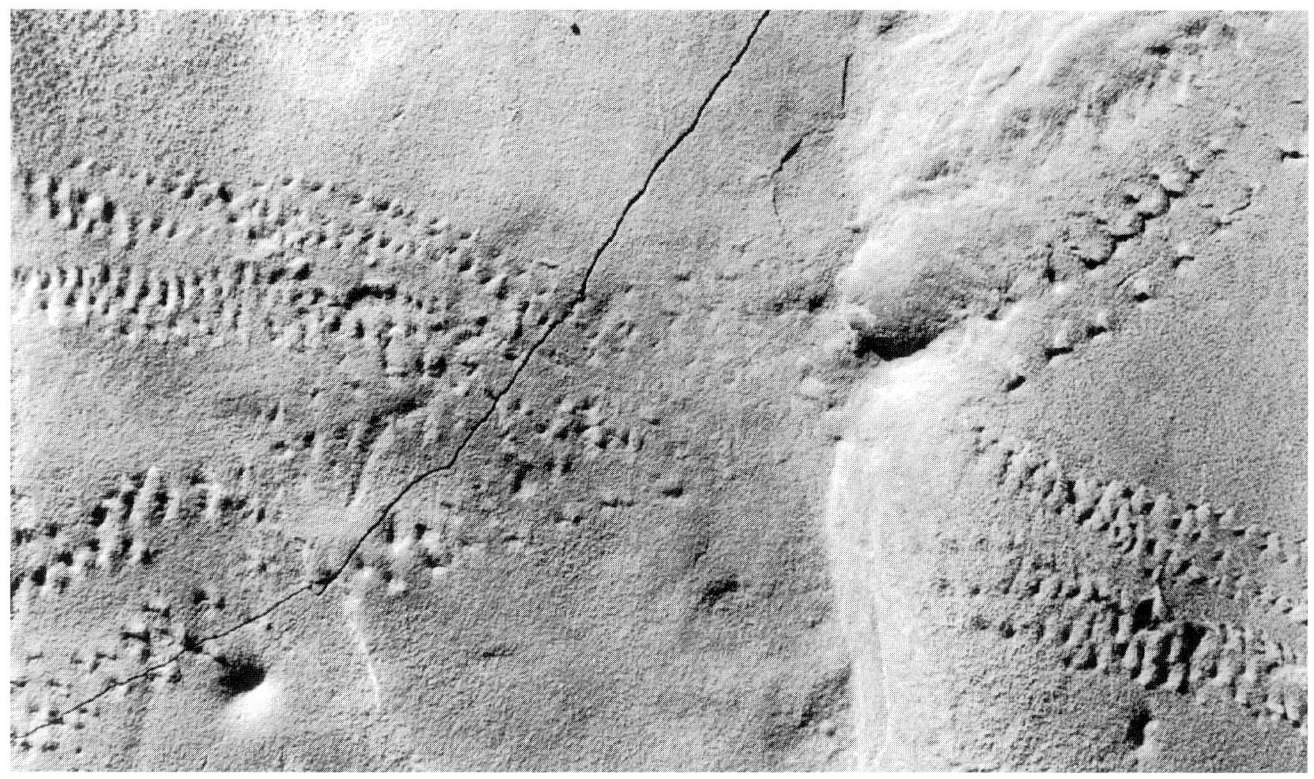

2

Glossary

Terms that are **boldface** in the various chapters of this book are defined here. The groups to which these terms apply are listed in SMALL CAPITALS in brackets following the definition. Some terms are noted as applying to several, many, or all groups; to Ohio geology; or to general geology or general paleontology. Terms within a definition that are defined in the glossary are in **boldface** type. For terms that are not in this glossary, see the *Glossary of geology* (Bates and Jackson, 1987).

abaxial Refers to the portion of a structure facing away from the **axis**; the underside or lower surface of a leaf. [PLANTS]

abdomen The most **posterior** body segment, behind the **thorax** (or cephalothorax). [ARTHROPODA]

aboral cup The lowest plates of the body near the **column**, plates between the **arms** and the column. May consist either of **basal plates** and **radial plates** (**monocyclic**) or **infrabasal plates, basal plates**, and **radial plates** (**dicyclic**). [ECHINODERMATA: CRINOIDEA]

acanthostyle A spinelike structure embedded in the **zooecial** wall between **apertures**. [BRYOZOA]

acetate peel A replica of the surface of a rock or fossil that has been polished and etched with acid. The peel is prepared by pressing an acetate film, the surface of which has been dissolved in acetone, onto the surface of the specimen, allowing it to dry, and removing it for examination. See Chapter 2. [GENERAL PALEONTOLOGY]

acline Refers to the body of a shell that is perpendicular to the **hinge axis**. [PELECYPODA]

adapertural In the direction toward the **aperture**. [GASTROPODA; CEPHALOPODA]

adapical In the direction away from the **aperture**; in an **orthoconic** cephalopod, this direction is toward the **apex** of the shell. [GASTROPODA; CEPHALOPODA]

adaxial Refers to the part of a structure facing toward the **axis**; the upper surface of a leaf. [PLANTS]

adductor muscles A pair of muscles that contract to close the **valves**, observed as scars on the floors of both valves. In a brachiopod, the adductor muscle scars commonly are inside the **diductor muscle scars** on the **pedicle valve**. [PELECYPODA; BRACHIOPODA]

adventitious roots Roots that arise from the stem above the level of the soil surface. [PLANTS]

aff. Abbreviation for Latin term "affinis," meaning "related to." Used in biological nomenclature to indicate a specimen that appears to be a certain species, but cannot be identified with certainty. [ALL GROUPS]

algae (singular = **alga**; adjective = **algal**) An informal term referring to relatively simple (unicellular, **colonial**, or simple multicellular) aquatic, photosynthetic organisms belonging to several kingdoms and divisions. [PLANTS]

alternate Refers to the arrangement of leaves or other structures singly along the length of a branch or axis, in contrast to **opposite** or **whorled** arrangments. [PLANTS]

alveolus (plural = **alveoli**; adjective = **alveolar**) A small pit **anterior** to the **cardinal process** in some brachiopods. [BRACHIOPODA]

ambulacra (singular = **ambulacrum**; adjective = **ambulacral**) The areas along the **rays** of an echinoderm where the water-vascular soft tissue is or was present. In the Crinoidea, Asteroidea, and Ophiuroidea, the ambulacra are elevated above the main body in **arms**. In the Blastoidea, Echinoidea, Rhombifera, Diplopora, and Edrioasteroidea, the ambulacra are directly plated into the body wall of the **theca**. [ECHINODERMATA]

ammonite In general, an **ammonoid** cephalopod that has **ammonitic sutures**; more precisely, a member of the ammonoid suborder Ammonitina. See discussion under **ammonoid.** [CEPHALOPODA]

ammonitic Refers to an **ammonoid suture** in which both the main **lobes** and the main **saddles** are subdivided into smaller lobes and saddles. Also see **ceratitic** and **goniatitic**. [CEPHALOPODA]

ammonoid A member of the cephalopod subclass Ammonoidea. Some people incorrectly use the term "**ammonite**" as a synonym for "ammonoid." In a general sense, an ammonite is any ammonoid cephalopod that has ammonitic sutures; more precisely, an ammonite is a member of the ammonoid order Ammonitida. None of the ammonoids reported from Ohio in this volume is an ammonite in either sense of the word. [CEPHALOPODA]

amniote A vertebrate that reproduces by means of a shell-covered egg. Includes all **tetrapods** except amphibians. [VERTEBRATES]

anaerobic Refers to environmental conditions in which free oxygen is absent. [GENERAL GEOLOGY]

anal sac On an inadunate crinoid, a structure that is plated into the **CD** (**posterior**) **interray**. It may be small and inconspicuous or large and elaborate. The anal opening is on the terminus or on the side of the anal sac, but the anal sac may have served functions in addition to waste disposal. [ECHINODERMATA: CRINOIDEA]

anal tube On a camerate crinoid, a short to long tubular structure that is plated into the **tegmen**. The anal opening is commonly at the terminus of the anal tube, and its principal function may have been for waste disposal. [ECHINODERMATA: CRINOIDEA]

anaptychus A single plate that may be found in the **body chamber** of an **ammonoid** cephalopod; it may have served to block the **aperture** of the shell of the living animal, or it may have been the lower jaw of the animal. [CEPHALOPODA]

anastomosing (verb = **anastomose**) Branching and rejoining to form a network. In a bryozoan, refers to the netlike or **reticulate** form of a branching **colony**; also called **cribrate**. In a plant, refers to the network (reticulum) formed by cross-veins. [SEVERAL GROUPS]

angiosperm A seed plant that has true flowers and seeds that are enclosed in an ovary. [PLANTS]

angulate Refers to a **pectiniform element** that is arched, comb shaped, and has two main branches (examples: *Ozarkodina, Plectodina*). [CONODONTA]

anguliplanate Refers to an **angulate pectiniform element** that has platformlike lateral extensions and a flattened attachment surface under the platform (example: *Polygnathus*). [CONODONTA]

anguliscaphate Refers to an **angulate pectiniform element** that has platformlike lateral extensions and a scoop-shaped attachment surface under the platform (examples: *Idiognathodus, Streptognathodus*). [CONODONTA]

annulation (adjective = **annulate**) A strong ridge or **plication** in a shell that extends across the shell at a right angle to the length, or nearly so. [PELECYPODA; CEPHALOPODA]

annulet A small transverse ring between larger rings on the surface of the **conch**. [TENTACULITOIDS]

anoxic See **anaerobic**.

antenna (plural = **antennae**) A multijointed sensory appendage attached to the front, **ventral** part of the **cephalon**. [TRILOBITA]

anterior In most animals, toward the head or the forward direction in which the mouth faces. In an ostracode, the front of the **carapace**. In a brachiopod, the direction away from the **pedicle** and toward the **valve** opening. [MANY GROUPS]

AP Abbreviation for **A**rboreal **P**ollen, the pollen of woody trees and larger shrubs. [PLANTS]

apertural lip The margin or edge of the **aperture**. [GASTROPODA]

aperture (adjective = **apertural**) An opening. In a conulariid or a tentaculitoid, the widest end of the **exoskeleton**. In a gastropod or cephalopod, the shell opening from which head and other organs are extended or withdrawn. In a plant, an opening in a wall or other structure. [MANY GROUPS]

apex (adjective = **apical**) The beginning point of **exoskeleton** formation of many invertebrates. In a conulariid, the narrowest termination of the exoskeleton, where the four **faces** meet at a closed point. In a cone-shaped gastropod or an **orthoconic** cephalopod, the point of the shell. In a brachiopod, the tip of the **beak**. In a plant, the tip of a stem or the most distal extension of a leaf or other structure. [MANY GROUPS]

aphlebia (plural = **aphlebiae**) A conspicuous leaflike **bract** at the base (point of attachment) of the **rachis** of a fern or fernlike leaf. [PLANTS]

apical wall The broadly rounded internal wall or partition of the **exoskeleton** that lacks **rods**; located in the apical region of the exoskeleton. [CONULARIIDA]

apodeme A small knob or inbent process of the **exoskeleton**, for attachment of muscles or ligaments. [TRILOBITA]

apparatus The entire group of **elements** making up the mineralized skeleton of a conodont. [CONODONTA]

aptychus One of a pair of plates that may be found in the **aperture** of an **ammonoid** cephalopod that, together, are believed to have served to block the aperture when the animal was alive. [CEPHALOPODA]

arborescent Treelike in size, form, and aspect. [PLANTS]

arm An appendage used for feeding, locomotion, and swimming. [ECHINODERMATA: CRINOIDEA, ASTEROIDEA, OPHIUROIDEA]

arm facet The surface on which a **free arm** articulates to the **aboral cup** or **calyx**. If articulated to an **aboral cup**, the arm facet is on the radial plate; if articulated to a **calyx**, the arm facet is on a **fixed brachial**. [ECHINODERMATA: CRINOIDEA]

articular facet The surface on a plate that is in contact with an adjacent plate. [ECHINODERMATA]

articulate Refers to one of two brachiopod classes, the Articulata, which is characterized by a **tooth** and **socket** arrangement along a **hinge line** or **hinge axis** and a shell of **calcareous** composition. [BRACHIOPODA]

articulating half-ring The **anterior** extension of an **axial ring**; bends downward anteriorly to pass under the **posterior** edge of the preceding segment. [TRILOBITA]

astrorhizae (singular = **astrorhiza**) A group of radiating, branching grooves, commonly centering on a **mamelon**. [STROMATOPOROIDS]

auricle (adjective = **auricular**, **auriculate**) In a pelecypod, an earlike extension along the **dorsal** margin of the shell. In a plant, a basal or lateral, **bilaterally symmetrical**, earlike lobe or appendage at the base of a leaf. [PELECYPODA; PLANTS]

axial furrow The groove separating the axial region of the **cephalon**, **thorax**, and **pygidium** from a **pleural lobe**. [TRILOBITA]

axial lobe The raised medial region of the **dorsal exoskeleton**; outlined by **axial furrows**. [TRILOBITA]

axial ring The medial portion of a **thoracic segment** or the **pygidium**. [TRILOBITA]

axial structure A collective term for various longitudinal structures, including the **columella**, in the **axial** region of a **corallum**. [CNIDARIA]

axial zone The central zone of a branching **colony**, made up of elongate, thin-walled, polygonal **zooecia**. Also called the endozone. [BRYOZOA]

axil The angle formed by two plant parts, such as a **petiole** with a stem. [PLANTS]

axis (adjective = **axial**) In a coral, the central region of a **corallum**. In a trilobite, the **axial lobe**. [CNIDARIA; TRILOBITA]

basal disk The fleshy part of a coral **polyp**; located on the side opposite the mouth and typically subcircular in outline. [CNIDARIA]

basal plate In a coral, the thin, initially secreted part of the **exoskeleton** from which **septa** begin to be built upward. In a crinoid **aboral cup**, one of the plates immediately below the **radial plates**. In a **monocyclic** crinoid the basal plates articulate to the **column**; in a **dicyclic** crinoid the basal plates are between the radial plates and the **infrabasal plates**. In a blastoid, the basal plates are the lowest plates of the **theca** that articulate with the **column**. [CNIDARIA; ECHINODERMATA: CRINOIDEA, BLASTOIDEA]

base The part of a conodont **element** that includes the attachment pit or surface. [CONODONTA]

beak In a rostroconch or pelecypod, the noselike angle of shell extended above the **hinge line** where growth begins. In an **ammonoid** cephalopod, part of the mouth apparatus. In a brachiopod, the **posterior** pointed or rounded region of a **valve** where growth begins. [SEVERAL GROUPS]

benthic (noun = **benthos**) Refers to an organism that lives on or is attached to the bottom or to other objects on the bottom of a body of water. [MANY GROUPS]

bicarinate Having two **carinae**. [CEPHALOPODA]

biconvex Refers to a **profile** view in which both **valves** are curved or convex. [BRACHIOPODA]

bifoliate Refers to an erect **colony** that has a vertical wall separating **zooids**, which face outward in both directions away from the central wall. [BRYOZOA]

bifurcation (adjective = **bifurcated**) The more or less equal branching of a leaf vein. [PLANTS]

bilateral symmetry A characteristic in which the plane of symmetry of an organism or a part(s) of an organism is divided into two halves that are essentially mirror images of each other. [MANY GROUPS]

biome A large-scale regional terrestrial vegetational assemblage, controlled by climate, which can be recognized on the basis of similarity in growth forms, vegetation structure, and seasonal response to climate; examples: tundra, boreal forest (taiga), temperate deciduous forest, tropical rain forest. [PLANTS]

biramous Refers to an appendage that is two branched beyond the **coxa**; the branches are the **exite** (**dorsal**) and the **telepod** (**ventral**). [TRILOBITA]

biserial In a crinoid, refers to **arms** in which the main arm is composed of a double row of **brachials**. In a graptolite, refers to a **rhabdosome** that has two rows of **thecae**. [ECHINODERMATA: CRINOIDEA; GRAPTOLITHINA]

bisporangiate Refers to a reproductive structure that produces both **microsporangia** and **megasporangia**. [PLANTS]

blue-green algae Photosynthetic, plantlike organisms of the division Cyanobacteria in the kingdom Monera, characterized by small cells that have a simple organization; growth forms range from unicellular to simple **colonies** (aggregates, filaments, sheets). [PLANTS]

body chamber See **living chamber**.

body fossil A fossil that preserves the actual remains of an organism or direct evidence of its existence, as opposed to an **ichnofossil**. [ALL GROUPS]

bog A general term for a range of freshwater habitats characterized by waterlogged, spongy ground in which relatively pure **peat** accumulates. In Ohio, bogs typically represent the intermediate successional stages in the history of ponds and small lakes formed as a result of glacial activity. Also see **fen**, **marsh**, **swamp**. [PLANTS]

bordered pit A slitlike, oval or circular opening or perforation in the **tracheid** wall characterized by a thickened border or annular ring. [PLANTS]

B.P. Abbreviation for **B**efore **P**resent; a term used to designate **radiocarbon** dates in a manner that avoids the ambiguity and social sensitivity associated with historical divisions in the civil calendar (B.C., B.C.E., A.D., C.E., etc.). Although the term may be used with older dates based on other approaches to radiometric dating, the error range in dating typically exceeds any ambiguity introduced by historically based calendar practices. [GENERAL GEOLOGY]

brachial An individual plate in an **arm**. [ECHINODERMATA: CRINOIDEA]

brachial ridges Narrow, looplike elevations of shell material extending laterally from the **brachial-valve adductor-muscle** field in some **articulate** brachiopods. [BRACHIOPODA]

brachial valve The **valve** to which the **lophophore** is attached, as well as the lophophore support (**brachidium**), if any; also the valve bearing the **sockets**. The brachial valve commonly is smaller than **pedicle valve**. Also called the dorsal valve. [BRACHIOPODA]

brachidium (plural = **brachidia**) A hard or **calcareous** internal **lophophore** support, commonly resembling a loop or spires, which attaches to the **posterior** part of the **brachial-valve** interior. [BRACHIOPODA]

brachiole A small, erect, food-gathering appendage on the **ambulacral** area of some echinoderms. [ECHINODERMATA: BLASTOIDEA, RHOMBIFERA]

brackish Refers to water that is intermediate in salt content between fresh water and sea water; typically present where rivers empty into the ocean, particularly in estuaries, and in coastal freshwater swamps that are subject to marine incursion as a result of tides or storm surges. [GENERAL GEOLOGY]

bract A modified leaflike structure, generally smaller or of different shape than other leaves. [PLANTS]

breviconic (**brevicone**) Refers to an **orthoconic** or **cyrtoconic** cephalopod in which the **conch** is short and stout. [CEPHALOPODA]

breviseptum A **median septum** in the **brachial-valve** interior that does not extend **posteriorly** to fuse with the **cardinal process**. [BRACHIOPODA]

bulb A prominent, hemispheroidal or elongate raised bump that may project above the **hinge** line of the **valve**. [OSTRACODA]

calcareous Refers to a substance composed of or containing calcium carbonate ($CaCO_3$), or an organism (such as calcareous algae) that secretes calcium carbonate. [GENERAL GEOLOGY]

calcified (noun = **calcification**) Refers to wood or other material **permineralized** by calcium carbonate ($CaCO_3$). [PLANTS]

calice The upper surface of a **corallite**; it is generally bowl shaped. [CNIDARIA]

calyx (plural = **calyces**) The portion of the **crown** between the **column** and the position where **free arms** begin. If the **free arms** begin on **radial plates**, the calyx equals the **aboral cup**; if the **free arms** become free at a position above the **radials**, the calyx equals the **aboral cup**, the **fixed brachials**, and typically the **interradial plates**. [ECHINODERMATA: CRINOIDEA]

camera (plural = **camerae**, adjective = **cameral**) The space inside the shell of a cephalopod or tentaculitoid between any two **septa**. [CEPHALOPODA; TENTACULITOIDS]

cameral deposits Calcium carbonate material produced within **camerae** by some **nautiloid** cephalopods. [CEPHALOPODA]

carapace In an ostracode, the complete skeleton, including both hinged **valves**. In some crustaceans, the covering of the top and commonly also the sides of the head and **thoracic** regions. [OSTRACODA; OTHER ARTHROPODA]

carbonization (adjective = **carbonized**) The removal of volatile organic material, typically from plant remains, resulting in a film of carbonaceous (coaly) material. [GENERAL GEOLOGY]

cardinal area The area that includes, and is immediately adjacent to, the **cardinal septum**. [CNIDARIA]

cardinal extremities Lateral terminations of the **posterior** margin. [BRACHIOPODA]

cardinal fossula The relatively prominent space developed in the position of the **cardinal septum**. [CNIDARIA]

cardinal process A blade or knobs of shell material located in the middle of the **posterior** end of the **brachial-valve** interior; used for **diductor-muscle** attachment. [BRACHIOPODA]

cardinal septum One of the first-formed **septa**, in the plane of **bilateral symmetry** of the **corallite**; distinguished from other first-formed septa by the presence of major septa adjacent to it on both sides. [CNIDARIA]

cardinal side The side of a coral where the **cardinal septum** is present. [CNIDARIA]

carina (plural = **carinae**; adjective = **carinate**) In a conulariid, an internal thickening that extends the length of a **face**, along the **midline**. In a coral, a keel-like ridge on a **septum**. In an ostracode, a well-defined, narrow, projecting ridge on the lateral surface of the **valves**. In a chitinozoan, a flared, netlike skirt at the base. [SEVERAL GROUPS]

carminate Refers to a comblike, unarched, **pectiniform element** that has two main branches (examples: *Hindeodus*, *Ozarkodina*); one branch is represented in some conodonts, such as *Hindeodus*, by a sharp edge along one side of the main **denticle**, which may not bear denticles at all stages of development. [CONODONTA]

carminiscaphate Refers to a **carminate pectiniform element** that has lateral, platformlike extensions and a scoop-shaped attachment surface under the platform (examples: *Cavusgnathus*, *Gnathodus*, *Neognathodus*). [CONODONTA]

cartilaginous Refers to skeletal material that is not hardened into bone; especially common in sharks and rays. [VERTEBRATES]

cast A three-dimensional replica of the external form of an object, such as a fossil shell or tree trunk, created by the infilling of a natural cavity (**mold**) in sediments formed by the decay or dissolution of the original object after burial. [ALL GROUPS]

CD interray The **posterior interray**, which is opposite the A ray when viewed from an oral or aboral perspective. [ECHINODERMATA: CRINOIDEA, BLASTOIDEA]

cephalon (plural = **cephala**; adjective = **cephalic**) The head shield; the **anterior** portion of the **dorsal exoskeleton**. [TRILOBITA]

ceratitic Refers to an **ammonoid suture** in which the main **lobes** are subdivided into smaller lobes and **saddles**, but the main saddles are not subdivided. Also see **ammonitic**, **goniatitic**. [CEPHALOPODA]

cf. Abbreviation for Latin word "confer," which means "compare." Used in **taxonomic nomenclature** to indicate a specimen of uncertain identity should be compared to a specimen of the indicated known species. [ALL GROUPS]

chamber Same as **camera**. [CEPHALOPODA]

cheek A **pleural lobe** of the **cephalon**. [TRILOBITA]

chilidium A triangular plate covering the **apex** of the central opening in the **posterior** margin of the **brachial valve**. [BRACHIOPODA]

chitin A complex celluloselike organic material that forms the **exoskeleton** of some invertebrates, especially arthropods. [SEVERAL GROUPS]

cirrus (plural = **cirri**) An unbranched appendage on the **column** of a stalked echinoderm. [ECHINODERMATA: CRINOIDEA, BLASTOIDEA]

cnidoblast A cell that contains a stinging organ (**nematocyst**). [CNIDARIA]

coal ball A mass of **peat** that has been **permineralized** (typically by calcium or magnesium carbonate) prior to the alteration of the surrounding peat into coal. A coal ball is thus a hard, stony mass embedded in a coal seam and commonly preserves the fine cellular detail of the plant parts making up the original peat deposit. [PLANTS]

coalification The sequence of physical and chemical changes involved in the transformation of **peat** and wood into the various grades of coal. Terms such as **carbonization**, fusinization, and vitrinization may be applied to specific components of the peat or to specific processes or stages that are part of the coalification process. [PLANTS]

coenosteum (plural = **coenostea**) The entire skeleton of a stromatoporoid, or the **exoskeletal** tissue that is deposited between **corallites** in a **colonial** coral. [STROMATOPOROIDS; CNIDARIA]

colony (adjective = **colonial**) A population of physically united, genetically identical individuals. [CNIDARIA; BRYOZOA; GRAPTOLITHINA]

columella In a coral, the **axial structure** formed by a modification of the inner edges of **septa**. In a gastropod, the internal pillar surrounding the axis of coiling. [CNIDARIA; GASTROPODA]

column In a stalked echinoderm, the stem or stalk that elevates the **crown** or **theca** above the sea floor, between the crown or theca and the **holdfast**. Typically composed of individual plates called **columnals**. [ECHINODERMATA: CRINOIDEA, BLASTOIDEA, RHOMBIFERA, DIPLOPORIDA]

columnal An individual plate of the **column** in a stalked echinoderm. [ECHINODERMATA: CRINOIDEA, BLASTOIDEA, RHOMBIFERA, DIPLOPORIDA]

comarginal Refers to any **ornamentation** that more or less parallels the growth margin of the shell. [SEVERAL GROUPS]

commissure The line or junction between the edges or margins of the **valves**. [PELECYPODA; BRACHIOPODA]

composite An **internal mold** that includes both **valves**. [PELECYPODA]

compound Refers to a leaf or **frond** composed of multiple separate, distinct leaflike units that may be variously arranged (**palmate**, **pinnate**, etc). The opposite term is **simple**. [PLANTS]

compressed Refers to a tube of a cephalopod shell in which the cross-sectional shape is taller than wide. [CEPHALOPODA]

compression The remains of a fossil (typically a leaf or other relatively small plant part) that has been flattened by the vertical pressure of overlying rocks but which retains some original organic material. This organic component may range from a simple carbon film to a relatively well-preserved original structure. [PLANTS]

concavo-convex Refers to a **profile** view of a brachiopod that has a concave **brachial valve** and a convex **pedicle valve**. [BRACHIOPODA]

conceptacle The modified region in the body (**thallus**) of marine brown algae (Division Phaeophyta) and *Protosalvinia* (*Foerstia*) that encloses the sexual phase of the life cycle. [PLANTS]

conch The shell of a mollusk or a tentaculitoid. [CEPHALOPODA; TENTACULITOIDS]

coniform Refers to simple, cone-shaped **elements** that have a single **apex** and no serrated or **denticulated** branches. [CONODONTA]

conispiral Refers to the **spire** of a shell that is cone shaped. [GASTROPODA]

convexi-concave Refers to a **profile** view of a brachiopod that has a convex **brachial valve** and a concave **pedicle valve**. [BRACHIOPODA]

convexi-plane Refers to a **profile** view of a brachiopod that has a convex **brachial valve** and a plane (flat) **pedicle valve**. [BRACHIOPODA]

coprophagous Refers to an organism that feeds upon the waste products of another organism. [GASTROPODA]

corallite The **exoskeleton** formed by a single **polyp**, either as an independent individual or in a **colony**. [CNIDARIA]

corallum (plural = **coralla**) The **exoskeleton** formed by the fusion of the **corallites** within a coral **colony**. [CNIDARIA]

cordate Refers to a leaf that is heart shaped. [PLANTS]

corner groove The longitudinal infolding of the **exoskeleton** that develops where two adjacent **faces**

meet. [CONULARIIDA]

cortex (adjective = **cortical**) The zone of tissues in a stem between the bark, **periderm**, or other external protective or reinforcing tissues (epidermis) and the more centrally located **vascular cylinder** (stele). [PLANTS]

costa (plural = **costae**, adjective = **costate**) A ridge of **exoskeletal** material forming **ornamentation** on the exterior surface. May be **comarginal** or at some angle to the growth margin (radial, spiral, etc.). Also called a rib, especially in a brachiopod. In an ostracode, a costa is not as prominent as a **carina**. [SEVERAL GROUPS]

coxa (plural = **coxae**) The proximal (basal) joint of a **biramous** appendage. [TRILOBITA]

cranidium (plural = **cranidia**) The central portion of the **cephalon**, bounded by the **facial sutures**. [TRILOBITA]

cranium (plural = **crania**, adjective = **cranial**) That portion of the skull of a vertebrate that encloses the brain. [VERTEBRATES]

crest A small, narrow, raised surface extending from, and at right angles to, a ridge; the external expression of a **spine**. [CONULARIIDA]

cribrate See **anastomosing**.

crown The body above the **column**, including the **arms** and **calyx** or **aboral cup**. [ECHINODERMATA: CRINOIDEA]

crura (singular = **crus**) Two blades or knobs of shell material that extend from the inner surface of the **interarea** or from the **median septum** in the **brachial valve** to support the **posterior** end of the **lophophore**. [BRACHIOPODA]

crural plate A plate of shell material extending from the base of the **crus** to the floor of the **brachial valve**. This plate may fuse medially with its counterpart on the **pedicle valve** to form a septalium. [BRACHIOPODA]

cuticle (adjective = **cuticular**) A waxlike layer that covers the surface of leaves and other appendages of land plants. Cuticle is more resistant to decay than many of the other components of a leaf and typically retains the cellular pattern of the upper or lower leaf surface. [PLANTS]

cyrtoconic (**cyrtocone**) Refers to a cephalopod shell that is curved but not coiled. [CEPHALOPODA]

cyst (adjective = **cystose**) In a coral, a bubble-shaped or blister-shaped structure in the wall. In a plant, a single-celled resting spore or other intermediate stage in the life cycle of a freshwater or marine alga. [CNIDARIA; PLANTS]

decorticated Refers to a stem that has lost some of its external bark, **periderm**, or **cortical** tissues as a result of decay and/or abrasion. [PLANTS]

decurrent Refers to a leaf base that extends downward along the axis below the point of attachment. [PLANTS]

delthyrial plate A single plate covering the **delthyrium** in some spiriferid brachiopods. [BRACHIOPODA]

delthyrium A median triangular or subtriangular opening beneath the **beak** of the **pedicle valve** that serves as a **pedicle opening**. [BRACHIOPODA]

deltidial plates Two plates of shell material growing inward from the sides of the **delthyrium**, partly or completely covering it. [BRACHIOPODA]

deltoid plates The circlet of plates between and above the **radial plates** that form the summit of the **theca**. [ECHINODERMATA: BLASTOIDEA]

dental plates Plates or blades of shell material beneath and supporting the **hinge teeth** and attached to the floor of the **pedicle valve**. [BRACHIOPODA]

denticle (adjective = **denticulate**) In a rostroconch, a toothlike structure or ridge of shell material along the margin of the **gape**. In a brachiopod, a small ridge that alternates with a small **socket** along the **hinge line** of both **valves**, giving a notched appearance. In a conodont, a spinelike or conical component of the serrated upper edge or surface of an **element**. In a plant, a toothlike indentation on a leaf margin, at right angles to the margin. (For vertebrates, see **dermal denticle**.) [SEVERAL GROUPS]

dentition The **teeth** and **sockets** and/or ridges and grooves that control movement of the **valves** of a shell. [PELECYPODA; BRACHIOPODA]

depressed Refers to a tube of a cephalopod shell in which the cross-sectional shape is wider than tall. [CEPHALOPODA]

dermal denticle A small, specialized, toothlike scale that forms the outer covering of some sharks and other lower vertebrates. [VERTEBRATES]

diagenesis (adjective = **diagenetic**) The complex of physical, chemical, and biological processes affecting sediments (and any entombed fossils), from the time of deposition through **lithification**, excluding metamorphism and weathering. [GENERAL GEOLOGY]

diagnosis The written description of a **taxon** that is part of the formal process of designating a new name. [ALL GROUPS]

diameter In **orthoconic** and **cyrtoconic** cephalopods, the distance across the tube of the shell; in coiled forms, the distance across the coil. The diameter of an orthoconic or cyrtoconic shell is equivalent to the **whorl width** or **whorl height** of a coiled form. [CEPHALOPODA]

dichotomous (noun = **dichotomy**) Refers to branching of a stem or axis into two essentially equal branches; generally considered to represent the earliest branching mode in land-plant evolution. Also see **monopodial**, **sympodial**. [PLANTS]

dicyclic Refers to an **aboral cup** that has two circlets of plates—**infrabasal plates** and **basal plates**—below the **radial plates**. [ECHINODERMATA: CRINOIDEA]

diductor muscles A pair of muscles that contract to open the **valves**. They extend from the **cardinal process** in the **brachial valve** to the floor of the **pedicle valve**, where they commonly form a large **muscle scar** outside the **adductor muscle** scars. [BRACHIOPODA]

dimorphism, sexual dimorphism The characteristic of having two distinct forms within a species, commonly owing to differences in shape between males and females. [OSTRACODA; CEPHALOPODA]

diplopores Double pores that penetrate through plates. Several diplopores may penetrate a single plate. [ECHINODERMATA: DIPLOPORIDA]

disk The central portion of an asteroid or ophiuroid that encases the main body tissues. [ECHINODERMATA: ASTEROIDEA, OPHIUROIDEA]

dissected Refers to a leaf that is cut or divided into lobes or segments. [PLANTS]

dissepiment In a coral, a small domed plate forming a blisterlike enclosure, generally in the marginal region of a **corallum**. In a **fenestrate** bryozoan **colony**, a cross-strut connecting thin branches. In a dendroid graptolite, a ribbonlike connection between branches. [CNIDARIA; BRYOZOA; GRAPTOLITHINA]

dissepimentarium The peripheral zone of the interior of a **corallum**; occupied by **dissepiments**. [CNIDARIA]

distal Refers to those portions of a branch system or other structure located at the greatest distance from the point of attachment to the next lower order of branching or attachment. The opposite term is **proximal**. [PLANTS]

dolabrate Refers to a pick-shaped **ramiform element** (example: *Ozarkodina*) that has a prominent **denticle** at one end and a single denticulate branch extending from it. [CONODONTA]

dorsal Refers to the upper side or part of an organism. In an ostracode, the upper part of the **carapace** or **valves** where the **hinge** is located. In a mollusk, toward or at the top of the animal when it is in life position. In a brachiopod, the direction away from the **pedicle valve** and toward the **brachial valve**; the brachial valve is called the dorsal valve by some writers. The opposite term is **ventral**. [MANY GROUPS]

dorsolateral Refers to the top part of the side (or the side part of the top). [CEPHALOPODA]

dorsum The top of an animal when it is in life position. The opposite term is **venter**. [CEPHALOPODA]

doublure The rim on the **ventral** surface formed by a reflexed continuation of the **dorsal exoskeleton**. [TRILOBITA]

ear A flattened or pointed extremity of the shell extending between the **hinge line** and the **commissure**. [BRACHIOPODA]

element A general term for individual components of the mineralized **apparatus** of a conodont. [CONODONTA]

encrusting Refers to a **colony** that grows as a flat crust on a hard surface. [BRYOZOA]

endocone One of the cone-shaped structures composed of calcium carbonate ($CaCO_3$) and deposited in the **siphuncle** by some kinds of cephalopods. [CEPHALOPODA]

endozone See **axial zone**.

entire Refers to a leaf margin that is smooth, not lobed or **toothed**. [PLANTS]

epifaunal Refers to an organism, either mobile or attached, that lives on the surface, as opposed to under the surface (**infaunal**). [MANY GROUPS]

epiphyte (adjective = **epiphytic**) A plant (generally of small stature) that lives on another plant (typically a woody tree) without depending on the host plant for water or nutrients. [PLANTS]

epitheca The thin external sheath covering the **exoskeleton**. [CNIDARIA]

erect Refers to **colonies** that grow vertically above the attachment surface. [BRYOZOA]

evolute Refers to a **planispirally** coiled cephalopod shell in which successive **whorls** are in contact with one another but overlap little or not at all, so that there is a wide **umbilicus**. [CEPHALOPODA]

exite The **dorsal** featherlike leg of a **biramous** appendage; presumably a gill-bearing leg. [TRILOBITA]

exoskeleton The external skeleton of an animal. In conulariids, a four-sided pyramidal structure composed of calcium phosphate, open at the **aperture** and closed at the **apex** and strengthened by internal thickenings called **rods**. In corals, the **calcareous** skeleton secreted by a **polyp**. In trilobites, the **chitinous**, and generally **calcitic**, structure covering the **dorsal** surface and parts of the **ventral** surface of the body. [MANY GROUPS]

exozone The outer zone in a branching **colony** made up of thick-walled **zooecia**. [BRYOZOA]

extant Refers to an organism that is still living today. [GENERAL PALEONTOLOGY]

external mold A **mold** or **impression** in the surrounding sediment or rock showing the surface form and markings of the outer hard parts of a fossil shell or other organic structure. Also see **internal mold**, **cast**. [MANY GROUPS]

external suture That portion of the **suture** of a coiled cephalopod that is visible outside the **umbilical seam**; it is between the umbilical seam and the **venter** of the **whorl**. [CEPHALOPODA]

eye tubercle A slightly raised, transparent or translucent spot in the anterodorsal region of the **valve** that forms the lens of the eye. [OSTRACODA]

eye A visual organ on the **cephalon**; generally bears eye lenses (facets). [TRILOBITA]

face One of the four sides of the **exoskeleton**; crossed by ridges. [CONULARIIDA]

facial suture One of two symmetrical lateral **sutures** that cross the **cephalon**. [TRILOBITA]

fen A **calcareous** (alkaline) **bog**. Also see **marsh**, **swamp**. [PLANTS]

fenestrate Refers to a **colony** that has thin branches joined by cross-struts, leaving open "windows" or fenestrules. [BRYOZOA]

fertile Refers to plant material (typically leaves or cones) that bears reproductive structures. [PLANTS]

fixed arm That portion of an **arm** that is incorporated into the plating of the **calyx**. [ECHINODERMATA: CRINOIDEA]

fixed brachial An **arm** plate that is rigidly sutured into a **calyx** as part of a **fixed arm**. [ECHINODERMATA: CRINOIDEA]

fixigena (plural = **fixigenae**) The portion of the **cranidium** between the **glabella** and the **facial suture**. Also called fixed cheek. [TRILOBITA]

flank In a coiled cephalopod, the portion of the **whorl** on the side, between the **dorsum** and the **venter**. [CEPHALOPODA]

fold A major rounded elevation of exterior and interior shell surfaces along the midline that radiates from the **umbo**; generally a feature of the **brachial valve**. [BRACHIOPODA]

fossula (plural = **fossulae**) A space between **septa** that is distinguished from other spaces between septa by its unusual shape and larger size. [CNIDARIA]

free arm An **arm** that is a movable appendage, rather than fixed within the **calyx** plating; may be either the entire arm or the upper arm. [ECHINODERMATA: CRINOIDEA]

free margin The peripheral area of the **carapace** or **valves** exclusive of the **hinge**. [OSTRACODA]

friil A relatively wide, ridgelike projection extending beyond the **free margin** of the **valves**. [OSTRACODA]

frond (adjective = **frondose**) The basic unit of foliage of ferns and other fernlike plants, ranging in organization from **simple** to multiply **compound**. Or, a plant structure that resembles a fern frond. [PLANTS]

fructification A structure, typically a highly modified leaf or branch system (cone/**strobilus**), bearing reproductive material (**spores**, **ovules**, pollen). [PLANTS]

gallery Space between two **laminae**; traversed by **pillars**. [STROMATOPOROIDS]

gametangia (singular = **gametangium**) Axes or processes (primarily in the various algae), bearing gametes or sex cells. [PLANTS]

gametophyte An inconspicuous, nonvascular, haploid

thallus in land-plant life cycles that bears male and/or female reproductive structures. In free-sporing plants, the gametophyte stage is free living. In seed-plant life cycles, gametophytes constitute pollen grains or portions of the **ovule**. [PLANTS]

gape An opening between the **valves** of the shell when the valves are closed. [ROSTROCONCHIA; PELECYPODA]

genal angle The posterolateral corner of the **cephalon**. [TRILOBITA]

genal spine A **spine** projecting from the posterolateral corner of the **cephalon**. [TRILOBITA]

geniculate, geniculated Refers to a skeletal part that is bent abruptly at an angle. In a brachiopod, an angular bend in lateral profile as a result of an abrupt change in the direction of **valve** growth. In a conodont, a pincer-shaped **coniform element** (example: *Phragmodus undatus*) that has a longitudinal axis that is bent sharply to form an acute angle. [SEVERAL GROUPS]

glabella The raised **axial** portion of the **cephalon**; bounded by **axial furrows** and the **occipital furrow**. [TRILOBITA]

gonatoparian suture A type of **facial suture** in which the **posterior** section intersects the **genal angle**. [TRILOBITA]

goniatitic Refers to an **ammonoid suture** in which neither the **lobes** nor the **saddles** are subdivided into smaller lobes and saddles. Also see **ammonitic**, **ceratitic**. [CEPHALOPODA]

granulae (singular = **granula**, adjective = **granulose**) Small, closely spaced, raised bumps, like the grains on sandpaper. [OSTRACODA; PLANTS]

growth lines Fine, commonly concentric lines paralleling the shell or **epithecal** margin and indicating growth increments. [MANY GROUPS]

guide fossil See **index fossil**.

gymnosperm (adjective = **gymnospermous**) A seed plant without true flowers or seed enclosed in an ovarian wall. [PLANTS]

gyroconic (**gyrocone**) Refers to a coiled cephalopod in which the **whorls** do not touch one another. [CEPHALOPODA]

hardground A surface formed by early **lithification** of sediment, typically a layer of limestone, formed on the sea floor. Such zones commonly are bored by, and **encrusted** with, marine organisms. [GENERAL GEOLOGY]

herbaceous Refers to a vascular plant that does not have persistent woody tissue. [PLANTS]

heterospory (adjective = **heterosporous**) Bearing two types of **spores**, distinguished on the basis of size (**megaspores** are large and **microspores** are small) and sexual expression of the derived **gametophytes** (megaspores produce egg-bearing gametophytes and microspores produce sperm-bearing gametophytes). [PLANTS]

hinge The line along which the **valves** of a shell articulate or are held together. [OSTRACODA; PELECYPODA; BRACHIOPODA]

hinge axis The axis about which the **valves** of a shell pivot. [PELECYPODA; BRACHIOPODA]

hinge line The **posterior** margin where the two **valves** of a shell articulate. [PELECYPODA; BRACHIOPODA]

hinge plate A divided or undivided platform of shell material in the **beak** region of the **brachial-valve** interior, generally joined to the **sockets** and the bases of the **crura**. [BRACHIOPODA]

holaspid stage The stage of growth beginning with the acquisition of the last **thoracic segment** and ending with death; the adult stage. The animal may continue to grow by **molting** during the holaspid stage, but segments are not added to the **posterior** of the **thorax**. Also see **protaspid stage**, **meraspid stage**. [TRILOBITA]

holdfast In a stalked echinoderm, the structure at the lower end of the **column** that attaches the organism to a hard surface. In a plant, a basal discoid or rootlike structure by which an algal **thallus** is attached to a surface. [ECHINODERMATA: CRINOIDEA, BLASTOIDEA, RHOMBIFERA, DIPLOPORIDA; PLANTS]

holochroal eye A compound **eye** consisting of numerous biconvex lenses covered with a single cornea. [TRILOBITA]

holotype The single **type specimen** from which a species is orginally described. Also see **hypotype**, **lectotype**, **neotype**, **paratype**, **syntype**, **topotype**. [ALL GROUPS]

homeomorphic Refers to a superficial, external similarity of form between two unrelated species, each of which is called a homeomorph. Internal structures of two such species are generally very different from each other. [ALL GROUPS]

homospore (adjective = **homosporous**; noun for condition = **homospory**) A **spore** of relatively uniform size and form that develops into a bisexual **gametophyte**. [PLANTS]

hood Broad, outward extension of shell material. [ROSTROCONCHIA]

hyponome A muscular tube through which a cephalopod directs water when swimming by "jet propulsion"; it is **ventral** in position. [CEPHALOPODA]

hyponomic sinus An **adaperturally** concave structure in the **aperture** of a cephalopod that is expressed in the **growth lines**; it marks the position of the **hyponome** and allowed mobility of the hyponome so that the animal could swim in a variety of directions. [CEPHALOPODA]

hypostome See **labrum**.

hypotype A described or illustrated specimen that is used to extend or correct the knowledge of a species. Also see **holotype**, **lectotype**, **neotype**, **paratype**, **syntype**, **topotype**, **type specimen**. [ALL GROUPS]

ichnofossil Any indirect evidence of an organism preserved in the rock record, including tracks, trails, burrows, borings, and even fossilized eggs and fecal material. Ichnofossils are also called trace fossils. [ICHNOFOSSILS]

ichnogenus (plural = **ichnogenera**) A genus of **ichnofossil**. [ICHNOFOSSILS]

ichnospecies A species of **ichnofossil**. [ICHNOFOSSILS]

impression The imprint or mark left in or on a rock or other sediment by an animal or a plant in which none of the original material remains. [MANY GROUPS]

inarticulate Refers to one of two classes of brachiopods, the Inarticulata, which is characterized by a lack of any rigid **hinge** mechanism between the **valves** and by a shell commonly composed of interlayers of **chitin** and calcium phosphate. [BRACHIOPODA]

index fossil A fossil that is useful in identifying and dating the strata or succession of strata in which it is found. An index fossil is generally a genus (rarely a species), is relatively common or very abundant, and has a wide geographic range and a relatively narrow stratigraphic range. [MANY GROUPS]

infaunal Refers to an organism that lives below the surface, as opposed to on the surface (**epifaunal**). [MANY GROUPS]

infiltration The crystallization of mineral material in the open spaces of fossils. Also see **permineralization**, **replacement**. [GENERAL GEOLOGY]

inflated Refers to a feature that is broad or swollen. [SEVERAL GROUPS]

infrabasal plate One of the lowest circle of plates in the **aboral cup** of a **dicyclic** crinoid that articulates with the **column**. [ECHINODERMATA: CRINOIDEA]

infranodal canal In casts of calamitean stems, a small, oval scar or bump marking a loose patch of soft (aerating?) tissue on the upper end of each rib just below a **node**. [PLANTS]

initial chamber The first-formed part of the **conch**, located at its proximal, pointed end. [TENTACULITOIDS]

inner lamella (plural = **lamellae**) A thin interior fold of the **valve**, apparent in the inside view of the **free margin**. [OSTRACODA]

instar A stage in the life of an arthropod between two **molts**. [TRILOBITA]

integument In an echinoderm, the outer leathery covering enclosing the plates. In a conulariid, the outer covering or **exoskeleton** of the animal. In a plant, the external tissue layer(s) of an **ovule**, derived from the **megasporangium**. Following fertilization of the ovule, the modified integument forms the seed coat. [ECHINODERMATA; CONULARIIDA; PLANTS]

interarea The planar or curved surface between the **beak** and the **posterior** margin of the **valve**. [BRACHIOPODA]

intercalary, **intercalated** Refers to **pinnules** that are inserted between main pinnules. [PLANTS]

internal mold A **mold** or **impression** showing the form and markings of the inner surfaces of a fossil shell or other organic structure. Also called a **steinkern**. Also see **cast**, **external mold**. [ALL GROUPS]

internode (adjective = **internodal**) The zone of a plant stem between successive **nodes**. [PLANTS]

interpleural furrow A transverse groove extending from the **axial furrow** across a **pleural lobe** of the **pygidium**, indicating the boundary of fused **pleurae**; generally shorter than a **pleural furrow**. [TRILOBITA]

interradial plate A typically hexagonal plate located between **fixed brachials** from adjacent **rays**. [ECHINODERMATA: CRINOIDEA]

interray The area of the body between adjacent **arms** or **ambulacra**. [ECHINODERMATA: CRINOIDEA]

involute Refers to a coiled cephalopod in which the sides of each **whorl** overlap the next whorl toward the center of the coil. [CEPHALOPODA]

keel A sharp ridge or angulation of the shell. In a cephalopod it is on the **venter**. [GASTROPODA; CEPHALOPODA]

labrum (plural = **labra**) The plate **anterior** to or covering the mouth opening on the **ventral** surface of the **cephalon**. Also called the **hypostome**. [TRILOBITA]

lacuna (plural = **lacunae**) A small opening between **corallites**. [CNIDARIA]

lamella (plural = **lamellae**, adjective = **lamellose**) A sheetlike or platelike extension of shell material on the external surface of the **valve** or **conch**; an extension of a growth increment. [SEVERAL GROUPS]

lamina (plural = **laminae**) In a stromatoporoid, one of the thin (≤0.1 mm), parallel or concentric layers making up the **coenosteum**. In a stromatolite, one of the layers of the mat or pillar. In a plant, the leaf blade—the expanded, flattened portion of a leaf above the **petiole**. [STROMATOPOROIDS; PLANTS]

lanceolate Refers to a leaf that is shaped like a lance point; it is notably longer than wide and the greatest diameter is near the base, tapering to a point at the **apex**. An oblanceolate leaf has the greatest diameter at the apex and tapers to a point at the base. [PLANTS]

last whorl The final 360° volution of the shell, termed body whorl in many earlier publications. [GASTROPODA]

lateral glabellar furrow A narrow groove extending inward from one side of the **glabella**; lateral glabellar furrows are counted from **posterior** to **anterior**. [TRILOBITA]

lateral glabellar lobe The portion of the **glabella** outlined and separated by successive pairs of **lateral glabellar furrows**; lateral glabellar lobes are counted from **posterior** to **anterior**. [TRILOBITA]

latilamina (plural = **latilaminae**) A thick (1-20 mm) layer of the **coenosteum**, composed of many **laminae**. [STROMATOPOROIDS]

lectotype A **type specimen** chosen after the original description to take the place of the **holotype**. Also see **hypotype**, **neotype**, **paratype**, **syntype**, **topotype**. [ALL GROUPS]

left valve The **valve** that is on the left if the shell is oriented with the **anterior** end up and viewed from the **dorsal** side (see fig. 1-15.1). [PELECYPODA]

librigena (plural = **librigenae**) The lateral portion of the **cephalon** outside the **facial suture**. Also called free cheek. [TRILOBITA]

lira (plural = **lirae**; adjective = **lirate**) In a cephalopod, a raised line on the exterior of the shell. In a tentaculitoid, a minute, raised, longitudinal rib on the exterior of the **conch**. [CEPHALOPODA; TENTACULITOIDS]

lithification (adjective = **lithified**) The complex physical (commonly heat and/or pressure) and chemical processes that turn unconsolidated sediment (sand, mud, etc.) into various types of sedimentary rock. [GENERAL GEOLOGY]

littoral Refers to marine communities developed in the zone between the limits of high and low tide. [GENERAL GEOLOGY]

living chamber That portion of the **conch** not subdivided by **septa**; it is adjacent to the **aperture** and was occupied in life by the body of the animal. Also called the **body chamber**. [CEPHALOPODA; TENTACULITOIDS]

lobe In an ostracode, a raised or domed, typically elongate portion of the **valve**. In a cephalopod, a wiggle of a **suture** that points away from the **aperture**; a lobe may be more-or-less smooth or may be divided into smaller wiggles (see **ammonitic**, **ceratitic**, **goniatitic**). [OSTRACODA; CEPHALOPODA]

loculi (singular = **locula**, adjective = **loculate**) Small chambers, appearing as round holes, generally in a line along the **ventral** and anteroventral margins of a **valve**. [OSTRACODA]

longiconic (**longicone**) Refers to an **orthoconic** or **cyrtoconic** cephalopod in which the **conch** is long and thin. [CEPHALOPODA]

longitudinal In an **orthoconic** or **cyrtoconic** cephalopod, refers to a structure that is parallel to the length of the shell; in a coiled cephalopod, refers to a structure that parallels the direction of coiling. The opposite term is **transverse**. [CEPHALOPODA]

lophophore A coiled fleshy organ in the **mantle cavity** that is rarely if ever preserved in fossil specimens. It is typically attached to the interior of the **brachial valve**. Two arms or brachia are edged with fringelike filaments that create currents to bring food and oxygen to the mouth of the animal. The two lophophore arms in some cases were supported internally by **calcareous brachidia**. [BRACHIOPODA]

lumen The central hole through a **columnal** of a stalked echinoderm. [ECHINODERMATA: CRINOIDEA, BLASTOIDEA, RHOMBIFERA, DIPLOPORIDA]

lunarium (plural = **lunaria**) A crescent-shaped rim or hood on one side of a **zooecial aperture**. [BRYOZOA]

M region The part of an **apparatus** occupied by a pair of pick-shaped **elements**. [CONODONTA]

macrofossil Fossil remains large enough to be studied without the aid of a microscope or powerful hand lens. A synonym is megafossil. [MOST GROUPS]

macrophyte (adjective = **macrophytic**) A large-bodied alga (primarily marine) such as a kelp or a seaweed. [PLANTS]

macroscopic Refers to an object such as a fossil that is easily seen without the aid of a magnifying lens or microscope. The opposite term is microscopic. [GENERAL GEOLOGY]

major face The wider of two adjacent **faces**. [CONULARIIDA]

mamelon A rounded elevation of the surface of a **coenosteum**. [STROMATOPOROIDS]

mandible A mouth part of an arthropod used for biting food. [ARTHROPODA]

mantle In a mollusk, the sheet of tissue that encloses the soft parts of the animal. In a mollusk that has a shell, the mantle is located between the other soft parts and the shell and secretes the shell. In a brachiopod, the thin sheet of tissue lining the **valve** interiors of the living animal. [MOLLUSCA; BRACHIOPODA]

mantle cavity In a mollusk, the space between the **mantle** and the other soft parts of the animal; expulsion of water from the mantle cavity of a cephalopod propels the animal. In a brachiopod, the **anterior** space between the **valves** lined by the mantle and separated from the internal organs by the body-cavity wall; the mantle cavity is filled with seawater and contains the **lophophore**. [MOLLUSCA; BRACHIOPODA]

marginal area Peripheral part of the interior of a **corallite**. Also called the peripheral zone. [CNIDARIA]

marsh A water-saturated, poorly drained, intermittently or permanently water-covered area that has aquatic and grasslike vegetation, but essentially without the formation of **peat**. Also see **bog**, **fen**, **swamp**. [PLANTS]

mature modification A change in the shell of a cephalopod that took place during the **ontogeny** of the animal as sexual maturity was approached. Common mature modifications include constriction of the **aperture**, change in coiling, change in cross-sectional shape, and closer spacing of the last few **septa**. [CEPHALOPODA]

median septum A long, narrow blade of shell material attached to the interior floor of the **valve** along the midline. In some brachiopods, the median septum may be double bladed or there may be additional septa or ridges of shell material. [BRACHIOPODA]

medusa (plural = **medusae**) The free-living, umbrella-shaped, tentacled body form of a cnidarian. Also see **polyp**. [CNIDARIA]

megasporangium (adjective = **megasporangiate**) See **sporangium**.

megaspore The large **spore** produced by **heterosporous** plants. Megaspores develop into female or egg-bearing **gametophytes**. Also see **microspore**. [PLANTS]

meraspid stage The stage of growth during which segments are added to the **thorax**; it extends from the first appearance of a transverse joint in the **exoskeleton** until all but the last segment has been added to the thorax. Also see **protaspid stage**, **holaspid stage**. [TRILOBITA]

microfossil Fossil remains that generally require the use of a binocular or compound microscope for study. Typical microfossils include foraminiferans, ostracodes, conodonts, plant cysts, pollen grains, **spores**, and dispersed microscopic fragments derived from larger plants and animals. [ALL GROUPS]

microphyll (adjective = **microphyllous**) A very small leaf, such as the scalelike leaf of some lycopods and horsetails. [PLANTS]

micropyle (adjective = **micropylar**) The opening of the **megasporangium** through which pollen grains or pollen tubes enter to fertilize the **ovule**. [PLANTS]

microsporangium See **sporangium**.

microspore A small **spore** produced by **heterosporous** plants. Microspores develop into male or sperm-bearing **gametophytes**. Also see **megaspore**. [PLANTS]

midline The longitudinal line connecting points where either two adjacent **rods** on a **face** meet, or central to the facial terminations of each pair of adjacent rods if the rods do not meet. [CONULARIIDA]

minor face The narrower of two adjacent **faces**. [CONULARIIDA]

miospore Any dispersed **spore** smaller than 200 micrometers. [PLANTS]

mold An **impression** preserved in the surrounding rock or sediment of the three-dimensional form of the interior or exterior of a fossil shell, bone, seed, tree trunk, or other organic structure. Also see **cast**, **external mold**, **internal mold**. [ALL GROUPS]

molt, molting Shedding of an **exoskeleton** to allow for growth of the animal. The shed exoskeleton is called a molt. [TRILOBITA]

monocyclic Refers to an **aboral cup** that contains only **basal plates** and **radial plates**. [ECHINODERMATA: CRINOIDEA]

monolete A **spore** characterized by the presence of a single linear opening or scar marking the zone or point of contact with the other spores in the original **tetrad**. [PLANTS]

monopodial Refers to a mode of branching in plants in which secondary, smaller branches arise from a larger primary branch or axis. This form of branching in plants is the most advanced and is derived, through **pseudomonopodial** intermediate stages, from the more primitive **dichotomous** mode. [PLANTS]

monoporate Refers to pollen grains that have a single pore in the pollen wall. [PLANTS]

monoserial Refers to a **rhabdosome** that has a single row of **thecae**. [GRAPTOLITHINA]

monticules Regularly spaced small mounds or dark patches on a **colony** surface. [BRYOZOA]

mucronate Refers to a plant or animal part that ends in a sharp, pointed extension, as in the "wings" of the **hinge line** of some brachiopods. [SEVERAL GROUPS]

multiserial Refers to a **colony** that has no empty spaces between close-packed **zooids**. [BRYOZOA]

mural pore An opening through a wall connecting adjacent **corallites** of a tabulate coral. [CNIDARIA]

muscle scar A mark, impression, or platform on the interior of a **valve** surface marking where muscles attached to the shell. [OSTRACODA; PELECYPODA; BRACHIOPODA]

NAP Abbreviation for **N**on**A**rboreal **P**ollen, the pollen produced by grasses and other nonwoody seed plants. [PLANTS]

nautiloid In a general sense, any externally shelled cephalopod that has straight, gently curved, or slightly sinuous **sutures**. In a technical sense, any member of the cephalopod class Nautiloidea. [CEPHALOPODA]

nektic (noun = **nekton**) Refers to aquatic organisms that are active swimmers. [SEVERAL GROUPS]

nematocyst The stinging organ housed in a **cnidoblast**. [CNIDARIA]

neotype A single specimen designated as the **type specimen** when the **holotype** and all **paratypes** have been lost or destroyed. Also see **hypotype**, **lectotype**, **syntype**, **topotype**. [ALL GROUPS]

node (adjectives = **nodose**, **nodal**) In an animal, a bump or low, rounded prominence or distinctly raised, rounded or elongate portion of the outer surface. On an ostracode **valve**, a node is larger than a **tubercle** but smaller than a **bulb**. In a plant, the point along a plant stem where leaves and/or lateral buds are borne. [MANY GROUPS]

nomenclature The formal application of scientific names to living organisms and fossils. In order to assure validity and the maximum practical utility in the application and use of scientific names, plant and animal nomenclature is governed by formal rules and procedures of the Codes of Botanical and Zoological Nomenclature. [ALL GROUPS]

oblanceolate See **lanceolate**.

occipital ring The axial region of the **posterior** segment of the **cephalon**. It is bounded laterally by the **axial furrows**, **anteriorly** by the **occipital furrow**, and posteriorly by the posterior margin of the cephalon. [TRILOBITA]

ontogeny The life history of an organism—everything that happens to an organism between conception and death. [ALL GROUPS]

oogonium (plural = **oogonia**) An egg-bearing structure in algae or fungi. [PLANTS]

opisthocline Refers to a shell that slopes **posteriorly** at an angle with the **hinge** structure. [PELECYPODA]

opisthoparian suture A type of **facial suture** in which the **posterior** section intersects the posterior margin of the **cephalon**. [TRILOBITA]

opposite Refers to the arrangement of leaves or other structures that are in pairs at successive **nodes** or at the same level, in contrast to **alternate** or **whorled** arrangements. [PLANTS]

oral plate One of the plates directly around the mouth. [ECHINODERMATA: CRINOIDEA, BLASTOIDEA, EDRIOASTEROIDEA, ECHINOIDEA]

orbit (adjective = **orbital**) One of the bony cavities of a vertebrate skull that partially encloses the eyes. [VERTEBRATES]

ornament, ornamentation Any outgrowth or pattern on the exterior of an organism, including **costae**, frills, **granulae**, **tubercles**, wrinkles, **plications**, **spines**, **lamellae**, and ribs. [MANY GROUPS]

orthoconic (**orthocone**) Refers to a cephalopod shell that is basically a straight cone. [CEPHALOPODA]

outer zone See **exozone**. [BRYOZOA]

outline The contour or shape (circular, subcircular, ovate, triangular, etc.) of the whole shell, generally viewed from above the **brachial valve**. [BRACHIOPODA]

ovule The female sexual structure in a seed-plant life cycle, consisting of the female **gametophyte** containing one or more eggs and surrounded by one or more layers of **integument**. [PLANTS]

P region The part of an **apparatus** customarily occupied by two pairs of **pectiniform elements**, which may or may not have lateral platformlike extensions. [CONODONTA]

pallial line The line formed by attachment of soft parts of an organism on the inside of the shell near the shell margin. [PELECYPODA]

pallial markings Branching impressions on the interior of a **valve** marking fluid-filled extensions of the **mantle**, which aid in respiration in some inarticulates or house the gonads in **calcareous**-shelled forms. [BRACHIOPODA]

pallial sinus An indentation of the **pallial line** on the inside of the shell in the **posterior** region formed by the attachment of certain muscles. [PELECYPODA]

palmate, **palmately** Refers to a **compound** leaf or **frond** in which the leaflets arise at the **apex** of the **petiole**, creating a fanlike or fingerlike appearance. [PLANTS]

paratype Any of the specimens, other than the **holotype**, on which the original description of a species is based. Also see **hypotype**, **lectotype**, **neotype**, **syntype**, **topotype**, **type specimen**. [ALL GROUPS]

parichnos Scars within the leaf scar of a lycopod leaf bolster; they reflect the presence of aerating tissue extending from the **cortex**. [PLANTS]

pastinate Refers to a **pectiniform element** (example: *Phragmodus*) that has three branches and no lateral platformlike extensions. [CONODONTA]

peat An accumulation of partially decayed or altered plant debris, commonly in water where localized conditions (oxygen deficiency, high or low pH, and/or low temperatures) inhibit the decay of plant material. Coal is derived from highly altered peat deposits; also see **coalification**. [PLANTS]

pectiniform Refers to a shell that has **auricles**; a shell shaped more or less like the Shell Oil Co. symbol. [PELECYPODA]

pectiniform element A blade- or comb-shaped component of an **apparatus**; may have two, three, or four main branches. One or more of the branches of some pectiniform elements may develop brimlike or platformlike lateral extensions. [CONODONTA]

pedicle A fleshy stalk attached internally to the **pedicle valve** and protruding from the **posterior** end of many brachiopods through the **pedicle opening**; typically used to permanently attach the shell to a hard surface. [BRACHIOPODA]

pedicle opening A circular, subcircular, or triangular opening through which the **pedicle** passes. Also called the pedicle foramen. Also see **delthyrium**. [BRA-

CHIOPODA]

pedicle valve The valve to which the **pedicle** is attached and which bears the **teeth**; it is the **ventral** valve, and generally is larger than the **brachial** (**dorsal**) **valve**. [BRACHIOPODA]

pelagic Refers to the water of the open ocean as an environment, or to marine organisms who live in the open ocean, rather than on the ocean bottom or in nearshore areas. [SEVERAL GROUPS]

pentameral symmetry A type of **bilateral symmetry** characterized by repetition of morphological features in multiples of five. This type of symmetry is present only in the echinoderms. [ECHINODERMATA]

pentamere An individual part of a **columnal** that is subdivided into five plates. [ECHINODERMATA: CRINOIDEA]

periderm The outer rind or barklike tissue of **arborescent** lycopods. Leaves are borne on the outer surface of the periderm and leave characteristic rhomboidal (diamond-shaped) or circular scars on the periderm when shed. [PLANTS]

periglacial Refers to areas or conditions in the immediate vicinity of a glacier that are influenced by the cold temperatures. [GENERAL GEOLOGY]

permineralization (adjective = **permineralized**) The process by which silica, carbonate, or other mineral matter fills the internal voids or pore spaces of a plant or animal. Also see **infiltration**, **replacement**. [MANY GROUPS]

petiole The stalklike structure by which a leaf is attached to a stem. [PLANTS]

phloem See **vascular system**.

phragmocone That portion of the shell that is subdivided by **septa**. [CEPHALOPODA]

phytoplankton. See **planktic**.

pillar A small vertical structure between **laminae** or **latilaminae**. [STROMATOPOROIDS]

pinna (plural = **pinnae**) The primary subdivision of a **compound** fern or fernlike **frond**. [PLANTS]

pinnate, **pinnately** Refers to a **compound** leaf or **frond** in which the leaflets or **pinnae** are arranged in two ranks on either side of the **rachis** or midvein, creating a featherlike appearance. Pinnae may be further subdivided as bipinnate (secondary subdivisions), tripinnate (tertiary subdivisions), or quadripinnate (fourth-order subdivisions) fronds. [PLANTS]

pinnulate Refers to the style of **arm** branching in which every **brachial** in the **free arms** bears a small side branchlet (pinnule). Branchlets project from opposite sides of the arm. [ECHINODERMATA: CRINOIDEA]

pinnule The smallest subunit of a **compound** fern or fernlike **frond**. [PLANTS]

pit A more-or-less circular depression on the lateral surface of a **valve**. [OSTRACODA]

pith The spongy central tissue of a plant stem. [PLANTS]

pith cast A **cast** of the inside of a plant stem, formed by the decay of the soft tissue of the **pith** cavity, accompanied or followed by infilling of the void by mud or other sediments. [PLANTS]

planispiral Refers to a shell that is coiled in a single plane. [GASTROPODA; CEPHALOPODA]

planktic, **planktonic** (noun = **plankton**) Refers to microscopic plantlike (phytoplankton) and animal-like (zooplankton) organisms that float or swim weakly in open water. [MANY GROUPS]

plano-convex Refers to a **profile** view of a shell in which the **brachial valve** is flat (plane) and the **pedicle valve** is convex. [BRACHIOPODA]

pleura (plural = **pleurae**, adjective = **pleural**) The lateral portion of a **thoracic segment** or the **pygidium**. [TRILOBITA]

pleural field The area to the side of the **axis** of the **pygidium** that is crossed by **pleural furrows** and ridges. [TRILOBITA]

pleural furrow An oblique groove along the surface of the **pygidium** or a **thoracic segment**. [TRILOBITA]

pleural lobe The longitudinal lateral portion of the **exoskeleton** on each side of the **axial lobe**. [TRILOBITA]

plication A folding of the shell material affecting both the outer and inner shell surfaces. May be **radial**, **comarginal**, or spiraling in occurrence. [PELECYPODA; GASTROPODA]

pluricolumnals Two or more **columnals** preserved articulated together. [ECHINODERMATA: CRINOIDEA, BLASTOIDEA, RHOMBIFERA, DIPLOPORIDA]

polished section A rock or fossil surface that has been cut into a flat surface and ground and polished to a fine finish. [GENERAL GEOLOGY]

polymorphism (adjective = **polymorphic)** Different body forms that occur sequentially at different stages of the life cycle, or at the same time in different parts of an animal or plant or **colony**. In cnidarians the different body forms are a **polyp** and a **medusa**. [SEVERAL GROUPS]

polymorph A unit of a bryozoan **colony** smaller than a **zooid**; also termed mesozooecia and exilazooecia. [BRYOZOA]

polyp The sessile, hollow, sacklike, tentacled body form of a cnidarian. Also see **medusa**. [CNIDARIA]

polyporate Refers to pollen grains characterized by the presence of multiple pores in the pollen wall. [PLANTS]

pore rhombs A complex system of infolded calcite and tubes. A pore rhomb typically has a chevron-shaped pattern of pores near a plate boundary that is connected by tubes to a similar arrangement of pores on the immediately adjacent plate. [ECHINODERMATA: RHOMBIFERA]

posterior Situated toward the back of an animal. In a mollusk, the direction toward the back of the shell in which the anus faces. In a brachiopod, the direction toward the **pedicle** and internal organs and away from the shell opening. The opposite term is **anterior**. [MANY GROUPS]

prepollen Functional pollen grains that have some characteristics of **spores**, such as a **trilete** mark. Prepollen is typical of extinct primitive **gymnosperms**. [PLANTS]

primary xylem The **xylem** tissues formed by the initial lengthwise growth of a stem. [PLANTS]

profile The shape of the entire shell when viewed from the side. See **biconvex, concavo-convex, convexi-concave, convexi-plane, plano-convex, resupinate**. [BRACHIOPODA]

proloculus The initial, or first-formed, chamber in the skeleton of a foraminiferan. [PROTISTA—CHAPTER 1]

proparian suture A type of **facial suture** in which the **posterior** section intersects the lateral margin of the **cephalon**. [TRILOBITA]

prosocline Refers to a shell that slopes **anteriorly** at an angle with the **hinge** structure. [PELECYPODA]

protaspid stage The stage of growth during which there is no transverse joint in the **exoskeleton**. Also see **meraspid stage**, **holaspid stage**. [TRILOBITA]

proximal Refers to that portion of a leaf or other organ or appendage that is closest to the point of attachment to the next lower order branch system. The opposite term is **distal**. [PLANTS]

pseudodeltidium A single plate that partially or completely covers the **delthyrium**. [BRACHIOPODA]

pseudofossil Any of a number of inorganic structures, including concretions, crystal growths, and fracture patterns, that superficially resemble organic remains. [GENERAL GEOLOGY]

pseudomonopodial A type of branching simulating **monopodial** branching in which the two branches of a **dichotomy** develop unequally, resulting in a more or less zigzag extension of the main axis of the branch and the lesser developed fork appearing as a side branch. [PLANTS]

pseudoplanispiral Refers to a shell that is coiled nearly in a plane but that does not have **bilaterally symmetrical** sides. [GASTROPODA]

pseudoselenizone A marking on shell giving a false impression of a **selenizone**. [GASTROPODA]

punctae (singular = **puncta**; adjective = **punctate**) Holes. In an ostracode, punctae occur in the lateral **valve** surfaces and are small, like pinpricks, and generally numerous. In a brachiopod, punctae extend from the outer surface to the inner surface of the shell. [OSTRACODA; BRACHIOPODA]

pygidium (plural = **pygidia**) The tail shield; the **posterior** part of the **dorsal exoskeleton**. [TRILOBITA]

quadriserial Refers to a **rhabdosome** that has four rows of **thecae**. [GRAPTOLITHINA]

rachial vein An accessory vein in a fernlike leaf that arises from the **rachis** and enters the **pinnule** independently of the primary vein(s). [PLANTS]

rachis (adjective = **rachial**) The primary axis of a fernlike **frond**. [PLANTS]

radial Refers to **ornamentation** that trends from the beak to the shell margin, perpendicular to the growth margin of the shell. [MOLLUSCA; BRACHIOPODA]

radial plate In a crinoid **aboral cup**, a plate at the base of the **ray**. The **arms** articulate to the upper margin of the **radial plates**, and two **basal plates** support the **radial plates** from beneath. In a blastoid **theca**, the plate between the **basal plates** and the **deltoid plates** that encases the **ambulacrum**. [ECHINODERMATA: CRINOIDEA, BLASTOIDEA]

radiocarbon dating One of several radiometric analytical techniques for absolute dating of geological materials using radioactive isotopes. Radiocarbon dating is based on the ratio of the quantity of the radioactive isotope of carbon (^{14}C) to the quantity of stable carbon (primarily ^{12}C). Given the small quantity of ^{14}C present in living tissues (or their carbon-containing products) and the relatively short half-life of the isotope (about 5,730 years), the technique is generally limited to dating material less than 40,000 years old. Also called carbon-14 dating. [GENERAL GEOLOGY]

ramiform element An **element** in which one or several **denticulate** and generally fragile branches project from the base. [CONODONTA]

ramose Refers to a branching, twiglike **colony**. [BRYOZOA]

ramus A branch or process of a bone, particularly in reference to the jawbone of a mammal. [VERTEBRATES]

ray That portion of an echinoderm that is directly in line with the **arms** or the **ambulacra**. [ECHINODERMATA]

relict Refers to a limited stand of vegetation that represents a remnant of a previously more widespread flora. [PLANTS]

replacement A type of fossil preservation in which original skeletal material is dissolved and replaced by inorganic mineral material. [GENERAL GEOLOGY]

repository The museum or other location where fossil specimens are cataloged and maintained. [GENERAL GEOLOGY]

resupinate Refers to a reversal in the relative convexity of a shell during growth. For example, a brachiopod may initially have a **concavo-convex profile** but as it grows it may develop a **convexi-concave** profile. [BRACHIOPODA]

reticulate (noun = **reticulum**) Having a netlike or meshlike pattern. In an ostracode, the pattern is formed by the intersection of **tubercles**, threads, or crests. In a mollusk or brachiopod, the pattern is formed by the intersection of ribs and **growth lines**. In a bryozoan, the network is formed by the branches of a **colony**. In a plant, the term refers to the arrangement of structural elements on the surface of pollen grains and **spores** or to the network of fine veins in a leaf. [MANY GROUPS]

rhabdosome The preserved skeleton of a **colony**. [GRAPTOLITHINA]

rhizome An underground stem, typically growing on or just under the soil surface, as opposed to a true root. [PLANTS]

rib See **costa**.

ridge A raised line crossing a **face** from a **corner groove** to the **midline** area; the external expression of a **rod**. [CONULARIIDA]

right valve The **valve** that is on the right if the shell is oriented with the **anterior** end up and viewed from the **dorsal** side (see fig. 1-15.1). [PELECYPODA]

ring furrow A groove bounding successive rings in the **axis** of the **pygidium**. [TRILOBITA]

rod A narrow, elongate, transverse thickening within the **integument**; a rod extends from a **corner groove** to the **midline** of a **face** and is expressed as a ridge on the exterior of the **exoskeleton**. [CONULARIIDA]

roof rock The rocks, typically shales, that overlie a coal bed and form the roof of mine tunnels following removal of coal. These rocks typically represent sediment deposited over a **swamp** as a result of fluvial flooding or encroachment by the sea. [GENERAL GEOLOGY]

rostral face The **posterior**-facing shell surface. [ROSTROCONCHIA]

rugae (singular = **ruga**, adjective = **rugose**) Concentric wrinkling on the exterior shell surface. [BRACHIOPODA]

S region The part of an **apparatus** customarily occupied by several pairs of fragile **ramiform elements** that grade in form from **bilaterally symmetrical** to strongly asymmetrical. [CONODONTA]

saddle A wiggle in a **suture** that points toward the **aperture**; a saddle may be more-or-less smooth or may be divided into smaller wiggles (see **ammonitic**, **ceratitic**, **goniatitic**). [CEPHALOPODA]

schizochroal eye A compound eye that has a visual surface consisting of numerous, separate, biconvex lenses, each with an individual cornea. [TRILOBITA]

sclerite A hard **chitinous** or **calcareous** plate of a body segment. [TRILOBITA]

secondary xylem, also called **secondary wood** Tissue

laid down in concentric layers, resulting in the growth in diameter of a woody stem. When secondary xylem production is seasonal, the result is annual growth rings in the wood. [PLANTS]

segminiscaphate Refers to a **pectiniform element** that has just one basic branch, lateral platform projections, and a scoop-shaped surface under the platform (example: *Icriodus*). [CONODONTA]

selenizone A narrow band on the **whorl** surface formed by growth of the shell around a **slit** or narrow notch in the margin of the **aperture** of the shell. [GASTROPODA]

septal groove A longitudinal furrow on the outer side of a **corallum** wall, corresponding in position to a **septum** on the inner side of the wall. [CNIDARIA]

septal spine A small projection in a tabulate coral that substitutes for a fully formed **septum**. [CNIDARIA]

septum (plural = **septa**) In a coral, a radially disposed longitudinal partition of a **corallite**. Numerous septa radiate from the **axial structure** of a coral. Larger septa are called major septa; smaller septa between major septa are called minor septa. In a cephalopod or a tentaculitoid, a **transverse** partition dividing the shell into **camerae**. In a plant, a dividing wall or partition. (For brachiopods, see **median septum**.) [SEVERAL GROUPS]

seta (plural = **setae**) A rigid, hairlike sensory device that extends from a tiny pore in the **exoskeleton**. [TRILOBITA]

shaft The axis of the **cardinal process**. [BRACHIOPODA]

sicula The first-formed part of a **rhabdosome**. [GRAPTOLITHINA]

silicified Refers to fossil material that has been **permineralized** by silica (SiO_2). [MANY GROUPS]

simple Refers to a leaf or **frond** that is undivided, consisting of a single blade, which may be **entire** or variously lobed or **dissected**. The opposite term is **compound**. [PLANTS]

sinus The indentation between lobes in a leaf. [PLANTS]

siphuncle (adjective = **siphuncular**) The tube of shell material in a cephalopod shell that extends from the **living chamber** through all the **septa**; in life, this tube was filled by a strand of tissue called the **siphuncular cord**. Some writers refer to this tissue as well as the tube of shell material simply as the siphuncle. [CEPHALOPODA]

siphuncular cord The strand of tissue within the **siphuncle**. [CEPHALOPODA]

siphuncular deposits Calcium carbonate material secreted by some cephalopods within the **siphuncle**, especially near the **apex** of the shell. Also called siphonal deposits. [CEPHALOPODA]

slit A narrow notch in the margin of the **aperture** of the shell. [GASTROPODA]

snout The **anterior** portion of the shell. [ROSTROCONCHIA]

sockets Pits or depressions along the **hinge line** of one **valve** of a shell into which **teeth** on the opposite valve fit. Together, the teeth and sockets allow the valves to pivot and open and close the shell. In a brachiopod, the sockets are located in the **posterior** margin of the **brachial valve**. [PELECYPODA; BRACHIOPODA]

spatulate Refers to a shape that is broad and rounded at one end, tapering to a narrow base at the opposite end. [PELECYPODA; BRACHIOPODA; PLANTS]

spicule A small, single, skeletal element of a sponge. [SPONGES; STROMATOPOROIDS]

spine (adjective = **spinose**) An elongated projection of shell material extending outward from the shell or skeletal surface; may be solid or hollow, straight or curved, cylindrical or flattened. [MANY GROUPS]

spine ridge An elongated ridge on the exterior **valve** surface, bearing a **spine** at the **anterior** end. [BRACHIOPODA]

spinule A **spine** of small diameter and length of 1-2 mm. [BRACHIOPODA]

spire (adjective = **spiral**) That portion of the shell not including the last **whorl**. [GASTROPODA]

spondylium A curved, spoonlike platform for muscle attachment in the **beak** area of the **pedicle-valve** interior, formed by the union of two **dental plates** into a Y-shaped structure. The median part of this structure may be attached to the **valve** floor, or may be supported by a **median septum** or by a pair of septa. [BRACHIOPODA]

spongocoel The interior cavity of a sponge. [SPONGES]

sporangium (plural = **sporangia**) A structure associated with the production and dispersal of **spores** in fungi, ferns, lycopods, and other non-seed-bearing plants. In seed plants, megasporangia are associated with the production of **ovules** and seeds, and microsporangia are associated with the production and dispersal of pollen. [PLANTS]

sporangiophore A short, **sporangia**-bearing process representing a highly modified leaf. [PLANTS]

spore Any of various minute or small, typically unicellular reproductive bodies or resistant resting cells that are capable of developing into a new individual (**algae**, fungi) or into the gamete-bearing stage of a plant life cycle. [PLANTS]

sporophyll A modified, **spore**-bearing leaf, which is typically organized into a cone or **strobilus**. [PLANTS]

spreiten (singular = **spreite**) Concentric arcs of laminated sediment, such as those between the arms of U-shaped tubes of ichnofossils (example: *Diplocraterion*). [ICHNOFOSSILS]

stalk An elongate structure, possibly **chitinous**, that attached to the **apex**; distally the structure may have been attached to a shell or other object on the sea floor. [CONULARIIDA]

stegidium In some brachiopods, a convex plate of shell material deposited as concentric layers, covering the gap between the **delthyrial plates** as the **pedicle** atrophies. [BRACHIOPODA]

steinkern See **internal mold**.

stipe The axis of a large **alga** (**macrophyte**) such as kelps and seaweeds. [PLANTS]

stolon The slender, creeping tube from which the long chain of **zooids** with **zooecia** develop. [BRYOZOA]

stoma (plural = **stomata**) An opening or pore in the epidermis of a leaf that functions to regulate gas exchange. [PLANTS]

stratigraphy The study of rock layers, including their form, distribution, lithologic composition, fossil content, age relations, and geophysical and geochemical properties. [GENERAL GEOLOGY]

striae (singular = **stria**; adjective = **striated**) Narrow, generally parallel lines or bands. In **ichnofossils**, striae are typically distinguished by differences in elevation. [SEVERAL GROUPS]

strobilus (plural = **strobili**) A cone, formed by **sporophylls** (and in some cases sterile **bracts**), variously arranged on a common axis. [PLANTS]

subfossil A fossil that is younger than what is considered to be of typical fossil age (about 6,000 years old), but is not a present-day organism. [MANY GROUPS, ESPECIALLY PLANTS]

sulcus (plural = **sulci**) In an ostracode, an elongate valley or depression in the **valve** surface. In a pelecypod, a major, **radial** infolding of the shell. In a brachiopod, a major depression of the inner and outer valve surfaces along the midline, externally concave in **profile**, radiating from the **umbo**, and generally associated with the **pedicle valve**; called the sinus in older literature. [OSTRACODA; PELECYPODA; BRACHIOPODA]

suture In a gastropod, the line of juncture of two adjacent **whorls** of the shell. In a cephalopod, the line produced by the intersection of a **septum** with the wall of the **conch**; generally visible only on the **internal mold**; a cephalopod suture may be straight, gently curved, or decidedly wiggly. Also see **lobe**, **saddle**. [GASTROPODA; CEPHALOPODA]

swamp An area that has standing water for all or much of the growing season and in which shrubs and trees grow. Also see **bog**, **fen**, **marsh**. [PLANTS]

symbiosis (adjective = **symbiotic**) The relationship that exists between two different organisms that live in close association, with at least one of the organisms being helped without either being harmed. [GENERAL PALEONTOLOGY]

symphytium A **calcareous** plate that closed the **pedicle opening** in mature specimens of *Strophomena*, so that mature specimens of this genus were no longer attached by pedicles. [BRACHIOPODA]

sympodial Refers to a mode of growth or branching in which continued growth of the main axis is initiated by development of a lateral bud from the previous season's growth, so that the branches have a somewhat irregular or zigzag course instead of being essentially straight (**monopodial**). [PLANTS]

synangium (plural = **synangia**; adjective = **synangial**) An aggregate of **sporangia** clustered, fused, or coalesced to form **fertile** structures with a specific morphology. [PLANTS]

syntype A specimen (or specimens) on which the description of a species is based when no **holotype** has been designated. The term "cotype" is a less desirable synonym. Also see **hypotype**, **lectotype**, **neotype**, **paratype**, **topotype**, **type specimen**. [ALL GROUPS]

syrinx A tube of shell material located on the inner surface of the **delthyrial plate**. [BRACHIOPODA]

tabula (plural = **tabulae**) In a cnidarian, the transverse partition of a **corallite**; it is commonly planar, but may be concave or convex. In a bryozoan, a closely spaced transverse plate that partitions small **polymorphs** in bryozoan **colonies**. [CNIDARIA; BRYOZOA]

taphonomy Everything that happens to an organism between the time of its death and the time that the fossil is found. [ALL GROUPS]

taxon (plural = **taxa**) A general term for a named group of organisms of any rank (phylum, order, genus, etc). [ALL GROUPS]

taxonomy (adjective = **taxonomic**) The formal system or study of the classification of organisms. [ALL GROUPS]

teeth (singular = **tooth**; adjective = **toothed**) In a pelecypod or a brachiopod, small knobs or projections of shell material on one **valve** that fit into **sockets** in the opposite valve as part of a **hinge**. Together, the teeth and sockets form the **dentition** that allows the valves to pivot and open and close the shell. In brachiopods, the teeth are on the **posterior** margin of the **pedicle valve.** In a gastropod, a projection of shell material that extends into the **aperture**. In a plant, small, sharp points or serrations along the margin of a leaf. [SEVERAL GROUPS]

tegmen The plating over the top of the **aboral cup** or **calyx**. The tegmen is rigidly joined in a camerate crinoid but consists of more loosely sutured plates in inadunate and flexible crinoids. [ECHINODERMATA: CRINOIDEA]

telepod The **ventral** branch of a **biramous** leg; presumably a walking or swimming leg. [TRILOBITA]

telson The last body segment of a crustacean. It typically includes the anus. [OTHER ARTHROPODA]

terminal piece The last segment expressed in the **pygidial axis**. [TRILOBITA]

terrace lines Fine, scarplike, raised lines on the **exoskeleton**. [TRILOBITA]

test An external shell or supporting structure of an organism. The term is more commonly used for microscopic organisms such as foraminiferans and chitinozoans, but may be used as a synonym for shell. [SEVERAL GROUPS]

tetrad A cluster of four pollen grains or **spores** originating by meiotic division of a parental "mother cell." [PLANTS]

tetrapod An animal that has four limbs, such as an amphibian, reptile, or mammal. [VERTEBRATES; ICHNOFOSSILS]

thallus (plural = **thalli**) The body of a relatively simple plant, such as an **alga** or a bryophyte (mosses and liverworts), that is not differentiated into complex structures such as roots, stems, and leaves. [PLANTS]

theca (plural = **thecae**) In some echinoderms, the body exclusive of the **column** and **brachioles**. In a graptolite, the cuplike living chamber of a **zooid** in a **rhabdosome**. [ECHINODERMATA: BLASTOIDEA, RHOMBIFERA, DIPLOPORIDA; GRAPTOLITHINA]

thin section An extremely thin slice of a rock or a fossil, mounted on a microscope slide. The section is typically prepared by sawing and polishing the sample to a thickness that permits light to pass through the sample. Thin sections are generally studied under the high magnification of a microscope. [GENERAL GEOLOGY]

thoracic segment A bandlike transverse division of the **thorax**, consisting of two **pleura** separated by an **axial ring**. [TRILOBITA]

thorax (adjective = **thoracic**) In a trilobite, the area of the body between the **cephalon** and the **pygidium**, formed of a variable number of **thoracic segments**. In other arthropods, the area between the head and the **abdomen**. In a vertebrate, the portion of the body between the neck and the abdomen. [TRILOBITA; OTHER ARTHROPODA; VERTEBRATES]

tongue An **anterior**, tongue-shaped extension of the **valve**. [BRACHIOPODA]

tooth See **teeth**.

topotype A specimen of a particular species that comes from the same locality as the **type specimen** of the species. Also see **holotype**, **hypotype**, **lectotype**, **neotype**, **paratype**, **syntype**, **type specimen**. [ALL GROUPS]

trabecula (plural = **trabeculae**) A pillar of radiating **calcareous** fibers in the structure of a **septum**. [CNIDARIA]

tracheid The most primitive water-conducting cell of the **xylem** of vascular plants. [PLANTS]

transverse In a gastropod, refers to a structure or **orna-**

mentation that is at an angle to the axis of coiling. In an **orthoconic** or **cyrtoconic** cephalopod, refers to a structure that extends in a direction perpendicular to the length of the shell or nearly so; in a coiled cephalopod, refers to a structure that lies at a right angle to the direction of coiling or nearly so; the opposite term is **longitudinal**. In a brachiopod, refers to a feature that is elongate laterally, that is, from side to side (width is greater than length). [GASTROPODA; CEPHALOPODA; BRACHIOPODA]

tricolpate Refers to pollen grains characterized by the presence of three furrows (colpi) in the pollen wall. [PLANTS]

tricolporate Refers to **tricolpate** pollen in which each furrow contains a pore, typically located at the equatorial plane. [PLANTS]

trilete Refers to **spores** that have a three-armed opening or scar marking the zone of mutual contact of the spores in the original **tetrad**. [PLANTS]

triserial Refers to a **rhabdosome** that has three rows of **thecae**. [GRAPTOLITHINA]

trochospiral Refers to a shell that is coiled in more than one plane (for example, the threads of a screw are trochospiral). Also called torticonic or trochoceroid. [CEPHALOPODA]

tubercle (adjective = **tuberculate** or **tubercular**) A low, rounded prominence. [MANY GROUPS]

turreted Refers to the shape of some high-spired shells, which resemble castle turrets; **whorls** generally have projecting angulations. [GASTROPODA]

type species The species on which the original description of a genus is based. [ALL GROUPS]

type specimen A specific specimen (or specimens), selected by the author, to represent the characteristics of the species for which he or she has created a new name. Several categories of type specimens are recognized (see **holotype**, **hypotype**, **lectotype**, **neotype**, **paratype**, **syntype**, **topotype**) under definitions established in the Codes of Botanical Nomenclature and Zoological Nomenclature. Considerable effort is made to preserve type specimens, as they serve as examples of the author's intent in establishing a new name. [ALL GROUPS]

umbilical seam In an **involutely** coiled cephalopod, the line that marks the contact of an outer **whorl** with an inner whorl. [CEPHALOPODA]

umbilical shoulder In a coiled cephalopod, the strongly bent portion of the side of a **whorl** that is **dorsolateral** in position. [CEPHALOPODA]

umbilicus In a **planispirally** coiled cephalopod in which successive **whorls** are in contact with one another, the depression on each side of the **conch** that is centered on the axis of coiling of the shell. Also called the umbilical opening. [CEPHALOPODA]

umbo (plural = **umbones**, adjective = **umbonal**) The area of a **valve** immediately adjacent to the **beak** area; may be curved or convex. [PELECYPODA; BRACHIOPODA]

uniserial In a bryozoan, refers to a **colony** consisting of a linear chain of connected teardrop-shaped **zooids**. In a crinoid, refers to **arms** in which a single row of **brachials** makes up the main **arm**; uniserial **brachials** may be quadrangular or cuneate (wedge shaped). [BRYOZOA; ECHINODERMATA: CRINOIDEA]

valve One of the two shells that form the **carapace** or **exoskeleton** of an ostracode or a phyllocarid or the shell of a pelecypod or brachiopod. [SEVERAL GROUPS]

vascular bundle The fluid-conducting tissue, composed of strands of **xylem** and phloem, which appear as discrete bundles in a stem cross section. [PLANTS]

vascular cylinder The bundles of **xylem** and phloem and the **pith**, if present. Also called the stele. [PLANTS]

vascular system A two-part tissue system for conduction of water (the **xylem**) and nutrients produced by photosynthesis (the phloem). The main elements of the vascular system are developed in the stem, but extend into most of the structures of the plant both above and below ground. [PLANTS]

vegetative Generally refers to sterile or nonreproductive parts of plants (commonly leaves). [PLANTS]

venation The pattern made by the veins of a leaf or a leaf-like structure. [PLANTS]

venter That portion of an animal that was down in life position. In a coiled cephalopod, as the living animal grew, the former venter was rotated, eventually to be positioned at the top of the shell; thus, in a coiled cephalopod, the term "ventral" refers to the direction toward the outside of the coil. The opposite term is **dorsum**. [CEPHALOPODA]

ventral Refers to the lower side or part of an organism. In an ostracode, refers to the lower part that includes the **free margin**. In a rostroconch or a pelecypod, refers to the underside of the body or shell; opposite of **dorsal**. In a brachiopod, refers to the direction toward the **pedicle valve** and away from the **brachial valve**; equivalent to the pedicle valve of some writers. [MANY GROUPS]

ventral membrane An uncalcified extension of the **exoskeleton** across the **ventral** side. [TRILOBITA]

ventrolateral Between **ventral** and lateral. [CEPHALOPODA]

vesiculate Refers to pollen grains characterized by one or more bladders attached to the main body of the pollen grain. [PLANTS]

whorl (adjective = **whorled**) In a gastropod or cephalopod, one complete, 360° turn of a spiral shell. Also called a volution. In a plant, the arrangement of leaves or other structures in a circle around the axis, in contrast to **alternate** or **opposite** arrangments. [GASTROPODA; CEPHALOPODA; PLANTS]

whorl height In a coiled cephalopod shell, the vertical distance between the **venter** and the **dorsum** of a **whorl**. [CEPHALOPODA]

whorl width In a coiled cephalopod shell, the greatest horizontal distance from one side of a **whorl** to the opposite side of the same whorl. [CEPHALOPODA]

xylem The thick-walled water-conducting cells and fibers in the **vascular system** of land plants. In addition to its water-conducting function, xylem provides much of the mechanical support for plant stems and branches. [PLANTS]

zoarium (plural = **zoaria**; adjective = **zoarial**) The skeleton of a bryozoan **colony**. [BRYOZOA]

zooecium (plural = **zooecia**; adjective = **zooecial**) The skeleton of a bryozoan **zooid**. [BRYOZOA]

zooid In a bryozoan, the basic unit of a **colony;** it is capsule shaped, containing in life a tentacular apparatus for feeding and a complete digestive tract. In a graptolite, a general term for the animal inhabiting the **theca**. [BRYOZOA; GRAPTOLITHINA]

zooplankton See **planktic**.

References

All the references cited in the various chapters of this book are listed here. The group(s) to which the references apply are listed in SMALL CAPITALS in brackets following the definition. Some references are noted as applying to several, many, or all groups; to Ohio geology; or to general geology or general paleontology.

Abbott, M. L., 1958, The American species of *Asterophyllites*, *Annularia*, and *Sphenophyllum*: Bulletins of American Paleontology, v. 38, no. 174, p. 289-390. [PLANTS]

Amsden, T. W., 1983, Upper Bromide Formation and Viola Group (Middle and Upper Ordovician) in eastern Oklahoma, Part 3, The Late Ordovician brachiopod genera *Lepidocyclus* and *Hiscobeccus*: Oklahoma Geological Survey Bulletin 132, p. 36-42. [BRACHIOPODA]

Anderson, William, Davis, James, Habig, Laura, Patrouch, Kathy, and Patrouch, Jean, 1989, The 1989 Ohio Intercollegiate Geology Field Trip: University of Dayton, 34 p. [OHIO GEOLOGY]

Andreas, B. K., and Knoop, J. D., 1992, 100 years of changes in Ohio peatlands: Ohio Journal of Science, v. 92, p. 130-138. [PLANTS]

Andrews, E. B., 1875, Descriptions of fossil plants from the coal measures of Ohio: Ohio Division of Geological Survey, v. 2, part 2, Paleontology, p. 413-426. [PLANTS]

Arkell, W. J., and others, 1957, Part L, Mollusca 4, Cephalopoda, Ammonoidea, *in* Moore, R. C., ed., Treatise on Invertebrate Paleontology: Geological Society of America and University of Kansas Press, 490 p. [CEPHALOPODA]

Arnold, C. A., 1931, On *Callixylon newberryi* (Dawson) Elkins et Wieland: University of Michigan Museum of Paleontology Contributions, v. 3, no. 12, p. 207-232. [PLANTS]

________ 1949, Fossil flora of the Michigan coal basin: University of Michigan Museum of Paleontology Contributions, v. 7, no. 9, p. 131-269. [PLANTS]

________ 1952, A specimen of *Prototaxites* from the Kettle Point black shale of Ontario: Palaentographica, band 93, Abteilung B, nos. 1-3, p. 45-56. [PLANTS]

Aronoff, S. M., 1979, Orthoconic nautiloid morphology and the case of *Treptoceras* vs. *Orthonybyoceras*: Neues Jahrbuch für Geologie und Paläontologie Abhandlungen, v. 158, no. 1, p. 100-122. [CEPHALOPODA]

Ausich, W. I., 1985, New crinoids and revision of the superfamily Glyptocrinacea (Early Silurian, Ohio): Journal of Paleontology, v. 59, p. 793-808. [ECHINODERMATA: CRINOIDEA]

________ 1986a, Early Silurian rhodocrinitacean crinoids (Brassfield Formation, Ohio): Journal of Paleontology, v. 60, p. 84-106. [ECHINODERMATA: CRINOIDEA]

________ 1986b, Early Silurian inadunate crinoids (Brassfield Formation, Ohio): Journal of Paleontology, v. 60, p. 719-735. [ECHINODERMATA: CRINOIDEA]

________ 1987, John Bryan State Park, Ohio: Silurian stratigraphy: Geological Society of America, North-Central Section, Centennial Field Guide, p. 419-422. [OHIO GEOLOGY; BRACHIOPODA]

Babcock, L. E., 1991, The enigma of conulariid affinities, *in* Simonetta, A. M., and Conway Morris, Simon, eds., The early evolution of Metazoa and the significance of problematic taxa: New York, Cambridge University Press, p. 133-143. [CONULARIIDA]

________ 1992, Lectotype of *Phacops rana milleri* Stewart, 1927 (Trilobita, Devonian of Ohio): Journal of Paleontology, v. 66, p. 692-693. [TRILOBITA]

________ 1993, Trilobite malformations and the fossil record of behavioral asymmetry: Journal of Paleontology, v. 67, p. 217-229. [CNIDARIA; TRILOBITA]

________ 1994a, Biostratigraphic significance and paleogeographic implications of Cambrian fossils from a deep core, Warren County, Ohio: Journal of Paleontology, v. 68, p. 24-30. [TRILOBITA]

________ 1994b, Systematics and phylogenetics of polymeroid trilobites from the Henson Gletscher and Kap Stanton Formations (Middle Cambrian), North Greenland: Greenland Geological Survey Bulletin 169, p. 79-127. [TRILOBITA]

Babcock, L. E., and Feldmann, R. M., 1986a, Devonian and Mississippian conulariids of North America, Part A, General description and *Conularia*: Carnegie Museum Annals, v. 55, p. 349-410. [CONULARIIDA]

________ 1986b, Devonian and Mississippian conulariids of North America, Part B, *Paraconularia*, *Reticulaconularia*, new genus, and organisms rejected from Conulariida: Carnegie Museum Annals, v. 55, p. 411-479. [CONULARIIDA]

Babcock, L. E., and Robison, R. A., 1989, Preferences of Palaeozoic predators: Nature, v. 337, p. 695-696. [TRILOBITA]

Babcock, L. E., and Speyer, S. E., 1987, Enrolled trilobites from the Alden Pyrite Bed, Ledyard Shale (Middle Devonian) of western New York: Journal of Paleontology, v. 61, p. 539-548. [TRILOBITA]

Baird, Donald, 1952, Revision of the Pennsylvanian and Permian footprints *Limnopus*, *Allopus*, and *Baropus*: Journal of Paleontology, v. 26, p. 832-840. [VERTEBRATES]

________ 1964, The aïstopod amphibians surveyed: Museum of Comparative Zoology (Harvard University) Breviora, no. 206, 17 p. [VERTEBRATES]

________ 1978, Studies on Carboniferous freshwater fishes: American Museum of Natural History Novitates, no. 2641, p. 1-22. [VERTEBRATES]

Baird, G. C., Brett, C. E., and Frey, R. C., 1989, "Hitchhiking" epizoans on orthoconic cephalopods: preliminary review of the evidence and its implications: Senckenbergiana lethaea, v. 69, no. 5/6, p. 439-465. [CEPHALOPODA]

Baker, R. C., 1942, The age and fossils of the Olentangy Shale of central Ohio: American Journal of Science, v. 240, p. 137-143. [BRACHIOPODA]

Bassler, R. S., 1932, The stratigraphy of the Central Basin of Tennessee: Tennessee Division of Geology Bulletin 38, 268 p. [PORIFERA]

________ 1937, Memorial of August F. Foerste: Geological Society of America Proceedings, 1936, p. 143-158. [CEPHALOPODA]

________ 1953, Part G, Bryozoa, *in* Moore, R. C., ed., Treatise on Invertebrate Paleontology: Geological Society of America and University of Kansas Press, 253 p. [BRYOZOA]

Bates, R. L., and Jackson, J. A., eds., 1987, Glossary of geology (3rd ed.): American Geological Institute, 788 p. [GENERAL GEOLOGY]

Bayer, F. M., and others, 1956, Part F, Coelenterata, *in* Moore, R. C., ed., Treatise on Invertebrate Paleontology: Geological Society of America and University of Kansas Press, 498 p. [CNIDARIA]

Beaver, H. H., and others, 1967, Part S, Echinodermata 1, *in* Moore, R. C., ed., Treatise on Invertebrate Paleontology: Geological Society of America and The University of Kansas Press, 650 p. [ECHINODERMATA: BLASTOIDEA, RHOMBIFERA, DIPLOPORIDA]

Beck, C. B., 1960, The identity of *Archeopteris* and *Callixylon*: Brittonia, v. 12, p. 351-368. [PLANTS]

________ 1962, Reconstruction of *Archeopteris* and further consideration of its phylogenetic position: American Journal of Botany, v. 49, p. 373-382. [PLANTS]

________ 1964, The woody, fern-like trees of the Devonian: Torrey Botanical Club, v. 21, p. 26-37. [PLANTS]

Beecher, C. E., 1889, Brachiospongidae: a memoir on a group of Silurian sponges; with six plates: Peabody Museum of Natural History (Yale University) Memoir 2, no. 1, 28 p. [PORIFERA]

Beerbower, J. R., 1963, Morphology, paleoecology and phylogeny of the Permo-Carboniferous amphibian *Diploceraspis*: Museum of Comparative Zoology (Harvard University) Bulletin, v. 130, p. 31-108. [VERTEBRATES]

Bell, B. M., 1976, A study of North American Edrioasteroidea: New York State Museum and Science Service Memoir 21, 447 p. [ECHINODERMATA: EDRIOASTEROIDEA]

Bengtson, Peter, 1988, Open nomenclature: Palaeontology, v. 31, p. 223-227. [GENERAL PALEONTOLOGY]

Benson, R. H., and MacDonald, H. C., 1963, Postglacial (Holocene) ostracodes from Lake Erie: University of Kansas Paleontological Contributions, no. 33, Arthropoda, article 4, 26 p. [OSTRACODA]

Benson, R. H., and others, 1961, Part Q, Arthropoda 3, *in* Moore, R. C., ed., Treatise on Invertebrate Paleontology: Geological Society of America and University of Kansas Press, 442 p. [OSTRACODA]

Bergström, Jan, 1973, Organization, life, and systematics of trilobites: Fossils and Strata, v. 2, p. 1-69. [TRILOBITA]

Bergström, S. M., and Sweet, W. C., 1966, Conodonts from the Lexington Limestone (Middle Ordovician) of Kentucky and its lateral equivalents in Ohio and Indiana: Bulletins of American Paleontology, v. 50, no. 229, p. 271-441. [CONODONTA]

Bergström, S. M., and Mitchell, C. E., 1986, The graptolite correlation of the North American Upper Ordovician Standard: Lethaia, v. 19, p. 247-266. [GRAPTOLITHINA]

_________ 1990, Trans-Pacific graptolite faunal relations: the biostratigraphic position of the base of the Cincinnatian Series (Upper Ordovician) in the standard Australian graptolite zone succession: Journal of Paleontology, v. 64, p. 992-997. [GRAPTOLITHINA]

_________ 1992, The Ordovician Utica Shale in the eastern Midcontinent region: age, lithofacies, and regional relationships: Oklahoma Geological Survey Bulletin 145, p. 67-89. [GRAPTOLITHINA]

Berman, D. S., 1978, *Ctenospondylus ninevehensis*, a new species (Reptilia, Pelycosauria) from the Lower Permian Dunkard Group of Ohio: Carnegie Museum Annals, v. 47, p. 493-514. [VERTEBRATES]

Berman, D. S., and Berman, S. L., 1975, *Broiliellus hektotopos* sp. nov. (Temnospondyli: Amphibia) Washington Formation, Dunkard Group, Ohio, *in* Barlow, J. A., ed., Proceedings of the first I. C. White memorial symposium: the age of the Dunkard: West Virginia Geological and Economic Survey, p. 69-78. [VERTEBRATES]

Bernhagen, R. J., Forsyth, Jane, Larson, L. H., Nave, Floyd, Silva, Edwin, and White, J. F., 1960, Geology of the Yellow Springs region: Guide to the Thirty-Fifth Annual Field Conference of the Section Geology of the Ohio Academy of Science, Ohio Academy of Science, 23 p. [OHIO GEOLOGY; BRACHIOPODA]

Berry, E. W., 1934, A fossil willow from Ohio: American Midland Naturalist, v. 15, p. 781-783. [PLANTS]

Berry, W. B. N., 1966, *Orthograptus truncatus richmondensis* (Ruedemann) in the Arnheim Formation (Ordovician) of Indiana: Journal of Paleontology, v. 40, p. 1392-1394. [GRAPTOLITHINA]

Bjerstedt, T. W., and Feldmann, R. M., 1985, Stromatoporoid paleosynecology in the Lucas Dolostone (Middle Devonian) on Kelleys Island, Ohio: Journal of Paleontology, v. 59, p. 1033-1061. [STROMATOPOROIDS]

Blind, Wolfram, and Stürmer, Wilhelm, 1977, *Viriatellina fuchsi* Kutscher (Tentaculoidea) mit Sipho und Fangarmen: Neues Jahrbuch für Geologie and Paläontologie Monatshefte 1977, issue 9, p. 513-522. [TENTACULITOIDS]

Boardman, D. R., II, Work, D. M., Mapes, R. H., and Barrick, J. E., 1994, Biostratigraphy of Middle and Late Pennsylvanian (Desmoinesian-Virgilian) ammonoids: Kansas Geological Survey Bulletin 232, 121 p. [CEPHALOPODA]

Boardman, R. S., and others, 1983, Part G (revised), Bryozoa, v. 1, *in* Robison, R. A., ed., Treatise on Invertebrate Paleontology: Geological Society of America and the University of Kansas, 625 p. [BRYOZOA]

Boardman, R. S., Cheetham, A. H., and Rowell, A. J., eds., 1987, Fossil invertebrates: Palo Alto, California, Blackwell Scientific Publications, 713 p. [GENERAL PALEONTOLOGY; BRYOZOA]

Boston, W. B., and Mapes, R. H., 1991, Ectocochleate cephalopod taphonomy, *in* Donovan, S. K., ed., The process of fossilization: London, England, Belhaven Press, p. 220-240. [CEPHALOPODA]

Bouček, Bedřich, 1964, The tentaculites of Bohemia: their morphology, taxonomy, ecology, phylogeny, and biostratigraphy: Czechoslovak Academy of Sciences, p. 1-215. [TENTACULITOIDS]

Brandt, D. S., 1991, Aspects of *Flexicalymene* (Trilobita) paleobiology (abs.): Geological Society of America Abstracts with Programs, v. 23, no. 3, p. 4. [TRILOBITA]

_________ 1993, Ecdysis in *Flexicalymene meeki* (Trilobita): Journal of Paleontology, v. 67, p. 999-1005. [TRILOBITA]

Brandt Velbel, D. S., 1985, Ichnologic, taphonomic, and sedimentologic clues to the deposition of Cincinnatian shales (Upper Ordovician), Ohio, U.S.A., *in* Curran, H. A., ed., Biogenic structures: their use in interpreting depositional environment: Society of Economic Paleontologists and Mineralogists (SEPM) Special Publication 35, p. 299-307. [TRILOBITA]

Brezinski, D. K., 1988, Appalachian Carboniferous trilobites: Journal of Paleontology, v. 62, p. 934-945. [TRILOBITA]

Brezinski, D. K., Sturgeon, M. T., and Hoare, R. D., 1989, Pennsylvanian trilobites of Ohio: Ohio Division of Geological Survey Report of Investigations 142, 18 p. [TRILOBITA; VERTEBRATES]

Broadhead, T. W., ed., 1983, Sponges and spongiomorphs; notes for a short course: University of Tennessee, Department of Geological Sciences, Studies in Geology 7, 220 p. [PORIFERA]

Bromley, R. G., 1990, Trace fossils: biology and taphonomy: London, Unwin Hyman, 280 p. [ICHNOFOSSILS]

Brongniart, Adolphe, 1822, Sur la classification et la distribution des végétaux fossiles en general, et sur ceux des terrains de sediment supérieur en particular: Musée National d'Histoire Naturelle, Memoirs, v. 8, p. 203-348. [PLANTS]

_________ 1828-1838, Histoire des végétaux fossiles ou recherches botaniques et géologiques sur les végétaux renfermes dans les diverses couches du globe: Paris, G. Dufour and Ed. D'Ocagne, 10 parts in 2 volumes, 488 p. and 72 p., respectively, and 195 pls. in 2 volumes. [PLANTS]

Brooks, H. K., 1957, Chelicerata, Trilobitomorpha, Crustacea (exclusive of Ostracoda) and Myriapoda—annotated bibliography, *in* Ladd, H. S., ed., Paleoecology, v. 2 of Treatise on marine ecology and paleoecology: Geological Society of America Memoir 67, p. 895-929. [TRILOBITA]

Brower, J. C., 1995, Dendrocrinid crinoids from the Ordovician of northern Iowa and southern Minnesota: Journal of Paleontology, v. 69, p. 939-960. [ECHINODERMATA: CRINOIDEA]

Buehler, E. J., 1955, The morphology and taxonomy of the Halysitidae: Peabody Museum of Natural History Bulletin 8, 179 p. [CNIDARIA]

Bulman, O. M. B., 1932, On the graptolites prepared by Holm. 2. The structure and development of *Climacograptus typicalis* Hall: Arkiv för Zoologi, v. 24A, issue 9, p. 1-10. [GRAPTOLITHINA]

_________ 1970, Part V (revised), Graptolithina, with sections on Enteropneusta and Pterobranchia, *in* Teichert, Curt, ed., Treatise on Invertebrate Paleontology: Geological Society of America and University of Kansas Press, 163 p. [GRAPTOLITHINA]

Burch, J. B., 1962, The eastern land snails: Dubuque, Iowa, W. C. Brown Co., 214 p. [GASTROPODA]

_________ 1975, Freshwater Sphaeracean clams (Mollusca: Pelecypoda) of North America: Hamburg, Michigan, Malacological Publications, 96 p. [PELECYPODA]

Burke, C. D., 1985, Paleoecologic interpretation of Ostracoda from the Skelley Member, Conemaugh Group (Pennsylvanian), southeastern Ohio: Journal of Paleontology, v. 59, p. 839-848. [OSTRACODA]

Burns, G. W., 1958, Wisconsin age forests in western Ohio—I. Vegetation and burial conditions: Ohio Journal of Science, v. 58, p. 220-230. [PLANTS]

Campbell, K. S. W., 1975, The functional morphology of *Cryptolithus*: Fossils and Strata, v. 4, p. 65-86. [TRILOBITA]

Carlson, E. H., 1991, Minerals of Ohio: Ohio Division of Geological Survey Bulletin 69, 155 p. [OHIO GEOLOGY; PLANTS (SILICIFIED TREE TRUNKS)]

Carman, J. E., 1927, Fossil footprints from the Pennsylvanian System in Ohio: Geological Society of America Bulletin, v. 38, p. 385-395. [VERTEBRATES; ICHNOFOSSILS]

_________ 1960, The stratigraphy of the Devonian Holland Quarry Shale of Ohio: Fieldiana—Geology (Chicago Natural History Museum), v. 14, no. 1, 5 p. [VERTEBRATES]

Carpenter, F. M., 1992, Part R, Arthropoda 4, v. 3 and v. 4, Superclass Hexapoda, *in* Kaesler, R. L., ed., Treatise on Invertebrate Paleontology: Geological Society of America and University of Kansas Press, 655 p. [OTHER ARTHROPODA]

Carr, R. K., 1991, Reanalysis of *Heintzichthys gouldii* (Newberry), an aspinothoracid arthrodire (Placodermi) from the Famennian of northern Ohio, with a review of brachythoracid systematics: Zoological Journal of the Linnean Society, v. 103, p. 349-390. [VERTEBRATES]

_________ 1994, A redescription of *Gymnotrachelus* (Placodermi: Arthrodira) from the Cleveland Shale (Famennian) of northern Ohio, U.S.A.: Kirtlandia, no. 48, p. 3-21. [VERTEBRATES]

_________ 1996, *Stenosteus angustopectus* sp. nov. from the Cleveland Shale (Famennian) of northern Ohio with a review of selenosteid (Placodermi) systematics: Kirtlandia, no. 49, p. 19-43. [VERTEBRATES]

Carroll, R. L., 1988, Vertebrate paleontology and evolution: New York, W. H. Freeman and Company, 698 p. [VERTEBRATES]

Carroll, R. L., and Baird, Donald, 1968, *Tuditanus* (*Eosauravus*) and the distinction between microsaurs and reptiles: American Museum of Natural History Novitates, no. 2337, 50 p. [VERTEBRATES]

Chitaley, Shya, 1982, Preliminary report on some plants from the Cleveland Shale: Kirtlandia, no. 38, p. 89-104. [PLANTS]

_________ 1988, The wood *Callixylon* from the Late Devonian of Ohio, U.S.A.: Review of Palaeobotany and Palynology, v. 53, p. 349-357. [PLANTS]

_________ 1992, On the occurrence of *Prototaxites* in the Cleveland black shale of Ohio, U.S.A.: Review of Palaeobotany and Palynology, v. 72, p. 257-271. [PLANTS]

Christopher, C. C., Jr., Hoare, R. D., and Sturgeon, M. T., 1990, Pennsylvanian hollinacean and kirkbyacean ostracodes from the Appalachian Basin: Journal of Paleontology, v. 64, p. 967-987. [OSTRACODA]

Churkin, Michael, Jr., and Carter, Claire, 1970, Devonian tentaculitids of east-central Alaska: systematics and biostratigraphic significance: Journal of Paleontology, v. 44, p. 51-68. [TENTACULITOIDS]

Clark, D. L., and others, 1981, Part W, Miscellanea, Supplement 2, Conodonta, *in* Robison, R. A., ed., Treatise on Invertebrate Paleontology: Geological Society of America and University of Kansas Press, p. 1-102. [CONODONTA]

Clarkson, E. N. K., 1975, The evolution of the eye in trilobites: Fossils and Strata, v. 4, p. 7-31. [TRILOBITA]

Claypole, E. W., 1891, *Megalonyx* in Holmes County, Ohio, 1890: American Geologist, v. 7, no. 2, p. 122-132; no. 3, p. 149-153. [VERTEBRATES]

_________ 1893, The fossil fishes of Ohio: Ohio Division of Geological Survey, v. 7, p. 602-619. [VERTEBRATES]

Cleal, C. J., and Shute, C. H., 1991, The Carboniferous pteridosperm frond *Neuropteris heterophylla* (Brongniart) Sternberg: British Museum of Natural History Bulletin (Geology), v. 46, p. 153-174. [PLANTS]

Cleal, C. J., and Shute, C. H., 1995, A synopsis of neuropterid foliage from the Carboniferous and Lower Permian of Europe: British Museum of Natural History Bulletin (Geology), v. 51, p. 1-52. [PLANTS]

Cleal, C. J., Shute, C. H., and Zodrow, E. L., 1990, A revised taxonomy for Paleozoic neuropterid foliage: Taxon, v. 39, p. 486-492. [PLANTS]

Cleal, C. J., and Zodrow, E. L., 1989, Epidermal structure of some medullosan *Neuropteris* foliage from the Middle and Upper Carboniferous of Canada and Germany: Palaeontology, v. 32, p. 837-882. [PLANTS]

Clifton, H. E., 1957, The carbonate concretions of the Ohio Shale: Ohio Journal of Science, v. 57, p. 114-124. [VERTEBRATES]

Cloudsley-Thompson, J. L., 1988, Evolution and adaptation of terrestrial arthropods: Berlin, Springer-Verlag, 141 p. [OTHER ARTHROPODA]

Coates, A. G., and Oliver, W. A., Jr., 1973, Coloniality in zoantharian corals, *in* Boardman, R. S., Cheetham, A. H., and Oliver, W. A., Jr., eds., Animal colonies: development through time: Stroudsburg, Pennsylvania, Dowden, Hutchinson, & Ross, p. 3-27. [CNIDARIA]

Collins, H. R., 1979, The Mississippian and Pennsylvanian (Carboniferous) Systems in the United States—Ohio: U.S. Geological Survey Professional Paper 1110-E, 26 p. [OHIO GEOLOGY]

Coogan, A. H., Heimlich, R. A., Malcuit, R. J., Bork K. B., and Lewis, T. L., 1981, Early Mississippian deltaic sedimentation in central and northeastern Ohio, *in* Roberts, T. G., ed., GSA Cincinnati '81 Field Trip Guidebooks: American Geological Institute, v. 1, p. 113-152. [OHIO GEOLOGY; BRACHIOPODA]

Cooper, B. J., 1975, Multielement conodonts from the Brassfield Limestone (Silurian) of southern Ohio: Journal of Paleontology, v. 49, p. 984-1008. [CONODONTA]

Cope, E. D., 1875, Synopsis of the extinct Batrachia of Ohio: Ohio Division of Geological Survey, v. 2, part 2, Paleontology, p. 349-411. [VERTEBRATES]

Cox, L. R., and others, 1969, Part N, Mollusca 6, v. 1 and 2, *in* Moore, R. C., ed., Treatise on Invertebrate Paleontology: Geological Society of America and University of Kansas Press, p. 1-952. [PELECYPODA]

Cox, L. R., and others, 1971, Part N, Mollusca 6, v. 3, *in* Moore, R. C., ed., Treatise on Invertebrate Paleontology: Geological Society of America and University of Kansas Press, p. 953-1224. [PELECYPODA]

Criss, R. E., Cooke, G. A., and Day, S. D., 1988, An organic origin for the carbonate concretions of the Ohio Shale: U.S. Geological Survey Bulletin 1836, 21 p. [VERTEBRATES]

Cross, A. T., 1988, Upper Pennsylvanian coals and associated rocks—depositional environments, sedimentation, paleontology, and paleobotany, Upper Ohio River Valley: Ohio Journal of Science, v. 88, p. 65-66. [PLANTS]

Cross, A. T., Smith, W. H., and Arkle, Thomas, Jr., 1950, Field guide for the special field conference on stratigraphy, sedimentation, and nomenclature of the Upper Pennsylvanian and lower Permian (Monongahela, Washington, and Greene Series) in the northern portion of the Dunkard basin of Ohio: West Virginia Geological and Economic Survey and Ohio Division of Geological Survey, 104 p. [PLANTS]

Crowther, P. R., and Bergström, S. M., 1980, Cortical bandages in an Upper Ordovician glyptograptid graptolite from Ohio: Bollettino della Società Paleontologica Italiana, v. 19, p. 250-253. [GRAPTOLITHINA]

Cumings, E. R., 1908, The stratigraphy and paleontology of the Ordovician rocks of Indiana: Indiana Department of Geology and Natural Resources, 32nd Annual Report, p. 605-1190. [BRYOZOA]

Dachnowski, Alfred, 1910, A cedar bog in central Ohio: The Ohio Naturalist, v. 11, no. 1, p. 193-199. [PLANTS]

_________ 1911, The vegetation of Cranberry Island (Ohio) and its relation to the substratum, temperature, and evaporation: Botanical Gazette, v. 52, p. 15-21. [PLANTS]

_________ 1912, Peat deposits of Ohio: Ohio Division of Geological Survey Bulletin 16, 424 p. [PLANTS]

Davis, R. A., ed., 1985, Cincinnati fossils, an elementary guide to the Ordovician rocks and fossils of the Cincinnati, Ohio, region: Cincinnati Museum of Natural History Popular Publication Series 10, 60 p. [MANY GROUPS]

Davis, R. A., and Troike, D. E., 1990, Repository for the Welch Collection of Silurian cephalopods described by August F. Foerste: Journal of Paleontology, v. 64, p. 1041-1042. [CEPHALOPODA]

Dawson, J. W., 1881, *Saccamina*? *(Calcisphaera) eriana*. (An Erian rhizopod of uncertain affinity): Canadian Naturalist and Quarterly Journal of Science (new series), v. 10, p. 5-8. [PLANTS]

Dean, Bashford, 1909, Studies on fossil fishes (sharks, chimaeroids and arthrodires): American Museum of Natural History Memoirs, part V, no. 9, p. 211-287. [VERTEBRATES]

Deevey, E. S., 1949, Biogeography of the Pleistocene, Part I: Europe and North America: Geological Society of America Bulletin, v. 60, p. 1315-1416. [PLANTS]

Delcourt, H. R., and Delcourt, P. A., 1985, Quaternary palynology and vegetation history of the southeastern United States, *in* Bryant, V. M., Jr., and Holloway, R. G., eds., Pollen records of Late-Quaternary North America sediments: Dallas, Texas, American Association of Stratigraphic Palynologists Foundation, p. 1-37. [PLANTS]

Delo, D. M., 1940, Phacopid trilobites of North America: Geological Society of America Special Paper 29, 135 p. [TRILOBITA]

Denison, R. H., 1960, Fishes of the Devonian Holland Quarry Shale of Ohio: Fieldiana—Geology (Chicago Natural History Museum), v. 11, no. 10, p. 555-613. [VERTEBRATES]

_________ 1978, Placodermi, *in* Schultze, H.-P., ed., Handbook of paleoichthyology: Stuttgart, Gustav Fischer Verlag, v. 2, 128 p. [VERTEBRATES]

_________ 1979, Acanthodii, *in* Schultze, H.-P., ed., Handbook of paleoichthyology: Stuttgart, Gustav Fischer Verlag, v. 5, 62 p. [VERTEBRATES]

Doher, L. I., 1980, Palynomorph preparation procedures currently used in the paleontology and stratigraphy laboratories, U.S. Geological Survey: U.S. Geological Survey Circular 830, 29 p. [PLANTS]

Dott, R. H., and Batten, R. L., 1976, Evolution of the Earth: New York, McGraw-Hill Book Co., 504 p. [GENERAL GEOLOGY]

Douglass, R. C., 1987, Fusulinid biostratigraphy and correlations between the Appalachian and Eastern Interior basins: U.S. Geological Survey Professional Paper 1451, 95 p. [PROTISTA — CHAPTER 1]

Dow, J. W., 1962, Lower and Middle Devonian limestones in northeastern Ohio and adjacent areas: Ohio Division of Geological Survey Report of Investigations 42, 67 p. [OHIO GEOLOGY]

Dreimanis, Aleksis, 1968, Extinction of mastodons in eastern North America: testing a new climatic environmental hypothesis: Ohio Journal of Science, v. 68, p. 257-272. [PLANTS]

Droste, J. B., and Shaver, R. H., 1983, Atlas of Early and Middle Paleozoic paleogeography of the southern Great Lakes area: Indiana Geological Survey Special Report 32, 32 p. [GENERAL GEOLOGY]

Dunkle, D. H., 1947, A new genus and species of arthrodiran fish from the Upper Devonian Cleveland Shale: Cleveland Museum of Natural History Science Publications, v. 8, no. 10, p. 103-117. [VERTEBRATES]

_________ 1964, Preliminary description of a paleoniscoid fish from the Upper Devonian of Ohio: Cleveland Museum of Natural History Science Publications, new series, v. 3, no. 1, 16 p. [VERTEBRATES]

Dunkle, D. H., and Bungart, P. A., 1939, A new arthrodire from the Cleveland Shale Formation: Cleveland Museum of Natural History Science Publications, v. 8, no. 2, p. 13-28. [VERTEBRATES]

_________ 1940, One of the least known of the Cleveland Shale Arthrodira: Cleveland Museum of Natural History Science Publications, v. 8, no. 2, p. 29-47. [VERTEBRATES]

_________ 1942a, The inferognathal plates of *Titanichthys*: Cleveland Museum of Natural History Science Publications, v. 8, no. 4, p. 49-59. [VERTEBRATES]

_________ 1942b, A new genus and species of Arthrodira from the Cleveland Shale: Cleveland Museum of Natural History Science Publications, v. 8, no. 6, p. 65-71. [VERTEBRATES]

_________ 1943, Comments on *Diplognathus mirabilis* Newberry: Cleveland Museum of Natural History Science Publications, v. 8, no. 7, p. 73-84. [VERTEBRATES]

_________ 1945a, A new arthrodiran fish from Upper Devonian Ohio shales: Cleveland Museum of Natural History Science Publications, v. 8, no. 8, p. 85-95. [VERTEBRATES]

_________ 1945b, Preliminary notice of a remarkable arthrodiran gnathal plate: Cleveland Museum of Natural History Science Publications, v. 8, no. 9, p. 97-102. [VERTEBRATES]

_________ 1946, The antero-supragnathal of *Gorgonichthys*: American Museum of Natural History Novitates, no. 1316, 10 p. [VERTEBRATES]

Dunkle, D. H., and Shaeffer, Bobb, 1973, *Tegeolepis clarki* (Newberry), a palaeonisciform from the Upper Devonian Ohio Shale: Palaeontographica, Abteilung A, v. 143, pt. 1-6, p. 151-158. [VERTEBRATES]

Durham, J. W., and others, 1966, Part U, Echinodermata 3 (Asterozoa, Echinozoa), v. 1 and 2, *in* Moore, R. C., ed., Treatise on Invertebrate Paleontology: Geological Society of America and University of Kansas Press, v. 1, p. 1-366a; v. 2, p. 367-695. [ECHINODERMATA]

Ehlers, G. M., and Stumm, E. C., 1949, Corals of the Devonian Traverse Group of Michigan, Part II: *Cylindrophyllum*, *Depasophyllum*, *Disphyllum*, *Eridophyllum*, and *Synaptophyllum*: University of Michigan Museum of Paleontology Contributions, no. 8, p. 21-41. [CNIDARIA]

Eldredge, Niles, 1972, Systematics and evolution of *Phacops rana* (Green, 1832) and *Phacops iowensis* Delo, 1935 (Trilobita) from the Middle Devonian of North America: American Museum of Natural History Bulletin, v. 147, p. 45-114. [TRILOBITA]

_________ 1973, Systematics of Lower and lower Middle Devonian species of the trilobite *Phacops* Emmrich in North America: American Museum of Natural History Bulletin, v. 151, p. 285-338. [TRILOBITA]

Elias, R. J., 1982, Latest Ordovician solitary rugose corals of eastern North America: Bulletins of American Paleontology, v. 81, no. 314, 116 p. [CNIDARIA; ICHNOFOSSILS]

_________ 1983, Middle and Late Ordovician solitary rugose corals of the Cincinnati Arch region, *in* Pojeta, John, Jr., ed., Contributions to the Ordovician paleontology of Kentucky and nearby states: U.S. Geological Survey Professional Paper 1066-N, p. N1-N13. [CNIDARIA]

_________ 1984, Paleobiology of solitary rugose corals, Late Ordovician of North America: Palaeontographica Americana, v. 54, p. 533-537. [CNIDARIA]

_________ 1986, Symbiotic relationships between worms and solitary rugose corals in the Late Ordovician: Paleobiology, v. 12, p. 32-45. [CNIDARIA; ICHNOFOSSILS]

Erdtmann, B.-D., and Moor, D. W., 1973, Reevaluation and taxonomic status of *Climacograptus typicalis* Hall and its varieties: Journal of Paleontology, v. 47, p. 1081-1093. [GRAPTOLITHINA]

Evitt, W. R., 1953, Observations on the trilobite *Ceraurus*: Journal of Paleontology, v. 27, p. 33-48. [TRILOBITA]

_________ 1963, A discussion and proposals concerning fossil dinoflagellates, hystricospheres and acritarchs: National Academy of Science Proceedings, v. 49, no. 2, p. 158-164 (pt. I); no. 3, p. 298-302 (pt. II). [PLANTS]

Evitt, W. R., and Whittington, H. B., 1953, The exoskeleton of *Flexicalymene*: Journal of Paleontology, v. 27, p. 49-55. [TRILOBITA]

Faegri, Knut, and Iverson, Johs., 1975, Textbook of pollen analysis (3rd ed.): New York, Hafner, 296 p. [PLANTS]

Fagadau, S. F., 1952, Paleontology and stratigraphy of the Logan Formation: Ph.D. dissertation (unpub.), Ohio State University, 424 p. [OHIO GEOLOGY; BRACHIOPODA]

Fagerstrom, J. A., 1971, Brachiopods of the Detroit River Group (Devonian) of southwestern Ontario and adjacent areas of Michigan and Ohio: Geological Survey of Canada Bulletin 204, 113 p. [BRACHIOPODA]

_________ 1982, Stromatoporoids of the Detroit River Group and adjacent rocks (Devonian) in the vicinity of the Michigan Basin: Geological Survey of Canada Bulletin 339, 81 p. [STROMATOPOROIDS]

Farrand, W. R., Zahner, Robert, and Benninghoff, W. S., 1969, Carey-Port Huron Interstade: evidence from a buried bryophyte bed, Cheboygan County, Michigan, *in* Shumm, S. A., and Bradley, W. C., United States contributions to Quaternary research: Geological Society of America Special Publication 123, p. 249-269. [PLANTS]

Fay, R. O., 1961, Blastoid studies: University of Kansas Paleontological Contributions, Echinodermata, Article 3, 147 p. [ECHINODERMATA: BLASTOIDEA]

Feldmann, R. M., and Babcock, L. E., 1986, Exceptionally preserved conulariids from Ohio—reinterpretation of their anatomy: National Geographic Research, v. 2, p. 464-472. [CONULARIIDA]

Feldmann, R. M., Chapman, R. E., and Hannibal, J. T., 1989, Paleotechniques: The Paleontological Society Special Publication 4, 358 p. [GENERAL PALEONTOLOGY]

Fenton, C. L., 1938, *Heliophyllum* and *"Cystiphyllum,"* corals of Hall's "Illustrations of Devonian corals": Carnegie Museum Annals, v. 27, p. 207-250. [CNIDARIA]

Fenton, C. L., and Fenton, M. A., 1936, The "tabulate" corals of Hall's "Illustrations of Devonian fossils": Carnegie Museum Annals, v. 25, p. 17-58. [CNIDARIA]

Fillion, D., and Pickerill, R. K., 1984, On *Arthraria antiquata* Billings, 1872 and its relationship to *Diplocraterion* Torell, 1870: Journal of Paleontology, v. 58, p. 683-696. [ICHNOFOSSILS]

Finks, R. M., 1960, Late Paleozoic sponge faunas of the Texas region—the siliceous sponges: American Museum of Natural History Bulletin, v. 120, article 1, p. 1-160. [PORIFERA]

Fisher, D. C., Lepper, B. T., and Hooge, P. E., 1991, Taphonomic analysis of the Burning Tree mastodont: Current Research in the Pleistocene, v. 8, p. 88-91. [VERTEBRATES]

_________ 1994, Evidence for butchery of the Burning Tree mastodont, *in* Dancey, W. S., ed., The first discovery of America: archaeological evidence of the early inhabitants of the Ohio area: Columbus, The Ohio Archaeological Council, p. 43-57. [VERTEBRATES]

Fisher, D. W., 1962, Small conoidal shells of uncertain affinities, *in* Hass, W. H., and others, Part W, Miscellanea, *in* Moore, R. C., ed., Treatise on Invertebrate Paleontology: Geological Society of America and University of Kansas Press, p. 98-143. [TENTACULITOIDS]

Flower, R. H., 1955, Trails and tentacular impressions of orthoconic cephalopods: Journal of Paleontology, v. 29, p. 857-867. [CEPHALOPODA]

Foerste, A. F., 1887, The Clinton Group of Ohio, Part II: Bulletin of the Scientific Laboratories of Denison University, v. 2, p. 89-110. [TRILOBITA]

_________ 1888, Notes on Paleozoic fossils: Bulletin of the Scientific Laboratories of Denison University, v. 3, p. 117-137. [CNIDARIA; TRILOBITA]

_________ 1893, Fossils of the Clinton Group in Ohio and Indiana: Ohio Division of Geological Survey, v. 7, p. 516-601. [TRILOBITA; MOLLUSCA]

_________ 1909a, Fossils from the Silurian formations of Tennessee, Indiana, and Kentucky: Bulletin of the Scientific Laboratories of Denison University, v. 14, p. 61-116. [PORIFERA]

_________ 1909b, Preliminary notes on Cincinnatian fossils: Bulletin of the Scientific Laboratories of Denison University, v. 14, p. 209-232. [CNIDARIA]

_________ 1909c, Preliminary notes on Cincinnatian and Lexington fossils: Bulletin of the Scientific Laboratories of Denison University, v. 14, p. 289-334. [PORIFERA; CNIDARIA]

_________ 1910, Preliminary notes on Cincinnatian and Lexington fossils of Ohio, Indiana, Kentucky, and Tennessee: Bulletin of the Scientific Laboratories of Denison University, v. 16, p. 17-87. [PORIFERA; TRILOBITA; PLANTS]

_________ 1914, Notes on the Lorraine faunas of New York and the Province of Quebec: Bulletin of the Scientific Laboratories of Denison University, v. 17, p. 247-340. [PLANTS]

_________ 1916, Notes on Cincinnatian fossil types: Bulletin of the Scientific Laboratories of Denison University, v. 18, p. 285-355. [PORIFERA; CNIDARIA; PLANTS]

_________ 1917, Notes on Silurian fossils from Ohio and other central states: Ohio Journal of Science, v. 17, p. 187-269. [CNIDARIA]

_________ 1919a, Notes on *Isotelus*, *Acrolichas*, *Calymene*, and *Encrinurus*: Bulletin of the Scientific Laboratories of Denison University, v. 19, p. 65-81. [TRILOBITA]

_________ 1919b, Silurian fossils from Ohio, with notes on related species from other horizons: Ohio Journal of Science, v. 19, p. 367-408. [TRILOBITA]

_________ 1925, Notes on cephalopod genera; chiefly coiled Silurian forms: Journal of the Scientific Laboratories of Denison University, v. 21, p. 1-69. [CEPHALOPODA]

_________ 1928, A restudy of American orthoconic Silurian cephalopods: Journal of the Scientific Laboratories of Denison University, v. 23, p. 236-320. [CEPHALOPODA]

_________ 1930, Three studies of cephalopods: Journal of the Scientific Laboratories of Denison University, v. 24, p. 265-381 (date nominally December 1929, but published in January 1930). [CEPHALOPODA]

_________ 1935, Correlation of Silurian formations in southwestern Ohio, southeastern Indiana, Kentucky, and western Tennessee: Journal of the Scientific Laboratories of Denison University, v. 30, p. 119-205. [OHIO GEOLOGY]

Folger, Tim, 1992, Oldest living bacteria tell all: Discover Magazine, v. 13, no. 1, p. 30-31. [VERTEBRATES; PLANTS]

Fontaine, W. M., and White, I. C., 1880, The Permian or Upper Carboniferous flora of West Virginia and southwestern Pennsylvania: Pennsylvania Geological Survey (Second) Report of Progress PP, 143 p. [PLANTS]

Forsyth, J. L., 1963, Ice age census: Ohio Conservation Bulletin, v. 27, no. 9, p. 16-19, 31, back cover. [VERTEBRATES]

_________ 1965, Age of the buried soil in the Sidney, Ohio, area: American Journal of Science, v. 263, p. 571-597. [PLANTS]

Fortey, R. A., 1985, Pelagic trilobites as an example of deducing the life habits of extinct arthropods: Transactions of the Royal Society of Edinburgh, v. 76, p. 219-230. [TRILOBITA]

Foster, J. W., 1838, Organic remains, *in* Mather, W. W., Second annual report on the Geological Survey of Ohio: Ohio Division of Geological Survey, 286 p. [VERTEBRATES]

Frank, G. W., ed., 1969, Ohio Intercollegiate Field Trip Guides 1950-51 to 1969-70: Kent State University Printing Service, sections paged separately. [OHIO GEOLOGY; BRACHIOPODA]

Frey, R. C., 1981, *Narthecoceras* (Cephalopoda) from the Upper Ordovician (Richmondian) of southwest Ohio: Journal of Paleontology, v. 55, p. 1217-1224. [CEPHALOPODA]

_________ 1985, A well-preserved specimen of *Schuchertoceras* (Cephalopoda, Ascocerida) from the Upper Ordovician (basal

Richmondian) of southwest Ohio: Journal of Paleontology, v. 59, p. 1506-1511. [CEPHALOPODA]

Frey, R. C., 1988, Paleoecology of *Treptoceras duseri* (Michelinoceratida, Proteoceratidae) from Late Ordovician of southwestern Ohio: New Mexico Bureau of Mines & Mineral Resources Memoir 44, p. 79-101. [CEPHALOPODA]

_________ 1989, Paleoecology of a well-preserved nautiloid assemblage from a Late Ordovician shale unit, southwestern Ohio: Journal of Paleontology, v. 63, p. 604-620. [CEPHALOPODA]

_________ 1995, Middle and Upper Ordovician nautiloid cephalopods of the Cincinnati Arch region of Kentucky, Indiana, and Ohio, *in* Pojeta, John, Jr., ed., Contributions to the Ordovician paleontology of Kentucky and nearby states: U.S. Geological Survey Professional Paper 1066-P, 126 p. [CEPHALOPODA]

Frey, R. W., 1975, The study of trace fossils: a synthesis of principles, problems, and procedures in ichnology: New York, Springer-Verlag, 562 p. [ICHNOFOSSILS]

Fry, W. L., 1983, An algal flora from the Upper Ordovician of the Lake Winnipeg region, Manitoba, Canada: Review of Palaeobotany and Palynology, v. 39, p. 313-341. [PLANTS]

Fry, W. L., and Banks, H. P., 1955, Three new genera of algae from the Upper Devonian of New York: Journal of Paleontology, v. 29, p. 37-44. [PLANTS]

Frye, C. J., and Feldmann, R. M., 1991, North American Late Devonian cephalopod aptychi: Kirtlandia, no. 46, p. 49-71. [CEPHALOPODA]

Furtos, N. C., 1933, The Ostracoda of Ohio: Ohio Biological Survey Bulletin, v. 5, no. 29, p. 413-524. [OSTRACODA]

Galloway, J. J., 1957, Structure and classification of the Stromatoporoidea: Bulletins of American Paleontology, v. 37, no. 164, p. 341-480. [STROMATOPOROIDS]

Galloway, J. J., and St. Jean, Joseph, Jr., 1957, Middle Devonian Stromatoporoidea of Indiana, Kentucky and Ohio: Bulletins of American Paleontology, v. 37, no. 162, p. 25-308. [STROMATOPOROIDS]

Garrison, G. C., 1967, Pollen stratigraphy and age of an early postglacial beaver site near Columbus, Ohio: Ohio Journal of Science, v. 67, p. 96-105. [PLANTS]

Gass, K. C., Edgecombe, G. D., Ramsköld, Lars, Mikulic, D. G., and Watkins, Rodney, 1992, Silurian Encrinurinae (Trilobita) from the central United States: Journal of Paleontology, v. 66, p. 75-89. [TRILOBITA]

Gazlay, Sayrs, 1833, Notices of fossil wood in Ohio: American Journal of Science, v. 25, p. 104-107. [PLANTS]

Ghist, J. M., 1976, Devonian tentaculites of Ohio: M.S. thesis (unpub.), Ohio State University, 185 p. [TENTACULITOIDS]

Gillespie, W. H., and Clendening, J. A., 1968, A flora from proglacial Lake Monongahela: Castanea, v. 33, p. 267-300. [PLANTS]

Gillespie, W. H., Clendening, J. A., and Pfefferkorn, H. W., 1978, Plant fossils of West Virginia and adjacent areas: West Virginia Geological and Economic Survey Educational Series ED-3A (revised ed.), 172 p. [PLANTS]

Girty, G. H., 1908, On some new and old species of Carboniferous fossils: U.S. National Museum Proceedings, v. 34, p. 281-303. [PORIFERA]

_________ 1915, Fauna of the Wewoka Formation of Oklahoma: U.S. Geological Survey Bulletin 554, 270 p. [PORIFERA]

Goldfuss, G. A., 1826, Petrefacta Germaniae, I: Dusseldorf, Germany, Arnz & Co., p. 1-76. [CNIDARIA]

_________ 1829, Petrefacta Germaniae, II: Dusseldorf, Germany, Arnz & Co., p. 77-164. [CNIDARIA]

Goldman, Daniel, 1995, Taxonomy, evolution, and biostratigraphy of the *Orthograptus quadrimucronatus* species group (Ordovician, Graptolithina): Journal of Paleontology, v. 69, p. 516-540. [GRAPTOLITHINA]

Goldman, Daniel, and Mitchell, C. E., 1991, Revision of the Upper Ordovician graptolite *Diplograptus* (*Amplexograptus*) *recurrens richmondensis* Ruedemann: Journal of Paleontology, v. 65, p. 1016-1017. [GRAPTOLITHINA]

Goldthwait, R. P., 1952, Geological situation of the Orleton Farms mastodon: Ohio Journal of Science, v. 52, p. 5-9. [PLANTS]

_________ 1958, Wisconsin age forest in western Ohio—I. Age and glacial events: Ohio Journal of Science, v. 58, p. 209-219. [PLANTS]

_________ 1959, Scenes in Ohio during the last ice age: Ohio Journal of Science, v. 59, p. 193-216. [PLANTS]

Graham, Russell, 1986, Taxonomy of North American mammoths, *in* Frison, G. C., and Todd, L. C., eds., The Colby Mammoth site—taphonomy and archaeology of a Clovis kill in northern Wyoming: University of New Mexico Press, p. 165-229. [VERTEBRATES]

Guber, A. C., 1971, Problems of sexual dimorphism, population structure and taxonomy of the Ordovician genus *Tetradella* (Ostracoda): Journal of Paleontology, v. 45, p. 6-22. [OSTRACODA]

Guilday, J. E., 1968, Grizzly bears from eastern North America: American Midland Naturalist, v. 79, p. 247-250. [VERTEBRATES]

_________ 1971, The Pleistocene history of the Appalachian mammal fauna, *in* Holt, P. C., ed., The distributional history of the biota of the southern Appalachians, pt. III, vertebrates: Virginia Polytechnic Institute and State University, Research Division Monograph 4, p. 233-262. [VERTEBRATES]

Gutschick, R. C., and Lamborn, Richard, 1975, *Bifungites*, trace fossils from Devonian-Mississippian rocks of Pennsylvania and Montana, U.S.A.: Palaeogeography, Palaeoclimatology, Palaeoecology, v. 18, p. 193-212. [ICHNOFOSSILS]

Hajlasz, Barbara, 1974, Tentaculites of the Upper Silurian and Lower Devonian of Poland: Acta Palaeontologica Polonica, v. 19, p. 455-500. [TENTACULITOIDS]

Hall, James, 1847, Descriptions of the organic remains of the lower division of the New York System (equivalent of the lower Silurian rocks of Europe): New York State Geological Survey, Palaeontology of New York, v. 1, 338 p. [CNIDARIA]

_________ 1852, Descriptions of the organic remains of the lower middle division of the New York System (equivalent in part to the middle Silurian rocks of Europe): New York State Geological Survey, Palaeontology of New York, v. 2, 363 p. [CNIDARIA]

_________ 1876, Illustrations of Devonian fossils: Gasteropoda, Cephalopoda, Crustacea and corals of the Upper Helderberg, Hamilton and Chemung groups: New York State Geological Survey, Palaeontology of New York, 7 p. [CNIDARIA]

_________ 1879, Descriptions of the Gasteropoda, Pteropoda, and Cephalopoda of the upper Helderberg, Hamilton, Portage, and Chemung groups: New York State Geological Survey, Palaeontology of New York, v. 5, pt. 2, 492 p. [TENTACULITOIDS]

_________ 1888, Supplement, containing descriptions and illustrations of Pteropoda, Cephalopoda and Annelida: New York State Geological Survey, Palaeontology of New York, v. 5, p. 2 (suppl.), 42 p. [TENTACULITOIDS]

Hall, James, and Clarke, J. M., 1888, Descriptions of the trilobites and other Crustacea of the Oriskany, Upper Helderberg, Hamilton, Portage, Chemung, and Catskill Groups: New York State Geological Survey, Palaeontology of New York, v. 7, 236 p. [TRILOBITA; OTHER ARTHROPODA]

_________ 1898, A memoir on the Palaeozoic reticulate sponges constituting the family Dictyospongidae: New York State Museum Memoir 2, 350 p. [PORIFERA]

Hall, James, and Simpson, G. B., 1887, Corals and Bryozoa, descriptions and figures of species from the lower Helderberg, upper Helderberg, and Hamilton groups: New York State Geological Survey, Palaeontology of New York, v. 6, 298 p. [CNIDARIA]

Hall, James, and Whitfield, R. P., 1875, Descriptions of Silurian fossils: Ohio Division of Geological Survey, v. 2, pt. 2, Paleontology, p. 65-161. [TRILOBITA; MOLLUSCA; PLANTS]

Hannibal, J. T., and Davis, R. A., 1992, A guide to the building stones of downtown Cincinnati—a walking tour: Ohio Division of Geological Survey Guidebook 7, 44 p. [ICHNOFOSSILS]

Hannibal, J. T., and Feldmann, R. M., 1983, Arthropod trace fossils, interpreted as echinocarid escape burrows, from the Chagrin Shale (Late Devonian) of Ohio: Journal of Paleontology, v. 57, p. 705-716. [ICHNOFOSSILS]

_________ 1987, *Echinocaris*, a mid-Paleozoic crustacean: an annotated bibliography: Kirtlandia, v. 42, p. 25-52. [OTHER ARTHROPODA]

Hannibal, J. T., and Schmidt, M. T., 1988, Rocks of ages: Earth Science, v. 41, no. 1, p. 19-20. [GENERAL GEOLOGY]

Hansen, M. C., no date, Guide to the geology along Interstate 77 between Marietta and Cleveland: Ohio Division of Geological Survey Educational Leaflet 15, folded brochure. [OHIO GEOLOGY]

_________ 1984, "Creatures from the Black Lagoon"—coal-swamp vertebrates from Linton, Ohio: Ohio Division of Geological Survey, Ohio Geology, Spring, p. 1-5. [VERTEBRATES]

_________ 1985a, Systematic relationships of petalodontiform chondrichthyans, *in* Dutro, J. T., Jr., and Pfefferkorn, H. W., eds., Compte Rendu, Neuvième Congrès International de Stratigraphie et de Géologie du Carbonifère, v. 5: Carbondale, Illinois, Southern Illinois Press, p. 523-541. [VERTEBRATES]

_________ 1985b, *Isotelus*—Ohio's State Fossil: Ohio Division of Geological Survey, Ohio Geology, Summer, p. 1-4. [TRILOBITA]

_________ 1986, Microscopic chondrichthyan remains from Pennsylvanian marine rocks of Ohio and adjacent areas: Ph.D. dissertation (unpub.), Ohio State University, 536 p. [VERTEBRATES]

_________ 1988, When "Bullwinkle" roamed Ohio: Ohio Division of Geological Survey, Ohio Geology, Winter, p. 5-6. [VERTEBRATES]

_________ 1990, The Johnstown mastodon: Ohio Division of Geological Survey, Ohio Geology, Winter, p. 4-5. [VERTEBRATES]

_________ 1992a, Ohio's Pleistocene bestiary: Ohio Division of Geological Survey, Ohio Geology, Winter, p. 1, 3-6. [VERTEBRATES]

_________ 1992b, Indian Trail Caverns—a window on Ohio's Pleistocene bestiary: Ohio Division of Geological Survey, Ohio Geology, Spring, p. 1, 3. [VERTEBRATES]

_________ 1992c, Ohio's oldest fossils: Ohio Geology, Spring, p. 6. [TRILOBITA]

_________ 1994a, The Martins Creek mastodon: a tale of man and beast: Ohio Division of Geological Survey, Ohio Geology, Summer, p. 1, 3. [VERTEBRATES]

_________ 1994b, Concretions: the "ludus helmontii" of the Ohio Shale: Ohio Division of Geological Survey, Ohio Geology, Fall, p. 1, 3-6. [VERTEBRATES]

_________ 1996, Ohio elk: Ohio Division of Geological Survey, Ohio Geology, Spring, p. 4-6. [VERTEBRATES]

Hansen, M. C., and Mapes, R. H., 1990, A predator-prey relationship between sharks and cephalopods in the late Paleozoic, *in* Boucot, A. J., Evolutionary paleobiology of behavior and coevolution: Amsterdam, Elsevier, p. 189-192. [CEPHALOPODA; VERTEBRATES]

Häntzchel, Walter, 1975, Part W, Supplement 1, Trace fossils and problematica (2nd ed.), *in* Teichert, Curt, ed., Treatise on Invertebrate Paleontology: Geological Society of America and University of Kansas Press, 269 p. [ICHNOFOSSILS]

Harrington, H. J., and others, 1959, Part O, Arthropoda 1, Trilobita, *in* Moore, R. C., ed., Treatise on Invertebrate Paleontology: Geological Survey of America and University of Kansas Press, p. 38-560. [TRILOBITA]

Harris, J. E., 1951, *Diademodus hydei*, a new fossil shark from the Cleveland Shale: Zoological Society of London Proceedings, v. 120, p. 683-697. [VERTEBRATES]

Hay, H. B., Pope, J. K., and Frey, R. C., 1981, Lithostratigraphy, cyclic sedimentation, and paleoecology of the Cincinnatian Series in southwestern Ohio and southeastern Indiana, *in* Roberts, T. G., ed., GSA Cincinnati '81 Field Trip Guidebooks: American Geological Institute, v. 1, p. 73-86. [OHIO GEOLOGY; BRACHIOPODA]

Hay, O. P., 1914, The Pleistocene mammals of Iowa: Iowa Geological Survey Annual Report for 1912, v. 23, p. 1-662. [VERTEBRATES]

_________ 1923, The Pleistocene of North America and its vertebrated animals from the States east of the Mississippi River and from the Canadian provinces east of longitude 95°: Washington D.C., Carnegie Institution, Publication 322, 499 p. [VERTEBRATES]

Haynes, Gary, 1991, Mammoths, mastodonts, and elephants: biology, behavior, and the fossil record: Cambridge, England, Cambridge University Press, 413 p. [VERTEBRATES]

Henningsmoen, Gunnar, 1975, Moulting in trilobites: Fossils and Strata, v. 4, p. 179-200. [TRILOBITA]

Herrick, C. L., 1887, A sketch of the geological history of Licking County, accompanying an illustrated catalogue of Carboniferous fossils from Flint Ridge, Ohio: Bulletin of the Scientific Laboratories of Denison University, v. 2, p. 15-88. [TRILOBITA]

_________ 1893, Observations upon the so-called Waverly Group of Ohio: Ohio Division of Geological Survey, v. 7, p. 495-515. [MANY GROUPS]

Hildreth, S. P., 1836, Observations on the bituminous coal deposits of the valley of the Ohio, and the accompanying rock strata; with notices of the fossil organic remains and the relics of vegetable and animal bodies: American Journal of Science, v. 29, p. 1-148. [PLANTS]

Hill, Dorothy, 1981, Part F, Coelenterata, Supplement 1, *in* Teichert, Curt, ed., Treatise on Invertebrate Paleontology: Geological Society of America and University of Kansas Press, 762 p. [CNIDARIA]

Hlavin, W. J., 1968, Ohio's Permian formations—their history and fauna: Explorer (Cleveland Museum of Natural History), v. 10, no. 4, p. 22-25. [VERTEBRATES]

_________ 1976, Biostratigraphy of the Late Devonian black shales on the cratonal margin of the Appalachian geosyncline: Ph.D. dissertation (unpub.), Boston University, 194 p. [VERTEBRATES]

Hlavin, W. J., and Boreske, J. R., Jr., 1973, *Mylostoma variabile* Newberry, an Upper Devonian durophagous brachythoracid arthrodire, with notes on related taxa: Museum of Comparative Zoology (Harvard University) Breviora, no. 412, 12 p. [VERTEBRATES]

Hoare, R. D., 1978, Report of a Pennsylvanian sponge new to Ohio: *Heliospongia ramosa* Girty (Demospongea: Heliospongiidae): Ohio Journal of Science, v. 76, p. 296-297. [PORIFERA]

_________ 1989, Taxonomy and paleoecology of Devonian rostroconch mollusks from Ohio: Journal of Paleontology, v. 63, p. 838-846. [ROSTROCONCHIA]

_________ 1990, Mississippian rostroconch mollusks from Ohio: Journal of Paleontology, v. 64, p. 725-732. [ROSTROCONCHIA]

_________ 1991, Ontogeny and variation in *Glyptopleura costata* (McCoy) (Ostracoda: Mississippian, Chesterian) from Ohio: Journal of Paleontology, v. 65, p. 760-766. [OSTRACODA]

_________ 1993, Ostracodes from the Maxville Limestone (Mississippian, Chesterian) from Ohio: Journal of Paleontology, v. 67, p. 571-585. [OSTRACODA]

Hoare, R. D., Coash, J. R., Innis, Charles, and Hole, Thornton, 1964, Pleistocene peccary *Platygonus compressus* Leconte from Sandusky County, Ohio: Ohio Journal of Science, v. 64, p. 207-214. [VERTEBRATES]

Hoare, R. D., Hansen, M. C., and Merrill, G. K., 1994, *Kellettina prolata* n. sp. (Ostracoda) from the Pennsylvanian of Ohio: Journal of Paleontology, v. 68, p. 1416. [OSTRACODA]

Hoare, R. D., and Sturgeon, M. T., 1968, The genus *Wewokella* (Porifera) in the Pennsylvanian of Ohio: Journal of Paleontology, v. 42, p. 81-83. [PORIFERA]

Hoare, R. D., Sturgeon, M. T., and Kindt, E. A., 1979, Pennsylvanian marine Bivalvia and Rostroconchia of Ohio: Ohio Division of Geological Survey Bulletin 67, 77 p. [PELECYPODA; ROSTROCONCHIA; VERTEBRATES]

Hoffman, R. L., 1969, Myriapoda, exclusive of Insecta, *in* Brooks, H. K., and others, Part R, Arthropoda, *in* Moore, R. C., ed., Treatise on Invertebrate Paleontology: Geological Society of America and University of Kansas Press, p. 572-606. [OTHER ARTHROPODA]

Holloway, R. G., and Bryant, V. M., Jr., 1985, Late-Quaternary pollen records and vegetation history of the Great Lakes region: United States and Canada, *in* Bryant, V. M., Jr., and Holloway, R. G., eds., Pollen records of Late-Quaternary North American sediments: Dallas, Texas, American Association of Stratigraphic Palynologists Foundation, p. 205-245. [PLANTS]

Holman, J. A., 1986, Turtles from the Late Wisconsinan of west-central Ohio: American Midland Naturalist, v. 116, no. 1, p. 213-214. [VERTEBRATES]

Hook, R. W., 1983, *Colosteus scutellatus* (Newberry), a primitive temnospondyl amphibian from the Middle Pennsylvanian of Linton, Ohio: American Museum of Natural History Novitates, no. 2770, p. 1-41. [VERTEBRATES]

_________ 1986, Coal is not without its poetry—fossil traces from the Paleozoic: Timeline (Ohio Historical Society), v. 3, no. 1, p. 2-15. [VERTEBRATES]

Hook, R. W., and Baird, Donald, 1986, The Diamond Coal Mine of Linton, Ohio, and its Pennsylvanian-age vertebrates: Journal of Vertebrate Paleontology, v. 6, p. 174-190. [VERTEBRATES]

_________ 1988, An overview of the Upper Carboniferous fossil deposit at Linton, Ohio: Ohio Journal of Science, v. 88, p. 55-60. [VERTEBRATES]

_________ 1993, A new fish and tetrapod assemblage from the Allegheny Group (Late Westphalian, Upper Carboniferous) of eastern Ohio, USA, *in* Heidtke, U., compiler, New research on Permo-Carboniferous faunas: Bad Dürkheim, Germany, Pollichia-Buch 29, p. 143-154. [VERTEBRATES]

Hook, R. W., and Ferm, J. C., 1985, A depositional model for the Linton tetrapod assemblage (Westphalian D, Upper Carboniferous) and its palaeoenvironmental significance: Philosophical Transactions of the Royal Society of London, B311, p. 101-109. [VERTEBRATES]

_________ 1987, Paleoenvironmental controls on vertebrate-bearing abandoned channels in the Upper Carboniferous: Palaeoclimatology, Palaeogeography, Palaeoecology, v. 63, p. 159-181. [VERTEBRATES]

Hook, R. W., and Hansen, M. C., 1985, The ichthyodorulite *Euctenius* from the Middle Pennsylvanian cannel coal at Linton, Ohio, identified as an intromittent organ of xenacanth sharks (abs.): Geological Society of America Abstracts with Programs, v. 17, no. 2, p. 95. [VERTEBRATES]

Hook, R. W., and Miller, T. R., 1996, An underground forest: Ohio Division of Geological Survey, Ohio Geology, Spring, p. 1, 3-4. [PLANTS]

Hoover, K. V., 1960, Devonian-Mississippian shale sequence in Ohio: Ohio Division of Geological Survey Information Circular 27, 154 p. [OHIO GEOLOGY]

Horvath, A. L., 1969, Relationships of Middle Silurian strata in Ohio and West Virginia: Ohio Journal of Science, v. 69, p. 321-342. [OHIO GEOLOGY; BRACHIOPODA]

Horvath, A. L., and Sparling, Dale, 1967, Silurian geology of Western Ohio: Guide to the Forty-Second Annual Conference of the Section of Geology of the Ohio Academy of Science, University of Dayton, 25 p. [OHIO GEOLOGY]

Hoskins, J. H., and Blickle, A. H., 1940, Concretionary *Callixylon* from the Ohio Devonian Black Shale: American Midland Naturalist, v. 23, p. 472-481. [PLANTS]

Hotton, Nicholas, III, 1970, *Mauchchunkia bassa*, gen. et sp. nov., an anthracosaur (Amphibia, Labyrinthodontia), from the Upper Mississippian: Kirtlandia, no. 12, 38 p. [VERTEBRATES]

House, M. R., 1962, Observations on the ammonoid succession of the North American Devonian: Journal of Paleontology, v. 36, p. 247-284. [CEPHALOPODA]

_________ 1978, Devonian ammonoids from the Appalachians and their bearing on international zonation and correlation: Special Papers in Palaeontology 21, 70 p. [CEPHALOPODA]

House, M. R., Gordon, MacKenzie, Jr., and Hlavin, W. J., 1986, Late Devonian ammonoids from Ohio and adjacent states: Journal of Paleontology, v. 60, p. 126-144. [CEPHALOPODA]

Howard, Hildegarde, 1951, Pleistocene duck bones from Ohio: The Condor, v. 53, p. 205. [VERTEBRATES]

Hyde, J. E. (M. F. Marple, ed.), 1953, Mississippian formations of central and southern Ohio: Ohio Division of Geological Survey Bulletin 51, 355 p. [MANY GROUPS]

Imbrie, John, and Imbrie, K. P., 1979, Ice ages: Short Hills, New Jersey, Enslow Publishing Company, 224 p. [GENERAL GEOLOGY]

James, J. F., 1881, Catalogue of the fossils of the Cincinnati Group: Cincinnati, James Barclay, 27 p. [SEVERAL GROUPS]

_________ 1884-1885, The fucoids of the Cincinnati Group: Cincinnati Society of Natural History Journal, v. 7, p. 124-132 (1884) and p. 155-166 (1885). [ICHNOFOSSILS]

_________ 1892, Studies in problematic organisms—the genus *Scolithus*: Geological Society of America Bulletin, v. 3, p. 32-44. [ICHNOFOSSILS]

James, U. P., 1881, Contributions to paleontology: fossils of the Lower Silurian Formation: Ohio, Indiana and Kentucky: The Paleontologist, v. 5, p. 33-44. [PORIFERA]

Jansonius, Jan, and Jenkins, W. A., 1978, Chitinozoa, *in* Haq, B. U., and Boersma, Anne, eds., Introduction to marine micropaleontology: New York, Elsevier, p. 341-357. [PLANTS]

Jell, P. A., 1978, Trilobite respiration and genal caeca: Alcheringa, v. 2, p. 251-260. [TRILOBITA]

Jin, Jisuo, 1989, Late Ordovician-Early Silurian rhynchonellid brachiopods from Anticosti Island, Quebec: Biostratigraphie du Paléozoique, v. 10, p. 1-217. [BRACHIOPODA]

Kemp, J. F., 1893, Memorial of John Strong Newberry: Geological Society of America Bulletin, v. 4, p. 393-406. [GENERAL GEOLOGY]

Kerp, J. H. F., 1988a, Aspects of Permian paleobotany and palynology. VIII. On the reclassification of the west and central European species of the form genus *Callipteris* Brongniart 1849: Review of Paleobotany and Palynology, v. 54, p. 135-150. [PLANTS]

_________ 1988b, Aspects of Permian paleobotany and palynology. X. The west and central European species of *Autunia* Frasser emend. Kerp (Peltaspermaceae) and the form genus *Rhachiphyllum* Kerp (callipterid foliage): Review of Paleobotany and Palynology, v. 54, p. 249-360. [PLANTS]

Kesling, R. V., 1954, Ostracods from the Middle Devonian Dundee Limestone in northwestern Ohio: University of Michigan Museum of Paleontology Contributions, v. 11, p. 167-186. [OSTRACODA]

_________ 1971, *Strataster ohioensis*, a new Early Mississippian brittle-star, and the paleoecology of its community: University of Michigan Museum of Paleontology Contributions, v. 23, no. 20, p. 305-341. [ECHINODERMATA: OPHIUROIDEA]

Kesling, R. V., and Chilman, R. B., 1975, Strata and megafossils of the Middle Devonian Silica Formation: University of Michigan Museum of Paleontology Papers on Paleontology, No. 8, 408 p. [MANY GROUPS]

_________ 1978, Ostracods of the Middle Devonian Silica Formation: University of Michigan Museum of Paleontology Papers on Paleontology, No. 18 (2 v.), 169 p. [OSTRACODA]

Kesling, R. V., and Graham, Alan, 1962, *Ischadites* is a dasycladacean alga: Journal of Paleontology, v. 36, p. 943-952. [PLANTS]

Kindle, E. M., and Miller, A. K., 1939, Bibliographic index of North American Devonian Cephalopoda: Geological Society of America Special Paper 23, 179 p. [CEPHALOPODA]

King, R. H., 1943, New Carboniferous and Permian sponges: Kansas Geological Survey Bulletin 47, 36 p. [PORIFERA]

Kjellesvig-Waering, E. N., 1961, Eurypterids of the Devonian Holland Quarry Shale of Ohio: Fieldiana—Geology (Chicago Natural History Museum), v. 14, no. 5, p. 79-98. [OTHER ARTHROPODA]

Kleffner, M. A., 1987, Conodonts of the Estill Shale and Bisher Formation (Silurian, southern Ohio): biostratigraphy and distribution: Ohio Journal of Science, v. 87, p. 78-89. [CONODONTA]

_________ 1990, Wenlockian (Silurian) conodont biostratigraphy, depositional environments, and depositional history along the eastern flank of the Cincinnati Arch in southern Ohio: Journal of Paleontology, v. 64, p. 319-328. [CONODONTA]

Kleffner, M. A., and Ausich, W. I., 1988, Lower and Middle Silurian of the eastern flank of the Cincinnati Arch and the Appalachian Basin margin, Ohio: Society of Economic Paleontologists and Mineralogists, Fifth Mid-Year Meeting, Field Trip 1, 25 p. [OHIO GEOLOGY; BRACHIOPODA]

Klippart, J. H., 1875, Discovery of *Dicotyles* (*Platygonus*) *compressus*, Le Conte: American Association for the Advancement of Science Proceedings, v. 23, no. 2, p. 1-6. [VERTEBRATES]

Knight, J. B., and others, 1960, Part I, Mollusca 1, *in* Moore, R. C., ed., Treatise on Invertebrate Paleontology: Geological Society of America and University of Kansas Press, 351 p. [GASTROPODA]

Kohut, J. J., and Sweet, W. C., 1968, The American Upper Ordovician Standard. X. Upper Maysville and Richmond conodonts from the Cincinnati Region of Ohio, Indiana and Kentucky: Journal of Paleontology, v. 42, p. 1456-1477. [CONODONTA]

Kovach, Jack, 1974, Stratigraphy and paleontology of the pentamerinid brachiopods of the Niagaran rocks of western Ohio and eastern Indiana: Ph.D. dissertation (unpub.), Ohio State University, 375 p. [BRACHIOPODA]

Krausel, R., and Weyland, H., 1934, *Lennea schmidti*, eine pflanzenahnliche Tierspur aus dem Devon: Palaeontologische Zeitschrift, v. 16, nos. 1-2, p. 95-102. [PLANTS]

Kummel, Bernard, and Raup, David, 1965, Handbook of paleontological techniques: San Francisco, W. H. Freeman and Company, 852 p. [GENERAL PALEONTOLOGY]

Landman, N. H., and Cochran, J. K., 1987, Growth and longevity of *Nautilus*, *in* Saunders, W. B., and Landman, N. H., eds., *Nautilus*, the biology and paleobiology of a living fossil: New York, Plenum Press, p. 401-420. [CEPHALOPODA]

La Rocque, Aurèle, 1966, Pleistocene Mollusca of Ohio, part 1 (Introduction): Ohio Division of Geological Survey Bulletin 62, part 1, p. 1-111. [MOLLUSCA]

_________ 1967, Pleistocene Mollusca of Ohio, part 2 (Naiades and Sphaeriidae): Ohio Division of Geological Survey Bulletin 62, part 2, p. 112-356. [PELECYPODA]

_________ 1968, Pleistocene Mollusca of Ohio, part 3 (freshwater Gastropoda): Ohio Division of Geological Survey Bulletin 62, part 3, p. 357-553. [GASTROPODA]

_________ 1970, Pleistocene Mollusca of Ohio, part 4 (terrestrial Gastropoda): Ohio Division of Geological Survey Bulletin 62, part 4, p. 555-800. [GASTROPODA]

La Rocque, Aurèle, and Marple, M. F., 1955, Ohio fossils: Ohio Division of Geological Survey Bulletin 54, 152 p. [OHIO GEOLOGY; MANY GROUPS]

Larsen, G. E., 1994, Regional bedrock geology of the Ohio portion of the Lima, Ohio-Indiana 30 x 60 minute quadrangle: Ohio Division of Geological Survey Map 7. [OHIO GEOLOGY]

Larson, G. P., 1975, Fossil fish of the Silica Formation, *in* Kesling, R. V., and Chilman, R. B., Strata and megafossils of the Middle Devonian Silica Formation: University of Michigan Museum of Paleontology Papers on Paleontology, No. 8, p. 231-236. [VERTEBRATES]

Larsson, Kent, 1979, Silurian tentaculitids from Gotland and Scania: Fossils and Strata, v. 11, p. 1-180. [TENTACULITOIDS]

Laub, R. S., 1972, The auloporid genus *Cladochonus* McCoy, 1847: new data from the New York Devonian: Journal of Paleontology, v. 46, p. 364-370. [CNIDARIA]

_________ 1975, The ancestry, geographical extent, and fate of the Brassfield coral fauna (Middle Llandovery, North America): Bulletins of American Paleontology, v. 67, no. 287, p. 273-286. [CNIDARIA]

_________ 1979, The corals of the Brassfield Formation (mid-Llandovery; Lower Silurian) in the Cincinnati Arch region: Bulletins of American Paleontology, v. 75, no. 305, 433 p. [CNIDARIA]

Laubenfels, M. W., de, 1955, Part E, Porifera, *in* Moore, R. C., ed., Treatise on Invertebrate Paleontology: Geological Society of America and University of Kansas Press, p. 21-122. [PORIFERA]

Lepper, B. T., Frolking, T. A., Fischer, D. C., Goldstein, Gerald, Sanger, John, Wymer, D. A., Ogden, J. G., III, and Hooge, P. E., 1991, Intestinal contents of a late Pleistocene mastodont from midcontinental North America: Quaternary Research, v. 36, p. 120-125. [VERTEBRATES; PLANTS]

Lespérance, P. J., 1975, Stratigraphy and paleontology of the Synphoriidae (Lower and Middle Devonian dalmanitacean trilobites): Journal of Paleontology, v. 49, p. 91-137. [TRILOBITA]

Lespérance, P. J., and Bourque, P. A., 1971, The Synphoriinae: an evolutionary pattern of Lower and Middle Devonian trilobites: Journal of Paleontology, v. 45, p. 182-208. [TRILOBITA]

Lesquereux, Leo, 1879-1884, Description of the coal flora of the Carboniferous formation in Pennsylvania and throughout the United States: Pennsylvania Geological Survey (Second) Report of Progress, 977 p. (3 v.) plus atlas (1879). [PLANTS]

Levi-Setti, Riccardo, 1993 (2nd ed.), Trilobites: a photographic atlas: University of Chicago Press, 342 p. [TRILOBITA]

Long, J. A., 1991, Arthrodire predation by *Onychodus* (Pisces, Crossopterygii) from the Upper Devonian Gogo Formation, Western Australia: Records of the Western Australian Museum, v. 15, p. 369-371. [VERTEBRATES]

_________ 1995, The rise of fishes: 500 million years of evolution: Baltimore, The John Hopkins University Press, 223 p. [VERTEBRATES]

Lowney, K. A., 1980, A revision of the Family Haplolepidae (Actinopterygii, Paleonisciformes) from Linton, Ohio (Westphalian D, Pennsylvanian): Journal of Paleontology, v. 54, p. 942-953. [VERTEBRATES]

Ludvigsen, Rolf, 1977, The Ordovician trilobite *Ceraurinus* Barton in North America: Journal of Paleontology, v. 51, p. 959-972. [TRILOBITA]

_________ 1979, Fossils of Ontario, part 1: the trilobites: Royal Ontario Museum Life Sciences Miscellaneous Publications, 96 p. [TRILOBITA]

Ludvigsen, Rolf, and Tuffnell, P. A., 1983, A revision of the Ordovician olenid trilobite *Triarthrus* Green: Geological Magazine, v. 120, p. 567-577. [TRILOBITA]

Lund, Richard, 1970, Fossil fishes from southwestern Pennsylvania, part I, fishes from the Duquesne Limestones (Conemaugh, Pennsylvanian): Carnegie Museum Annals, v. 41, p. 231-161. [VERTEBRATES]

_________ 1973, Fossil fishes from southwestern Pennsylvania, part II, *Monongahela dunkardensis*, new species (Dipnoi, Lepidosirenidae) from the Dunkard Group: Carnegie Museum Annals, v. 44, p. 71-101. [VERTEBRATES]

Lund, Richard, and Lund, W. L., 1985, Coelacanths from the Bear Gulch Limestone (Namurian) of Montana and the evolution of the Coelacanthiformes: Carnegie Museum of Natural History Bulletin, v. 25, p. 1-74. [VERTEBRATES]

Lyons, P. C., Morey, E. D., and Wagner, R. H., 1995, Historical perspective of early twentieth century Carboniferous paleobotany in North America: Geological Society of America Memoir 185, 404 p. [PLANTS]

Maisey, J. G., 1982, Studies on the Paleozoic selachian genus *Ctenacanthus* Agassiz, no. 2, *Bythiacanthus* St. John and Worthen, *Amelacanthus*, new genus, *Eunemacanthus* St. John and Worthen, *Sphenacanthus* Agassiz, and *Wodnika* Munster: American Museum of Natural History Novitates, no. 2722, p. 1-24. [VERTEBRATES]

_________ 1984, Studies on the Paleozoic selachian genus *Ctenacanthus* Agassiz, no. 3, nominal species referred to *Ctenacanthus*: American Museum of Natural History Novitates, no. 2774, p. 1-20. [VERTEBRATES]

Manger, W. L., 1971, The Mississippian ammonoids *Karagandoceras* and *Kazakhstania* from Ohio: Journal of Paleontology, v. 45, p. 33-39. [CEPHALOPODA]

Mangold, K., 1987, Reproduction, *in* Boyle, P. R., ed., Cephalopod life cycles; v. II, comparative reviews: London, Academic Press, p. 157-200. [CEPHALOPODA]

Mann, D. N., Wingate, T. T., and Hanna, E. L., 1962, The Johnstown mastodon: Explorer (Cleveland Museum of Natural History), v. 4, no. 5, p. 14-21. [VERTEBRATES]

Mapes, R. H., and Hansen, M. C., 1984, Pennsylvanian shark-cephalopod predation: a case study: Lethaia, v. 17, p. 175-183. [CEPHALOPODA; VERTEBRATES]

Mapes, R. H., Sturgeon, M. T., Windle, D. L., and Hoare, R. D., in press, Pennsylvanian cephalopods of Ohio, part 2, ammonoid cephalopods: Ohio Division of Geological Survey Bulletin 71. [CEPHALOPODA]

Mark, C. G., 1912, The fossils of the Conemaugh formation in Ohio, *in* Condit, D. D., Conemaugh formation in Ohio: Ohio Division of Geological Survey Bulletin 17, p. 261-326. [MOLLUSCA]

Marple, M. F., 1952, Ostracodes from the Pottsville Series in Ohio: Journal of Paleontology, v. 26, p. 924-940. [OSTRACODA]

Martin, A. C., and Barkley, W. D., 1961, Seed identification manual: Berkeley, University of California Press, 221 p. [PLANTS]

McComas, G. A., and Mapes, R. H., 1988, Fauna associated with the Pennsylvanian floral zones of the 7-11 Mine, Columbiana County, northeastern Ohio: Ohio Journal of Science, v. 88, p. 53-55. [OTHER ARTHROPODA; PLANTS]

McComas, M. A., 1988, Upper Pennsylvanian compression floras of the 7-11 mine, Columbiana County, northeastern Ohio: Ohio Journal of Science, v. 88, p. 48-52. [PLANTS]

McDonald, H. G., 1988, Fossil muskoxen in Ohio: Cincinnati Museum of Natural History Quarterly, v. 21, no. 1, p. 11-12. [VERTEBRATES]

_________ 1989, New records of the elk-moose *Cervalces scotti* from Ohio: American Midland Naturalist, v. 122, p. 349-356. [VERTEBRATES]

_________ 1994, The Late Pleistocene vertebrate fauna in Ohio: coinhabitants with Ohio's Paleoindians, *in* Dancey, W. S., ed., The first discovery of America: archaeological evidence of the early inhabitants of the Ohio area: Columbus, The Ohio Archaeological Council, p. 23-41. [VERTEBRATES]

McDonald, H. G., and Davis, R. A., 1989, Fossil muskoxen of Ohio: Canadian Journal of Zoology, v. 67, p. 1159-1166. [VERTEBRATES]

McDonald, J. N., and Ray, C. E., 1989, The autochthonous North American muskoxen *Bootherium*, *Symbos*, and *Gidleya* (Mammalia: Artiodactyla: Bovidae): Smithsonian Contributions to Paleobiology, No. 66, 77 p. [VERTEBRATES]

Meek, F. B., 1873, Descriptions of invertebrate fossils of the Silurian and Devonian Systems: Ohio Division of Geological Survey, v. 1, part 2, Paleontology, p. 1-243. [MOLLUSCA]

_________ 1875, Descriptions of invertebrate fossils from the Carboniferous System: Ohio Division of Geological Survey, v. 2, part 2, Paleontology, p. 269-347. [MOLLUSCA]

Meek, F. B., and Worthen, A. H., 1868, Geological Survey of Illinois, v. III, part II, Palaeontology: p. 291-343. [TENTACULITOIDS]

Melvin, R. W., and McKenzie, G. D., 1992, Guide to the building stones of downtown Columbus: a walking tour: Ohio Division of Geological Survey Guidebook 6, 33 p. [GENERAL GEOLOGY; ICHNOFOSSILS]

Merrill, G. K., 1972, Taxonomy, phylogeny and biostratigraphy of *Neognathodus* in Appalachian Pennsylvanian rocks: Journal of Paleontology, v. 46, p. 817-829. [CONODONTA]

_________ 1973, Pennsylvanian nonplatform conodont genera. I. *Spathognathodus*: Journal of Paleontology, v. 47, p. 289-314. [CONODONTA]

_________ 1974, Pennsylvanian conodont localities in northeastern Ohio: Ohio Division of Geological Survey Guidebook 3, 25 p. [CONODONTA]

Meyer, D. L., 1990, Population paleoecology and comparative taphonomy of two edrioasteroid (Echinodermata) pavements: Upper Ordovician of Kentucky and Ohio: Historical Biology, v. 4, p. 155-178. [ECHINODERMATA: EDRIOASTEROIDEA]

Meyer, D. L., Tobin, R. C., Pryor, W. A., Harrison, W. B., and Osgood, R. G., 1981, Stratigraphy, sedimentology, and paleoecology of the Cincinnatian Series (Upper Ordovician) in the vicinity of Cincinnati, Ohio, *in* Roberts, T. G., ed., GSA Cincinnati '81 Field Trip Guidebooks: American Geological Institute, v. 1, p. 31-71. [OHIO GEOLOGY; BRACHIOPODA]

Meyer, D. L., Schumacher, G. A., Swinford, E. M., Jennette, D. C., and Brockman, C. S., 1985, Upper Ordovician stratigraphy, sedimentology, and paleontology along Backbone Creek, Clermont County, Ohio: Guidebook for the Geology Section field trip of the annual meeting (Cincinnati) of the Ohio Academy of Science, p. 1-14. [OHIO GEOLOGY; BRACHIOPODA]

Mickle, J. E., and Rothwell, G. W., 1982, Permineralized *Alethopteris* from the Upper Pennsylvanian of Ohio and Illinois: Journal of Paleontology, v. 56, p. 392-402. [PLANTS]

Middleman, A. A., 1976, Trace fossils of the Logan Formation (Lower Mississippian) in northern Hocking County, Ohio: M.S. thesis (unpub.), Ohio University, 132 p. [ICHNOFOSSILS]

Mikulic, D. G., 1981, Trilobites in Paleozoic carbonate buildups: Lethaia, v. 14, p. 45-56. [TRILOBITA]

Miller, B. B., and Szabo, J. P., 1987, Garfield Heights: Quaternary stratigraphy of northeastern Ohio, *in* Biggs, D. L., ed., Geological Society of America Centennial Field Guide, North-Central Section, p. 399-402. [MOLLUSCA]

Miller, G. S., Jr., 1899, A new fossil bear from Ohio: Biological Society of Washington, Proceedings, v. 13, p. 53-56. [VERTEBRATES]

Miller, John, 1976, The sensory fields and life mode of *Phacops rana* (Green, 1832) (Trilobita): Transactions of the Royal Society of Edinburgh, v. 69, p. 337-367. [TRILOBITA]

Miller, S. A., 1874a, Genus *Pasceolus* (Billings): Cincinnati Quarterly Journal of Science, v. 1, p. 4-7. [PLANTS]

_________ 1874b, *Tentaculites richmondensis*: Cincinnati Quarterly Journal of Science, v. 1, p. 234-235. [TENTACULITOIDS]

_________ 1879, Catalogue of fossils found in the Hudson River, Utica Slate and Trenton Groups, as exposed in the southeast part of Indiana, southwest part of Ohio, and northern part of Kentucky: 8th, 9th, and 10th Annual Reports (one volume) of the Geological Survey of Indiana, p. 22-56. [PORIFERA]

_________ 1882, Designation of two new genera and eight new species from the Hudson River Group, with remarks on others: Cincinnati Society of Natural History Journal, v. 5, p. 34-44. [PORIFERA]

_________ 1889, Class Porifera, *in* North American geology and palaeontology: Cincinnati, S. A. Miller (privately published), p. 152-167. [PORIFERA]

Miller, S. A., and Dyer, C. B., 1878, Contributions to paleontology: Cincinnati Society of Natural History Journal, v. 1, p. 24-39. [PORIFERA]

Miller, Wade, 1987, *Mammut americanum*, Utah's first record of the American mastodon: Journal of Paleontology, v. 61, p. 168-183. [VERTEBRATES]

Mills, R. S., 1975, A ground sloth, *Megalonyx*, from a Pleistocene site in Darke County, Ohio: Ohio Journal of Science, v. 75, p. 147-155. [VERTEBRATES]

Milne-Edwards, Henri, 1851, Monographie des polypiers fossiles des terrains paléozoïques: Muséum National d'Histoire Naturelle, Archives, v. 5, 502 p. [CNIDARIA]

Milne-Edwards, Henri, and Haime, Jules, 1850, A monograph of the British fossil corals: Palaeontographical Society Monographs, p. 1-71. [CNIDARIA]

Mitchell, C. E., 1975, The fauna and strata of a portion of the Arnheim Formation as exposed at Stonelick Lake State Park, southwestern Ohio: B.S. thesis (unpub.), Ohio State University, 47 p. [GRAPTOLITHINA]

_________ 1986, Morphometric studies of *Climacograptus* Hall and the phylogenetic significance of astogeny, *in* Hughes, C. P., and Rickards, R. B., eds., Palaeoecology and biostratigraphy of graptolites: Geological Society Special Publication 20, p. 199-129. [GRAPTOLITHINA]

_________ 1987, Evolution and phylogenetic classification of Diplograptacea: Palaeontology, v. 30, p. 353-405. [GRAPTOLITHINA]

Mitchell, C. E., and Bergström, S. M., 1977, Three-dimensionally preserved Richmondian graptolites from southwestern Ohio and the graptolite correlation of the North American Upper Ordovician Standard: Bollettino della Società Paleontologica Italiana, v. 16, p. 257-270. [GRAPTOLITHINA]

_________ 1991, New graptolite and lithostratigraphic evidence from the Cincinnati region, U.S.A., for the definition and correlation of the base of the Cincinnatian Series (Upper Ordovician): Geological Survey of Canada Paper 90-9, p. 59-77. [GRAPTOLITHINA]

Mitchell, R. H., 1931, Fossil footprints from the Pennsylvanian of Ohio: Ohio Journal of Science, v. 31, p. 501-504. [VERTEBRATES]

_________ 1933, Notes of another Pennsylvanian footprint from Ohio: Ohio Journal of Science, v. 33, p. 48-49. [VERTEBRATES]

Mitchell, S. W., 1971, A new occurrence of the Devonian arthrodire *Holonema*: Ohio Journal of Science, v. 71, p. 120-124. [VERTEBRATES]

Moodie, R. L., 1916, The coal measures Amphibia of North America: Washington, D. C., Carnegie Institution Publication No. 238, 222 p. [VERTEBRATES]

Moore, R. C., Lalicker, C. G., and Fischer, A. G., 1952, Invertebrate fossils: New York, McGraw-Hill Book Co., Inc., 766 p. [GENERAL PALEONTOLOGY]

Moran, W. E., 1952, Location and stratigraphy of known occurrences of fossil tetrapods in the Upper Pennsylvanian and Permian of Pennsylvania, West Virginia, and Ohio, *in* Fossil vertebrates of the tri-state area: Carnegie Museum Annals, v. 33, p. 1-44. [VERTEBRATES]

Morgan, A. V., and Morgan, Ann, 1990, Beetles, *in* Warner, B. G., ed., Methods in Quaternary ecology: Geoscience Canada Reprint Series, v. 5, p. 113-126. [OTHER ARTHROPODA]

Morgan, Jeanne, 1959, The morphology and anatomy of American species of the genus *Psaronius*: Illinois Biological Monograph 27, 108 p. [PLANTS]

Morningstar, Helen, 1922, Pottsville fauna of Ohio: Ohio Division of Geological Survey Bulletin 25, 312 p. [MOLLUSCA]

Morton, S. G., 1836, Being a notice and description of the organic remains embraced in the preceding paper [Hildreth, 1836]: American Journal of Science, v. 29, p. 149-154. [PLANTS]

Moy-Thomas, J. A., and Miles, R. S., 1971, Palaeozoic fishes: Philadelphia, W. B. Saunders Company, 259 p. [VERTEBRATES]

Murphy, J. L., 1971a, A *Physonemus* spine from the Lower Mercer limestone (Pennsylvanian) of Portage County, Ohio: Ohio Journal of Science, v. 71, p. 240-242. [VERTEBRATES]

_________ 1971b, Eryopsid remains from the Conemaugh Group, Braxton County, West Virginia: Southeastern Geology, v. 13, p. 265-273. [VERTEBRATES]

_________ 1973, *Protosalvinia* (*Foerstia*) Zone in the Upper Devonian sequence of eastern Ohio, northwestern Pennsylvania, and western New York: Geological Society of America Bulletin, v. 84, p. 3405-3410. [PLANTS]

Murphy, J. L., Dyer, D. L., and Walker, D. A., 1985, Prehistoric elk remains from Cranberry Prairie, Mercer County, Ohio: Ohio Journal of Science, v. 85, p. 112-115. [VERTEBRATES; PLANTS]

Murray, E. J., 1975, Trace fossils of the Brassfield Formation, Lower Silurian, in south-central Ohio and north-central Kentucky: M.S. thesis (unpub.), Western Michigan University, 101 p. [ICHNOFOSSILS]

Murray, R. C., ed., 1985, Atlas of invertebrate macrofossils: Harlow, England, Longman Group Limited (New York, Halstead Press), 241 p. [GENERAL PALEONTOLOGY; BRACHIOPODA]

Nave, F. R., 1969, Pleistocene mollusks of southwestern Ohio: Sterkiana, v. 34 p. 1-48. [MOLLUSCA]

Newberry, J. S., 1853, Fossil plants from the Ohio coal basin: Annals of Science (Cleveland), v. 1, p. 106-108. [PLANTS]

_________ 1873, Descriptions of fossil fishes: Ohio Division of Geological Survey, v. 1, part 2, Paleontology, p. 245-355. [VERTEBRATES]

_________ 1875, Descriptions of fossil fishes: Ohio Division of Geological Survey, v. 2, part 2, Paleontology, p. 1-64. [VERTEBRATES]

_________ 1889, The Paleozoic fishes of North America: U.S. Geological Survey Monograph 16, 340 p. [VERTEBRATES]

Nicholson, H. A., 1875, Description of the corals of the Silurian and Devonian systems; Descriptions of Amorphozoa from the Silurian and Devonian formations: Ohio Division of Geological Survey, v. 2, pt. 2, Paleontology, p. 181-255. [STROMATOPOROIDS; CNIDARIA]

_________ 1876, Notes on the Palaeozoic corals of the State of Ohio: Annals and Magazine of Natural History, 4th series, v. 18, no. 104, p. 85-95. [CNIDARIA]

Nickles, J. M., 1902, The geology of Cincinnati: Cincinnati Society of Natural History Journal, v. 20, p. 49-100. [PORIFERA]

Niklas, K. J., and Phillips, T. L., 1976, Morphology of *Protosalvinia* from Upper Devonian of Ohio and Kentucky: American Journal of Botany, v. 63, p. 9-29. [PLANTS]

Nitecki, M. H., 1970a, North American cyclocrinitid algae: Fieldiana—Geology (Chicago Natural History Museum), v. 21, 182 p. [PLANTS]

_________ 1970b, Gametangia of Silurian *Ischadites hemisphericus* (Receptaculitaceae, Dasycladales): Phycologia, v. 11, p. 1-4. [PLANTS]

_________ 1970c, The paleogeographic significance of receptaculitids: 24th International Geological Congress (1972), v. 7, p. 303-309. [PLANTS]

_________ 1971, *Ischadites abbottae*, a new North American Silurian species (Dasycladales): Phycologia, v. 10, p. 263-275. [PLANTS]

_________ 1972, North American Silurian receptaculitid algae: Fieldiana—Geology (Chicago Natural History Museum), v. 28, p. 1-108. [PLANTS]

Nitecki, M. H., and Toomey, D. F., 1979, Nature and classification of receptaculitids: Bulletin Centre de Recherches Exploration-Production Elf Aquitaine, v. 3, p. 725-732. [PLANTS]

Ogden, J. G., III, 1966, Forest history of Ohio. I. Radiocarbon dates and pollen stratigraphy of Silver Lake, Logan County, Ohio: Ohio Journal of Science, v. 66, p. 387-400. [PLANTS]

_________ 1967a, Radiocarbon and pollen evidence for a sudden change in climate in the Great Lakes region approximately 10,000 years ago, *in* Cushing, E. J., and Wright, H. E., Jr., eds., Quaternary paleoecology: New Haven, Connecticut, Yale University Press, p. 117-127. [PLANTS]

_________ 1967b, Radiocarbon determinations of sedimentation rates from hard and soft water lakes in northeastern North America, *in* Cushing, E. J., and Wright, H. E., Jr., eds., Quaternary paleoecology: New Haven, Connecticut, Yale University Press, p. 175-183. [PLANTS]

Ogden, J. G., III, and Hay, R. J., 1964, Ohio Wesleyan University natural radiocarbon measurements I: Radiocarbon, v. 6, p. 340-348. [PLANTS]

_________ 1965, Ohio Wesleyan University natural radiocarbon measurements II: Radiocarbon, v. 7, p. 166-173. [PLANTS]

_________ 1967, Ohio Wesleyan University natural radiocarbon measurements III: Radiocarbon, v. 9, p. 316-332. [PLANTS]

Ohio Division of Geological Survey, Report on Ohio mineral industries: published annually. [OHIO GEOLOGY]

Ohio Division of Parks and Recreation, no date, The fossils of Hueston Woods: Ohio Department of Natural Resources, 15 p. [OHIO GEOLOGY]

Oliver, F. W., and Scott, D. H., 1904, On the structures of the Paleozoic seed *Lagenostoma lomaxi* with a statement of the evidence upon which it is referred to *Lyginodendron*: Philosophical Transactions of the Royal Society of London, 197B, p. 193-247. [PLANTS]

Oliver, W. A., Jr., 1976, Biogeography of Devonian rugose corals: Journal of Paleontology, v. 50, p. 365-373. [CNIDARIA]

Oliver, W. A., Jr., and Coates, A. G., 1987, Phylum Cnidaria, *in* Boardman, R. S., Cheetham, A. H., and Rowell, A. J., eds., Fossil invertebrates: Palo Alto, California, Blackwell Scientific Publications, p. 140-193. [CNIDARIA]

Olsen, S. J., 1972, Osteology for the archaeologist: the American mastodon and the wooly mammoth: Papers of the Peabody Museum of Archaeology and Ethnology (Harvard University), v. 56, no. 3, p. 1-45. [VERTEBRATES]

Olson, E. C., 1970, *Trematops stonei* sp. nov. (Temnospondyli: Amphibia) from the Washington Formation, Dunkard Group, Ohio: Kirtlandia, no. 8, 12 p. [VERTEBRATES]

_________ 1975, Vertebrates and biostratigraphic position of the Dunkard, *in* Barlow, J. A., ed., Proceedings of the first I. C. White memorial symposium: the age of the Dunkard: West Virginia Geological and Economic Survey, p. 155-156. [VERTEBRATES]

Orton, Edward, 1870, On the occurrence of a peat bed beneath deposits of drift in southwestern Ohio: American Journal of Science and Arts (2nd series), v. 50, p. 54-57, 293. [PLANTS]

Osgood, R. G., Jr., 1970, Trace fossils of the Cincinnati area: Palaeontographica Americana, v. 6, no. 41, p. 277-444. [CEPHALOPODA; ICHNOFOSSILS]

_________ 1977, Selected Cincinnatian trace fossils, *in* Pope, J. K., and Martin, W. D., eds., Field guidebook to the biostratigraphy and paleoenvironments of the Cincinnatian Series of southeastern Indiana: 7th annual field conference, Great Lakes Section SEPM, Miami University, p. III-1 to III-24. [ICHNOFOSSILS]

_________ 1987, Trace fossils, *in* Boardman, R. S., Cheetham, A. H., and Rowell, A. J., eds., Fossil invertebrates: Palo Alto, California, Blackwell Scientific Publications, p. 663-674. [ICHNOFOSSILS]

Palmer, A. R., 1974, Search for the Cambrian world: American Scientist, v. 62, p. 216-224. [GENERAL GEOLOGY]

_________ 1983, compiler, The Decade of North American Geology 1983 geologic time scale: Geology, v. 11, p. 503-504. [GENERAL GEOLOGY]

Palmer, Douglas, and Rickards, Barrie, eds., 1991, Graptolites: writing in the rocks: Woodbridge, England, Boydell Press, p. 1-182. [GRAPTOLITHINA]

Parks, W. A., 1936, Devonian stromatoporoids of North America, Part I: University of Toronto Studies, Geological Series, no. 39, 125 p. [STROMATOPOROIDS]

Parsley, R. L., 1989, Latex casting of macroinvertebrate fossils, *in* Feldmann, R. M., Chapman, R. E., and Hannibal, J. T., Paleotechniques: Paleontological Society Special Publication 4, p. 275-281. [GENERAL PALEONTOLOGY]

Pashin, J. C., and Ettensohn, F. R., 1995, Reevaluation of the Bedford-Berea sequence in Ohio and adjacent states: forced regression in a foreland basin: Geological Society of America Special Paper 298, 74 p. [OHIO GEOLOGY]

Patterson, R. P., 1971, Fossil trackways from Upper Pennsylvanian Monongahela Formation in southeastern Ohio: Earth Science, v. 24, p. 181-185. [VERTEBRATES]

Peck, R. E., and Eyer, J. A., 1963, Pennsylvanian, Permian and Triassic Charophyta of North America: Journal of Paleontology, v. 37, p. 835-844. [PLANTS]

_________ 1964, Pennsylvanian, Permian and Triassic Charophyta of North America—a correction: Journal of Paleontology, v. 38, p. 426. [PLANTS]

Peck, R. E., and Morales, G. A., 1966, The Devonian and Lower Mississippian Charophyta of North America: Micropaleontology, v. 12, p. 303-324. [PLANTS]

Pemberton, S. G., and Frey, R. W., 1982, Trace fossil nomenclature and the *Planolites-Palaeophycus* dilemma: Journal of Paleontology, v. 56, p. 843-881. [ICHNOFOSSILS]

Penhallow, D. D., 1896, *Nematophyton ortoni*, n. sp.: Annals of Botany, v. 10, p. 41-48. [PLANTS]

Pettijohn, F. J., and Potter, P. E., 1964, Atlas and glossary of primary sedimentary structures: Berlin, Springer-Verlag, 370 p. [GENERAL GEOLOGY; ICHNOFOSSILS]

Pigg, K. B., and Rothwell, G. W., 1983, *Chaloneria* gen. nov.; heterosporous lycophytes from the Pennsylvanian of North America: Botanical Gazette, v. 144, p. 132-147. [PLANTS]

Pojeta, John, Jr., 1966, North American Ambonychiidae (Pelecypoda): Paleontographica Americana, v. 5, no. 36, p. 129-241. [PELECYPODA]

Pojeta John, Jr., and Runnegar, Bruce, 1976, The paleontology of rostroconch mollusks and the early history of the phylum Mollusca: U.S. Geological Survey Professional Paper 968, 88 p. [ROSTROCONCHIA]

Pope, J. K., 1976, Comparative morphology and shell histology of the Ordovician Strophomenacea (Brachiopoda): Palaeontographica Americana, v. 8, no. 49, p. 129-213. [BRACHIOPODA]

_________ 1982, Some silicified strophomenacean brachiopods from the Ordovician of Kentucky, with comments on the genus *Pionomena*, *in* Pojeta, John, Jr., ed., Contributions to the Ordovician paleontology of Kentucky and nearby states: U.S. Geological Survey Professional Paper 1066-L, p. L1-L30. [BRACHIOPODA]

Pulse, R. R., and Sweet, W. C., 1960, The American Upper Ordovician Standard. III. Conodonts from the Fairview and McMillan formations of Ohio, Kentucky and Indiana: Journal of Paleontology, v. 34, p. 237-264. [CONODONTA]

Rau, J. L., 1970, The Pennsylvanian System, *in* Banks, P. O., and Feldmann, R. M., eds., Guide to the geology of northeastern Ohio: Northern Ohio Geological Society, p. 69-124. [OHIO GEOLOGY; BRACHIOPODA]

Rauff, Hermann, 1893-1895, Palaeospongiologie: Palaeontographica, v. 40, p. 1-232; v. 41, p. 233-346; v. 43, p. 223-272. [PORIFERA]

Raymond, P. E., and Barton, D. C., 1913, A revision of the American species of *Ceraurus*: Museum of Comparative Zoology (Harvard University) Bulletin, v. 54, p. 525-543. [TRILOBITA]

Reisz, R. R., and Baird, Donald, 1983, Captorhinomorph "stem" reptiles from the Pennsylvanian coal-swamp deposit of Linton, Ohio: Carnegie Museum Annals, v. 52, p. 393-411. [VERTEBRATES]

Rexroad, C. B., 1967, Stratigraphy and conodont paleontology of the Brassfield (Silurian) in the Cincinnati Arch area: Indiana Geological Survey Bulletin 36, 71 p. [CONODONTA]

Richard, Benjamin, and Evers, Michael, 1990, Ohio Academy of Science 1990 Geology Field Trip through Glen Helen, 15 p. [OHIO GEOLOGY; BRACHIOPODA]

Richards, R. P., 1972, Autecology of Richmondian brachiopods (Late Ordovician of Indiana and Ohio): Journal of Paleontology, v. 46, p. 386-405. [BRACHIOPODA]

Rigby, J. K., 1966, Microstructure and classification of an Ordovician sponge, *Dystactospongia madisonensis* Foerste from Indiana: Journal of Paleontology, v. 40, p. 1127-1130. [PORIFERA]

_________ 1970, *Brachiospongia tuberculata* James from the Ordovician of central Ontario: Journal of Paleontology, v. 44, p. 1139-1142. [PORIFERA]

_________ 1978, Two wewokellid calcareous sponges in North America: Journal of Paleontology, v. 52, p. 705-716. [PORIFERA]

_________ 1983, Fossil Demospongia, *in* Broadhead, T. W., ed., Sponges and spongiomorphs; notes for a short course: University of Tennessee, Department of Geological Sciences, Studies in Geology 7, p. 12-39. [PORIFERA]

_________ 1986, Late Devonian sponges of Western Australia: Geological Survey of Western Australia Report 18, 59 p. [PORIFERA]

_________ 1987, Phylum Porifera, *in* Boardman, R. S., Cheetham, A. W., and Rowell, A. J., eds., Fossil invertebrates: Palo Alto, California, Blackwell Scientific Publications, p. 116-139. [PORIFERA]

Rixon, A. E., 1976, Fossil animal remains: their preparation and conservation: London, The Athlone Press, 304 p. [GENERAL PALEONTOLOGY]

Robison, R. A., 1987, Superclass Trilobitomorpha, *in* Boardman, R. S., Cheetham, A. H., and Rowell, A. J., eds., Fossil invertebrates: Palo Alto, California, Blackwell Scientific Publications, p. 221-241. [TRILOBITA]

Rolfe, W. D. I., 1969, Phyllocarida, *in* Brooks, H. K., and others, Part R, Arthropoda 4, v. 1, *in* Moore, R. C., ed., Treatise on Invertebrate Paleontology: Geological Society of America and University of Kansas Press, p. 296-333. [OTHER ARTHROPODA]

Romer, A. S., 1930, The Pennsylvanian tetrapods of Linton, Ohio: American Museum of Natural History Bulletin, v. 59, article 2, p. 77-147. [VERTEBRATES]

_________ 1952, Late Pennsylvanian and early Permian vertebrates of the Pittsburgh-West Virginia region, *in* Fossil vertebrates of the tri-state area: Carnegie Museum Annals, v. 33, p. 47-112. [VERTEBRATES]

_________ 1961, A large ophiacodont pelycosaur from the Pennsylvanian of the Pittsburgh region: Museum of Comparative Zoology (Harvard University) Breviora, no. 144, 7 p. [VERTEBRATES]

_________ 1963, The larger embolomerous amphibians of the American Carboniferous: Museum of Comparative Zoology (Harvard University) Bulletin, v. 128, no. 9, p. 415-454. [VERTEBRATES]

_________ 1969, A temnospondylous labyrinthodont from the Lower Carboniferous: Kirtlandia, no. 6, 20 p. [VERTEBRATES]

_________ 1970, A new anthracosaur labyrinthodont, *Proterogyrinus scheelei*, from the Lower Carboniferous: Kirtlandia, no. 10, 16 p. [VERTEBRATES]

Romer, A. S., and Price, L. W., 1940, Review of the Pelycosauria: Geological Society of America Special Paper 28, 538 p. [VERTEBRATES]

Rominger, C. L., 1876, Lower Peninsula. Palaeontology, fossil corals: Geological Survey of Michigan, v. 3, part 2, 161 p. [CNIDARIA]

Ross, R. J., Jr., 1967, Calymenid and other Ordovician trilobites from Kentucky and Ohio: U.S. Geological Survey Professional Paper 583-B, 18 p. [TRILOBITA]

_________ 1979, Additional trilobites from the Ordovician of Kentucky, *in* Pojeta, John, Jr., ed., Contributions to the Ordovician paleontology of Kentucky and nearby states: U.S. Geological Survey Professional Paper 1066-D, p. D1-D13. [TRILOBITA]

Rothwell, G. W., 1976, Petrified Pennsylvanian age plants of eastern Ohio: Ohio Journal of Science, v. 76, p. 128-132. [PLANTS]

_________ 1984, The apex of *Stigmaria* (Lycopsida): American Journal of Botany, v. 71, p. 1031-1034. [PLANTS]

_________ 1988a, Upper Pennsylvanian Steubenville coal-ball flora: Ohio Journal of Science, v. 88, p. 61-65. [PLANTS]

_________ 1988b, Cordaitales, Chapter 6 *in* Beck, C. B., ed., Origin and evolution of gymnosperms: New York, Columbia University Press, p. 298-337. [PLANTS]

_________ 1991, *Botryopteris forensis* (Botryopteridaceae), a trunk epiphyte of the tree fern *Psaronius*: American Journal of Botany, v. 78, p. 782-788. [PLANTS]

Rothwell, G. W., and Blickle, A. H., 1982, *Psaronius magnificus* n. comb., a marattialean fern from the Upper Pennsylvanian of North America: Journal of Paleontology, v. 56, p. 459-568. [PLANTS]

Rothwell, G. W., and Erwin, D. M., 1985, The rhizomorph apex of *Paurodendron*: implications for homologies among the rooting organs of lycopods: American Journal of Botany, v. 72, p. 86-98. [PLANTS]

Rothwell, G. W., Scheckler, S. E., and Gillespie, W. H., 1989, *Elkinsia*, gen. nov., a late Devonian gymnosperm with cupulate ovules: Botanical Gazette, v. 150, p. 170-189. [PLANTS]

Ruedemann, Rudolf, 1947, Graptolites of North America: Geological Society of America Memoir 19, 652 p. [GRAPTOLITHINA]

Sandy, M. R., 1992, Geologic glimpses from around the world—the geology of monuments in Woodland Cemetery and Arboretum, Dayton, Ohio: a self-guided tour: Ohio Division of Geological Survey Guidebook 8, 29 p. [ICHNOFOSSILS]

Sanger, J. E., and Crowl, G. H., 1979, Fossil pigments as a guide to the paleolimnology of Browns Lake, Ohio: Ohio Journal of Science, v. 11, p. 342-352. [PLANTS]

Sartenaer, Paul, 1961a, Étude nouvelle en deux parties, du genre *Camarotoechia* Hall et Clarke, 1893. Première partie: *Atrypa congregata* Conrad, espèce-type: Bulletin de l'Institut royal des Sciences naturelles de Belgique, v. 22, p. 1-9. [BRACHIOPODA]

_________ 1961b, Étude nouvelle en deux parties, du genre *Camarotoechia* Hall et Clarke, 1893. Deuxième partie: *Cupularostrum recticostatum* n. gen., n. sp.: Bulletin de l'Institut royal des Sciences naturelles de Belgique, v. 25, p. 1-15. [BRACHIOPODA]

Sass, J. E., 1958, Botanical microtechnique: Ames, Iowa State University Press, 228 p. [PLANTS]

Savage, K. M., and Lowell, T. V., 1992, Dynamics of the marginal Late Wisconsin Miami sublobe, Cincinnati, Ohio: Ohio Journal of Science, v. 92, p. 107-118. [OHIO GEOLOGY]

Schaeffer, Bobb, 1962, A coelacanth fish from the Upper Devonian of Ohio: Scientific Publications of the Cleveland Museum of Natural History, v. 1 (new series), no. 1, 13 p. [VERTEBRATES]

_________ 1967, Comments on elasmobranch evolution, *in* Gilbert, P. W., Mathewson, R. F., and Rall, D. P., eds., Sharks, skates, and rays: Baltimore, Johns Hopkins University Press, p. 3-35. [VERTEBRATES]

Schmalfuss, Helmut, 1981, Structure, patterns and function of cuticular terraces in trilobites: Lethaia, v. 14, p. 331-241. [TRILOBITA]

Schmid, R., 1976, Septal pores in *Prototaxites*, an enigmatic Devonian plant: Science, v. 191, p. 287-288. [PLANTS]

Schmidt, R. G., McFarlan, A. C., Nosow, Edmund, Bowman, R. S., and Alberts, Robert, 1961, Examination of Ordovician through Devonian stratigraphy and the Serpent Mound chaotic structure area: Geological Society of America, Guidebook for field trips, Cincinnati meeting, 1961, p. 261-293. [OHIO GEOLOGY; BRACHIOPODA]

Schopf, J. M., Ehlers, E. G., Stiles, D. V., and Birle, J. D., 1965, Fossil bacteria preserved in pyrite: American Philosophical Society Proceedings, v. 109, p. 288-308. [PLANTS]

Schopf, J. M., and Schwietering, J. F., 1970, The *Foerstia* zone of the Ohio and Chattanooga Shales: U.S. Geological Survey Bulletin 1294-H, p. H1-H15. [PLANTS]

Schopf, J. M., Wilson, L. R., and Bentall, Ray, 1944, An annotated synopsis of Paleozoic fossil spores and the definition of generic groups: Illinois State Geological Survey Report of Investigations 91, 73 p. [PLANTS]

Schram, F. R., Feldmann, R. M., and Copeland, M. J., 1978, The Late Devonian Palaeopalaemonidae and the earliest decapod crustaceans: Journal of Paleontology, v. 52, p. 1375-1387. [OTHER ARTHROPODA]

Schultze, H.-P., 1994, *Palaeophichthys parvulus* Eastman, 1908, a gnathorhizid dipnoan from the Middle Pennsylvanian of Illinois, USA: Carnegie Museum Annals, v. 63, p. 105-113. [VERTEBRATES]

Schumacher, G. A., 1993, Regional bedrock geology of the Ohio portion of the Piqua, Ohio-Indiana 30 x 60 minute quadrangle: Ohio Division of Geological Survey Map 6. [OHIO GEOLOGY]

Schumacher, G. A., and Ausich, W. I., 1983, New Upper Ordovician echinoderm site: Bull Fork Formation, Caesar Creek Reservoir (Warren County, Ohio): Ohio Journal of Science, v. 83, p. 60-64. [ECHINODERMATA: CRINOIDEA, ASTEROIDEA]

Schumacher, G. A., Shrake, D. L., Swinford, E. M., Brockman, C. S., and Wickstrom, L. H., 1987, Stratigraphy and depositional environments of the Cincinnati Group of southwestern Ohio: Field trip guidebook, 16th Annual Eastern Section Meeting, American Association of Petroleum Geologists, Ohio Geological Society, 73 p. [OHIO GEOLOGY]

Schwimmer, B. A., and Feldmann, R. M., 1990, Stratigraphic distribution of brachiopods and bivalves in the Upper Devonian (Famennian) Chagrin Shale of northeastern Ohio: Kirtlandia, no. 45, p. 7-31. [BRACHIOPODA]

Scotese, C. R., and Denham, C. R., 1988, Terra Mobilis: plate tectonics for the Macintosh: published by the authors. [GENERAL GEOLOGY]

Scott, A. C., and Taylor, T. N., 1983, Plant-animal interactions during the Upper Carboniferous: Botanical Review, v. 48, p. 259-307. [PLANTS]

Scrutton, C. T., 1965, Periodicity in Devonian coral growth: Palaeontology, v. 7, p. 552-558. [CNIDARIA]

Scudder, S. H., 1895, Revision of the American fossil cockroaches with descriptions of new forms: U.S. Geological Survey Bulletin 124, 176 p. [OTHER ARTHROPODA]

Sears, P. B., 1930, A record of post-glacial climate in northern Ohio: Ohio Journal of Science, v. 30, p. 205-217. [PLANTS]

_________ 1931, Pollen analysis of Mud Lake bog in Ohio: Ecology, v. 12, p. 650-655. [PLANTS]

_________ 1942, Forest sequences in the north-central states: Botanical Gazette, v. 103, p. 751-761. [PLANTS]

Sears, P. B., and Clisby, K. H., 1952, Pollen spectra associated with the Orleton Farms mastodon site: Ohio Journal of Science, v. 52, p. 9-10. [PLANTS]

Shackleton, N. J., and Opdyke, N. D., 1976, Oxygen isotope and paleomagnetic stratigraphy of equatorial Pacific core V28-238: oxygen isotope temperatures and ice volumes on a 10^5 and 10^6 year scale: Quaternary Research, v. 3, p. 39-55. [PLANTS]

Shane, L. C. K., 1975, Palynology and radiocarbon chronology of Battaglia Bog, Portage County, Ohio: Ohio Journal of Science, v. 75, p. 96-102. [PLANTS]

_________ 1994, Intensity and rate of vegetation and climate change in the Ohio region between 14,000 and 9,000 ^{14}C yr B.P., *in* Dancey, W. S., ed., The first discovery of America: archaeological evidence of the early inhabitants of the Ohio area: Columbus, The Ohio Archaeological Council, p. 7-21. [VERTEBRATES]

Shaw, F. C., and Lespérance, P. J., 1994, North American biogeography and taxonomy of *Cryptolithus* (Trilobita, Ordovician): Journal of Paleontology, v. 68, p. 808-823. [TRILOBITA]

Shear, W. A., and Kukalovà-Peck, Jarmila, 1990, The ecology of Paleozoic terrestrial arthropods: the fossil evidence: Canadian Journal of Zoology, v. 68, p. 1807-1834. [OTHER ARTHROPODA]

Shrake, D. L., 1990, Common trilobites of Ohio: Ohio Division of Geological Survey, Ohio Geology, Summer, p. 1-5. [TRILOBITA]

_________ 1992, Excursion to Caesar Creek State Park in Warren County, Ohio: a classic Upper Ordovician fossil-collecting locality: Ohio Division of Geological Survey Guidebook 12, 18 p. [OHIO GEOLOGY; MANY GROUPS]

Sinclair, G. W., and Walker, D. R., 1956, Redescription of *Aspidichthys*: Arthrodira, Devonian: Ohio Journal of Science, v. 56, p. 135-137. [VERTEBRATES]

Sisson, Peg, and Sisson, Ray, 1988, Elementary Cincinnati fossils: College of Mount St. Joseph, 52 p. [BRACHIOPODA]

Smith, H. P., 1887, *Bison latifrons*—Leidy: Cincinnati Society of Natural History Journal, v. 10, p. 19-53. [VERTEBRATES]

Smyth, Pauline, 1979, Bibliography of Ohio geology, 1755-1974: Ohio Division of Geological Survey Information Circular 48, 249 p. [OHIO GEOLOGY; VERTEBRATES]

Snigirevskaya, N. S., 1958, An anatomical study of the leaves (phylloids) of some lycopsids in the Donetz basin coal balls: Akademie Nauk SSSR, Botanical Journal, v. 43, p. 106-112. [PLANTS]

Solem, Alan, and Yochelson, E. L., 1979, North American Paleozoic land snails, with a summary of other Paleozoic nonmarine snails: U.S. Geological Survey Professional Paper 1072, 38 p. [GASTROPODA]

Sorauf, J. E., 1971, Microstructure in the exoskeleton of some Rugosa (Coelenterata): Journal of Paleontology, v. 45, p. 23-32. [CNIDARIA]

Sparling, D. R., 1981, Middle Devonian conodont apparatuses with seven types of elements: Journal of Paleontology, v. 55, p. 295-316. [CONODONTA]

_________ 1983, Conodont biostratigraphy and biofacies of lower Middle Devonian limestones, north-central Ohio: Journal of Paleontology, v. 57, p. 825-864. [CONODONTA]

_________ 1984, Paleoecologic and paleogeographic factors in the distribution of lower Middle Devonian conodonts from north-central Ohio, *in* Clark, D. L., ed., Conodont biofacies and provincialism: Geological Society of America Special Paper 196, p. 113-125. [CONODONTA]

_________ 1988, Middle Devonian stratigraphy and conodont biostratigraphy, north-central Ohio: Ohio Journal of Science, v. 88, p. 2-18. [CONODONTA]

Speyer, S. E., and Chatterton, B. D. E., 1989, Trilobite larvae and larval ecology: Historical Biology, v. 3, p. 27-60. [TRILOBITA]

Stauffer, C. R., 1909, The Middle Devonian of Ohio: Ohio Division of Geological Survey Bulletin 10, 204 p. [OHIO GEOLOGY; MOLLUSCA; BRACHIOPODA]

_________ 1938, Conodonts of the Olentangy Shale: Journal of Paleontology, v. 14, p. 417-435. [CONODONTA]

Stauffer, C. R., and Schroyer, C. R., 1920, The Dunkard Series of Ohio: Ohio Division of Geological Survey Bulletin 22, 167 p. [VERTEBRATES]

Stearn, C. W., 1972, The relationship of the stromatoporoids to the sclerosponges: Lethaia, v. 5, p. 369-388. [STROMATOPOROIDS]

_________ 1975, The stromatoporoid animal: Lethaia, v. 8, p. 89-100. [STROMATOPOROIDS]

_________ 1980, Classification of the Paleozoic stromatoporoids: Journal of Paleontology, v. 54, p. 881-902. [STROMATOPOROIDS]

Steen, M. C., 1931, The British Museum collection of Amphibia from the middle coal measures of Linton, Ohio: Zoological Society of London Proceedings, no. 55, part 4, p. 849-891. [VERTEBRATES]

Stephens, J. J., 1964, *Ophiacodon* from Ohio: Ohio Journal of Science, v. 64, p. 217-220. [VERTEBRATES]

Stevenson, J. J., 1893, John Strong Newberry: American Geologist, v. 12, no. 1, p. 1-25. [GENERAL GEOLOGY]

Stewart, D. P., and Miller, B. B., 1987, Hueston Woods State Park: Wisconsin glacial stratigraphy in southwestern Ohio, *in* Biggs, D. L., ed., Geological Society of America Centennial Field Guide, North-Central Section, p. 391-394. [MOLLUSCA]

Stewart, G. A., 1927, Fauna of the Silica Shale of Lucas County:

Ohio Division of Geological Survey Bulletin 32, 76 p. [MANY GROUPS]

_________ 1936, Ostracodes of the Silica Formation, Middle Devonian, of Ohio: Journal of Paleontology, v. 10, p. 739-763. [OSTRACODA]

_________ 1938, Middle Devonian corals of Ohio: Geological Society of America Special Paper 8, 120 p. [CNIDARIA]

_________ 1950, Ostracoda from Middle Devonian bone beds in central Ohio: Journal of Paleontology, v. 24, p. 652-666. [OSTRACODA]

_________ 1955, Age relations of the Middle Devonian limestones of Ohio: Ohio Journal of Science, v. 55, p. 147-181. [OHIO GEOLOGY; BRACHIOPODA]

Stewart, G. A., and Hendrix, W. E., 1945a, Ostracoda of the Plum Brook Shale, Erie County, Ohio: Journal of Paleontology, v. 19, p. 87-95. [OSTRACODA]

_________ 1945b, Ostracoda of the Olentangy Shale, Franklin and Delaware Counties, Ohio: Journal of Paleontology, v. 19, p. 96-115. [OSTRACODA]

Stewart, G. A., and Sweet, W. C., 1956, Conodonts from the Middle Devonian bone beds of central and west-central Ohio: Journal of Paleontology, v. 30, p. 261-263. [CONODONTA]

Stewart, W. N., and Delavoryas, Theodore, 1956, The medullosan pteridosperms: Botanical Review, v. 22, p. 45-80. [PLANTS]

Stewart, W. N., and Rothwell, G. W., 1993, Paleobotany and the evolution of plants (2nd ed.): New York, Cambridge University Press, 521 p. [PLANTS]

Stout, Wilber, 1943, Generalized section of coal bearing rocks of Ohio: Ohio Division of Geological Survey Information Circular 4, chart. [OHIO GEOLOGY]

Stukel, D. J., III, 1987, Ichnology and paleoenvironmental analysis of the Late Devonian (Famennian) Chagrin Shale of northeast Ohio: M.S. thesis (unpub.), Kent State University, 94 p. [ICHNOFOSSILS]

Stumm, E. C., 1942, Fauna and stratigraphic relations of the Prout Limestone and Plum Brook Shale of northern Ohio: Journal of Paleontology, v. 16, p. 549-563. [OHIO GEOLOGY; BRACHIOPODA]

_________ 1949, Revision of the families and genera of the Devonian tetracorals: Geological Society of America Memoir 40, 92 p. [CNIDARIA]

_________ 1950, Corals of the Devonian Traverse Group of Michigan, Part III: *Antholites*, *Pleurodictyum*, and *Procteria*: University of Michigan Museum of Paleontology Contributions, v. 8, no. 8, p. 205-220. [CNIDARIA]

_________ 1953, Lower Middle Devonian proetid trilobites from Michigan, southwestern Ontario, and northern Ohio: University of Michigan Museum of Paleontology Contributions, v. 11, no. 2, p. 11-31. [TRILOBITA]

_________ 1954, Lower Middle Devonian phacopid trilobites from Michigan, southwestern Ohio, and the Ohio Valley: University of Michigan Museum of Paleontology Contributions, v. 11, no. 11, p. 201-221. [TRILOBITA]

_________ 1963, Corals of the Traverse Group of Michigan, Part XI: *Tortophyllum*, *Bethanyphyllum*, *Aulacophyllum* and *Hallia*: University of Michigan Museum of Paleontology Contributions, v. 18, no. 8, p. 135-155. [CNIDARIA]

_________ 1965a, Silurian and Devonian corals of the Falls of the Ohio: Geological Society of America Memoir 93, 184 p. [CNIDARIA]

_________ 1965b, Two new species of trilobites from the Middle Devonian Silica Shale of northwestern Ohio: University of Michigan Museum of Paleontology Contributions, v. 19, no. 13, p. 163-166. [TRILOBITA]

_________ 1967a, Tabulate corals of the Silica Shale (Middle Devonian) of northwestern Ohio and southeastern Michigan: University of Michigan Museum of Paleontology Contributions, v. 21, no. 4, p. 86-104. [CNIDARIA]

_________ 1967b, Devonian trilobites from northwestern Ohio, northern Michigan, and western New York: University of Michigan Museum of Paleontology Contributions, v. 21, no. 6, p. 109-122. [TRILOBITA]

_________ 1968a, The corals of the Middle Devonian Tenmile Creek Dolomite of northwestern Ohio: University of Michigan Museum of Paleontology Contributions, v. 22, no. 3, p. 37-44. [CNIDARIA]

_________ 1968b, Rugose corals of the Silica Formation (Middle Devonian) of northwestern Ohio and southeastern Michigan: University of Michigan Museum of Paleontology Contributions, v. 22, no. 5, p. 61-70. [CNIDARIA]

Sturgeon, M. T., and Hoare, R. D., 1968, Pennsylvanian brachiopods of Ohio: Ohio Division of Geological Survey Bulletin 63, 95 p. [BRACHIOPODA; VERTEBRATES]

Sturgeon, M. T., Windle, D. L., Mapes, R. H., and Hoare, R. D., 1982, New and revised taxa of Pennsylvanian cephalopods in Ohio and West Viriginia: Journal of Paleontology, v. 56, p. 1453-1479. [CEPHALOPODA]

_________ in press, Pennsylvanian cephalopods of Ohio, part 1, nautiloid and bactritoid cephalopods: Ohio Division of Geological Survey Bulletin 71. [CEPHALOPODA]

Sturgeon, M. T., and Youngquist, Walter, 1949, Allegheny conodonts from eastern Ohio: Journal of Paleontology, v. 23, p. 380-386. [CONODONTA]

Sweet, W. C., 1979, Conodonts and conodont biostratigraphy of post-Tyrone Ordovician rocks of the Cincinnati region, *in* Pojeta, John, Jr., ed., Contributions to the Ordovician paleontology of Kentucky and nearby states: U.S. Geological Survey Professional Paper 1066-G, p. G1-G26. [CONODONTA]

_________ 1988, The Conodonta. Morphology, taxonomy, paleoecology, and evolutionary history of a long-extinct animal phylum: New York, Oxford University Press, 212 p. [CONODONTA]

Sweet, W. C., and Miller, A. K., 1956, Goniatites from the Middle Devonian Columbus Limestone of Ohio: Journal of Paleontology, v. 30, p. 811-817. [CEPHALOPODA]

Sweet, W. C., Turco, C. A., Warner, Earl, Jr., and Wilkie, L. C., 1959, The American Upper Ordovician Standard. I. Eden conodonts from the Cincinnati region of Ohio and Kentucky: Journal of Paleontology, v. 33, p. 1029-1068. [CONODONTA]

Swinford, E. M., and Slucher, E. R., 1995, Regional bedrock geology of the Bellefontaine, Ohio, 30 x 60 minute quadrangle: Ohio Division of Geological Survey Map 8. [OHIO GEOLOGY]

Szmuc, E. J., 1957, Stratigraphy and paleontology of the Cuyahoga formation of northern Ohio: Ph.D. dissertation (unpub.), Ohio State University, 623 p. [OHIO GEOLOGY; BRACHIOPODA]

_________ 1970a, The Devonian System, *in* Banks, P. O., and Feldmann, R. M., eds., Guide to the geology of northeastern Ohio: Northern Ohio Geological Society, p. 9-21. [OHIO GEOLOGY; BRACHIOPODA]

_________ 1970b, The Mississippian System, *in* Banks, P. O., and Feldmann, R. M., eds., Guide to the geology of northeastern Ohio: Northern Ohio Geological Society, p. 23-68. [OHIO GEOLOGY; BRACHIOPODA]

Szmuc, E. J., Osgood, R. G., and Meinke, D. W., 1976, *Lingulichnites*, a new trace fossil genus for lingulid brachiopod burrows: Lethaia, v. 9, p. 163-167. [ICHNOFOSSILS]

Taggart, R. E., and Parker, L. R., 1976, A new fossil alga from the Silurian of Michigan: American Journal of Botany, v. 63, p. 1390-1392. [PLANTS]

Tasch, Paul, 1969, Branchiopoda, *in* Brooks, H. K., and others, Part R, Arthropoda 4, v. 1, *in* Moore, R. C., ed., Treatise on Invertebrate Paleontology: Geological Society of America and University of Kansas Press, p. R128-R191. [OTHER ARTHROPODA]

Taylor, P. D., and Wilson, M. A., 1996, *Cuffeyella*, a new bryozoan genus from the Late Ordovician of North America, and its bearing on the origin of the post-Paleozoic cyclostomates, *in* Gordon, D. P., Smith, A. M., and Grant-Mackie, J. A., eds., Bryozoans in space and time: Wellington, New Zealand, Proceedings of the 10th International Bryozoology Conference (1995), National Institute of Water & Atmospheric Research, Ltd., p. 351-360. [BRYOZOA]

Teeter, J. W., 1970, Paleoecology of a Pleistocene microfossil assemblage at the Fairlawn, Ohio, mastodon site: American Midland Naturalist, v. 83, p. 583-594, 18 figs. [OSTRACODA]

Teichert, Curt, and others, 1964, Part K, Mollusca 3, Cephalopoda—General features—Endoceratoidea—Actinoceratoidea—Nautiloidea—Bactritoidea, *in* Moore, R. C., ed., Treatise on Invertebrate Paleontology: Geological Society of America and University of Kansas Press, 519 p. [CEPHALOPODA]

Thomas, A. T., 1977, Classification and phylogeny of homalonotid trilobites: Palaeontology, v. 20, p. 159-178. [TRILOBITA]

Thomas, E. S., 1952, The Orleton Farms mastodon: Ohio Journal of Science, v. 52, p. 1-5. [VERTEBRATES]

Thompson, T. L., Ford, N. S., and Sweet, W. C., 1971, Conodonts from the Rushville Formation (Mississippian) of Ohio: Journal of Paleontology, v. 45, p. 704-712. [CONODONTA]

Tillman, J. R., 1970, The age, stratigraphic relationships, and correlation of the lower part of the Olentangy Shale of central Ohio: Ohio Journal of Science, v. 70, p. 202-217. [OSTRACODA]

_________ 1984, Ostracodes of the superfamilies Beyrichiacea and Drepanellacea from Middle Devonian rocks of central Ohio: Journal of Paleontology, v. 58, p. 234-253. [OSTRACODA]

Tillman, J. R., and Murphy, S. E., 1978, Ostracodes of the superfamily Hollinacea from Middle Devonian rocks of central Ohio: Journal of Paleontology, v. 52, p. 411-439. [OSTRACODA]

Todd, T. N., 1973, A Pleistocene record of a North American mudminnow, *Umbra*: Copeia, no. 3, p. 587-588. [VERTEBRATES]

Totten, S. M., 1988, Glacial geology of Medina County, Ohio: Ohio Division of Geological Survey Report of Investigations 141, 38 p. [VERTEBRATES]

Traverse, Alfred, 1988, Paleopalynology: Boston, Unwin Hyman, 600 p. [PLANTS]

Ubaghs, Georges, and others, 1966, Part U, Echinodermata 3, *in* Moore, R. C., ed., Treatise on Invertebrate Paleontology: Geological Society of America and University of Kansas Press, 695 p. [ECHINODERMATA: ASTEROIDEA, ECHINOIDEA, OPHIUROIDEA]

Ubaghs, Georges, and others, 1978, Part T, Echinodermata 2, *in* Moore, R. C., and Teichert, Curt, eds., Treatise on Invertebrate Paleontology: Geological Society of America and University of Kansas Press, 1,027 p. [ECHINODERMATA: CRINOIDEA]

Ulrich, E. O., 1879, Descriptions of new genera and species of fossils from the lower Silurian about Cincinnati: Cincinnati Society of Natural History Journal, v. 2, p. 8-30. [PLANTS]

_________ 1880, Catalogue of fossils occurring in the Cincinnati Group of Ohio, Indiana, and Kentucky: Cincinnati, Ohio, James Barclay, 31 p. [PORIFERA]

_________ 1886, Descriptions of new Silurian and Devonian fossils: Contributions to American Paleontology (published by Ulrich in Cincinnati), v. 1 (only volume published), p. 3-35. [PLANTS]

_________ 1889, Preliminary description of new Lower Silurian sponges: American Geologist, v. 3, p. 233-248. [PORIFERA]

_________ 1890, American Palaeozoic sponges: Geological Survey of Illinois, v. 8, p. 209-241. [PORIFERA]

_________ 1890-1891, New and little known American Paleozoic Ostracoda: Cincinnati Society of Natural History Journal, v. 13, no. 3 (1890), p. 104-137; no. 4 (1891), p. 173-211. [OSTRACODA]

_________ 1893, New and little known Lamellibranchiata from the lower Silurian rocks of Ohio and adjacent states: Ohio Division of Geological Survey, v. 7, p. 627-693. [PELECYPODA]

U.S. Forest Service, 1948, Woody plant seed manual: U.S. Department of Agriculture Miscellaneous Publication 654, 416 p. [PLANTS]

Vaughn, P. P., 1971, A *Platyhystrix*-like amphibian with fused vertebrae, from the Upper Pennsylvanian of Ohio: Journal of Paleontology, v. 45, p. 464-469. [VERTEBRATES]

Wagner, R. H., 1959, Flora fosile stratigrafia del Carbonifero en Espana N.W. y Portugal N.: Estudios Geologicos, v. XV (tomo homenaj S. Miguel de la Camara), p. 393-420. [PLANTS]

Walker, L. G., 1982, The brachiopod genera *Hebertella, Dalmanella*, and *Heterorthina* from the Ordovician of Kentucky, *in* Pojeta, John, Jr., ed., Contributions to the Ordovician paleontology of Kentucky and nearby states: U.S. Geological Survey Professional Paper 1066-M, p. M1-M17. [BRACHIOPODA]

Wall, D., 1962, Evidence from recent plankton regarding the biological affinities of *Tasmanites* Newton 1875 and *Leiosphaeridia* Eisenack, 1958: Geological Magazine, v. 94, p. 353-362. [PLANTS]

Waller, A., E., 1943, The breadth of vision of Dr. John Strong Newberry: Ohio State Archaeological and Historical Society Quarterly, v. 52, p. 324-346. [GENERAL GEOLOGY]

Warn, J. M., and Strimple, H. L., 1977, The disparid inadunate superfamilies Homocrinacea and Cincinnaticrinacea (Echinodermata: Crinoidea), Ordovician-Silurian, North America: Bulletins of American Paleontology, v. 70, no. 296, 138 p. [ECHINODERMATA: CRINOIDEA]

Warshauer, S. M., and Berdan, J. M., 1982, Palaeocopid and podocopid Ostracoda from the Lexington Limestone and Clays Ferry Formation (Middle and Upper Ordovician) of central Kentucky, *in* Pojeta, John, Jr., ed., Contributions to the Ordovician paleontology of Kentucky and nearby states: U.S. Geological Survey Professional Paper 1066-H, p. H1-H80. [OSTRACODA]

Watkins, J. L., 1959, Middle Devonian auloporid corals from the Traverse Group of Michigan: Journal of Paleontology, v. 33, p. 793-808. [CNIDARIA]

Watts, W. A., 1983, Vegetation history of the Eastern United States 25,000 to 10,000 years ago, *in* Wright, H. E., Jr., and Porter, S. C., eds., Late Quaternary environments of the United States: University of Minnesota Press, v. 1, p. 294-310. [PLANTS]

Weir, G. W., Peterson, W. L., and Swadley, W C, 1984, Lithostratigraphy of Upper Ordovician strata exposed in Kentucky: U.S. Geological Survey Professional Paper 1151-E, 121 p. [GENERAL GEOLOGY]

Wells, J. W., 1939, Association of crinoids with *Callixylon* in the lower Ohio Shale: Palaeobiologica (Wien), v. 7, p. 105-110. [PLANTS]

_________ 1941, Crinoids and *Callixylon*: American Journal of Science, v. 239, p. 454-456. [PLANTS]

_________ 1943, A new species of *Astraeospongia* from the Middle Devonian of Ohio: Ohio Journal of Science, v. 43, p. 210-211. [PORIFERA]

_________ 1944a, A new fish spine from the Pennsylvanian of Ohio: Ohio Journal of Science, v. 44, p. 65-67. [VERTEBRATES]

_________ 1944b, Fish remains from the Middle Devonian bone beds of the Cincinnati arch region: Palaeontographica Americana, v. 3, no. 16, 62 p. [VERTEBRATES]

_________ 1963, Coral growth and geochronometry: Nature, v. 197, p. 948-950. [CNIDARIA]

Wellstead, C. F., 1991, Taxonomic revision of the Lysorophia, Permo-Carboniferous lepospondyl amphibians: American Museum of Natural History Bulletin, v. 209, p. 1-90. [VERTEBRATES]

White, David, 1899, Fossil flora of the Lower Coal Measures of Missouri: U.S. Geological Survey Monograph 37, 467 p. [PLANTS]

_________ 1901, Two new species of algae of the genus *Buthotrephis*, from the Upper Silurian of Indiana: Proceedings of the U.S. National Museum, v. 24, p. 265-270. [PLANTS]

_________ 1902, A new name for *Buthotrephis divaricata* D.W.: Proceedings of the Biological Society of Washington, v. 15, p.

86. [PLANTS]

White, G. W., 1967, Glacial geology of Wayne County, Ohio: Ohio Division of Geological Survey Report of Investigations 62, 39 p. [PLANTS]

_________ 1968, Age and correlation of Pleistocene deposits at Garfield Heights (Cleveland), Ohio: Geological Society of America Bulletin, v. 79, p. 749-752. [PLANTS]

_________ 1982, Glacial geology of northeastern Ohio: Ohio Division of Geological Survey Bulletin 68, 75 p. [OHIO GEOLOGY; PLANTS]

Whitfield, R. P., 1893, Contributions to the paleontology of Ohio: Ohio Division of Geological Survey, v. 7, p. 407-494. [MANY GROUPS]

Whittington, H. B., 1968, *Cryptolithus* (Trilobita): specific characters and occurrence in Ordovician of eastern North America: Journal of Paleontology, v. 42, p. 702-714. [TRILOBITA]

_________ 1971, Silurian calymenid trilobites from United States, Norway, and Sweden: Palaeontology, v. 14, p. 455-577. [TRILOBITA]

_________ 1992, Trilobites: Woodbridge, England, Boydell Press, 145 p. [TRILOBITA]

Wicander, E. R., 1974, Upper Devonian-Lower Mississippian acritarchs and prasinophycean algae from Ohio, U.S.A.: Palaeontographica, Abteilung B, v. 148, p. 9-43. [PLANTS]

_________ 1984, Middle Devonian acritarch biostratigraphy of North America: Journal of Micropalaeontology, v. 3, no. 2, p. 19-24. [PLANTS]

Wicander, E. R., and Wood, G. D., 1981, Systematics and biostratigraphy of the organic-walled microplankton from the Middle Devonian (Givetian) Silica Formation, Ohio, U.S.A.: American Association of Stratigraphic Palynologists Contribution Series No. 8, 137 p. [PLANTS]

Wicander, E. R., and Wright, R. P., 1983, Organic-walled microphytoplankton abundance and stratigraphic distribution from the Middle Devonian Columbus and Delaware Limestones of the Hamilton Quarry, Marion County, Ohio: Ohio Journal of Science, v. 83, p. 2-13. [PLANTS]

Williams, Alwyn, and others, 1965, Part H, Brachiopoda, *in* Moore, R. C., ed., Treatise on Invertebrate Paleontology: Geological Society of America and University of Kansas Press, 927 p. [BRACHIOPODA]

Williams, M. E., 1972, The origin of "spiral coprolites": University of Kansas Paleontological Contributions, Paper 59, 19 p. [VERTEBRATES]

_________ 1985, The "cladodont level" sharks of the Pennsylvanian black shales of central North America: Palaeontographica, v. 190, p. 83-158. [VERTEBRATES]

_________ 1990, Feeding behavior in Cleveland Shale fishes, *in* Boucot, A. J., Evolutionary paleobiology of behavior and coevolution: Amsterdam, Elsevier, p. 272-287. [VERTEBRATES]

_________ 1992, Jaws, the early years: feeding behavior in Cleveland Shale sharks: The Explorer (Cleveland Museum of Natural History), v. 34, p. 4-8. [VERTEBRATES]

Williamson, W. C., 1880, On the organization of fossil plants of the Coal Measures—Part 10, including an examination of supposed radiolarians of the Carboniferous rocks: Philosophical Transactions of the Royal Society of London, v. 171, p. 493-539. [PLANTS]

Williston, S. W., 1910, *Cacops*, *Desmospondylus*: new genera of Permian vertebrates: Geological Society of America Bulletin, v. 21, p. 249-284. [VERTEBRATES]

Wilson, L. R., 1958, Oklahoma's oldest fossil trees: Oklahoma Geology Notes, v. 18, p. 173-177. [PLANTS]

Wilson, M. A., and Palmer, T. J., 1988, Nomenclature of a bivalve boring from the Upper Ordovician of the midwestern United States: Journal of Paleontology, v. 62, p. 306-308. [ICHNOFOSSILS]

_________ 1989, Preparation of acetate peels, *in* Feldmann, R. M., Chapman, R. E., and Hannibal, J. T., eds., Paleotechniques: Paleontological Society Special Publication 4, p. 142-145. [BRYOZOA]

Winkler, E. M., 1962, Two late Pleistocene (Cary) freshwater ostracode faunas: Journal of Paleontology, v. 36, p. 1021-1034. [OSTRACODA]

Winslow, M. R., 1962, Plant spores and other microfossils from Upper Devonian and Lower Mississippian rocks of Ohio: U.S. Geological Survey Professional Paper 364, 93 p. [PLANTS]

Wolberg, D. L., and Gil, April VanCamp, 1988, Bibliography of Rousseau H. Flower: New Mexico Bureau of Mines & Mineral Resources Memoir 44, p. xi-xiv. [CEPHALOPODA]

Wood, G. D., 1974, Chitinozoa of the Silica Formation (Middle Devonian), Ohio: vesicle ornamentation and paleoecology: Michigan State University Museum, Paleontological Series, v. 1, no. 4, p. 127-162. [PLANTS]

Wood, Rachel, 1990, Reef-building sponges: American Scientist, v. 78, p. 224-235. [STROMATOPOROIDS]

Wright, A. A., 1893, On the ventral armor of *Dinichthys*: Ohio Division of Geological Survey, v. 7, p. 620-626. [VERTEBRATES]

Wright, C. P., 1976, Occurrence, stratigraphic distribution and abundance of Chitinozoa from the Middle Devonian Columbus Limestone of Ohio: Ohio Journal of Science, v. 76, p. 214-224. [PLANTS]

_________ 1978, Biogeography of the Middle Devonian Chitinozoa of the midwestern United States: Palinologia, Numero extraordinario 1 (I Coloquio International de Palinologia, 1977, Leon), p. 501-505. [PLANTS]

Yoder, R. L., and Erdtmann, B.-D., 1975, *Tentaculites attenuatus* Hall and *T. bellulus* Hall: a redescription and interpretation of these species as dimorphs: Journal of Paleontology, v. 49, p. 374-386. [TENTACULITOIDS]

Zangerl, Rainer, 1981, Chondrichthyes I, Paleozoic Elasmobranchii, *in* Schultze, H.-P., ed., Handbook of paleoichthyology: Stuttgart, Gustav Fischer Verlag, v. 3A, 115 p. [VERTEBRATES]

_________ 1984, On the microscopic anatomy and possible function of the spine-"brush" complex of *Stethacanthus* (Elasmobranchii: Symmoriida): Journal of Vertebrate Paleontology, v. 4, p. 372-378. [VERTEBRATES]

Zeiller, R., 1894, Notes sur la flore des couches permiennes de Trienbach (Alsace): Société géologique de France Bulletin (3rd ser.), v. 22, p. 163-182. [PLANTS]

Zidek, Jiri, 1980, *Acanthodes lundi*, new species (Acanthodii), and associated coprolites from uppermost Mississippian Heath Formation of central Montana: Carnegie Museum Annals, v. 49, p. 49-78. [VERTEBRATES]

_________ 1981, *Machaeracanthus* Newberry (Acanthodii: Ischnacanthiformes)—morphology and systematic position: Neues Jahrbuch für Geologie und Paläontologie, v. 12, p. 742-748. [VERTEBRATES]

Index to genera

The names of genera listed in Chapters 1 to 25 are indexed here. Qualifying notations such as quotation marks, question marks, cf., etc. have been ignored.

Index to species

Names of species listed in Chapters 1 to 25 are indexed here. Qualifying notations such as quotation marks, question marks, cf., etc. have been ignored.